2020

MINNESOTA
RESIDENTIAL CODE
• Administration • Construction • Radon • Energy

INTERNATIONAL
CODE COUNCIL

**DEPARTMENT OF
LABOR AND INDUSTRY**

2020 Minnesota Residential Code

First Printing: March 2020

ISBN: 978-1-60983-988-8

COPYRIGHT © 2020
by
INTERNATIONAL CODE COUNCIL, INC.

T026014

mn DEPARTMENT OF LABOR AND INDUSTRY

Additional information on the Minnesota State Building Code can be found at the Minnesota Department of Labor & Industry's website:
http://www.dli.mn.gov/business/codes-and-laws

There you can find reference guides, maps, charts, fact sheets, archived references, Statute and Rule excerpts and other helpful information to assist you in using the Minnesota State Building Code.

Minnesota Rules material is published with the permission of the Office of the Revisor of Statutes.

Important Disclaimer

Note: Minnesota Rules included in this document have been extracted from Minnesota Rules 2015 and from Minnesota Rules proposed for adoption in 2019. Although efforts have been made to ensure the accuracy of the Minnesota Rules included herein, the official Minnesota Rules are as published by the Office of the Revisor of Statutes: https://www.revisor.mn.gov/rules/

If there is a difference between the Minnesota Rules included herein and the official rules published by the Office of the Revisor of Statutes, the official rules published by the Office of the Revisor of Statutes take precedence.

The official rules published by the Office of the Revisor of Statutes must be used for any notice or legal documentation used in conjunction with the application or enforcement of the Minnesota State Building Code.

Neither the state of Minnesota nor its employees or agents make any representations or warranties, express or implied, with respect to the use or reliance on the information provided herein and the user assumes all risks and responsibilities associated with its use.

In no event shall the State of Minnesota or its employees be liable for any direct, indirect, incidental, special, exemplary, or consequential damages arising in any way out of the use of this material.

PREFACE

Introduction

The *International Residential Code*® (IRC®) establishes minimum requirements for one- and two-family dwellings and townhouses using prescriptive provisions. It is founded on broad-based principles that make possible the use of new materials and new building designs. This 2018 edition is fully compatible with all of the *International Codes*® (I-Codes®) published by the International Code Council® (ICC®), including the *International Building Code*®, *International Energy Conservation Code*®, *International Existing Building Code*®, *International Fire Code*®, *International Fuel Gas Code*®, *International Green Construction Code*®, *International Mechanical Code*®, *International Plumbing Code*®, *International Private Sewage Disposal Code*®, *International Property Maintenance Code*®, *International Swimming Pool and Spa Code*®, *International Wildland-Urban Interface Code*®, *International Zoning Code*® and *International Code Council Performance Code*®.

The I-Codes, including this *International Residential Code*, are used in a variety of ways in both the public and private sectors. Most industry professionals are familiar with the I-Codes as the basis of laws and regulations in communities across the U.S. and in other countries. However, the impact of the codes extends well beyond the regulatory arena, as they are used in a variety of nonregulatory settings, including:

- Voluntary compliance programs such as those promoting sustainability, energy efficiency and disaster resistance.

- The insurance industry, to estimate and manage risk, and as a tool in underwriting and rate decisions.

- Certification and credentialing of individuals involved in the fields of building design, construction and safety.

- Certification of building and construction-related products.

- U.S. federal agencies, to guide construction in an array of government-owned properties.

- Facilities management.

- "Best practices" benchmarks for designers and builders, including those who are engaged in projects in jurisdictions that do not have a formal regulatory system or a governmental enforcement mechanism.

- College, university and professional school textbooks and curricula.

- Reference works related to building design and construction.

In addition to the codes themselves, the code development process brings together building professionals on a regular basis. It provides an international forum for discussion and deliberation about building design, construction methods, safety, performance requirements, technological advances and innovative products.

Development

This 2018 edition presents the code as originally issued, with changes reflected in the 2003 through 2015 editions and further changes approved by the ICC Code Development Process through 2017. Residential electrical provisions are based on the 2017 *National Electrical Code*® (NFPA 70). A new edition such as this is promulgated every 3 years.

Fuel gas provisions have been included through an agreement with the American Gas Association (AGA). Electrical provisions have been included through an agreement with the National Fire Protection Association (NFPA).

This code is founded on principles intended to establish provisions consistent with the scope of a residential code that adequately protects public health, safety and welfare; provisions that do not unnecessarily increase construction costs; provisions that do not restrict the use of new materials, products or methods of construction; and provisions that do not give preferential treatment to particular types or classes of materials, products or methods of construction.

Maintenance

The *International Residential Code* is kept up-to-date through the review of proposed changes submitted by code enforcement officials, industry representatives, design professionals and other interested parties. Proposed changes are carefully considered through an open code development process in which all interested and affected parties may participate.

The ICC Code Development Process reflects principles of openness, transparency, balance, due process and consensus, the principles embodied in OMB Circular A-119, which governs the federal government's use of private-sector standards. The ICC process is open to anyone; there is no cost to participate, and people can participate without travel cost through the ICC's cloud-based app, cdp-Access®. A broad cross section of interests are represented in the ICC Code Development Process. The codes, which are updated regularly, include safeguards that allow for emergency action when required for health and safety reasons.

In order to ensure that organizations with a direct and material interest in the codes have a voice in the process, the ICC has developed partnerships with key industry segments that support the ICC's important public safety mission. Some code development committee members were nominated by the following industry partners and approved by the ICC Board:

- National Association of Home Builders (NAHB)
- National Council of Structural Engineers Association (NCSEA)

The code development committees evaluate and make recommendations regarding proposed changes to the codes. Their recommendations are then subject to public comment and council-wide votes. The ICC's governmental members—public safety officials who have no financial or business interest in the outcome—cast the final votes on proposed changes.

The contents of this work are subject to change through the code development cycles and by any governmental entity that enacts the code into law. For more information regarding the code development process, contact the Codes and Standards Development Department of the International Code Council.

The maintenance process for the fuel gas provisions is based on the process used to maintain the *International Fuel Gas Code*, in conjunction with the American Gas Association. The maintenance process for the electrical provisions is undertaken by the National Fire Protection Association.

While the I-Code development procedure is thorough and comprehensive, the ICC, its members and those participating in the development of the codes disclaim any liability resulting from the publication or use of the I-Codes, or from compliance or noncompliance with their provisions. The ICC does not have the power or authority to police or enforce compliance with the contents of this code.

Code Development Committee Responsibilities

In each code development cycle, proposed changes to the code are considered at the Committee Action Hearings by the applicable International Code Development Committee as follows:

[RB] = IRC—Building Code Development Committee

[RE] = International Residential Energy Conservation Code Development Committee;

[MP] = IRC—Mechanical/Plumbing Code Development Committee

The [RE] committee is also responsible for the IECC—Residential Provisions and Appendix T.

For the development of the 2021 edition of the I-Codes, there will be two groups of code development committees and they will meet in separate years.

Group A Codes (Heard in 2018, Code Change Proposals Deadline: January 8, 2018)	Group B Codes (Heard in 2019, Code Change Proposals Deadline: January 7, 2019)
International Building Code – Egress (Chapters 10, 11, Appendix E) – Fire Safety (Chapters 7, 8, 9, 14, 26) – General (Chapters 2–6, 12, 27–33, Appendices A, B, C, D, K, N)	Administrative Provisions (Chapter 1 of all codes except IECC, IRC and IgCC, administrative updates to currently referenced standards, and designated definitions)
International Fire Code	**International Building Code** – Structural (Chapters 15–25, Appendices F, G, H, I, J, L, M)
International Fuel Gas Code	**International Existing Building Code**
International Mechanical Code	**International Energy Conservation Code—Commercial**
International Plumbing Code	**International Energy Conservation Code—Residential** – IECC—Residential – IRC—Energy (Chapter 11)
International Property Maintenance Code	**International Green Construction Code** (Chapter 1)
International Private Sewage Disposal Code	**International Residential Code** – IRC—Building (Chapters 1–10, Appendices E, F, H, J, K, L, M, O, Q, R, S, T)
International Residential Code – IRC—Mechanical (Chapters 12–23) – IRC—Plumbing (Chapters 25–33, Appendices G, I, N, P)	
International Swimming Pool and Spa Code	
International Wildland-Urban Interface Code	
International Zoning Code	

Note: Proposed changes to the ICC *Performance Code*™ will be heard by the code development committee noted in brackets [ ] in the text of the ICC *Performance Code*™.

Code change proposals submitted to Chapters 1 and 3 through 10, Appendices E, F, H, J, K, L, M, O, Q, R, S, T and Definitions designated [RB] of the *International Residential Code* are heard by the IRC—Building Committee during the Group B (2019) cycle code development hearing. Code change proposals submitted to Chapter 11 are heard by the International Energy Conservation Code Development Committee during the Group B (2019) cycle code development hearing. Proposed changes to all other chapters are heard by the IRC Plumbing and Mechanical Committee during the Group A (2018) code development cycle.

It is very important that anyone submitting code change proposals understand which code development committee is responsible for the section of the code that is the subject of the code change proposal. For further information on the code development committee responsibilities, please visit the ICC website at www.iccsafe.org/scoping.

Marginal Markings

➡ = Indicates where a paragraph or item has been deleted from the requirements of the 2015 *International Residential Code*.

\> = Indicates model code language deleted by the State of Minnesota.

▌ = Indicates a technical change from the requirements of the 2015 *International Residential Code*.

ᴹ ₙ = Indicates a State of Minnesota amendment has been made to the 2018 *International Residential Code*.

Solid vertical lines in the margins within the body of the code indicate a technical change from the requirements of the 2015 edition. Deletion indicators in the form of an arrow (➡) are provided in the margin where an entire section, paragraph, exception or table has been deleted or an item in a list of items or a table has been deleted.

A single asterisk [*] placed in the margin indicates that text or a table has been relocated within the code. A double asterisk [**] placed in the margin indicates that the text or table immediately following it has been relocated there from elsewhere in the code. The following table indicates such relocations in the 2018 edition of the *International Residential Code*.

2018 LOCATION	2015 LOCATION
R703.3.1.2	R703.11.1.4

Coordination of the International Codes

The coordination of technical provisions is one of the strengths of the ICC family of model codes. The codes can be used as a complete set of complementary documents, which will provide users with full integration and coordination of technical provisions. Individual codes can also be used in subsets or as stand-alone documents. To make sure that each individual code is as complete as possible, some technical provisions that are relevant to more than one subject area are duplicated in some of the model codes. This allows users maximum flexibility in their application of the I-Codes.

Italicized Terms

Selected words and terms defined in Chapter 2, Definitions, are italicized where they appear in code text and the Chapter 2 definition applies. Where such words and terms are not italicized, common-use definitions apply. The words and terms selected have code-specific definitions that the user should read carefully to facilitate better understanding of the code.

Adoption

The International Code Council maintains a copyright in all of its codes and standards. Maintaining copyright allows the ICC to fund its mission through sales of books, in both print and electronic formats. The ICC welcomes adoption of its codes by jurisdictions that recognize and acknowledge the ICC's copyright in the code, and further acknowledge the substantial shared value of the public/private partnership for code development between jurisdictions and the ICC.

The ICC also recognizes the need for jurisdictions to make laws available to the public. All I-Codes and I-Standards, along with the laws of many jurisdictions, are available for free in a nondownloadable form on the ICC's website. Jurisdictions should contact the ICC at adoptions@iccsafe.org to learn how to adopt and distribute laws based on the *International Residential Code* in a manner that provides necessary access, while maintaining the ICC's copyright.

To facilitate adoption, several sections of this code contain blanks for fill-in information that needs to be supplied by the adopting jurisdiction as part of the adoption legislation. For this code, please see:

Section R101.1. Insert: **[NAME OF JURISDICTION]**

Table R301.2(1)—Jurisdictions to fill in details as directed by provisions of the code.

Section P2603.5.1 Insert: **[NUMBER OF INCHES IN TWO LOCATIONS]**

EFFECTIVE USE OF THE INTERNATIONAL RESIDENTIAL CODE

Effective Use of the International Residential Code

The *International Residential Code®* (IRC®) was created to serve as a complete, comprehensive code regulating the construction of single-family houses, two-family houses (duplexes) and buildings consisting of three or more townhouse units. All buildings within the scope of the IRC are limited to three stories above grade plane. For example, a four-story single-family house would fall within the scope of the *International Building Code®* (IBC®), not the IRC. The benefits of devoting a separate code to residential construction include the fact that the user need not navigate through a multitude of code provisions that do not apply to residential construction in order to locate that which is applicable. A separate code also allows for residential and nonresidential code provisions to be distinct and tailored to the structures that fall within the appropriate code's scopes.

The IRC contains coverage for all components of a house or townhouse, including structural components, fireplaces and chimneys, thermal insulation, mechanical systems, fuel gas systems, plumbing systems and electrical systems.

The IRC is a prescriptive-oriented (specification) code with some examples of performance code language. It has been said that the IRC is the complete cookbook for residential construction. Section R301.1, for example, is written in performance language, but states that the prescriptive requirements of the code will achieve such performance.

It is important to understand that the IRC contains coverage for what is conventional and common in residential construction practice. While the IRC will provide all of the needed coverage for most residential construction, it might not address construction practices and systems that are atypical or rarely encountered in the industry. Sections such as R301.1.3, R301.2.2.1.1, R320.1, M1301.1, G2401.1 and P2601.1 refer to other codes either as an alternative to the provisions of the IRC or where the IRC lacks coverage for a particular type of structure, design, system, appliance or method of construction. In other words, the IRC is meant to be all inclusive for typical residential construction and it relies on other codes only where alternatives are desired or where the code lacks coverage for the uncommon aspect of residential construction. Of course, the IRC constantly evolves to address new technologies and construction practices that were once uncommon, but are now common.

The IRC is unique in that much of it, including Chapters 3 through 9 and Chapters 34 through 43, is presented in an ordered format that is consistent with the normal progression of construction, starting with the design phase and continuing through the final trim-out phase. This is consistent with the "cookbook" philosophy of the IRC.

The IRC is divided into eight main parts, specifically: Part I—Administration; Part II—Definitions; Part III—Building Planning and Construction; Part IV—Energy Conservation; Part V—Mechanical; Part VI—Fuel Gas; Part VII—Plumbing; and Part VIII—Electrical.

The following provides a brief description of the content of each chapter and appendix of the IRC:

Chapter 1. Deleted.

Chapter 2 Definitions. Terms defined in the code are listed alphabetically in Chapter 2. It is important to note that two chapters have their own definitions sections: Chapter 11 for the defined terms unique to energy conservation, Chapter 24 for the defined terms that are unique to fuel gas and Chapter 35 containing terms that are applicable to electrical Chapters 34 through 43. Where Chapter 24 or 35 defines a term differently than it is defined in Chapter 2, the definition applies in that chapter only. Chapter 2 definitions apply in all other locations in the code.

Where understanding a term's definition is key to or necessary for understanding a particular code provision, the term is shown in italics where it appears in the code. This is true only for those terms that have a meaning that is unique to the code. In other words, the generally understood meaning of a term or phrase might not be sufficient or consistent with the meaning prescribed by the code; therefore, it is essential that the code-defined meaning be known.

Guidance regarding not only tense, gender and plurality of defined terms, but also terms not defined in this code, is provided.

Chapter 3 Building Planning. Chapter 3 provides guidelines for a minimum level of structural integrity, life safety, fire safety and livability for inhabitants of dwelling units regulated by this code. Chapter 3 is a compilation of the code requirements specific to the building planning sector of the design and construction process. This chapter sets forth code requirements dealing with light, ventilation, sanitation, minimum room size, ceiling height and environmental comfort. Chapter 3 establishes life-safety provisions including limitations on glazing used in hazardous areas, specifications on stairways, use of guards at elevated surfaces, window and fall protection, and rules for means of egress. Snow, wind and seismic design live and dead loads and flood-resistant construction, as well as solar energy systems, and swimming pools, spas and hot tubs, are addressed in this chapter.

Chapter 4 Foundations. Chapter 4 provides the requirements for the design and construction of foundation systems for buildings regulated by this code. Provisions for seismic load, flood load and frost protection are contained in this chapter. A foundation system consists of two interdependent components: the foundation structure itself and the supporting soil.

The prescriptive provisions of this chapter provide requirements for constructing footings and walls for foundations of wood, masonry, concrete and precast concrete. In addition to a foundation's ability to support the required design loads, this chapter addresses several other factors that can affect foundation performance. These include controlling surface water and subsurface drainage, requiring soil tests where conditions warrant and evaluating proximity to slopes and minimum depth requirements. The chapter also provides requirements to minimize adverse effects of moisture, decay and pests in basements and crawl spaces.

Chapter 5 Floors. Chapter 5 provides the requirements for the design and construction of floor systems that will be capable of supporting minimum required design loads. This chapter covers four different types: wood floor framing, wood floors on the ground, cold-formed steel floor framing and concrete slabs on the ground. Allowable span tables are provided that greatly simplify the determination of joist, girder and sheathing sizes for raised floor systems of wood framing and cold-formed steel framing. This chapter also contains prescriptive requirements for wood-framed exterior decks and their attachment to the main building.

Chapter 6 Wall Construction. Chapter 6 contains provisions that regulate the design and construction of walls. The wall construction covered in Chapter 6 consists of five different types: wood framed, cold-formed steel framed, masonry, concrete and structural insulated panel (SIP). The primary concern of this chapter is the structural integrity of wall construction and transfer of all imposed loads to the supporting structure. This chapter provides the requirements for the design and construction of wall systems that are capable of supporting the minimum design vertical loads (dead, live and snow loads) and lateral loads (wind or seismic loads). This chapter contains the prescriptive requirements for wall bracing and/or shear walls to resist the imposed lateral loads due to wind and seismic.

Chapter 6 also regulates exterior windows and doors installed in walls. This chapter contains criteria for the performance of exterior windows and doors and includes provisions for testing and labeling, garage doors, wind-borne debris protection and anchorage details.

Chapter 7 Wall Covering. Chapter 7 contains provisions for the design and construction of interior and exterior wall coverings. This chapter establishes the various types of materials, materials standards and methods of application permitted for use as interior coverings, including interior plaster, gypsum board, ceramic tile, wood veneer paneling, hardboard paneling, wood shakes and wood shingles. Chapter 7 also contains requirements for the use of vapor retarders for moisture control in walls.

Exterior wall coverings provide the weather-resistant exterior envelope that protects the building's interior from the elements. Chapter 7 provides the requirements for wind resistance and water-resistive barrier for exterior wall coverings. This chapter prescribes the exterior wall coverings as well as the water-resistive barrier required beneath the exterior materials. Exterior wall coverings regulated by this section include aluminum, stone and masonry veneer, wood, hardboard, particleboard, wood structural panel siding, wood shakes and shingles, exterior plaster, steel, vinyl, fiber cement and exterior insulation finish systems.

Chapter 8 Roof–ceiling Construction. Chapter 8 regulates the design and construction of roof-ceiling systems. This chapter contains two roof-ceiling framing systems: wood framing and cold-formed steel framing. Allowable span tables are provided to simplify the selection of rafter and ceiling joist size for wood roof framing and cold-formed steel framing. Chapter 8 also provides requirements for the application of ceiling finishes, the proper ventilation of concealed spaces in roofs (e.g., enclosed attics and rafter spaces), unvented attic assemblies and attic access.

Chapter 9 Roof Assemblies. Chapter 9 regulates the design and construction of roof assemblies. A roof assembly includes the roof deck, vapor retarder, substrate or thermal barrier, insulation, vapor retarder and roof covering. This chapter provides the requirement for wind resistance of roof coverings.

The types of roof covering materials and installation regulated by Chapter 9 are: asphalt shingles, clay and concrete tile, metal roof shingles, mineral-surfaced roll roofing, slate and slate-type shingles, wood shakes and shingles, built-up roofs, metal roof panels, modified bitumen roofing, thermoset and thermoplastic single-ply roofing, sprayed polyurethane foam roofing, liquid applied coatings and photovoltaic shingles. Chapter 9 also provides requirements for roof drainage, flashing, above deck thermal insulation, rooftop-mounted photovoltaic systems and recovering or replacing an existing roof covering.

Chapter 10 Chimneys and Fireplaces. Chapter 10 contains requirements for the safe construction of masonry chimneys and fireplaces and establishes the standards for the use and installation of factory-built chimneys, fireplaces and masonry heaters. Chimneys and fireplaces constructed of masonry rely on prescriptive requirements for the details of their construction; the factory-built type relies on the listing and labeling method of approval. Chapter 10 provides the requirements for seismic reinforcing and anchorage of masonry fireplaces and chimneys.

Chapters 11 through 28. Deleted.   MN <

Section P2904 Dwelling Unit Fire Sprinkler Systems. Section P2904 regulates the design   MN
and installation of residential fire sprinkler systems and is considered equivalent to NFPA 13D.   MN

Chapters 30 through 43. Deleted.   MN <

Chapter 44 Referenced Standards. The code contains numerous references to standards that are used to regulate materials and methods of construction. Chapter 44 contains a comprehensive list of all standards that are referenced in the code. The standards are part of the code to the extent of the reference to the standard. Compliance with the referenced standard is necessary for compliance with this code. By providing specifically adopted standards, the construction and installation requirements necessary for compliance with the code can be readily determined. The basis for code compliance is, therefore, established and available on an equal basis to the code official, contractor, designer and owner.

Chapter 44 is organized in a manner that makes it easy to locate specific standards. It lists all of the referenced standards, alphabetically, by acronym of the promulgating agency of the standard. Each agency's standards are then listed in either alphabetical or numeric order based upon the standard identification. The list also contains the title of the standard; the edition (date) of the standard referenced; any addenda included as part of the ICC adoption; and the section or sections of this code that reference the standard.

Appendices A through J. Deleted.   MN <

Appendix K Sound Transmission. Appendix K regulates the sound transmission of wall and floor-ceiling assemblies separating dwelling units and townhouse units. Airborne sound insulation is required for walls. Airborne sound insulation and impact sound insulation are required for floor-ceiling assemblies. The provisions in Appendix K set forth a minimum Sound Transmission Class (STC) rating for common walls and floor-ceiling assemblies between dwelling units. In addition, a minimum Impact Insulation Class (IIC) rating is also established to limit structureborne sound through common floor-ceiling assemblies separating dwelling units.

Appendices L through P. Deleted.

Appendix Q Tiny Houses. For dwelling units that are 400 square feet (37 m^2) or less in floor area, excluding lofts, Appendix Q provides relaxed provisions as compared to those in the body of the code. These provisions primarily address reduced ceiling heights for loft areas and specific stair and ladder detail requirements that allow for more compact designs where accessing lofts.

Appendices R through T. Deleted.

TABLE OF CONTENTS

CHAPTER 1

SCOPE AND ADMINISTRATION

This code shall be administered according to Minnesota Rules, Chapter 1300.
(See 1309.0100 for additional information)

2020 MINNESOTA BUILDING CODE ADMINISTRATION

1300.0010
ADMINISTRATION

Subpart 1. Scope. This chapter provides administrative provisions for all *Minnesota State Building Code* rule chapters identified in part 1300.0050. If specific administrative provisions are provided in a statute or rule chapter, the specific administrative provisions apply.

Subp. 2. Minnesota Electrical Act. Chapter 1315 shall be administered according to Chapter 3801 and the Minnesota Electrical Act, Minnesota Statutes, Sections 326B.31 to 326B.399. Provisions of this chapter that do not conflict with the Minnesota Electrical Act also apply.

Subp. 3. Minnesota Plumbing Code. Chapter 4714, the *Minnesota Plumbing Code*, and applicable provisions of this chapter shall be administered and enforced statewide by the commissioner under Minnesota Statutes, Section 326B.106, subdivision 3, unless an agreement exists between the commissioner and a municipality to enforce the *Minnesota Plumbing Code* under Minnesota Statutes, Section 326B.43, subdivision 2.

1300.0020
TITLE

The chapters listed in part 1300.0050, including the standards they adopt by reference, are the *Minnesota State Building Code* and may be cited as or referred to as the "code."

1300.0030
PURPOSE AND APPLICATION

Subpart 1. Purpose. The purpose of this code is to establish minimum requirements to safeguard the public health, safety, and general welfare through structural strength, means of egress facilities, stability, sanitation, adequate light and ventilation, energy conservation, and safety to life and property from fire and other hazards attributed to the built environment and to provide safety to firefighters and emergency responders during emergency operations.

The purpose of the code is not to create, establish, or designate a particular class or group of persons who will or should be especially protected or benefited by the terms of the code.

Subp. 2. Application.

A. The *State Building Code* is the standard that applies statewide for the construction, reconstruction, alteration, and repair of buildings and other structures of the type governed by the code, except as provided in Minnesota Statutes, Section 326B.121.

The *State Building Code* supersedes the building code of any municipality. The *State Building Code* does not apply to agricultural buildings except with respect to state inspections required or rulemaking authorized by Minnesota Statutes, Sections 103F.141,

326B.36, and 326B.121, subdivision 1, paragraph (c), clause (2).

B. The codes and standards referenced in a rule chapter are considered part of the requirements of the code to the prescribed extent of each reference. If differences occur between provisions of the code and referenced codes and standards, the provisions of the code apply.

C. In the event that a new edition of the code is adopted after a permit has been issued, the edition of the code current at the time of permit application shall remain in effect throughout the work authorized by the permit.

1300.0040
SCOPE

Subpart 1. Applicability. The code applies to the design, construction, addition, alteration, moving, replacement, demolition, repair, equipment, installation, use and occupancy, location, maintenance, and inspection of any building, structure, or building service equipment in a municipality, except work located primarily in a public way, public utility towers and poles, mechanical equipment not specifically regulated in the code, and hydraulic flood control structures.

Exception: When approved by the building official, buildings, structures, or portions thereof, used exclusively by military personnel, police, fire, or first responders for training purposes may be designed to reflect actual conditions that may be encountered in field operations, maneuvers, or tactics, however, structural provisions must apply.

Subp. 2. Compliance. Structures classified under part 1300.0070, subpart 12b, as IRC-1, IRC-2, IRC-3, and IRC-4 occupancies not more than three stories above grade plane in height with a separate means of egress shall comply with Chapter 1309 and other applicable rules. Other buildings and structures and appurtenances connected or attached to them shall comply with Chapter 1305 and other applicable rules.

Exception: The following structures that meet the scope of Chapter 1305 shall be permitted to be designed to comply with Minnesota Rules, Chapter 1311:

(1) existing buildings undergoing repair, alteration, change of occupancy, addition, or being moved; and

(2) historic buildings.

If different provisions of the code specify different materials, methods of construction, or other requirements, the most restrictive provision governs. If there is a conflict between a general requirement and a specific requirement, the specific requirement applies.

If reference is made in the code to an appendix, the provisions in the appendix do not apply unless specifically adopted by the code. Optional appendix chapters of the code identified in part 1300.0060 do not apply unless a municipality has specifically adopted them.

1300.0050
CHAPTERS OF MINNESOTA
STATE BUILDING CODE

The *Minnesota State Building Code* adopted under Minnesota Statutes, Section 326B.106, subdivision 1, includes the following chapters:

- A. 1300, Minnesota Building Code Administration;
- B. 1301, Building Official Certification;
- C. 1302, State Building Code Construction Approvals;
- D. 1303, Special Provisions;
- E. 1305, Minnesota Building Code;
- F. 1306, Special Fire Protection Systems;
- G. 1307, Elevators and Related Devices;
- H. 1309, Minnesota Residential Code;
- I. 1311, Minnesota Conservation Code for Existing Buildings;
- J. 1315, Minnesota Electrical Code;
- K. 1325, Solar Energy Systems;
- L. 1335, Floodproofing Regulations;
- M. 1341, Minnesota Accessibility Code;
- N. 1346, Minnesota Mechanical Code;
- O. 1350, Manufactured Homes;
- P. 1360, Prefabricated Structures;
- Q. 1361, Industrialized/Modular Buildings;
- R. 1370, Storm Shelters (Manufactured Home Parks);
- S. 4714, Minnesota Plumbing Code;
- T. 1322 and 1323, Minnesota Energy Codes; and
- U. 5230, Minnesota High Pressure Piping Systems.

1300.0060
OPTIONAL ADMINISTRATION

The following chapters of the code are not mandatory but may be adopted without change by a municipality which has adopted the code:

- A. Chapter 1306, Special Fire Protection Systems; and
- B. grading, IBC Appendix chapter J.

1300.0070
DEFINITIONS

Subpart 1. Scope; incorporation by reference. The definitions in this part apply to parts 1300.0010 to 1300.0250. For terms that are not defined through the methods authorized by this chapter, the Merriam-Webster Collegiate Dictionary, available at www.m-w.com, shall be considered as providing ordinarily accepted meanings. The dictionary is incorporated by reference, is subject to frequent change, and is available through the Minitex interlibrary loan system.

Subp. 2. Administrative authority. "Administrative authority" means a municipality's governing body or its assigned administrative authority.

Subp. 3. [Repealed].

Subp. 4. Agricultural building. "Agricultural building" means a building that meets the requirements of Minnesota Statutes, Section 326B.103, subdivision 3.

Subp. 4a. Approved. "Approved" means approval by the building official, pursuant to the *Minnesota State Building Code*, by reason of:

- A. inspection, investigation, or testing;
- B. accepted principles;
- C. computer simulations;
- D. research reports; or
- E. testing performed by either a licensed engineer or by a locally or nationally recognized testing laboratory.

Subp. 5. Building official. "Building official" means the municipal building code official certified under Minnesota Statutes, Section 326B.133, subdivisions 2 and 3.

Subp. 6. Building service equipment. "Building service equipment" refers to the plumbing, mechanical, electrical, and elevator equipment, including piping, wiring, fixtures, and other accessories, that provides sanitation, lighting, heating, ventilation, cooling, refrigeration, firefighting, and transportation facilities essential to the occupancy of the building or structure for its designated use and occupancy.

Subp. 7. City. "City" means a home rule charter or statutory city.

Subp. 8. Code. For the purposes of chapter 1300, "Code" means the *Minnesota State Building Code* adopted under Minnesota Statutes, Section 326B.106, subdivision 1, and includes the chapters identified in part 1300.0020.

Subp. 9. Commissioner. "Commissioner" means the commissioner of labor and industry.

Subp. 10. Designate. "Designate" means the formal designation by a municipality's administrative authority of a certified building official accepting responsibility for code administration.

Subp. 10a. [Repealed].

Subp. 11. [Repealed].

Subp. 11a. Electric substation. "Electric substation" means an enclosed assemblage of equipment, including switches, circuit breakers, buses, and transformers that are accessible only to employees of an electric utility or persons acting under the electric utility's control or direction, through which electric energy is passed for the purpose of switching or modifying the electric energy's characteristics to increase or decrease voltage or control frequency.

Subp. 12. [Repealed].

Subp. 12a. Historical building. "Historical building" means any building or structure that is listed in the National Register of Historic Places, designated as a historic property under local or state designation law; certified as a contributing resource within a National Register listed or locally designated historic district; or with an opinion or certification that the property is eligible to be listed on the National or State Register of Historic Places either individually or as a contributing building to a historic district by the State Historic Preservation Officer or the Keeper of the National Register of Historic Places.

Subp. 12b. *International Residential Code* **(IRC) occupancy classifications.** *International Residential Code* (IRC) occupancy classifications are as follows:

IRC-1 single-family dwellings;

IRC-2 two-family dwellings;

IRC-3 townhouses; and

IRC-4 accessory structures:

    A. garages;

    B. storage sheds; and

    C. similar structures.

Subp. 13. Mandatory terms. "Mandatory terms" include "must" and "shall," which have the same meaning.

Subp. 14. Manufactured home. "Manufactured home" has the meaning given in Minnesota Statutes, Section 327.31, subdivision 3, and for the purpose of determining occupancy separations, is considered a Group IRC-1 occupancy.

Subp. 15. Master plan. "Master plan" is a plan that has been reviewed for code compliance by the building official and stamped "Reviewed for Code Compliance."

Subp. 16. Mayor and city council. "Mayor" and "city council" mean governing body whenever they appear in the code.

Subp. 17. Municipality. "Municipality" means a city, county, or town; the University of Minnesota; or the state of Minnesota for public buildings and state licensed facilities.

Subp. 18. [Repealed].

Subp. 19. Performance-based design. An engineering approach to design elements of a building based on agreed upon performance goals and objectives, engineering analysis, and quantitative assessment of alternatives against the design goals and objectives, using accepted engineering tools, methodologies, and performance criteria.

Subp. 19a. Public building. "Public building" means a building and its grounds the cost of which is paid for by the state or a state agency regardless of its cost, and a building project for a school district or charter school the cost of which is $100,000 or more.

Subp. 20. Recyclable materials. "Recyclable materials" means materials that are separated from mixed municipal solid waste for the purpose of recycling, including paper, glass, plastic, metals, automobile oil, and batteries. Refuse-derived fuel or other material that is destroyed by incineration is not a recyclable material.

Subp. 21. Recycling. "Recycling" means the process of collecting and preparing recyclable materials and reusing the materials in their original form or using them in manufacturing processes that do not cause the destruction of recyclable materials in a manner that precludes further use.

Subp. 22. [Repealed].

Subp. 23. [Repealed].

Subp. 24. State building official. "State building official" means the person who, under the direction and supervision of the commissioner, administers the code.

Subp. 25. State licensed facilities. "State licensed facilities" means, pursuant to Minnesota Statutes, Section 326B.103,

subdivision 13, a building and its grounds that are licensed by the state as a hospital, nursing home, supervised living facility, free-standing outpatient surgical center, correctional facility, boarding care home, or residential hospice.

Subp. 26. State-owned buildings. "State-owned buildings" means buildings and structures financed in whole or in part by state funds that are under the exclusive jurisdiction and custodial control of one or more state department or agency.

1300.0080
CODE ADOPTION AND AMENDMENTS

Under Minnesota Statutes, Section 326B.106, the code is adopted and periodically updated to include current editions of national model codes in general use and existing statewide specialty codes and their amendments.

Under Minnesota Statutes, Section 326B.13, subdivisions 5 and 6, amendments to the code may be proposed and initiated by any interested person. Proposed amendments must be submitted in writing on a form provided by the commissioner.

1300.0090
DEPARTMENT OF BUILDING SAFETY

Subpart 1. Creation of enforcement agency. There is hereby established in the municipality a code enforcement agency and the official in charge is the designated building official. The agency is referred to in the code as the "Department of Building Safety."

Subp. 2. Appointment. The building official shall be designated by the municipality according to Minnesota Statutes, Section 326B.133.

1300.0110
DUTIES AND POWERS OF BUILDING OFFICIAL

Subpart 1. General. The building official is authorized and directed to enforce the provisions of this code. The building official has the authority to render interpretations of the code and adopt policies and procedures in order to clarify the application of the provisions. The interpretations, policies, and procedures shall comply with the intent and purpose of the code. The policies and procedures shall not have the effect of waiving requirements specifically provided for in the code.

Subp. 2. Deputies. According to the prescribed procedures of the municipality and with the concurrence of the appointing authority, the building official may designate a deputy building official and related technical officers, inspectors, plan examiners, and other employees. The employees have the powers delegated by the building official.

Subp. 3. Applications and permits. The building official shall receive applications, review construction documents, and issue permits for the erection, alteration, demolition, moving, and repair of buildings and structures, including all other equipment and systems regulated by the code. When requested by a permit applicant, the building official shall meet with the permit applicant prior to the application for a construction permit to discuss plans for the proposed work. The meeting shall be held at a mutually agreeable location. Municipalities may establish a fee for this service.

Subp. 4. Notices and orders. The building official shall issue all necessary notices and orders to ensure compliance with the code. Notices and orders shall be in writing unless waived by the permit applicant, contractor, owner, or owner's agent. Notices and orders shall be based on the edition of the code under which the permit has been issued.

Subp. 5. Inspections. The building official shall make all of the required inspections or accept reports of inspection by approved agencies or individuals. Results of inspections shall be documented on the job site inspection card and in the official records of the municipality, including type of inspection, date of inspection, identification of the responsible individual making the inspection, and comments regarding approval or disapproval of the inspection. The building official is authorized to engage an expert opinion as deemed necessary to report on any unusual technical issues that arise.

Subp. 6. Identification. The building official and deputies shall carry proper identification when inspecting structures or premises in the performance of duties under the code.

Subp. 7. Right of entry. If it is necessary to make an inspection to enforce the code or if the building official has reasonable cause to believe that there exists in a structure or upon a premises a condition contrary to or in violation of the code that makes the structure or premises unsafe, dangerous, or hazardous, the building official or designee may enter the structure or premises at reasonable times to inspect or to perform the duties imposed by the code, provided that if the structure or premises is occupied, credentials must be presented to the occupant and entry requested. If the structure or premises is unoccupied, the building official shall first make a reasonable effort to locate the owner or other person having charge or control of the structure or premises and request entry. If entry is refused, the building official shall have recourse to the remedies provided by law to secure entry.

Subp. 8. Department records. The building official shall be responsible for official records of the local Department of Building Safety for permit applications received, plans, specifications, surveys, plot plans, plan reviews, permits and certificates issued, reports of inspections, and notices and orders issued by the department. The records shall be kept according to the records management schedule of the municipality required by Minnesota Statutes, Section 138.17.

Subp. 9. Liability. The building official, member of the Board of Appeals, or employee charged with the enforcement of the code, while acting for the jurisdiction in good faith and without malice in the discharge of the duties required by the code or other pertinent laws or ordinances, is not rendered personally liable and is relieved from personal liability for any damage accruing to persons or property as a result of any act or by reason of an act or omission in the discharge of official duties. Any suit instituted against an officer or employee because of an act performed by that officer or employee in the lawful discharge of duties and under the code shall be defended by the legal representative of the jurisdiction until the final termination of the proceedings. The building official, member of the Board of Appeals, or an employee charged with the enforcement of the code, is not liable for costs in any action, suit, or proceeding that is instituted in pursuance of the provisions of this code.

Subp. 10. Approved materials and equipment. Materials, equipment, and devices approved by the building official shall be constructed and installed in the approved manner.

Subp. 11. Used material and equipment. The use of used materials that meet the requirements of the code for new materials is permitted. Used equipment and devices shall not be reused unless approved by the building official.

Subp. 12. Modifications. If there are practical difficulties involved in carrying out the provisions of the code, the building official may grant modifications for individual cases, upon application by the owner or owner's representative, provided the building official finds that special individual reason makes the strict letter of the code impractical, the modification is in compliance with the intent and purpose of the code, and the modification does not lessen health, life, and fire safety or structural requirements. The details of action granting modifications shall be recorded and entered in the files of the Department of Building Safety.

Subp. 13. Alternative materials, design, and methods of construction and equipment. The code is not intended to prevent the installation of any material or to prohibit any design or method of construction not specifically prescribed by the code, provided that any alternative has been approved. An alternative material, design, or method of construction shall be approved where the building official finds that the proposed design is satisfactory and complies with the intent of the code, and that the material, method, or work offered is, for the purpose intended, at least the equivalent of that prescribed in the code in quality, strength, effectiveness, fire resistance, durability, and safety. The details of any action granting or denying approval of an alternate shall be recorded and entered in the files of the Department of Building Safety. The permit applicant may request written documentation of the denial, including the reasons for the denial.

Subp. 14. Performance-based fire and life safety design. The code official may approve performance-based fire and life safety designs if the code official finds that the proposed design has been conducted by an approved method. Approved performance-based designs are evidence of compliance with the intent of the code. Approvals under this subpart are subject to the approval of the building code official whenever the design involves matters regulated by the building code.

   A. Design goals, objectives, and performance criteria shall be approved by the code official before submission of a performance-based design report, calculations, or analysis results. As a minimum, an approved performance-based design shall address the following objectives:

      (1) life safety of occupants;

      (2) firefighter safety;

      (3) property protection;

      (4) continuity of operations; and

      (5) safeguarding of the environment.

B. To determine the acceptability of a performance-based design, the code official may require the owner or agent to provide, without charge to the jurisdiction, a technical opinion and report. The code official may require the technical opinion and report to be prepared by, and bear the stamp of, a licensed design professional.

C. Performance-based designs shall be prepared by, and bear the stamp of, a licensed design professional competent in the area of work. The design professional shall provide written confirmation to the code official before a certificate of occupancy is issued that the performance-based design has been properly implemented, the operation or use of the building is within the limitations of the design, and adequate controls are in place to maintain compliance with the conditions of the design throughout the life of the building.

Subp. 15. Tests. If there is insufficient evidence of compliance with the code, or evidence that a material or method does not conform to the requirements of the code, or in order to substantiate claims for alternative materials or methods, the building official shall have the authority to require tests as evidence of compliance to be made at no expense to the municipality. Test methods shall be as specified in the code or by other recognized test standards. In the absence of recognized and accepted test methods, the building official shall approve the testing procedures. Tests shall be performed by an approved agency. Reports of the tests shall be retained by the building official.

1300.0120
PERMITS

Subpart 1. Required. An owner or authorized agent who intends to construct, enlarge, alter, repair, move, demolish, or change the occupancy of a building or structure, or to erect, install, enlarge, alter, repair, remove, convert, or replace any gas, mechanical, electrical, plumbing system, or other equipment, the installation of which is regulated by the code; or cause any such work to be done, shall first make application to the building official and obtain the required permit.

Subp. 2. Annual permit. In lieu of an individual permit for each alteration to an already approved electrical, gas, mechanical, or plumbing installation, the building official may issue an annual permit upon application for the permit to any person, firm, or corporation regularly employing one or more qualified trade persons in the building, structure, or on the premises owned or operated by the applicant for the permit.

Subp. 3. Annual permit records. The person to whom an annual permit is issued shall keep a detailed record of alterations made under the annual permit. The building official shall have access to the records at all times or the records shall be filed with the building official as designated.

Subp. 4. Work exempt from permit. Exemptions from permit requirements of the code do not authorize work to be done in any manner in violation of the code or any other laws or ordinances of this jurisdiction. Permits shall not be required for the following:

A. Building:

(1) One-story detached accessory structures, used as tool and storage sheds, playhouses, and similar uses, provided the floor area does not exceed 200 square feet (18.58 m²);

(2) Fences not over 7 feet (2,134 mm) high;

(3) Oil derricks;

(4) Retaining walls that are not over 4 feet (1,219 mm) in height measured from the bottom of the footing to the top of the wall, unless supporting a surcharge or impounding Class I, II, or III-A liquids;

(5) Water tanks supported directly upon grade if the capacity does not exceed 5,000 gallons (18,927 L) and the ratio of height to diameter or width does not exceed 2 to 1;

(6) Sidewalks and driveways that are not part of an accessible route;

(7) Decks and platforms not more than 30 inches (762 mm) above adjacent grade and not attached to a structure with frost footings and which is not part of an accessible route;

(8) Painting, papering, tiling, carpeting, cabinets, countertops, and similar finish work;

(9) Temporary motion picture, television, and theater stage sets and scenery;

(10) Prefabricated swimming pools installed entirely above ground accessory to dwelling units constructed to the provisions of the *International Residential Code* or R-3 occupancies constructed to the provisions of the *International Building Code*, which do not exceed both 5,000 gallons in capacity (18 925 L) and a 24-inch (610 mm) depth;

(11) Window awnings supported by an exterior wall that do not project more than 54 inches (1372 mm) from the exterior wall and do not require additional support, when constructed under the *International Residential Code* or Group R-3 and Group U occupancies constructed to the provisions of the *International Building Code*;

(12) Movable cases, counters, and partitions not over five feet, nine inches (1753 mm) in height;

(13) Swings and other playground equipment; and

(14) Electric substation facilities, including:

    (a) foundations that support electrical equipment;

    (b) foundations and enclosures affixed with an Interstate Industrialized Buildings Commission (IIBC) label that contain electrical equipment only; and

(c) fencing that encloses the substation facilities or any part thereof.

Unless otherwise exempted, plumbing, electrical, and mechanical permits are required for subitems (1) to (14).

B. Gas:

(1) Portable heating, cooking, or clothes drying appliances;

(2) Replacement of any minor part that does not alter approval of equipment or make the equipment unsafe; and

(3) portable fuel cell appliances that are not connected to a fixed piping system and are not interconnected to a power grid.

C. Mechanical:

(1) Portable heating appliances;

(2) Portable ventilation appliances and equipment;

(3) Portable cooling units;

(4) Steam, hot, or chilled water piping within any heating or cooling equipment regulated by this code;

(5) Replacement of any part that does not alter approval of equipment or make the equipment unsafe;

(6) Portable evaporative coolers;

(7) Self-contained refrigeration systems containing ten pounds (4.5 kg) or less of refrigerant or that are actuated by motors of one horsepower (0.75 kW) or less; and

(8) Portable fuel cell appliances that are not connected to a fixed piping system and are not interconnected to a power grid.

D. Electrical: a municipality must not require an electrical permit if the work falls under the jurisdiction of the commissioner or if the work is exempt from inspection under Minnesota Statutes, Section 326B.36, subdivision 7. This exemption does not exempt the work from other *State Building Code* requirements relating to electrical equipment.

Subp. 5. Emergency repairs. If equipment replacements and repairs must be performed in an emergency situation, the permit application shall be submitted to the building official within the next working business day.

Subp. 6. Repairs. Application or notice to the building official is not required for ordinary repairs to structures. The repairs shall not include the opening or removal of any wall, partition, or portion of a wall or partition, the removal or cutting of any structural beam or load bearing support, or the removal or change of any required means of egress, or rearrangement of parts of a structure affecting the egress requirements; nor shall ordinary repairs include addition to, alteration of, replacement, or relocation of any standpipe, water supply, sewer, drainage, drain leader, gas, soil, waste, vent or similar piping, electric wiring, or mechanical or other work affecting public health or general safety.

Subp. 7. Application for permit. To obtain a permit, the applicant shall file an application in writing on a form furnished by the Department of Building Safety for that purpose. The application shall:

A. Identify and describe the work to be covered by the permit for which application is made;

B. Describe the land on which the proposed work is to be done by legal description, street address, or similar description that will readily identify and definitely locate the proposed building or work;

C. Indicate the use and occupancy for which the proposed work is intended;

D. Indicate the type of construction;

E. Be accompanied by construction documents and other information as required by the code;

F. State the valuation of the proposed work;

G. Be signed by the applicant, or the applicant's authorized agent; and

H. Give other data and information required by the building official.

Subp. 8. Action on application. The building official shall examine or cause to be examined applications for permits and amendments within a reasonable time after filing. If the application or the construction documents do not conform to the requirements of pertinent laws, the building official shall reject the application and notify the applicant of the reasons. The building official shall document the reasons for rejecting the application. The applicant may request written documentation of the rejection and the reasons for the rejection. When the building official is satisfied that the proposed work conforms to the requirements of the code and applicable laws and ordinances, the building official shall issue a permit.

Subp. 9. Time limitation of application. An application for a permit for any proposed work shall be considered abandoned 180 days after the date of filing, unless the application has been pursued in good faith or a permit has been issued; except that the building official is authorized to grant one or more extensions of time for additional periods not exceeding 180 days each. The extension shall be requested in writing and justifiable cause demonstrated.

Subp. 10. Validity of permit. The issuance or granting of a permit or approval of plans, specifications, and computations, shall not be construed to be a permit for any violation of the code or of any other ordinance of the jurisdiction. Permits presuming to give authority to violate or cancel the provisions of the code or other ordinances of the jurisdiction are not valid. Any permit issued becomes invalid if the work authorized by the permit is suspended or abandoned for more than 180 days. The 180 days commences the first day the work was suspended or abandoned.

Subp. 11. Expiration. Every permit issued expires unless the work authorized by the permit is commenced within 180 days after its issuance. The building official shall grant, in writing, extensions of time, for periods not more than 180 days each if the applicant demonstrates justifiable cause for the extension to the building official.

Subp. 12. Suspension or revocation. The building official may suspend or revoke a permit issued under the code if the permit is issued in error; on the basis of incorrect, inaccurate, or incomplete information; or in violation of any ordinance or regulation or the code.

Subp. 13. Information and placement of permit. The building permit or a copy shall be kept on the site of the work until the completion of the project. Pursuant to Minnesota Statutes, Section 15.41, the permit shall specify the name and address of the applicant, and the general contractor, if one exists. All construction permits shall be posted in a conspicuous and accessible place at the premises or site of construction.

Subp. 14. Responsibility. Every person who performs work for the installation or repair of building, structure, electrical, gas, mechanical, or plumbing systems, for which the code is applicable, shall comply with the code. The person, firm, or organization securing the permit is responsible for code compliance for the work being performed.

1300.0130
CONSTRUCTION DOCUMENTS

Subpart 1. Submittal documents. Construction documents, special inspection and structural observation programs, and other data shall be submitted in one or more sets with each application for a permit.

> **Exception:** The building official may waive the submission of construction documents and other data if the nature of the work applied for is such that reviewing of construction documents is not necessary to obtain compliance with the code.

The building officer may require plans or other data be prepared according to the rules of the Board of Architecture, Engineering, Land Surveying, Landscape Architecture, Geoscience and Interior Design, Chapter 1800, and Minnesota Statutes, Sections 326.02 to 326.15, and other state laws relating to plan and specification preparation by occupational licenses. If special conditions exist, the building official may require additional construction documents to be prepared by a licensed design professional.

Subp. 2. Information on construction documents. Construction documents shall be dimensioned and drawn upon suitable material. Electronic media documents are permitted to be submitted when approved by the building official. Construction documents shall be of sufficient clarity to indicate the location, nature, and extent of the work proposed and show in detail that it will conform to the code and relevant laws, ordinances, rules, and regulations, as determined by the building official.

Subp. 3. Manufacturer's installation instructions. When required by the building official, manufacturer's installation instructions for construction equipment and components regulated by the code, shall be available on the job site at the time of inspection.

Subp. 4. Site plan. The construction documents submitted with the application for permit shall be accompanied by a site plan drawn to scale, showing the size and location of new construction and existing structures on the site, distances from lot lines, the established street grades, and the proposed finished grades, and it shall be drawn according to an accurate boundary line survey. In the case of demolition, the site plan shall show construction to be demolished and the location and size of existing structures and construction that are to remain on the site or plot. The building official may waive or modify the requirement for a site plan if the application for permit is for alteration or repair or when otherwise warranted.

Subp. 5. Examination of documents. The building official shall examine or cause to be examined the accompanying construction documents to ascertain whether the construction indicated and described complies with the requirements of the code and other pertinent laws and ordinances.

Subp. 6. Approval of construction documents.

A. If the building official issues a permit, the construction documents shall be approved in writing or by a stamp, stating "Reviewed for Code Compliance," dated, and signed by the building official or an authorized representative. One set of the construction documents that were reviewed shall be retained by the building official. The other set shall be returned to the applicant, kept at the site of the work, and open to inspection by the building official or an authorized representative.

B. Any code deficiencies identified by the building official during the plan review process for construction documents that are prepared by a design professional who is licensed or certified under Minnesota Statutes, Sections 326.02 to 326.15, must be itemized by the building official through a comprehensive plan review letter only. Any code deficiencies identified by the building official during the plan review process for construction documents that are not prepared by a licensed or certified design professional may be marked directly on the document or itemized by the building official through a comprehensive plan review letter. The issuance of a permit based on construction documents and other data does not prevent the building official from requiring the correction of errors in the construction documents and other data. All sets of required construction documents, including the site copy, municipality copy, or inspector copy, must be marked identically by the building official, with one copy retained by the building official after construction is completed. Work regulated by the code must be installed according to the reviewed construction documents. Work that does not comply with approved construction documents must not proceed until the applicant submits changes that are approved by the building official.

Subp. 7. Previous approvals. The code in effect at the time of application shall be applicable.

Subp. 8. Phased approval. The building official may issue a permit for the construction of foundations or any other part of a building or structure before the construction documents for the whole building or structure have been submitted, provided that adequate information and detailed statements have been filed complying with pertinent requirements of the code. The holder of the permit for the foundation or other parts of a building or structure shall proceed at the holder's own risk with the building operation and without assurance that a permit for the entire structure will be granted.

Subp. 9. Design professional in responsible charge.

A. The building official may require the owner to engage and designate on the building permit application a licensed design professional who shall act as the licensed design professional in responsible charge. If the circumstances require, the owner shall designate a substitute licensed design professional in responsible charge who shall perform the duties required of the original licensed design professional in responsible charge. The building official shall be notified in writing by the owner if the licensed design professional in responsible charge is changed or is unable to continue to perform the duties.

The licensed design professional in responsible charge shall be responsible for reviewing and coordinating submittal documents prepared by others, including phased and deferred submittal items, for compatibility with the design of the building.

When structural observation is required by the code, the inspection program shall name the individual or firms who are to perform structural observation and describe the stages of construction at which structural observation is to occur.

B. For the purposes of this part, deferred submittals are defined as those portions of the design that are not submitted at the time of the application and that are to be submitted to the building official within a specified period.

Deferral of any submittal items shall have the prior approval of the building official. The licensed design professional in responsible charge shall list the deferred submittals on the construction documents for review by the building official.

Submittal documents for deferred submittal items shall be submitted to the licensed design professional in responsible charge who shall review them and forward them to the building official with a notation indicating that the deferred submittal documents have been reviewed and that they have been found to be in general conformance with the design of the building. The deferred submittal items shall not be installed until their design and submittal documents have been approved by the building official.

C. Work regulated by the code shall be installed according to the reviewed construction documents, and any changes made during construction that are not in compliance with the approved construction documents shall be resubmitted for approval as an amended set of construction documents.

1300.0140
VIOLATIONS

It is unlawful for any person, firm, or corporation to erect, construct, alter, extend, repair, move, remove, demolish, or occupy any building, structure, or equipment regulated by the code, or cause any of those actions, in conflict with or in violation of the code. The building official may serve a notice of violation or order on the person responsible for the erection, construction, alteration, extension, repair, moving, removal, demolition, or occupancy of a building or structure in violation of the code, or in violation of a permit or certificate issued under the code. The order shall direct the discontinuance of the illegal action or condition and the abatement of the violation.

1300.0150
VIOLATIONS, PENALTY

A violation of the code is a misdemeanor under Minnesota Statutes, Section 326B.082.

1300.0160
FEES

Subpart 1. Schedule of permit fees. The applicant for a permit for a building; structure; or electrical, gas, mechanical, or plumbing system or alterations requiring a permit shall pay the fee set forth by a fee schedule adopted by the municipality.

When submittal documents are required to be submitted by this chapter, a plan review fee shall be required. The plan review fee shall be established by the fee schedule adopted by the municipality.

Exception: The fee schedule adopted by the municipality may exempt minor work from plan review fees.

Subp. 2. Fees commensurate with service. Fees established by the municipality must be by legal means and must be fair, reasonable, and proportionate to the actual cost of the service for which the fee is imposed.

Subp. 3. Building permit valuations. The applicant for a permit shall provide an estimated permit value at time of application. Permit valuations shall include total value of all construction work, including materials and labor, for which the permit is being issued, such as electrical, gas, mechanical, plumbing equipment, and permanent systems. Building permit valuation shall be set by the building official.

Exceptions: Building permit valuations for the following structures shall be based on the valuation of on-site work only:

A. Manufactured homes containing a Housing and Urban Development (HUD) certification label;

B. Prefabricated buildings with a Department of Labor and Industry prefabrication label; and

C. Industrialized/modular buildings with an Interstate Industrialized Buildings Commission (IIBC) label.

Subp. 4. Building permit fees. Building permit fees shall be based on valuation.

Exceptions:

A. one- and two-family dwelling maintenance permits for roofing, siding, windows, doors, or other minor projects may be charged a fixed fee; and

B. permits for plumbing, mechanical, electrical, or other building service equipment systems may be based on valuation or charged a fixed fee.

Subp. 5. Plan review fees for similar plans. When submittal documents for similar plans are approved under subpart 6, plan review fees shall not exceed 25 percent of the normal building permit fee established and charged by the jurisdiction for the same structure.

Subp. 6. Plan review of similar plans.

A. Any number of similar buildings may be built from a master plan if:

(1) Plan review fees have been paid for the master plan;

(2) A code change has not occurred that impacts the design of a master plan;

(3) The similar building has the same physical dimensions and structural design as the master plan;

> **Exception:** The following modifications to the master plan are not considered to be significant modifications, according to Minnesota Statutes, Section 326B.106, subdivision 1, and are permitted for dwelling units and their accessory structures built to the *International Residential Code*, and residential occupancies built to the *International Building Code* that are three stories or less in height and their accessory structures:
>
> (a) foundation configurations of walkout, lookout, and full basements;
>
> (b) alternate foundation materials approved by the building official;
>
> (c) roof design changed by a revised truss plan approved by the building official; and
>
> (d) other modifications approved by the building official;

(4) Occupancy groups other than those identified in the exceptions listed in part 1300.0160, subpart 6, item A, subitem (3), must be the same type of construction and occupancy classification and must have the same exit system;

> **Exception:** Minor changes to the exit access; and

(5) The similar plan is based on a master plan for which the municipality has issued a permit within the last 12 months.

B. Plan review fees for similar building plans must be based on the costs commensurate with the direct and indirect cost of the service, but must not exceed 25 percent of the normal building permit fee established and charged by the municipality for the same structure.

C. The plan review fee charged for similar building plans applies to all buildings regulated by the code regardless of occupancy classification including industrialized/

modular buildings constructed under a program specified in Minnesota Statutes, Section 326B.194.

D. The applicant must submit a new plan set and other information as required by the building official for each building reviewed as a similar building.

Subp. 7. Payment of fees. A permit shall not be issued until the fees prescribed by the municipality have been paid.

Subp. 8. Work commencing before permit issuance. If work for which a permit is required by the code has been commenced without first obtaining a permit, a special investigation shall be made before a permit may be issued for the work. An investigation fee established by the municipality shall be collected whether or not a permit is issued and is in addition to the required permit fees, but it may not exceed the permit fee. The investigation fee must comply with requirements for fees in subpart 2.

Subp. 9. Fee refunds. The municipality shall establish a permit and plan review fee refund policy.

Subp. 10. State surcharge fees. All municipal permits issued for work under the code are subject to a surcharge fee. The fees are established by Minnesota Statutes, Section 326B.148. Reports and remittances by municipalities must be filed with the commissioner.

Surcharge fees imposed by the state are in addition to municipal permit fees. Surcharge report forms and information may be obtained by writing the commissioner.

1300.0170
STOP WORK ORDER

If the building official finds any work regulated by the code being performed in a manner contrary to the provisions of the code or in a dangerous or unsafe manner, the building official is authorized to issue a stop work order or a notice or order pursuant to part 1300.0110, subpart 4.

The stop work order shall be in writing and issued to the owner of the property involved, to the owner's agent, or to the person doing the work. Upon issuance of a stop work order, the cited work shall immediately cease. A person who continues work after having been served with a stop work order, except for work that the person is directed to perform to remove a violation or unsafe condition, is subject to penalties as prescribed by law. The stop work order shall state the reason for the order and the conditions under which the cited work will be permitted to resume.

1300.0180
UNSAFE BUILDINGS OR STRUCTURES

A building or structure regulated by the code is unsafe, for purposes of this part, if it is structurally unsafe, not provided with adequate egress, a fire hazard, or otherwise dangerous to human life.

Building service equipment that is regulated by the code is unsafe, for purposes of this part, if it is a fire, electrical, or health hazard; an unsanitary condition; or otherwise dangerous to human life. Use of a building, structure, or building service equipment constituting a hazard to safety, health, or public welfare by reason of inadequate maintenance, dilapidation, obsolescence, fire hazard, disaster, damage, or abandonment is, for the purposes of this part, an unsafe use. Parapet walls, cornices, spires, towers, tanks, statuary, and other appendages or structural members that are supported by, attached to, or a part of a building and that are in deteriorated condition or otherwise unable to sustain the design loads that are specified in the code are unsafe building appendages.

The building official shall order any building or portion of a building to be vacated if continued use is dangerous to life, health, or safety of the occupants. The building official shall have the authority to order disconnection of utility services to the building, structure, or system, regulated by the code, in case of an emergency to eliminate a hazard to life or property. The order shall be in writing and state the reasons for the action.

All unsafe buildings, structures, or appendages are public nuisances and must be abated by repair, rehabilitation, demolition, or removal according to Minnesota Statutes, Sections 463.15 to 463.26.

1300.0190
TEMPORARY STRUCTURES AND USES

Subpart 1. General. The building official may issue a permit for temporary structures and temporary uses.

Subp. 2. Conformance. Temporary structures and uses shall conform to the structural strength, fire safety, means of egress, accessibility, light, ventilation, and sanitary requirements of the code as necessary to ensure the public health, safety, and general welfare.

Subp. 3. Termination of approval. The building official may terminate the permit for a temporary structure or use and order the temporary structure or use to be discontinued if the conditions required in this part have not been complied with.

1300.0210
INSPECTIONS

Subpart 1. General. Construction or work for which a permit is required is subject to inspection by the building official and the construction or work shall remain accessible and exposed for inspection purposes until approved. Approval as a result of an inspection is not approval of a violation of the code or of other ordinances of the jurisdiction. Inspections presuming to give authority to violate or cancel the provisions of the code or of other ordinances of the jurisdiction are not valid. It shall be the duty of the permit applicant to cause the work to remain accessible and exposed for inspection purposes. Neither the building official nor the jurisdiction is liable for expense entailed in the removal or replacement of any material required to allow inspection.

Subp. 2. Preliminary inspection. Before issuing a permit, the building official may examine, or cause to be examined, buildings, structures, and sites for which an application has been filed.

Subp. 3. Inspection record card. The building official shall identify which inspections are required for the work requiring a permit. Work requiring a permit shall not be commenced until the permit holder or an agent of the permit holder has posted or otherwise made available an inspection record card that allows the building official to conveniently make all required entries regarding inspection of the work. This card shall be maintained and made available by the permit holder until final approval has been granted by the building official.

Subp. 4. Inspection requests. The building official shall provide the applicant with policies, procedures, and a timeline for requesting inspections. The person doing the work authorized by a permit shall notify the building official that the work is ready for inspection. The person requesting an inspection required by the code shall provide access to and means for inspection of the work.

Subp. 5. Approval required. Work shall not be done beyond the point indicated in each successive inspection without first obtaining the approval of the building official. The building official, upon notification, shall make the requested inspections and shall either indicate the portion of the construction that is satisfactory as completed or notify the permit holder or an agent of the permit holder of any failures to comply with the code. Any portion that does not comply shall be corrected and the portion shall not be covered or concealed until authorized by the building official.

Subp. 6. Required inspections. The building official, upon notification, shall make the inspections in this part. In addition to the inspections identified in this subpart, see applicable rule chapters in part 1300.0050 for specific inspection and testing requirements.

   A. Footing inspections shall be made after excavations for footings are complete and any required reinforcing steel is in place. Materials for the foundation shall be on the job, except that concrete need not be on the job if the concrete is ready mixed according to approved nationally recognized standards.

   B. Foundations:

   (1) Foundation inspections for poured walls shall be made after all forms are in place with any required reinforcing steel and bracing in place, and prior to pouring concrete.

   (2) All foundation walls shall be inspected prior to backfill for specific code requirements.

   (3) The foundation inspection shall include excavations for thickened slabs intended for the support of bearing walls, partitions, structural supports, or equipment.

   C. Concrete slab and under-floor inspections shall be made after in-slab or under-floor reinforcing steel and building service equipment, conduit, piping accessories, and other ancillary equipment items are in place, but before any concrete is placed or floor sheathing installed, including the subfloor.

   D. Rough-in inspections of plumbing, mechanical, gas, sprinklers, alarms, and electrical systems shall be made before covering or concealment, before fixtures or appliances are set or installed, and before framing inspection.

E. Inspection of framing and masonry construction shall be made after the roof, masonry, framing, firestopping, draftstopping, and bracing are in place and after the plumbing, mechanical, and electrical rough inspections are approved.

F. Energy efficiency inspections shall be made to determine compliance with *Minnesota Energy Code* requirements.

G. Lath and gypsum board inspections shall be made after lathing and gypsum board, interior and exterior, are in place, but before any plastering is applied or before gypsum board joints and fasteners are taped and finished.

> **Exception:** Gypsum board that is not part of a fire-resistive assembly or a shear assembly.

H. Protection of joints and penetrations in fire-resistance-rated or smoke-resistance-rated assemblies shall not be concealed from view until inspected and approved.

I. Installation of manufactured homes (mobile homes) shall be made after the installation of the support systems and all utility service connections are in place, but before any covering material or skirting is in place. Evaluation of an approved anchoring system is part of the installation inspection.

J. Fireplaces must be inspected for compliance with applicable requirements of the code and the manufacturer's installation instructions.

K. A final inspection shall be made for all work for which a permit is issued.

L. Special inspections shall be as required by the code.

M. In addition to the inspections in items A to K, the building official is authorized to make or require other inspections of any construction work to ascertain compliance with the code and other laws that are enforced by the Department of Building Safety.

Subp. 7. Inspection agencies. The building official is authorized to accept inspection reports by approved agencies.

1300.0215
PLUMBING

Subpart 1. Inspections, testing, and permits.

A. For purposes of this part, "administrative authority" is defined in part 4714.0203.

B. Except as provided in item C, new plumbing systems or parts of existing plumbing systems that have been altered, extended, or repaired shall be tested and approved by the administrative authority before the plumbing system is put into use. The administrative authority shall perform the final inspection and witness the test. The administrative authority shall approve the plumbing system if the system complies with the requirements of this code, any permit

requirements, and the requirements of any plan approved pursuant to subpart 6. Plumbing system tests shall comply with chapter 4714.

C. Unless the plumbing work poses an unsanitary or hazardous condition, the administrative authority is authorized to waive the permit, inspection, and testing requirements for the following plumbing work performed in one- and two-family dwellings:

(1) the reconnection of an existing water supply line to a replacement appliance that does not involve the replacement or alteration of the existing water supply line;

(2) replacement of the internal working components of existing water closets, faucets, or valves;

(3) replacement of sink faucets when the work does not include alterations to the existing plumbing piping system; or

(4) replacement or resetting of water closets when the work does not include alterations to the existing plumbing piping systems.

D. The administrative authority is permitted to waive testing requirements for plumbing work that does not include any addition to or replacement, alteration, or relocation of any water supply, drainage, or vent piping, if it does not create a hazardous or unsanitary condition.

Subp. 2. [Repealed].

Subp. 3. Covering of work. No building drainage or plumbing system or part thereof shall be covered until it has been inspected, tested, and approved as herein prescribed.

If any building drainage or plumbing system or part thereof is covered before being regularly inspected, tested, and approved, as herein prescribed, it shall be uncovered upon the direction of the proper administrative authority.

Subp. 4. Building sewer. The building sewer shall be inspected by the proper administrative authority to ensure compliance with the provisions of the code.

Subp. 5. Certificate of approval. Upon the satisfactory completion and final inspection of the plumbing system, a certificate of approval shall be issued by the proper administrative authority.

Subp. 6. Plans and specifications. Prior to the installation by any person, corporation, or public agency, of a system of plumbing that serves the public or that serves any considerable number of persons, or any plumbing system that shall affect the public health in any manner, complete plans and specifications, together with any additional information that the commissioner of labor and industry may require, shall be submitted and approved by the commissioner. The appraisal of the commissioner shall reflect the degree to which these plans and specifications affect the public health and conform to the provisions of the *Minnesota Plumbing Code*. No construction shall proceed except in accordance with approved plans and specifications. Any material alteration or extension of the existing system shall be subject to these same requirements. This rule shall not apply to cities of the first class, except those plumbing installations in state-licensed health care facilities or in buildings in these cities owned by the state government.

Except as approved in Chapter 4714, there shall be no physical connection between water supply systems that are safe for domestic use and those that are unsafe for domestic use. There shall be no apparatus through which unsafe water may be discharged or drawn into a safe water supply system.

1300.0220
CERTIFICATE OF OCCUPANCY

Subpart 1. Use and occupancy. No building or structure shall be used or occupied, and no change in the existing occupancy classification of a building, structure, or portion of a building or structure shall be made until the building official has issued a certificate of occupancy for the building or structure under this part. Issuance of a certificate of occupancy is not approval of a violation of the code or other ordinances of the municipality. Certificates presuming to give authority to violate or cancel the code or other ordinances of the municipality are not valid.

Exception: A municipality has the option of requiring certificates of occupancy for:

A. "U" occupancies constructed under the *International Building Code*;

B. Accessory structures constructed under the *International Residential Code*; or

C. Used manufactured homes moved into or within a jurisdiction.

Subp. 2. Existing structures. The legal occupancy of any structure existing on the date of adoption of the code shall be permitted to continue without change.

Subp. 3. Change in use. Changes in the character or use of an existing structure must comply with Chapter 1305 or 1311.

Subp. 4. Moved buildings. Buildings or structures moved into or within a jurisdiction shall comply with the provisions of the code for new buildings or structures.

Exception:

A. Buildings designed to comply with Chapter 1311; or

B. A residential building relocated within or into a municipality need not comply with the *Minnesota Energy Code* or Minnesota Statutes, Section 326B.439.

Subp. 5. Certificate issued. After the building official inspects a building or structure and finds no violations of the code or other laws that are enforced by the Department of Building Safety, the building official shall issue a certificate of occupancy containing the following:

A. The building permit number;

B. The address of the structure;

C. The name and address of the owner;

D. A statement that the described portion of the structure has been inspected for compliance with the requirements of the code for the occupancy and division of

occupancy and the use for which the proposed occupancy is classified;

E. The name of the building official;

F. The edition of the code under which the permit was issued;

G. The use and occupancy classification;

H. The type of construction;

I. If an automatic sprinkler system is provided; and

J. Any special stipulations and conditions of the building permit.

Subp. 6. Temporary occupancy. The building official is authorized to issue a temporary certificate of occupancy before the completion of the entire work covered by the permit, provided that the portion or portions shall be occupied safely. The building official shall set a time period during which the temporary certificate of occupancy is valid.

Subp. 7. Revocation. The building official may issue a written suspension or revocation of a certificate of occupancy issued under the code if the certificate is issued in error or on the basis of incorrect information supplied, or if the building or use of the building, structure, or portion of the building or structure is in violation of any ordinance or regulation or a provision of the code.

1300.0225
MAINTENANCE

All buildings and structures, both existing and new, and all parts of the buildings or structures, shall be maintained in a safe and sanitary condition. All devices or safeguards required by this code shall be maintained in conformance with the code editions under which the devices or safeguards are installed. The owner or the owner's designated agent shall be responsible for the maintenance of buildings and structures. A building official is authorized to require reinspection of a building or structure if the building official is unable to determine whether or not the building or structure complies with this part.

1300.0230
BOARD OF APPEALS

Subpart 1. Local board of appeals. In order to hear and decide appeals of orders, decisions, or determinations made by the building official relative to the application and interpretation of this code, there shall be and is hereby created a board of appeals. The building official shall be an ex officio member of said board but shall have no vote on any matter before the board. The board of appeals shall be designated by the governing body. Appeals hearings must occur within ten working days from the date the municipality receives a properly completed application for appeal. If an appeals hearing is not held within this time, the applicant may appeal directly to the State Building Code Appeals Board.

The board shall adopt rules of procedures for conducting its business and shall render all decisions and findings in writing to the appellant with a duplicate copy to the building official and to the state building official within five working days of the decision. For jurisdictions without a board of appeals, the appellant may appeal to an appeals board assembled by the state of Minnesota, Department of Labor and Industry's Construction Codes and Licensing Division.

Subp. 2. Qualifications. The board of appeals shall consist of members who are qualified by experience and training to pass on matters pertaining to building construction and are not employees of the affected jurisdiction.

Subp. 3. Limitations on authority. An application for appeal shall be based on a claim that the true intent of this code or the rules legally adopted thereunder have been incorrectly interpreted, the provisions of this code do not fully apply, or an equally good or better form of construction is proposed. The board shall have no authority to waive requirements of this code.

Subp. 4. [Repealed].

Subp. 5. Final interpretive authority. In accordance with Minnesota Statutes, Section 326B.127, subdivision 5, the commissioner has final interpretive authority to all codes adopted as part of the *State Building Code*, except for the *State Plumbing Code*, the *State Electrical Code*, and the *State High Pressure Piping Code*.

1300.0240
DISCLAIMER CLAUSE

The inclusion of specific requirements relative to the manner of installation of any building or portion of any building or building equipment in one or more parts of the code does not limit this procedure to any particular type of installer or provide a basis upon which determination of the right to perform a procedure shall be made. The authority for this determination is in the various licensing statutes or ordinances for each type of installer who performs the work.

1300.0250
SEVERABILITY

The invalidity of any provision of the *Minnesota State Building Code* does not affect any other provisions of the code that can be given effect without the invalid provision and, to this end, the provisions of the code are declared to be severable.

2020 MINNESOTA PROVISIONS TO THE MINNESOTA STATE BUILDING CODE (INCLUDING RADON)

1303.1000
TITLE

This chapter shall be known as "Minnesota provisions."

1303.1100
PURPOSE

This chapter contains requirements of the code that are mandated by Minnesota Statutes, are needed to address Minnesota's climatic conditions, or are otherwise determined necessary to provide a safe minimum level of construction in an area not appropriately regulated in the *International Building Code* or *International Residential Code*.

1303.1200
RESTROOM FACILITIES
IN PUBLIC ACCOMMODATIONS

Subpart 1. Ratio. In a place of public accommodation subject to this part, the ratio of water closets for women to the total of water closets and urinals provided for men must be at least three to two, unless there are two or fewer fixtures for men.

Subp. 2. Application. This part applies only to the construction of buildings or structures of public accommodation or where the cost of alterations to an existing place of public accommodation exceeds 50 percent of the estimated replacement value of the existing facility.

Subp. 3. Definition. For purposes of this part, "place of public accommodation" means a publicly or privately owned sports or entertainment arena, stadium, theater, community or convention hall, special event center, amusement facility, or special event center in a public park, that is designed for occupancy by 200 or more people.

1303.1300
SPACE FOR COMMUTER VANS

Every parking ramp or other parking facility must include spaces for the parking of motor vehicles having a capacity of seven to 16 persons. The number of required spaces must be determined by two percent of the gross designed parking area with a minimum of two spaces. The minimum vertical clearance to and within required spaces is 98 inches.

1303.1400
AUTOMATIC GARAGE DOOR OPENING SYSTEMS

All automatic garage door opening systems that are installed, serviced, or repaired for garages serving residential buildings must comply with the provisions of Minnesota Statutes, Sections 325F.82 and 325F.83.

1303.1500
RECYCLING SPACE

Subpart 1. Requirement. Space must be provided for the collection, separation, and temporary storage of recyclable materials within or adjacent to all new or significantly remodeled buildings or structures that contain 1,000 square feet or more.

> **Exception:** Residential structures with fewer than four dwelling units.

Subp. 2. Location. Space designated for recycling shall be located so it is at least as convenient as the location where other solid waste is collected. If feasible, recycling space should be adjacent to other solid waste collection space. Recycling space must be located and designed in accordance with the provisions of this code and ordinances of the jurisdiction.

Subp. 3. Identification on plans. Space designated for recycling must be identified on plans submitted for a building permit.

Subp. 4. Minimum space. Space designated for recycling must be sufficient to contain all the recyclable materials generated from the building. The minimum amount of recycling space required must be the number of square feet determined by multiplying the gross square feet of floor areas assigned to each use within a building as set forth in subpart 5, Table 1-A, times the corresponding factor.

Subp. 5.

TABLE 1-A
MINIMUM RECYCLING SPACE REQUIREMENTS

USE[1]	FACTOR
1. Aircraft hangers (no repair)	.001
2. Auction rooms	.0025
3[2]. Auditoriums, reviewing stands, stadiums, gymnasiums, public swimming pools, skating rinks	.001
4. Lodge rooms, conference rooms, lounges, stages, exhibit rooms	.0025
5. Dance floors, churches[3] and chapels, lobby	.001
6. Dining rooms	.003
7[3]. Drinking establishments	.004
8[3]. Bowling alleys (excluding lanes)	.0025
9[3]. Children's homes and homes for the aged	.0025
10. Classrooms	.002
11. Courtrooms	.001
12. Dormitories	.0025
13. Exercise rooms	.001
14. Garages, parking	.001
15[3]. Hospitals and sanitariums, nursing homes	.0025
16[3]. Hotels	.002
17. Apartments	.0025

(continued)

TABLE 1-A
MINIMUM RECYCLING SPACE REQUIREMENTS—continued

18. Kitchens – commercial	.003
19[3]. Libraries	.002
20. Locker rooms	.001
21. Malls	.0025
22. Manufacturing areas	.0025
23. Mechanical equipment rooms	.001
24[3]. Nurseries for children (day care)	.002
25. Offices	.0025
26. School shops and vocational rooms	.0025
27. Storage and stock rooms	.0025
28. Warehouses	.001
29. All others	.0025

1. The area of a use must include all areas serving or accessory to a use (corridors, accessory use areas, etc.).
2. Excludes playing areas, courts, fields, and like areas.
3. The factors for these uses are intended to include all incidental uses typical of these types of facilities.

If the provisions of Table 1-A are excessive due to a specific use, space for recycling may be considered individually by the administrative authority.

1303.1600
FOOTING DEPTH FOR FROST PROTECTION

Subpart 1. Minimum footing depth. In the absence of a determination by an engineer competent in soil mechanics, the minimum allowable footing depth in feet due to freezing is five feet in Zone I and $3^{1}/_{2}$ feet in Zone II.

Zone I includes the counties of: Aitkin, Becker, Beltrami, Carlton, Cass, Clay, Clearwater, Cook, Crow Wing, Douglas, Grant, Hubbard, Itasca, Kanabec, Kittson, Koochiching, Lake, Lake of the Woods, Mahnomen, Marshall, Mille Lacs, Morrison, Norman, Otter Tail, Pennington, Pine, Polk, Red Lake, Roseau, St. Louis, Todd, Traverse, Wadena, and Wilkin.

Zone II shall include the counties of: Anoka, Benton, Big Stone, Blue Earth, Brown, Carver, Chippewa, Chisago, Cottonwood, Dakota, Dodge, Faribault, Fillmore, Freeborn, Goodhue, Hennepin, Houston, Isanti, Jackson, Kandiyohi, Lac qui Parle, Le Sueur, Lincoln, Lyon, McLeod, Martin, Meeker, Mower, Murray, Nicollet, Nobles, Olmsted, Pipestone, Pope, Ramsey, Redwood, Renville, Rice, Rock, Scott, Sibley, Sherburne, Stearns, Steele, Stevens, Swift, Wabasha, Waseca, Washington, Watonwan, Winona, Wright, and Yellow Medicine.

Less depths may be permitted when supporting evidence is presented by an engineer competent in soil mechanics.

Subp. 2. Soil under slab on grade construction for buildings. When soil, natural or fill, is sand or pit run sand and gravel, and of depth in accordance with minimum footing depth requirements for each zone, slab on grade construction which is structurally designed to support all applied loads is permitted. Sand must contain less than 70 percent material that will pass through a U.S. Standard No. 40 sieve and less than five percent material that will pass through a No. 200 sieve (five percent fines), or be approved by an engineer competent in soil mechanics.

Exception: Slab on grade construction may be placed on any soil except peat or muck for detached one-story private garage, carport, and shed buildings not larger than 1,000 square feet.

Footings for interior bearing walls or columns may be constructed to be integral with the slab on grade for any height building. Footings for exterior bearing walls or columns may be similarly constructed for any height building when supporting soil is as described in this subpart. Footing design must reflect eccentric loading conditions at slab edges, soil bearing capacity, and the requirements of *International Building Code*, Chapter 19.

1303.1700
GROUND SNOW LOAD

The ground snow load, P_g, to be used in determining the design snow loads for buildings and other structures shall be 60 pounds per square foot in the following counties: Aitkin, Becker, Beltrami, Carlton, Cass, Clearwater, Cook, Crow Wing, Hubbard, Itasca, Kanabec, Kittson, Koochiching, Lake, Lake of the Woods, Mahnomen, Marshall, Mille Lacs, Morrison, Norman, Otter Tail, Pennington, Pine, Polk, Red Lake, Roseau, St. Louis, Todd, and Wadena. The ground snow load, P_g, to be used in determining the design snow loads for buildings and other structures shall be 50 pounds per square foot in all other counties.

1303.2000
EXTERIOR WOOD DECKS, PATIOS, AND BALCONIES

The decking surface and upper portions of exterior wood decks, patios, and balconies may be constructed of any of the following materials:

A. the heartwood from species of wood having natural resistance to decay or termites, including redwood and cedars;

B. grades of lumber which contain sapwood from species of wood having natural resistance to decay or termites, including redwood and cedars; or

C. treated wood.

The species and grades of wood products used to construct the decking surface and upper portions of exterior decks, patios, and balconies must be made available to the building official on request before final construction approval.

1303.2100
BLEACHER SAFETY

All new bleachers, manufactured, installed, sold, or distributed where the bleachers or bleacher open spaces will be over 55 inches above grade or the floor below, and all bleacher guardrails if any part of the guardrail will be over 30 inches above grade or the floor below must comply with the *State Building Code* in effect and the provisions of Minnesota Statutes, Section 326B.112.

1303.2200
SIMPLIFIED WIND LOADS

Subpart 1. Section 2200.

A. This section applies to the wind loads for the main wind force-resisting systems only.

B. In order to utilize wind loads from this part, the building shall meet the following requirements:

    (1) 60 feet or less in height;

    (2) height not to exceed least horizontal dimension;

    (3) enclosed building;

    (4) roof shape—flat, gabled, or hip;

    (5) roof slope of 45 degrees maximum;

    (6) simple diaphragm building;

    (7) not a flexible building;

    (8) regular shape and approximately symmetrical;

    (9) no expansion joints or separations; and

    (10) no unusual response characteristics (for example: vortex shedding, galloping, or buffeting).

Subp. 2. Simplified design wind pressures. P_s represents the net pressures (sum of internal and external) to be applied to the horizontal and vertical projections of building surfaces. For the horizontal pressures, P_s is the combination of the windward and leeward net pressures. P_s may be determined from the following equation:

$$P_s = K_{zt} (V_{ult}^2 / 115^2) P_{alt}$$

where:

K_{zt} = Topographic factor as defined in Chapter 26 of ASCE 7.

P_{alt} = Alternative simplified design wind pressure from Table P_{alt}.

TABLE P_{alt}[a]

HORIZONTAL AND VERTICAL PRESSURE[b]	
Exp B	25 psf
Exp C	30 psf
Exp D	35 psf
OVERHANG VERTICAL PRESSURE[c]	
Exp B	-40 psf
Exp C	-48 psf
Exp D	-56 psf

a. Values are for ultimate wind design (V_{ult}). Multiply by 0.6 for allowable stress design (ASD).

b. For vertical pressure, the above values are negative (upward).

c. Negative values are upward.

1303.2400
PURPOSE AND SCOPE

Subpart 1. Applicability; residential structures. The purpose of parts 1303.2400 to 1303.2402 is to establish minimum requirements for passive radon control systems that apply to all new residential structures listed in items A to H:

A. one-family dwellings;

B. two-family dwellings;

C. townhouses;

D. apartment buildings;

E. condominiums;

F. multistory buildings that include any residential occupancy;

G. mixed-occupancy buildings that include any residential occupancy; and

H. any addition to an existing dwelling that currently has a radon control system incorporated into the existing building.

If a fan is installed in a passive radon control system, this creates an active radon control system that must comply with the requirements of parts 1303.2400 to 1303.2403.

Subp. 2. Applicability; design features. The requirements in parts 1303.2400 to 1303.2402 shall apply to any structure identified in subpart 1, items A to H, if the structure is designed with any of the features identified in items A to F:

A. a basement concrete slab in contact with the earth;

B. a crawl space within the building's conditioned space that has a concrete or earth floor;

C. a wood foundation floor constructed on or directly above the earth;

D. slab on grade construction designs;

E. attached or tuck-under garages, unless the floor, wall, and ceiling assemblies separating the garage from the dwellings are sealed; and

F. any building configuration that allows radon gas to enter the residential dwelling.

Exceptions:

    1. Crawl spaces outside the conditioned space of the residential dwelling, when the crawl space is ventilated directly to the outside atmosphere according to IRC Sections R408.1 and R408.2; IBC Sections 1203.3 and 1203.3.1; Code of Federal Regulations, Section 3285.505; and Minnesota Rules, Chapter 1350.

    2. Hotels and motels.

    3. Additions to existing dwellings that do not currently have a radon control system incorporated into the existing dwelling.

Subp. 3. Mixed occupancy or multistory mixed occupancy buildings. When the nonresidential occupancy is in contact with the earth, all assemblies that separate the occupancies must be sealed to prevent the movement of air and airborne gases between the nonresidential and residential occupancies. When the residential occupancy is in contact with the earth and adjacent to a nonresidential occupancy, the residential occupancy shall incorporate a radon control system and all assemblies that separate the nonresidential and residential occupancy shall be sealed to prevent the movement of air or airborne gases.

1303.2401
DEFINITIONS

Subpart 1. Terms not defined. For purposes of parts 1303.2400 to 1303.2403, where terms are not defined in parts 1303.2400 to 1303.2403, Merriam-Webster's Collegiate Dictionary, available at www.m-w.com, shall be considered as providing ordinarily accepted meanings. The dictionary is incorporated by reference, is subject to frequent change, and is available through the Minitex interlibrary loan system.

Subp. 2. Definitions. For the purposes of parts 1303.2400 to 1303.2403, the terms defined in this part have the meanings given them.

ACTIVE RADON CONTROL SYSTEM. "Active radon control system" means a system designed to achieve lower air pressure below the soil-gas membrane relative to the indoor air pressure by use of a fan that has been added to the passive radon control system.

APPROVED. "Approved" means approval by the building official, pursuant to the *Minnesota State Building Code*, by reason of inspection, investigation, or testing; accepted principles; computer simulations; research reports; or testing performed by either a licensed engineer or by a locally or nationally recognized testing laboratory.

CFR. "CFR" means Code of Federal Regulations, title 24, Chapter 3285.

GAS PERMEABLE MATERIAL. A "gas permeable material" means any of the following:

1. A uniform layer of clean aggregate, a minimum of 4 inches (102 mm) thick. The aggregate shall consist of material that will pass through a 2-inch (51 mm) sieve and be retained by a $^1/_4$-inch (6.4 mm) sieve.

2. A uniform layer of sand, native or fill, a minimum of 4 inches (102 mm) thick, overlain by a layer or strips of geotextile drainage matting designed to allow the lateral flow of soil gases.

3. Other materials, systems, or floor designs if the material, system, or floor design is professionally engineered to provide depressurization under the entire soil-gas membrane.

IBC. "IBC" means the *International Building Code* incorporated by reference except as qualified and amended in Minnesota Rules, Chapter 1305.

IRC. "IRC" means the *International Residential Code* incorporated by reference except as qualified and amended in Minnesota Rules, Chapter 1309.

PASSIVE RADON CONTROL SYSTEM. "Passive radon control system" means a system designed to achieve lower air pressure below the soil-gas membrane relative to the indoor air pressure by use of a vent pipe that relies on stack effect to provide an upward flow of air from beneath the soil-gas membrane.

RADON GAS. "Radon gas" means a naturally occurring, chemically inert, radioactive gas.

SEALED. "Sealed" means to prevent the movement of air or airborne gases through a floor, wall, or ceiling assembly.

SOIL-GAS MEMBRANE. "Soil-gas membrane" means a continuous membrane of 6-mil (0.15 mm) polyethylene, or 3-mil (0.075 mm) cross-laminated polyethylene.

VENT PIPE. "Vent pipe" means a 3-inch (76 mm) or 4-inch (102 mm) diameter ABS or PVC pipe used to vent subsoil gases that have collected under the soil-gas membrane to the exterior of the dwelling.

1303.2402
REQUIREMENTS FOR PASSIVE
RADON CONTROL SYSTEMS

Subpart 1. Gas permeable material preparation. A gas-permeable material shall be placed on the prepared subgrade under all floor systems.

Subp. 2. Soil-gas membrane installation. A soil-gas membrane shall be placed on top of the gas-permeable material prior to placing a floor on top of or above the soil. The soil-gas membrane shall cover the entire floor area. Separate sections of membrane must be lapped at least 12 inches (305 mm). The membrane shall fit closely around any penetration of the membrane to reduce the leakage of soil gases. All punctures or tears in the soil-gas membrane shall be repaired by sealing and patching the soil-gas membrane with the same kind of material, maintaining a minimum 12-inch (305 mm) lap.

Subp. 3. "T" fitting. A "T" fitting shall be installed beneath the soil-gas membrane with a minimum of 10 feet of perforated pipe connected to any two openings of the "T" fitting, or by connecting the two openings to the interior drain tile system. The third opening of the "T" fitting shall be connected to the vent pipe. The perforated pipe or drain tile and the "T" fitting shall be the same size as the vent pipe. All connections to the "T" fitting shall be tight fitting.

Subp. 4. Potential entry routes. Potential entry routes for radon gas shall be sealed according to this subpart, as applicable.

A. **Floor openings.** Floor openings around bathtubs, showers, water closets, pipes, wires, or other objects that penetrate the soil-gas membrane and the concrete slab or other floor systems shall be sealed.

B. **Concrete joints.** All control joints, isolation joints, construction joints, or any other joints in the concrete slab, or the joint between the concrete slab and a foundation wall, shall be sealed. All gaps and joints shall be cleared of all loose material prior to sealing.

C. **Foundation walls.** Penetrations of all foundation wall types shall be sealed. Joints, cracks, or other openings around all penetrations of both exterior and interior surfaces of foundation walls shall be sealed.

    (1) Hollow block masonry foundation walls shall be constructed with either:

        (a) a continuous course of solid masonry at or above the exterior ground surface;

        (b) one course of masonry grouted solid at or above the exterior ground surface; or

        (c) a solid concrete beam at or above the finished exterior ground surface.

    (2) When a brick veneer or other masonry ledge is installed, the masonry course immediately below the veneer or ledge shall be solid or filled.

D. **Unconditioned crawl spaces.** All penetrations through floors or walls into unconditioned crawl spaces shall be sealed. Access doors into unconditioned crawl spaces shall be gasketed. Crawl space ventilation shall be provided according to part 1303.2400.

E. **Sumps.** A sump connected to interior drain tile may serve as the termination point for the vent pipe, if the sump cover is sealed or gasketed and designed to accommodate the vent pipe. The sump pump water discharge pipe shall have a backflow preventer installed.

Subp. 5. Vent pipes.

A. **Single vent pipe.** The vent pipe shall be primed and glued at all fittings and shall extend up from the radon control system's collection point to a point terminating a minimum of 12 inches (305 mm) above the roof. The vent pipe shall be located at least 10 feet (3,048 mm) away from any window or other opening into the conditioned spaces of the building. Vent pipes routed through unconditioned spaces shall be insulated with a minimum of R-4 insulation. Vent pipes within the conditioned envelope of the building shall not be insulated.

B. **Multiple vent pipes.** In buildings where interior footings or other barriers separate the gas-permeable material into two or more areas, each area shall be fitted with an individual radon control system in accordance with item A, or connected to a single radon gas vent pipe terminating above the roof in accordance with item A.

C. **Vent pipe drainage.** All components of the radon gas vent pipe system shall be installed to provide drainage to the ground beneath the soil-gas membrane.

D. **Vent pipe accessibility.** Radon gas vent pipes shall be provided with space around the vent pipe for future installation of a fan. The space required for the future fan installation shall be a minimum of 24 inches in diameter, centered on the axis of the vent pipe, and shall extend a minimum distance of 3 vertical feet.

    Exception: Accessibility to the radon gas vent pipe is not required if the future fan installation is above the roof system and there is an approved rooftop electrical supply provided.

E. **Vent pipe identification.** All radon gas vent pipes shall be identified with at least 1 label on each story and in attics and crawl spaces. The label shall read: "Radon Gas Vent System."

F. **Combination foundations.** Combination basement/crawl space or slab-on grade/crawl space foundations shall have separate radon gas vent pipes installed in each type of foundation area. Each radon gas vent pipe shall terminate above the roof or shall be connected to a single vent pipe that terminates above the roof.

Subp. 6. Power source. A power source consisting of an electrical circuit terminating in an approved electrical box shall be installed during construction in the anticipated location of the vent pipe fan to allow for the future installation of a fan into a passive radon control system to make the system an active radon control system. The power source shall not be installed in any conditioned space, basement, or crawl space.

1303.2403
REQUIREMENTS FOR ACTIVE
RADON CONTROL SYSTEMS

When an active radon control system is installed, all the requirements for the passive radon control system in parts 1303.2400 to 1303.2402 shall be met. In addition, an active radon control system shall incorporate items A to C in this part.

A. **Radon gas vent pipe fan.** A radon gas vent pipe fan manufactured for radon control systems and rated for continuous operation that provides a minimum measurement of 50 cubic feet per minute at $1/_2$-inch water column shall be installed in the vertical vent pipe. The fan shall be attached to a radon gas vent pipe that connects the air below the soil-gas membrane with outdoor air and relies on the fan to provide upward air flow in the vent pipe. The radon gas vent pipe fan shall be installed outdoors, in attics, or in garages. The radon gas vent pipe fan shall not be installed in conditioned spaces of a building, basement, or crawl space. The radon gas vent pipe fan shall not be located where it positively pressurizes any portion of the vent pipe that is located inside conditioned space.

B. **System monitoring device.** An audible alarm, a manometer, or other similar device shall be installed to indicate when the fan is not operating.

C. **Luminaire and receptacle outlet.** A switch-controlled luminaire and the receptacle outlet near the fan shall be installed according to the *Minnesota Electrical Code*. The requirements of the *International Mechanical Code*, Section 306, do not apply.

2015 MINNESOTA RESIDENTIAL ENERGY CODE

1322.0010
ADOPTION OF INTERNATIONAL ENERGY CONSERVATION CODE (IECC) BY REFERENCE

Subpart 1. General. Chapters 2(RE) to 5(RE) of the Residential Provisions of the 2012 edition of the *International Energy Conservation Code* (IECC) as promulgated by the International Code Council, Inc. (ICC), Washington, DC, is incorporated by reference and made part of the *Minnesota State Building Code* except as qualified by the applicable provisions in Minnesota Rules, Chapter 1300, and as amended in this chapter. Portions of this publication reproduce excerpts from the 2012 IECC, International Code Council, Inc. Washington, DC, copyright 2012, reproduced with permission, all rights reserved. The 2012 IECC is not subject to frequent change and a copy of the 2012 IECC with amendments for use in Minnesota is available in the office of the commissioner of labor and industry.

Subp. 2. Mandatory chapters. Chapters 2(RE) to 5(RE) of the Residential Provisions of the 2012 IECC shall be administered by any municipality that has adopted the *Minnesota State Building Code*, except as qualified by applicable provisions in Minnesota Rules, Chapter 1300, and as amended by this chapter.

Subp. 3. Replacement chapters. Chapter 1 of the Residential Provisions of the IECC and any references to code administration are deleted and replaced with Minnesota Rules, Chapter 1300, Minnesota Building Code Administration.

1322.0015
ADMINISTRATION AND PURPOSE

Subpart 1. Administration. This code shall be administered according to Chapter 1300.

Subp. 2. Purpose. The purpose of this chapter is to establish a minimum code of standards for the construction, reconstruction, alteration, and repair of residential buildings governing matters including design and construction standards regarding heat loss control, illumination, and climate control, pursuant to Minnesota Statutes, Sections 326B.101, 326B.106, and 326B.13.

1322.0030
REFERENCES TO OTHER INTERNATIONAL CODE COUNCIL (ICC) CODES

Subpart 1. Generally. References to other codes and standards promulgated by the International Code Council in the *International Energy Conservation Code* are modified in this part.

Subp. 2. Building code. References to the International Building Code mean the *Minnesota Building Code*, Minnesota Rules, Chapter 1305, and adopted pursuant to Minnesota Statutes, Section 326B.106, subdivision 1.

Subp. 3. Residential code. References to the *International Residential Code* mean the *Minnesota Residential Code*, Minnesota Rules, Chapter 1309, and adopted pursuant to Minnesota Statutes, Section 326B.106, subdivision 1.

Subp. 4. Electrical code. References to the *National Electrical Code* mean the *Minnesota Electrical Code*, Minnesota Rules, Chapter 1315, adopted pursuant to Minnesota Statutes, Section 326B.35.

Subp. 5. Fuel gas code. References to the *International Fuel Gas Code* mean the *Minnesota Mechanical and Fuel Gas Code*, Minnesota Rules, Chapter 1346, adopted pursuant to Minnesota Statutes, Section 326B.106, subdivision 1.

Subp. 6. Mechanical code. References to the *International Mechanical Code* mean the *Minnesota Mechanical and Fuel Gas Code*, Minnesota Rules, Chapter 1346, adopted pursuant to Minnesota Statutes, Section 326B.106, subdivision 1.

Subp. 7. Plumbing code. References to the *International Plumbing Code* mean the *Minnesota Plumbing Code*, Minnesota Rules, Chapter 4715, adopted pursuant to Minnesota Statutes, Section 326B.435.

Subp. 8. Private sewage disposal code. References to the *International Private Sewage Disposal Code* mean the Minnesota Pollution Control Agency's minimum standards and criteria for individual sewage treatment systems in Minnesota Rules, Chapters 7080, 7082, and 7083, adopted pursuant to Minnesota Statutes, Chapters 103F, 103G, 115, and 116.

Subp. 9. Energy conservation code. References to the *International Energy Conservation Code* mean the *Minnesota Energy Code*, Minnesota Rules, Chapters 1322 and 1323, adopted pursuant to Minnesota Statutes, Section 326B.106.

Subp. 10. Property maintenance code. References to the *International Property Maintenance Code* do not apply.

Subp. 11. Accessibility code. References to accessibility mean the *Minnesota Accessibility Code*, Minnesota Rules, Chapter 1341.

1322.0040
ADMINISTRATIVE PROCEDURE CRITERIA

Procedures relating to the administration and enforcement pursuant to Minnesota Statutes, Section 326B.101, are contained in Minnesota Rules, Chapter 1300, Minnesota Building Code Administration, which govern the application of this code.

1322.0100
ADMINISTRATION FOR RESIDENTIAL ENERGY

Subpart 1. Administration. In addition to the application of Minnesota Rules, Chapter 1300, the administrative requirements in this part shall apply.

Subp. 2. Scope. This code applies to residential buildings and associated systems and equipment as defined in the Residential Provisions of the 2012 IECC.

Subp. 3. Applicability.

A. Additions, alterations, renovations, or repairs. Additions, alterations, renovations, or repairs to an existing building, building system, or portion of a building shall conform to the provisions of this code as they relate to new construction without requiring the unaltered portion of the existing building or building system to comply with this code. Additions, alterations, renovations, or repairs shall not create an unsafe or hazardous condition or overload existing building systems. An addition shall comply with this code if the addition alone complies or if the existing building and addition comply with this code as a single building. Attic insulation shall not be installed unless accessible attic bypasses have been sealed. An attic bypass is any air passageway between a conditioned space and an unconditioned attic.

Exceptions: The following are excepted from this part provided the energy use of the building is not increased:

1. Storm windows installed over existing windows.

2. Glass only replacements in an existing sash and frame.

3. Existing ceiling, wall, or floor cavities exposed during construction provided that these cavities are filled with insulation.

4. Construction where the existing roof, wall, or floor cavity is not exposed.

5. Reroofing and residing.

6. Replacement of existing doors that separate conditioned space from the exterior do not require the installation of a vestibule or revolving door; provided that an existing vestibule that separates a conditioned space from the exterior shall not be removed.

7. Alterations that replace less than 50 percent of the luminaires in a space, provided that the alterations do not increase the installed interior lighting power.

8. Alterations that replace only the bulb and ballast within the existing luminaires in a space, provided that the alteration does not increase the installed interior lighting power.

9. Insulation *R*-value, air barrier, and vapor retarder requirements are not applicable to existing foundations, crawl space walls, and basements in existing dwellings or dwelling units when the alteration or repair requires a permit if the original dwelling or dwelling unit permit was issued before June 1, 2009.

B. Change in occupancy or use. Spaces undergoing a change in occupancy that would result in an increase in demand for either fossil fuel or electrical energy shall comply with this code.

C. Change in space conditioning. Any nonconditioned space that is altered to become conditioned space shall be brought into full compliance with this code.

D. Mixed occupancy. Where a building includes both residential and commercial occupancies, each occupancy shall be separately considered and meet the applicable provisions of this chapter and Chapter 1323.

Subp. 4. Compliance. Residential buildings shall meet the requirements of Minnesota Rules, Chapter 1322. Commercial buildings shall meet the requirements of Minnesota Rules, Chapter 1323.

A. Compliance materials. The building official is permitted to approve specific computer software, worksheets, compliance manuals, and other similar materials that meet the intent of this code.

B. Low energy buildings. The following buildings, or portions thereof, separated from the remainder of the building by building thermal envelope assemblies complying with this code are exempt from the building thermal envelope provisions of this code:

(1) those with a peak design rate of energy usage less than 3.4 Btu/h · ft^2 (10.7 W/m^2) or 1.0 watt/ft^2 (10.7 W/m^2) of floor area for space conditioning purposes; and

(2) those that do not contain conditioned space.

1322.0103
CONSTRUCTION DOCUMENTS

Construction documents shall be drawn to scale upon suitable material. Electronic media documents are permitted to be submitted when approved by the building official. Construction documents shall be of sufficient clarity to indicate the location; nature, and extent of the work proposed, and show in sufficient detail pertinent data and features of the building, systems, and equipment as herein governed. The details shall include the following when applicable:

A. Insulation materials and their R-values;

B. Fenestration U-factors and SHGCs;

C. Area-weighted U-factor and SHGC calculations;

D. Mechanical system design criteria;

E. Mechanical and service water heating system and equipment types, sizes, and efficiencies;

F. Equipment and systems controls;

G. Fan motor horsepower (hp) and controls;

H. Duct sealing, and the location and insulation of ducts and pipes;

I. Lighting fixture schedule with wattage and control narrative; and

J. Air sealing details.

CHAPTER 2 [RE]
DEFINITIONS

SECTION R201
GENERAL

R201.1 Scope. Unless stated otherwise, the following words and terms in this code shall have the meanings indicated in this chapter.

R201.2 Interchangeability. Words used in the present tense include the future; words in the masculine gender include the feminine and neuter; the singular number includes the plural and the plural includes the singular.

R201.3 Terms defined in other codes. Terms that are not defined in this code but are defined in the *International Building Code, International Fire Code, International Fuel Gas Code, International Mechanical Code, International Plumbing Code* or the *International Residential Code* shall have the meanings ascribed to them in those codes.

R201.4 Terms not defined. Where terms are not defined through the methods authorized by this chapter, the Merriam-Webster Collegiate Dictionary, available at www.m-w.com, shall be considered as providing ordinarily accepted meanings. The dictionary is incorporated by reference, is subject to frequent change, and is available through the Minitex interlibrary loan system.

SECTION R202
GENERAL DEFINITIONS

ABOVE-GRADE WALL. A wall more than 50 percent above grade and enclosing *conditioned space*. This includes between-floor spandrels, peripheral edges of floors, roof and basement knee walls, dormer walls, gable end walls, walls enclosing a mansard roof and skylight shafts.

ACCESSIBLE. Signifies access that requires the removal of an access panel or similar removable obstruction.

ACCESSIBLE, READILY. Signifies access without the necessity for removing a panel or similar obstruction.

ADDITION. An extension or increase in the *conditioned space* floor area or height of a building or structure.

AIR BARRIER. Material(s) assembled and joined together to provide a barrier to air leakage through the building envelope. An air barrier may be a single material or a combination of materials.

AIR CIRCULATION, FORCED. A means of providing space conditioning using movement of air through ducts or plenums by mechanical means.

AIR, EXHAUST. Air discharged from any space to the outside by the residential ventilation system.

AIR, OUTDOOR. The air that is taken from the external atmosphere, and therefore not previously circulated through the HVAC system or the conditioned space.

AIR-CONDITIONING SYSTEM. A system that consists of heat exchangers, blowers, filters, and supply, exhaust, and return-air systems, and includes any apparatus installed in connection with the system.

ALTERATION. Any construction or renovation to an existing structure other than repair or addition that requires a permit. Also, a change in a mechanical system that involves an extension, addition or change to the arrangement, type or purpose of the original installation that requires a permit.

APPROVED. "Approved" means approval by the building official, pursuant to the *State Building Code*, by reason of: inspection, investigation, or testing; accepted principles; computer simulations; research reports; or testing performed by either a licensed engineer or by a locally or nationally recognized testing laboratory.

AUTOMATIC. Self-acting, operating by its own mechanism when actuated by some impersonal influence, as, for example, a change in current strength, pressure, temperature or mechanical configuration (see "Manual").

BALANCED SYSTEM. A ventilation system in which the air intake is within ten percent of the exhaust output.

BASEMENT WALL. A wall 50 percent or more below grade and enclosing *conditioned space*.

BUILDING. Any structure used or intended for supporting or sheltering any use or occupancy, including any mechanical systems, service water heating systems and electric power and lighting systems located on the building site and supporting the building.

BUILDING SITE. A contiguous area of land that is under the ownership or control of one entity.

BUILDING THERMAL ENVELOPE. The basement walls, exterior walls, floor, roof, and any other building elements that enclose *conditioned space* or provides a boundary between *conditioned space* and exempt or unconditioned space.

C-FACTOR (THERMAL CONDUCTANCE). The coefficient of heat transmission (surface to surface) through a building component or assembly, equal to the time rate of heat flow per unit area and the unit temperature difference between the warm side and cold side surfaces (Btu/h ft^2 × °F) [W/(m^2 × K)].

CODE. For purposes of this chapter, "this code" or "the code" means the *Minnesota Residential Energy Code*, Minnesota Rules, Chapter 1322.

CODE OFFICIAL. The officer or other designated authority charged with the administration and enforcement of this code, or a duly authorized representative.

COMMERCIAL BUILDING. For this code, all buildings that are not included in the definition of "Residential buildings."

CONDITIONED FLOOR AREA. The horizontal projection of the floors associated with the *conditioned space*.

CONDITIONED SPACE. An area or room within a building being heated or cooled, containing uninsulated ducts, or with a fixed opening directly into an adjacent *conditioned space*.

CONTINUOUS AIR BARRIER. A combination of materials and assemblies that restrict or prevent the passage of air through the building thermal envelope.

CRAWL SPACE WALL. The opaque portion of a wall that encloses a crawl space and is partially or totally below grade.

CUBIC FEET PER MINUTE (CFM). The quantity of air moved in one minute. A measurement typically applied to ventilation equipment.

CURTAIN WALL. Fenestration products used to create an external nonload-bearing wall that is designed to separate the exterior and interior environments.

DEMAND RECIRCULATION WATER SYSTEM. A water distribution system where pump(s) prime the service hot water piping with heated water upon demand for hot water.

DUCT. A tube or conduit utilized for conveying air. The air passages of self-contained systems are not to be construed as air ducts.

DUCT SYSTEM. A continuous passageway for the transmission of air that, in addition to ducts, includes duct fittings, dampers, plenums, fans and accessory air-handling equipment and appliances.

[B] DWELLING UNIT. A single unit providing complete independent living facilities for one or more persons, including permanent provisions for living, sleeping, eating, cooking and sanitation.

ENERGY ANALYSIS. A method for estimating the annual energy use of the *proposed design* and *standard reference design* based on estimates of energy use.

ENERGY COST. The total estimated annual cost for purchased energy for the building functions regulated by this code, including applicable demand charges.

ENERGY RECOVERY VENTILATOR (ERV). A device or combination of devices applied to transfer energy and moisture from the exhaust air stream for use within the dwelling.

ENERGY SIMULATION TOOL. An *approved* software program or calculation-based methodology that projects the annual energy use of a building.

ENTRANCE DOOR. Fenestration products used for ingress, egress and access in nonresidential buildings, including, but not limited to, exterior entrances that utilize latching hardware and automatic closers and contain over 50-percent glass specifically designed to withstand heavy use and possibly abuse.

EXTERIOR WALL. Walls including both above-grade walls and basement walls.

FENESTRATION. Skylights, roof windows, vertical windows (fixed or moveable), opaque doors, glazed doors, glazed block and combination opaque/glazed doors. Fenestration includes products with glass and nonglass glazing materials.

FENESTRATION PRODUCT, SITE-BUILT. A fenestration designed to be made up of field-glazed or field-assembled units using specific factory cut or otherwise factory-formed framing and glazing units. Examples of site-built fenestration include storefront systems, curtain walls, and atrium roof systems.

F-FACTOR. The perimeter heat loss factor for slab-on-grade floors (Btu/h × ft × °F) [W/(m × K)].

FURNACE. A vented heating appliance designed or arranged to discharge heated air into a conditioned space or through a duct or ducts.

HEAT RECOVERY VENTILATOR (HRV). A device or combination of devices applied to transfer energy from the exhaust air stream for use within the dwelling.

HEATED SLAB. Slab-on-grade construction in which the heating elements, hydronic tubing, or hot air distribution system is in contact with, or placed within or under, the slab.

HIGH-EFFICACY LAMPS. Compact fluorescent lamps, T-8 or smaller diameter linear fluorescent lamps, or lamps with a minimum efficacy of:

1. 60 lumens per watt for lamps over 40 watts;

2. 50 lumens per watt for lamps over 15 watts to 40 watts; and

3. 40 lumens per watt for lamps 15 watts or less.

INFILTRATION. The uncontrolled inward air leakage into a building caused by the pressure effects of wind or the effect of differences in the indoor and outdoor air density or both.

INSULATING SHEATHING. An insulating board with a core material having a minimum *R*-value of R-2.

LABELED. Equipment, materials or products to which have been affixed a label, seal, symbol or other identifying mark of a nationally recognized testing laboratory, inspection agency or other organization concerned with product evaluation that maintains periodic inspection of the production of the above-labeled items and whose labeling indicates either that the equipment, material or product meets identified standards or has been tested and found suitable for a specified purpose.

LISTED. Equipment, materials, products or services included in a list published by an organization acceptable to the *code official* and concerned with evaluation of products or services that maintains periodic inspection of production of *listed* equipment or materials or periodic evaluation of services and whose listing states either that the equipment, material, product or service meets identified standards or has been tested and found suitable for a specified purpose.

LOW-VOLTAGE LIGHTING. Lighting equipment powered through a transformer such as a cable conductor, a rail conductor and track lighting.

MANUAL. Capable of being operated by personal intervention (see "Automatic").

MANUFACTURER'S INSTALLATION INSTRUCTIONS. Printed instructions included with equipment, the provision of which is one of the conditions for listing and labeling.

MECHANICAL VENTILATION. The mechanical process of supplying conditioned or unconditioned air to, or removing it from, any space.

PROPOSED DESIGN. A description of the proposed building used to estimate annual energy use for determining compliance based on total building performance.

REPAIR. The reconstruction or renewal of any part of an existing building.

RESIDENTIAL BUILDING. For this code, includes detached one- and two-family dwellings and multiple single-family dwellings (townhouses) as well as Group R-2, R-3 and R-4 buildings three stories or less in height above grade plane.

ROOF ASSEMBLY. A system designed to provide weather protection and resistance to design loads. The system consists of a roof covering and roof deck or a single component serving as both the roof covering and the roof deck. A roof assembly includes the roof covering, underlayment, roof deck, insulation, vapor retarder and interior finish.

R-VALUE (THERMAL RESISTANCE). The inverse of the time rate of heat flow through a body from one of its bounding surfaces to the other surface for a unit temperature difference between the two surfaces, under steady state conditions, per unit area ($h \cdot ft^2 \cdot °F/Btu$) [($m^2 \cdot K$)/W].

SERVICE WATER HEATING. Supply of hot water for purposes other than comfort heating.

SKYLIGHT. Glass or other transparent or translucent glazing material installed at a slope of less than 60 degrees (1.05 rad) from horizontal. Glazing material in skylights, including unit skylights, solariums, sunrooms, roofs and sloped walls is included in this definition.

SOLAR HEAT GAIN COEFFICIENT (SHGC). The ratio of the solar heat gain entering the space through the fenestration assembly to the incident solar radiation. Solar heat gain includes directly transmitted solar heat and absorbed solar radiation which is then reradiated, conducted or convected into the space.

STANDARD REFERENCE DESIGN. A version of the *proposed design* that meets the minimum requirements of this code and is used to determine the maximum annual energy use requirement for compliance based on total building performance.

SUNROOM. A one-story structure attached to a dwelling with a glazing area in excess of 40 percent of the gross area of the structure's exterior walls and roof.

THERMAL ISOLATION. Physical and space conditioning separation from *conditioned space(s)*. The *conditioned space*(s) shall be controlled as separate zones for heating and cooling or conditioned by separate equipment.

THERMOSTAT. An automatic control device used to maintain temperature at a fixed or adjustable set point.

U-FACTOR (THERMAL TRANSMITTANCE). The coefficient of heat transmission (air to air) through a building component or assembly, equal to the time rate of heat flow per unit area and unit temperature difference between the warm side and cold side air films (Btu/h $\cdot$ ft^2 $\cdot$ °F) [W/(m^2 $\cdot$ K)].

VENTILATION. The natural or mechanical process of supplying conditioned or unconditioned air to, or removing such air from, any space.

VENTILATION AIR. That portion of supply air that comes from outside (outdoors) plus any recirculated air that has been treated to maintain the desired quality of air within a designated space.

VISIBLE TRANSMITTANCE [VT]. The ratio of visible light entering the space through the fenestration product assembly to the incident visible light, Visible Transmittance, includes the effects of glazing material and frame and is expressed as a number between 0 and 1.

WHOLE HOUSE MECHANICAL VENTILATION SYSTEM. An exhaust system, supply system, or combination thereof that is designed to mechanically exchange indoor air with outdoor air when operating continuously or through a programmed intermittent schedule to satisfy the whole house ventilation rates.

ZONE. A space or group of spaces within a building with heating or cooling requirements that are sufficiently similar so that desired conditions can be maintained throughout using a single controlling device.

CHAPTER 3 [RE]
GENERAL REQUIREMENTS

SECTION R301
CLIMATE ZONES

R301.1 General. Climate zones from Figure R301.1 or Table R301.1 shall be used in determining the applicable requirements from Chapter 4. Locations not in Table R301.1 (outside the United States) shall be assigned a climate zone based on Section R301.3.

R301.2 Warm humid counties. Warm humid counties are identified in Table R301.1 by an asterisk.

R301.3 International climate zones. The climate zone for any location outside the United States shall be determined by applying Table R301.3(1) and then Table R301.3(2).

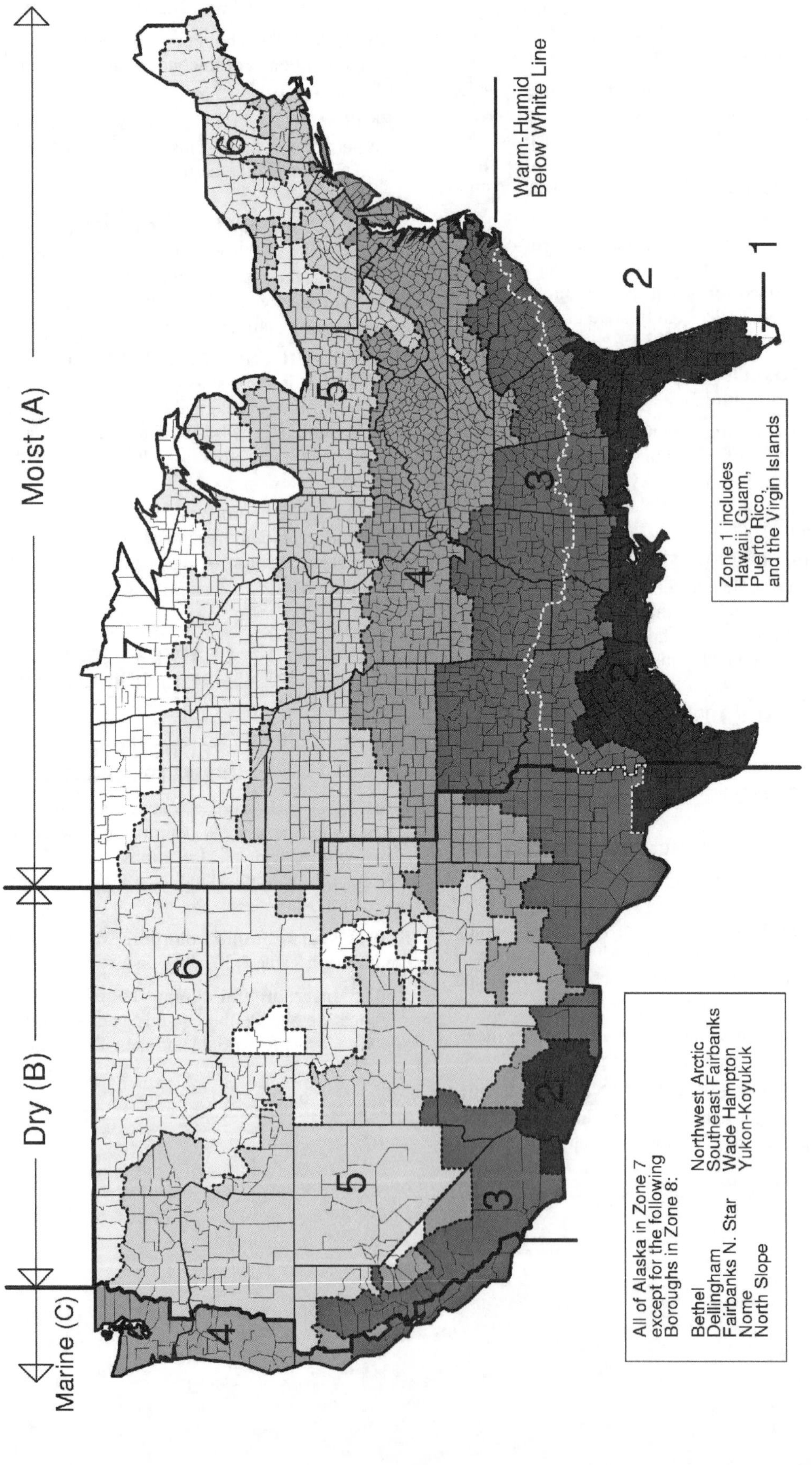
Marine (C)
Dry (B)
Moist (A)
Warm-Humid
Below White Line
1
2
3
4
5
6
7
All of Alaska in Zone 7
except for the following
Boroughs in Zone 8:
Bethel
Dellingham
Fairbanks N. Star
Nome
North Slope
Northwest Arctic
Southeast Fairbanks
Wade Hampton
Yukon-Koyukuk
Zone 1 includes
Hawaii, Guam,
Puerto Rico,
and the Virgin Islands

FIGURE R301.1
CLIMATE ZONES

TABLE R301.1
CLIMATE ZONES, MOISTURE REGIMES, AND WARM-HUMID
DESIGNATIONS BY STATE, COUNTY AND TERRITORY

Key: A – Moist, B – Dry, C – Marine. Absence of moisture designation indicates moisture regime is irrelevant. Asterisk (*) indicates a warm-humid location.

US STATES

ALABAMA

3A Autauga*
2A Baldwin*
3A Barbour*
3A Bibb
3A Blount
3A Bullock*
3A Butler*
3A Calhoun
3A Chambers
3A Cherokee
3A Chilton
3A Choctaw*
3A Clarke*
3A Clay
3A Cleburne
3A Coffee*
3A Colbert
3A Conecuh*
3A Coosa
3A Covington*
3A Crenshaw*
3A Cullman
3A Dale*
3A Dallas*
3A DeKalb
3A Elmore*
3A Escambia*
3A Etowah
3A Fayette
3A Franklin
3A Geneva*
3A Greene
3A Hale
3A Henry*
3A Houston*
3A Jackson
3A Jefferson
3A Lamar
3A Lauderdale
3A Lawrence

3A Lee
3A Limestone
3A Lowndes*
3A Macon*
3A Madison
3A Marengo*
3A Marion
3A Marshall
2A Mobile*
3A Monroe*
3A Montgomery*
3A Morgan
3A Perry*
3A Pickens
3A Pike*
3A Randolph
3A Russell*
3A Shelby
3A St. Clair
3A Sumter
3A Talladega
3A Tallapoosa
3A Tuscaloosa
3A Walker
3A Washington*
3A Wilcox*
3A Winston

ALASKA

7 Aleutians East
7 Aleutians West
7 Anchorage
8 Bethel
7 Bristol Bay
7 Denali
8 Dillingham
8 Fairbanks North Star
7 Haines
7 Juneau
7 Kenai Peninsula
7 Ketchikan Gateway

7 Kodiak Island
7 Lake and Peninsula
7 Matanuska-Susitna
8 Nome
8 North Slope
8 Northwest Arctic
7 Prince of Wales
  Outer Ketchikan
7 Sitka
7 Skagway-Hoonah-
  Angoon
8 Southeast Fairbanks
7 Valdez-Cordova
8 Wade Hampton
7 Wrangell-Petersburg
7 Yakutat
8 Yukon-Koyukuk

ARIZONA

5B Apache
3B Cochise
5B Coconino
4B Gila
3B Graham
3B Greenlee
2B La Paz
2B Maricopa
3B Mohave
5B Navajo
2B Pima
2B Pinal
3B Santa Cruz
4B Yavapai
2B Yuma

ARKANSAS

3A Arkansas
3A Ashley
4A Baxter
4A Benton
4A Boone
3A Bradley

3A Calhoun
4A Carroll
3A Chicot
3A Clark
3A Clay
3A Cleburne
3A Cleveland
3A Columbia*
3A Conway
3A Craighead
3A Crawford
3A Crittenden
3A Cross
3A Dallas
3A Desha
3A Drew
3A Faulkner
3A Franklin
4A Fulton
3A Garland
3A Grant
3A Greene
3A Hempstead*
3A Hot Spring
3A Howard
3A Independence
4A Izard
3A Jackson
3A Jefferson
3A Johnson
3A Lafayette*
3A Lawrence
3A Lee
3A Lincoln
3A Little River*
3A Logan
3A Lonoke
4A Madison
4A Marion
3A Miller*
3A Mississippi

3A Monroe
3A Montgomery
3A Nevada
4A Newton
3A Ouachita
3A Perry
3A Phillips
3A Pike
3A Poinsett
3A Polk
3A Pope
3A Prairie
3A Pulaski
3A Randolph
3A Saline
3A Scott
4A Searcy
3A Sebastian
3A Sevier*
3A Sharp
3A St. Francis
4A Stone
3A Union*
3A Van Buren
4A Washington
3A White
3A Woodruff
3A Yell

CALIFORNIA

3C Alameda
6B Alpine
4B Amador
3B Butte
4B Calaveras
3B Colusa
3B Contra Costa
4C Del Norte
4B El Dorado
3B Fresno
3B Glenn

(continued)

TABLE R301.1—continued
CLIMATE ZONES, MOISTURE REGIMES, AND WARM-HUMID
DESIGNATIONS BY STATE, COUNTY AND TERRITORY

4C Humboldt
2B Imperial
4B Inyo
3B Kern
3B Kings
4B Lake
5B Lassen
3B Los Angeles
3B Madera
3C Marin
4B Mariposa
3C Mendocino
3B Merced
5B Modoc
6B Mono
3C Monterey
3C Napa
5B Nevada
3B Orange
3B Placer
5B Plumas
3B Riverside
3B Sacramento
3C San Benito
3B San Bernardino
3B San Diego
3C San Francisco
3B San Joaquin
3C San Luis Obispo
3C San Mateo
3C Santa Barbara
3C Santa Clara
3C Santa Cruz
3B Shasta
5B Sierra
5B Siskiyou
3B Solano
3C Sonoma
3B Stanislaus
3B Sutter
3B Tehama
4B Trinity
3B Tulare
4B Tuolumne
3C Ventura
3B Yolo

3B Yuba

COLORADO

5B Adams
6B Alamosa
5B Arapahoe
6B Archuleta
4B Baca
5B Bent
5B Boulder
6B Chaffee
5B Cheyenne
7 Clear Creek
6B Conejos
6B Costilla
5B Crowley
6B Custer
5B Delta
5B Denver
6B Dolores
5B Douglas
6B Eagle
5B Elbert
5B El Paso
5B Fremont
5B Garfield
5B Gilpin
7 Grand
7 Gunnison
7 Hinsdale
5B Huerfano
7 Jackson
5B Jefferson
5B Kiowa
5B Kit Carson
7 Lake
5B La Plata
5B Larimer
4B Las Animas
5B Lincoln
5B Logan
5B Mesa
7 Mineral
6B Moffat
5B Montezuma
5B Montrose

5B Morgan
4B Otero
6B Ouray
7 Park
5B Phillips
7 Pitkin
5B Prowers
5B Pueblo
6B Rio Blanco
7 Rio Grande
7 Routt
6B Saguache
7 San Juan
6B San Miguel
5B Sedgwick
7 Summit
5B Teller
5B Washington
5B Weld
5B Yuma

CONNECTICUT

5A (all)

DELAWARE

4A (all)

DISTRICT OF COLUMBIA

4A (all)

FLORIDA

2A Alachua*
2A Baker*
2A Bay*
2A Bradford*
2A Brevard*
1A Broward*
2A Calhoun*
2A Charlotte*
2A Citrus*
2A Clay*
2A Collier*
2A Columbia*
2A DeSoto*
2A Dixie*
2A Duval*

2A Escambia*
2A Flagler*
2A Franklin*
2A Gadsden*
2A Gilchrist*
2A Glades*
2A Gulf*
2A Hamilton*
2A Hardee*
2A Hendry*
2A Hernando*
2A Highlands*
2A Hillsborough*
2A Holmes*
2A Indian River*
2A Jackson*
2A Jefferson*
2A Lafayette*
2A Lake*
2A Lee*
2A Leon*
2A Levy*
2A Liberty*
2A Madison*
2A Manatee*
2A Marion*
2A Martin*
1A Miami-Dade*
1A Monroe*
2A Nassau*
2A Okaloosa*
2A Okeechobee*
2A Orange*
2A Osceola*
2A Palm Beach*
2A Pasco*
2A Pinellas*
2A Polk*
2A Putnam*
2A Santa Rosa*
2A Sarasota*
2A Seminole*
2A St. Johns*
2A St. Lucie*
2A Sumter*
2A Suwannee*

2A Taylor*
2A Union*
2A Volusia*
2A Wakulla*
2A Walton*
2A Washington*

GEORGIA

2A Appling*
2A Atkinson*
2A Bacon*
2A Baker*
3A Baldwin
4A Banks
3A Barrow
3A Bartow
3A Ben Hill*
2A Berrien*
3A Bibb
3A Bleckley*
2A Brantley*
2A Brooks*
2A Bryan*
3A Bulloch*
3A Burke
3A Butts
3A Calhoun*
2A Camden*
3A Candler*
3A Carroll
4A Catoosa
2A Charlton*
2A Chatham*
3A Chattahoochee*
4A Chattooga
3A Cherokee
3A Clarke
3A Clay*
3A Clayton
2A Clinch*
3A Cobb
3A Coffee*
2A Colquitt*
3A Columbia
2A Cook*
3A Coweta

(continued)

TABLE R301.1—continued
CLIMATE ZONES, MOISTURE REGIMES, AND WARM-HUMID
DESIGNATIONS BY STATE, COUNTY AND TERRITORY

3A Crawford	2A Lanier*	3A Taylor*	5B Cassia	4A Crawford
3A Crisp*	3A Laurens*	3A Telfair*	6B Clark	5A Cumberland
4A Dade	3A Lee*	3A Terrell*	5B Clearwater	5A DeKalb
4A Dawson	2A Liberty*	2A Thomas*	6B Custer	5A De Witt
2A Decatur*	3A Lincoln	3A Tift*	5B Elmore	5A Douglas
3A DeKalb	2A Long*	2A Toombs*	6B Franklin	5A DuPage
3A Dodge*	2A Lowndes*	4A Towns	6B Fremont	5A Edgar
3A Dooly*	4A Lumpkin	3A Treutlen*	5B Gem	4A Edwards
3A Dougherty*	3A Macon*	3A Troup	5B Gooding	4A Effingham
3A Douglas	3A Madison	3A Turner*	5B Idaho	4A Fayette
3A Early*	3A Marion*	3A Twiggs*	6B Jefferson	5A Ford
2A Echols*	3A McDuffie	4A Union	5B Jerome	4A Franklin
2A Effingham*	2A McIntosh*	3A Upson	5B Kootenai	5A Fulton
3A Elbert	3A Meriwether	4A Walker	5B Latah	4A Gallatin
3A Emanuel*	2A Miller*	3A Walton	6B Lemhi	5A Greene
2A Evans*	2A Mitchell*	2A Ware*	5B Lewis	5A Grundy
4A Fannin	3A Monroe	3A Warren	5B Lincoln	4A Hamilton
3A Fayette	3A Montgomery*	3A Washington	6B Madison	5A Hancock
4A Floyd	3A Morgan	2A Wayne*	5B Minidoka	4A Hardin
3A Forsyth	4A Murray	3A Webster*	5B Nez Perce	5A Henderson
4A Franklin	3A Muscogee	3A Wheeler*	6B Oneida	5A Henry
3A Fulton	3A Newton	4A White	5B Owyhee	5A Iroquois
4A Gilmer	3A Oconee	4A Whitfield	5B Payette	4A Jackson
3A Glascock	3A Oglethorpe	3A Wilcox*	5B Power	4A Jasper
2A Glynn*	3A Paulding	3A Wilkes	5B Shoshone	4A Jefferson
4A Gordon	3A Peach*	3A Wilkinson	6B Teton	5A Jersey
2A Grady*	4A Pickens	3A Worth*	5B Twin Falls	5A Jo Daviess
3A Greene	2A Pierce*		6B Valley	4A Johnson
3A Gwinnett	3A Pike	**HAWAII**	5B Washington	5A Kane
4A Habersham	3A Polk	1A (all)*		5A Kankakee
4A Hall	3A Pulaski*		**ILLINOIS**	5A Kendall
3A Hancock	3A Putnam	**IDAHO**	5A Adams	5A Knox
3A Haralson	3A Quitman*	5B Ada	4A Alexander	5A Lake
3A Harris	4A Rabun	6B Adams	4A Bond	5A La Salle
3A Hart	3A Randolph*	6B Bannock	5A Boone	4A Lawrence
3A Heard	3A Richmond	6B Bear Lake	5A Brown	5A Lee
3A Henry	3A Rockdale	5B Benewah	5A Bureau	5A Livingston
3A Houston*	3A Schley*	6B Bingham	5A Calhoun	5A Logan
3A Irwin*	3A Screven*	6B Blaine	5A Carroll	5A Macon
3A Jackson	2A Seminole*	6B Boise	5A Cass	4A Macoupin
3A Jasper	3A Spalding	6B Bonner	5A Champaign	4A Madison
2A Jeff Davis*	4A Stephens	6B Bonneville	4A Christian	4A Marion
3A Jefferson	3A Stewart*	6B Boundary	5A Clark	5A Marshall
3A Jenkins*	3A Sumter*	6B Butte	4A Clay	5A Mason
3A Johnson*	3A Talbot	6B Camas	4A Clinton	4A Massac
3A Jones	3A Taliaferro	5B Canyon	5A Coles	5A McDonough
3A Lamar	2A Tattnall*	6B Caribou	5A Cook	5A McHenry

(continued)

TABLE R301.1—continued
CLIMATE ZONES, MOISTURE REGIMES, AND WARM-HUMID DESIGNATIONS BY STATE, COUNTY AND TERRITORY

5A McLean	5A Boone	5A Miami	5A Appanoose	5A Jasper
5A Menard	4A Brown	4A Monroe	5A Audubon	5A Jefferson
5A Mercer	5A Carroll	5A Montgomery	5A Benton	5A Johnson
4A Monroe	5A Cass	5A Morgan	6A Black Hawk	5A Jones
4A Montgomery	4A Clark	5A Newton	5A Boone	5A Keokuk
5A Morgan	5A Clay	5A Noble	6A Bremer	6A Kossuth
5A Moultrie	5A Clinton	4A Ohio	6A Buchanan	5A Lee
5A Ogle	4A Crawford	4A Orange	6A Buena Vista	5A Linn
5A Peoria	4A Daviess	5A Owen	6A Butler	5A Louisa
4A Perry	4A Dearborn	5A Parke	6A Calhoun	5A Lucas
5A Piatt	5A Decatur	4A Perry	5A Carroll	6A Lyon
5A Pike	5A De Kalb	4A Pike	5A Cass	5A Madison
4A Pope	5A Delaware	5A Porter	5A Cedar	5A Mahaska
4A Pulaski	4A Dubois	4A Posey	6A Cerro Gordo	5A Marion
5A Putnam	5A Elkhart	5A Pulaski	6A Cherokee	5A Marshall
4A Randolph	5A Fayette	5A Putnam	6A Chickasaw	5A Mills
4A Richland	4A Floyd	5A Randolph	5A Clarke	6A Mitchell
5A Rock Island	5A Fountain	4A Ripley	6A Clay	5A Monona
4A Saline	5A Franklin	5A Rush	6A Clayton	5A Monroe
5A Sangamon	5A Fulton	4A Scott	5A Clinton	5A Montgomery
5A Schuyler	4A Gibson	5A Shelby	5A Crawford	5A Muscatine
5A Scott	5A Grant	4A Spencer	5A Dallas	6A O'Brien
4A Shelby	4A Greene	5A Starke	5A Davis	6A Osceola
5A Stark	5A Hamilton	5A Steuben	5A Decatur	5A Page
4A St. Clair	5A Hancock	5A St. Joseph	6A Delaware	6A Palo Alto
5A Stephenson	4A Harrison	4A Sullivan	5A Des Moines	6A Plymouth
5A Tazewell	5A Hendricks	4A Switzerland	6A Dickinson	6A Pocahontas
4A Union	5A Henry	5A Tippecanoe	5A Dubuque	5A Polk
5A Vermilion	5A Howard	5A Tipton	6A Emmet	5A Pottawattamie
4A Wabash	5A Huntington	5A Union	6A Fayette	5A Poweshiek
5A Warren	4A Jackson	4A Vanderburgh	6A Floyd	5A Ringgold
4A Washington	5A Jasper	5A Vermillion	6A Franklin	6A Sac
4A Wayne	5A Jay	5A Vigo	5A Fremont	5A Scott
4A White	4A Jefferson	5A Wabash	5A Greene	5A Shelby
5A Whiteside	4A Jennings	5A Warren	6A Grundy	6A Sioux
5A Will	5A Johnson	4A Warrick	5A Guthrie	5A Story
4A Williamson	4A Knox	4A Washington	6A Hamilton	5A Tama
5A Winnebago	5A Kosciusko	5A Wayne	6A Hancock	5A Taylor
5A Woodford	5A Lagrange	5A Wells	6A Hardin	5A Union
	5A Lake	5A White	5A Harrison	5A Van Buren
INDIANA	5A La Porte	5A Whitley	5A Henry	5A Wapello
	4A Lawrence		6A Howard	5A Warren
5A Adams	5A Madison	**IOWA**	6A Humboldt	5A Washington
5A Allen	5A Marion		6A Ida	5A Wayne
5A Bartholomew	5A Marshall	5A Adair	5A Iowa	6A Webster
5A Benton	4A Martin	5A Adams	5A Jackson	6A Winnebago
5A Blackford		6A Allamakee		

(continued)

TABLE R301.1—continued
CLIMATE ZONES, MOISTURE REGIMES, AND WARM-HUMID
DESIGNATIONS BY STATE, COUNTY AND TERRITORY

6A Winneshiek
5A Woodbury
6A Worth
6A Wright

KANSAS

4A Allen
4A Anderson
4A Atchison
4A Barber
4A Barton
4A Bourbon
4A Brown
4A Butler
4A Chase
4A Chautauqua
4A Cherokee
5A Cheyenne
4A Clark
4A Clay
5A Cloud
4A Coffey
4A Comanche
4A Cowley
4A Crawford
5A Decatur
4A Dickinson
4A Doniphan
4A Douglas
4A Edwards
4A Elk
5A Ellis
4A Ellsworth
4A Finney
4A Ford
4A Franklin
4A Geary
5A Gove
5A Graham
4A Grant
4A Gray
5A Greeley
4A Greenwood
5A Hamilton
4A Harper
4A Harvey

4A Haskell
4A Hodgeman
4A Jackson
4A Jefferson
5A Jewell
4A Johnson
4A Kearny
4A Kingman
4A Kiowa
4A Labette
5A Lane
4A Leavenworth
4A Lincoln
4A Linn
5A Logan
4A Lyon
4A Marion
4A Marshall
4A McPherson
4A Meade
4A Miami
5A Mitchell
4A Montgomery
4A Morris
4A Morton
4A Nemaha
4A Neosho
5A Ness
5A Norton
4A Osage
5A Osborne
4A Ottawa
4A Pawnee
5A Phillips
4A Pottawatomie
4A Pratt
5A Rawlins
4A Reno
5A Republic
4A Rice
4A Riley
5A Rooks
4A Rush
4A Russell
4A Saline
5A Scott

4A Sedgwick
4A Seward
4A Shawnee
5A Sheridan
5A Sherman
5A Smith
4A Stafford
4A Stanton
4A Stevens
4A Sumner
5A Thomas
5A Trego
4A Wabaunsee
5A Wallace
4A Washington
5A Wichita
4A Wilson
4A Woodson
4A Wyandotte

KENTUCKY

4A (all)

LOUISIANA

2A Acadia*
2A Allen*
2A Ascension*
2A Assumption*
2A Avoyelles*
2A Beauregard*
3A Bienville*
3A Bossier*
3A Caddo*
2A Calcasieu*
3A Caldwell*
2A Cameron*
3A Catahoula*
3A Claiborne*
3A Concordia*
3A De Soto*
2A East Baton Rouge*
3A East Carroll
2A East Feliciana*
2A Evangeline*
3A Franklin*
3A Grant*
2A Iberia*

2A Iberville*
3A Jackson*
2A Jefferson*
2A Jefferson Davis*
2A Lafayette*
2A Lafourche*
3A La Salle*
3A Lincoln*
2A Livingston*
3A Madison*
3A Morehouse
3A Natchitoches*
2A Orleans*
3A Ouachita*
2A Plaquemines*
2A Pointe Coupee*
2A Rapides*
3A Red River*
3A Richland*
3A Sabine*
2A St. Bernard*
2A St. Charles*
2A St. Helena*
2A St. James*
2A St. John the
Baptist*
2A St. Landry*
2A St. Martin*
2A St. Mary*
2A St. Tammany*
2A Tangipahoa*
3A Tensas*
2A Terrebonne*
3A Union*
2A Vermilion*
3A Vernon*
2A Washington*
3A Webster*
2A West Baton
Rouge*
3A West Carroll
2A West Feliciana*
3A Winn*

MAINE

6A Androscoggin
7   Aroostook

6A Cumberland
6A Franklin
6A Hancock
6A Kennebec
6A Knox
6A Lincoln
6A Oxford
6A Penobscot
6A Piscataquis
6A Sagadahoc
6A Somerset
6A Waldo
6A Washington
6A York

MARYLAND

4A Allegany
4A Anne Arundel
4A Baltimore
4A Baltimore (city)
4A Calvert
4A Caroline
4A Carroll
4A Cecil
4A Charles
4A Dorchester
4A Frederick
5A Garrett
4A Harford
4A Howard
4A Kent
4A Montgomery
4A Prince George's
4A Queen Anne's
4A Somerset
4A St. Mary's
4A Talbot
4A Washington
4A Wicomico
4A Worcester

MASSACHSETTS

5A (all)

MICHIGAN

6A Alcona
6A Alger

(continued)

TABLE R301.1—continued
CLIMATE ZONES, MOISTURE REGIMES, AND WARM-HUMID
DESIGNATIONS BY STATE, COUNTY AND TERRITORY

5A Allegan	7 Mackinac	6A Carver	7 Otter Tail	3A Clarke
6A Alpena	5A Macomb	7 Cass	7 Pennington	3A Clay
6A Antrim	6A Manistee	6A Chippewa	7 Pine	3A Coahoma
6A Arenac	6A Marquette	6A Chisago	6A Pipestone	3A Copiah*
7 Baraga	6A Mason	7 Clay	7 Polk	3A Covington*
5A Barry	6A Mecosta	7 Clearwater	6A Pope	3A DeSoto
5A Bay	6A Menominee	7 Cook	6A Ramsey	3A Forrest*
6A Benzie	5A Midland	6A Cottonwood	7 Red Lake	3A Franklin*
5A Berrien	6A Missaukee	7 Crow Wing	6A Redwood	3A George*
5A Branch	5A Monroe	6A Dakota	6A Renville	3A Greene*
5A Calhoun	5A Montcalm	6A Dodge	6A Rice	3A Grenada
5A Cass	6A Montmorency	6A Douglas	6A Rock	2A Hancock*
6A Charlevoix	5A Muskegon	6A Faribault	7 Roseau	2A Harrison*
6A Cheboygan	6A Newaygo	6A Fillmore	6A Scott	3A Hinds*
7 Chippewa	5A Oakland	6A Freeborn	6A Sherburne	3A Holmes
6A Clare	6A Oceana	6A Goodhue	6A Sibley	3A Humphreys
5A Clinton	6A Ogemaw	7 Grant	6A Stearns	3A Issaquena
6A Crawford	7 Ontonagon	6A Hennepin	6A Steele	3A Itawamba
6A Delta	6A Osceola	6A Houston	6A Stevens	2A Jackson*
6A Dickinson	6A Oscoda	7 Hubbard	7 St. Louis	3A Jasper
5A Eaton	6A Otsego	6A Isanti	6A Swift	3A Jefferson*
6A Emmet	5A Ottawa	7 Itasca	6A Todd	3A Jefferson Davis*
5A Genesee	6A Presque Isle	6A Jackson	6A Traverse	3A Jones*
6A Gladwin	6A Roscommon	7 Kanabec	6A Wabasha	3A Kemper
7 Gogebic	5A Saginaw	6A Kandiyohi	7 Wadena	3A Lafayette
6A Grand Traverse	6A Sanilac	7 Kittson	6A Waseca	3A Lamar*
5A Gratiot	7 Schoolcraft	7 Koochiching	6A Washington	3A Lauderdale
5A Hillsdale	5A Shiawassee	6A Lac qui Parle	6A Watonwan	3A Lawrence*
7 Houghton	5A St. Clair	7 Lake	7 Wilkin	3A Leake
6A Huron	5A St. Joseph	7 Lake of the Woods	6A Winona	3A Lee
5A Ingham	5A Tuscola	6A Le Sueur	6A Wright	3A Leflore
5A Ionia	5A Van Buren	6A Lincoln	6A Yellow	3A Lincoln*
6A Iosco	5A Washtenaw	6A Lyon	Medicine	3A Lowndes
7 Iron	5A Wayne	7 Mahnomen		3A Madison
6A Isabella	6A Wexford	7 Marshall	**MISSISSIPPI**	3A Marion*
5A Jackson		6A Martin		3A Marshall
5A Kalamazoo	**MINNESOTA**	6A McLeod	3A Adams*	3A Monroe
6A Kalkaska		6A Meeker	3A Alcorn	3A Montgomery
5A Kent	7 Aitkin	7 Mille Lacs	3A Amite*	3A Neshoba
7 Keweenaw	6A Anoka	6A Morrison	3A Attala	3A Newton
6A Lake	7 Becker	6A Mower	3A Benton	3A Noxubee
5A Lapeer	7 Beltrami	6A Murray	3A Bolivar	3A Oktibbeha
6A Leelanau	6A Benton	6A Nicollet	3A Calhoun	3A Panola
5A Lenawee	6A Big Stone	6A Nobles	3A Carroll	2A Pearl River*
5A Livingston	6A Blue Earth	7 Norman	3A Chickasaw	3A Perry*
7 Luce	6A Brown	6A Olmsted	3A Choctaw	3A Pike*
	7 Carlton		3A Claiborne*	

(continued)

TABLE R301.1—continued
CLIMATE ZONES, MOISTURE REGIMES, AND WARM-HUMID
DESIGNATIONS BY STATE, COUNTY AND TERRITORY

3A Pontotoc
3A Prentiss
3A Quitman
3A Rankin*
3A Scott
3A Sharkey
3A Simpson*
3A Smith*
2A Stone*
3A Sunflower
3A Tallahatchie
3A Tate
3A Tippah
3A Tishomingo
3A Tunica
3A Union
3A Walthall*
3A Warren*
3A Washington
3A Wayne*
3A Webster
3A Wilkinson*
3A Winston
3A Yalobusha
3A Yazoo

MISSOURI

5A Adair
5A Andrew
5A Atchison
4A Audrain
4A Barry
4A Barton
4A Bates
4A Benton
4A Bollinger
4A Boone
5A Buchanan
4A Butler
5A Caldwell
4A Callaway
4A Camden
4A Cape Girardeau
4A Carroll
4A Carter
4A Cass
4A Cedar

5A Chariton
4A Christian
5A Clark
4A Clay
5A Clinton
4A Cole
4A Cooper
4A Crawford
4A Dade
4A Dallas
5A Daviess
5A DeKalb
4A Dent
4A Douglas
4A Dunklin
4A Franklin
4A Gasconade
5A Gentry
4A Greene
5A Grundy
5A Harrison
4A Henry
4A Hickory
5A Holt
4A Howard
4A Howell
4A Iron
4A Jackson
4A Jasper
4A Jefferson
4A Johnson
5A Knox
4A Laclede
4A Lafayette
4A Lawrence
5A Lewis
4A Lincoln
5A Linn
5A Livingston
5A Macon
4A Madison
4A Maries
5A Marion
4A McDonald
5A Mercer
4A Miller

4A Mississippi
4A Moniteau
4A Monroe
4A Montgomery
4A Morgan
4A New Madrid
4A Newton
5A Nodaway
4A Oregon
4A Osage
4A Ozark
4A Pemiscot
4A Perry
4A Pettis
4A Phelps
5A Pike
4A Platte
4A Polk
4A Pulaski
5A Putnam
5A Ralls
4A Randolph
4A Ray
4A Reynolds
4A Ripley
4A Saline
5A Schuyler
5A Scotland
4A Scott
4A Shannon
5A Shelby
4A St. Charles
4A St. Clair
4A Ste. Genevieve
4A St. Francois
4A St. Louis
4A St. Louis (city)
4A Stoddard
4A Stone
5A Sullivan
4A Taney
4A Texas
4A Vernon
4A Warren
4A Washington
4A Wayne

4A Webster
5A Worth
4A Wright

MONTANA

6B (all)

NEBRASKA

5A (all)

NEVADA

5B Carson City (city)
5B Churchill
3B Clark
5B Douglas
5B Elko
5B Esmeralda
5B Eureka
5B Humboldt
5B Lander
5B Lincoln
5B Lyon
5B Mineral
5B Nye
5B Pershing
5B Storey
5B Washoe
5B White Pine

NEW HAMPSHIRE

6A Belknap
6A Carroll
5A Cheshire
6A Coos
6A Grafton
5A Hillsborough
6A Merrimack
5A Rockingham
5A Strafford
6A Sullivan

NEW JERSEY

4A Atlantic
5A Bergen
4A Burlington
4A Camden
4A Cape May

4A Cumberland
4A Essex
4A Gloucester
4A Hudson
5A Hunterdon
5A Mercer
4A Middlesex
4A Monmouth
5A Morris
4A Ocean
5A Passaic
4A Salem
5A Somerset
5A Sussex
4A Union
5A Warren

NEW MEXICO

4B Bernalillo
5B Catron
3B Chaves
4B Cibola
5B Colfax
4B Curry
4B DeBaca
3B Dona Ana
3B Eddy
4B Grant
4B Guadalupe
5B Harding
3B Hidalgo
3B Lea
4B Lincoln
5B Los Alamos
3B Luna
5B McKinley
5B Mora
3B Otero
4B Quay
5B Rio Arriba
4B Roosevelt
5B Sandoval
5B San Juan
5B San Miguel
5B Santa Fe
4B Sierra
4B Socorro

(continued)

TABLE R301.1—continued
CLIMATE ZONES, MOISTURE REGIMES, AND WARM-HUMID
DESIGNATIONS BY STATE, COUNTY AND TERRITORY

5B Taos	4A Queens	4A Clay	4A Orange	7 Divide
5B Torrance	5A Rensselaer	4A Cleveland	3A Pamlico	6A Dunn
4B Union	4A Richmond	3A Columbus*	3A Pasquotank	7 Eddy
4B Valencia	5A Rockland	3A Craven	3A Pender*	6A Emmons
	5A Saratoga	3A Cumberland	3A Perquimans	7 Foster
NEW YORK	5A Schenectady	3A Currituck	4A Person	6A Golden Valley
	6A Schoharie	3A Dare	3A Pitt	7 Grand Forks
5A Albany	6A Schuyler	3A Davidson	4A Polk	6A Grant
6A Allegany	5A Seneca	4A Davie	3A Randolph	7 Griggs
4A Bronx	6A Steuben	3A Duplin	3A Richmond	6A Hettinger
6A Broome	6A St. Lawrence	4A Durham	3A Robeson	7 Kidder
6A Cattaraugus	4A Suffolk	3A Edgecombe	4A Rockingham	6A LaMoure
5A Cayuga	6A Sullivan	4A Forsyth	3A Rowan	6A Logan
5A Chautauqua	5A Tioga	4A Franklin	4A Rutherford	7 McHenry
5A Chemung	6A Tompkins	3A Gaston	3A Sampson	6A McIntosh
6A Chenango	6A Ulster	4A Gates	3A Scotland	6A McKenzie
6A Clinton	6A Warren	4A Graham	3A Stanly	7 McLean
5A Columbia	5A Washington	4A Granville	4A Stokes	6A Mercer
5A Cortland	5A Wayne	3A Greene	4A Surry	6A Morton
6A Delaware	4A Westchester	4A Guilford	4A Swain	7 Mountrail
5A Dutchess	6A Wyoming	4A Halifax	4A Transylvania	7 Nelson
5A Erie	5A Yates	4A Harnett	3A Tyrrell	6A Oliver
6A Essex		4A Haywood	3A Union	7 Pembina
6A Franklin	**NORTH**	4A Henderson	4A Vance	7 Pierce
6A Fulton	**CAROLINA**	4A Hertford	4A Wake	7 Ramsey
5A Genesee		3A Hoke	4A Warren	6A Ransom
5A Greene	4A Alamance	3A Hyde	3A Washington	7 Renville
6A Hamilton	4A Alexander	4A Iredell	5A Watauga	6A Richland
6A Herkimer	5A Alleghany	4A Jackson	3A Wayne	7 Rolette
6A Jefferson	3A Anson	3A Johnston	4A Wilkes	6A Sargent
4A Kings	5A Ashe	3A Jones	3A Wilson	7 Sheridan
6A Lewis	5A Avery	4A Lee	4A Yadkin	6A Sioux
5A Livingston	3A Beaufort	3A Lenoir	5A Yancey	6A Slope
6A Madison	4A Bertie	4A Lincoln		6A Stark
5A Monroe	3A Bladen	4A Macon	**NORTH DAKOTA**	7 Steele
6A Montgomery	3A Brunswick*	4A Madison		7 Stutsman
4A Nassau	4A Buncombe	3A Martin	6A Adams	7 Towner
4A New York	4A Burke	4A McDowell	7 Barnes	7 Traill
5A Niagara	3A Cabarrus	3A Mecklenburg	7 Benson	7 Walsh
6A Oneida	4A Caldwell	5A Mitchell	6A Billings	7 Ward
5A Onondaga	3A Camden	3A Montgomery	7 Bottineau	7 Wells
5A Ontario	3A Carteret*	3A Moore	6A Bowman	7 Williams
5A Orange	4A Caswell	4A Nash	7 Burke	
5A Orleans	4A Catawba	3A New Hanover*	6A Burleigh	**OHIO**
5A Oswego	4A Chatham	4A Northampton	7 Cass	
6A Otsego	4A Cherokee	3A Onslow*	7 Cavalier	4A Adams
5A Putnam	3A Chowan		6A Dickey	5A Allen

(continued)

TABLE R301.1—continued
CLIMATE ZONES, MOISTURE REGIMES, AND WARM-HUMID
DESIGNATIONS BY STATE, COUNTY AND TERRITORY

5A Ashland	5A Mahoning	3A Bryan	3A Okfuskee	4C Linn
5A Ashtabula	5A Marion	3A Caddo	3A Oklahoma	5B Malheur
5A Athens	5A Medina	3A Canadian	3A Okmulgee	4C Marion
5A Auglaize	5A Meigs	3A Carter	3A Osage	5B Morrow
5A Belmont	5A Mercer	3A Cherokee	3A Ottawa	4C Multnomah
4A Brown	5A Miami	3A Choctaw	3A Pawnee	4C Polk
5A Butler	5A Monroe	4B Cimarron	3A Payne	5B Sherman
5A Carroll	5A Montgomery	3A Cleveland	3A Pittsburg	4C Tillamook
5A Champaign	5A Morgan	3A Coal	3A Pontotoc	5B Umatilla
5A Clark	5A Morrow	3A Comanche	3A Pottawatomie	5B Union
4A Clermont	5A Muskingum	3A Cotton	3A Pushmataha	5B Wallowa
5A Clinton	5A Noble	3A Craig	3A Roger Mills	5B Wasco
5A Columbiana	5A Ottawa	3A Creek	3A Rogers	4C Washington
5A Coshocton	5A Paulding	3A Custer	3A Seminole	5B Wheeler
5A Crawford	5A Perry	3A Delaware	3A Sequoyah	4C Yamhill
5A Cuyahoga	5A Pickaway	3A Dewey	3A Stephens	
5A Darke	4A Pike	3A Ellis	4B Texas	**PENNSYLVANIA**
5A Defiance	5A Portage	3A Garfield	3A Tillman	5A Adams
5A Delaware	5A Preble	3A Garvin	3A Tulsa	5A Allegheny
5A Erie	5A Putnam	3A Grady	3A Wagoner	5A Armstrong
5A Fairfield	5A Richland	3A Grant	3A Washington	5A Beaver
5A Fayette	5A Ross	3A Greer	3A Washita	5A Bedford
5A Franklin	5A Sandusky	3A Harmon	3A Woods	5A Berks
5A Fulton	4A Scioto	3A Harper	3A Woodward	5A Blair
4A Gallia	5A Seneca	3A Haskell		5A Bradford
5A Geauga	5A Shelby	3A Hughes	**OREGON**	4A Bucks
5A Greene	5A Stark	3A Jackson	5B Baker	5A Butler
5A Guernsey	5A Summit	3A Jefferson	4C Benton	5A Cambria
4A Hamilton	5A Trumbull	3A Johnston	4C Clackamas	6A Cameron
5A Hancock	5A Tuscarawas	3A Kay	4C Clatsop	5A Carbon
5A Hardin	5A Union	3A Kingfisher	4C Columbia	5A Centre
5A Harrison	5A Van Wert	3A Kiowa	4C Coos	4A Chester
5A Henry	5A Vinton	3A Latimer	5B Crook	5A Clarion
5A Highland	5A Warren	3A Le Flore	4C Curry	6A Clearfield
5A Hocking	4A Washington	3A Lincoln	5B Deschutes	5A Clinton
5A Holmes	5A Wayne	3A Logan	4C Douglas	5A Columbia
5A Huron	5A Williams	3A Love	5B Gilliam	5A Crawford
5A Jackson	5A Wood	3A Major	5B Grant	5A Cumberland
5A Jefferson	5A Wyandot	3A Marshall	5B Harney	5A Dauphin
5A Knox		3A Mayes	5B Hood River	4A Delaware
5A Lake	**OKLAHOMA**	3A McClain	4C Jackson	6A Elk
4A Lawrence	3A Adair	3A McCurtain	5B Jefferson	5A Erie
5A Licking	3A Alfalfa	3A McIntosh	4C Josephine	5A Fayette
5A Logan	3A Atoka	3A Murray	5B Klamath	5A Forest
5A Lorain	4B Beaver	3A Muskogee	5B Lake	5A Franklin
5A Lucas	3A Beckham	3A Noble	4C Lane	5A Fulton
5A Madison	3A Blaine	3A Nowata	4C Lincoln	5A Greene

(continued)

TABLE R301.1—continued
CLIMATE ZONES, MOISTURE REGIMES, AND WARM-HUMID
DESIGNATIONS BY STATE, COUNTY AND TERRITORY

5A Huntingdon	3A Bamberg*	5A Bennett	6A Minnehaha	4A Gibson
5A Indiana	3A Barnwell*	5A Bon Homme	6A Moody	4A Giles
5A Jefferson	3A Beaufort*	6A Brookings	6A Pennington	4A Grainger
5A Juniata	3A Berkeley*	6A Brown	6A Perkins	4A Greene
5A Lackawanna	3A Calhoun	6A Brule	6A Potter	4A Grundy
5A Lancaster	3A Charleston*	6A Buffalo	6A Roberts	4A Hamblen
5A Lawrence	3A Cherokee	6A Butte	6A Sanborn	4A Hamilton
5A Lebanon	3A Chester	6A Campbell	6A Shannon	4A Hancock
5A Lehigh	3A Chesterfield	5A Charles Mix	6A Spink	3A Hardeman
5A Luzerne	3A Clarendon	6A Clark	6A Stanley	3A Hardin
5A Lycoming	3A Colleton*	5A Clay	6A Sully	4A Hawkins
6A McKean	3A Darlington	6A Codington	5A Todd	3A Haywood
5A Mercer	3A Dillon	6A Corson	5A Tripp	3A Henderson
5A Mifflin	3A Dorchester*	6A Custer	6A Turner	4A Henry
5A Monroe	3A Edgefield	6A Davison	5A Union	4A Hickman
4A Montgomery	3A Fairfield	6A Day	6A Walworth	4A Houston
5A Montour	3A Florence	6A Deuel	5A Yankton	4A Humphreys
5A Northampton	3A Georgetown*	6A Dewey	6A Ziebach	4A Jackson
5A Northumberland	3A Greenville	5A Douglas		4A Jefferson
5A Perry	3A Greenwood	6A Edmunds	**TENNESSEE**	4A Johnson
4A Philadelphia	3A Hampton*	6A Fall River	4A Anderson	4A Knox
5A Pike	3A Horry*	6A Faulk	4A Bedford	3A Lake
6A Potter	3A Jasper*	6A Grant	4A Benton	3A Lauderdale
5A Schuylkill	3A Kershaw	5A Gregory	4A Bledsoe	4A Lawrence
5A Snyder	3A Lancaster	6A Haakon	4A Blount	4A Lewis
5A Somerset	3A Laurens	6A Hamlin	4A Bradley	4A Lincoln
5A Sullivan	3A Lee	6A Hand	4A Campbell	4A Loudon
6A Susquehanna	3A Lexington	6A Hanson	4A Cannon	4A Macon
6A Tioga	3A Marion	6A Harding	4A Carroll	3A Madison
5A Union	3A Marlboro	6A Hughes	4A Carter	4A Marion
5A Venango	3A McCormick	5A Hutchinson	4A Cheatham	4A Marshall
5A Warren	3A Newberry	6A Hyde	3A Chester	4A Maury
5A Washington	3A Oconee	5A Jackson	4A Claiborne	4A McMinn
6A Wayne	3A Orangeburg	6A Jerauld	4A Clay	3A McNairy
5A Westmoreland	3A Pickens	6A Jones	4A Cocke	4A Meigs
5A Wyoming	3A Richland	6A Kingsbury	4A Coffee	4A Monroe
4A York	3A Saluda	6A Lake	3A Crockett	4A Montgomery
	3A Spartanburg	6A Lawrence	4A Cumberland	4A Moore
RHODE ISLAND	3A Sumter	6A Lincoln	4A Davidson	4A Morgan
5A (all)	3A Union	6A Lyman	4A Decatur	4A Obion
	3A Williamsburg	6A Marshall	4A DeKalb	4A Overton
SOUTH CAROLINA	3A York	6A McCook	4A Dickson	4A Perry
		6A McPherson	3A Dyer	4A Pickett
3A Abbeville	**SOUTH DAKOTA**	6A Meade	3A Fayette	4A Polk
3A Aiken	6A Aurora	5A Mellette	4A Fentress	4A Putnam
3A Allendale*	6A Beadle	6A Miner	4A Franklin	4A Rhea
3A Anderson				

(continued)

TABLE R301.1—continued
CLIMATE ZONES, MOISTURE REGIMES, AND WARM-HUMID
DESIGNATIONS BY STATE, COUNTY AND TERRITORY

4A Roane	3B Brewster	3B Ector	3B Howard	3B McCulloch
4A Robertson	4B Briscoe	2B Edwards*	3B Hudspeth	2A McLennan*
4A Rutherford	2A Brooks*	3A Ellis*	3A Hunt*	2A McMullen*
4A Scott	3A Brown*	3B El Paso	4B Hutchinson	2B Medina*
4A Sequatchie	2A Burleson*	3A Erath*	3B Irion	3B Menard
4A Sevier	3A Burnet*	2A Falls*	3A Jack	3B Midland
3A Shelby	2A Caldwell*	3A Fannin	2A Jackson*	2A Milam*
4A Smith	2A Calhoun*	2A Fayette*	2A Jasper*	3A Mills*
4A Stewart	3B Callahan	3B Fisher	3B Jeff Davis	3B Mitchell
4A Sullivan	2A Cameron*	4B Floyd	2A Jefferson*	3A Montague
4A Sumner	3A Camp*	3B Foard	2A Jim Hogg*	2A Montgomery*
3A Tipton	4B Carson	2A Fort Bend*	2A Jim Wells*	4B Moore
4A Trousdale	3A Cass*	3A Franklin*	3A Johnson*	3A Morris*
4A Unicoi	4B Castro	2A Freestone*	3B Jones	3B Motley
4A Union	2A Chambers*	2B Frio*	2A Karnes*	3A Nacogdoches*
4A Van Buren	2A Cherokee*	3B Gaines	3A Kaufman*	3A Navarro*
4A Warren	3B Childress	2A Galveston*	3A Kendall*	2A Newton*
4A Washington	3A Clay	3B Garza	2A Kenedy*	3B Nolan
4A Wayne	4B Cochran	3A Gillespie*	3B Kent	2A Nueces*
4A Weakley	3B Coke	3B Glasscock	3B Kerr	4B Ochiltree
4A White	3B Coleman	2A Goliad*	3B Kimble	4B Oldham
4A Williamson	3A Collin*	2A Gonzales*	3B King	2A Orange*
4A Wilson	3B Collingsworth	4B Gray	2B Kinney*	3A Palo Pinto*
	2A Colorado*	3A Grayson	2A Kleberg*	3A Panola*
TEXAS	2A Comal*	3A Gregg*	3B Knox	3A Parker*
	3A Comanche*	2A Grimes*	3A Lamar*	4B Parmer
2A Anderson*	3B Concho	2A Guadalupe*	4B Lamb	3B Pecos
3B Andrews	3A Cooke	4B Hale	3A Lampasas*	2A Polk*
2A Angelina*	2A Coryell*	3B Hall	2B La Salle*	4B Potter
2A Aransas*	3B Cottle	3A Hamilton*	2A Lavaca*	3B Presidio
3A Archer	3B Crane	4B Hansford	2A Lee*	3A Rains*
4B Armstrong	3B Crockett	3B Hardeman	2A Leon*	4B Randall
2A Atascosa*	3B Crosby	2A Hardin*	2A Liberty*	3B Reagan
2A Austin*	3B Culberson	2A Harris*	2A Limestone*	2B Real*
4B Bailey	4B Dallam	3A Harrison*	4B Lipscomb	3A Red River*
2B Bandera*	3A Dallas*	4B Hartley	2A Live Oak*	3B Reeves
2A Bastrop*	3B Dawson	3B Haskell	3A Llano*	2A Refugio*
3B Baylor	4B Deaf Smith	2A Hays*	3B Loving	4B Roberts
2A Bee*	3A Delta	3B Hemphill	3B Lubbock	2A Robertson*
2A Bell*	3A Denton*	3A Henderson*	3B Lynn	3A Rockwall*
2A Bexar*	2A DeWitt*	2A Hidalgo*	2A Madison*	3B Runnels
3A Blanco*	3B Dickens	2A Hill*	3A Marion*	3A Rusk*
3B Borden	2B Dimmit*	4B Hockley	3B Martin	3A Sabine*
2A Bosque*	4B Donley	3A Hood*	3B Mason	3A San Augustine*
3A Bowie*	2A Duval*	3A Hopkins*	2A Matagorda*	2A San Jacinto*
2A Brazoria*	3A Eastland	2A Houston*	2B Maverick*	2A San Patricio*
2A Brazos*				

(continued)

TABLE R301.1—continued
CLIMATE ZONES, MOISTURE REGIMES, AND WARM-HUMID
DESIGNATIONS BY STATE, COUNTY AND TERRITORY

3A San Saba*	3A Young	4C Clark	4A Gilmer	**WISCONSIN**
3B Schleicher	2B Zapata*	5B Columbia	5A Grant	6A Adams
3B Scurry	2B Zavala*	4C Cowlitz	5A Greenbrier	7 Ashland
3B Shackelford	**UTAH**	5B Douglas	5A Hampshire	6A Barron
3A Shelby*	5B Beaver	6B Ferry	5A Hancock	7 Bayfield
4B Sherman	6B Box Elder	5B Franklin	5A Hardy	6A Brown
3A Smith*	6B Cache	5B Garfield	5A Harrison	6A Buffalo
3A Somervell*	6B Carbon	5B Grant	4A Jackson	7 Burnett
2A Starr*	6B Daggett	4C Grays Harbor	4A Jefferson	6A Calumet
3A Stephens	5B Davis	4C Island	4A Kanawha	6A Chippewa
3B Sterling	6B Duchesne	4C Jefferson	5A Lewis	6A Clark
3B Stonewall	5B Emery	4C King	4A Lincoln	6A Columbia
3B Sutton	5B Garfield	4C Kitsap	4A Logan	6A Crawford
4B Swisher	5B Grand	5B Kittitas	5A Marion	6A Dane
3A Tarrant*	5B Iron	5B Klickitat	5A Marshall	6A Dodge
3B Taylor	5B Juab	4C Lewis	4A Mason	6A Door
3B Terrell	5B Kane	5B Lincoln	4A McDowell	7 Douglas
3B Terry	5B Millard	4C Mason	4A Mercer	6A Dunn
3B Throckmorton	6B Morgan	6B Okanogan	5A Mineral	6A Eau Claire
3A Titus*	5B Piute	4C Pacific	4A Mingo	7 Florence
3B Tom Green	6B Rich	6B Pend Oreille	5A Monongalia	6A Fond du Lac
2A Travis*	5B Salt Lake	4C Pierce	4A Monroe	7 Forest
2A Trinity*	5B San Juan	4C San Juan	4A Morgan	6A Grant
2A Tyler*	5B Sanpete	4C Skagit	5A Nicholas	6A Green
3A Upshur*	5B Sevier	5B Skamania	5A Ohio	6A Green Lake
3B Upton	6B Summit	4C Snohomish	5A Pendleton	6A Iowa
2B Uvalde*	5B Tooele	5B Spokane	4A Pleasants	7 Iron
2B Val Verde*	6B Uintah	6B Stevens	5A Pocahontas	6A Jackson
3A Van Zandt*	5B Utah	4C Thurston	5A Preston	6A Jefferson
2A Victoria*	6B Wasatch	4C Wahkiakum	4A Putnam	6A Juneau
2A Walker*	3B Washington	5B Walla Walla	5A Raleigh	6A Kenosha
2A Waller*	5B Wayne	4C Whatcom	5A Randolph	6A Kewaunee
3B Ward	5B Weber	5B Whitman	4A Ritchie	6A La Crosse
2A Washington*		5B Yakima	4A Roane	6A Lafayette
2B Webb*	**VERMONT**		5A Summers	7 Langlade
2A Wharton*	6A (all)	**WEST VIRGINIA**	5A Taylor	7 Lincoln
3B Wheeler		5A Barbour	5A Tucker	6A Manitowoc
3A Wichita	**VIRGINIA**	4A Berkeley	4A Tyler	6A Marathon
3B Wilbarger	4A (all)	4A Boone	5A Upshur	6A Marinette
2A Willacy*		4A Braxton	4A Wayne	6A Marquette
2A Williamson*	**WASHINGTON**	5A Brooke	5A Webster	6A Menominee
2A Wilson*	5B Adams	5A Cabell	5A Wetzel	6A Milwaukee
3B Winkler	5B Asotin	4A Calhoun	4A Wirt	6A Monroe
3A Wise	5B Benton	4A Clay	4A Wood	6A Oconto
3A Wood*	5B Chelan	5A Doddridge	4A Wyoming	7 Oneida
4B Yoakum	4C Clallam	5A Fayette		6A Outagamie

(continued)

TABLE R301.1—continued
CLIMATE ZONES, MOISTURE REGIMES, AND WARM-HUMID
DESIGNATIONS BY STATE, COUNTY AND TERRITORY

6A Ozaukee	7 Taylor	6B Big Horn	6B Sheridan	**NORTHERN**
6A Pepin	6A Trempealeau	6B Campbell	7 Sublette	**MARIANA**
6A Pierce	6A Vernon	6B Carbon	6B Sweetwater	**ISLANDS**
6A Polk	7 Vilas	6B Converse	7 Teton	1A (all)*
6A Portage	6A Walworth	6B Crook	6B Uinta	**PUERTO RICO**
7 Price	7 Washburn	6B Fremont	6B Washakie	1A (all)*
6A Racine	6A Washington	5B Goshen	6B Weston	
6A Richland	6A Waukesha	6B Hot Springs	**US TERRITORIES**	**VIRGIN ISLANDS**
6A Rock	6A Waupaca	6B Johnson		1A (all)*
6A Rusk	6A Waushara	6B Laramie	**AMERICAN**	
6A Sauk	6A Winnebago	7 Lincoln	**SAMOA**	
7 Sawyer	6A Wood	6B Natrona	1A (all)*	
6A Shawano		6B Niobrara		
6A Sheboygan	**WYOMING**	6B Park	**GUAM**	
6A St. Croix	6B Albany	5B Platte	1A (all)*	

TABLE R301.3(1)
INTERNATIONAL CLIMATE ZONE DEFINITIONS

MAJOR CLIMATE TYPE DEFINITIONS
Marine (C) Definition—Locations meeting all four criteria: 1. Mean temperature of coldest month between -3°C (27°F) and 18°C (65°F).   2. Warmest month mean < 22°C (72°F).   3. At least four months with mean temperatures over 10°C (50°F).   4. Dry season in summer. The month with the heaviest precipitation in the cold season has at least three times as much precipitation as the month with the least precipitation in the rest of the year. The cold season is October through March in the Northern Hemisphere and April through September in the Southern Hemisphere.
Dry (B) Definition—Locations meeting the following criteria: Not marine and $P_{in} < 0.44 \times (TF - 19.5)$ [$P_{cm} < 2.0 \times (TC + 7)$ in SI units]   where: P_{in} = Annual precipitation in inches (cm) T = Annual mean temperature in °F (°C)
Moist (A) Definition—Locations that are not marine and not dry.
Warm-humid Definition—Moist (A) locations where either of the following wet-bulb temperature conditions shall occur during the warmest six consecutive months of the year: 1. 67°F (19.4°C) or higher for 3,000 or more hours; or   2. 73°F (22.8°C) or higher for 1,500 or more hours.

For SI: °C = [(°F)-32]/1.8, 1 inch = 2.54 cm.

TABLE R301.3(2)
INTERNATIONAL CLIMATE ZONE DEFINITIONS

ZONE NUMBER	THERMAL CRITERIA	
	IP Units	**SI Units**
1	9000 < CDD50°F	5000 < CDD10°C
2	6300 < CDD50°F ≤ 9000	3500 < CDD10°C ≤ 5000
3A and 3B	4500 < CDD50°F ≤ 6300 AND HDD65°F ≤ 5400	2500 < CDD10°C ≤ 3500 AND HDD18°C ≤ 3000
4A and 4B	CDD50°F ≤ 4500 AND HDD65°F ≤ 5400	CDD10°C ≤ 2500 AND HDD18°C ≤ 3000
3C	HDD65°F ≤ 3600	HDD18°C ≤ 2000
4C	3600 < HDD65°F ≤ 5400	2000 < HDD18°C ≤ 3000
5	5400 < HDD65°F ≤ 7200	3000 < HDD18°C ≤ 4000
6	7200 < HDD65°F ≤ 9000	4000 < HDD18°C ≤ 5000
7	9000 < HDD65°F ≤ 12600	5000 < HDD18°C ≤ 7000
8	12600 < HDD65°F	7000 < HDD18°C

For SI: °C = [(°F)-32]/1.8.

SECTION R302
DESIGN CONDITIONS

R302.1 Interior design conditions. The interior design temperatures used for heating and cooling load calculations shall be a maximum of 72°F (22°C) for heating and minimum of 75°F (24°C) for cooling.

SECTION R303
MATERIALS, SYSTEMS AND EQUIPMENT

R303.1 Identification. Materials, systems, and equipment shall be identified in a manner that will allow a determination of compliance with the applicable provisions of this code. Materials used shall be: (1) listed for the intended use; (2) installed in accordance with the manufacturer's installation instructions; and (3) installed by an installer who is certified by a manufacturer to install that specific product, if such certification exists.

R303.1.1 Building thermal envelope insulation. An R-value identification mark shall be applied by the manufacturer to each piece of *building thermal envelope* insulation 12 inches (305 mm) or greater in width. Alternately, the insulation installers shall provide a certification listing the type, manufacturer and R-value of insulation installed in each element of the *building thermal envelope*. For blown or sprayed insulation (fiberglass and cellulose), the initial installed thickness, settled thickness, settled R-value, installed density, coverage area and number of bags installed shall be *listed* on the certification. For sprayed polyurethane foam (SPF) insulation, the installed thickness of the areas covered and R-value of installed thickness shall be *listed* on the certification. The insulation installer shall sign, date and post the certification in a conspicuous location on the job site.

R303.1.1.1 Blown or sprayed roof/ceiling insulation. The thickness of blown-in or sprayed roof/ceiling insulation (fiberglass or cellulose) shall be written in inches (mm) on markers that are installed at least one for every 300 square feet (28 m²) throughout the attic space. The markers shall be affixed to the trusses or joists and marked with the minimum initial installed thickness with numbers a minimum of 1 inch (25 mm) in height. Each marker shall face the attic access opening. Spray polyurethane foam thickness and installed R-value shall be *listed* on certification provided by the insulation installer.

R303.1.2 Insulation mark installation. Insulating materials shall be installed such that the manufacturer's R-value mark is readily observable upon inspection.

R303.1.3 Fenestration product rating. U-factors of fenestration products (windows, doors and skylights) shall be determined in accordance with NFRC 100 by an accredited, independent laboratory, and labeled and certified by the manufacturer. Products lacking such a labeled U-factor shall be assigned a default U-factor from Table R303.1.3(1) or R303.1.3(2). The solar heat gain coefficient (SHGC) and *visible transmittance* (VT) of glazed fenestration products (windows, glazed doors and skylights) shall be determined in accordance with NFRC 200 by an accredited, independent laboratory, and labeled and certified by the manufacturer. Products lacking such a labeled SHGC or VT shall be assigned a default SHGC or VT from Table R303.1.3(3).

TABLE R303.1.3(1)
DEFAULT GLAZED FENESTRATION U-FACTOR

FRAME TYPE	SINGLE PANE	DOUBLE PANE	SKYLIGHT	
			Single	Double
Metal	1.20	0.80	2.00	1.30
Metal with Thermal Break	1.10	0.65	1.90	1.10
Nonmetal or Metal Clad	0.95	0.55	1.75	1.05
Glazed Block	0.60			

TABLE R303.1.3(2)
DEFAULT DOOR U-FACTORS

DOOR TYPE	U-FACTOR
Uninsulated Metal	1.20
Insulated Metal	0.60
Wood	0.50
Insulated, nonmetal edge, max 45% glazing, any glazing double pane	0.35

TABLE R303.1.3(3)
DEFAULT GLAZED FENESTRATION SHGC AND VT

	SINGLE GLAZED		DOUBLE GLAZED		GLAZED BLOCK
	Clear	Tinted	Clear	Tinted	
SHGC	0.8	0.7	0.7	0.6	0.6
VT	0.6	0.3	0.6	0.3	0.6

R303.1.4 Insulation product rating. The thermal resistance (R-value) of insulation shall be determined in accordance with the U.S. Federal Trade Commission R-value rule (CFR Title 16, Part 460) in units of h × ft² × °F/Btu at a mean temperature of 75°F (24°C).

R303.1.5 Minnesota thermal insulation standards. Thermal insulation shall comply with Minnesota Rules, Chapter 7640, Minnesota Thermal Insulation Standards, adopted by the Department of Commerce.

R303.2 Installation. All materials, systems and equipment shall be installed in accordance with the manufacturer's installation instructions and the *International Building Code*.

R303.2.1 Protection of exposed foundation insulation. Insulation applied to the exterior of basement walls, crawl-space walls and the perimeter of slab-on-grade floors shall have a rigid, opaque and weather-resistant protective covering to prevent the degradation of the insulation's thermal performance. The protective covering shall cover the exposed exterior insulation and extend a minimum of 6 inches (153 mm) below grade.

R303.3 Maintenance information. Maintenance instructions shall be furnished for equipment and systems that require preventive maintenance. Required regular maintenance actions shall be clearly stated and incorporated on a readily accessible label. The label shall include the title or publication number for the operation and maintenance manual for that particular model and type of product.

CHAPTER 4 [RE]
RESIDENTIAL ENERGY EFFICIENCY

SECTION R401
GENERAL

R401.1 Scope. This chapter applies to residential buildings.

R401.2 Compliance. Projects shall comply with Sections identified as "mandatory" and with either sections identified as "prescriptive" or the performance approach in Section R405.

R401.3 Certificate (mandatory). A building certificate shall be completed and posted on or in the electrical distribution panel by the builder or registered design professional. The certificate shall not cover or obstruct the visibility of the circuit directory label, service disconnect label, or other required labels. The certificate shall list: the date the certificate is installed; the dwelling address; residential contractor name and contractor license number, or homeowner name, if acting as the general contractor; the predominant installed R-values, their location, and type of insulation installed in or on ceiling/roof, walls, rim/band joist, foundation, slab, basement wall, crawl space wall or floor, and ducts outside conditioned spaces; U-factors for fenestration and the solar heat gain coefficient (SHGC) of fenestration; and the results of any required duct system and building envelope air leakage testing done on the building. Where there is more than one value for each component, the certificate shall list the value covering the largest area. The certificate shall list the types, input ratings, manufacturers, model numbers and efficiencies of heating, cooling, and service water heating equipment. The certificate shall also list the structure's calculated heat loss, calculated cooling load, and calculated heat gain. Where an electric furnace or baseboard electric heater is installed in the residence, the certificate shall list "electric furnace" or "baseboard electric heater," as appropriate. An efficiency shall not be listed for electric furnaces or electric baseboard heaters. The certificate shall list the mechanical ventilation system type, location, and capacity, and the building's designated continuous and total ventilation rates. The certificate shall also list the type, size, and location of any make-up air system installed and the location or future location of the radon fan.

SECTION R402
BUILDING THERMAL ENVELOPE

R402.1 General (Prescriptive). The *building thermal envelope* shall meet the requirements of Sections R402.1.1 through R402.1.4.

R402.1.1 Insulation, waterproofing, and fenestration criteria. The building thermal envelope shall meet the requirements of Table R402.1.1 based on the climate zone specified in Chapter 3, and the requirements contained in Section R402.2. Cast-in-place concrete and masonry block foundation walls shall be waterproofed according to IRC Section R406 and the following requirements:

1. The waterproofing shall extend from the top interior wall edge, across the top of the wall, and down the exterior wall face to the top of the footing. If a full width, closed-cell material is installed to create a seal between the sill plate and the top of the foundation wall, the installation is deemed to meet the requirements for the top of the wall waterproofing.

2. If the walls are exposed to the exterior environment, the waterproofing system shall have a rigid, opaque,

TABLE R402.1.1
INSULATION AND FENESTRATION REQUIREMENTS BY COMPONENT[a]

CLIMATE ZONE	FENESTRATION U-FACTOR[b]	SKYLIGHT[b] U-FACTOR	GLAZED FENESTRATION SHGC[b,e]	CEILING[j] R-VALUE	WOOD FRAME WALL R-VALUE[f]	MASS WALL R-VALUE[i,g,h]	FLOOR R-VALUE	BASEMENT[c,i] WALL R-VALUE	SLAB[d] R-VALUE & DEPTH	CRAWL SPACE[c,i] WALL R-VALUE
6	0.32	0.55	NR	49	20, 13+5	15/20	30[e]	15	10, 3.5 ft	15
7	0.32	0.55	NR	49	21	19/21	38[e]	15	10, 5 ft	15

For SI: 1 foot = 304.8 mm.

a. R-values are minimums. U-factors and SHGC are maximums. When insulation is installed in a cavity that is less than the label or design thickness of the insulation, the installed R-value of the insulation shall not be less than the R-value specified in the table.

b. The fenestration U-factor column excludes skylights. The SHGC column applies to all glazed fenestration.

c. See Section R402.2.8.

d. Insulation R-values for heated slabs shall be installed to the depth indicated or to the top of the footing, whichever is less.

e. Or insulation sufficient to fill the framing cavity, R-19 minimum.

f. First value is cavity insulation, second is continuous insulation or insulated siding, so "13+5" means R-13 cavity insulation plus R-5 continuous insulation or insulated siding. If structural sheathing covers 40 percent or less of the exterior, continuous insulation R-value shall be permitted to be reduced by no more than R-3 in the locations where structural sheathing is used to maintain a consistent total sheathing thickness.

g. The second R-value applies when more than half the insulation is on the interior of the mass wall.

h. When using log-type construction for thermal mass walls the following applies:
   (1) a minimum of a 7-inch diameter log shall be used; and
   (2) the U-value of fenestration products shall be 0.29 overall on average or better.

i. See Section 402.2.8. A minimum R-19 cavity insulation is required in wood foundation walls.

j. Roof/ceiling assemblies shall have a minimum 6-inch energy heel.

and weather-resistant protective covering to prevent degradation of the waterproofing system. The protective covering shall cover the exposed waterproofing and extend a minimum of 6 inches (152 mm) below grade. The protective covering system shall be flashed in accordance with IRC Section R703.8.

R402.1.1.1 Integral foundation insulation requirements. Any insulation assembly installed integral to the foundation walls shall be manufactured for that intended use and installed according to the manufacturer's installation instructions.

R402.1.1.2 Exterior draining foundation insulation requirements. Any insulation assembly installed on the exterior of the foundation walls and on the perimeter of slabs-on-grade that permits water drainage shall:

1. be made of water-resistant materials manufactured for that intended use;

2. be installed according to the manufacturer's installation instructions;

3. comply with either ASTM C 578, C 612, or C 1029, as applicable; and

4. have a rigid, opaque, and weather-resistant protective covering to prevent the degradation of the insulation's thermal performance. The protective covering shall cover the exposed exterior insulation and extend a minimum of 6 inches (152 mm) below grade. The insulation and protective covering system shall be flashed in accordance with IRC Section R703.8.

R402.1.1.3 Exterior nondraining foundation insulation requirements. Any insulation assembly installed on the exterior of the foundation walls or on the perimeter of slabs-on-grade that does not permit bulk water drainage shall:

1. be made of water-resistant materials manufactured for that intended use;

2. be installed according to the manufacturer's installation instructions;

3. comply with either ASTM C 578 or C 1029, as applicable;

4. be covered with a 6-mil polyethylene slip sheet over the entire exterior surface; and

5. have a rigid, opaque, and weather-resistant protective covering to prevent degradation of the insulation's thermal performance. The protective covering shall cover the exposed exterior insulation and extend a minimum of 6 inches (152 mm) below grade. The insulation and protective covering system shall be flashed in accordance with IRC Section R703.8.

R402.1.1.4 Interior foundation insulation requirements. Any insulation assembly installed on the interior of foundation walls shall meet the following requirements:

1. Masonry foundation walls shall be drained through each masonry block core to an approved interior drainage system.

2. If a frame wall is installed, it shall not be in direct contact with the foundation wall.

3. The insulation assembly shall comply with the interior air barrier requirements of Section R402.4.

4. The insulation assembly shall comply with Section R402.1.1.5, R402.1.1.6, or R402.1.1.7, as applicable.

R402.1.1.5 Rigid interior insulation. Rigid interior insulation shall comply with ASTM C 578 or ASTM C 1289 and the following requirements:

1. For installation:

   a. the insulation shall be in contact with the foundation wall surface;

   b. vertical edges shall be sealed with acoustic sealant;

   c. all interior joints, edges, and penetrations shall be sealed against air and water vapor penetration;

   d. continuous acoustic sealant shall be applied horizontally between the foundation wall and the insulation at the top of the foundation wall; and

   e. continuous acoustic sealant shall be applied horizontally between the basement floor and the bottom insulation edge.

2. The insulation shall not be penetrated by the placement of utilities, fasteners, or connectors used to install a frame wall, with the exception of through penetrations.

3. Through penetrations shall be sealed around the penetrating products.

R402.1.1.6 Spray-applied interior foam insulation. Spray-applied interior foam insulation shall comply with the following:

1. Closed-cell foam:

   a. the foam shall comply with ASTM C 1029 and have a permeance not greater than 0.8, in accordance with ASTM E 96 procedure A, and a permeance of not less than 0.3, in accordance with ASTM E 96 procedure B.

   b. the foam shall be sprayed directly onto the foundation wall surface. There shall be a 1-inch (25.4 mm) minimum gap between the foundation wall surface and any framing.

   c. the insulation surface shall not be penetrated by the placement of utilities, fasteners, or connectors used to install a frame wall, with the exception of through penetrations.

   d. through penetrations shall be sealed around the penetrating products.

2. Open-cell foam:

   a. The foam shall be sprayed directly onto the foundation wall surface. There shall be a 1-inch (25.4 mm) minimum gap between the foundation wall surface and any framing.

   b. The insulation surface shall not be penetrated by the placement of utilities, fasteners, or connectors used to install a frame wall, with the exception of through penetrations.

   c. Through penetrations shall be sealed around the penetrating product.

   d. A vapor retarder and air barrier shall be applied to the warm-in-winter side of the assembly with a permeance not greater than 1.0, in accordance with ASTM E 96 procedure A, and a permeance not less than 0.3, in accordance with ASTM E 96 procedure B.

R402.1.1.7 Fiberglass batt interior insulation. Fiberglass batt insulation shall comply with the following:

1. The above-grade exposed foundation wall height shall not exceed 1.5 feet (457 mm).

2. The top and bottom plates shall be air sealed to the foundation wall surface and the basement floor.

3. A vapor retarder and air barrier shall be applied to the warm in winter side of the wall with a permeance not greater than 1.0 in accordance with ASTM E 96 procedure A and a permeance not less than 0.3 in accordance with ASTM E 96 procedure B meeting the following requirements:

   a. the vapor and air barrier shall be sealed to the framing with construction adhesive or equivalent at the top and bottom plates and where the adjacent wall is insulated;

   b. the vapor and air barrier shall be sealed around utility boxes and other penetrations; and

   c. all seams in the vapor and air barrier shall be overlapped at least 6 inches (152 mm) and sealed with compatible sealing tape or equivalent.

R402.1.1.8 Foundation wall insulation performance option. Insulated foundation systems designed and installed under the performance option shall meet the requirements of this section and the foundation, basement, or crawl space wall equivalent U-factor from Table 402.1.3.

1. **Water separation plane.** The foundation shall be designed and built to have a continuous water separation plane between the interior and exterior. The interior side of the water separation plane shall:

   a. have a stable annual wetting and drying cycle whereby foundation wall system water (solid, liquid, and vapor) transport processes produce no net accumulation of ice or water over a full calendar year and the foundation wall system is free of absorbed water for at least 4 months over a full calendar year;

   b. prevent conditions of moisture and temperature to prevail for a time period favorable to mold growth for the material used; and

   c. prevent liquid water from the foundation wall system from reaching the foundation floor system at any time during a full calendar year.

2. **Documentation.** The foundation insulation system designer shall provide documentation certified by a professional engineer licensed in Minnesota demonstrating how the requirements of this section are fulfilled. The foundation insulation system designer shall also specify the design conditions for the wall and the design conditions for the interior space for which the water separation plane will meet the requirements of this section. The foundation insulation system designer shall provide a label disclosing these design conditions. The label shall be posted according to Section R401.3.

3. **Installation.** The water separation plane shall be designed and installed to prevent external liquid or capillary water flow across it after the foundation is backfilled.

4. **Foundation air barrier.** The foundation insulation system shall be designed and installed to have a foundation air barrier system between the interior and the exterior. The foundation air barrier system shall be a material or combination of materials that is continuous with all joints sealed and is durable for the intended application. Material used for the foundation air barrier system shall have an air permeability not to exceed 0.004 ft^3/min.ft^2 under a pressure differential of 0.3 inches water (l.57 psf) (0.02 L/s.m^2 at 75 Pa) as determined by either commonly accepted engineering tables or by being labeled by the manufacturer as having these values when tested according to ASTM E 2178.

R402.1.2 R-value computation. Insulation material used in layers, such as framing cavity insulation and insulating sheathing, shall be summed to compute the component R-value. The manufacturer's settled R-value shall be used for blown insulation. Computed R-values shall not include an R-value for other building materials or air films.

R402.1.3 U-factor alternative. An assembly with a U-factor equal to or less than that specified in Table R402.1.3 shall be permitted as an alternative to the R-value in Table R402.1.1.

R402.1.4 Total UA alternative. If the total *building thermal envelope* UA (sum of U-factor times assembly area) is less than or equal to the total UA resulting from using the U-factors in Table R402.1.3 (multiplied by the same assembly area as in the proposed building), the building shall be considered in compliance with Table R402.1.1. The UA calculation shall be done using a method consis-

TABLE R402.1.3
EQUIVALENT U-FACTORS[a]

CLIMATE ZONE	FENESTRATION U-FACTOR	SKYLIGHT U-FACTOR	CEILING U-FACTOR	FRAME WALL U-FACTOR	MASS WALL U-FACTOR[b]	FLOOR U-FACTOR	BASEMENT WALL U-FACTOR	CRAWL SPACE WALL U-FACTOR
1	0.50	0.75	0.035	0.082	0.197	0.064	0.360	0.477
2	0.40	0.65	0.030	0.082	0.165	0.064	0.360	0.477
3	0.35	0.55	0.030	0.057	0.098	0.047	0.091[c]	0.136
4 except Marine	0.35	0.55	0.026	0.057	0.098	0.047	0.059	0.065
5 and Marine 4	0.32	0.55	0.026	0.057	0.082	0.033	0.050	0.055
6	0.32	0.55	0.026	0.048	0.060	0.033	0.050	0.055
7 and 8	0.32	0.55	0.026	0.048	0.057	0.028	0.050	0.055

a. Nonfenestration U-factors shall be obtained from measurement, calculation or an approved source.

b. When more than half the insulation is on the interior, the mass wall U-factors shall be a maximum of 0.17 in Climate Zone 1, 0.14 in Climate Zone 2, 0.12 in Climate Zone 3, 0.087 in Climate Zone 4 except Marine, 0.065 in Climate Zone 5 and Marine 4, and 0.057 in Climate Zones 6 through 8.

c. Basement wall U-factor of 0.360 in warm-humid locations as defined by Figure R301.1 and Table R301.1.

tent with the ASHRAE *Handbook of Fundamentals* and shall include the thermal bridging effects of framing materials. The SHGC requirements shall be met in addition to UA compliance.

R402.2 Specific insulation requirements (Prescriptive). In addition to the requirements of Section R402.1, insulation shall meet the specific requirements of Sections R402.2.1 through R402.2.12.

R402.2.1 Ceilings with attic spaces. When Section R402.1.1 would require R-38 in the ceiling, R-30 shall be deemed to satisfy the requirement for R-38 wherever the full height of uncompressed R-30 insulation extends over the wall top plate at the eaves. Similarly, R-38 shall be deemed to satisfy the requirement for R-49 wherever the full height of uncompressed R-38 insulation extends over the wall top plate at the eaves. This reduction shall not apply to the U-factor alternative approach in Section R402.1.3 and the total UA alternative in Section R402.1.4.

R402.2.2 Ceilings without attic spaces. Where Section R402.1.1 would require insulation levels above R-30 and the design of the roof/ceiling assembly does not allow sufficient space for the required insulation, the minimum required insulation for such roof/ceiling assemblies shall be R-30. This reduction of insulation from the requirements of Section R402.1.1 shall be limited to 500 square feet (46 m²) or 20 percent of the total insulated ceiling area, whichever is less. This reduction shall not apply to the U-factor alternative approach in Section R402.1.3 and the total UA alternative in Section R402.1.4.

R402.2.3 Eave baffle. For air permeable insulations in vented attics, a baffle shall be installed adjacent to soffit and eave vents. Baffles shall maintain an opening equal or greater than the size of the vent. The baffle shall extend over the top of the attic insulation. The baffle shall be permitted to be any solid material.

R402.2.4 Access hatches and doors. Access doors from conditioned spaces to unconditioned spaces (e.g., attics and crawl spaces) shall be weatherstripped and insulated to a level equivalent to the insulation on the surrounding surfaces. Access shall be provided to all equipment that prevents damaging or compressing the insulation. A wood

framed or equivalent baffle or retainer is required to be provided when loose fill insulation is installed, the purpose of which is to prevent the loose fill insulation from spilling into the living space when the attic access is opened, and to provide a permanent means of maintaining the installed R-value of the loose fill insulation.

R402.2.5 Mass walls. Mass walls for the purposes of this chapter shall be considered above-grade walls of concrete block, concrete, insulated concrete form (ICF), masonry cavity, brick (other than brick veneer), earth (adobe, compressed earth block, rammed earth) and solid timber/logs.

R402.2.6 Steel-frame ceilings, walls, and floors. Steel-frame ceilings, walls, and floors shall meet the insulation requirements of Table R402.2.6 or shall meet the U-factor requirements of Table R402.1.3. The calculation of the U-factor for a steel-frame envelope assembly shall use a series-parallel path calculation method.

R402.2.7 Floors. Floor insulation shall be installed to maintain permanent contact with the underside of the sub-floor decking.

R402.2.8 Basement walls. Walls associated with conditioned basements shall be insulated from the top of the basement wall down to 10 feet (3048 mm) below grade or to the top of the footing, whichever is less. Foundation insulation shall be installed according to the manufacturer's installation instructions. Walls associated with unconditioned basements shall meet the requirements of this section unless the floor overhead is insulated in accordance with Sections R402.1.1 and R402.2.7 and the following requirements:

a. R-15 insulation for concrete and masonry foundations shall be installed according to R402.1.1.1 to R402.1.1.8 and a minimum of a R-10 shall be installed on the exterior of the wall. Interior insulation, other than closed cell spray foam, shall not exceed R-11. Foundations shall be waterproofed in accordance with the applicable provisions of the *International Residential Code* (IRC).

> **Exception:** R-10 continuous insulation on the exterior of each foundation wall shall be permitted to comply with this code if the tested air leakage rate required in Section R402.4.1.2 does not

exceed 2.6 air changes per hour and the total square feet between the finished grade and the top of each foundation wall does not exceed 1.5 multiplied by the total lineal feet of each foundation wall that encloses conditioned space. Interior insulation, other than closed cell spray foam, shall not exceed R-11. See footnote c to Table R402.2.l.

b. Minimum R-19 cavity insulation is required in wood foundation walls. See footnote 1 to Table R402.2.l.

R402.2.9 Slab-on-grade floors. Slab-on-grade floors with a floor surface less than 12 inches (305 mm) below grade shall be insulated in accordance with Table R402.1.1. The insulation shall extend downward from the top of the slab on the outside or inside of the foundation wall. Insulation located below grade shall be extended the distance provided in Table R402.1.1 by any combination of vertical insulation, insulation extending under the slab or insulation extending out from the building. Insulation extending

TABLE R402.2.6
STEEL-FRAME CEILING, WALL AND FLOOR INSULATION (R-VALUE)

WOOD FRAME R-VALUE REQUIREMENT	COLD-FORMED STEEL EQUIVALENT R-VALUE[a]
Steel Truss Ceilings[b]	
R-30	R-38 or R-30 + 3 or R-26 + 5
R-38	R-49 or R-38 + 3
R-49	R-38 + 5
Steel Joist Ceilings[b]	
R-30	R-38 in 2 × 4 or 2 × 6 or 2 × 8 R-49 in any framing
R-38	R-49 in 2 × 4 or 2 × 6 or 2 × 8 or 2 × 10
Steel-Framed Wall 16″ O.C.	
R-13	R-13 + 4.2 or R-19 + 2.1 or R-21 + 2.8 or R-0 + 9.3 or R-15 + 3.8 or R-21 + 3.1
R-13 + 3	R-0 + 11.2 or R-13 + 6.1 or R-15 + 5.7 or R-19 + 5.0 or R-21 + 4.7
R-20	R-0 + 14.0 or R-13 + 8.9 or R-15 + 8.5 or R-19 + 7.8 or R-19 + 6.2 or R-21 + 7.5
R-20 + 5	R-13 + 12.7 or R-15 + 12.3 or R-19 + 11.6 or R-21 + 11.3 or R-25 + 10.9
R-21	R-0 + 14.6 or R-13 + 9.5 or R-15 + 9.1 or R-19 + 8.4 or R-21 + 8.1 or R-25 + 7.7
Steel Framed Wall, 24″ O.C	
R-13	R-0 + 9.3 or R-13 + 3.0 or R-15 + 2.4
R-13 + 3	R-0 + 11.2 or R-13 + 4.9 or R-15 + 4.3 or R-19 + 3.5 or R-21 + 3.1
R-20	R-0 + 14.0 or R-13 + 7.7 or R-15 + 7.1 or R-19 + 6.3 or R-21 + 5.9
R-20 + 5	R-13 + 11.5 or R-15 + 10.9 or R-19 + 10.1 or R-21 + 9.7 or R-25 + 9.1
R-21	R-0 + 14.6 or R-13 + 8.3 or R-15 + 7.7 or R-19 + 6.9 or R-21 + 6.5 or R-25 + 5.9
Steel Joist Floor	
R-13	R-19 in 2 × 6, or R-19 + 6 in 2 × 8 or 2 × 10
R-19	R-19 + 6 in 2 × 6, or R-19 + 12 in 2 × 8 or 2 × 10

a. Cavity insulation R-value is listed first, followed by continuous insulation R-value.

b. Insulation exceeding the height of the framing shall cover the framing.

away from the building shall be protected by pavement or by a minimum of 10 inches (254 mm) of soil. The top edge of the insulation installed between the *exterior wall* and the edge of the interior slab shall be permitted to be cut at a 45-degree (0.79 rad) angle away from the *exterior wall*. Slab-edge insulation is not required in jurisdictions designated by the *code official* as having a very heavy termite infestation.

R402.2.10 Crawl space walls. As an alternative to insulating floors over crawl spaces, crawl space walls shall be permitted to be insulated when the crawl space is not vented to the outside. Crawl space wall insulation shall be permanently fastened to the wall and extend downward from the floor to the finished grade level and then vertically and/or horizontally for at least an additional 24 inches (610 mm). Exposed earth in unvented crawl space foundations shall be covered with a continuous Class I vapor retarder in accordance with the *International Building Code* or *International Residential Code*, as applicable. All joints of the vapor retarder shall overlap by 6 inches (153 mm) and be sealed or taped. The edges of the vapor retarder shall extend at least 6 inches (153 mm) up the stem wall and shall be attached to the stem wall.

R402.2.11 Masonry veneer. Insulation shall not be required on the horizontal portion of the foundation that supports a masonry veneer.

R402.2.12 Sunroom insulation. All *sunrooms* enclosing conditioned space shall meet the insulation requirements of this code.

> **Exception:** For *sunrooms* with *thermal isolation*, and enclosing conditioned space, the following exceptions to the insulation *requirements* of this code shall apply:
>
> 1. The minimum ceiling insulation R-values shall be R-19 in Climate Zones 1 through 4 and R-24 in Climate Zones 5 through 8; and
>
> 2. The minimum wall R-value shall be R-13 in all climate zones. Wall(s) separating a *sunroom* with a *thermal isolation* from *conditioned space* shall meet the *building thermal envelope* requirements of this code.

R402.3 Fenestration (Prescriptive). In addition to the requirements of Section R402, fenestration shall comply with Sections R402.3.1 through R402.3.6.

R402.3.1 U-factor. An area-weighted average of fenestration products shall be permitted to satisfy the U-factor requirements.

R402.3.2 Glazed fenestration SHGC. An area-weighted average of fenestration products more than 50-percent glazed shall be permitted to satisfy the SHGC requirements.

R402.3.3 Glazed fenestration exemption. Up to 15 square feet (1.4 m^2) of glazed fenestration per dwelling unit shall be permitted to be exempt from U-factor and SHGC requirements in Section R402.1.1. This exemption shall not apply to the U-factor alternative approach in Section R402.1.3 and the Total UA alternative in Section R402.1.4.

R402.3.4 Opaque door exemption. One side-hinged opaque door assembly up to 24 square feet (2.22 m²) in area is exempted from the U-factor requirement in Section R402.1.1. This exemption shall not apply to the U-factor alternative approach in Section R402.1.3 and the total UA alternative in Section R402.1.4.

R402.3.5 Sunroom U-factor. All *sunrooms* enclosing conditioned space shall meet the fenestration requirements of this code.

> **Exception:** For *sunrooms* with *thermal isolation* and enclosing conditioned space, in Climate Zones 4 through 8, the following exceptions to the fenestration requirements of this code shall apply:
>
> 1. The maximum fenestration U-factor shall be 0.45; and
>
> 2. The maximum skylight U-factor shall be 0.70. New fenestration separating the *sunroom* with *thermal isolation* from *conditioned space* shall meet the *building thermal envelope* requirements of this code.

R402.3.6 Replacement fenestration. Where some or all of an existing fenestration unit is replaced with a new fenestration product, including sash and glazing, the replacement fenestration unit shall meet the applicable requirements for U-factor and SHGC in Table R402.1.1.

R402.4 Air leakage (Mandatory). The building thermal envelope shall be constructed to limit air leakage in accordance with the requirements of Sections R402.4.1 through R402.4.4.

R402.4.1 Building thermal envelope. The *building thermal envelope* shall comply with Sections R402.4.1.1 and R402.4.1.2. The sealing methods between dissimilar materials shall allow for differential expansion and contraction.

R402.4.1.1 Installation. The components of the *building thermal envelope* as listed in Table R402.4.1.1 shall be installed in accordance with the manufacturer's instructions and the criteria listed in Table R402.4.1.1, as applicable to the method of construction. Where required by the *code official*, an *approved* third party shall inspect all components and verify compliance.

R402.4.1.2 Testing. The building or dwelling unit shall be tested and verified as having an air leakage rate of not exceeding 5 air changes per hour in Climate Zones 1 and 2, and 3 air changes per hour in Climate Zones 3 through 8. Testing shall be conducted with a blower door at a pressure of 0.2 inches w.g. (50 Pascals). Where required by the *code official*, testing shall be conducted by an *approved* third party. A written report of the results of the test shall be signed by the party conducting the test and provided to the *code official*. Testing shall be performed at any time after creation of all penetrations of the *building thermal envelope*.

During testing:

1. Exterior windows and doors, fireplace and stove doors shall be closed, but not sealed, beyond the intended weatherstripping or other infiltration control measures;

2. Dampers including exhaust, intake, makeup air, backdraft and flue dampers shall be closed, but not sealed beyond intended infiltration control measures;

3. Interior doors, if installed at the time of the test, shall be open;

4. Exterior doors for continuous ventilation systems and heat recovery ventilators shall be closed and sealed;

5. Heating and cooling systems, if installed at the time of the test, shall be turned off; and

6. Supply and return registers, if installed at the time of the test, shall be fully open.

R402.4.2 Fireplaces. New wood-burning fireplaces shall have tight-fitting flue dampers and outdoor combustion air.

R402.4.3 Fenestration air leakage. Windows, skylights and sliding glass doors shall have an air infiltration rate of no more than 0.3 cfm per square foot (1.5 L/s/m²), and swinging doors no more than 0.5 cfm per square foot (2.6 L/s/m²), when tested according to NFRC 400 or AAMA/WDMA/CSA 101/I.S.2/A440 by an accredited, independent laboratory and *listed* and *labeled* by the manufacturer.

> **Exception:** Site-built windows, skylights and doors.

R402.4.4 Recessed lighting. Recessed luminaires installed in the *building thermal envelope* shall be sealed to limit air leakage between conditioned and unconditioned spaces. All recessed luminaires shall be IC-rated and *labeled* as having an air leakage rate not more than 2.0 cfm (0.944 L/s) when tested in accordance with ASTM E 283 at a 1.57 psf (75 Pa) pressure differential. All recessed luminaires shall be sealed with a gasket or caulk between the housing and the interior wall or ceiling covering.

R402.5 Maximum fenestration U-factor and SHGC (Mandatory). The area-weighted average maximum fenestration U-factor permitted using tradeoffs from Section R402.1.4 or R405 shall be 0.48 in Climate Zones 4 and 5 and 0.40 in Climate Zones 6 through 8 for vertical fenestration, and 0.75 in Climate Zones 4 through 8 for skylights. The area-weighted average maximum fenestration SHGC permitted using tradeoffs from Section R405 in Climate Zones 1 through 3 shall be 0.50.

SECTION R403
SYSTEMS

R403.1 Controls (Mandatory). At least one thermostat shall be provided for each separate heating and cooling system.

R403.1.1 Programmable thermostat. Where the primary heating system is a forced-air furnace, at least one thermostat per dwelling unit shall be capable of controlling the heating and cooling system on a daily schedule to maintain different temperature set points at different times of

TABLE R402.4.1.1
AIR BARRIER AND INSULATION INSTALLATION

COMPONENT	CRITERIA[a]
Air barrier and thermal barrier	A continuous air barrier shall be installed in the building envelope. Exterior thermal envelope contains a continuous air barrier. Breaks or joints in the air barrier shall be sealed. Air-permeable insulation shall not be used as a sealing material.
Ceiling/attic	The air barrier in any dropped ceiling/soffit shall be aligned with the insulation and any gaps in the air barrier sealed. Access openings, drop down stair or knee wall doors to unconditioned attic spaces shall be sealed.
Walls	Corners and headers shall be insulated and the junction of the foundation and sill plate shall be sealed. The junction of the top plate and top of exterior walls shall be sealed. Exterior thermal envelope insulation for framed walls shall be installed in substantial contact and continuous alignment with the air barrier. Knee walls shall be sealed.
Windows, skylights and doors	The space between window/door jambs and framing and skylights and framing shall be sealed.
Rim joists	Rim joists shall be insulated and include the air barrier.
Floors (including above-garage and cantilevered floors)	Insulation shall be installed to maintain permanent contact with underside of subfloor decking. The air barrier shall be installed at any exposed edge of insulation.
Crawl space walls	Where provided in lieu of floor insulation, insulation shall be permanently attached to the crawlspace walls. Exposed earth in unvented crawl spaces shall be covered with a Class I vapor retarder with overlapping joints taped.
Shafts, penetrations	Duct shafts, utility penetrations, and flue shafts opening to exterior or unconditioned space shall be sealed.
Narrow cavities	Batts in narrow cavities shall be cut to fit, or narrow cavities shall be filled by insulation that on installation readily conforms to the available cavity space.
Garage separation	Air sealing shall be provided between the garage and conditioned spaces.
Recessed lighting	Recessed light fixtures installed in the building thermal envelope shall be air tight, IC rated, and sealed to the drywall.
Plumbing and wiring	Batt insulation shall be cut neatly to fit around wiring and plumbing in exterior walls, or insulation that on installation readily conforms to available space shall extend behind piping and wiring.
Shower/tub on exterior wall	Exterior walls adjacent to showers and tubs shall be insulated and the air barrier installed separating them from the showers and tubs.
Electrical/phone box on exterior walls	The air barrier shall be installed behind electrical or communication boxes or air sealed boxes shall be installed.
HVAC register boots	HVAC register boots that penetrate building thermal envelope shall be sealed to the subfloor or drywall.
Fireplace	An air barrier shall be installed on fireplace walls. Fireplaces shall have gasketed doors.

a. In addition, inspection of log walls shall be in accordance with the provisions of ICC-400.

the day. This thermostat shall include the capability to set back or temporarily operate the system to maintain *zone* temperatures down to 55°F (13°C) or up to 85°F (29°C). The thermostat shall initially be programmed with a heating temperature set point no higher than 70°F (21°C) and a cooling temperature set point no lower than 78°F (26°C).

R403.1.2 Heat pump supplementary heat (Mandatory). Heat pumps having supplementary electric-resistance heat shall have controls that, except during defrost, prevent supplemental heat operation when the heat pump compressor can meet the heating load.

R403.2 Ducts. Ducts and air handlers shall be in accordance with Sections R403.2.1 through R403.2.3.

R403.2.1 Insulation (prescriptive). All exhaust, supply, and return air ducts and plenums shall be insulated according to Table R403.2.l.

For the purposes of Table R403.2.1, the following applies:

a. Insulation is only required in the conditioned space for a distance of 3 feet (914 mm) from the exterior or unconditioned space.

b. V means the vapor retarder in accordance with IMC Section 604.11. When a vapor retarder is required, duct insulation required by this section shall be installed without respect to other building envelope insulation.

c. W means an approved weatherproof barrier.

TABLE R403.2.1
MINIMUM REQUIRED DUCT AND PLENUM
INSULATION FOR DWELLING UNITS

DUCT TYPE/LOCATION	REQUIREMENTS
Exterior of building	R-8, V and W
Attics, garages, and ventilated crawl spaces	R-8 and V
Outdoor air intakes within conditioned spaces	R3.3 and V
Exhaust ducts within conditioned spaces	R3.3 and V
Within concrete slab or within ground	R3-5 and V
Within conditioned spaces and in basements with insulated walls	None Required

R403.2.2 Sealing (Mandatory). Ducts, air handlers, and filter boxes shall be sealed. Joints and seams shall comply with either the *International Mechanical Code* or *International Residential Code*, as applicable.

Exceptions:

1. Air-impermeable spray foam products shall be permitted to be applied without additional joint seals.

2. Where a duct connection is made that is partially inaccessible, three screws or rivets shall be equally spaced on the exposed portion of the joint so as to prevent a hinge effect.

3. Continuously welded and locking-type longitudinal joints and seams in ducts operating at static pressures less than 2 inches of water column (500 Pa) pressure classification shall not require additional closure systems.

Duct tightness shall be verified by either of the following:

1. Postconstruction test: Total leakage shall be less than or equal to 4 cfm (113.3 L/min) per 100 square feet (9.29 m^2) of conditioned floor area when tested at a pressure differential of 0.1 inches w.g. (25 Pa) across the entire system, including the manufacturer's air handler enclosure. All register boots shall be taped or otherwise sealed during the test.

2. Rough-in test: Total leakage shall be less than or equal to 4 cfm (113.3 L/min) per 100 square feet (9.29 m^2) of conditioned floor area when tested at a pressure differential of 0.1 inches w.g. (25 Pa) across the system, including the manufacturer's air handler enclosure. All registers shall be taped or otherwise sealed during the test. If the air handler is not installed at the time of the test, total leakage shall be less than or equal to 3 cfm (85 L/min) per 100 square feet (9.29 m^2) of conditioned floor area.

   Exception: The total leakage test is not required for ducts and air handlers located entirely within the building thermal envelope.

R403.2.2.1 Sealed air handler. Air handlers shall have a manufacturer's designation for an air leakage of no more than 2 percent of the design air flow rate when tested in accordance with ASHRAE 193.

R403.2.3 Building cavities (Mandatory). Building framing cavities shall not be used as ducts or plenums.

R403.3 Mechanical system piping insulation (Mandatory). Mechanical system piping capable of carrying fluids above 105°F (41°C) or below 55°F (13°C) shall be insulated to a minimum of R-3.

R403.3.1 Protection of piping insulation. Piping insulation exposed to weather shall be protected from damage, including that caused by sunlight, moisture, equipment maintenance, and wind, and shall provide shielding from solar radiation that can cause degradation of the material. Adhesive tape shall not be permitted.

R403.4 Service hot water systems. Energy conservation measures for service hot water systems shall be in accordance with Sections R403.4.1 and R403.4.2.

R403.4.1 Circulating hot water systems (Mandatory). Circulating hot water systems shall be provided with an automatic or readily *accessible* manual switch that can turn off the hot-water circulating pump when the system is not in use.

R403.4.2 Hot water pipe insulation (Prescriptive). Insulation for hot water pipe with a minimum thermal resistance (R-value) of R-3 shall be applied to the following:

1. Piping larger than $^3/_4$ inch nominal diameter.

2. Piping serving more than one dwelling unit.

3. Piping from the water heater to kitchen outlets.

4. Piping located outside the conditioned space.

5. Piping from the water heater to a distribution manifold.

6. Piping located under a floor slab.

7. Buried piping.

8. Supply and return piping in recirculation systems other than demand recirculation systems.

9. Piping with run lengths greater than the maximum run lengths for the nominal pipe diameter given in Table R403.4.2.

All remaining piping shall be insulated to at least R-3 or meet the run length requirements of Table R403.4.2.

TABLE R403.4.2
MAXIMUM RUN LENGTH (feet)[a]

Nominal Pipe Diameter of Largest Diameter Pipe in the Run (inch)	$^3/_8$	$^1/_2$	$^3/_4$	$> ^3/_4$
Maximum Run Length	30	20	10	5

For SI: 1 inch = 25.4 mm, 1 foot = 304.8 mm.

a. Total length of all piping from the distribution manifold or the recirculation loop to a point of use.

R403.5 Mechanical ventilation (mandatory). The building shall be provided with a balanced mechanical ventilation system that is +/-10 percent of the system's design capacity and meets the requirements of Section R403.5.5, which establishes the continuous and total mechanical ventilation requirements for dwelling unit ventilation. All conditioned unfinished basements, conditioned crawl spaces, and conditioned levels shall be provided with a minimum ventilation rate of 0.02 cfm (0.57 L/min) per square foot or a minimum of 1 supply duct and 1 return duct. The supply and return ducts shall be separated by $^1/_2$ the diagonal dimension of the basement to avoid a short circuit of the air circulation. Outdoor air intakes and exhausts shall have automatic or gravity dampers that close when the ventilation system is not operating.

Exception: Kitchen and bath fans that are not included as part of the mechanical ventilation system are exempt from these requirements.

R403.5.l Alterations. Alterations to existing buildings are exempt from meeting the requirements of Section R403.5.

R403.5.2 Total ventilation rate. The mechanical ventilation system shall provide sufficient outdoor air to equal the total ventilation rate average for each 1-hour period in accordance with Table R403.5.2, or Equation R403.5.2, based on the number of bedrooms and square footage of conditioned space, including the basement and conditioned crawl spaces.

For the purposes of Table R403.5.2 and Section R403.5.3, the following applies:

a. Equation R403.5.2 Total ventilation rate: Total ventilation rate (cfm) = (0.02 × square feet of conditioned space) + (15 × (number of bedrooms + 1))

b. Equation R403.5.2.1 Continuous ventilation rate: Continuous ventilation rate (cfm) = Total ventilation rate/2

R403.5.3 Continuous ventilation rate. Continuous ventilation rate (CVR) is a minimum of 50 percent of the total ventilation rate (TVR). The CVR shall not be less than 40 cfm (1133 L/min) and shall provide a continuous average cfm rate according to Table R403.5.2 or according to Equation R403.5.2 for every 1-hour period. The portion of the ventilation system that is intended to be continuous may have automatic cycling controls to provide the average flow rate for each hour.

R403.5.4 Intermittent ventilation rate. Intermittent ventilation rate means the difference between the total ventilation rate and the continuous ventilation rate.

R403.5.5 Balanced and HRV/ERV systems. All balanced systems shall be balanced so that the air intake is within 10 percent of the exhaust output. A heat recovery ventilator (HRV) or energy recovery ventilator (ERV) shall meet either:

1. The requirements of HVI Standard 920, 72 hours minus 13°F (-l0°C) cold weather test; or

2. Certified by a registered professional engineer and installed per manufacturer's installation instructions.

An HRV or ERV intended to comply with both the continuous and total ventilation rate requirements shall meet the rated design capacity of the continuous ventilation rate specified in Section R403.5.3 under low capacity and meet the total ventilation rate specified in Section R403.5.2 under high capacity.

Exception: The balanced system and HRV/ERV system may include exhaust fans to meet the intermittent ventilation rate. Surface mounted fans shall have a maximum 1.0 sone per HVI Standard 915.

TABLE R403.5.1
MECHANICAL VENTILATION SYSTEM FAN EFFICACY

FAN LOCATION	AIR FLOW RATE MINIMUM (CFM)	MINIMUM EFFICACY (CFM/WATT)	AIR FLOW RATE MAXIMUM (CFM)
Range hoods	Any	2.8 cfm/watt	Any
In-line fan	Any	2.8 cfm/watt	Any
Bathroom, utility room	10	1.4 cfm/watt	< 90
Bathroom, utility room	90	2.8 cfm/watt	Any

For SI: 1 cfm = 28.3 L/min.

TABLE R403.5.2
NUMBER OF BEDROOMS

Conditioned space[1] (in sq. ft.)	1 Total/Continuous	2 Total/Continuous	3 Total/Continuous	4 Total/Continuous	5 Total/Continuous	6[2] Total/Continuous
1000-1500	60/40	75/40	90/45	105/53	120/60	135/68
1501-2000	70/40	85/43	100/50	115/58	130/65	145/73
2001-2500	80/40	95/48	110/55	125/63	140/70	155/78
2501-3000	90/45	105/53	120/60	135/68	150/75	165/83
3001-3500	100/50	115/58	130/65	145/73	160/80	175/88
3501-4000	110/55	125/63	140/70	155/78	170/85	185/93
4001-4500	120/60	135/68	150/75	165/83	180/90	195/98
4501-5000	130/65	145/73	160/80	175/88	190/95	205/103
5001-5500	140/70	155/78	170/85	185/93	200/100	215/108
5501-6000[2]	150/75	165/83	180/90	195/98	210/105	225/113

1. Conditioned space includes the basement and conditioned crawl spaces.
2. If conditioned space exceeds 6000 sq. ft. or there are more than 6 bedrooms, use Equation R403.5.2.

R403.5.6 Installation requirements. All mechanical systems shall meet the requirements of Section R403.5.6. The mechanical ventilation system and its components shall also be installed according to the *Minnesota Mechanical Code*, Minnesota Rules, Chapter 1346, and the equipment manufacturer's installation instructions.

R403.5.6.1 Air distribution/circulation. Outdoor air shall be delivered to each habitable space by a forced air circulation system, separate duct system, or individual inlets.

R403.5.6.1.1 Forced air circulation systems. When outdoor air is supplied directly through a forced air circulation system, the requirements of this section shall be met using one of the following methods:

a. When an outdoor air supply is not ducted to the forced air system, controls shall be installed to allow the forced air system to provide an average circulation flow rate each hour of not less than 0.15 cfm (4.25 L/min) per square foot of the conditioned floor area; or

b. When the outdoor air supply is ducted to the forced air system, the mixed air temperature shall not be less than the heating equipment manufacturer's installation instructions. The controls shall be installed to allow the forced air circulation system to provide an average flow rate not less than 0.075 cfm (2.12 L/min) per square foot of conditioned floor area.

R403.5.6.1.2 Directly ducted and individual room inlets. When outdoor air is supplied directly to habitable spaces with an airflow of 20 cfm (566 L/min) or greater, the system shall be designed and installed to temper incoming air to not less than 40°F (4°C) measured at the point of distribution into the space.

R403.5.6.l.3 Airflow verification. All mechanical ventilation system airflows greater than 30 cfm (849 L/min) at the building exhaust or intake shall be tested and verified. The airflow verification results shall be made available to the building official upon request.

R403.5.7 Fans. When used as part of the mechanical ventilation system, fans shall be capable of delivering the designed air flow at the point of air discharge or intake as determined by Section R403.5.2 and according to HVI Standard 916. Fans shall be designed and certified by the equipment manufacturer to be capable of continuous operation at the maximum fan-rated cfm. Surface mounted fans used to comply with the continuous ventilation requirement of the mechanical ventilation system shall have a maximum 1.0 sone, according to HVI Standard 915. Fans used to comply with the intermittent ventilation requirement of the mechanical ventilation system shall have a maximum 2.5 sone,

according to HVI Standard 915. Mechanical ventilation system fans shall meet the efficacy requirements of Table R403.5.l.

Exception to sone requirements: Sone requirements do not apply to forced air circulation systems and remotely mounted fans. If the remotely mounted fan is not in a habitable space and there are at least 4 feet (1219 mm) of ductwork between the fan and grille, then the fan sone rating shall be 2.5 sone or less. Where mechanical ventilation fans are integral to tested and listed HVAC equipment, the fans shall be powered by an electronically commutated motor.

R403.5.8 Multifan systems. When two or more fans in a dwelling unit share a common duct, each fan shall be equipped with a backdraft damper to prevent recirculation of exhaust air into another room.

R403.5.9 Connection to forced air circulation systems. When air ducts are directly connected to the forced air circulation system, the outdoor air shall be supplied directly to the forced air circulation system, or the exhaust air shall be drawn directly from the forced air circulation system, but not both. To meet the mechanical ventilation system requirements, the air duct shall be installed according to the manufacturer's installation instructions.

Exception: Both outdoor air and exhaust air may be connected to the forced air circulation system only if controls are installed to operate the forced air circulation system when the mechanical ventilation system is operating or other means are provided to prevent short circuiting of ventilation air in accordance with the manufacturer's recommendations.

R403.5.10 Dampers. The mechanical ventilation system supply and exhaust ducts shall be provided with accessible backflow dampers to minimize flow to or from the outdoors when the ventilation system is off.

R403.5.11 Intake openings. Exterior air intake openings shall be accessible for inspection and maintenance. Intake openings shall be located according to the *Minnesota Mechanical Code*, Minnesota Rules, Chapter 1346, and shall be covered with a corrosion-resistant screen of not less than $1/_4$-inch (6.4 mm) mesh. Intake openings shall be located at least 12 inches (305 mm) above adjoining grade level.

Exception: Combination air intake and exhaust hoods may be approved by the building official when specifically allowed by the equipment manufacturer's installation instructions.

R403.5.12 Filtration. All mechanically supplied outdoor air shall have a filter with a designated minimum efficiency of MERV 4 as defined by ASHRAE Standard 52.2. The filter location shall be prior to the air entering the thermal conditioning components, blower, or habitable space. The filter shall be installed so it is readily accessible and facilitates regular service.

R403.5.13 Noise and vibration. Mechanical ventilation system components shall be installed to minimize transmission of noise and vibration. The equipment manufacturer's installation instructions shall be followed and any materials provided by the equipment manufacturer for installation shall be used. In the absence of specific materials or instructions, vibration dampening materials, such as rubber grommets and flexible straps, shall be used when connecting fans and heat exchangers to the building structure. Isolation duct connectors shall be used to mitigate noise transmission.

R403.5.14 Controls. Balanced mechanical ventilation system controls shall comply with all the following:

1. When the mechanical ventilation system is not designed to operate whenever the forced air circulation system is operating, the mechanical ventilation system shall incorporate an accessible backflow damper to prevent flow from the outside when the mechanical ventilation system is off.

2. Controls shall be compatible with the mechanical ventilation system, its components, and the manufacturer's installation and operating instructions.

3. Controls shall be installed to operate the mechanical ventilation system as designed.

4. Each control shall be readily accessible to occupants and shall be labeled to indicate the control's function.

R403.5.15 Labeling. All ventilation intake and exhaust outlets shall include permanent, weather-resistant identification labels on the building's exterior.

R403.5.16 Documentation. Documentation, which includes proper operation and maintenance instructions, shall accompany all mechanical ventilation systems. The documentation shall be in a conspicuous and readily accessible location.

R403.5.17 Climatic design conditions.

A. HVAC equipment shall be sized according to the ACCA Manual S or an equivalent method, based on the building's heating and cooling load calculations by using ASHRAE Handbook of Fundamentals or the ACCA Manual J. Oversizing of heating equipment shall not exceed 40 percent of the calculated load requirements and oversizing of cooling equipment shall not exceed 15 percent of the calculated load requirements.

B. Design conditions shall be determined according to Table 403.5.17. Design condition adjustments may be determined by the building official if local climates differ from the tabulated temperatures based on local climate data.

TABLE R403.5.17
CLIMATIC DATA DESIGN CONDITIONS

CITY	SUMMER Db/Wb °F	WINTER Db °F
Aitkin	82/72	-24
Albert Lea	85/72	-15
Alexandria	86/70	-21
Bemidji	84/68	-24
Cloquet	82/68	-20
Crookston	84/70	-27
Duluth	81/67	-20
Ely	82/68	-29
Eveleth	82/68	-26
Faribault	86/73	-16
Fergus Falls	86/71	-21
Grand Rapids	81/67	-23
Hibbing	82/68	-19
International Falls	83/67	-28
Litchfield	85/71	-18
Little Falls	86/71	-20
Mankato	86/72	-15
Minneapolis/St. Paul	88/72	-15
Montevideo	86/72	-17
Mora	84/70	-21
Morris	84/72	-21
New Ulm	87/73	-15
Owatonna	86/73	-16
Pequot Lakes	84/68	-23
Pipestone	85/73	-15
Redwood Falls	89/73	-17
Rochester	85/72	-17
Roseau	82/70	-29
St. Cloud	86/71	-20
Thief River Falls	82/68	-25
Tofte	75/61	-14
Warroad	83/67	-29
Wheaton	84/71	-20
Willmar	85/71	-20
Winona	88/74	-13
Worthington	84/71	-14

For SI: °C = [(°F)-32]/1.8.
Db = dry bulb temperature, degrees Fahrenheit
Wb = wet bulb temperature, degrees Fahrenheit

R403.6 Equipment Sizing (Mandatory). Heating and cooling equipment shall be sized in accordance with ACCA Manual S based on building loads calculated in accordance with ACCA Manual J or other *approved* heating and cooling calculation methodologies.

R403.7 Systems serving multiple dwelling units (Mandatory). Systems serving multiple dwelling units shall comply with Sections C403 and C404 of the IECC—Commercial Provisions in lieu of Section R403.

R403.8 Snow melt system controls (Mandatory). Snow- and ice-melting systems, supplied through energy service to the building, shall include automatic controls capable of shutting off the system when the pavement temperature is above 50°F, and no precipitation is falling and an automatic or manual control that will allow shutoff when the outdoor temperature is above 40°F.

R403.9 Pools and inground permanently installed spas (Mandatory). Pools and inground permanently installed spas shall comply with Sections R403.9.1 through R403.9.3.

R403.9.1 Heaters. All heaters shall be equipped with a readily *accessible* on-off switch that is mounted outside of the heater to allow shutting off the heater without adjusting the thermostat setting. Gas-fired heaters shall not be equipped with constant burning pilot lights.

R403.9.2 Time switches. Time switches or other control method that can automatically turn off and on heaters and pumps according to a preset schedule shall be installed on all heaters and pumps. Heaters, pumps and motors that have built in timers shall be deemed in compliance with this requirement.

Exceptions:

1. Where public health standards require 24-hour pump operation.

2. Where pumps are required to operate solar- and waste-heat-recovery pool heating systems.

R403.9.3 Covers. Heated pools and inground permanently installed spas shall be provided with a vapor-retardant cover.

Exception: Pools deriving over 70 percent of the energy for heating from site-recovered energy, such as a heat pump or solar energy source computed over an operating season.

R403.12 Photovoltaic modules and systems: Installation of photovoltaic modules and systems shall meet the requirements of Minnesota Rules, Chapter 1315.

SECTION R404
ELECTRICAL POWER AND LIGHTING SYSTEMS
(MANDATORY)

R404.1 Lighting equipment (Mandatory). A minimum of 75 percent of the lamps in permanently installed lighting fixtures shall be high-efficacy lamps or a minimum of 75 percent of the permanently installed lighting fixtures shall contain only high efficacy lamps.

Exception: Low-voltage lighting shall not be required to utilize high-efficiency lamps.

R404.1.1 Lighting equipment (Mandatory). Fuel gas lighting systems shall not have continuously burning pilot lights.

SECTION R405
SIMULATED PERFORMANCE ALTERNATIVE
(PERFORMANCE)

R405.1 Scope. This section establishes criteria for compliance using simulated energy performance analysis. Such analysis shall include heating, cooling, and service water heating energy only.

R405.2 Mandatory requirements. Compliance with this section requires that the mandatory provisions identified in Section R401.2 be met. All supply and return ducts not completely inside the *building thermal envelope* shall be insulated to a minimum of R-6.

R405.3 Performance-based compliance. Compliance based on simulated energy performance requires that a proposed residence (*proposed design*) be shown to have an annual energy cost that is less than or equal to the annual energy cost of the *standard reference design*. Energy prices shall be taken from a source *approved* by the *code official,* such as the Department of Energy, Energy Information Administration's *State Energy Price and Expenditure Report. Code officials* shall be permitted to require time-of-use pricing in energy cost calculations.

Exception: The energy use based on source energy expressed in Btu or Btu per square foot of *conditioned floor area* shall be permitted to be substituted for the energy cost. The source energy multiplier for electricity shall be 3.16. The source energy multiplier for fuels other than electricity shall be 1.1.

R405.4 Documentation. Documentation of the software used for the performance design and the parameters for the building shall be in accordance with Sections R405.4.1 through R405.4.3.

R405.4.1 Compliance software tools. Documentation verifying that the methods and accuracy of the compliance software tools conform to the provisions of this section shall be provided to the *code official.*

R405.4.2 Compliance report. Compliance software tools shall generate a report that documents that the *proposed design* complies with Section R405.3. The compliance documentation shall include the following information:

1. Address or other identification of the residence;

2. An inspection checklist documenting the building component characteristics of the *proposed design* as listed in Table R405.5.2(1). The inspection checklist shall show results for both the *standard reference design* and the *proposed design,* and shall document all inputs entered by the user necessary to reproduce the results;

3. Name of individual completing the compliance report; and

4. Name and version of the compliance software tool.

Exception: Multiple orientations. When an otherwise identical building model is offered in multiple orientations, compliance for any orientation shall be permitted by documenting that the building meets the performance requirements in each of the four cardinal (north, east, south and west) orientations.

R405.4.3 Additional documentation. The *code official* shall be permitted to require the following documents:

1. Documentation of the building component characteristics of the *standard reference design.*

2. A certification signed by the builder providing the building component characteristics of the *proposed design* as given in Table R405.5.2(1).

3. Documentation of the actual values used in the software calculations for the *proposed design.*

R405.5 Calculation procedure. Calculations of the performance design shall be in accordance with Sections R405.5.1 and R405.5.2.

R405.5.1 General. Except as specified by this section, the *standard reference design* and *proposed design* shall be configured and analyzed using identical methods and techniques.

R405.5.2 Residence specifications. The *standard reference design* and *proposed design* shall be configured and analyzed as specified by Table R405.5.2(1). Table R405.5.2(1) shall include by reference all notes contained in Table R402.1.1.

R405.6 Calculation software tools. Calculation software, where used, shall be in accordance with Sections R405.6.1 through R405.6.3.

R405.6.1 Minimum capabilities. Calculation procedures used to comply with this section shall be software tools capable of calculating the annual energy consumption of all building elements that differ between the *standard reference design* and the *proposed design* and shall include the following capabilities:

1. Computer generation of the *standard reference design* using only the input for the *proposed design.* The calculation procedure shall not allow the user to directly modify the building component characteristics of the *standard reference design.*

2. Calculation of whole-building (as a single *zone*) sizing for the heating and cooling equipment in the *standard reference design* residence in accordance with Section R403.6.

3. Calculations that account for the effects of indoor and outdoor temperatures and part-load ratios on the performance of heating, ventilating and air-conditioning equipment based on climate and equipment sizing.

4. Printed *code official* inspection checklist listing each of the *proposed design* component characteristics from Table R405.5.2(1) determined by the analysis to provide compliance, along with their respective performance ratings (e.g., *R*-value, *U*-factor, SHGC, HSPF, AFUE, SEER, EF, etc.).

R405.6.2 Specific approval. Performance analysis tools meeting the applicable sections of Section R405 shall be permitted to be *approved.* Tools are permitted to be *approved* based on meeting a specified threshold for a jurisdiction. The *code official* shall be permitted to approve tools for a specified application or limited scope.

R405.6.3 Input values. When calculations require input values not specified by Sections R402, R403, R404 and R405, those input values shall be taken from an *approved* source.

TABLE R405.5.2(1)
SPECIFICATIONS FOR THE STANDARD REFERENCE AND PROPOSED DESIGNS

BUILDING COMPONENT	STANDARD REFERENCE DESIGN	PROPOSED DESIGN
Above-grade walls	Type: mass wall if proposed wall is mass; otherwise wood frame. Gross area: same as proposed U-factor: from Table R402.1.3 Solar absorptance = 0.75 Remittance = 0.90	As proposed As proposed As proposed As proposed As proposed
Basement and crawl space walls	Type: same as proposed Gross area: same as proposed U-factor: from Table R402.1.3, with insulation layer on interior side of walls.	As proposed As proposed As proposed
Above-grade floors	Type: wood frame Gross area: same as proposed U-factor: from Table R402.1.3	As proposed As proposed As proposed
Ceilings	Type: wood frame Gross area: same as proposed U-factor: from Table R402.1.3	As proposed As proposed As proposed
Roofs	Type: composition shingle on wood sheathing Gross area: same as proposed Solar absorptance = 0.75 Emittance = 0.90	As proposed As proposed As proposed As proposed
Attics	Type: vented with aperture = 1 ft^2 per 300 ft^2 ceiling area	As proposed
Foundations	Type: same as proposed foundation wall area above and below grade and soil characteristics: same as proposed.	As proposed As proposed
Doors	Area: 40 ft^2 Orientation: North U-factor: same as fenestration from Table R402.1.3.	As proposed As proposed As proposed

Glazing[a]	Total area[b] =
	   (a) The proposed glazing area; where proposed glazing area is less than 15% of the conditioned floor area.
	   (b) 15% of the conditioned floor area; where the proposed glazing area is 15% or more of the conditioned floor area.
	
	Orientation: equally distributed to four cardinal compass orientations (N, E, S & W).
	
	U-factor: from Table R402.1.3
	
	SHGC: From Table R402.1.1 except that for climates with no requirement (NR) SHGC = 0.40 shall be used.
	Interior shade fraction: 0.92-(0.21 × SHGC for the standard reference design)
	External shading: none
		As proposed
		
		As proposed
		
		As proposed
		
		As proposed
		
		0.92-(0.21 × SHGC as proposed)
		As proposed

Skylights	None	As proposed
Thermally isolated sunrooms	None	As proposed

(continued)

TABLE R405.5.2(1)—continued
SPECIFICATIONS FOR THE STANDARD REFERENCE AND PROPOSED DESIGNS

BUILDING COMPONENT	STANDARD REFERENCE DESIGN	PROPOSED DESIGN
Air exchange rate	Air leakage rate of 5 air changes per hour in Climate Zones 1 and 2, and 3 air changes per hour in Climate Zones 3 through 8 at a pressure of 0.2 inches w.g (50 Pa). The mechanical ventilation rate shall be in addition to the air leakage rate and the same as in the proposed design, but no greater than $0.01 \times CFA + 7.5 \times (N_{br} + 1)$ where: CFA = conditioned floor area N_{br} = number of bedrooms Energy recovery shall not be assumed for mechanical ventilation.	For residences that are not tested, the same air leakage rate as the standard reference design. For tested residences, the measured air exchange rate[c]. The mechanical ventilation rate[d] shall be in addition to the air leakage rate and shall be as proposed.
Mechanical ventilation	None, except where mechanical ventilation is specified by the proposed design, in which case: Annual vent fan energy use: kWh/yr = $0.03942 \times CFA + 29.565 \times (N_{br} + 1)$ where: CFA = conditioned floor area N_{br} = number of bedrooms	As proposed
Internal gains	IGain = $17,900 + 23.8 \times CFA + 4104 \times N_{br}$ (Btu/day per dwelling unit)	Same as standard reference design.
Internal mass	An internal mass for furniture and contents of 8 pounds per square foot of floor area.	Same as standard reference design, plus any additional mass specifically designed as a thermal storage element[e] but not integral to the building envelope or structure.
Structural mass	For masonry floor slabs, 80% of floor area covered by R-2 carpet and pad, and 20% of floor directly exposed to room air. For masonry basement walls, as proposed, but with insulation required by Table R402.1.3 located on the interior side of the walls For other walls, for ceilings, floors, and interior walls, wood frame construction	As proposed As proposed As proposed
Heating systems[f, g]	As proposed for other than electric heating without a heat pump. Where the proposed design utilizes electric heating without a heat pump the standard reference design shall be an air source heat pump meeting the requirements of Section R403 of the IECC—Commercial Provisions. Capacity: sized in accordance with Section R403.6	As proposed
Cooling systems[f, h]	As proposed Capacity: sized in accordance with Section R403.6.	As proposed
Service water Heating[f, g, h, i]	As proposed Use: same as proposed design	As proposed gal/day = $30 + (10 \times N_{br})$
Thermal distribution systems		Thermal distribution system efficiency shall be as tested or as specified in Table R405.5.2(2) if not tested. Duct insulation shall be as proposed.
Thermostat	Type: Manual, cooling temperature setpoint = 75°F; Heating temperature setpoint = 72°F	Same as standard reference

(continued)

TABLE R405.5.2(1)—continued
SPECIFICATIONS FOR THE STANDARD REFERENCE AND PROPOSED DESIGNS

For SI: 1 square foot = 0.93 m², 1 British thermal unit = 1055 J, 1 pound per square foot = 4.88 kg/m², 1 gallon (U.S.) = 3.785 L,
    °C = (°F-3)/1.8, 1 degree = 0.79 rad.

a. Glazing shall be defined as sunlight-transmitting fenestration, including the area of sash, curbing or other framing elements, that enclose conditioned space. Glazing includes the area of sunlight-transmitting fenestration assemblies in walls bounding conditioned basements. For doors where the sunlight-transmitting opening is less than 50 percent of the door area, the glazing area is the sunlight transmitting opening area. For all other doors, the glazing area is the rough frame opening area for the door including the door and the frame.

b. For residences with conditioned basements, R-2 and R-4 residences and townhouses, the following formula shall be used to determine glazing area:

$$AF = A_s \times FA \times F$$

where:

AF = Total glazing area.

A_s = Standard reference design total glazing area.

FA = (Above-grade thermal boundary gross wall area)/(above-grade boundary wall area + 0.5 × below-grade boundary wall area).

F = (Above-grade thermal boundary wall area)/(above-grade thermal boundary wall area + common wall area) or 0.56, whichever is greater.

and where:

Thermal boundary wall is any wall that separates conditioned space from unconditioned space or ambient conditions.

Above-grade thermal boundary wall is any thermal boundary wall component not in contact with soil.

Below-grade boundary wall is any thermal boundary wall in soil contact.

Common wall area is the area of walls shared with an adjoining dwelling unit.

L and CFA are in the same units.

c. Where required by the *code official*, testing shall be conducted by an *approved* party. Hourly calculations as specified in the ASHRAE *Handbook of Fundamentals,* or the equivalent shall be used to determine the energy loads resulting from infiltration.

d. The combined air exchange rate for infiltration and mechanical ventilation shall be determined in accordance with Equation 43 of 2001 ASHRAE *Handbook of Fundamentals,* page 26.24 and the "Whole-house Ventilation" provisions of 2001 ASHRAE *Handbook of Fundamentals*, page 26.19 for intermittent mechanical ventilation.

e. Thermal storage element shall mean a component not part of the floors, walls or ceilings that is part of a passive solar system, and that provides thermal storage such as enclosed water columns, rock beds, or phase-change containers. A thermal storage element must be in the same room as fenestration that faces within 15 degrees (0.26 rad) of true south, or must be connected to such a room with pipes or ducts that allow the element to be actively charged.

f. For a proposed design with multiple heating, cooling or water heating systems using different fuel types, the applicable standard reference design system capacities and fuel types shall be weighted in accordance with their respective loads as calculated by accepted engineering practice for each equipment and fuel type present.

g. For a proposed design without a proposed heating system, a heating system with the prevailing federal minimum efficiency shall be assumed for both the standard reference design and proposed design.

h. For a proposed design home without a proposed cooling system, an electric air conditioner with the prevailing federal minimum efficiency shall be assumed for both the standard reference design and the proposed design.

i. For a proposed design with a nonstorage-type water heater, a 40-gallon storage-type water heater with the prevailing federal minimum energy factor for the same fuel as the predominant heating fuel type shall be assumed. For the case of a proposed design without a proposed water heater, a 40-gallon storage-type water heater with the prevailing federal minimum efficiency for the same fuel as the predominant heating fuel type shall be assumed for both the proposed design and standard reference design.

TABLE R405.5.2(2)
DEFAULT DISTRIBUTION SYSTEM EFFICIENCIES FOR PROPOSED DESIGNS[a]

DISTRIBUTION SYSTEM CONFIGURATION AND CONDITION	FORCED AIR SYSTEMS	HYDRONIC SYSTEMS[b]
Distribution system components located in unconditioned space	—	0.95
Untested distribution systems entirely located in conditioned space[c]	0.88	1
"Ductless" systems[d]	1	—

For SI: 1 cubic foot per minute = 0.47 L/s, 1 square foot = 0.093m², 1 pound per square inch = 6895 Pa, 1 inch water gauge = 1250 Pa.

a. Default values given by this table are for untested distribution systems, which must still meet minimum requirements for duct system insulation.

b. Hydronic systems shall mean those systems that distribute heating and cooling energy directly to individual spaces using liquids pumped through closed-loop piping and that do not depend on ducted, forced airflow to maintain space temperatures.

c. Entire system in conditioned space shall mean that no component of the distribution system, including the air-handler unit, is located outside of the conditioned space.

d. Ductless systems shall be allowed to have forced airflow across a coil but shall not have any ducted airflow external to the manufacturer's air-handler enclosure.

CHAPTER 5 [RE]
REFERENCED STANDARDS

This chapter lists the standards that are referenced in various sections of this document. The standards are listed herein by the promulgating agency of the standard, the standard identification, the effective date and title, and the section or sections of this document that reference the standard. The application of the referenced standards shall be as specified in Section R106.

AAMA

American Architectural Manufacturers Association
1827 Walden Office Square
Suite 550
Schaumburg, IL 60173-4268

Standard reference number	Title	Referenced in code section number
AAMA/WDMA/CSA 101/I.S.2/A C440—11	North American Fenestration Standard/ Specifications for Windows, Doors and Unit Skylights	R402.4.3

ACCA

Air Conditioning Contractors of America
2800 Shirlington Road, Suite 300
Arlington, VA 22206

Standard reference number	Title	Referenced in code section number
Manual J—11	Residential Load Calculation Eighth Edition	R403.6
Manual S—10	Residential Equipment Selection	R403.6

ASHRAE

American Society of Heating, Refrigerating and Air-Conditioning Engineers, Inc.
1791 Tullie Circle, NE
Atlanta, GA 30329-2305

Standard reference number	Title	Referenced in code section number
ASHRAE—52.2	Method of Testing General Ventilation Air-cleaning Devices for Removal Efficiency by Particle Size	R403.5.12
ASHRAE—2009	ASHRAE Handbook of Fundamentals	R402.1.4, Table R405.5.2(1)
ASHRAE 193—2010	Method of Test for Determining the Airtightness of HVAC Equipment	R403.2.2.1

M
N
M

ASTM

ASTM International
100 Barr Harbor Drive
West Conshohocken, PA 19428-2859

Standard reference number	Title	Referenced in code section number
E 283—04	Test Method for Determining the Rate of Air Leakage Through Exterior Windows, Curtain Walls and Doors Under Specified Pressure Differences Across the Specimen	R402.4.4

CSA

Canadian Standards Association
5060 Spectrum Way
Mississauga, Ontario, Canada L4W 5N6

Standard reference number	Title	Referenced in code section number
AAMA/WDMA/CSA 101/I.S.2/A440—11	North American Fenestration Standard/Specification for Windows, Doors and Unit Skylights	R402.4.3

HVI

Home Ventilating Institute
3317 E. Bell Road, Ste 101122
Phoenix, AZ 85032

Standard reference number	Title	Referenced in code section number
HVI 915	Loudness Testing and Rating Procedure...	R403.5.7
HVI 916	Airflow Test Procedure...	R403.5.7
HVI 920	Product Performance Certification Procedure	R403.5.5

ICC

International Code Council, Inc.
500 New Jersey Avenue, NW
6th Floor
Washington, DC 20001

Standard reference number	Title	Referenced in code section number
IBC—12	International Building Code®	R201.3, R303.2, R402.2.10
ICC 400—12	Standard on the Design and Construction of Log Structures	Table R402.4.1.1
IFC—12	International Fire Code®	R201.3
IFGC—12	International Fuel Gas Code®	R201.3
IMC—12	International Mechanical Code®	R201.3, R403.2.2, R403.5
IPC—12	International Plumbing Code®	R201.3
IRC—12	International Residential Code®	R201.3, R303.2, R402.2.10, R403.2.2, R403.5

NFRC

National Fenestration Rating Council, Inc.
6305 Ivy Lane, Suite 140
Greenbelt, MD 20770

Standard reference number	Title	Referenced in code section number
100—2010	Procedure for Determining Fenestration Products U-factors	R303.1.3
200—2010	Procedure for Determining Fenestration Product Solar Heat Gain Coefficients and Visible Transmittance at Normal Incidence...............................	R303.1.3
400—2010	Procedure for Determining Fenestration Product Air Leakage	R402.4.3

US-FTC

United States-Federal Trade Commission
600 Pennsylvania Avenue NW
Washington, DC 20580

Standard reference number	Title	Referenced in code section number
CFR Title 16 (May 31, 2005)	R-value Rule	R303.1.4

WDMA

Window and Door Manufacturers Association
1400 East Touhy Avenue, Suite 470
Des Plaines, IL 60018

Standard reference number	Title	Referenced in code section number
AAMA/WDMA/CSA 101/I.S.2/A440—11	North American Fenestration Standard/Specification for Windows, Doors and Unit Skylights...	R402.4.3

1309.0010
ADOPTION OF INTERNATIONAL
RESIDENTIAL CODE (IRC) BY REFERENCE

Subpart 1. Generally.

The 2018 edition of the *International Residential Code* ("IRC") as promulgated by the International Code Council, Inc. ("ICC"), Washington, D.C., is incorporated by reference and made part of the *Minnesota State Building Code* except as qualified by the applicable provisions in Minnesota Rules, Chapter 1300, and as amended in this chapter. Portions of this publication reproduce excerpts from the 2018 IRC, International Code Council, Inc., Washington, D.C., copyright 2017, reproduced with permission, all rights reserved. The IRC is not subject to frequent change and a copy of the IRC, with amendments for use in Minnesota, is available in the office of the commissioner of labor and industry.

Subp. 1a. Deleted appendices.

All of the IRC appendices are deleted except Appendix K and Appendix Q.

Subp. 2. Mandatory chapters.

The 2018 IRC Chapters 2 to 10, 44, Section P2904 of Chapter 29, Appendix K, and Appendix Q shall be administered by any municipality that has adopted the *Minnesota State Building Code*, except as qualified by the applicable provisions in Minnesota Rules, Chapter 1300, and as amended by this chapter.

Subp. 3. Replacement chapters.

The following 2018 IRC chapters are being deleted and replaced with the provisions in items A to E:

    A. Chapter 1 of the 2018 IRC is deleted and replaced as provided in Minnesota Rules, part 1309.0100, subpart 1.

    B. Chapter 11 of the 2018 IRC and any references to residential or commercial energy in this code are deleted and replaced with Minnesota Rules, Chapters 1322 and 1323, *Minnesota Energy Code*.

    C. Chapters 12 to 24 of the 2018 IRC and any references to mechanical matters in this code are deleted and replaced with Minnesota Rules, Chapter 1346, *Minnesota Mechanical Code*.

    D. Chapters 25 to 33 of the 2018 IRC and any references to plumbing in this code are deleted and replaced with Minnesota Rules, Chapter 4714, *Minnesota Plumbing Code*, except that Section P2904 of IRC Chapter 29 is not deleted.

    E. Chapters 34 to 43 of the 2018 IRC and references to electrical matters in this code, other than Sections R314 Smoke Alarms and R315 Carbon Monoxide Alarms, are deleted and replaced with Minnesota Rules, Chapter 1315, *Minnesota Electrical Code*.

Subp. 4. REPEALED

Subp. 5. Flood hazard or floodproofing provisions.

Any flood hazard or floodproofing provisions in the IRC, and any reference to those provisions, are deleted in their entirety.

Requirements for floodproofing are located in Chapter 1335, floodproofing regulations.

Subp. 6. Elevator and platform lift provisions.

Any elevator and platform lift provisions in the IRC and any reference to those provisions are deleted in their entirety. Requirements for elevators or platform lifts are located in Chapter 1307, elevators and related devices.

1309.0020
REFERENCES TO OTHER ICC CODES

Subpart 1. Generally.

References to other codes and standards promulgated by the ICC in the 2018 IRC are modified in subparts 2 to 11.

Subp. 2. Building code.

References to the *International Building Code* in this code mean the *Minnesota Building Code*, adopted pursuant to Minnesota Rules, Chapter 1305, and Minnesota Statutes, Section 326B.106, subdivision 1.

Subp. 3. Residential code.

References to the IRC in this code mean the *Minnesota Residential Code*, adopted under Minnesota Rules, Chapter 1309, and Minnesota Statutes, Section 326B.106, subdivision 1.

Subp. 4. Electrical code.

References to the ICC *Electrical Code* in this code mean the *Minnesota Electrical Code*, Minnesota Rules, Chapter 1315, adopted under Minnesota Statutes, Section 326B.35.

Subp. 5. Fuel gas code.

References to the *International Fuel Gas Code* in this code mean the *Minnesota Mechanical Code*, Minnesota Rules, Chapter 1346, adopted under Minnesota Statutes, Section 326B.106, subdivision 1.

Subp. 6. Mechanical code.

References to the *International Mechanical Code* in this code mean the *Minnesota Mechanical Code*, Minnesota Rules, Chapter 1346, adopted under Minnesota Statutes, Section 326B.106, subdivision 1.

Subp. 7. Plumbing code.

References to the *International Plumbing Code* in this code mean the *Minnesota Plumbing Code*, Minnesota Rules, Chapter 4714, adopted under Minnesota Statutes, Section 326B.435.

Subp. 8. Private sewage disposal code.

References to the *International Private Sewage Disposal Code* in this code mean the Minnesota Pollution Control Agency's minimum standards and criteria for individual sewage treatment systems in Minnesota Rules, Chapter 7080, adopted under Minnesota Statutes, Chapters 103F, 103G, 115, and 116.

Subp. 9. Energy conservation code.

References to the *International Energy Conservation Code* in this code mean the *Minnesota Energy Code*, adopted under Minnesota Rules, Chapters 1322 and 1323.

Subp. 10. Property maintenance code.

References to the *International Property Maintenance Code* in this code do not apply.

Subp. 11. Accessibility code.

References to accessibility in this code mean the *Minnesota Accessibility Code*, Minnesota Rules, Chapter 1341.

1309.0030
ADMINISTRATIVE PROCEDURE CRITERIA

Procedures relating to the administration and enforcement of this code under Minnesota Statutes, Section 326B.101, are contained in Minnesota Rules, Chapter 1300, Minnesota Building Code Administration. Minnesota Rules, Chapter 1300, governs the application of this code.

1309.0100
CHAPTER 1, ADMINISTRATION

Subpart 1. IRC chapter 1.

IRC Chapter 1 is deleted and replaced with the following:

CHAPTER 1
ADMINISTRATION

This code shall be administered according to Minnesota Rules, Chapter 1300.

Subp. 2. Existing buildings and structures.

Additions, alterations, or repairs to existing buildings and structures meeting the scope of the *International Residential Code* shall be exempt from Minnesota Rules, Chapter 1311, *Minnesota Conservation Code for Existing Buildings*.

Additions, alterations, or repairs to existing one- and two-family dwellings including townhouses may be made without requiring the existing building or structure to comply with all the requirements of this code provided that any addition or alteration conforms to this code. Repairs to existing buildings or structures may be made that are nonstructural and do not adversely affect any structural member or required fire-resistive element with the same methods and materials of which the building or structure is constructed.

> **Exception:** The installation or replacement of glass shall be as required for new installations in accordance with IRC Section R308.

Subp. 3. Transient use.

Buildings constructed for transient use and required to be licensed by any Minnesota state agency shall be constructed in accordance with the requirements for Group R occupancies located in Minnesota Rules, Chapter 1305.

CHAPTER 2

DEFINITIONS

User notes:

About this chapter: Codes, by their very nature, are technical documents. Every word, term and punctuation mark can add to or change the meaning of a technical requirement. It is necessary to maintain a consensus on the specific meaning of each term contained in the code. Chapter 2 performs this function by stating clearly what specific terms mean for the purpose of the code.

Code development reminder: Code change proposals to definitions in this chapter preceded by a bracketed letter are considered by the IRC—Building Code Development Committee [RB], the IRC—Mechanical/Plumbing Code Development Committee [MP] or the IECC—Residential Code Development Committee [RE] during the Group B (2019) Code Development cycle. See page iv for explanation.

SECTION R201
GENERAL

R201.1 Scope. Unless otherwise expressly stated, the following words and terms shall, for the purposes of this code, have the meanings indicated in this chapter.

R201.2 Interchangeability. Words used in the present tense include the future; words in the masculine gender include the feminine and neuter; the singular number includes the plural and the plural, the singular.

R201.3 Terms defined in other codes. Where terms are not defined in this code such terms shall have the meanings ascribed in other code publications of the International Code Council.

R201.4 Terms not defined. Where terms are not defined through the methods authorized by this chapter, the Merriam-Webster Collegiate Dictionary, available at www.m-w.com, shall be considered as providing ordinarily accepted meanings. The dictionary is incorporated by reference, is subject to frequent change, and is available through the Minitex interlibrary loan system.

SECTION R202
DEFINITIONS

[RB] ACCESS (TO). That which enables a device, an appliance or equipment to be reached by ready access or by a means that first requires the removal or movement of a panel, door or similar obstruction.

[RB] ACCESSORY STRUCTURE. A structure that is accessory to and incidental to that of the *dwelling(s)* and that is located on the same *lot*.

[RB] ADDITION. An extension or increase in floor area, number of stories or height of a building or structure.

[RB] ADHERED STONE OR MASONRY VENEER. Stone or masonry veneer secured and supported through the adhesion of an *approved* bonding material applied to an *approved* backing.

[RB] AIR-IMPERMEABLE INSULATION. An insulation having an air permanence equal to or less than 0.02 L/s-m² at

75 Pa pressure differential as tested in accordance with ASTM E2178 or E283. For the definition applicable in Chapter 11, see Section N1101.6.

[RB] ALTERATION. Any construction, retrofit or renovation to an existing structure other than repair or addition that requires a permit. Also, a change in a building, electrical, gas, mechanical or plumbing system that involves an extension, addition or change to the arrangement, type or purpose of the original installation that requires a permit.

[RB] ALTERNATING TREAD DEVICE. A device that has a series of steps between 50 and 70 degrees (0.87 and 1.22 rad) from horizontal, usually attached to a center support rail in an alternating manner so that the user does not have both feet on the same level at the same time.

[RB] ANCHORED STONE OR MASONRY VENEER. Stone or masonry veneer secured with *approved* mechanical fasteners to an *approved* backing.

[MP] ANCHORS. See "Supports."

[MP] APPLIANCE. A device or apparatus that is manufactured and designed to utilize energy.

[RB] APPROVED. "Approved" means approval by the *building official*, pursuant to the *Minnesota State Building Code*, by reason of:

   a. inspection, investigation, or testing;

   b. accepted principles;

   c. computer simulations;

   d. research reports; or

   e. testing performed by either a licensed engineer or by a locally or nationally recognized testing laboratory.

[RB] APPROVED AGENCY. An established and recognized agency that is regularly engaged in conducting tests, furnishing inspection services or furnishing product certification, and has been *approved* by the building official.

[RB] ASPECT RATIO. The ratio of longest to shortest perpendicular dimensions, or for wall sections, the ratio of height to length.

[RB] ATTIC. The unfinished space between the ceiling assembly and the roof assembly.

[RB] ATTIC, HABITABLE. A finished or unfinished *habitable space* within an *attic*.

[RB] BASEMENT. A *story* that is not a *story above grade plane*. (see "Story above grade plane").

[RE] BASEMENT WALL. For the definition applicable in Chapter 11, see Section N1101.6.

[RB] BASIC WIND SPEED. Three-second gust speed at 33 feet (10 058 mm) above the ground in Exposure C (see Section R301.2.1) as given in Figure R301.2(5)A.

[RB] BATTERY SYSTEM, STATIONARY STORAGE. A rechargeable energy storage system consisting of electrochemical storage batteries, battery chargers, controls and associated electrical *equipment* designed to provide electrical power to a building. The system is typically used to provide standby or emergency power, an uninterruptable power supply, load shedding, load sharing or similar capabilities.

[RB] BOND BEAM. A horizontal grouted element within masonry in which reinforcement is embedded.

[RB] BRACED WALL LINE. A straight line through the building plan that represents the location of the lateral resistance provided by the wall bracing.

[RB] BRACED WALL LINE, CONTINUOUSLY SHEATHED. A *braced wall line* with structural sheathing applied to all sheathable surfaces including the areas above and below openings.

[RB] BRACED WALL PANEL. A full-height section of wall constructed to resist in-plane shear loads through interaction of framing members, sheathing material and anchors. The panel's length meets the requirements of its particular bracing method, and contributes toward the total amount of bracing required along its *braced wall line* in accordance with Section R602.10.1.

[RB] BUILDING. Any one- or two-family dwelling or portion thereof, including *townhouses*, used or intended to be used for human habitation, for living, sleeping, cooking or eating purposes, or any combination thereof, or any *accessory structure*.

[RB] BUILDING, EXISTING. Existing building is a building erected prior to the adoption of this code, or one for which a legal building *permit* has been issued.

[RB] BUILDING-INTEGRATED PHOTOVOLTAIC PRODUCT. A building product that incorporates photovoltaic modules and functions as a component of the building envelope.

[RB] BUILDING-INTEGRATED PHOTOVOLTAIC ROOF PANEL (BIPV Roof Panel). A *photovoltaic panel* that functions as a component of the building envelope.

[RB] BUILDING LINE. The line established by law, beyond which a building shall not extend, except as specifically provided by law.

[RB] BUILDING OFFICIAL. The officer or other designated authority charged with the administration and enforcement of this code, or a duly authorized representative.

[RB] BUILT-UP ROOF COVERING. Two or more layers of felt cemented together and surfaced with a cap sheet, mineral aggregate, smooth coating or similar surfacing material.

[RB] CAP PLATE. The top plate of the double top plates used in structural insulated panel (SIP) construction. The cap plate is cut to match the panel thickness such that it overlaps the wood structural panel facing on both sides.

[RB] CARBON MONOXIDE ALARM. A single- or multiple-station alarm intended to detect carbon monoxide gas and alert occupants by a distinct audible signal. It incorporates a sensor, control components and an alarm notification appliance in a single unit.

[RB] CARBON MONOXIDE DETECTOR. A device with an integral sensor to detect carbon monoxide gas and transmit an alarm signal to a connected alarm control unit.

[RB] CEILING HEIGHT. The clear vertical distance from the finished floor to the finished ceiling.

[RB] CEMENT PLASTER. A mixture of portland or blended cement, Portland cement or blended cement and hydrated lime, masonry cement or plastic cement and aggregate and other *approved* materials as specified in this code.

[MP] CHIMNEY. A primary vertical structure containing one or more flues, for the purpose of carrying gaseous products of combustion and air from a fuel-burning *appliance* to the outside atmosphere.

[RB] CHANGE OF OCCUPANCY. A change in the use of a building or portion of a building that involves a change in the application of the requirements of this code.

[RB] CLADDING. The exterior materials that cover the surface of the building envelope that is directly loaded by the wind.

[RB] CLOSET. A small room or chamber used for storage.

CODE. For purposes of this chapter, "the code" or "this code" means the *Minnesota Residential Code*, Minnesota Rules, Chapter 1309.

[RB] COLLAPSIBLE SOILS. Soils that exhibit volumetric reduction in response to partial or full wetting under load.

[RB] COMBUSTIBLE MATERIAL. Any material not defined as noncombustible.

[RB] COMPRESSIBLE SOILS. Soils that exhibit volumetric reduction in response to the application of load even in the absence of wetting or drying.

[RB] CONDITIONED AIR. Air treated to control its temperature, relative humidity or quality.

[RB] CONSTRUCTION DOCUMENTS. Written, graphic and pictorial documents prepared or assembled for describing the design, location and physical characteristics of the elements of a project necessary for obtaining a building *permit*. Construction drawings shall be drawn to an appropriate scale.

[RB] CORE. The lightweight middle section of a structural insulated panel, composed of foam plastic insulation, that provides the link between the two facing shells.

[RB] CORROSION RESISTANCE. The ability of a material to withstand deterioration of its surface or its properties where exposed to its environment.

[RB] COURT. A space, open and unobstructed to the sky, located at or above *grade* level on a *lot* and bounded on three or more sides by walls or a building.

[RB] CRAWL SPACE. Areas or rooms with less than 6 feet 4 inches (1931 mm) ceiling height measured to the finished floor or grade below.

[RB] CRIPPLE WALL. A framed wall extending from the top of the foundation to the underside of the floor framing of the first *story above grade plane.*

[RB] CROSS-LAMINATED TIMBER. A prefabricated engineered wood product consisting of not less than three layers of solid-sawn lumber or *structural composite lumber* where the adjacent layers are cross-oriented and bonded with structural adhesive to form a solid wood element.

[RB] DALLE GLASS. A decorative composite glazing material made of individual pieces of glass that are embedded in a cast matrix of concrete or epoxy.

[RB] DEAD LOADS. The weight of the materials of construction incorporated into the building, including but not limited to walls, floors, roofs, ceilings, stairways, built-in partitions, finishes, cladding, and other similarly incorporated architectural and structural items, and fixed service *equipment.*

[RB] DECORATIVE GLASS. A carved, leaded or Dalle glass or glazing material with a purpose that is decorative or artistic, not functional; with coloring, texture or other design qualities or components that cannot be removed without destroying the glazing material; and with a surface, or assembly into which it is incorporated, that is divided into segments.

[MP] DESIGN PROFESSIONAL. See *"Registered design professional."*

[MP] DIAMETER. Unless specifically stated, the term "diameter" is the nominal diameter as designated by the *approved* material standard.

[RB] DIAPHRAGM. A horizontal or nearly horizontal system acting to transmit lateral forces to the vertical resisting elements. Where the term "*diaphragm*" is used, it includes horizontal bracing systems.

[RB] DRAFT STOP. A material, device or construction installed to restrict the movement of air within open spaces of concealed areas of building components such as crawl spaces, floor-ceiling assemblies, roof-ceiling assemblies and *attics.*

[RB] DWELLING.

SINGLE-FAMILY. Any building that contains one dwelling unit used, intended, or designed to be built, used, rented, leased, let or hired out to be occupied, or occupied for living purposes.

TWO-FAMILY. Any building that contains two separate dwelling units with separation either horizontal or vertical on one lot that is used, intended, or designed to be built,

used, rented, leased, let or hired out to be occupied, or occupied for living purposes.

TOWNHOUSE. A single-family dwelling unit constructed in a group of two or more attached units in which each unit extends from the foundation to the roof and having open space on at least two sides of each unit. Each single-family dwelling unit shall be considered to be a separate building. Separate building service utilities shall be provided to each single-family dwelling unit when required by other chapters of the *State Building Code.*

[RB] DWELLING UNIT. A single unit providing complete independent living facilities for one or more persons, including permanent provisions for living, sleeping, eating, cooking and sanitation.

[RB] EMERGENCY ESCAPE AND RESCUE OPENING. An operable exterior window, door or similar device that provides for a means of escape and access for rescue in the event of an emergency. (See also "Grade floor opening.")

[RB] ENGINEERED WOOD RIM BOARD. A full-depth structural composite lumber, wood structural panel, structural glued laminated timber or prefabricated wood I-joist member designed to transfer horizontal (shear) and vertical (compression) loads, provide attachment for *diaphragm* sheathing, siding and exterior deck ledgers and provide lateral support at the ends of floor or roof joists or rafters.

[RB] ESCARPMENT. With respect to topographic wind effects, a cliff or steep slope generally separating two levels or gently sloping areas.

[RB] EXPANSIVE SOILS. Soils that exhibit volumetric increase or decrease (swelling or shrinking) in response to partial or full wetting or drying under load.

[RB] EXTERIOR INSULATION AND FINISH SYSTEMS (EIFS). EIFS are nonstructural, nonload-bearing *exterior wall* cladding systems that consist of an insulation board attached either adhesively or mechanically, or both, to the substrate; an integrally reinforced base coat; and a textured protective finish coat.

[RB] EXTERIOR INSULATION AND FINISH SYSTEMS (EIFS) WITH DRAINAGE. An EIFS that incorporates a means of drainage applied over a water-resistive barrier.

[RB] EXTERIOR WALL COVERING. A material or assembly of materials applied on the exterior side of exterior walls for the purpose of providing a weather-resistive barrier, insulation or for aesthetics, including but not limited to, veneers, siding, exterior insulation and finish systems, architectural trim and embellishments such as cornices, soffits, and fascias.

[RB] FACING. The wood structural panel facings that form the two outmost rigid layers of the structural insulated panel.

[MP] FACTORY-BUILT CHIMNEY. A *listed* and *labeled* chimney composed of factory-made components assembled in the field in accordance with the manufacturer's instructions and the conditions of the *listing.*

FENESTRATION. Products classified as either vertical fenestration or skylights and sloped glazing, installed in such a manner as to preserve the weather-resistant barrier of the wall or roof in which they are installed. Fenestration includes products with glass or other transparent materials.

FENESTRATION, VERTICAL. Windows that are fixed or movable, opaque doors, glazed doors, glazed block and combination opaque and glazed doors installed in a wall at less than 15-degrees from vertical.

[RB] FIBER-CEMENT (BACKERBOARD, SIDING, SOFFIT, TRIM AND UNDERLAYMENT) PRODUCTS. Manufactured thin section composites of hydraulic cementitious matrices and discrete nonasbestos fibers.

[RB] FIRE SEPARATION DISTANCE. The distance measured from the building face to one of the following:

1. To the closest interior *lot line*.

2. To the centerline of a street, an alley or public way.

3. To an imaginary line between two buildings on the *lot*.

The distance shall be measured at a right angle from the face of the wall.

[RB] FIREBLOCKING. Building materials or materials *approved* for use as fireblocking, installed to resist the free passage of flame to other areas of the building through concealed spaces.

[RB] FIREPLACE. An assembly consisting of a hearth and fire chamber of noncombustible material and provided with a chimney, for use with solid fuels.

> **Factory-built fireplace.** A *listed* and *labeled* fireplace and chimney system composed of factory-made components, and assembled in the field in accordance with manufacturer's instructions and the conditions of the listing.

> **Masonry fireplace.** A field-constructed fireplace composed of *solid masonry* units, bricks, stones or concrete.

[RB] FIREPLACE THROAT. The opening between the top of the firebox and the smoke chamber.

[RB] FIRE-RETARDANT-TREATED WOOD. Pressure-treated lumber and plywood that exhibit reduced surface burning characteristics and resist propagation of fire.

> **Other means during manufacture.** A process where the wood raw material is treated with a fire-retardant formulation while undergoing creation as a finished product.

> **Pressure process.** A process for treating wood using an initial vacuum followed by the introduction of pressure above atmospheric.

[RB] FLAME SPREAD. The propagation of flame over a surface.

[RB] FLAME SPREAD INDEX. A comparative measure, expressed as a dimensionless number, derived from visual measurements of the spread of flame versus time for a material tested in accordance with ASTM E84 or UL 723.

FLASHING. Approved corrosion-resistive material provided in such a manner as to deflect and resist entry of water into the construction assembly.

[RB] FLIGHT. A continuous run of rectangular treads or winders or combination thereof from one landing to another.

FLOOR AREA. The calculated square footage of the floor within the inside perimeter of the exterior walls of the building under consideration without deduction for hallways, stairways, closets, the thickness of interior walls, columns, or other features.

[MP] FLUE. See "Vent."

[RB] FOAM BACKER BOARD. Foam plastic used in siding applications where the foam plastic is a component of the siding.

[RB] FOAM PLASTIC INSULATION. A plastic that is intentionally expanded by the use of a foaming agent to produce a reduced-density plastic containing voids consisting of open or closed cells distributed throughout the plastic for thermal insulating or acoustic purposes and that has a density less than 20 pounds per cubic foot (320 kg/m^3) unless it is used as interior trim.

[RB] FOAM PLASTIC INTERIOR TRIM. Exposed foam plastic used as picture molds, chair rails, crown moldings, baseboards, handrails, ceiling beams, door trim and window trim and similar decorative or protective materials used in fixed applications.

[RB] GLAZING AREA. The interior surface area of all glazed fenestration, including the area of sash, curbing or other framing elements, that enclose *conditioned space*. Includes the area of glazed fenestration assemblies in walls bounding conditioned *basements*.

[RB] GRADE. The finished ground level adjoining the building at all *exterior walls*.

[RB] GRADE FLOOR OPENING. A window or other opening located such that the sill height of the opening is not more than 44 inches (1118 mm) above or below the finished ground level adjacent to the opening. (See also "Emergency escape and rescue opening.")

[RB] GRADE PLANE. A reference plane representing the average of the finished ground level adjoining the building at all *exterior walls*. Where the finished ground level slopes away from the *exterior walls*, the reference plane shall be established by the lowest points within the area between the building and the *lot line* or, where the *lot line* is more than 6 feet (1829 mm) from the building between the structure and a point 6 feet (1829 mm) from the building.

[RB] GUARD. A building component or a system of building components located near the open sides of elevated walking surfaces that minimizes the possibility of a fall from the walking surface to the lower level.

[RB] GUESTROOM. Any room or rooms used or intended to be used by one or more guests for living or sleeping purposes.

[RB] GYPSUM BOARD. The generic name for a family of sheet products consisting of a noncombustible core primarily of gypsum with paper surfacing. Gypsum wallboard, gypsum sheathing, gypsum base for gypsum *veneer* plaster, exterior gypsum soffit board, predecorated gypsum board and water-resistant gypsum backing board complying with the standards listed in Section R702.3 and Part IX of this code are types of gypsum board.

[RB] GYPSUM PANEL PRODUCT. The general name for a family of sheet products consisting essentially of gypsum.

[RB] HABITABLE SPACE. A space in a building for living, sleeping, eating or cooking. Bathrooms, toilet rooms, closets, halls, storage or utility spaces and similar areas are not considered *habitable spaces*.

[RB] HANDRAIL. A horizontal or sloping rail intended for grasping by the hand for guidance or support.

[RB] HEIGHT, BUILDING. The vertical distance from *grade plane* to the average height of the highest roof surface.

[RB] HEIGHT, STORY. The vertical distance from top to top of two successive tiers of beams or finished floor surfaces; and, for the topmost *story*, from the top of the floor finish to the top of the ceiling joists or, where there is not a ceiling, to the top of the roof rafters.

[RB] HILL. With respect to topographic wind effects, a land surface characterized by strong relief in any horizontal direction.

[RB] HISTORIC BUILDING. A "Historic building" has the meaning given in part 1300.0070, subpart 12a.

[RB] HURRICANE-PRONE REGIONS. Areas vulnerable to hurricanes, defined as the U.S. Atlantic Ocean and Gulf of Mexico coasts where the ultimate design wind speed, V_{ult}, is greater than 115 miles per hour (51 m/s), and Hawaii, Puerto Rico, Guam, Virgin Islands and America Samoa.

[RB] IMPACT PROTECTIVE SYSTEM. Construction that has been shown by testing to withstand the impact of test missiles and that is applied, attached, or locked over exterior glazing.

[RB] INSULATED SIDING. A type of continuous insulation, with manufacturer-installed insulating material as an integral part of the cladding product, having a minimum *R*-value of R-2. For the definition applicable in Chapter 11, see Section N1101.6.

[RB] INSULATED VINYL SIDING. A vinyl cladding product, with manufacturer-installed foam plastic insulating material as an integral part of the cladding product, having a thermal resistance of not less than R-2.

[RB] INSULATING CONCRETE FORM (ICF). A concrete forming system using stay-in-place forms of rigid foam plastic insulation, a hybrid of cement and foam insulation, a hybrid of cement and wood chips, or other insulating material for constructing cast-in-place concrete walls.

[RB] INSULATING SHEATHING. An insulating board having a thermal resistance of not less than R-2 of the core material.

[RB] JURISDICTION. The governmental unit that has adopted this code.

KICK-OUT FLASHING. Flashing used to divert water where the lower portion of a sloped roof stops within the plane of an intersecting wall cladding.

[RB] KITCHEN. Kitchen shall mean an area used, or designated to be used, for the preparation of food.

[RB] LABEL. An identification applied on a product by the manufacturer that contains the name of the manufacturer, the function and performance characteristics of the product or material, and the name and identification of an *approved agency* and that indicates that the representative sample of the product or material has been tested and evaluated by an *approved agency*. (See also "Manufacturer's designation" and "Mark.")

[RB] LABELED. *Equipment*, materials or products to which have been affixed a *label*, seal, symbol or other identifying *mark* of a nationally recognized testing laboratory, approved agency or other organization concerned with product evaluation that maintains periodic inspection of the production of such *labeled* items and whose labeling indicates either that the *equipment*, material or product meets identified standards or has been tested and found suitable for a specified purpose.

[RB] LIGHT-FRAME CONSTRUCTION. Construction whose vertical and horizontal structural elements are primarily formed by a system of repetitive wood or cold-formed steel framing members.

[RB] LISTED. *Equipment*, materials, products or services included in a list published by an organization acceptable to the code official and concerned with evaluation of products or services that maintains periodic inspection of production of *listed equipment* or materials or periodic evaluation of services and whose listing states either that the *equipment*, material, product or service meets identified standards or has been tested and found suitable for a specified purpose.

[RB] LIVE LOADS. Those loads produced by the use and occupancy of the building or other structure and do not include construction or environmental loads such as wind load, snow load, rain load, earthquake load, flood load or dead load.

[MP] LIVING SPACE. Space within a *dwelling unit* utilized for living, sleeping, eating, cooking, bathing, washing and sanitation purposes.

[RB] LODGING HOUSE. A one-family dwelling where one or more occupants are primarily permanent in nature, and rent is paid for guestrooms.

[RB] LOT. A portion or parcel of land considered as a unit.

[RB] LOT LINE. A line dividing one *lot* from another, or from a street or any public place.

[RB] MANUFACTURER'S DESIGNATION. An identification applied on a product by the manufacturer indicating that a product or material complies with a specified standard or set of rules. (See also "Mark" and "Label.")

[RB] MANUFACTURER'S INSTALLATION INSTRUCTIONS. Printed instructions included with *equipment* as part of the conditions of their *listing* and *labeling*.

[RB] MARK. An identification applied on a product by the manufacturer indicating the name of the manufacturer and the function of a product or material. (See also "Manufacturer's designation" and "Label.")

[RB] MASONRY CHIMNEY. A field-constructed chimney composed of solid masonry units, bricks, stones or concrete.

[RB] MASONRY HEATER. A masonry heater is a solid fuel burning heating *appliance* constructed predominantly of concrete or solid masonry having a mass of not less than 1,100 pounds (500 kg), excluding the chimney and foundation. It is designed to absorb and store a substantial portion of heat from a fire built in the firebox by routing exhaust gases through internal heat exchange channels in which the flow path downstream of the firebox includes not less than one 180-degree (3.14-rad) change in flow direction before entering the chimney and that deliver heat by radiation through the masonry surface of the heater.

[RB] MASONRY, SOLID. Masonry consisting of solid masonry units laid contiguously with the joints between the units filled with mortar.

[RB] MASONRY UNIT. Brick, tile, stone, architectural cast stone, glass block or concrete block conforming to the requirements specified in Section 2103 of the *International Building Code.*

> **Clay.** A building unit larger in size than a brick, composed of burned clay, shale, fire clay or mixtures thereof.

> **Concrete.** A building unit or block larger in size than 12 inches by 4 inches by 4 inches (305 mm by 102 mm by 102 mm) made of cement and suitable aggregates.

> **Glass.** Nonload-bearing masonry composed of glass units bonded by mortar.

> **Hollow.** A masonry unit with a net cross-sectional area in any plane parallel to the loadbearing surface that is less than 75 percent of its gross cross-sectional area measured in the same plane.

> **Solid.** A masonry unit with a net cross-sectional area in every plane parallel to the loadbearing surface that is 75 percent or more of its cross-sectional area measured in the same plane.

[RB] MEAN ROOF HEIGHT. The average of the roof eave height and the height to the highest point on the roof surface, except that eave height shall be used for roof angle of less than or equal to 10 degrees (0.18 rad).

[MP] MECHANICAL EXHAUST SYSTEM. A system for removing air from a room or space by mechanical means.

[RB] METAL ROOF PANEL. An interlocking metal sheet having an installed weather exposure of not less than 3 square feet (0.28 m^2) per sheet.

[RB] METAL ROOF SHINGLE. An interlocking metal sheet having an installed weather exposure less than 3 square feet (0.28 m^2) per sheet.

[RB] MEZZANINE. An intermediate level or levels between the floor and ceiling of any *story.*

[RB] MODIFIED BITUMEN ROOF COVERING. One or more layers of polymer modified asphalt sheets. The sheet materials shall be fully adhered or mechanically attached to the substrate or held in place with an *approved* ballast layer.

[RB] MULTIPLE-STATION SMOKE ALARM. Two or more single-station alarm devices that are capable of inter-connection such that actuation of one causes all integral or separate audible alarms to operate.

[RB] NAILABLE SUBSTRATE. A product or material such as framing, sheathing or furring, composed of wood or wood-based materials, or other materials and fasteners providing equivalent fastener withdrawal resistance.

[RB] NATURALLY DURABLE WOOD. The heartwood of the following species with the exception that an occasional piece with corner sapwood is permitted if 90 percent or more of the width of each side on which it occurs is heartwood.

> **Decay resistant.** Redwood, cedar, black locust and black walnut.

> **Termite resistant.** Alaska yellow cedar, redwood, Eastern red cedar and Western red cedar including all sapwood of Western red cedar.

[RB] NONCOMBUSTIBLE MATERIAL. Materials that pass the test procedure for defining noncombustibility of elementary materials set forth in ASTM E136.

[RB] NOSING. The leading edge of treads of stairs and of landings at the top of stairway flights.

OCCUPANCY CLASSIFICATIONS.

> IRC-1 - Single-family dwellings

> IRC-2 - Two-family dwellings

> IRC-3 - Townhouses

> IRC-4 - Accessory structures:

>> a. Garages;

>> b. Storage sheds; and

>> c. Similar structures.

[RB] OCCUPIED SPACE. The total area of all buildings or structures on any *lot* or parcel of ground projected on a horizontal plane, excluding permitted projections as allowed by this code.

[RB] OWNER. Any person, agent, firm or corporation having a legal or equitable interest in the property.

[RB] PAN FLASHING. Corrosion-resistant flashing at the base of an opening that is integrated into the building exterior wall to direct water to the exterior and is premanufactured, fabricated, formed or applied at the job site.

[RB] PANEL THICKNESS. Thickness of core plus two layers of structural wood panel facings.

[RB] PERFORMANCE CATEGORY. A designation of wood structural panels as related to the panel performance used in Chapters 4, 5, 6 and 8.

[RB] PERMIT. An official document or certificate issued by the *building official* that authorizes performance of a specified activity.

[RB] PERSON. An individual, heirs, executors, administrators or assigns, and a firm, partnership or corporation, its or their successors or assigns, or the agent of any of the aforesaid.

[RB] PHOTOVOLTAIC MODULE. A complete, environmentally protected unit consisting of solar cells, optics and other components, exclusive of a tracker, designed to generate DC power where exposed to sunlight.

[RB] PHOTOVOLTAIC PANEL. A collection of photovoltaic modules mechanically fastened together, wired, and designed to provide a field-installable unit.

[RB] PHOTOVOLTAIC PANEL SYSTEM. A system that incorporates discrete photovoltaic panels that convert solar radiation into electricity, including rack support systems.

[RB] PHOTOVOLTAIC SHINGLES. A *roof covering* that resembles shingles and that incorporates photovoltaic modules.

[MP] PITCH. See "Slope."

[RB] PLASTIC COMPOSITE. A generic designation that refers to wood-plastic composites and plastic lumber.

[RB] PLATFORM CONSTRUCTION. A method of construction by which floor framing bears on load bearing walls that are not continuous through the *story* levels or floor framing.

[MP] PLUMBING FIXTURE. A receptacle or device that is connected to a water supply system or discharges to a drainage system or both. Such receptacles or devices require a supply of water; or discharge liquid waste or liquidborne solid waste; or require a supply of water and discharge waste to a drainage system.

[RB] POLYPROPYLENE SIDING. A shaped material, made principally from polypropylene homopolymer, or copolymer, that in some cases contains fillers or reinforcements, that is used to clad *exterior walls* or buildings.

[RB] POSITIVE ROOF DRAINAGE. The drainage condition in which consideration has been made for the loading deflections of the roof deck, and additional slope has been provided to ensure drainage of the roof within 48 hours of precipitation.

[RB] PRECAST CONCRETE. A structural concrete element cast elsewhere than its final position in the structure.

[RB] PRECAST CONCRETE FOUNDATION WALLS. Preengineered, precast concrete wall panels that are designed to withstand specified stresses and used to build below-*grade* foundations.

[RB] PUBLIC WAY. Any street, alley or other parcel of land open to the outside air leading to a public street, that has been deeded, dedicated or otherwise permanently appropriated to the public for public use and that has a clear width and height of not less than 10 feet (3048 mm).

[RB] RAMP. A walking surface that has a running slope steeper than 1 unit vertical in 20 units horizontal (5-percent slope).

[RB] READY ACCESS (TO). That which enables a device, *appliance* or *equipment* to be directly reached, without requiring the removal or movement of any panel, door or similar obstruction.

[RB] REGISTERED DESIGN PROFESSIONAL. An individual who is registered or licensed to practice their respective design profession as defined by the statutory

requirements of the professional registration laws of the state or *jurisdiction* in which the project is to be constructed.

[RB] REPAIR. The reconstruction, replacement or renewal of any part of an existing building for the purpose of its maintenance or to correct damage.

[RB] REROOFING. The process of recovering or replacing an existing roof covering. See "Roof recover." For the definition applicable in Chapter 11, see Section N1101.6.

[MP] RETURN AIR. Air removed from an *approved conditioned space* or location and recirculated or exhausted.

[RB] RIDGE. With respect to topographic wind effects, an elongated crest of a *hill* characterized by strong relief in two directions.

[RB] RISER (STAIR). The vertical component of a step or stair.

[RB] ROOF ASSEMBLY. A system designed to provide weather protection and resistance to design loads. The system consists of a roof covering and roof deck or a single component serving as both the roof covering and the roof deck. A roof assembly includes the roof deck, underlayment and *roof covering,* and can also include a thermal barrier, ignition barrier, insulation or a vapor retarder.

[RB] ROOF COATING. A fluid-applied, adhered coating used for roof maintenance or *roof repair*, or as a component of a *roof covering* system or *roof assembly*.

[RB] ROOF COVERING. The covering applied to the roof deck for weather resistance, fire classification or appearance.

[RB] ROOF COVERING SYSTEM. See "Roof assembly."

[RB] ROOF DECK. The flat or sloped surface not including its supporting members or vertical supports.

[RB] ROOF RECOVER. The process of installing an additional *roof covering* over a prepared existing roof covering without removing the existing roof covering. For the definition applicable in Chapter 11, see Section N1101.6.

[RB] ROOF REPAIR. Reconstruction or renewal of any part of an existing roof for the purposes of its maintenance.

[RB] ROOF REPLACEMENT. The process of removing the existing *roof covering*, repairing any damaged substrate and installing a new *roof covering*. For the definition applicable in Chapter 11, see Section N1101.6.

[RB] RUNNING BOND. The placement of masonry units such that head joints in successive courses are horizontally offset not less than one-quarter the unit length.

[RB] SEISMIC DESIGN CATEGORY (SDC). A classification assigned to a structure based on its occupancy category and the severity of the design earthquake ground motion at the site.

[RB] SHALL. "Shall" is a mandatory term. See Minnesota Rules, part 1300.0070, subpart 13.

[RB] SHEAR WALL. A general term for walls that are designed and constructed to resist racking from seismic and wind by use of masonry, concrete, cold-formed steel or wood framing in accordance with Chapter 6 of this code and the associated limitations in Section R301.2 of this code.

[RB] SHINGLE FASHION. A method of installing roof or wall coverings, water-resistive barriers, flashing or other building components such that upper layers of material are placed overlapping lower layers of material to provide drainage and protect against water intrusion at unsealed penetrations and joints or in combination with sealed joints.

SILL HEIGHT. The lowest part of the window opening of an operable window measured from the finished floor.

[RB] SINGLE-PLY MEMBRANE. A roofing membrane that is field applied using one layer of membrane material (either homogeneous or composite) rather than multiple layers.

[RB] SINGLE-STATION SMOKE ALARM. An assembly incorporating the detector, control *equipment* and alarm sounding device in one unit that is operated from a power supply either in the unit or obtained at the point of installation.

[RB] SKYLIGHT, UNIT. A factory assembled, glazed fenestration unit, containing one panel of glazing material, that allows for natural daylighting through an opening in the roof assembly while preserving the weather-resistant barrier of the roof.

[RB] SKYLIGHTS AND SLOPED GLAZING. Glass or other transparent or translucent glazing material installed at a slope of 15 degrees (0.26 rad) or more from vertical. Unit skylights, tubular daylighting devices and glazing materials in solariums, sunrooms, roofs and sloped walls are included in this definition. For the definition applicable in Chapter 11, see Section N1101.6.

[MP] SLOPE. The fall (pitch) of a line of pipe in reference to a horizontal plane. In drainage, the slope is expressed as the fall in units vertical per units horizontal (percent) for a length of pipe.

[RB] SMOKE-DEVELOPED INDEX. A comparative measure, expressed as a dimensionless number, derived from measurements of smoke obscuration versus time for a material tested in accordance with ASTM E84 or UL 723.

[RB] SOLAR ENERGY SYSTEM. A system that converts solar radiation to usable energy, including *photovoltaic panel systems* and *solar thermal systems*.

[MP] SOLAR THERMAL SYSTEM. A system that converts solar radiation to thermal energy for use in heating or cooling.

[RB] SOLID MASONRY. Load-bearing or nonload-bearing construction using masonry units where the net cross-sectional area of each unit in any plane parallel to the bearing surface is not less than 75 percent of its gross cross-sectional area. Solid masonry units shall conform to ASTM C55, C62, C73, C145 or C216.

[RB] SPLINE. A strip of wood structural panel cut from the same material used for the panel facings, used to connect two structural insulated panels. The strip (spline) fits into a groove cut into the vertical edges of the two structural insulated panels to be joined. Splines are used behind each facing of the structural insulated panels being connected as shown in Figure R610.8.

[RB] STACK BOND. The placement of masonry units in a bond pattern is such that head joints in successive courses are vertically aligned. For the purpose of this code, requirements for stack bond shall apply to all masonry laid in other than running bond.

[RB] STAIR. A change in elevation, consisting of one or more risers.

[RB] STAIRWAY. One or more flights of stairs, either interior or exterior, with the necessary landings and connecting platforms to form a continuous and uninterrupted passage from one level to another within or attached to a building, porch or deck.

[RB] STAIRWAY, SPIRAL. A stairway with a plan view of closed circular form and uniform section-shaped treads radiating from a minimum-diameter circle.

[RB] STANDARD TRUSS. Any construction that does not permit the roof-ceiling insulation to achieve the required *R*-value over the *exterior walls*.

[RB] STORY. That portion of a building included between the upper surface of a floor and the upper surface of the floor or roof next above.

[RB] STORY ABOVE GRADE PLANE. Any *story* having its finished floor surface entirely above *grade plane*, or in which the finished surface of the floor next above is either of the following:

1. More than 6 feet (1829 mm) *above grade plane.*

2. More than 12 feet (3658 mm) above the finished ground level at any point.

[RB] STRUCTURAL COMPOSITE LUMBER. Structural members manufactured using wood elements bonded together with exterior adhesives.

Examples of structural composite lumber are:

Laminated strand lumber (LSL). A composite of wood strand elements with wood fibers primarily oriented along the length of the member, where the least dimension of the wood strand elements is 0.10 inch (2.54 mm) or less and their average lengths are not less than 150 times the least dimension of the wood strand elements.

Laminated veneer lumber (LVL). A composite of wood veneer elements with wood fibers primarily oriented along the length of the member, where the veneer element thicknesses are 0.25 inch (6.4 mm) or less.

Oriented strand lumber (OSL). A composite of wood strand elements with wood fibers primarily oriented along the length of the member, where the least dimension of the wood strand elements is 0.10 inch (2.54 mm) or less and their average lengths are not less than 75 times and less than 150 times the least dimension of the wood strand elements.

Parallel strand lumber (PSL). A composite of wood strand elements with wood fibers primarily oriented along the length of the member, where the least dimension of the wood strand elements is 0.25 inch (6.4 mm) or less and their average lengths are not less than 300 times the least dimension of the wood strand elements.

[RB] STRUCTURAL INSULATED PANEL (SIP). A structural sandwich panel that consists of a lightweight foam plastic core securely laminated between two thin, rigid wood structural panel facings.

[RB] STRUCTURE. That which is built or constructed.

[RB] SUBSOIL DRAIN. A drain that collects subsurface water or seepage water and conveys such water to a place of disposal.

[MP] SUMP. A tank or pit that receives sewage or waste, located below the normal *grade* of the gravity system and that must be emptied by mechanical means.

[MP] SUMP PUMP. A pump installed to empty a sump. These pumps are used for removing storm water only. The pump is selected for the specific head and volume of the load and is usually operated by level controllers.

[RB] SUNROOM. A one-story structure attached to a *dwelling* with a *glazing area* in excess of 40 percent of the gross area of the structure's *exterior walls* and roof.

[MP] SUPPLY AIR. Air delivered to a *conditioned space* through ducts or plenums from the heat exchanger of a heating, cooling or ventilating system.

[MP] SUPPORTS. Devices for supporting, hanging and securing pipes, fixtures and *equipment*.

[RB] TERMITE-RESISTANT MATERIAL. Pressure-preservative-treated wood in accordance with the AWPA standards in Section R317.1, naturally durable termite-resistant wood, steel, concrete, masonry or other *approved* material.

[RE] THERMAL ISOLATION. For the definition applicable in Chapter 11, see Section N1101.6.

[RB] TOWNHOUSE. See "Dwelling."

TRANSIENT. Occupancy of a dwelling unit or sleeping unit for not more than 30 days.

[RB] TRIM. Picture molds, chair rails, baseboards, handrails, door and window frames, and similar decorative or protective materials used in fixed applications.

[RB] TRUSS DESIGN DRAWING. The graphic depiction of an individual truss, that describes the design and physical characteristics of the truss.

[RB] TUBULAR DAYLIGHTING DEVICE (TDD). A nonoperable fenestration unit primarily designed to transmit daylight from a roof surface to an interior ceiling via a tubular conduit. The basic unit consists of an exterior glazed weathering surface, a light-transmitting tube with a reflective interior surface, and an interior-sealing device such as a translucent ceiling panel. The unit may be factory assembled, or field assembled from a manufactured kit.

[RB] UNDERLAYMENT. One or more layers of felt, sheathing paper, nonbituminous saturated felt, or other *approved* material over which a roof covering, with a slope of 2 to 12 (17-percent slope) or greater, is applied.

[RB] VAPOR DIFFUSION PORT. A passageway for conveying water vapor from an unvented *attic* to the outside atmosphere.

[RB] VAPOR PERMEABLE. The property of having a moisture vapor permeance rating of 5 perms (2.9×10^{-10} kg/Pa $\cdot$ s $\cdot$ m^2) or greater, where tested in accordance with the desiccant method using Procedure A of ASTM E96. A vapor permeable material permits the passage of moisture vapor.

[RB] VAPOR RETARDER CLASS. A measure of the ability of a material or assembly to limit the amount of moisture that passes through that material or assembly. Vapor retarder class shall be defined using the desiccant method with Procedure A of ASTM E96 as follows:

Class I: ≤ 0.1 perm rating

Class II: > 0.1 to ≤ 1.0 perm rating

Class III: > 1.0 to ≤ 10 perm rating

[MP] VENT. A passageway for conveying a flue gases from fuel-fired appliances, or their vent connectors, to the outside atmosphere.

[RB] VENTILATION. The natural or mechanical process of supplying conditioned or unconditioned air to, or removing such air from, any space.

[MP] VENTING. Removal of combustion products to the outdoors.

[MP] VENTING SYSTEM. A continuous open passageway from the flue collar of an *appliance* to the outside atmosphere for the purpose of removing flue or vent gases. A venting system is usually composed of a vent or a chimney and vent connector, if used, assembled to form the open passageway.

[RB] VINYL SIDING. A shaped material, made principally from rigid polyvinyl chloride (PVC), that is used to cover exterior walls of buildings.

[RB] WALL, RETAINING. A wall not laterally supported at the top, that resists lateral soil load and other imposed loads.

[RB] WALLS. Walls shall be defined as follows:

Load-bearing wall. A wall supporting any vertical load in addition to its own weight.

Nonbearing wall. A wall which does not support vertical loads other than its own weight.

[RB] WATER-RESISTIVE BARRIER. A material behind an *exterior wall* covering that is intended to resist liquid water that has penetrated behind the exterior covering from further intruding into the *exterior wall* assembly.

WATERPROOFING. Treatment of a surface or structure located below grade to resist the passage of water in liquid form, under hydrostatic pressure that bridges nonstructural cracks.

[MP] WHOLE-HOUSE MECHANICAL VENTILATION SYSTEM. An exhaust system, supply system, or combination thereof that is designed to mechanically exchange indoor air for outdoor air where operating continuously or through a programmed intermittent schedule to satisfy the whole-house ventilation rate.

[RB] WINDBORNE DEBRIS REGION. Areas within *hurricane-prone regions* located in accordance with one of the following:

1. Within 1 mile (1.61 km) of the coastal mean high-water line where the ultimate design wind speed, V_{ult}, is 130 mph (58 m/s) or greater.

2. In areas where the ultimate design wind speed, V_{ult}, is 140 mph (63.6 m/s) or greater; or Hawaii.

[RB] WINDER. A tread with nonparallel edges.

[RB] WOOD STRUCTURAL PANEL. A panel manufactured from veneers; or wood strands or wafers; bonded together with waterproof synthetic resins or other suitable bonding systems. Examples of wood structural panels are plywood, orientated strand board (OSB) or composite panels.

[RB] YARD. An open space, other than a court, unobstructed from the ground to the sky, except where specifically provided by this code, on the *lot* on which a building is situated.

CHAPTER 3

BUILDING PLANNING

User note:

About this chapter: Chapter 3 contains a wide array of building planning requirements that are critical to designing a safe and usable building. This includes, but is not limited to, requirements related to: general structural design, fire-resistant construction, light, ventilation, sanitation, plumbing fixture clearances, minimum room area and ceiling height, safety glazing, means of egress, automatic fire sprinkler systems, smoke and carbon monoxide alarm systems, accessibility, solar energy systems, swimming pools, spas and hot tubs.

SECTION R300
CLASSIFICATION

R300.1 Occupancy classification. Structures or portions of structures shall be classified with respect to occupancy in one or more of the groups in accordance with Table R300.1.

TABLE R300.1
OCCUPANCY CLASSIFICATIONS

IRC-1	Dwelling, single-family
IRC-2	Dwelling, two-family
IRC-3	Townhouse
IRC-4	Accessory structures

SECTION R301
DESIGN CRITERIA

R301.1 Application. Buildings and structures, and parts thereof, shall be constructed to safely support all loads, including dead loads, live loads, roof loads, flood loads, snow loads, wind loads and seismic loads as prescribed by this code. The construction of buildings and structures in accordance with the provisions of this code shall result in a system that provides a complete load path that meets the requirements for the transfer of loads from their point of origin through the load-resisting elements to the foundation. Buildings and structures constructed as prescribed by this code are deemed to comply with the requirements of this section.

R301.1.1 Alternative provisions. As an alternative to the requirements in Section R301.1, the following standards are permitted subject to the limitations of this code and the limitations therein. Where engineered design is used in conjunction with these standards, the design shall comply with the *International Building Code.*

1. AWC *Wood Frame Construction Manual* (WFCM).

2. AISI *Standard for Cold-Formed Steel Framing— Prescriptive Method for One- and Two-Family Dwellings* (AISI S230).

3. ICC *Standard on the Design and Construction of Log Structures* (ICC 400).

R301.1.2 Construction systems. The requirements of this code are based on platform and balloon-frame construction for light-frame buildings. The requirements for concrete and masonry buildings are based on a balloon framing system. Other framing systems must have equivalent detailing to ensure force transfer, continuity and compatible deformations.

R301.1.3 Engineered design. Where a building of otherwise conventional construction contains structural elements exceeding the limits of Section R301 or otherwise not conforming to this code, these elements shall be designed in accordance with accepted engineering practice. The extent of such design need only demonstrate compliance of nonconventional elements with other applicable provisions and shall be compatible with the performance of the conventional framed system. Engineered design in accordance with the *International Building Code* is permitted for buildings and structures, and parts thereof, included in the scope of this code.

R301.2 Climatic and geographic design criteria. Buildings shall be constructed in accordance with the provisions of this code as limited by the provisions of this section. Additional criteria shall be established by the local *jurisdiction* and set forth in Table R301.2(1).

R301.2.1 Wind design criteria. Buildings and portions thereof shall be constructed in accordance with the wind provisions of this code using the ultimate design wind speed in Table R301.2(1) as determined from Figure R301.2(5)A. The structural provisions of this code for wind loads are not permitted where wind design is required as specified in Section R301.2.1.1. Where different construction methods and structural materials are used for various portions of a building, the applicable requirements of this section for each portion shall apply. Where not otherwise specified, the wind loads listed in Table R301.2(2) adjusted for height and exposure using Table R301.2(3) shall be used to determine design load performance requirements for wall coverings, curtain walls, roof coverings, exterior windows, skylights, garage doors and exterior doors. Asphalt shingles shall be designed for wind speeds in accordance with Section R905.2.4. A continuous load path shall be provided to transmit the applicable uplift forces in Section R802.11.1 from the roof assembly to the foundation.

R301.2.1.1 Wind limitations and wind design required. The wind provisions of this code shall not apply to the design of buildings where wind design is required in accordance with Figure R301.2(5)B.

Exceptions:

1. For concrete construction, the wind provisions of this code shall apply in accordance with the limitations of Sections R404 and R608.

2. For structural insulated panels, the wind provisions of this code shall apply in accordance with the limitations of Section R610.

3. For cold-formed steel light-frame construction, the wind provisions of this code shall apply in accordance with the limitations of Sections R505, R603 and R804.

In regions where wind design is required in accordance with Figure R301.2(5)B, the design of buildings for wind loads shall be in accordance with one or more of the following methods:

1. AWC *Wood Frame Construction Manual* (WFCM).

2. ICC *Standard for Residential Construction in High-Wind Regions* (ICC 600).

3. ASCE *Minimum Design Loads for Buildings and Other Structures* (ASCE 7).

4. AISI *Standard for Cold-Formed Steel Framing— Prescriptive Method For One- and Two-Family Dwellings* (AISI S230).

5. *International Building Code.*

The elements of design not addressed by the methods in Items 1 through 5 shall be in accordance with the provisions of this code.

Where ASCE 7 or the *International Building Code* is used for the design of the building, the wind speed map and exposure category requirements as specified in ASCE 7 and the *International Building Code* shall be used.

R301.2.1.1.1 Sunrooms. *Sunrooms* shall comply with AAMA/NPEA/NSA 2100. For the purpose of applying the criteria of AAMA/NPEA/NSA 2100 based on the intended use, *sunrooms* shall be identified as one of the following categories by the permit applicant, design professional or the property owner or owner's agent in the construction documents. Component and cladding pressures shall be used for the design of elements that do not qualify as main windforce-resisting systems. Main windforce-resisting system pressures shall be used for the design of elements assigned to provide support and stability for the overall *sunroom.*

Category I: A thermally isolated *sunroom* with walls that are open or enclosed with insect screening or 0.5 mm (20 mil) maximum thickness plastic film. The space is nonhabitable and unconditioned.

Category II: A thermally isolated *sunroom* with enclosed walls. The openings are enclosed with translucent or transparent plastic or glass. The space is nonhabitable and unconditioned.

Category III: A thermally isolated *sunroom* with enclosed walls. The openings are enclosed with translucent or transparent plastic or glass. The sunroom fenestration complies with additional requirements for air infiltration resistance and water penetration resistance. The space is nonhabitable and unconditioned.

Category IV: A thermally isolated *sunroom* with enclosed walls. The sunroom is designed to be heated or cooled by a separate temperature control or system and is thermally isolated from the primary structure. The *sunroom* fenestration complies with additional requirements for water penetration resistance, air infiltration resistance and thermal performance. The space is nonhabitable and conditioned.

Category V: A *sunroom* with enclosed walls. The sunroom is designed to be heated or cooled and is open to the main structure. The *sunroom* fenestration complies with additional requirements for water penetration resistance, air infiltration resistance and thermal performance. The space is habitable and conditioned.

R301.2.1.2 Protection of openings. Exterior glazing in buildings located in windborne debris regions shall be protected from windborne debris. Glazed opening protection for windborne debris shall meet the requirements of the Large Missile Test of ASTM E1996 and ASTM E1886 as modified in Section 301.2.1.2.1. Garage door glazed opening protection for windborne debris shall meet the requirements of an *approved* impact-resisting standard or ANSI/DASMA 115.

Exception: Wood structural panels with a thickness of not less than $^7/_{16}$ inch (11 mm) and a span of not more than 8 feet (2438 mm) shall be permitted for opening protection. Panels shall be precut and attached to the framing surrounding the opening containing the product with the glazed opening. Panels shall be predrilled as required for the anchorage method and shall be secured with the attachment hardware provided. Attachments shall be designed to resist the component and cladding loads determined in accordance with either Table R301.2(2) or ASCE 7, with the permanent corrosion-resistant attachment hardware provided and anchors permanently installed on the building. Attachment in accordance with Table R301.2.1.2 is permitted for buildings with a *mean roof height* of 45 feet (13 728 mm) or less where the ultimate design wind speed, V_{ult}, is 180 mph (290 kph) or less.

R301.2.1.2.1 Application of ASTM E1996. The text of Section 2.2 of ASTM E1996 shall be substituted as follows:

2.2 ASCE Standard:

ASCE 7-10 American Society of Civil Engineers *Minimum Design Loads for Buildings and Other Structures*

The text of Section 6.2.2 of ASTM E1996 shall be substituted as follows:

6.2.2 Unless otherwise specified, select the wind zone based on the ultimate design wind speed, V_{ult}, as follows:

6.2.2.1 Wind Zone 1–130 mph ≤ ultimate design wind speed, V_{ult} < 140 mph.

6.2.2.2 Wind Zone 2–140 mph ≤ ultimate design wind speed, V_{ult} < 150 mph at greater than 1 mile (1.6 km) from the coastline. The coastline shall be measured from the mean high-water mark.

6.2.2.3 Wind Zone 3–150 mph (58 m/s) ≤ ultimate design wind speed, V_{ult} ≤ 170 mph (76 m/s), or 140 mph (54 m/s) ≤ ultimate design wind speed, V_{ult} ≤ 170 mph (76 m/s) and within 1 mile (1.6 km) of the coastline. The coastline shall be measured from the mean high-water mark.

6.2.2.4 Wind Zone 4–ultimate design wind speed, V_{ult} > 170 mph (76 m/s).

TABLE R301.2.1.2
WINDBORNE DEBRIS PROTECTION FASTENING SCHEDULE FOR WOOD STRUCTURAL PANELS[a, b, c, d]

FASTENER TYPE	FASTENER SPACING (inches)[a, b]		
	Panel span ≤ 4 feet	4 feet < panel span ≤ 6 feet	6 feet < panel span ≤ 8 feet
No. 8 wood-screw-based anchor with 2-inch embedment length	16	10	8
No. 10 wood-screw-based anchor with 2-inch embedment length	16	12	9
$^1/_4$-inch lag-screw-based anchor with 2-inch embedment length	16	16	16

For SI: 1 inch = 25.4 mm, 1 foot = 304.8 mm, 1 pound = 4.448 N, 1 mile per hour = 0.447 m/s.

a. This table is based on 180 mph ultimate design wind speeds, V_{ult}, and a 45-foot mean roof height.

b. Fasteners shall be installed at opposing ends of the wood structural panel. Fasteners shall be located not less than 1 inch from the edge of the panel.

c. Anchors shall penetrate through the exterior wall covering with an embedment length of not less than 2 inches into the building frame. Fasteners shall be located not less than $2^1/_2$ inches from the edge of concrete block or concrete.

d. Panels attached to masonry or masonry/stucco shall be attached using vibration-resistant anchors having an ultimate withdrawal capacity of not less than 1,500 pounds.

R301.2.1.3 Wind speed conversion. Where referenced documents are based on nominal design wind speeds and do not provide the means for conversion between ultimate design wind speeds and nominal design wind speeds, the ultimate design wind speeds, V_{ult}, of Figure R301.2(5)A shall be converted to nominal design wind speeds, V_{asd}, using Table R301.2.1.3.

R301.2.1.4 Exposure category. For each wind direction considered, an exposure category that adequately reflects the characteristics of ground surface irregularities shall be determined for the site at which the building or structure is to be constructed. For a site located in the transition zone between categories, the category resulting in the largest wind forces shall apply. Account shall be taken of variations in ground surface roughness that arise from natural topography and vegetation as well as from constructed features. For a site where multiple detached one- and two-family *dwellings*, *townhouses* or other structures are to be constructed as part of a subdivision or master-planned community, or are otherwise designated as a developed area by the authority having jurisdiction, the exposure category for an individual structure shall be based on the site conditions that will exist at the time when all adjacent structures on the site have been constructed, provided that their construction is expected to begin within 1 year of the start of construction for the structure for which the exposure category is determined. For any given wind direction, the exposure in which a specific building or other structure is sited shall be assessed as being one of the following categories:

1. Exposure B. Urban and suburban areas, wooded areas or other terrain with numerous closely spaced obstructions having the size of single-family *dwellings* or larger. Exposure B shall be assumed unless the site meets the definition of another type exposure.

2. Exposure C. Open terrain with scattered obstructions, including surface undulations or other irregularities, having heights generally less than 30 feet (9144 mm) extending more than 1,500 feet (457 m) from the building site in any quadrant. This exposure shall apply to any building located within Exposure B type terrain where the building is directly adjacent to open areas of Exposure C type terrain in any quadrant for a distance of more than 600 feet (183 m). This category includes flat, open country and grasslands.

3. Exposure D. Flat, unobstructed areas exposed to wind flowing over open water, smooth mud flats, salt flats and unbroken ice for a distance of not less than 5,000 feet (1524 m). This exposure shall apply only to those buildings and other structures exposed to the wind coming from over the unobstructed area. Exposure D extends downwind from the edge of the unobstructed area a distance of 600 feet (183 m) or 20 times the height of the building or structure, whichever is greater.

TABLE R301.2(1)
CLIMATIC AND GEOGRAPHIC DESIGN CRITERIA

ROOF SNOW LOAD[f]	WIND DESIGN		SEISMIC DESIGN CATEGORY[l]	SUBJECT TO DAMAGE FROM			WINTER DESIGN TEMP[e]	ICE BARRIER UNDERLAYMENT REQUIRED[h]	FLOOD HAZARDS[g]	AIR FREEZING INDEX[i]	MEAN ANNUAL TEMP[j]
	Speed[d] (mph)	Topographic effects[k]		Weathering[a]	Frost line depth[b]	Termite[c]					
$p_f = 0.7 * p_g$	115	Yes	A	Severe	See MR part 1303.1600	See Footnote "c"	See MR Chapter 1322	Yes	See MR Chapter 1335	See Table R403.3(2)	See Footnote "j"

For SI: 1 pound per square foot = 0.0479 kPa, 1 mile per hour = 0.447 m/s.

a. Weathering may require a higher strength concrete or grade of masonry than necessary to satisfy the structural requirements of this code. The weathering column shall be filled in with the weathering index, "negligible," "moderate," or "severe," for concrete as determined from the Weathering Probability Map Figure R301.2(4). The grade of masonry units shall be determined from ASTM C34, C55, C62, C73, C90, C129, C145, C216 or C652.

b. See Minnesota Rules, part 1303.1600, Footing Depth for Frost Protection, to verify whether the county requires Zone I or Zone II frost protection.

c. The jurisdiction shall fill in this part of the table to indicate the need for protection depending on whether there has been a history of local subterranean termite damage.

d. See wind speed map Figure R301.2(5)A. Wind exposure category shall be determined on a site-specific basis in accordance with Section R301.2.1.4.

e. See Minnesota Rules, Chapter 1322, Climate Data Design Conditions, to verify by city.

f. The ground snow loads to be used in determining the design snow loads for buildings and other structures are given in Minnesota Rules, part 1303.1700, Ground Snow Load to verify by county. The roof snow load is a uniform load on the horizontal projection of the roof.

g. See Minnesota Rules, Chapter 1335, Flood Proofing Regulations.

h. In accordance with Sections R905.1.2, R905.2.7, R905.4.3.1, R905.5.3.1, R905.6.3.1, R905.7.3.1 and R905.8.3.1, where there has been a history of local damage from the effects of ice damming.

i. The jurisdiction shall fill in this part of the table with the 100-year return period air freezing index (BF-days) from Figure R403.3(2) or from the 100-year (99 percent) value on the National Climatic Data Center data table "Air Freezing Index-USA Method (Base 32°F)" at www.ncdc.noaa.gov.sites/default/files/attachments/Air-Freezing-Index-Return-Periods-and-Associated-Probabilities.pdf.

j. The jurisdiction shall fill in this part of the table with the mean annual temperature from the National Climatic Data Center data table "Average Mean Temperature Index" at www.ncdc.noaa.gov.sites/default/files/attachments/Air-Freezing-Index-Return-Periods-and-Associated-Probabilities.pdf.

k. In accordance with Section R301.2.1.5.

l. Assigned to allow the application of the least restrictive topographic provisions of the code.

TABLE R301.2(2)
COMPONENT AND CLADDING LOADS FOR A BUILDING WITH A MEAN ROOF HEIGHT OF 30 FEET LOCATED IN EXPOSURE B (ASD) (psf)[a, b, c, d, e]

	ZONE	EFFECTIVE WIND AREA (feet²)	ULTIMATE DESIGN WIND SPEED, V_{ULT} (mph)															
			110		115		120		130		140		150		160		170		180	
Roof 0 to 7 degrees	1	10	10.0	-13.0	10.0	-14.0	10.0	-15.0	10.0	-18.0	10.0	-21.0	9.9	-24.0	11.2	-27.0	12.6	-31.0	14.2	-35.0
	1	20	10.0	-12.0	10.0	-13.0	10.0	-15.0	10.0	-17.0	10.0	-20.0	9.2	-23.0	10.6	-26.0	11.9	-30.0	13.3	-34.1
	1	50	10.0	-12.0	10.0	-13.0	10.0	-14.0	10.0	-17.0	10.0	-19.0	8.5	-22.0	10.0	-26.0	10.8	-29.0	12.2	-32.9
	1	100	10.0	-11.0	10.0	-13.0	10.0	-14.0	10.0	-16.0	10.0	-19.0	7.8	-22.0	10.0	-25.0	10.0	-28.0	11.3	-32.0
	2	10	10.0	-21.0	10.0	-23.0	10.0	-26.0	10.0	-30.0	10.0	-35.0	9.9	-40.0	11.2	-46.0	12.6	-52.0	14.2	-58.7
	2	20	10.0	-19.0	10.0	-21.0	10.0	-23.0	10.0	-27.0	10.0	-31.0	9.2	-36.0	10.6	-41.0	11.9	-46.0	13.3	-52.4
	2	50	10.0	-16.0	10.0	-18.0	10.0	-19.0	10.0	-23.0	10.0	-26.0	8.5	-30.0	10.0	-34.0	10.8	-39.0	12.2	-44.1
	2	100	10.0	-14.0	10.0	-15.0	10.0	-16.0	10.0	-19.0	10.0	-22.0	7.8	-26.0	10.0	-30.0	10.0	-33.0	11.3	-37.9
	3	10	10.0	-33.0	10.0	-36.0	10.0	-39.0	10.0	-46.0	10.0	-53.0	9.9	-61.0	11.2	-69.0	12.6	-78.0	14.2	-88.3
	3	20	10.0	-27.0	10.0	-29.0	10.0	-32.0	10.0	-38.0	10.0	-44.0	9.2	-50.0	10.6	-57.0	11.9	-65.0	13.3	-73.1
	3	50	10.0	-19.0	10.0	-21.0	10.0	-23.0	10.0	-27.0	10.0	-32.0	8.5	-36.0	10.0	-41.0	10.8	-47.0	12.2	-53.1
	3	100	10.0	-14.0	10.0	-15.0	10.0	-16.0	10.0	-19.0	10.0	-22.0	7.8	-26.0	10.0	-30.0	10.0	-33.0	11.3	-37.9
Roof > 7 to 27 degrees	1	10	10.0	-11.0	10.0	-13.0	10.0	-14.0	10.5	-16.0	12.2	-19.0	14.0	-22.0	15.9	-25.0	17.9	-28.0	20.2	-32.0
	1	20	10.0	-11.0	10.0	-12.0	10.0	-13.0	10.0	-16.0	11.1	-18.0	12.8	-21.0	14.5	-24.0	16.4	-27.0	18.4	-31.1
	1	50	10.0	-11.0	10.0	-12.0	10.0	-13.0	10.0	-15.0	10.0	-18.0	11.1	-20.0	12.7	-23.0	14.3	-26.0	16.0	-29.9
	1	100	10.0	-10.0	10.0	-11.0	10.0	-12.0	10.0	-15.0	10.0	-17.0	9.9	-20.0	11.2	-22.0	12.6	-25.0	14.2	-29.0
	2	10	10.0	-20.0	10.0	-22.0	10.0	-24.0	10.5	-29.0	12.2	-33.0	14.0	-38.0	15.9	-44.0	17.9	-49.0	20.2	-55.8
	2	20	10.0	-19.0	10.0	-20.0	10.0	-22.0	10.0	-26.0	11.1	-31.0	12.8	-35.0	14.5	-40.0	16.4	-45.0	18.4	-51.2
	2	50	10.0	-16.0	10.0	-18.0	10.0	-20.0	10.0	-23.0	10.0	-27.0	11.1	-31.0	12.7	-35.0	14.3	-40.0	16.0	-45.4
	2	100	10.0	-15.0	10.0	-16.0	10.0	-18.0	10.0	-21.0	10.0	-24.0	9.9	-28.0	11.2	-32.0	12.6	-36.0	14.2	-40.9
	3	10	10.0	-30.0	10.0	-33.0	10.0	-36.0	10.5	-43.0	12.2	-49.0	14.0	-57.0	15.9	-65.0	17.9	-73.0	20.2	-82.4
	3	20	10.0	-28.0	10.0	-31.0	10.0	-34.0	10.0	-40.0	11.1	-46.0	12.8	-53.0	14.5	-60.0	16.4	-68.0	18.4	-77.0
	3	50	10.0	-26.0	10.0	-28.0	10.0	-31.0	10.0	-36.0	10.0	-42.0	11.1	-48.0	12.7	-55.0	14.3	-62.0	16.0	-69.9
	3	100	10.0	-24.0	10.0	-26.0	10.0	-28.0	10.0	-33.0	10.0	-39.0	9.9	-44.0	11.2	-51.0	12.6	-57.0	14.2	-64.6
Roof > 27 to 45 degrees	1	10	11.9	-13.0	13.1	-14.0	14.2	-15.0	16.7	-18.0	19.4	-21.0	22.2	-24.0	25.3	-27.0	28.5	-31.0	32.0	-35.0
	1	20	11.6	-12.0	12.7	-13.0	13.8	-14.0	16.2	-17.0	18.8	-20.0	21.6	-23.0	24.6	-26.0	27.7	-29.0	31.1	-33.2
	1	50	11.2	-11.0	12.2	-12.0	13.3	-13.0	15.6	-16.0	18.1	-18.0	20.8	-21.0	23.6	-24.0	26.7	-27.0	29.9	-30.8
	1	100	10.9	-10.0	11.9	-11.0	12.9	-12.0	15.1	-15.0	17.6	-17.0	20.2	-20.0	22.9	-22.0	25.9	-25.0	29.0	-29.0
	2	10	11.9	-15.0	13.1	-16.0	14.2	-18.0	16.7	-21.0	19.4	-24.0	22.2	-28.0	25.3	-32.0	28.5	-36.0	32.0	-40.9
	2	20	11.6	-14.0	12.7	-16.0	13.8	-17.0	16.2	-20.0	18.8	-23.0	21.6	-27.0	24.6	-30.0	27.7	-34.0	31.1	-39.1
	2	50	11.2	-13.0	12.2	-15.0	13.3	-16.0	15.6	-19.0	18.1	-22.0	20.8	-25.0	23.6	-29.0	26.7	-32.0	29.9	-36.8
	2	100	10.9	-13.0	11.9	-14.0	12.9	-15.0	15.1	-18.0	17.6	-21.0	20.2	-24.0	22.9	-27.0	25.9	-31.0	29.0	-35.0
	3	10	11.9	-15.0	13.1	-16.0	14.2	-18.0	16.7	-21.0	19.4	-24.0	22.2	-28.0	25.3	-32.0	28.5	-36.0	32.0	-40.9
	3	20	11.6	-14.0	12.7	-16.0	13.8	-17.0	16.2	-20.0	18.8	-23.0	21.6	-27.0	24.6	-30.0	27.7	-34.0	31.1	-39.1
	3	50	11.2	-13.0	12.2	-15.0	13.3	-16.0	15.6	-19.0	18.1	-22.0	20.8	-25.0	23.6	-29.0	26.7	-32.0	29.9	-36.8
	3	100	10.9	-13.0	11.9	-14.0	12.9	-15.0	15.1	-18.0	17.6	-21.0	20.2	-24.0	22.9	-27.0	25.9	-31.0	29.0	-35.0
Wall	4	10	13.1	-14.0	14.3	-15.0	15.5	-16.0	18.2	-19.0	21.2	-22.0	24.3	-26.0	27.7	-30.0	31.2	-33.0	35.0	-37.9
	4	20	12.5	-13.0	13.6	-14.0	14.8	-16.0	17.4	-19.0	20.2	-22.0	23.2	-25.0	26.4	-28.0	29.7	-32.0	33.4	-36.4
	4	50	11.7	-12.0	12.8	-14.0	13.9	-15.0	16.3	-17.0	19.0	-20.0	21.7	-23.0	24.7	-27.0	27.9	-30.0	31.3	-34.3
	4	100	11.1	-12.0	12.1	-13.0	13.2	-14.0	15.5	-17.0	18.0	-19.0	20.6	-22.0	23.5	-25.0	26.5	-29.0	29.8	32.7
	4	500	10.0	-10.0	10.6	-11.0	11.6	-12.0	13.6	-15.0	15.8	-17.0	18.1	-20.0	20.6	-22.0	23.2	-25.0	26.1	-29.0
	5	10	13.1	-17.0	14.3	-19.0	15.5	-20.0	18.2	-24.0	21.2	-28.0	24.3	-32.0	27.7	-37.0	31.2	-41.0	35.0	-46.8
	5	20	12.5	-16.0	13.6	-17.0	14.8	-19.0	17.4	-22.0	20.2	-26.0	23.2	-30.0	26.4	-34.0	29.7	-39.0	33.4	-43.7
	5	50	11.7	-14.0	12.8	-16.0	13.9	-17.0	16.3	-20.0	19.0	-23.0	21.7	-27.0	24.7	-31.0	27.9	-35.0	31.3	-39.5
	5	100	11.1	-13.0	12.1	-14.0	13.2	-16.0	15.5	-19.0	18.0	-22.0	20.6	-25.0	23.5	-28.0	26.5	-32.0	29.8	-36.4
	5	500	10.0	-10.0	10.6	-11.0	11.6	-12.0	13.6	-15.0	15.8	-17.0	18.1	-20.0	20.6	-22.0	23.2	-25.0	26.1	-29.0

For SI: 1 foot = 304.8 mm, 1 square foot = 0.0929 m², 1 mile per hour = 0.447 m/s, 1 pound per square foot = 0.0479 kPa.

a. The effective wind area shall be equal to the span length multiplied by an effective width. This width shall be permitted to be not less than one-third the span length. For cladding fasteners, the effective wind area shall not be greater than the area that is tributary to an individual fastener.

b. For effective areas between those given, the load shall be interpolated or the load associated with the lower effective area shall be used.

c. Table values shall be adjusted for height and exposure by multiplying by the adjustment coefficient in Table R301.2(3).

d. See Figure R301.2(8) for location of zones.

e. Plus and minus signs signify pressures acting toward and away from the building surfaces.

TABLE R301.2(3)
HEIGHT AND EXPOSURE ADJUSTMENT COEFFICIENTS FOR TABLE R301.2(2)

MEAN ROOF HEIGHT	EXPOSURE		
	B	C	D
15	1.00	1.21	1.47
20	1.00	1.29	1.55
25	1.00	1.35	1.61
30	1.00	1.40	1.66
35	1.05	1.45	1.70
40	1.09	1.49	1.74
45	1.12	1.53	1.78
50	1.16	1.56	1.81
55	1.19	1.59	1.84
60	1.22	1.62	1.87

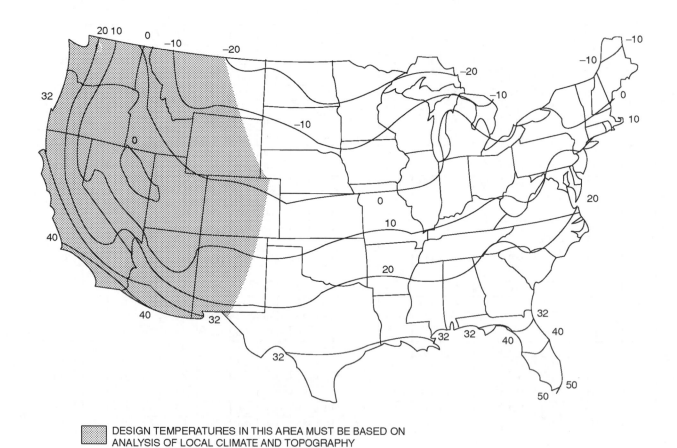

DESIGN TEMPERATURES IN THIS AREA MUST BE BASED ON ANALYSIS OF LOCAL CLIMATE AND TOPOGRAPHY

For SI: °C = [(°F)-32]/1.8.

FIGURE R301.2(1)
ISOLINES OF THE 97$^{1}/_{2}$-PERCENT WINTER (DECEMBER, JANUARY AND FEBRUARY) DESIGN TEMPERATURES (°F)

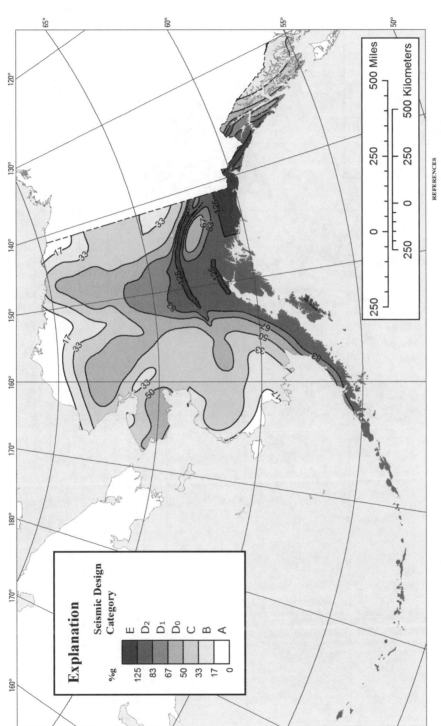

Map prepared by U.S. Geological Survey in collaboration with the Federal Emergency Management Agency (FEMA) funded Building Seismic Safety Council's (BSSC) Code Resource Support Committee (CRSC).

REFERENCES

Building Seismic Safety Council, 2015, NEHRP Recommended Seismic Provisions for New Buildings and Other Structures: FEMA P-1050, Federal Emergency Management Agency, Washington, DC.

Huang, Yin-Nan, Whittaker, A.S., and Luco, Nicolas, 2008, Maximum spectral demands in the near-fault region, Earthquake Spectra Volume 24, Issue 1, pp. 319-341.

Luco, Nicolas, Ellingwood, B.R., Hamburger, R.O., Hooper, J.D., Kimball, J.K., and Kircher, C.A., 2007, Risk-Targeted versus Current Seismic Design Maps for the Conterminous United States, Structural Engineers Association of California 2007 Convention Proceedings, pp. 163-175.

Wesson, Robert L., Boyd, Oliver S., Mueller, Charles S., Bufe, Charles G., Frankel, Arthur D., Petersen, Mark D., 2007, Revision of time-independent probabilistic seismic hazard maps for Alaska: U.S. Geological Survey Open-File Report 2007-1043.

FIGURE R301.2(2)
SEISMIC DESIGN CATEGORIES

(continued)

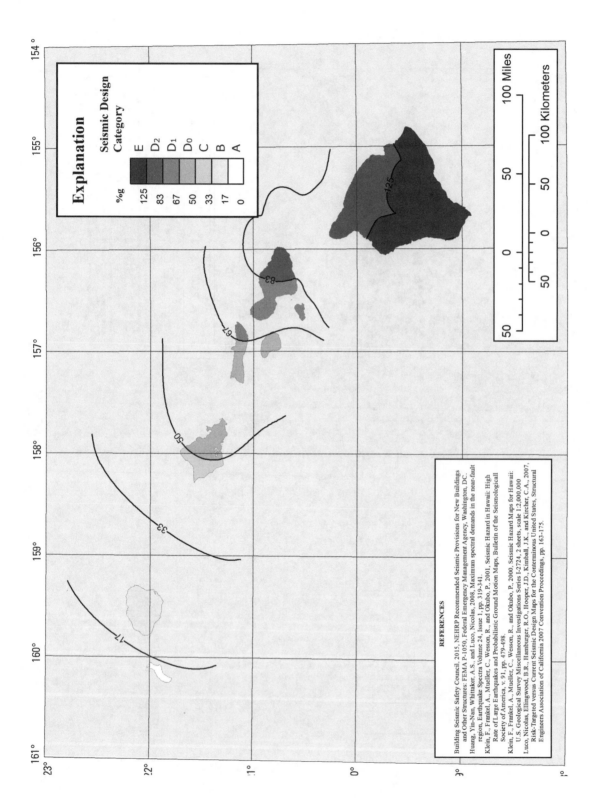

REFERENCES

Building Seismic Safety Council, 2015, NEHRP Recommended Seismic Provisions for New Buildings and Other Structures: FEMA P-1050, Federal Emergency Management Agency, Washington, DC.

Huang, Yin-Nan, Whittaker, A.S., and Luco, Nicolas, 2008, Maximum spectral demands in the near-fault region, Earthquake Spectra Volume 24, Issue 1, pp. 319-341.

Klein, F., Frankel, A., Mueller, C., Wesson, R., and Okubo, P., 2001, Seismic Hazard in Hawaii: High Rate of Large Earthquakes and Probabilistic Ground Motion Maps, Bulletin of the Seismologicall Society of America, v. 91, pp. 479-498.

Klein, F. Frankel, A., Mueller, C., Wesson, R., and Okubo, P., 2000, Seismic Hazard Maps for Hawaii: U. S. Geological Survey Miscellaneous Investigations Series I-2724, 2 sheets, scale 1:2,000,000

Luco, Nicolas, Ellingwood, B.R., Hamburger, R.O., Hooper, J.D., Kimball, J.K., and Kircher, C.A., 2007, Risk-Targeted versus Current Seismic Design Maps for the Conterminous United States, Structural Engineers Association of California 2007 Convention Proceedings, pp. 163-175.

FIGURE R301.2(2)—continued
SEISMIC DESIGN CATEGORIES

(continued)

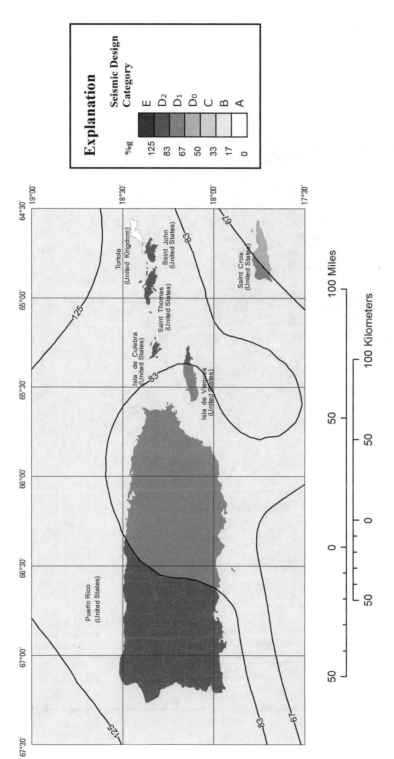

Explanation

Seismic Design Category

%g	
125	E
83	D₂
67	D₁
50	D₀
33	C
17	B
0	A

100 Miles

100 Kilometers

REFERENCES

Building Seismic Safety Council, 2015, NEHRP Recommended Seismic Provisions for New Buildings and Other Structures: FEMA P-1050, Federal Emergency Management Agency, Washington, DC.

Huang, Yin-Nan, Whittaker, A.S., and Luco, Nicolas, 2008, Maximum spectral demands in the near-fault region, Earthquake Spectra Volume 24, Issue 1, pp. 319-341.

Luco, Nicolas, Ellingwood, B.R., Hamburger, R.O., Hooper, J.D., Kimball, J.K., and Kircher, C.A., 2007, Risk-Targeted versus Current Seismic Design Maps for the Conterminous United States, Structural Engineers Association of California 2007 Convention Proceedings, pp. 163-175.

Mueller, C., Frankel, A., Petersen, M., and Leyendecker, E., 2003, Documentation for 2003 USGS Seismic Hazard Maps for Puerto Rico and the U.S. Virgin Islands, U.S. Geological Survey Open-File Report 03-379.

Map prepared by U.S. Geological Survey in collaboration with the Federal Emergency Management Agency (FEMA)-funded Building Seismic Safety Council's (BSSC) Code Resource Support Committee (CRSC).

FIGURE R301.2(2)—continued
SEISMIC DESIGN CATEGORIES

(continued)

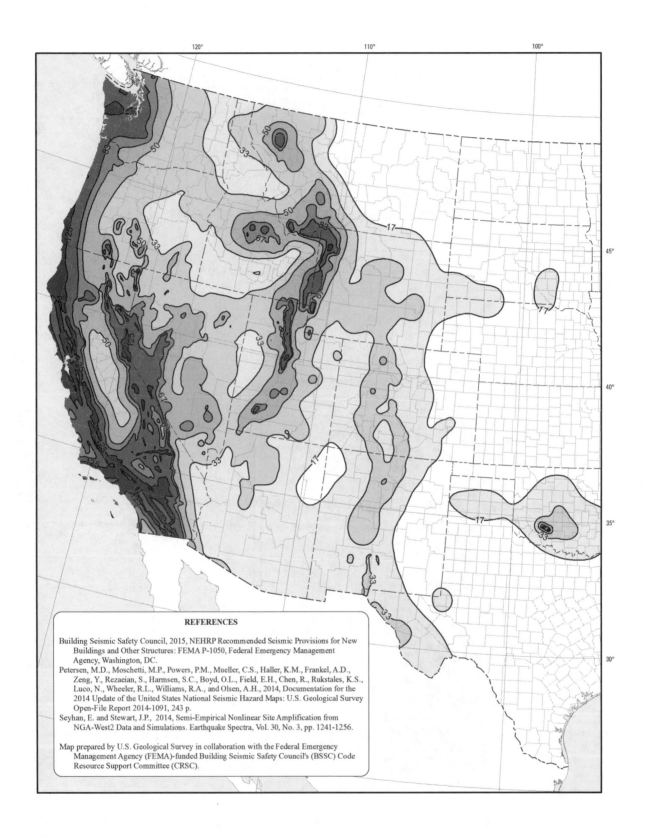

REFERENCES

Building Seismic Safety Council, 2015, NEHRP Recommended Seismic Provisions for New
    Buildings and Other Structures: FEMA P-1050, Federal Emergency Management
    Agency, Washington, DC.
Petersen, M.D., Moschetti, M.P., Powers, P.M., Mueller, C.S., Haller, K.M., Frankel, A.D.,
    Zeng, Y., Rezaeian, S., Harmsen, S.C., Boyd, O.L., Field, E.H., Chen, R., Rukstales, K.S.,
    Luco, N., Wheeler, R.L., Williams, R.A., and Olsen, A.H., 2014, Documentation for the
    2014 Update of the United States National Seismic Hazard Maps: U.S. Geological Survey
    Open-File Report 2014-1091, 243 p.
Seyhan, E. and Stewart, J.P., 2014, Semi-Empirical Nonlinear Site Amplification from
    NGA-West2 Data and Simulations. Earthquake Spectra, Vol. 30, No. 3, pp. 1241-1256.

Map prepared by U.S. Geological Survey in collaboration with the Federal Emergency
    Management Agency (FEMA)-funded Building Seismic Safety Council's (BSSC) Code
    Resource Support Committee (CRSC).

**FIGURE R301.2(2)—continued
SEISMIC DESIGN CATEGORIES**

(continued)

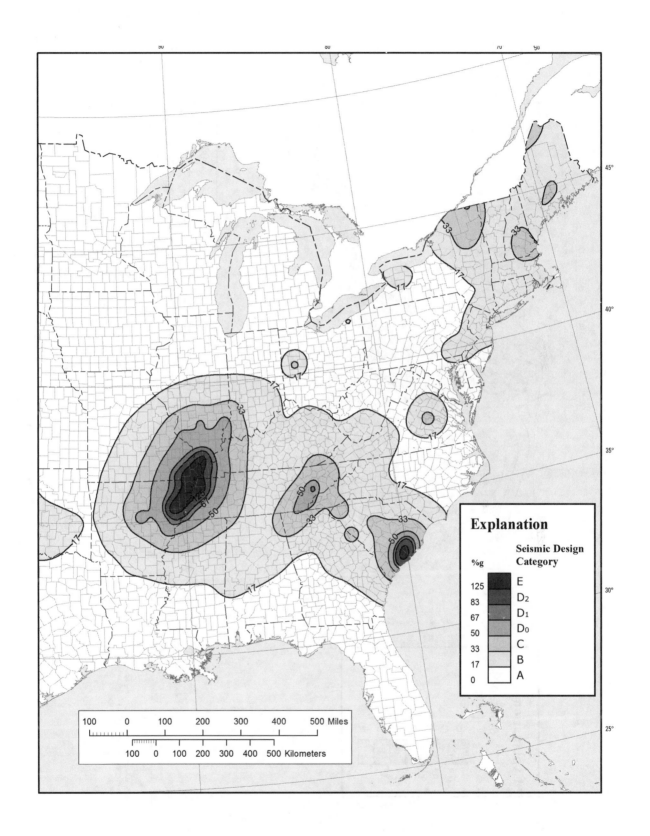

**FIGURE R301.2(2)—continued
SEISMIC DESIGN CATEGORIES**

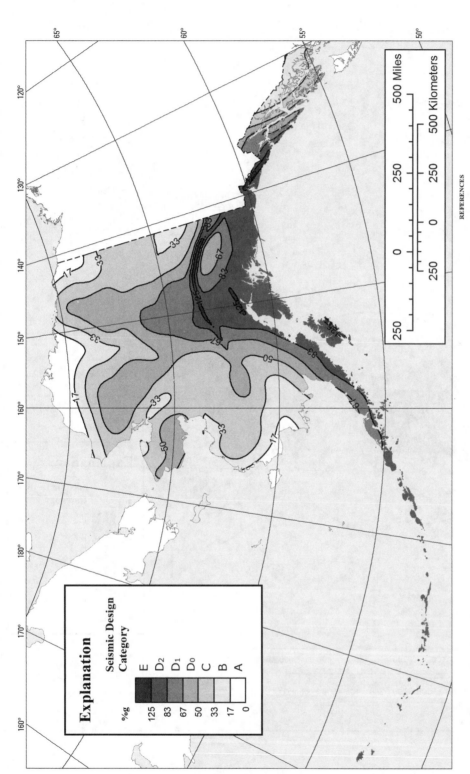

Map prepared by U.S. Geological Survey in collaboration with the Federal Emergency Management Agency (FEMA)-funded Building Seismic Safety Council's (BSSC) Code Resource Support Committee (CRSC).

REFERENCES

Building Seismic Safety Council, 2015, NEHRP Recommended Seismic Provisions for New Buildings and Other Structures: FEMA P-1050, Federal Emergency Management Agency, Washington, DC.

Huang, Yin-Nan, Whitaker, A.S., and Luco, Nicolas, 2008, Maximum spectral demands in the near-fault region, Earthquake Spectra Volume 24, Issue 1, pp. 319-341.

Luco, Nicolas, Ellingwood, B.R., Hamburger, R.O., Hooper, J.D., Kimball, J.K., and Kircher, C.A., 2007, Risk-Targeted versus Current Seismic Design Maps for the Conterminous United States, Structural Engineers Association of California 2007 Convention Proceedings, pp. 163-175.

Wesson, Robert L., Boyd, Oliver S., Mueller, Charles S., Bufe, Charles G., Frankel, Arthur D., Petersen, Mark D., 2007, Revision of time-independent probabilistic seismic hazard maps for Alaska: U.S. Geological Survey Open-File Report 2007-1043.

FIGURE R301.2(3)
ALTERNATE SEISMIC DESIGN CATEGORIES

(continued)

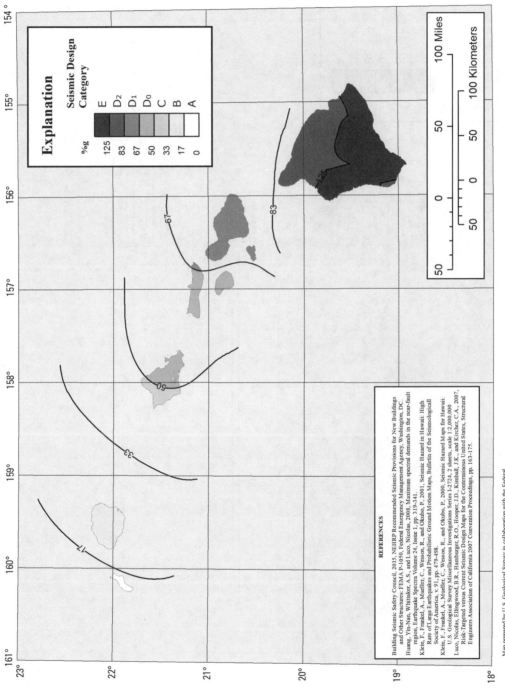

REFERENCES

Building Seismic Safety Council, 2015, NEHRP Recommended Seismic Provisions for New Buildings and Other Structures: FEMA P-1050, Federal Emergency Management Agency, Washington, DC.

Huang, Yin-Nan, Whitaker, A.S., and Luco, Nicolas, 2008, Maximum spectral demands in the near-fault region, Earthquake Spectra Volume 24, Issue 1, pp. 319-341.

Klein, F., Frankel, A., Mueller, C., Wesson, R., and Okubo, P., 2001, Seismic Hazard in Hawaii: High Rate of Large Earthquakes and Probabilistic Ground Motion Maps, Bulletin of the Seismologicall Society of America, v. 91, pp. 479-498.

Klein, F., Frankel, A., Mueller, C., Wesson, R., and Okubo, P., 2000, Seismic Hazard Maps for Hawaii: U.S. Geological Survey Miscellaneous Investigations Series I-2724, 2 sheets, scale 1:2,000,000

Luco, Nicolas, Ellingwood, B.R., Hamburger, R.O., Hooper, J.D., Kimball, J.K., and Kircher, C.A., 2007, Risk-Targeted versus Current Seismic Design Maps for the Conterminous United States, Structural Engineers Association of California 2007 Convention Proceedings, pp. 163-175.

Map prepared by U.S. Geological Survey in collaboration with the Federal Emergency Management Agency (FEMA)-funded Building Seismic Safety Council's (BSSC) Code Resource Support Committee (CRSC).

FIGURE R301.2(3)—continued
ALTERNATE SEISMIC DESIGN CATEGORIES

(continued)

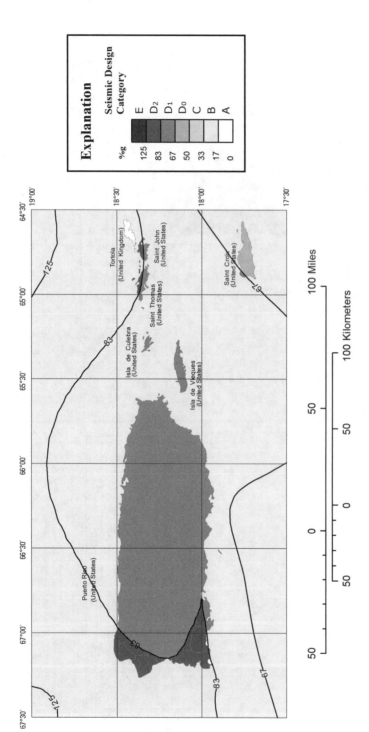

Explanation

Seismic Design Category

%g	
125	E
83	D₂
67	D₁
50	D₀
33	C
17	B
0	A

REFERENCES

Building Seismic Safety Council, 2015, NEHRP Recommended Seismic Provisions for New Buildings and Other Structures: FEMA P-1050, Federal Emergency Management Agency, Washington, DC.

Huang, Yin-Nan, Whittaker, A.S., and Luco, Nicolas, 2008, Maximum spectral demands in the near-fault region, Earthquake Spectra Volume 24, Issue 1, pp. 319-341.

Luco, Nicolas, Ellingwood, B.R., Hamburger, R.O., Hooper, J.D., Kimball, J.K., and Kircher, C.A., 2007, Risk-Targeted versus Current Seismic Design Maps for the Conterminous United States, Structural Engineers Association of California 2007 Convention Proceedings, pp. 163-175.

Mueller, C., Frankel, A., Petersen, M., and Leyendecker, E. 2003, Documentation for 2003 USGS Seismic Hazard Maps for Puerto Rico and the U.S. Virgin Islands, U.S. Geological Survey Open-File Report 03-379.

Map prepared by U.S. Geological Survey in collaboration with the Federal Emergency Management Agency (FEMA)-funded Building Seismic Safety Council's (BSSC) Code Resource Support Committee (CRSC).

FIGURE R301.2(3)—continued
ALTERNATE SEISMIC DESIGN CATEGORIES

(continued)

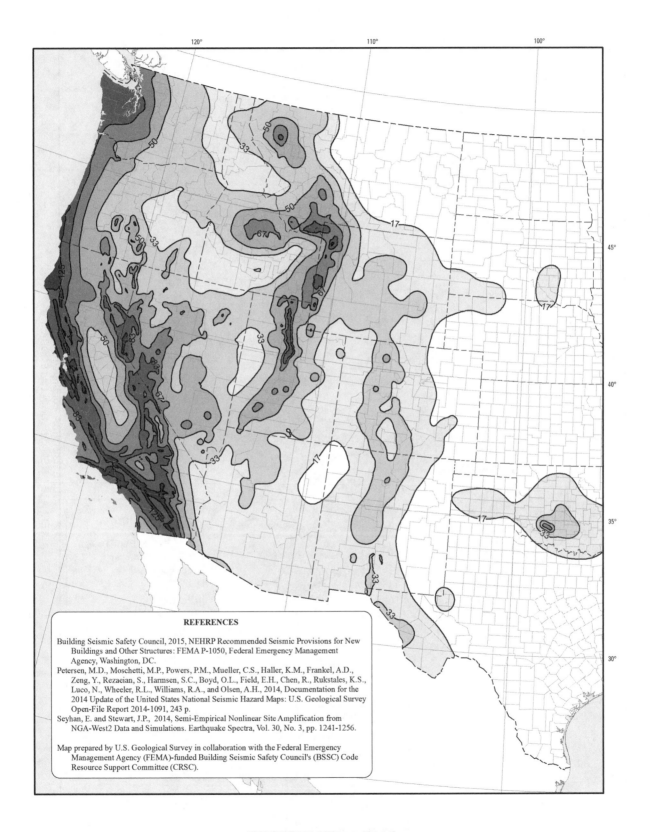

REFERENCES

Building Seismic Safety Council, 2015, NEHRP Recommended Seismic Provisions for New
  Buildings and Other Structures: FEMA P-1050, Federal Emergency Management
  Agency, Washington, DC.
Petersen, M.D., Moschetti, M.P., Powers, P.M., Mueller, C.S., Haller, K.M., Frankel, A.D.,
  Zeng, Y., Rezaeian, S., Harmsen, S.C., Boyd, O.L., Field, E.H., Chen, R., Rukstales, K.S.,
  Luco, N., Wheeler, R.L., Williams, R.A., and Olsen, A.H., 2014, Documentation for the
  2014 Update of the United States National Seismic Hazard Maps: U.S. Geological Survey
  Open-File Report 2014-1091, 243 p.
Seyhan, E. and Stewart, J.P., 2014, Semi-Empirical Nonlinear Site Amplification from
  NGA-West2 Data and Simulations. Earthquake Spectra, Vol. 30, No. 3, pp. 1241-1256.

Map prepared by U.S. Geological Survey in collaboration with the Federal Emergency
  Management Agency (FEMA)-funded Building Seismic Safety Council's (BSSC) Code
  Resource Support Committee (CRSC).

FIGURE R301.2(3)—continued
ALTERNATE SEISMIC DESIGN CATEGORIES

(continued)

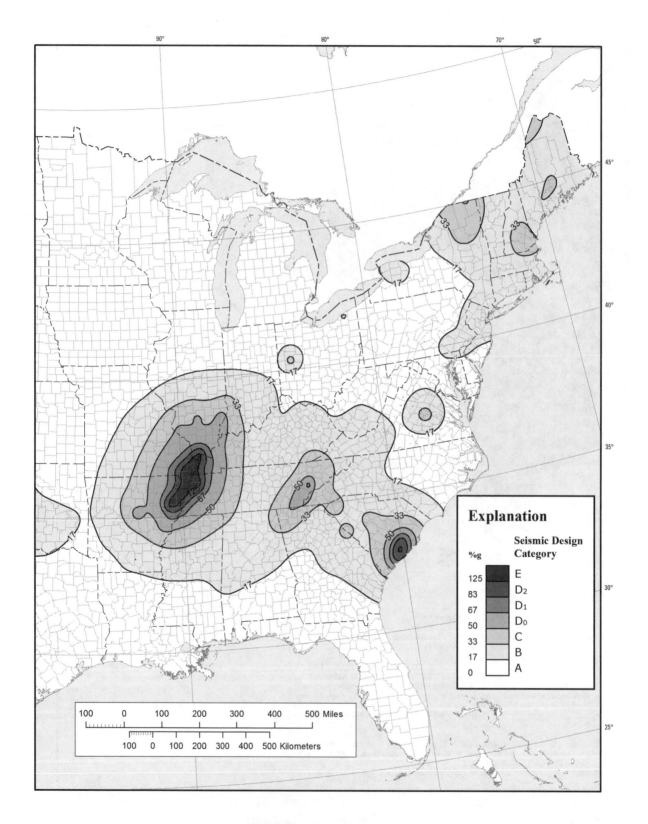

FIGURE R301.2(3)—continued
ALTERNATE SEISMIC DESIGN CATEGORIES

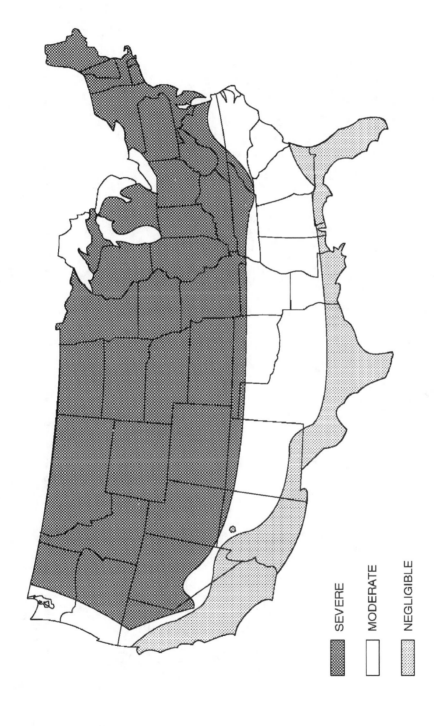

SEVERE

MODERATE

NEGLIGIBLE

FIGURE R301.2(4)
WEATHERING PROBABILITY MAP FOR CONCRETE[a, b]

a. Alaska and Hawaii are classified as severe and negligible, respectively.
b. Lines defining areas are approximate only. Local conditions may be more or less severe than indicated by region classification. A severe classification is where weather conditions result in significant snowfall combined with extended periods during which there is little or no natural thawing causing deicing salts to be used extensively.

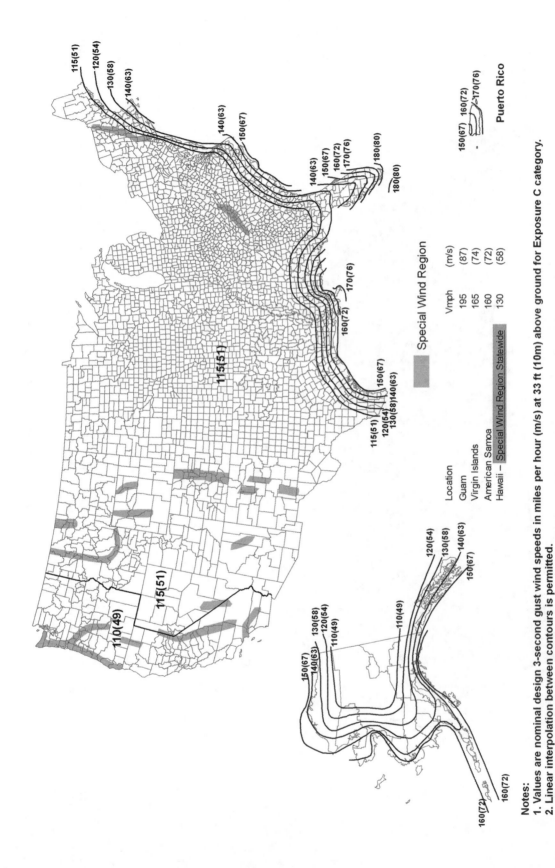

Location	Vmph	(m/s)
Guam	195	(87)
Virgin Islands	165	(74)
American Samoa	160	(72)
Hawaii – Special Wind Region Statewide	130	(58)

Special Wind Region

FIGURE R301.2(5)A
ULTIMATE DESIGN WIND SPEEDS

Notes:
1. Values are nominal design 3-second gust wind speeds in miles per hour (m/s) at 33 ft (10m) above ground for Exposure C category.
2. Linear interpolation between contours is permitted.
3. Islands and coastal areas outside the last contour shall use the last wind speed contour of the coastal area.
4. Mountainous terrain, gorges, ocean promontories, and special wind regions shall be examined for unusual wind conditions.
5. Wind speeds correspond to approximately a 7% probability of exceedance in 50 years (Annual Exceedance Probability = 0.00143, MRI = 700 Years).

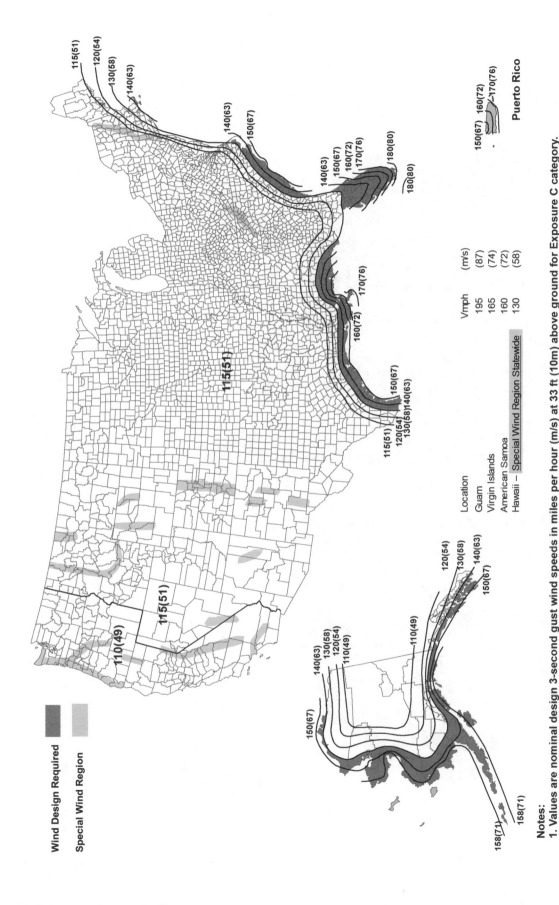

Notes:

1. Values are nominal design 3-second gust wind speeds in miles per hour (m/s) at 33 ft (10m) above ground for Exposure C category.
2. Linear interpolation between contours is permitted.
3. Islands and coastal areas outside the last contour shall use the last wind speed contour of the coastal area.
4. Mountainous terrain, gorges, ocean promontories, and special wind regions shall be examined for unusual wind conditions.
5. Wind speeds correspond to approximately a 7% probability of exceedance in 50 years (Annual Exceedance Probability = 0.00143, MRI = 700 Years).

Location	Vmph	(m/s)
Guam	195	(87)
Virgin Islands	165	(74)
American Samoa	160	(72)
Hawaii – Special Wind Region Statewide	130	(58)

FIGURE R301.2(5)B
REGIONS WHERE WIND DESIGN IS REQUIRED

Wind Design Required

Special Wind Region

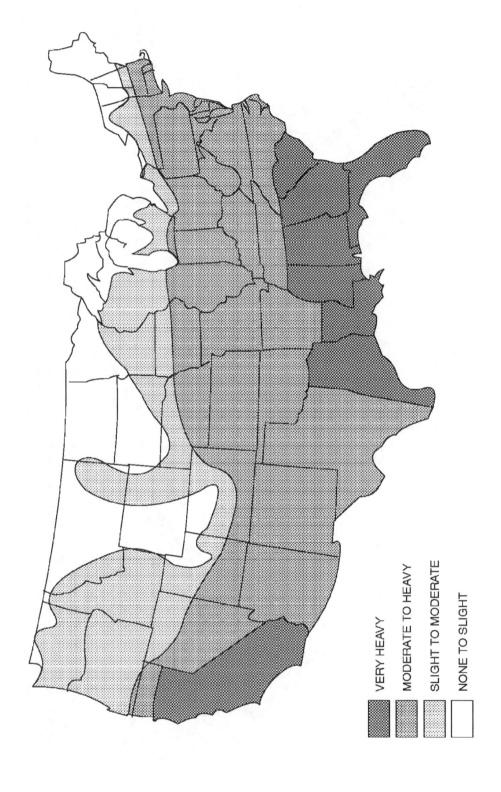

VERY HEAVY

MODERATE TO HEAVY

SLIGHT TO MODERATE

NONE TO SLIGHT

Note: Lines defining areas are approximate only. Local conditions may be more or less severe than indicated by the region classification.

FIGURE R301.2(7)
TERMITE INFESTATION PROBABILITY MAP

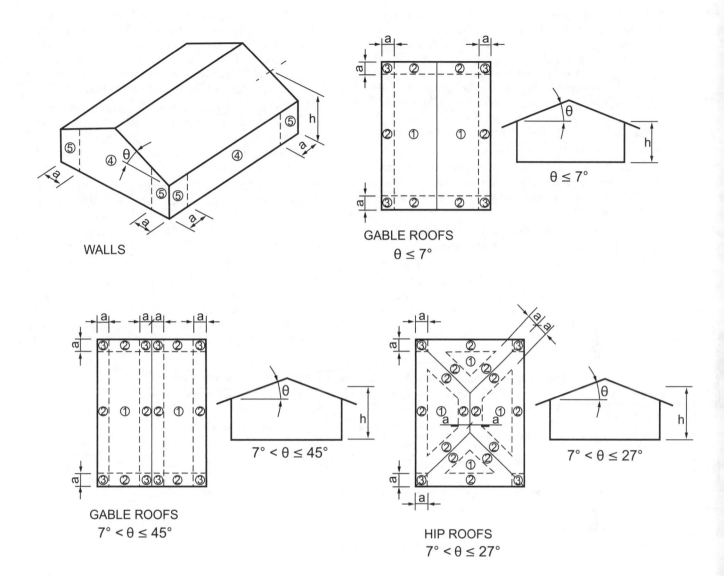

For SI: 1 foot = 304.8 mm, 1 degree = 0.0175 rad.
Note: a = 4 feet in all cases.

FIGURE R301.2(8)
COMPONENT AND CLADDING PRESSURE ZONES

TABLE R301.2.1.3
WIND SPEED CONVERSIONS[a]

V_{ult}	110	115	120	130	140	150	160	170	180	190	200
V_{asd}	85	89	93	101	108	116	124	132	139	147	155

For SI: 1 mile per hour = 0.447 m/s.
a. Linear interpolation is permitted.

R301.2.1.5 Topographic wind effects. In areas designated in Table R301.2(1) as having local historical data documenting structural damage to buildings caused by wind speed-up at isolated hills, ridges and escarpments that are abrupt changes from the general topography of the area, topographic wind effects shall be considered in the design of the building in accordance with Section R301.2.1.5.1 or in accordance with the provisions of ASCE 7. See Figure R301.2.1.5.1(1) for topographic features for wind speed-up effect.

In these designated areas, topographic wind effects shall apply only to buildings sited on the top half of an isolated hill, ridge or escarpment where all of the following conditions exist:

1. The average slope of the top half of the hill, ridge or escarpment is 10 percent or greater.

2. The hill, ridge or escarpment is 60 feet (18 288 mm) or greater in height for Exposure B, 30 feet (9144 mm) or greater in height for Exposure C, and 15 feet (4572 mm) or greater in height for Exposure D.

3. The hill, ridge or escarpment is isolated or unobstructed by other topographic features of similar height in the upwind direction for a distance measured from its high point of 100 times its height or 2 miles (3.2 km), whichever is less. See Figure R301.2.1.5.1(3) for upwind obstruction.

4. The hill, ridge or escarpment protrudes by a factor of two or more above the height of other upwind topographic features located in any quadrant within a radius of 2 miles (3.2 km) measured from its high point.

R301.2.1.5.1 Simplified topographic wind speed-up method. As an alternative to the ASCE 7 topographic wind provisions, the provisions of Section R301.2.1.5.1 shall be permitted to be used to design for wind speed-up effects, where required by Section R301.2.1.5.

Structures located on the top half of isolated hills, ridges or escarpments meeting the conditions of Section R301.2.1.5 shall be designed for an increased basic wind speed as determined by Table R301.2.1.5.1. On the high side of an escarpment, the

TABLE R301.2.1.5.1
ULTIMATE DESIGN WIND SPEED MODIFICATION FOR TOPOGRAPHIC WIND EFFECT[a, b]

ULTIMATE DESIGN WIND SPEED FROM FIGURE R301.2(5)A (mph)	AVERAGE SLOPE OF THE TOP HALF OF HILL, RIDGE OR ESCARPMENT (percent)						
	0.10	0.125	0.15	0.175	0.20	0.23	0.25
	Required ultimate design wind speed-up, modified for topographic wind speed-up (mph)						
110	132	137	142	147	152	158	162
115	138	143	148	154	159	165	169
120	144	149	155	160	166	172	176
130	156	162	168	174	179	NA	NA
140	168	174	181	NA	NA	NA	NA
150	180	NA	NA	NA	NA	NA	NA

For SI: 1 mile per hour = 0.447 m/s, 1 foot = 304.8 mm.

NA = Not Applicable.

a. Table applies to a feature height of 500 feet or less and dwellings sited a distance equal or greater than half the feature height.

b. Where the ultimate design wind speed as modified by Table R301.2.1.5.1 equals or exceeds 140 miles per hour, the building shall be considered as "wind design required" in accordance with Section R301.2.1.1.

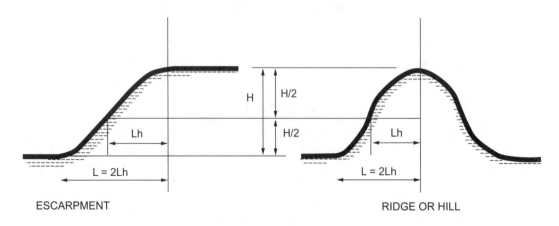

ESCARPMENT

RIDGE OR HILL

Note: H/2 determines the measurement point for Lh. L is twice Lh.

FIGURE R301.2.1.5.1(1)
TOPOGRAPHIC FEATURES FOR WIND SPEED-UP EFFECT

increased basic wind speed shall extend horizontally downwind from the edge of the escarpment 1.5 times the horizontal length of the upwind slope (1.5L) or 6 times the height of the escarpment (6H), whichever is greater. See Figure R301.2.1.5.1(2) for where wind speed increase is applied.

R301.2.2 Seismic provisions. Buildings in Seismic Design Categories C, D_0, D_1, and D_2 shall be constructed in accordance with the requirements of this section and other seismic requirements of this code. The seismic provisions of this code shall apply as follows:

1. *Townhouses* in Seismic Design Categories C, D_0, D_1 and D_2.

2. Detached one- and two-family *dwellings* in Seismic Design Categories, D_0, D_1 and D_2.

Buildings in Seismic Design Category E shall be designed to resist seismic loads in accordance with the *International Building Code*, except where the seismic design category is reclassified to a lower seismic design category in accordance with Section R301.2.2.1. Compo-

nents of buildings not required to be designed to resist seismic loads shall be constructed in accordance with the provisions of this code.

R301.2.2.1 Determination of seismic design category. Buildings shall be assigned a seismic design category in accordance with Figure R301.2(2).

R301.2.2.1.1 Alternate determination of seismic design category. The seismic design categories and corresponding short-period design spectral response accelerations, S_{DS}, shown in Figure R301.2(2), are based on soil Site Class D, used as an assumed default, as defined in Section 1613.2.2 of the *International Building Code*. If soil conditions are determined by the building official to be Site Class A, B, or D, the seismic design category and short-period design spectral response accelerations, S_{DS}, for a site shall be allowed to be determined in accordance with Figure R301.2(3), or Section 1613.2 of the *International Building Code*. The value of S_{DS} determined in accordance with Section 1613.2 of the *International*

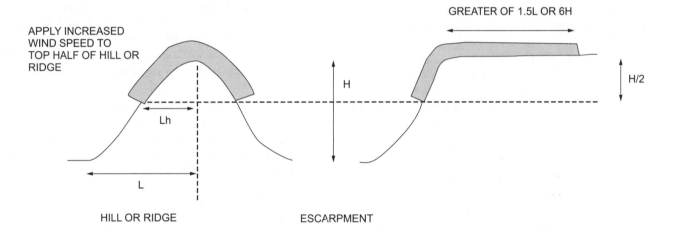

FIGURE R301.2.1.5.1(2)
ILLUSTRATION OF WHERE ON A TOPOGRAPHIC FEATURE, WIND SPEED INCREASE IS APPLIED

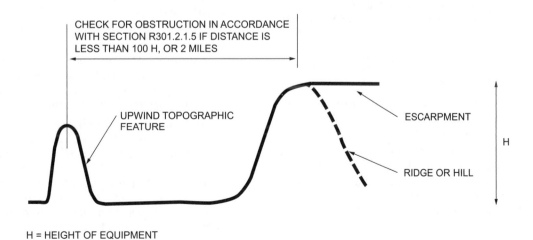

FIGURE R301.2.1.5.1(3)
UPWIND OBSTRUCTION

Building Code is permitted to be used to set the seismic design category in accordance with Table R301.2.2.1.1, and to interpolate between values in Tables R602.10.3(3), R603.9.2(1) and other seismic design requirements of this code.

TABLE R301.2.2.1.1
SEISMIC DESIGN CATEGORY DETERMINATION

CALCULATED S_{DS}	SEISMIC DESIGN CATEGORY
$S_{DS} \leq 0.17g$	A
$0.17g < S_{DS} \leq 0.33g$	B
$0.33g < S_{DS} \leq 0.50g$	C
$0.50g < S_{DS} \leq 0.67g$	D_0
$0.67g < S_{DS} \leq 0.83g$	D_1
$0.83g < S_{DS} \leq 1.25g$	D_2
$1.25g < S_{DS}$	E

R301.2.2.1.2 Alternative determination of Seismic Design Category E. Buildings located in Seismic Design Category E in accordance with Figure R301.2(2), or Figure R301.2(3) where applicable, are permitted to be reclassified as being in Seismic Design Category D_2 provided that one of the following is done:

1. A more detailed evaluation of the seismic design category is made in accordance with the provisions and maps of the *International Building Code*. Buildings located in Seismic Design Category E in accordance with Table R301.2.2.1.1, but located in Seismic Design Category D in accordance with the *International Building Code*, shall be permitted to be designed using the Seismic Design Category D_2 requirements of this code.

2. Buildings located in Seismic Design Category E that conform to the following additional restrictions are permitted to be constructed in accordance with the provisions for Seismic Design Category D_2 of this code:

   2.1. All exterior shear wall lines or *braced wall panels* are in one plane vertically from the foundation to the uppermost *story*.

   2.2. Floors shall not cantilever past the *exterior walls*.

   2.3. The building is within the requirements of Section R301.2.2.2.6 for being considered as regular.

R301.2.2.2 Weights of materials. Average dead loads shall not exceed 15 pounds per square foot (720 Pa) for the combined roof and ceiling assemblies (on a horizontal projection) or 10 pounds per square foot (480 Pa) for floor assemblies, except as further limited by

Section R301.2.2. Dead loads for walls above *grade* shall not exceed:

1. Fifteen pounds per square foot (720 Pa) for exterior light-frame wood walls.

2. Fourteen pounds per square foot (670 Pa) for exterior light-frame cold-formed steel walls.

3. Ten pounds per square foot (480 Pa) for interior light-frame wood walls.

4. Five pounds per square foot (240 Pa) for interior light-frame cold-formed steel walls.

5. Eighty pounds per square foot (3830 Pa) for 8-inch-thick (203 mm) masonry walls.

6. Eighty-five pounds per square foot (4070 Pa) for 6-inch-thick (152 mm) concrete walls.

7. Ten pounds per square foot (480 Pa) for SIP walls.

Exceptions:

1. Roof and ceiling dead loads not exceeding 25 pounds per square foot (1190 Pa) shall be permitted provided that the wall bracing amounts in Section R602.10.3 are increased in accordance with Table R602.10.3(4).

2. Light-frame walls with stone or masonry veneer shall be permitted in accordance with the provisions of Sections R702.1 and R703.

3. Fireplaces and chimneys shall be permitted in accordance with Chapter 10.

R301.2.2.3 Stone and masonry veneer. Anchored stone and masonry veneer shall comply with the requirements of Sections R702.1 and R703.

R301.2.2.4 Masonry construction. Masonry construction in Seismic Design Categories D_0 and D_1 shall comply with the requirements of Section R606.12.1. Masonry construction in Seismic Design Category D_2 shall comply with the requirements of Section R606.12.4.

R301.2.2.5 Concrete construction. Buildings with exterior above-*grade* concrete walls shall comply with PCA 100 or shall be designed in accordance with ACI 318.

Exception: Detached one- and two-family dwellings in Seismic Design Category C with exterior above-grade concrete walls are allowed to comply with the requirements of Section R608.

R301.2.2.6 Irregular buildings. The seismic provisions of this code shall not be used for structures, or portions thereof, located in Seismic Design Categories C, D_0, D_1 and D_2 and considered to be irregular in accordance with this section. A building or portion of a building shall be considered to be irregular where one or more of the conditions defined in Items 1 through 7 occur. Irregular structures, or irregular portions of structures, shall be designed in accordance with accepted engineering practice to the extent the irregular features affect the performance of the remaining structural system. Where the forces associated with the irregularity are resisted by a structural system designed in accordance with accepted engineering practice, the remainder of the building shall be permitted to be designed using the provisions of this code.

1. **Shear wall or braced wall offsets out of plane.** Conditions where exterior shear wall lines or *braced wall panels* are not in one plane vertically from the foundation to the uppermost story in which they are required.

   Exception: For wood light-frame construction, floors with cantilevers or setbacks not exceeding four times the nominal depth of the wood floor joists are permitted to support *braced wall panels* that are out of plane with *braced wall panels* below provided that all of the following are satisfied:

   1. Floor joists are nominal 2 inches by 10 inches (51 mm by 254 mm) or larger and spaced not more than 16 inches (406 mm) on center.

   2. The ratio of the back span to the cantilever is not less than 2 to 1.

   3. Floor joists at ends of *braced wall panels* are doubled.

   4. For wood-frame construction, a continuous rim joist is connected to ends of cantilever joists. Where spliced, the rim joists shall be spliced using a galvanized metal tie not less than 0.058 inch (1.5 mm) (16 gage) and $1^1/_2$ inches (38 mm) wide fastened with six 16d nails on each side of the splice; or a block of the same size as the rim joist and of sufficient length to fit securely between the joist space at which the splice occurs, fastened with eight 16d nails on each side of the splice.

   5. Gravity loads carried at the end of cantilevered joists are limited to uniform wall and roof loads and the reactions from headers having a span of 8 feet (2438 mm) or less.

2. **Lateral support of roofs and floors.** Conditions where a section of floor or roof is not laterally supported by shear walls or *braced wall lines* on all edges.

   Exception: Portions of floors that do not support shear walls, braced wall panels above, or roofs shall be permitted to extend not more than 6 feet (1829 mm) beyond a shear wall or *braced wall line*.

3. **Shear wall or braced wall offsets in plane.** Conditions where the end of a *braced wall panel* occurs over an opening in the wall below and extends more than 1 foot (305 mm) horizontally past the edge of the opening. This provision is applicable to shear walls and braced wall panels offset in plane and to braced wall panels offset out of plane in accordance with the exception to Item 1.

   Exception: For wood light-frame wall construction, one end of a *braced wall panel* shall be permitted to extend more than 1 foot (305 mm) over an opening not more than 8 feet (2438 mm) in width in the wall below provided that the opening includes a header in accordance with all of the following:

   1. The building width, loading condition and framing member species limitations of Table R602.7(1) shall apply.

   2. The header is composed of:

      2.1. Not less than one 2 × 12 or two 2 × 10 for an opening not more than 4 feet (1219 mm) wide.

      2.2. Not less than two 2 × 12 or three 2 × 10 for an opening not more than 6 feet (1829 mm) in width.

      2.3. Not less than three 2 × 12 or four 2 × 10 for an opening not more than 8 feet (2438 mm) in width.

   3. The entire length of the *braced wall panel* does not occur over an opening in the wall below.

4. **Floor and roof opening.** Conditions where an opening in a floor or roof exceeds the lesser of 12 feet (3658 mm) or 50 percent of the least floor or roof dimension.

5. **Floor level offset.** Conditions where portions of a floor level are vertically offset.

   Exceptions:

   1. Framing supported directly by continuous foundations at the perimeter of the building.

   2. For wood light-frame construction, floors shall be permitted to be vertically offset where the floor framing is lapped or tied together as required by Section R502.6.1.

6. **Perpendicular shear wall and wall bracing.** Conditions where shear walls and *braced wall lines* do not occur in two perpendicular directions.

7. **Wall bracing in stories containing masonry or concrete construction.** Conditions where stories above *grade plane* are partially or completely braced by wood wall framing in accordance with Section R602 or cold-formed steel wall framing in accordance with Section R603 include masonry or concrete construction. Where this irregularity applies, the entire story shall be

designed in accordance with accepted engineering practice.

> **Exceptions:** Fireplaces, chimneys and masonry veneer in accordance with this code.

R301.2.2.7 Height limitations. Wood-framed buildings shall be limited to three stories above *grade plane* or the limits given in Table R602.10.3(3). Cold-formed steel-framed buildings shall be limited to less than or equal to three stories above *grade plane* in accordance with AISI S230. Mezzanines as defined in Section R202 that comply with Section R325 shall not be considered as stories. Structural insulated panel buildings shall be limited to two stories above *grade plane*.

R301.2.2.8 Cold-formed steel framing in Seismic Design Categories D₀, D₁ and D₂. In Seismic Design Categories D_0, D_1 and D_2 in addition to the requirements of this code, cold-formed steel framing shall comply with the requirements of AISI S230.

R301.2.2.9 Masonry chimneys. In Seismic Design Categories D_0, D_1 and D_2, masonry chimneys shall be reinforced and anchored to the building in accordance with Sections R1003.3 and R1003.4.

R301.2.2.10 Anchorage of water heaters. In Seismic Design Categories D_0, D1 and D_2, water heaters shall be anchored against movement and overturning in accordance with Section M1307.2.

R301.2.3 Snow loads. Wood-framed construction, cold-formed, steel-framed construction and masonry and concrete construction, and structural insulated panel construction in regions with ground snow loads 70 pounds per square foot (3.35 kPa) or less, shall be in accordance with Chapters 5, 6 and 8. Buildings in regions with ground snow loads greater than 70 pounds per square foot (3.35 kPa) shall be designed in accordance with accepted engineering practice.

R301.2.4 Floodplain construction. Buildings and structures constructed in whole or in part in flood hazard areas (including A or V Zones) as established in Table R301.2(1), and substantial improvement and *repair* of substantial damage of buildings and structures in flood hazard areas, shall be designed and constructed in accordance with Section R322. Buildings and structures that are located in more than one flood hazard area shall comply with the provisions associated with the most restrictive flood hazard area. Buildings and structures located in whole or in part in identified floodways shall be designed and constructed in accordance with ASCE 24.

R301.2.4.1 Alternative provisions. As an alternative to the requirements in Section R322, ASCE 24 is permitted subject to the limitations of this code and the limitations therein.

R301.3 Story height. The wind and seismic provisions of this code shall apply to buildings with *story heights* not exceeding the following:

1. For wood wall framing, the *story height* shall not exceed 11 feet 7 inches (3531 mm) and the laterally unsupported bearing wall stud height permitted by Table R602.3(5).

2. For cold-formed steel wall framing, the *story height* shall be not more than 11 feet 7 inches (3531 mm) and the unsupported bearing wall stud height shall be not more than 10 feet (3048 mm).

3. For masonry walls, the *story height* shall be not more than 13 feet 7 inches (4140 mm) and the bearing wall clear height shall be not more than 12 feet (3658 mm).

> **Exception:** An additional 8 feet (2438 mm) of bearing wall clear height is permitted for gable end walls.

4. For insulating concrete form walls, the maximum story height shall not exceed 11 feet 7 inches (3531 mm) and the maximum unsupported wall height per *story* as permitted by Section R608 tables shall not exceed 10 feet (3048 mm).

5. For structural insulated panel (SIP) walls, the story height shall be not more than 11 feet 7 inches (3531 mm) and the bearing wall height per *story* as permitted by Section R610 tables shall not exceed 10 feet (3048 mm).

Individual walls or wall studs shall be permitted to exceed these limits as permitted by Chapter 6 provisions, provided that *story heights* are not exceeded. An engineered design shall be provided for the wall or wall framing members where the limits of Chapter 6 are exceeded. Where the *story height* limits of this section are exceeded, the design of the building, or the noncompliant portions thereof, to resist wind and seismic loads shall be in accordance with the *International Building Code*.

R301.4 Dead load. The actual weights of materials and construction shall be used for determining dead load with consideration for the dead load of fixed service *equipment*.

R301.5 Live load. The minimum uniformly distributed live load shall be as provided in Table R301.5.

TABLE R301.5
MINIMUM UNIFORMLY DISTRIBUTED LIVE LOADS
(in pounds per square foot)

USE	LIVE LOAD
Uninhabitable attics without storage[b]	10
Uninhabitable attics with limited storage[b, g]	20
Habitable attics and attics served with fixed stairs	30
Balconies (exterior) and decks[e]	40
Fire escapes	40
Guards and handrails[d]	200[h]
Guard in-fill components[f]	50[h]
Passenger vehicle garages[a]	50[a]
Rooms other than sleeping rooms	40
Sleeping rooms	30
Stairs	40[c]

For SI: 1 pound per square foot = 0.0479 kPa, 1 square inch = 645 mm², 1 pound = 4.45 N.

a. Elevated garage floors shall be capable of supporting a 2,000-pound load applied over a 20-square-inch area.

(continued)

TABLE R301.5—continued
MINIMUM UNIFORMLY DISTRIBUTED LIVE LOADS
(in pounds per square foot)

b. Uninhabitable attics without storage are those where the clear height between joists and rafters is not more than 42 inches, or where there are not two or more adjacent trusses with web configurations capable of accommodating an assumed rectangle 42 inches in height by 24 inches in width, or greater, within the plane of the trusses. This live load need not be assumed to act concurrently with any other live load requirements.

c. Individual stair treads shall be designed for the uniformly distributed live load or a 300-pound concentrated load acting over an area of 4 square inches, whichever produces the greater stresses.

d. A single concentrated load applied in any direction at any point along the top.

e. See Section R507.1 for decks attached to exterior walls.

f. Guard in-fill components (all those except the handrail), balusters and panel fillers shall be designed to withstand a horizontally applied normal load of 50 pounds on an area equal to 1 square foot. This load need not be assumed to act concurrently with any other live load requirement.

g. Uninhabitable attics with limited storage are those where the clear height between joists and rafters is 42 inches or greater, or where there are two or more adjacent trusses with web configurations capable of accommodating an assumed rectangle 42 inches in height by 24 inches in width, or greater, within the plane of the trusses.

The live load need only be applied to those portions of the joists or truss bottom chords where all of the following conditions are met:

1. The attic area is accessed from an opening not less than 20 inches in width by 30 inches in length that is located where the clear height in the attic is not less than 30 inches.

2. The slopes of the joists or truss bottom chords are not greater than 2 inches vertical to 12 units horizontal.

3. Required insulation depth is less than the joist or truss bottom chord member depth.

The remaining portions of the joists or truss bottom chords shall be designed for a uniformly distributed concurrent live load of not less than 10 pounds per square foot.

h. Glazing used in handrail assemblies and guards shall be designed with a safety factor of 4. The safety factor shall be applied to each of the concentrated loads applied to the top of the rail, and to the load on the in-fill components. These loads shall be determined independent of one another, and loads are assumed not to occur with any other live load.

R301.6 Roof load. The roof shall be designed for the live load indicated in Table R301.6 or the snow load indicated in Table R301.2(1), whichever is greater.

TABLE R301.6
MINIMUM ROOF LIVE LOADS IN POUNDS-FORCE PER SQUARE FOOT OF HORIZONTAL PROJECTION

ROOF SLOPE	TRIBUTARY LOADED AREA IN SQUARE FEET FOR ANY STRUCTURAL MEMBER		
	0 to 200	201 to 600	Over 600
Flat or rise less than 4 inches per foot (1:3)	20	16	12
Rise 4 inches per foot (1:3) to less than 12 inches per foot (1:1)	16	14	12
Rise 12 inches per foot (1:1) and greater	12	12	12

For SI: 1 square foot = 0.0929 m², 1 pound per square foot = 0.0479 kPa, 1 inch per foot = 83.3 mm/m.

R301.7 Deflection. The allowable deflection of any structural member under the live load listed in Sections R301.5 and R301.6 or wind loads determined by Section R301.2.1 shall not exceed the values in Table R301.7.

R301.8 Nominal sizes. For the purposes of this code, dimensions of lumber specified shall be deemed to be nominal dimensions unless specifically designated as actual dimensions.

SECTION R302
FIRE-RESISTANT CONSTRUCTION

R302.1 Exterior walls. Construction, projections, openings and penetrations of *exterior walls* of *dwellings* and accessory buildings shall comply with Table R302.1(1); or *dwellings* equipped throughout with an *automatic sprinkler system* installed in accordance with Section P2904 shall comply with Table R302.1(2).

Exceptions:

1. Walls, projections, openings or penetrations in walls perpendicular to the line used to determine the *fire separation distance*.

2. Walls of *individual dwelling units* and their *accessory structures* located on the same *lot*.

3. Detached tool sheds and storage sheds, playhouses and similar structures exempted from permits are not required to provide wall protection based on location on the *lot*. Projections beyond the *exterior wall* shall not extend over the *lot line*.

4. Detached garages accessory to a *dwelling* located within 2 feet (610 mm) of a *lot line* are permitted to

TABLE R301.7
ALLOWABLE DEFLECTION OF STRUCTURAL MEMBERS[b, c]

STRUCTURAL MEMBER	ALLOWABLE DEFLECTION
Rafters having slopes greater than 3:12 with finished ceiling not attached to rafters	$L/180$
Interior walls and partitions	$H/180$
Floors	$L/360$
Ceilings with brittle finishes (including plaster and stucco)	$L/360$
Ceilings with flexible finishes (including gypsum board)	$L/240$
All other structural members	$L/240$
Exterior walls—wind loads[a] with plaster or stucco finish	$H/360$
Exterior walls—wind loads[a] with other brittle finishes	$H/240$
Exterior walls—wind loads[a] with flexible finishes	$H/120$[d]
Lintels supporting masonry veneer walls[e]	$L/600$

Note: L = span length, H = span height.

a. For the purpose of the determining deflection limits herein, the wind load shall be permitted to be taken as 0.7 times the component and cladding (ASD) loads obtained from Table R301.2(2).

b. For cantilever members, L shall be taken as twice the length of the cantilever.

c. For aluminum structural members or panels used in roofs or walls of sunroom additions or patio covers, not supporting edge of glass or sandwich panels, the total load deflection shall not exceed $L/60$. For continuous aluminum structural members supporting edge of glass, the total load deflection shall not exceed $L/175$ for each glass lite or $L/60$ for the entire length of the member, whichever is more stringent. For sandwich panels used in roofs or walls of sunroom additions or patio covers, the total load deflection shall not exceed $L/120$.

d. Deflection for exterior walls with interior gypsum board finish shall be limited to an allowable deflection of $H/180$.

e. Refer to Section R703.8.2.

have roof eave projections not exceeding 4 inches (102 mm).

5. Foundation vents installed in compliance with this code are permitted.

R302.2 Townhouses. Walls separating townhouse units shall be constructed in accordance with Section R302.2.1 or R302.2.2.

R302.2.1 Double walls. Each townhouse shall be separated by two 1-hour fire-resistance-rated wall assemblies tested in accordance with ASTM E119, UL 263 or Section 703.3 of the *International Building Code*.

R302.2.2 Common walls. Common walls separating *townhouses* shall be assigned a fire-resistance rating in accordance with Item 1 or 2. The common wall shared by

TABLE R302.1(1)
EXTERIOR WALLS

EXTERIOR WALL ELEMENT		MINIMUM FIRE-RESISTANCE RATING	MINIMUM FIRE SEPARATION DISTANCE
Walls	Fire-resistance rated	1 hour—tested in accordance with ASTM E119, UL 263, or Section 703.3 of the *International Building Code* with exposure from both sides	0 feet
	Not fire-resistance rated	0 hours	≥ 5 feet
Projections	Not allowed	NA	< 2 feet
	Fire-resistance rated	1 hour on the underside, or heavy timber, or fire-retardant-treated wood[a, b, c]	≥ 2 feet to < 5 feet
	Not fire-resistance rated	0 hours	≥ 5 feet
Openings in walls	Not allowed	NA	< 3 feet
	25% maximum of wall area	0 hours	3 feet
	Unlimited	0 hours	5 feet
Penetrations	All	Comply with Section R302.4	< 3 feet
		None required	3 feet

For SI: 1 foot = 304.8 mm.

NA = Not Applicable.

a. The fire-resistance rating shall be permitted to be reduced to 0 hours on the underside of the eave overhang if fireblocking is provided from the wall top plate to the underside of the roof sheathing.

b. The fire-resistance rating shall be permitted to be reduced to 0 hours on the underside of the rake overhang where gable vent openings are not installed.

c. One hour on the underside equates to one layer of $^5/_8$-inch type X gypsum sheathing. Openings are not allowed.

TABLE R302.1(2)
EXTERIOR WALLS—DWELLINGS WITH FIRE SPRINKLERS

EXTERIOR WALL ELEMENT		MINIMUM FIRE-RESISTANCE RATING	MINIMUM FIRE SEPARATION DISTANCE
Walls	Fire-resistance rated	1 hour—tested in accordance with ASTM E119, UL 263, or Section 703.3 of the *International Building Code* with exposure from the outside	0 feet
	Not fire-resistance rated	0 hours	3 feet[a]
Projections	Not allowed	NA	< 2 feet
	Fire-resistance rated	1 hour on the underside, or heavy timber, or fire-retardant-treated wood[b, c, d]	2 feet[a]
	Not fire-resistance rated	0 hours	3 feet
Openings in walls	Not allowed	NA	< 3 feet
	Unlimited	0 hours	3 feet[a]
Penetrations	All	Comply with Section R302.4	< 3 feet
		None required	3 feet[a]

For SI: 1 foot = 304.8 mm.

NA = Not Applicable.

a. For residential subdivisions where all dwellings are equipped throughout with an automatic sprinkler system installed in accordance with Section P2904, the fire separation distance for exterior walls not fire-resistance rated and for fire-resistance-rated projections shall be permitted to be reduced to 0 feet, and unlimited unprotected openings and penetrations shall be permitted, where the adjoining lot provides an open setback yard that is 6 feet or more in width on the opposite side of the property line.

b. The fire-resistance rating shall be permitted to be reduced to 0 hours on the underside of the eave overhang if fireblocking is provided from the wall top plate to the underside of the roof sheathing.

c. The fire-resistance rating shall be permitted to be reduced to 0 hours on the underside of the rake overhang where gable vent openings are not installed.

d. One hour on the underside equates to one layer of $^5/_8$-inch type X gypsum sheathing. Openings are not allowed.

two *townhouses* shall be constructed without plumbing or mechanical equipment, ducts or vents in the cavity of the common wall. The wall shall be rated for fire exposure from both sides and shall extend to and be tight against exterior walls and the underside of the roof sheathing. Electrical installations shall be in accordance with Chapters 34 through 43. Penetrations of the membrane of common walls for electrical outlet boxes shall be in accordance with Section R302.4.

1. Where a fire sprinkler system in accordance with Section P2904 is provided, the common wall shall be not less than a 1-hour fire-resistance-rated wall assembly tested in accordance with ASTM E119, UL 263 or Section 703.3 of the *International Building Code*.

2. Where a fire sprinkler system in accordance with Section P2904 is not provided, the common wall shall be not less than a 2-hour fire-resistance-rated wall assembly tested in accordance with ASTM E119, UL 263 or Section 703.3 of the *International Building Code*.

R302.2.3 Continuity. The fire-resistance-rated wall or assembly separating *townhouses* shall be continuous from the foundation to the underside of the roof sheathing, roof deck, or roof slab. The fire-resistance rating shall extend the full length of the wall or assembly, including wall extensions through and separating attached enclosed *accessory structures*. The separation shall extend through enclosed soffits, overhangs, and similar projections.

R302.2.4 Parapets for townhouses. Parapets constructed in accordance with Section R302.2.5 shall be constructed for *townhouses* as an extension of exterior walls or common walls in accordance with the following:

1. Where roof surfaces adjacent to the wall or walls are at the same elevation, the parapet shall extend not less than 30 inches (762 mm) above the roof surfaces.

2. Where roof surfaces adjacent to the wall or walls are at different elevations and the higher roof is not more than 30 inches (762 mm) above the lower roof, the parapet shall extend not less than 30 inches (762 mm) above the lower roof surface.

   Exception: A parapet is not required in the preceding two cases where the roof covering complies with a minimum Class C rating as tested in accordance with ASTM E108 or UL 790 and the roof decking or sheathing is of noncombustible materials or fire-retardant-treated wood for a distance of 4 feet (1219 mm) on each side of the wall or walls, or one layer of $^5/_8$-inch (15.9 mm) Type X gypsum board is installed directly beneath the roof decking or sheathing, supported by not less than nominal 2-inch (51 mm) ledgers attached to the sides of the roof framing members, for a distance of not less than 4 feet (1219 mm) on each side of the wall or walls and any openings or penetrations in the roof are not within 4 feet (1219 mm) of the common walls. Fire-retardant-treated wood shall meet the requirements of Sections R802.1.5 and R803.2.1.2.

3. A parapet is not required where roof surfaces adjacent to the wall or walls are at different elevations and the higher roof is more than 30 inches (762 mm) above the lower roof. The common wall construction from the lower roof to the underside of the higher roof deck shall have not less than a 1-hour fire-resistance rating. The wall shall be rated for exposure from both sides.

R302.2.5 Parapet construction. Parapets shall have the same fire-resistance rating as that required for the supporting wall or walls. On any side adjacent to a roof surface, the parapet shall have noncombustible faces for the uppermost 18 inches (457 mm), to include counterflashing and coping materials. Where the roof slopes toward a parapet at slopes greater than 2 units vertical in 12 units horizontal (16.7-percent slope), the parapet shall extend to the same height as any portion of the roof within a distance of 3 feet (914 mm), and the height shall be not less than 30 inches (762 mm).

R302.2.6 Structural independence. Each individual *townhouse* shall be structurally independent.

Exceptions:

1. Foundations supporting *exterior walls* or common walls.

2. Structural roof and wall sheathing from each unit fastened to the common wall framing.

3. Nonstructural wall and roof coverings.

4. Flashing at termination of roof covering over common wall.

5. *Townhouses* separated by a common wall as provided in Section R302.2.2, Item 1 or 2.

R302.2.7 Sound transmission. Townhouses constructed in accordance with Section R302.2 shall comply with the sound transmission requirements of IRC Appendix K.

R302.3 Two-family dwellings. *Dwelling units* in two-family dwellings shall be separated from each other by wall and floor assemblies having not less than a 1-hour fire-resistance rating where tested in accordance with ASTM E119, UL 263 or Section 703.3 of the *International Building Code*. Fire-resistance-rated floor/ceiling and wall assemblies shall extend to and be tight against the *exterior wall*, and wall assemblies shall extend from the foundation to the underside of the roof sheathing.

Exceptions:

1. A fire-resistance rating of $^1/_2$ hour shall be permitted in buildings equipped throughout with an automatic sprinkler system installed in accordance with NFPA 13.

2. Wall assemblies need not extend through *attic* spaces where the ceiling is protected by not less than $^5/_8$-inch (15.9 mm) Type X gypsum board, an *attic* draft stop constructed as specified in Section R302.12.1 is provided above and along the wall assembly separating the *dwellings* and the structural framing supporting the ceiling is protected by not less than $^1/_2$-inch (12.7 mm) gypsum board or equivalent.

R302.3.1 Supporting construction. Where floor assemblies are required to be fire-resistance rated by Section R302.3, the supporting construction of such assemblies shall have an equal or greater fire-resistance rating.

R302.3.2 Sound transmission. Two-family dwellings constructed in accordance with Section R302.3 shall comply with the sound transmission requirements of IRC Appendix K.

R302.4 Dwelling unit rated penetrations. Penetrations of wall or floor-ceiling assemblies required to be fire-resistance rated in accordance with Section R302.2 or R302.3 shall be protected in accordance with this section.

R302.4.1 Through penetrations. Through penetrations of fire-resistance-rated wall or floor assemblies shall comply with Section R302.4.1.1 or R302.4.1.2.

Exception: Where the penetrating items are steel, ferrous or copper pipes, tubes or conduits, the annular space shall be protected as follows:

1. In concrete or masonry wall or floor assemblies, concrete, grout or mortar shall be permitted where installed to the full thickness of the wall or floor assembly or the thickness required to maintain the fire-resistance rating, provided that both of the following are complied with:

   1.1. The nominal diameter of the penetrating item is not more than 6 inches (152 mm).

   1.2. The area of the opening through the wall does not exceed 144 square inches (92 900 mm²).

2. The material used to fill the annular space shall prevent the passage of flame and hot gases sufficient to ignite cotton waste where subjected to ASTM E119 or UL 263 time temperature fire conditions under a positive pressure differential of not less than 0.01 inch of water (3 Pa) at the location of the penetration for the time period equivalent to the fire-resistance rating of the construction penetrated.

R302.4.1.1 Fire-resistance-rated assembly. Penetrations shall be installed as tested in the *approved* fire-resistance-rated assembly.

R302.4.1.2 Penetration firestop system. Penetrations shall be protected by an *approved* penetration firestop system installed as tested in accordance with ASTM E814 or UL 1479, with a positive pressure differential of not less than 0.01 inch of water (3 Pa) and shall have an F rating of not less than the required fire-resistance rating of the wall or floor-ceiling assembly penetrated.

R302.4.2 Membrane penetrations. Membrane penetrations shall comply with Section R302.4.1. Where walls are required to have a fire-resistance rating, recessed fixtures shall be installed so that the required fire-resistance rating will not be reduced.

Exceptions:

1. Membrane penetrations of not more than 2-hour fire-resistance-rated walls and partitions by steel electrical boxes that do not exceed 16 square inches (0.0103 m²) in area provided that the aggregate area of the openings through the membrane does not exceed 100 square inches (0.0645 m²) in any 100 square feet (9.29 m²) of wall area. The annular space between the wall membrane and the box shall not exceed ¹/₈ inch (3.1 mm). Such boxes on opposite sides of the wall shall be separated by one of the following:

   1.1. By a horizontal distance of not less than 24 inches (610 mm) where the wall or partition is constructed with individual noncommunicating stud cavities.

   1.2. By a horizontal distance of not less than the depth of the wall cavity where the wall cavity is filled with cellulose loose-fill, rockwool or slag mineral wool insulation.

   1.3. By solid fireblocking in accordance with Section R302.11.

   1.4. By protecting both boxes with *listed* putty pads.

   1.5. By other *listed* materials and methods.

2. Membrane penetrations by *listed* electrical boxes of any materials provided that the boxes have been tested for use in fire-resistance-rated assemblies and are installed in accordance with the instructions included in the *listing*. The annular space between the wall membrane and the box shall not exceed ¹/₈ inch (3.1 mm) unless *listed* otherwise. Such boxes on opposite sides of the wall shall be separated by one of the following:

   2.1. By the horizontal distance specified in the *listing* of the electrical boxes.

   2.2. By solid fireblocking in accordance with Section R302.11.

   2.3. By protecting both boxes with *listed* putty pads.

   2.4. By other *listed* materials and methods.

3. The annular space created by the penetration of a fire sprinkler provided that it is covered by a metal escutcheon plate.

4. Ceiling membrane penetrations by *listed* luminaires or by luminaires protected with *listed* materials that have been tested for use in fire-resistance-rated assemblies and are installed in accordance with the instructions included in the *listing*.

R302.5 Dwelling-garage opening and penetration protection. Openings and penetrations through the walls or ceilings separating the *dwelling* from the garage shall be in accordance with Sections R302.5.1 through R302.5.3.

R302.5.1 Opening protection. Openings from a private garage directly into a room used for sleeping purposes shall not be permitted. Other openings between the garage and residence shall be equipped with solid wood doors not less than $1^3/_8$ inches (35 mm) in thickness, solid or honeycomb-core steel doors not less than $1^3/_8$ inches (35 mm) thick, or 20-minute fire-rated doors.

R302.5.2 Duct penetration. Ducts in the garage and ducts penetrating the walls or ceilings separating the *dwelling* from the garage shall be constructed of a minimum No. 26 gage (0.48 mm) sheet steel or other *approved* material and shall not have openings into the garage.

R302.5.3 Other penetrations. Penetrations through the separation required in Section R302.6 shall be protected as required by Section R302.11, Item 4.

R302.6 Dwelling-garage fire separation. The garage shall be separated as required by Table R302.6. Openings in garage walls shall comply with Section R302.5.

R302.7 Under-stair protection. Enclosed space under stairs that is *accessed* by a door or access panel shall have walls, under-stair surface and any soffits protected on the enclosed side with $^1/_2$-inch (12.7 mm) gypsum board.

R302.8 Foam plastics. For requirements for foam plastics, see Section R316.

R302.9 Flame spread index and smoke-developed index for wall and ceiling finishes. Flame spread and smoke-developed indices for wall and ceiling finishes shall be in accordance with Sections R302.9.1 through R302.9.4.

R302.9.1 Flame spread index. Wall and ceiling finishes shall have a flame spread index of not greater than 200.

Exception: Flame spread index requirements for finishes shall not apply to trim defined as picture molds, chair rails, baseboards and handrails; to doors and windows or their frames; or to materials that are less than $^1/_{28}$ inch (0.91 mm) in thickness cemented to the surface of walls or ceilings if these materials exhibit flame spread index values not greater than those of paper of this thickness cemented to a noncombustible backing.

R302.9.2 Smoke-developed index. Wall and ceiling finishes shall have a smoke-developed index of not greater than 450.

R302.9.3 Testing. Tests shall be made in accordance with ASTM E84 or UL 723.

R302.9.4 Alternative test method. As an alternative to having a flame spread index of not greater than 200 and a smoke-developed index of not greater than 450 where tested in accordance with ASTM E84 or UL 723, wall and ceiling finishes shall be permitted to be tested in accordance with NFPA 286. Materials tested in accordance with NFPA 286 shall meet the following criteria:

The interior finish shall comply with the following:

1. During the 40 kW exposure, flames shall not spread to the ceiling.

2. The flame shall not spread to the outer extremity of the sample on any wall or ceiling.

3. Flashover, as defined in NFPA 286, shall not occur.

4. The peak heat release rate throughout the test shall not exceed 800 kW.

5. The total smoke released throughout the test shall not exceed 1,000 m².

R302.10 Flame spread index and smoke-developed index for insulation. Flame spread and smoke-developed index for insulation shall be in accordance with Sections R302.10.1 through R302.10.5.

TABLE R302.6[a]
DWELLING-GARAGE SEPARATION

SEPARATION	MATERIAL
From the residence and attics	Not less than $^1/_2$-inch gypsum board or equivalent applied to the garage side. Vertical separation between the garage and the residence attic shall extend to the roof sheathing or rafter blocking.
From all habitable rooms above the garage	Not less than $^5/_8$-inch Type X gypsum board or equivalent.
Structural members supporting floor/ceiling assemblies or garage ceiling used for separation required by this section	Not less than $^1/_2$-inch gypsum board or equivalent applied to the garage side of structural members supporting the floor/ceiling assemblies or garage ceiling. Structural members include, but are not limited to: walls, columns, beams, girders, and trusses.
Garages located less than 3 feet from a dwelling unit on the same lot	Not less than $^1/_2$-inch gypsum board or equivalent applied to the interior side of exterior walls that are within this area. This provision does not apply to garage walls that are perpendicular to the adjacent dwelling unit wall.

For SI: 1 inch = 25.4 mm, 1 foot = 304.8 mm.

a. Attachment of gypsum board shall comply with Table R702.3.5.

R302.10.1 Insulation. Insulating materials installed within floor-ceiling assemblies, roof-ceiling assemblies, wall assemblies, crawl spaces and *attics* shall comply with the requirements of this section. They shall exhibit a flame spread index not to exceed 25 and a smoke-developed index not to exceed 450 where tested in accordance with ASTM E84 or UL 723. Insulating materials, where tested in accordance with the requirements of this section, shall include facings, where used, such as vapor retarders, vapor permeable membranes and similar coverings.

Exceptions:

1. Where such materials are installed in concealed spaces, the flame spread index and smoke-developed index limitations do not apply to the facings, provided that the facing is installed in substantial contact with the unexposed surface of the ceiling, floor or wall finish.

2. Cellulose fiber loose-fill insulation that is not spray applied and that complies with the requirements of Section R302.10.3 shall not be required to meet the flame spread index requirements but shall be required to meet a smoke-developed index of not more than 450 where tested in accordance with CAN/ULC S102.2.

3. Foam plastic insulation shall comply with Section R316.

R302.10.2 Loose-fill insulation. Loose-fill insulation materials that cannot be mounted in the ASTM E84 or UL 723 apparatus without a screen or artificial supports shall comply with the flame spread and smoke-developed limits of Section R302.10.1 where tested in accordance with CAN/ULC S102.2.

Exception: Cellulosic fiber loose-fill insulation shall not be required to be tested in accordance with CAN/ULC S102.2, provided that such insulation complies with the requirements of Sections R302.10.1 and R302.10.3.

R302.10.3 Cellulosic fiber loose-fill insulation. Cellulosic fiber loose-fill insulation shall comply with CPSC 16 CFR, Parts 1209 and 1404. Each package of such insulating material shall be clearly *labeled* in accordance with CPSC 16 CFR, Parts 1209 and 1404.

R302.10.4 Exposed attic insulation. Exposed insulation materials installed on *attic* floors shall have a critical radiant flux of not less than 0.12 watt per square centimeter.

R302.10.5 Testing. Tests for critical radiant flux shall be made in accordance with ASTM E970.

R302.11 Fireblocking. In combustible construction, fireblocking shall be provided to cut off both vertical and horizontal concealed draft openings and to form an effective fire barrier between stories, and between a top *story* and the roof space.

Fireblocking shall be provided in wood-framed construction in the following locations:

1. In concealed spaces of stud walls and partitions, including furred spaces and parallel rows of studs or staggered studs, as follows:

   1.1. Vertically at the ceiling and floor levels.

   1.2. Horizontally at intervals not exceeding 10 feet (3048 mm).

2. At interconnections between concealed vertical and horizontal spaces such as occur at soffits, drop ceilings and cove ceilings.

3. In concealed spaces between stair stringers at the top and bottom of the run. Enclosed spaces under stairs shall comply with Section R302.7.

4. At openings around vents, pipes, ducts, cables and wires at ceiling and floor level, with an *approved* material to resist the free passage of flame and products of combustion. The material filling this annular space shall not be required to meet the ASTM E136 requirements.

5. For the fireblocking of chimneys and fireplaces, see Section R1003.19.

6. Fireblocking of cornices of a two-family *dwelling* is required at the line of *dwelling unit* separation.

R302.11.1 Fireblocking materials. Except as provided in Section R302.11, Item 4, fireblocking shall consist of the following materials.

1. Two-inch (51 mm) nominal lumber.

2. Two thicknesses of 1-inch (25.4 mm) nominal lumber with broken lap joints.

3. One thickness of $^{23}/_{32}$-inch (18.3 mm) wood structural panels with joints backed by $^{23}/_{32}$-inch (18.3 mm) wood structural panels.

4. One thickness of $^{3}/_{4}$-inch (19.1 mm) particleboard with joints backed by $^{3}/_{4}$-inch (19.1 mm) particleboard.

5. One-half-inch (12.7 mm) gypsum board.

6. One-quarter-inch (6.4 mm) cement-based millboard.

7. Batts or blankets of mineral wool or glass fiber or other *approved* materials installed in such a manner as to be securely retained in place.

8. Cellulose insulation installed as tested in accordance with ASTM E119 or UL 263, for the specific application.

R302.11.1.1 Batts or blankets of mineral or glass fiber. Batts or blankets of mineral or glass fiber or other *approved* nonrigid materials shall be permitted for compliance with the 10-foot (3048 mm) horizontal fireblocking in walls constructed using parallel rows of studs or staggered studs.

R302.11.1.2 Unfaced fiberglass. Unfaced fiberglass batt insulation used as fireblocking shall fill the entire cross section of the wall cavity to a height of not less than 16 inches (406 mm) measured vertically. Where piping, conduit or similar obstructions are encountered, the insulation shall be packed tightly around the obstruction.

R302.11.1.3 Loose-fill insulation material. Loose-fill insulation material shall not be used as a fireblock unless specifically tested in the form and manner intended for use to demonstrate its ability to remain in place and to retard the spread of fire and hot gases.

R302.11.2 Fireblocking integrity. The integrity of fireblocks shall be maintained.

R302.12 Draftstopping. In combustible construction where there is usable space both above and below the concealed space of a floor-ceiling assembly, draftstops shall be installed so that the area of the concealed space does not exceed 1,000 square feet (92.9 m²). Draftstopping shall divide the concealed space into approximately equal areas. Where the assembly is enclosed by a floor membrane above and a ceiling membrane below, draftstopping shall be provided in floor-ceiling assemblies under the following circumstances:

1. Ceiling is suspended under the floor framing.

2. Floor framing is constructed of truss-type open-web or perforated members.

R302.12.1 Materials. Draftstopping materials shall be not less than $^1/_2$-inch (12.7 mm) gypsum board, $^3/_8$-inch (9.5 mm) wood structural panels or other *approved* materials adequately supported. Draftstopping shall be installed parallel to the floor framing members unless otherwise *approved* by the *building official*. The integrity of the draftstops shall be maintained.

R302.13 Fire protection of floors. Floor assemblies that are not required elsewhere in this code to be fire-resistance rated, shall be provided with a $^1/_2$-inch (12.7 mm) gypsum wallboard membrane, $^5/_8$-inch (16 mm) wood structural panel membrane, or equivalent on the underside of the floor framing member. Penetrations or openings for ducts, vents, electrical outlets, lighting, devices, luminaires, wires, speakers, drainage, piping and similar openings or penetrations shall be permitted.

Exceptions:

1. Floor assemblies located directly over a space protected by an automatic sprinkler system in accordance with Section P2904, NFPA 13D, or other approved equivalent sprinkler system.

2. Floor assemblies located directly over a crawl space not intended for storage or for the installation of fuel-fired or electric-powered heating appliances.

3. Portions of floor assemblies shall be permitted to be unprotected where complying with the following:

   3.1. The aggregate area of the unprotected portions does not exceed 80 square feet (7.4 m²) per story.

   3.2. Fireblocking in accordance with Section R302.11.1 is installed along the perimeter of the unprotected portion to separate the unprotected portion from the remainder of the floor assembly.

4. Wood floor assemblies using dimension lumber or structural composite lumber equal to or greater than 2-inch by 10-inch (50.8 mm by 254 mm) nominal dimension, or other approved floor assemblies demonstrating equivalent fire performance.

R302.14 Combustible insulation clearance. Combustible insulation shall be separated not less than 3 inches (76 mm) from recessed luminaires, fan motors and other heat-producing devices.

Exception: Where heat-producing devices are *listed* for lesser clearances, combustible insulation complying with 3the listing requirements shall be separated in accordance with the conditions stipulated in the listing.

Recessed luminaires installed in the *building thermal envelope* shall meet the requirements of Section N1102.4.5 of this code.

SECTION R303
LIGHT, VENTILATION AND HEATING

R303.1 Habitable rooms. Habitable rooms shall have an aggregate glazing area of not less than 8 percent of the floor area of such rooms. Natural *ventilation* shall be through windows, skylights, doors, louvers or other *approved* openings to the outdoor air. Such openings shall be provided with ready access or shall otherwise be readily controllable by the building occupants. The openable area to the outdoors shall be not less than 4 percent of the floor area being ventilated.

Exceptions:

1. The glazed areas need not be openable where the opening is not required by Section R310 and a whole-house mechanical *ventilation* system is installed in accordance with Section M1505.

2. The glazed areas need not be installed in rooms where Exception 1 is satisfied and artificial light is provided that is capable of producing an average illumination of 6 footcandles (65 lux) over the area of the room at a height of 30 inches (762 mm) above the floor level.

3. Use of sunroom and patio covers, as defined in Section R202, shall be permitted for natural *ventilation* if in excess of 40 percent of the exterior sunroom walls are open, or are enclosed only by insect screening.

R303.2 Adjoining rooms. For the purpose of determining light and *ventilation* requirements, rooms shall be considered to be a portion of an adjoining room where not less than one-half of the area of the common wall is open and unobstructed and provides an opening of not less than one-tenth of the floor area of the interior room and not less than 25 square feet (2.3 m²).

Exception: Openings required for light or *ventilation* shall be permitted to open into a sunroom with thermal isolation or a patio cover, provided that there is an openable area between the adjoining room and the sunroom or patio cover of not less than one-tenth of the floor area of the interior room and not less than 20 square feet (2 m²). The minimum openable area to the outdoors shall be based on the total floor area being ventilated.

R303.3 Bathrooms. Bathrooms, water closet compartments and other similar rooms shall be provided with aggregate glazing area in windows of not less than 3 square feet (0.3 m²), one-half of which shall be openable.

Exception: The glazed areas shall not be required where artificial light and a local exhaust system are provided. The minimum local exhaust rates shall be determined in accordance with Section M1505. Exhaust air from the space shall be exhausted directly to the outdoors.

R303.4 Mechanical ventilation. Mechanical ventilation of a dwelling unit shall comply with either Minnesota Rules, Chapter 1322 or 1346.

R303.5 Opening location. Outdoor intake and exhaust openings shall be located in accordance with Sections R303.5.1 and R303.5.2.

R303.5.1 Intake openings. Mechanical and gravity outdoor air intake openings shall be located not less than 10 feet (3048 mm) from any hazardous or noxious contaminant, such as vents, chimneys, plumbing vents, streets, alleys, parking lots and loading docks.

For the purpose of this section, the exhaust from *dwelling* unit toilet rooms, bathrooms and kitchens shall not be considered as hazardous or noxious.

Exceptions:

1. The 10-foot (3048 mm) separation is not required where the intake opening is located 3 feet (914 mm) or greater below the contaminant source.

2. Vents and chimneys serving fuel-burning appliances shall be terminated in accordance with the applicable provisions of Chapters 18 and 24.

3. Clothes dryer exhaust ducts shall be terminated in accordance with Section M1502.3.

R303.5.2 Exhaust openings. Exhaust air shall not be directed onto walkways.

R303.6 Outside opening protection. Air exhaust and intake openings that terminate outdoors shall be protected with corrosion-resistant screens, louvers or grilles having an opening size of not less than ¹/₄ inch (6 mm) and a maximum opening size of ¹/₂ inch (13 mm), in any dimension. Openings shall be protected against local weather conditions. Outdoor air exhaust and intake openings shall meet the provisions for *exterior wall* opening protectives in accordance with this code.

R303.7 Interior stairway illumination. Interior stairways shall be provided with an artificial light source to illuminate the landings and treads. The light source shall be capable of illuminating treads and landings to levels of not less than 1 foot-candle (11 lux) as measured at the center of treads and

landings. There shall be a wall switch at each floor level to control the light source where the stairway has six or more risers.

Exception: A switch is not required where remote, central or automatic control of lighting is provided.

R303.8 Exterior stairway illumination. Exterior stairways shall be provided with an artificial light source located at the top landing of the stairway. Exterior stairways providing access to a *basement* from the outdoor *grade* level shall be provided with an artificial light source located at the bottom landing of the stairway.

R303.9 Required glazed openings. Required glazed openings shall open directly onto a street or public alley, or a *yard* or court located on the same *lot* as the building.

Exceptions:

1. Required glazed openings that face into a roofed porch where the porch abuts a street, *yard* or court and the longer side of the porch is not less than 65 percent unobstructed and the ceiling height is not less than 7 feet (2134 mm).

2. Eave projections shall not be considered as obstructing the clear open space of a *yard* or court.

3. Required glazed openings that face into the area under a deck, balcony, bay or floor cantilever where a clear vertical space not less than 36 inches (914 mm) in height is provided.

R303.9.1 Sunroom additions. Required glazed openings shall be permitted to open into sunroom *additions* or patio covers that abut a street, *yard* or court if in excess of 40 percent of the exterior sunroom walls are open, or are enclosed only by insect screening, and the ceiling height of the sunroom is not less than 7 feet (2134 mm).

R303.10 Required heating. Where the winter design temperature in Table R301.2(1) is below 60°F (16°C), every *dwelling unit* shall be provided with heating facilities capable of maintaining a room temperature of not less than 68°F (20°C) at a point 3 feet (914 mm) above the floor and 2 feet (610 mm) from exterior walls in habitable rooms at the design temperature. The installation of one or more portable space heaters shall not be used to achieve compliance with this section.

SECTION R304
MINIMUM ROOM AREAS

R304.1 Minimum area. Habitable rooms shall have a floor area of not less than 70 square feet (6.5 m²).

Exception: Kitchens.

R304.2 Minimum dimensions. Habitable rooms shall be not less than 7 feet (2134 mm) in any horizontal dimension.

Exception: Kitchens.

R304.3 Height effect on room area. Portions of a room with a sloping ceiling measuring less than 5 feet (1524 mm) or a furred ceiling measuring less than 7 feet (2134 mm) from the finished floor to the finished ceiling shall not be considered as contributing to the minimum required habitable area for that room.

SECTION R305
CEILING HEIGHT

R305.1 Minimum height, new buildings. *Habitable space*, hallways, bathrooms, toilet rooms, laundry rooms, and portions of basements containing these spaces shall have a ceiling height of not less than 7 feet (2134 mm). The required height shall be measured from the finish floor to the lowest projection from the ceiling.

Exceptions:

1. For rooms with sloped ceilings, at least 50 percent of the required floor area of the room shall have a ceiling height of at least 7 feet (2134 mm) and no portion of the required floor area may have a ceiling height of less than 5 feet (1524 mm).

2. Bathrooms shall have a minimum ceiling height of 6 feet 8 inches (2032 mm) at the center of the front clearance area for water closets, bidets, or sinks. The ceiling height above fixtures shall be such that the fixture is capable of being used for its intended purpose. A shower or tub equipped with a showerhead shall have a minimum ceiling height of 6 feet 8 inches (2032 mm) above a minimum area 30 inches (762 mm) by 30 inches (762 mm) at the showerhead.

R305.1.1 Basements, new buildings. Portions of basements that do not contain habitable space, hallways, bathrooms, toilet rooms, and laundry rooms shall have a ceiling height of not less than 6 feet 8 inches (2032 mm).

Exception: Beams, girders, ducts, or other obstructions may project to within 6 feet 4 inches (1931 mm) of the finished floor.

R305.2 Alterations to existing building basements. Alterations to portions of existing basements shall comply with the provisions of this section.

R305.2.1 Minimum ceiling height, existing buildings. Alterations to existing basements or portions thereof shall have a ceiling height of not less than 6 feet 4 inches (1931 mm), including beams, girders, ducts, or other obstructions.

R305.2.1.1 Bathroom plumbing fixture clearance. Bathrooms shall have a minimum ceiling height of 6 feet 4 inches (1931 mm) at the center of the front clearance area for water closets, bidets, or sinks. A shower or tub equipped with a showerhead shall have a minimum ceiling height of 6 feet 4 inches (1931 mm) above a minimum area 30 inches (762 mm) by 30 inches (762 mm) at the wall where the showerhead is placed. The ceiling may have slopes or soffits that do not infringe on the height required for the plumbing fixture.

R305.2.2 Minimum stairway headroom, existing buildings. Alterations to existing basement stairways shall have a minimum headroom in all parts of the stairway not less than 6 feet 4 inches (1931 mm) measured vertically from the sloped line adjoining the tread nosing or from the floor surface of the landing or platform on that portion of the stairway.

Exception: Where the nosings of treads at the side of a flight extend under the edge of a floor opening through which the stair passes, the floor opening shall be allowed to project horizontally into the required headroom a maximum of $4^3/_4$ inches (121 mm).

SECTION R306
SANITATION

R306.1 Toilet facilities. Every *dwelling* unit shall be provided with a water closet, lavatory, and a bathtub or shower.

R306.2 Kitchen. Each *dwelling* unit shall be provided with a kitchen area and every kitchen area shall be provided with a sink.

R306.3 Sewage disposal. Plumbing fixtures shall be connected to a sanitary sewer or to an *approved* private sewage disposal system.

R306.4 Water supply to fixtures. Plumbing fixtures shall be connected to an *approved* water supply. Kitchen sinks, lavatories, bathtubs, showers, bidets, laundry tubs and washing machine outlets shall be provided with hot and cold water.

SECTION R307
TOILET, BATH AND SHOWER SPACES

R307.1 Space required. Plumbing fixtures shall be installed in accordance with Minnesota Rules, Chapter 4714, *Minnesota Plumbing Code.*

R307.2 Bathtub and shower spaces. Bathtub and shower floors and walls above bathtubs with installed shower heads and in shower compartments shall be finished with a nonabsorbent surface. Such wall surfaces shall extend to a height of not less than 6 feet (1829 mm) above the floor.

SECTION R308
GLAZING

R308.1 Identification. Except as indicated in Section R308.1.1 each pane of glazing installed in hazardous locations as defined in Section R308.4 shall be provided with a manufacturer's designation specifying who applied the designation, the type of glass and the safety glazing standard with which it complies, and that is visible in the final installation. The designation shall be acid etched, sandblasted, ceramic-fired, laser etched, embossed, or be of a type that once applied cannot be removed without being destroyed. A *label* shall be permitted in lieu of the manufacturer's designation.

Exceptions:

1. For other than tempered glass, manufacturer's designations are not required provided that the *building official* approves the use of a certificate, affidavit or other evidence confirming compliance with this code.

2. Tempered spandrel glass is permitted to be identified by the manufacturer with a removable paper designation.

R308.1.1 Identification of multiple assemblies. Multipane assemblies having individual panes not exceeding 1 square foot (0.09 m^2) in exposed area shall have not less than one pane in the assembly identified in accordance with Section R308.1. Other panes in the assembly shall be *labeled* "CPSC 16 CFR 1201" or "ANSI Z97.1" as appropriate.

R308.2 Louvered windows or jalousies. Regular, float, wired or patterned glass in jalousies and louvered windows shall be not less than nominal $^3/_{16}$ inch (5 mm) thick and not more than 48 inches (1219 mm) in length. Exposed glass edges shall be smooth.

R308.2.1 Wired glass prohibited. Wired glass with wire exposed on longitudinal edges shall not be used in jalousies or louvered windows.

R308.3 Human impact loads. Individual glazed areas, including glass mirrors in hazardous locations such as those indicated as defined in Section R308.4, shall pass the test requirements of Section R308.3.1.

Exceptions:

1. Louvered windows and jalousies shall comply with Section R308.2.

2. Mirrors and other glass panels mounted or hung on a surface that provides a continuous backing support.

3. Glass unit masonry complying with Section R607.

R308.3.1 Impact test. Where required by other sections of the code, glazing shall be tested in accordance with CPSC 16 CFR 1201. Glazing shall comply with the test criteria for Category II unless otherwise indicated in Table R308.3.1(1).

Exception: Glazing not in doors or enclosures for hot tubs, whirlpools, saunas, steam rooms, bathtubs and showers shall be permitted to be tested in accordance with ANSI Z97.1. Glazing shall comply with the test criteria for Class A unless otherwise indicated in Table R308.3.1(2).

R308.4 Hazardous locations. The locations specified in Sections R308.4.1 through R308.4.7 shall be considered to be specific hazardous locations for the purposes of glazing.

R308.4.1 Glazing in doors. Glazing in fixed and operable panels of swinging, sliding and bifold doors shall be considered to be a hazardous location.

Exceptions:

1. Glazed openings of a size through which a 3-inch-diameter (76 mm) sphere is unable to pass.

2. Decorative glazing.

R308.4.2 Glazing adjacent to doors. Glazing in an individual fixed or operable panel adjacent to a door shall be considered to be a hazardous location where the bottom exposed edge of the glazing is less than 60 inches (1524 mm) above the floor or walking surface and it meets either of the following conditions:

1. Where the glazing is within 24 inches (610 mm) of either side of the door in the plane of the door in a closed position.

2. Where the glazing is on a wall less than 180 degrees (3.14 rad) from the plane of the door in a closed position and within 24 inches (610 mm) of the hinge side of an in-swinging door.

Exceptions:

1. Decorative glazing.

2. Where there is an intervening wall or other permanent barrier between the door and the glazing.

3. Where access through the door is to a closet or storage area 3 feet (914 mm) or less in depth. Glazing in this application shall comply with Section R308.4.3.

TABLE R308.3.1(1)
MINIMUM CATEGORY CLASSIFICATION OF GLAZING USING CPSC 16 CFR 1201

EXPOSED SURFACE AREA OF ONE SIDE OF ONE LITE	GLAZING IN STORM OR COMBINATION DOORS (Category Class)	GLAZING IN DOORS (Category Class)	GLAZED PANELS REGULATED BY SECTION R308.4.3 (Category Class)	GLAZED PANELS REGULATED BY SECTION R308.4.2 (Category Class)	GLAZING IN DOORS AND ENCLOSURES REGULATED BY SECTION 308.4.5 (Category Class)	SLIDING GLASS DOORS PATIO TYPE (Category Class)
9 square feet or less	I	I	NR	I	II	II
More than 9 square feet	II	II	II	II	II	II

For SI: 1 square foot = 0.0929 m^2.
NR = No Requirement.

TABLE R308.3.1(2)
MINIMUM CATEGORY CLASSIFICATION OF GLAZING USING ANSI Z97.1

EXPOSED SURFACE AREA OF ONE SIDE OF ONE LITE	GLAZED PANELS REGULATED BY SECTION R308.4.3 (Category Class)	GLAZED PANELS REGULATED BY SECTION R308.4.2 (Category Class)	DOORS AND ENCLOSURES REGULATED BY SECTION R308.4.5[a] (Category Class)
9 square feet or less	No requirement	B	A
More than 9 square feet	A	A	A

For SI: 1 square foot = 0.0929 m^2.

a. Use is permitted only by the exception to Section R308.3.1.

4. Glazing that is adjacent to the fixed panel of patio doors.

R308.4.3 Glazing in windows. Glazing in an individual fixed or operable panel that meets all of the following conditions shall be considered to be a hazardous location:

1. The exposed area of an individual pane is larger than 9 square feet (0.836 m^2).

2. The bottom edge of the glazing is less than 18 inches (457 mm) above the floor.

3. The top edge of the glazing is more than 36 inches (914 mm) above the floor.

4. One or more walking surfaces are within 36 inches (914 mm), measured horizontally and in a straight line, of the glazing.

   Exceptions:

   1. Decorative glazing.

   2. Where glazing is adjacent to a walking surface and a horizontal rail is installed 34 to 38 inches (864 to 965 mm) above the walking surface. The rail shall be capable of withstanding a horizontal load of 50 pounds per linear foot (730 N/m) without contacting the glass and have a cross-sectional height of not less than 1$^1/_2$ inches (38 mm).

   3. Outboard panes in insulating glass units and other multiple glazed panels where the bottom edge of the glass is 25 feet (7620 mm) or more above *grade*, a roof, walking surfaces or other horizontal [within 45 degrees (0.79 rad) of horizontal] surface adjacent to the glass exterior.

R308.4.4 Glazing in guards and railings. Glazing in *guards* and railings, including structural baluster panels and nonstructural in-fill panels, regardless of area or height above a walking surface shall be considered to be a hazardous location.

R308.4.4.1 Structural glass baluster panels. Guards with structural glass baluster panels shall be installed with an attached top rail or handrail. The top rail or handrail shall be supported by not less than three glass baluster panels, or shall be otherwise supported to remain in place should one glass baluster panel fail.

Exception: An attached top rail or handrail is not required where the glass baluster panels are laminated glass with two or more glass plies of equal thickness and of the same glass type.

R308.4.5 Glazing and wet surfaces. Glazing in walls, enclosures or fences containing or facing hot tubs, spas, whirlpools, saunas, steam rooms, bathtubs, showers and indoor or outdoor swimming pools where the bottom exposed edge of the glazing is less than 60 inches (1524 mm) measured vertically above any standing or walking surface shall be considered to be a hazardous location. This shall apply to single glazing and each pane in multiple glazing.

Exception: Glazing that is more than 60 inches (1524 mm), measured horizontally and in a straight line, from the water's edge of a bathtub, hot tub, spa, whirlpool or swimming pool or from the edge of a shower, sauna or steam room.

R308.4.6 Glazing adjacent to stairs and ramps. Glazing where the bottom exposed edge of the glazing is less than 36 inches (914 mm) above the plane of the adjacent walking surface of stairways, landings between flights of stairs and ramps shall be considered to be a hazardous location.

Exceptions:

1. Where glazing is adjacent to a walking surface and a horizontal rail is installed at 34 to 38 inches (864 to 965 mm) above the walking surface. The rail shall be capable of withstanding a horizontal load of 50 pounds per linear foot (730 N/m) without contacting the glass and have a cross-sectional height of not less than 1$^1/_2$ inches (38 mm).

2. Glazing 36 inches (914 mm) or more measured horizontally from the walking surface.

R308.4.7 Glazing adjacent to the bottom stair landing. Glazing adjacent to the landing at the bottom of a stairway where the glazing is less than 36 inches (914 mm) above the landing and within a 60-inch (1524 mm) horizontal arc less than 180 degrees (3.14 rad) from the bottom tread nosing shall be considered to be a hazardous location. (See Figure R308.4.7.)

Exception: Where the glazing is protected by a *guard* complying with Section R312 and the plane of the glass is more than 18 inches (457 mm) from the *guard*.

R308.5 Site-built windows. Site-built windows shall comply with Section 2404 of the *International Building Code*.

R308.6 Skylights and sloped glazing. Skylights and sloped glazing shall comply with the following sections.

R308.6.1 Definitions. The following terms are defined in Chapter 2:

SKYLIGHT, UNIT.

SKYLIGHTS AND SLOPED GLAZING.

TUBULAR DAYLIGHTING DEVICE (TDD).

R308.6.2 Materials. Glazing materials shall be limited to the following:

1. Laminated glass with not less than a 0.015-inch (0.38 mm) polyvinyl butyral interlayer for glass panes 16 square feet (1.5 m^2) or less in area located such that the highest point of the glass is not more than 12 feet (3658 mm) above a walking surface; for higher or larger sizes, the interlayer thickness shall be not less than 0.030 inch (0.76 mm).

2. Fully tempered glass.

3. Heat-strengthened glass.

4. Wired glass.

5. *Approved* rigid plastics.

R308.6.3 Screens, general. For fully tempered or heat-strengthened glass, a retaining screen meeting the requirements of Section R308.6.7 shall be installed below the glass, except for fully tempered glass that meets either condition listed in Section R308.6.5.

R308.6.4 Screens with multiple glazing. Where the inboard pane is fully tempered, heat-strengthened or wired glass, a retaining screen meeting the requirements of Section R308.6.7 shall be installed below the glass, except for either condition listed in Section R308.6.5. Other panes in the multiple glazing shall be of any type listed in Section R308.6.2.

R308.6.5 Screens not required. Screens shall not be required where fully tempered glass is used as single glazing or the inboard pane in multiple glazing and either of the following conditions are met:

1. The glass area is 16 square feet (1.49 m²) or less; the highest point of glass is not more than 12 feet (3658 mm) above a walking surface; the nominal glass thickness is not more than $^3/_{16}$ inch (4.8 mm); and (for multiple glazing only) the other pane or panes are fully tempered, laminated or wired glass.

2. The glass area is greater than 16 square feet (1.49 m²); the glass is sloped 30 degrees (0.52 rad) or less from vertical; and the highest point of glass is not more than 10 feet (3048 mm) above a walking surface.

R308.6.6 Glass in greenhouses. Any glazing material is permitted to be installed without screening in the sloped areas of greenhouses, provided that the greenhouse height at the ridge does not exceed 20 feet (6096 mm) above *grade*.

R308.6.7 Screen characteristics. The screen and its fastenings shall be capable of supporting twice the weight of the glazing, be firmly and substantially fastened to the framing members, and have a mesh opening of not more than 1 inch by 1 inch (25 mm by 25 mm).

R308.6.8 Curbs for skylights. Unit skylights installed in a roof with a pitch of less than three units vertical in 12 units horizontal (25-percent slope) shall be mounted on a curb extending not less than 4 inches (102 mm) above the plane of the roof, unless otherwise specified in the manufacturer's installation instructions.

R308.6.9 Testing and labeling. Unit skylights and tubular daylighting devices shall be tested by an *approved* independent laboratory, and bear a *label* identifying manufacturer, performance grade rating and *approved* inspection agency to indicate compliance with the requirements of AAMA/WDMA/CSA 101/I.S.2/A440.

R308.6.9.1 Comparative analysis for glass-glazed unit skylights. Structural wind load design pressures for glass-glazed unit skylights different than the size tested in accordance with Section R308.6.9 shall be permitted to be different than the design value of the tested unit where determined in accordance with one of the following comparative analysis methods:

1. Structural wind load design pressures for glass-glazed unit skylights smaller than the size tested in accordance with Section R308.6.9 shall be permitted to be higher than the design value of the tested unit provided that such higher pressures are determined by accepted engineering analysis. Components of the smaller unit shall be the same as those of the tested unit. Such calculated design pressures shall be validated by an additional test of the glass-glazed unit skylight having the highest allowable design pressure.

2. In accordance with WDMA I.S. 11.

SECTION R309
GARAGES AND CARPORTS

R309.1 Floor surface. Garage floor surfaces may be concrete, asphalt, sand, gravel, crushed rock, or natural earth.

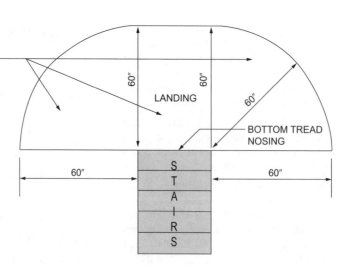

GLAZING LESS THAN 36″ ABOVE LANDINGS WITHIN THIS AREA ARE CONSIDERED TO BE IN HAZARDOUS LOCATIONS, UNLESS THE EXCEPTION TO SECTION R308.4.7 IS SATISFIED

LANDING

BOTTOM TREAD NOSING

STAIRS

For SI: 1 inch = 25.4 mm.

FIGURE R308.4.7
HAZARDOUS GLAZING LOCATIONS AT BOTTOM STAIR LANDINGS

R309.2 Carports. Carports shall be open on at least two sides. Carport floor surfaces may be concrete, asphalt, sand, gravel, crushed rock, or natural earth. Carports not open on at least two sides shall be considered a garage and shall comply with the provisions of this section for garages.

R309.3 Flood hazard areas. See Minnesota Rules, Chapter 1335.

R309.4 Automatic garage door opening systems. All automatic garage door opening systems that are installed, serviced, or repaired for garages serving residential buildings shall comply with the provisions of Minnesota Statutes, Sections 325F.82 and 325F.83.

R309.5 Fire sprinklers. Attached garages of two-family dwellings and townhouses shall be protected by fire sprinklers and installed in compliance with Section R313.3.

SECTION R310
EMERGENCY ESCAPE AND RESCUE OPENINGS

R310.1 Emergency escape and rescue opening required. *Basements, habitable attics,* and every sleeping room shall have not less than one operable emergency escape and rescue opening. Where *basements* contain one or more sleeping rooms, an emergency egress and rescue opening shall be required in each sleeping room, but not be required in adjoining areas of the basement. Emergency escape and rescue openings shall open directly into a public way, or to a *yard* or court that opens to a public way.

Exceptions:

1. Storm shelters and *basements* used only to house mechanical *equipment* not exceeding a total floor area of 200 square feet (18.58 m²).

2. Basements or basement bedrooms when the building is protected with an automatic sprinkler system installed in accordance with IRC Section P2904 or NFPA 13D.

3. Basements or basement bedrooms where the entire basement area, including all portions of the means of egress to the level of exit discharge, and all areas on the level of exit discharge that are open to the means of egress is protected with an automatic sprinkler system in accordance with IRC Section P2904 or NFPA 13D.

R310.1.1 Operational constraints and opening control devices. Emergency escape and rescue openings shall be operational from the inside of the room without the use of keys, tools or special knowledge. Window opening control devices on windows serving as a required emergency escape and rescue opening shall comply with ASTM F2090.

R310.2 Emergency escape and rescue openings. Emergency escape and rescue openings shall have minimum dimensions as specified in this section.

R310.2.1 Minimum opening area. Emergency and escape rescue openings shall have a net clear opening of not less than 5.7 square feet (0.530 m²). The net clear opening

dimensions required by this section shall be obtained by the normal operation of the emergency escape and rescue opening from the inside. The net clear height of the opening shall be not less than 24 inches (610 mm) and the net clear width shall be not less than 20 inches (508 mm).

Exception: *Grade floor openings* or *below-grade openings* shall have a net clear opening area of not less than 5 square feet (0.465 m²).

R310.2.2 Window sill height. Where a window is provided as the emergency escape and rescue opening, it shall have a sill height of not more than 44 inches (1118 mm) above the floor; where the sill height is below *grade*, it shall be provided with a window well in accordance with Section R310.2.3.

R310.2.3 Window wells. The horizontal area of the window well shall be not less than 9 square feet (0.9 m²), with a horizontal projection and width of not less than 36 inches (914 mm). The area of the window well shall allow the emergency escape and rescue opening to be fully opened.

Exception: The ladder or steps required by Section R310.2.3.1 shall be permitted to encroach not more than 6 inches (152 mm) into the required dimensions of the window well.

R310.2.3.1 Ladder and steps. Window wells with a vertical depth greater than 44 inches (1118 mm) shall be equipped with a permanently affixed ladder or steps usable with the window in the fully open position. Ladders or steps required by this section shall not be required to comply with Section R311.7. Ladders or rungs shall have an inside width of not less than 12 inches (305 mm), shall project not less than 3 inches (76 mm) from the wall and shall be spaced not more than 18 inches (457 mm) on center vertically for the full height of the window well.

R310.2.3.2 Drainage. Window wells shall be designed for proper drainage by connecting to the building's foundation drainage system required by Section R405.1 or by an approved alternative method.

Exception: A drainage system for window wells is not required where the foundation is on well-drained soil or sand-gravel mixture soils in accordance with the United Soil Classification System, Group I Soils, as detailed in Table R405.1.

R310.2.4 Emergency escape and rescue openings under decks and porches. Emergency escape and rescue openings installed under decks and porches shall be fully openable and provide a path not less than 36 inches (914 mm) in height to a *yard* or court.

R310.2.5 Replacement windows. Replacement windows installed in buildings meeting the scope of this code shall be exempt from the maximum sill height requirements of Section R310.2.2 and the requirements of Section R310.2.1, provided that the replacement window meets the following conditions:

1. The replacement window is the manufacturer's largest standard size window that will fit within the existing frame or existing rough opening. The

replacement window is of the same operating style as the existing window or a style that provides for an equal or greater window opening area than the existing window.

2. The replacement window is not part of a change of occupancy.

R310.2.5.1 Licensed facilities. Windows in rooms used for foster care or day care licensed or registered by the state of Minnesota shall comply with the provisions of Section R310.2.5, or all of the following conditions, whichever is more restrictive:

1. Minimum of 20 inches (508 mm) in clear opening width;

2. Minimum of 20 inches (508 mm) in clear opening height;

3. Minimum of 648 square inches (4.5 square feet) clear opening; and

4. Maximum of 48 inches (1219 mm) from the floor to the sill height.

R310.3 Emergency escape and rescue doors. Where a door is provided as the required emergency escape and rescue opening, it shall be a side-hinged door or a slider. Where the opening is below the adjacent grade, it shall be provided with an area well.

R310.3.1 Minimum door opening size. The minimum net clear height opening for any door that serves as an emergency and escape rescue opening shall be in accordance with Section R310.2.1.

R310.3.2 Area wells. Area wells shall have a width of not less than 36 inches (914 mm). The area well shall be sized to allow the emergency escape and rescue door to be fully opened.

R310.3.2.1 Ladder and steps. Area wells with a vertical depth greater than 44 inches (1118 mm) shall be equipped with a permanently affixed ladder or steps usable with the door in the fully open position. Ladders or steps required by this section shall not be required to comply with Section R311.7. Ladders or rungs shall have an inside width of not less than 12 inches (305 mm), shall project not less than 3 inches (76 mm) from the wall and shall be spaced not more than 18 inches (457 mm) on center vertically for the full height of the exterior stairwell.

R310.3.2.2 Drainage. Area wells shall be designed for proper drainage by connecting to the building's foundation drainage system required by Section R405.1 or by an *approved* alternative method.

Exception: A drainage system for area wells is not required where the foundation is on well-drained soil or sand-gravel mixture soils in accordance with the United Soil Classification System, Group I Soils, as detailed in Table R405.1.

R310.4 Bars, grilles, covers and screens. Where bars, grilles, covers, screens or similar devices are placed over emergency escape and rescue openings, area wells, or win-dow wells, the minimum net clear opening size shall comply with Sections R310.2.1 through R310.2.3, and such devices shall be releasable or removable from the inside without the use of a key, tool, special knowledge or force greater than that required for the normal operation of the escape and rescue opening.

R310.5 Dwelling additions. Where *dwelling additions* contain sleeping rooms, an emergency escape and rescue opening shall be provided in each new sleeping room. Where *dwelling additions* have *basements*, an emergency escape and rescue opening shall be provided in the new *basement*.

Exceptions:

1. An emergency escape and rescue opening is not required in a new *basement* that contains a sleeping room with an emergency escape and rescue opening.

2. An emergency escape and rescue opening is not required in a new *basement* where there is an emergency escape and rescue opening in an existing *basement* that is *accessed* from the new *basement*.

R310.6 Alterations or repairs of existing basements. An emergency escape and rescue opening is not required where existing *basements* undergo alterations or repairs.

R310.6.1 Sleeping rooms in existing basements. New sleeping rooms created in an existing basement shall be provided with emergency escape and rescue openings in accordance with Section R310.1.

Exception: Emergency escape and rescue openings are not required to be provided where the entire basement area, including all portions of the means of egress to the level of exit discharge, and all areas on the level of exit discharge that are open to the means of egress are protected with an automatic sprinkler system in accordance with IRC Section P2904 or NFPA 13D.

SECTION R311
MEANS OF EGRESS

R311.1 Means of egress. *Dwellings* shall be provided with a means of egress in accordance with this section. The means of egress shall provide a continuous and unobstructed path of vertical and horizontal egress travel from all portions of the *dwelling* to the required egress door without requiring travel through a garage. The required egress door shall open directly into a public way or to a *yard* or court that opens to a public way.

R311.2 Egress door. Not less than one egress door shall be provided for each *dwelling* unit. The egress door shall be side-hinged, and shall provide a clear width of not less than 32 inches (813 mm) where measured between the face of the door and the stop, with the door open 90 degrees (1.57 rad). The clear height of the door opening shall be not less than 78 inches (1981 mm) in height measured from the top of the threshold to the bottom of the stop. Other doors shall not be required to comply with these minimum dimensions. Egress doors shall be readily openable from inside the *dwelling* without the use of a key or special knowledge or effort.

R311.3 Floors and landings at exterior doors. There shall be a landing or floor on each side of each exterior door. The width of each landing shall be not less than the door served. Landings shall have a dimension of not less than 36 inches (914 mm) measured in the direction of travel. The slope at exterior landings shall not exceed $^{1}/_{4}$ unit vertical in 12 units horizontal (2 percent).

Exception: Exterior balconies less than 60 square feet (5.6 m^2) and only *accessed* from a door are permitted to have a landing that is less than 36 inches (914 mm) measured in the direction of travel.

R311.3.1 Floor elevations at the required egress doors. Landings or finished floors at the required egress door shall be not more than $1^{1}/_{2}$ inches (38 mm) lower than the top of the threshold.

Exception: The landing or floor on the exterior side shall be not more than $7^{3}/_{4}$ inches (196 mm) below the top of the threshold provided that the door does not swing over the landing or floor.

Where exterior landings or floors serving the required egress door are not at *grade*, they shall be provided with access to *grade* by means of a ramp in accordance with Section R311.8 or a stairway in accordance with Section R311.7.

R311.3.2 Floor elevations at other exterior doors. Doors other than the required egress door shall be provided with landings or floors not more than $7^{3}/_{4}$ inches (196 mm) below the top of the threshold.

Exception: A landing is not required if a stairway less than 30 inches (762 mm) in height is located on the exterior side of the door, provided the door does not swing over the stairway. The stairway height shall be measured vertically from the interior floor surface to the finished grade.

R311.3.3 Storm and screen doors. Storm and screen doors shall be permitted to swing over exterior stairs and landings.

R311.4 Vertical egress. Egress from habitable levels including habitable attics and *basements* that are not provided with an egress door in accordance with Section R311.2 shall be by a ramp in accordance with Section R311.8 or a stairway in accordance with Section R311.7.

R311.5 Landing, deck, balcony and stair construction and attachment. Exterior landings, decks, balconies, stairs and similar facilities shall be positively anchored to the primary structure to resist both vertical and lateral forces or shall be designed to be self-supporting. Attachment shall not be accomplished by use of toenails or nails subject to withdrawal.

R311.6 Hallways. The width of a hallway shall be not less than 3 feet (914 mm).

R311.7 Stairways.

R311.7.1 Stairways; general.

R311.7.1.1 Stairways serving dwellings or accessory structures. All stairways serving a dwelling or accessory structure, or any part thereof, shall comply with this section. This shall include exterior stairs from a dwelling or garage to grade and those stairs serving decks, porches, balconies, sun rooms, and similar structures.

Exceptions:

1. Stairs serving attics or crawl spaces.

2. Stairs that only provide access to plumbing, mechanical, or electrical equipment.

R311.7.1.2 Width. Stairways shall be not less than 36 inches (914 mm) in clear width at all points above the permitted handrail height and below the required headroom height. Handrails shall not project more than 4.5 inches (114 mm) on either side of the stairway and the minimum clear width of the stairway at and below the handrail height, including treads and landings, shall be not less than $31^{1}/_{2}$ inches (787 mm) where a handrail is installed on one side and 27 inches (698 mm) where handrails are provided on both sides.

Exception: The width of spiral stairways shall be in accordance with Section R311.7.10.1.

R311.7.2 Headroom. The minimum headroom in all parts of the stairway shall be not less than 6 feet 8 inches (2032 mm) measured vertically from the sloped line adjoining the tread nosing or from the floor surface of the landing or platform on that portion of the stairway.

Exceptions:

1. Where the nosings of treads at the side of a flight extend under the edge of a floor opening through which the stair passes, the floor opening shall be allowed to project horizontally into the required headroom a maximum of $4^{3}/_{4}$ inches (121 mm).

2. The minimum headroom for existing buildings shall be in accordance with Section R305.2.2.

3. The headroom for spiral stairways shall be in accordance with Section R311.7.10.1.

R311.7.3 Vertical rise. A flight of stairs shall not have a vertical rise larger than 151 inches (3835 mm) between floor levels or landings.

R311.7.4 Walkline. The walkline across winder treads and landings shall be concentric to the turn and parallel to the direction of travel entering and exiting the turn. The walkline shall be located 12 inches (305 mm) from the inside of the turn. The 12-inch (305 mm) dimension shall be measured from the widest point of the clear stair width at the walking surface. Where winders are adjacent within a flight, the point of the widest clear stair width of the adjacent winders shall be used.

R311.7.5 Stair treads and risers. Stair treads and risers shall meet the requirements of this section. For the purposes of this section, dimensions and dimensioned surfaces shall be exclusive of carpets, rugs or runners.

R311.7.5.1 Risers. The riser height shall be not more than $7^{3}/_{4}$ inches (196 mm). The riser shall be measured vertically between leading edges of the adjacent treads. The greatest riser height within any flight of stairs shall not exceed the smallest by more than $^3/_8$ inch (9.5 mm). Risers shall be vertical or sloped from the underside of the nosing of the tread above at an angle not more than 30 degrees (0.51 rad) from the vertical. At open risers, openings located more than 30 inches (762 mm), as measured vertically, to the floor or grade below shall not permit the passage of a 4-inch-diameter (102 mm) sphere.

Exceptions:

1. The opening between adjacent treads is not limited on spiral stairways.

2. The riser height of spiral stairways shall be in accordance with Section R311.7.10.1.

R311.7.5.2 Treads. The tread depth shall be not less than 10 inches (254 mm). The tread depth shall be measured horizontally between the vertical planes of the foremost projection of adjacent treads and at a right angle to the tread's leading edge. The greatest tread depth within any flight of stairs shall not exceed the smallest by more than $^3/_8$ inch (9.5 mm).

R311.7.5.2.1 Winder treads. Winder treads shall have a tread depth of not less than 10 inches (254 mm) measured between the vertical planes of the foremost projection of adjacent treads at the intersections with the walkline. Winder treads shall have a tread depth of not less than 6 inches (152 mm) at any point within the clear width of the stair. Within any flight of stairs, the largest winder tread depth at the walkline shall not exceed the smallest winder tread by more than $^3/_8$ inch (9.5 mm). Consistently shaped winders at the walkline shall be allowed within the same flight of stairs as rectangular treads and shall not be required to be within $^3/_8$ inch (9.5 mm) of the rectangular tread depth.

Exception: The tread depth at spiral stairways shall be in accordance with Section R311.7.10.1.

R311.7.5.3 Nosings. Nosings at treads, landings and floors of stairways shall have a radius of curvature at the nosing not greater than $^9/_{16}$ inch (14 mm) or a bevel not greater than $^1/_2$ inch (12.7 mm). A nosing projection not less than $^3/_4$ inch (19 mm) and not more than $1^1/_4$ inches (32 mm) shall be provided on stairways. The greatest nosing projection shall not exceed the smallest nosing projection by more than $^3/_8$ inch (9.5 mm) within a stairway.

Exception: A nosing projection is not required where the tread depth is not less than 11 inches (279 mm).

R311.7.5.4 Exterior plastic composite stair treads. Plastic composite exterior stair treads shall comply with the provisions of this section and Section R507.2.2.

R311.7.6 Landings for stairways. There shall be a floor or landing at the top and bottom of each stairway. The width perpendicular to the direction of travel shall be not less than the width of the flight served. For landings of shapes other than square or rectangular, the depth at the walk line and the total area shall be not less than that of a quarter circle with a radius equal to the required landing width. Where the stairway has a straight run, the depth in the direction of travel shall be not less than 36 inches (914 mm).

Exception: A floor or landing is not required at the top of an interior flight of stairs, including stairs in an enclosed garage, provided that a door does not swing over the stairs.

R311.7.7 Stairway walking surface. The walking surface of treads and landings of stairways shall be sloped not steeper than one unit vertical in 48 inches horizontal (2-percent slope).

R311.7.8 Handrails. Handrails shall be provided on not less than one side of each flight of stairs with four or more risers.

R311.7.8.1 Height. Handrail height, measured vertically from the sloped plane adjoining the tread nosing, or finish surface of ramp slope, shall be not less than 34 inches (864 mm) and not more than 38 inches (965 mm).

Exceptions:

1. The use of a volute, turnout or starting easing shall be allowed over the lowest tread.

2. Where handrail fittings or bendings are used to provide continuous transition between flights, transitions at winder treads, the transition from handrail to *guard*, or used at the start of a flight, the handrail height at the fittings or bendings shall be permitted to exceed 38 inches (956 mm).

R311.7.8.2 Handrail projection. Handrails shall not project more than $4^1/_2$ inches (114 mm) on either side of the stairway.

Exception: Where nosings of landings, floors or passing flights project into the stairway reducing the clearance at passing handrails, handrails shall project not more than $6^1/_2$ inches (165 mm) into the stairway, provided that the stair width and handrail clearance are not reduced to less than that required.

R311.7.8.3 Handrail clearance. Handrails adjacent to a wall shall have a space of not less than $1^1/_2$ inches (38 mm) between the wall and the handrails.

R311.7.8.4 Continuity. Handrails shall be continuous for the full length of the flight, from a point directly above the top riser of the flight to a point directly above the lowest riser of the flight. Handrail ends shall be returned or shall terminate in newel posts or safety terminals.

Exceptions:

1. Handrail continuity shall be permitted to be interrupted by a newel post at a turn in a flight with winders, at a landing, or over the lowest tread.

2. A volute, turnout or starting easing shall be allowed to terminate over the lowest tread.

R311.7.8.5 Grip size. Required handrails shall be of one of the following types or provide equivalent graspability.

1. Type I. Handrails with a circular cross section shall have an outside diameter of not less than $1^1/_4$ inches (32 mm) and not greater than 2 inches (51 mm). If the handrail is not circular, it shall have a perimeter of not less than 4 inches (102 mm) and not greater than $6^1/_4$ inches (160 mm) and a cross section of not more than $2^1/_4$ inches (57 mm). Edges shall have a radius of not less than 0.01 inch (0.25 mm).

2. Type II. Handrails with a perimeter greater than $6^1/_4$ inches (160 mm) shall have a graspable finger recess area on both sides of the profile. The finger recess shall begin within $^3/_4$ inch (19 mm) measured vertically from the tallest portion of the profile and have a depth of not less than $^5/_{16}$ inch (8 mm) within $^7/_8$ inch (22 mm) below the widest portion of the profile. This required depth shall continue for not less than $^3/_8$ inch (10 mm) to a level that is not less than $1^3/_4$ inches (45 mm) below the tallest portion of the profile. The width of the handrail above the recess shall be not less than $1^1/_4$ inches (32 mm) and not more than $2^3/_4$ inches (70 mm). Edges shall have a radius of not less than 0.01 inch (0.25 mm).

R311.7.8.6 Exterior plastic composite handrails. Plastic composite exterior handrails shall comply with the requirements of Section R507.2.2.

R311.7.9 Illumination. Stairways shall be provided with illumination in accordance with Sections R303.7 and R303.8.

R311.7.10 Special stairways. Spiral stairways and bulkhead enclosure stairways shall comply with the requirements of Section R311.7 except as specified in Sections R311.7.10.1 and R311.7.10.2.

R311.7.10.1 Spiral stairways. The clear width at and below the handrails at spiral stairways shall be not less than 26 inches (660 mm) and the walkline radius shall be not greater than $24^1/_2$ inches (622 mm). Each tread shall have a depth of not less than $6^3/_4$ inches (171 mm) at the walkline. Treads shall be identical, and the rise shall be not more than $9^1/_2$ inches (241 mm). Headroom shall be not less than 6 feet 6 inches (1982 mm).

R311.7.10.2 Bulkhead enclosure stairways. Stairways serving bulkhead enclosures, not part of the required building egress, providing access from the outside *grade* level to the *basement* shall be exempt from the requirements of Sections R311.3 and R311.7 where the height from the *basement* finished floor level to *grade* adjacent to the stairway is not more than 8 feet (2438 mm) and the *grade* level opening to the stairway is covered by a bulkhead enclosure with hinged doors or other *approved* means.

R311.7.11 Alternating tread devices. Alternating tread devices shall not be used as an element of a means of egress. Alternating tread devices shall be permitted pro-vided that a required means of egress stairway or ramp serves the same space at each adjoining level or where a means of egress is not required. The clear width at and below the handrails shall be not less than 20 inches (508 mm).

Exception: Alternating tread devices are allowed to be used as an element of a means of egress for lofts, mezzanines and similar areas of 200 gross square feet (18.6 m^2) or less where such devices do not provide exclusive access to a kitchen or bathroom.

R311.7.11.1 Treads of alternating tread devices. Alternating tread devices shall have a tread depth of not less than 5 inches (127 mm), a projected tread depth of not less than $8^1/_2$ inches (216 mm), a tread width of not less than 7 inches (178 mm) and a riser height of not more than $9^1/_2$ inches (241 mm). The tread depth shall be measured horizontally between the vertical planes of the foremost projections of adjacent treads. The riser height shall be measured vertically between the leading edges of adjacent treads. The riser height and tread depth provided shall result in an angle of ascent from the horizontal of between 50 and 70 degrees (0.87 and 1.22 rad). The initial tread of the device shall begin at the same elevation as the platform, landing or floor surface.

R311.7.11.2 Handrails of alternating tread devices. Handrails shall be provided on both sides of alternating tread devices and shall comply with Sections R311.7.8.2 to R311.7.8.6. Handrail height shall be uniform, not less than 30 inches (762 mm) and not more than 34 inches (864 mm).

R311.7.12 Ships ladders. Ships ladders shall not be used as an element of a means of egress. Ships ladders shall be permitted provided that a required means of egress stairway or ramp serves the same space at each adjoining level or where a means of egress is not required. The clear width at and below the handrails shall be not less than 20 inches.

Exception: Ships ladders are allowed to be used as an element of a means of egress for lofts, mezzanines and similar areas of 200 gross square feet (18.6 m^2) or less that do not provide exclusive access to a kitchen or bathroom.

R311.7.12.1 Treads of ships ladders. Treads shall have a depth of not less than 5 inches (127 mm). The tread shall be projected such that the total of the tread depth plus the nosing projection is not less than $8^1/_2$ inches (216 mm). The riser height shall be not more than $9^1/_2$ inches (241 mm).

R311.7.12.2 Handrails of ships ladders. Handrails shall be provided on both sides of ships ladders and shall comply with Sections R311.7.8.2 to R311.7.8.6. Handrail height shall be uniform, not less than 30 inches (762 mm) and not more than 34 inches (864 mm).

R311.8 Ramps.

R311.8.1 Maximum slope. Ramps serving the egress door required by Section R311.2 shall have a slope of not more than 1 unit vertical in 12 units horizontal (8.3-percent slope). Other ramps shall have a maximum slope of 1 unit vertical in 8 units horizontal (12.5 percent).

> **Exception:** Where it is technically infeasible to comply because of site constraints, ramps shall have a slope of not more than 1 unit vertical in 8 units horizontal (12.5 percent).

R311.8.2 Landings required. There shall be a floor or landing at the top and bottom of each ramp, where doors open onto ramps, and where ramps change directions. The width of the landing perpendicular to the ramp slope shall be not less than 36 inches (914 mm).

R311.8.3 Handrails required. Handrails shall be provided on not less than one side of ramps exceeding a slope of one unit vertical in 12 units horizontal (8.33-percent slope).

R311.8.3.1 Height. Handrail height, measured above the finished surface of the ramp slope, shall be not less than 34 inches (864 mm) and not more than 38 inches (965 mm).

R311.8.3.2 Grip size. Handrails on ramps shall comply with Section R311.7.8.5.

R311.8.3.3 Continuity. Handrails where required on ramps shall be continuous for the full length of the ramp. Handrail ends shall be returned or shall terminate in newel posts or safety terminals. Handrails adjacent to a wall shall have a space of not less than $1^1/_2$ inches (38 mm) between the wall and the handrails.

SECTION R312
GUARDS AND WINDOW FALL PROTECTION

R312.1 Guards. *Guards* shall be provided in accordance with Sections R312.1.1 through R312.1.4.

R312.1.1 Where required. *Guards* shall be located along the open sides of floors, stairs, ramps, and landings that are located more than 30 inches (762 mm) measured vertically to the floor or *grade* below. Insect screening shall not be considered as a *guard*.

R312.1.2 Height. Required *guards* at open-sided walking surfaces, including stairs, porches, balconies or landings, shall be not less than 36 inches (914 mm) in height as measured vertically above the adjacent walking surface or the line connecting the *nosings*.

Exceptions:

1. *Guards* on the open sides of stairs shall have a height of not less than 34 inches (864 mm) measured vertically from a line connecting the *nosings*.

2. Where the top of the *guard* serves as a handrail on the open sides of stairs, the top of the *guard* shall be not less than 34 inches (864 mm) and not more than 38 inches (965 mm) as measured vertically from a line connecting the *nosings*.

R312.1.3 Opening limitations. Required *guards* shall not have openings from the walking surface to the required

guard height that allow passage of a sphere 4 inches (102 mm) in diameter.

Exceptions:

1. The triangular openings at the open side of stair, formed by the riser, tread and bottom rail of a *guard*, shall not allow passage of a sphere 6 inches (153 mm) in diameter.

2. *Guards* on the open side of stairs shall not have openings that allow passage of a sphere $4^3/_8$ inches (111 mm) in diameter.

R312.1.4 Exterior plastic composite guards. Plastic composite exterior *guards* shall comply with the requirements of Section R317.4.

R312.2 Window fall protection. Window fall protection shall be provided in accordance with Sections R312.2.1 and R312.2.2.

R312.2.1 Window sills. In dwelling units, where the lowest part of the opening of an operable window is located more than 72 inches (1829 mm) above the finished *grade* or surface below, the lowest part of the window opening shall be a minimum of 36 inches (914 mm) above the finished floor of the room in which the window is located. Operable sections of windows shall not permit openings that allow passage of a 4-inch diameter (102 mm) sphere where such openings are located within 36 inches (914 mm) of the finished floor.

Exceptions:

1. Windows with openings that will not allow a 4-inch-diameter (102 mm) sphere to pass through the opening when the window is in its largest opened position.

2. Openings that are provided with window fall prevention devices that comply with ASTM F2090.

3. Windows that are provided with window opening control devices that comply with Section R312.2.2.

4. Replacement windows.

R312.2.2 Window opening control devices. Window opening control devices shall comply with ASTM F2090. The window opening control device, after operation to release the control device allowing the window to fully open, shall not reduce the net clear opening area of the window unit to less than the area required by Section R310.2.1.

SECTION R313
AUTOMATIC FIRE SPRINKLER SYSTEMS

R313.1 Townhouse automatic fire sprinkler systems. An automatic residential fire sprinkler system shall be installed in *townhouses*.

Exceptions:

1. An automatic residential fire sprinkler system shall not be required to be installed in a two-unit townhouse, unless required by Section R313.4.

2. An automatic residential fire sprinkler system shall not be required when additions or alterations are made to existing townhouses that do not have an automatic residential fire sprinkler system installed.

R313.1.1 Design and installation. Automatic residential fire sprinkler systems for *townhouses* shall be designed and installed in accordance with IRC Section P2904 or NFPA 13D.

> **R313.2 One- and two-family dwellings automatic fire systems.** An automatic residential fire sprinkler system shall not be required to be installed in one- and two-family *dwellings*, unless required by Section R313.4.

> **R313.2.1 Design and installation.** Automatic residential fire sprinkler systems shall be designed and installed in accordance with IRC Section P2904 or NFPA 13D.

R313.3 Installation requirements. When an automatic sprinkler system is required in two-family dwellings, it shall be installed in accordance with IRC Section P2904 or NFPA 13D.

Automatic sprinkler systems required in two-family dwellings and townhouse buildings shall be installed in accordance with the following:

1. Attached garages are required to have one dry head sprinkler located within 5 lineal feet (1524 mm) of each door installed in the common wall separating the dwelling unit and the attached garage;

2. Attached covered patios, covered decks, covered porches, and similar structures are required to have automatic sprinklers with a minimum of one dry head for every 20 lineal feet (6.096 m) of common wall between the dwelling unit and the covered patio, covered deck, covered porch, or similar structure.

   Exception: Attached roofs of covered patios, covered decks, covered porches, or similar structures that do not exceed 40 square feet (3716 m^2) of floor area.

R313.4 State-licensed facilities. One- and two-family dwellings and townhouse buildings containing facilities required to be licensed or registered by the state of Minnesota shall be provided with an automatic sprinkler system required by the applicable licensing provisions of that agency or according to this part, whichever is more restrictive.

SECTION R314
SMOKE ALARMS

R314.1 General. Smoke alarms shall comply with NFPA 72 and Section R314.

R314.1.1 Listings. Smoke alarms shall be *listed* in accordance with UL 217. Combination smoke and carbon monoxide alarms shall be *listed* in accordance with UL 217 and UL 2034.

R314.2 Where required. Smoke alarms shall be provided in accordance with this section.

R314.2.1 New construction. Smoke alarms shall be provided in *dwelling units*.

R314.2.2 Alterations, repairs and additions. An individual *dwelling unit* shall be equipped with smoke alarms located as required for new *dwellings* when:

1. Alterations, repairs (including installation or replacement of windows or doors), or additions requiring a building permit occur; or

2. One or more sleeping rooms are added or created in existing dwellings.

Exceptions:

1. Work involving the exterior surfaces of *dwellings*, such as the replacement of roofing or siding, or the addition of a an open porch or deck, or chimney repairs.

2. Installation, alteration, or repairs of plumbing, electrical, or mechanical systems.

R314.3 Location. Smoke alarms shall be installed in the following locations:

1. In each sleeping room.

2. Outside each separate sleeping area in the immediate vicinity of the bedrooms.

3. On each additional *story* of the *dwelling*, including *basements* and *habitable attics* and not including crawl spaces and uninhabitable *attics*. In *dwellings* or *dwelling units* with split levels and without an intervening door between the adjacent levels, a smoke alarm installed on the upper level shall suffice for the adjacent lower level provided that the lower level is less than one full *story* below the upper level.

4. Smoke alarms shall be installed not less than 3 feet (914 mm) horizontally from the door or opening of a bathroom that contains a bathtub or shower unless this would prevent placement of a smoke alarm required by this section.

R314.3.1 Installation near cooking appliances. Smoke alarms shall not be installed in the following locations unless this would prevent placement of a smoke alarm in a location required by Section R314.3.

1. Ionization smoke alarms shall not be installed less than 20 feet (6096 mm) horizontally from a permanently installed cooking *appliance*.

2. Ionization smoke alarms with an alarm-silencing switch shall not be installed less than 10 feet (3048 mm) horizontally from a permanently installed cooking *appliance*.

3. Photoelectric smoke alarms shall not be installed less than 6 feet (1828 mm) horizontally from a permanently installed cooking *appliance*.

R314.4 Interconnection. Where more than one smoke alarm is required to be installed within an individual dwelling unit in accordance with Section R314.3, the alarm devices shall be interconnected in such a manner that the actuation of one alarm will activate all of the alarms in the individual *dwelling unit*. Physical interconnection of smoke alarms shall not be required where listed wireless alarms are installed and all alarms sound upon activation of one alarm.

Exception: Interconnection of smoke alarms in existing areas shall not be required where alterations or repairs do not result in removal of interior wall or ceiling finishes exposing the structure.

R314.5 Combination alarms. Combination smoke and carbon monoxide alarms shall be permitted to be used in lieu of smoke alarms.

R314.6 Power source. Smoke alarms shall receive their primary power from the building wiring where such wiring is served from a commercial source and, where primary power is interrupted, shall receive power from a battery. Wiring shall be permanent and without a disconnecting switch other than those required for overcurrent protection.

Exceptions:

1. Smoke alarms shall be permitted to be battery operated where installed in buildings without commercial power.

2. Smoke alarms installed in existing areas shall be permitted to be battery powered provided any alterations or repairs do not result in the removal of interior wall or ceiling finishes exposing the structure.

R314.7 Fire alarm systems. Fire alarm systems shall be permitted to be used in lieu of smoke alarms and shall comply with Sections R314.7.1 through R314.7.4.

R314.7.1 General. Fire alarm systems shall comply with the provisions of this code and the household fire warning *equipment* provisions of NFPA 72. Smoke detectors shall be *listed* in accordance with UL 268.

R314.7.2 Location. Smoke detectors shall be installed in the locations specified in Section R314.3.

R314.7.3 Permanent fixture. Where a household fire alarm system is installed, it shall become a permanent fixture of the occupancy, owned by the homeowner.

R314.7.4 Combination detectors. Combination smoke and carbon monoxide detectors shall be permitted to be installed in fire alarm systems in lieu of smoke detectors, provided that they are *listed* in accordance with UL 268 and UL 2075.

SECTION R315
CARBON MONOXIDE ALARMS

R315.1 General. Carbon monoxide alarms shall comply with Section R315.

R315.1.1 Listings. Carbon monoxide alarms shall be *listed* in accordance with UL 2034. Combination carbon monoxide and smoke alarms shall be *listed* in accordance with UL 2034 and UL 217.

R315.2 Where required. Carbon monoxide alarms shall be provided in accordance with Sections R315.2.1 and R315.2.2.

R315.2.1 New construction. For new construction, every one-family dwelling unit, each unit in a two-family dwelling unit, and each townhouse dwelling unit shall be provided with an approved and operational carbon monoxide alarm where one or both of the following conditions exist.

1. The *dwelling unit* contains a fuel-fired *appliance*.

2. The *dwelling unit* has an attached garage with an opening that communicates with the dwelling unit.

R315.2.2 Alterations, repairs, and additions. An individual *dwelling unit* shall be equipped with carbon monoxide alarms located as required for new *dwellings* where:

1. Alterations, repairs (including installation or replacement of windows or doors), or additions requiring a building permit occur; or

2. One or more sleeping rooms are added or created in existing dwellings.

Exceptions:

1. Work involving the exterior surfaces of *dwellings*, such as the replacement of roofing or siding, the addition of an open porch or deck, or chimney repairs.

2. Installation, alteration, or repairs of plumbing, electrical, or mechanical systems.

R315.3 Location. Carbon monoxide alarms in *dwelling units* shall be installed outside of and not more than 10 feet (3048 mm) from each separate sleeping area or bedroom. Alarms shall be installed on each level containing sleeping areas or bedrooms. Where a fuel-burning *appliance* is located within a bedroom or its attached bathroom, a carbon monoxide alarm shall be installed within the bedroom.

R315.4 Combination alarms. Combination carbon monoxide and smoke alarms shall be permitted to be used in lieu of carbon monoxide alarms.

R315.5 Interconnectivity. Where more than one carbon monoxide alarm is required to be installed within an individual *dwelling unit* in accordance with Section R315.3, the alarm devices shall be interconnected in such a manner that the actuation of one alarm will activate all of the alarms in the individual *dwelling unit*. Physical interconnection of carbon monoxide alarms shall not be required where *listed* wireless alarms are installed and all alarms sound upon activation of one alarm.

Exception: Interconnection of carbon monoxide alarms in existing areas shall not be required where *alterations* or *repairs* do not result in removal of interior wall or ceiling finishes exposing the structure.

R315.6 Power source. Carbon monoxide alarms shall receive their primary power from the building wiring where such wiring is served from a commercial source and, where primary power is interrupted, shall receive power from a battery. Wiring shall be permanent and without a disconnecting switch other than those required for overcurrent protection.

Exceptions:

1. Carbon monoxide alarms shall be permitted to be battery operated where installed in buildings without commercial power.

2. Carbon monoxide alarms installed in existing areas shall be permitted to be battery powered provided any alterations or repairs do not result in the removal of interior wall or ceiling finishes exposing the structure.

R315.7 Carbon monoxide detection systems. Carbon monoxide detection systems shall be permitted to be used in lieu of carbon monoxide alarms and shall comply with Sections R315.7.1 through R315.7.4.

R315.7.1 General. Household carbon monoxide detection systems shall comply with NFPA 720. Carbon monoxide detectors shall be *listed* in accordance with UL 2075.

R315.7.2 Location. Carbon monoxide detectors shall be installed in the locations specified in Section R315.3. These locations supersede the locations specified in NFPA 720.

R315.7.3 Permanent fixture. Where a household carbon monoxide detection system is installed, it shall become a permanent fixture of the occupancy and owned by the homeowner.

R315.7.4 Combination detectors. Combination carbon monoxide and smoke detectors installed in carbon monoxide detection systems in lieu of carbon monoxide detectors shall be *listed* in accordance with UL 2075 and UL 268.

SECTION R316
FOAM PLASTIC

R316.1 General. The provisions of this section shall govern the materials, design, application, construction and installation of foam plastic materials.

R316.2 Labeling and identification. Packages and containers of foam plastic insulation and foam plastic insulation components delivered to the job site shall bear the *label* of an *approved agency* showing the manufacturer's name, the product listing, product identification and information sufficient to determine that the end use will comply with the requirements.

R316.3 Surface burning characteristics. Unless otherwise allowed in Section R316.5, foam plastic, or foam plastic cores used as a component in manufactured assemblies, used in building construction shall have a flame spread index of not more than 75 and shall have a smoke-developed index of not more than 450 when tested in the maximum thickness and density intended for use in accordance with ASTM E84 or UL 723. Loose-fill-type foam plastic insulation shall be tested as board stock for the flame spread index and smoke-developed index.

Exception: Foam plastic insulation more than 4 inches (102 mm) thick shall have a flame spread index of not more than 75 and a smoke-developed index of not more than 450 where tested at a thickness of not more than 4 inches (102 mm), provided that the end use is *approved* in accordance with Section R316.6 using the thickness and density intended for use.

R316.4 Thermal barrier. Unless otherwise allowed in Section R316.5, foam plastic shall be separated from the interior of a building by an *approved* thermal barrier of not less than $^1/_2$-inch (12.7 mm) gypsum wallboard, $^{23}/_{32}$-inch (18.2 mm) wood structural panel or a material that is tested in accordance with and meets the acceptance criteria of both the Temperature Transmission Fire Test and the Integrity Fire Test of NFPA 275.

R316.5 Specific requirements. The following requirements shall apply to these uses of foam plastic unless specifically *approved* in accordance with Section R316.6 or by other sections of the code or the requirements of Sections R316.2 through R316.4 have been met.

R316.5.1 Masonry or concrete construction. The thermal barrier specified in Section R316.4 is not required in a masonry or concrete wall, floor or roof where the foam plastic insulation is separated from the interior of the building by not less than a 1-inch (25 mm) thickness of masonry or concrete.

R316.5.2 Roofing. The thermal barrier specified in Section R316.4 is not required where the foam plastic in a roof assembly or under a roof covering is installed in accordance with the code and the manufacturer's instructions and is separated from the interior of the building by tongue-and-groove wood planks or wood structural panel sheathing, in accordance with Section R803, that is not less than $^{15}/_{32}$ inch (11.9 mm) thick bonded with exterior glue, identified as Exposure 1 and with edges supported by blocking or tongue-and-groove joints or an equivalent material. The smoke-developed index for roof applications shall not be limited.

R316.5.3 Attics. The thermal barrier specified in Section R316.4 is not required where all of the following apply:

1. *Attic* access is required by Section R807.1.

2. The space is entered only for purposes of repairs or maintenance.

3. The foam plastic insulation has been tested in accordance with Section R316.6 or the foam plastic insulation is protected against ignition using one of the following ignition barrier materials:

   3.1. $1^1/_2$-inch-thick (38 mm) mineral fiber insulation.

   3.2. $^1/_4$-inch-thick (6.4 mm) wood structural panels.

   3.3. $^3/_8$-inch (9.5 mm) particleboard.

   3.4. $^1/_4$-inch (6.4 mm) hardboard.

   3.5. $^3/_8$-inch (9.5 mm) gypsum board.

   3.6. Corrosion-resistant steel having a base metal thickness of 0.016 inch (0.406 mm).

3.7. $1^1/_2$-inch-thick (38 mm) cellulose insulation.

3.8. $^1/_4$-inch (6.4 mm) fiber-cement panel, soffit or backer board.

The ignition barrier is not required where the foam plastic insulation has been tested in accordance with Section R316.6.

R316.5.4 Crawl spaces. The thermal barrier specified in Section R316.4 is not required where all of the following apply:

1. Crawl space access is required by Section R408.4.

2. Entry is made only for purposes of repairs or maintenance.

3. The foam plastic insulation has been tested in accordance with Section R316.6 or the foam plastic insulation is protected against ignition using one of the following ignition barrier materials:

   3.1. $1^1/_2$-inch-thick (38 mm) mineral fiber insulation.

   3.2. $^1/_4$-inch-thick (6.4 mm) wood structural panels.

   3.3. $^3/_8$-inch (9.5 mm) particleboard.

   3.4. $^1/_4$-inch (6.4 mm) hardboard.

   3.5. $^3/_8$-inch (9.5 mm) gypsum board.

   3.6. Corrosion-resistant steel having a base metal thickness of 0.016 inch (0.406 mm).

   3.7. $^1/_4$-inch (6.4 mm) fiber-cement panel, soffit or backer board.

R316.5.5 Foam-filled exterior doors. Foam-filled exterior doors are exempt from the requirements of Sections R316.3 and R316.4.

R316.5.6 Foam-filled garage doors. Foam-filled garage doors in attached or detached garages are exempt from the requirements of Sections R316.3 and R316.4.

R316.5.7 Foam backer board. The thermal barrier specified in Section R316.4 is not required where siding backer board foam plastic insulation has a thickness of not more than 0.5 inch (12.7 mm) and a potential heat of not more than 2000 Btu per square foot (22 720 kJ/m^2) when tested in accordance with NFPA 259 and it complies with one or more of the following:

1. The foam plastic insulation is separated from the interior of the building by not less than 2 inches (51 mm) of mineral fiber insulation.

2. The foam plastic insulation is installed over existing *exterior wall* finish in conjunction with re-siding.

3. The foam plastic insulation has been tested in accordance with Section R316.6.

R316.5.8 Re-siding. The thermal barrier specified in Section R316.4 is not required where the foam plastic insulation is installed over existing *exterior wall* finish in conjunction with re-siding provided that the foam plastic has a thickness of not more than 0.5 inch (12.7 mm) and a

potential heat of not more than 2000 Btu per square foot (22 720 kJ/m^2) when tested in accordance with NFPA 259.

R316.5.9 Interior trim. The thermal barrier specified in Section R316.4 is not required for exposed foam plastic interior trim, provided that all of the following are met:

1. The density is not less than 20 pounds per cubic foot (320 kg/m^3).

2. The thickness of the trim is not more than 0.5 inch (12.7 mm) and the width is not more than 8 inches (204 mm).

3. The interior trim shall not constitute more than 10 percent of the aggregate wall and ceiling area of any room or space.

4. The flame spread index does not exceed 75 when tested in accordance with ASTM E84 or UL 723. The smoke-developed index is not limited.

R316.5.10 Interior finish. Foam plastics used as interior finishes shall comply with Section R316.6 and shall meet the flame spread index and smoke-developed index requirements of Sections R302.9.1 and R302.9.2.

R316.5.11 Sill plates and headers. Foam plastic be spray applied to sill plates and headers or installed in the perimeter joist space without the thermal barrier specified in Section R316.4 shall comply with all of the following:

1. The thickness of the foam plastic shall be not more than $3^1/_4$ inches (83 mm).

2. The density of the foam plastic shall be in the range of 0.5 to 2.0 pounds per cubic foot (8 to 32 kg/m^3).

3. The foam plastic shall have a flame spread index of 25 or less and an accompanying smoke-developed index of 450 or less when tested in accordance with ASTM E84 or UL 723.

R316.5.12 Sheathing. Foam plastic insulation used as sheathing shall comply with Section R316.3 and Section R316.4. Where the foam plastic sheathing is exposed to the *attic* space at a gable or kneewall, the provisions of Section R316.5.3 shall apply. Where foam plastic insulation is used as *exterior wall* sheathing on framed wall assemblies, it shall comply with Section R316.8.

R316.5.13 Floors. The thermal barrier specified in Section R316.4 is not required to be installed on the walking surface of a structural floor system that contains foam plastic insulation where the foam plastic is covered by not more than a nominal $^1/_2$-inch-thick (12.7 mm) wood structural panel or equivalent. The thermal barrier specified in Section R316.4 is required on the underside of the structural floor system that contains foam plastic insulation where the underside of the structural floor system is exposed to the interior of the building.

R316.6 Specific approval. Foam plastic not meeting the requirements of Sections R316.3 through R316.5 shall be specifically *approved* on the basis of one of the following *approved* tests: NFPA 286 with the acceptance criteria of Section R302.9.4, FM 4880, UL 1040 or UL 1715, or fire tests related to actual end-use configurations. Approval shall be based on the actual end-use configuration and shall be performed on the finished foam plastic assembly in the maximum thickness intended for use. Assemblies tested shall include seams, joints and other typical details used in the installation of the assembly and shall be tested in the manner intended for use.

R316.7 Termite damage. The use of foam plastics in areas of "very heavy" termite infestation probability shall be in accordance with Section R318.4.

R316.8 Wind resistance. Foam plastic insulation complying with ASTM C578 and ASTM C1289 and used as *exterior wall* sheathing on framed wall assemblies shall comply with SBCA FS 100 for wind pressure resistance unless installed directly over a sheathing material that is separately capable of resisting the wind load or otherwise exempted from the scope of SBCA FS 100.

SECTION R317
PROTECTION OF WOOD AND
WOOD-BASED PRODUCTS AGAINST DECAY

R317.1 Location required. Protection of wood and wood-based products from decay shall be provided in the following locations by the use of naturally durable wood or wood that is preservative-treated in accordance with AWPA U1.

1. Wood joists or the bottom of a wood structural floor where closer than 18 inches (457 mm) or wood girders where closer than 12 inches (305 mm) to the exposed ground in crawl spaces or unexcavated area located within the periphery of the building foundation.

2. Wood framing members that rest on concrete or masonry exterior foundation walls and are less than 8 inches (203 mm) from the exposed ground.

3. Sills and sleepers on a concrete or masonry slab that is in direct contact with the ground unless separated from such slab by an impervious moisture barrier.

4. The ends of wood girders entering exterior masonry or concrete walls having clearances of less than $^1/_2$ inch (12.7 mm) on tops, sides and ends.

5. Wood siding, sheathing and wall framing on the exterior of a building having a clearance of less than 6 inches (152 mm) from the ground or less than 2 inches (51 mm) measured vertically from concrete steps, porch slabs, patio slabs and similar horizontal surfaces exposed to the weather.

6. Wood structural members supporting moisture-permeable floors or roofs that are exposed to the weather, such as concrete or masonry slabs, unless separated from such floors or roofs by an impervious moisture barrier.

7. Wood furring strips or other wood framing members attached directly to the interior of exterior masonry walls or concrete walls below *grade* except where an *approved* vapor retarder is applied between the wall and the furring strips or framing members.

R317.1.1 Field treatment. Field-cut ends, notches and drilled holes of preservative-treated wood shall be treated in the field in accordance with AWPA M4.

R317.1.2 Ground contact. All wood in contact with the ground, embedded in concrete in direct contact with the ground or embedded in concrete exposed to the weather that supports permanent structures intended for human occupancy shall be *approved* pressure-preservative-treated wood suitable for ground contact use, except that untreated wood used entirely below groundwater level or continuously submerged in fresh water shall not be required to be pressure-preservative treated.

R317.1.3 Geographical areas. In geographical areas where experience has demonstrated a specific need, *approved* naturally durable or pressure-preservative-treated wood shall be used for those portions of wood members that form the structural supports of buildings, balconies, porches or similar permanent building appurtenances where those members are exposed to the weather without adequate protection from a roof, eave, overhang or other covering that would prevent moisture or water accumulation on the surface or at joints between members. Depending on local experience, such members typically include:

1. Horizontal members such as girders, joists and decking.

2. Vertical members such as posts, poles and columns.

3. Both horizontal and vertical members.

R317.1.4 Wood columns. Wood columns shall be *approved* wood of natural decay resistance or *approved* pressure-preservative-treated wood.

Exceptions:

1. Columns exposed to the weather or in *basements* where supported by concrete piers or metal pedestals projecting 1 inch (25 mm) above a concrete floor or 6 inches (152 mm) above exposed earth and the earth is covered by an *approved* impervious moisture barrier.

2. Columns in enclosed crawl spaces or unexcavated areas located within the periphery of the building where supported by a concrete pier or metal pedestal at a height more than 8 inches (203 mm) from exposed earth and the earth is covered by an impervious moisture barrier.

3. Deck posts supported by concrete piers or metal pedestals projecting not less than 1 inch (25 mm) above a concrete floor or 6 inches (152 mm) above exposed earth.

R317.1.5 Exposed glued-laminated timbers. The portions of glued-laminated timbers that form the structural supports of a building or other structure and are exposed to weather and not properly protected by a roof, eave or similar covering shall be pressure treated with preservative, or be manufactured from naturally durable or preservative-treated wood.

R317.2 Quality mark. Lumber and plywood required to be pressure-preservative treated in accordance with Section R318.1 shall bear the quality *mark* of an *approved* inspection agency that maintains continuing supervision, testing and inspection over the quality of the product and that has been *approved* by an accreditation body that complies with the requirements of the American Lumber Standard Committee treated wood program.

R317.2.1 Required information. The required quality *mark* on each piece of pressure-preservative-treated lumber or plywood shall contain the following information:

1. Identification of the treating plant.

2. Type of preservative.

3. The minimum preservative retention.

4. End use for which the product was treated.

5. Standard to which the product was treated.

6. Identity of the *approved* inspection agency.

7. The designation "Dry," if applicable.

Exception: Quality *mark*s on lumber less than 1 inch (25 mm) nominal thickness, or lumber less than nominal 1 inch by 5 inches (25 mm by 127 mm) or 2 inches by 4 inches (51 mm by 102 mm) or lumber 36 inches (914 mm) or less in length shall be applied by stamping the faces of exterior pieces or by end labeling not less than 25 percent of the pieces of a bundled unit.

R317.3 Fasteners and connectors in contact with preservative-treated and fire-retardant-treated wood. Fasteners, including nuts and washers, and connectors in contact with preservative-treated wood and fire-retardant-treated wood shall be in accordance with this section. The coating weights for zinc-coated fasteners shall be in accordance with ASTM A153. Stainless steel driven fasteners shall be in accordance with the material requirements of ASTM F1667.

R317.3.1 Fasteners for preservative-treated wood. Fasteners, including nuts and washers, for preservative-treated wood shall be of hot-dipped, zinc-coated galvanized steel, stainless steel, silicon bronze or copper. Staples shall be of stainless steel. Coating types and weights for connectors in contact with preservative-treated wood shall be in accordance with the connector manufacturer's recommendations. In the absence of manufacturer's recommendations, not less than ASTM A653 type G185 zinc-coated galvanized steel, or equivalent, shall be used.

Exceptions:

1. $\frac{1}{2}$-inch-diameter (12.7 mm) or greater steel bolts.

2. Fasteners other than nails, staples and timber rivets shall be permitted to be of mechanically deposited zinc-coated steel with coating weights in accordance with ASTM B695, Class 55 minimum.

3. Plain carbon steel fasteners in SBX/DOT and zinc borate preservative-treated wood in an interior, dry environment shall be permitted.

R317.3.2 Fastenings for wood foundations. Fastenings, including nuts and washers, for wood foundations shall be as required in AWC PWF.

R317.3.3 Fasteners for fire-retardant-treated wood used in exterior applications or wet or damp locations. Fasteners, including nuts and washers, for fire-retardant-treated wood used in exterior applications or wet or damp locations shall be of hot-dipped, zinc-coated galvanized steel, stainless steel, silicon bronze or copper. Fasteners other than nails, staples and timber rivets shall be permitted to be of mechanically deposited zinc-coated steel with coating weights in accordance with ASTM B695, Class 55 minimum.

R317.3.4 Fasteners for fire-retardant-treated wood used in interior applications. Fasteners, including nuts and washers, for fire-retardant-treated wood used in interior locations shall be in accordance with the manufacturer's recommendations. In the absence of the manufacturer's recommendations, Section R317.3.3 shall apply.

R317.4 Plastic composites. Plastic composite exterior deck boards, stair treads, guards and handrails containing wood, cellulosic or other biodegradable materials shall comply with the requirements of Section R507.2.2.

SECTION R318
PROTECTION AGAINST
SUBTERRANEAN TERMITES

R318.1 Subterranean termite control methods. In areas subject to damage from termites as indicated by Table R301.2(1), protection shall be by one, or a combination, of the following methods:

1. Chemical termiticide treatment in accordance with Section R318.2.

2. Termite-baiting system installed and maintained in accordance with the *label*.

3. Pressure-preservative-treated wood in accordance with the provisions of Section R317.1.

4. Naturally durable termite-resistant wood.

5. Physical barriers in accordance with Section R318.3 and used in locations as specified in Section R317.1.

6. Cold-formed steel framing in accordance with Sections R505.2.1 and R603.2.1.

R318.1.1 Quality mark. Lumber and plywood required to be pressure-preservative treated in accordance with Section R318.1 shall bear the quality *mark* of an *approved* inspection agency that maintains continuing supervision, testing and inspection over the quality of the product and that has been *approved* by an accreditation body that complies with the requirements of the American Lumber Standard Committee treated wood program.

R318.1.2 Field treatment. Field-cut ends, notches and drilled holes of pressure-preservative-treated wood shall be retreated in the field in accordance with AWPA M4.

R318.2 Chemical termiticide treatment. Chemical termiticide treatment shall include soil treatment or field-applied wood treatment. The concentration, rate of application and method of treatment of the chemical termiticide shall be in strict accordance with the termiticide *label*.

R318.3 Barriers. *Approved* physical barriers, such as metal or plastic sheeting or collars specifically designed for termite prevention, shall be installed in a manner to prevent termites from entering the structure. Shields placed on top of an exterior foundation wall shall be used only if in combination with another method of protection.

R318.4 Foam plastic protection. In areas where the probability of termite infestation is "very heavy" as indicated in Figure R301.2(7), extruded and expanded polystyrene, polyisocyanurate and other foam plastics shall not be installed on the exterior face or under interior or exterior foundation walls or slab foundations located below *grade*. The clearance between foam plastics installed above *grade* and exposed earth shall be not less than 6 inches (152 mm).

Exceptions:

1. Buildings where the structural members of walls, floors, ceilings and roofs are entirely of noncombustible materials or pressure-preservative-treated wood.

2. Where in *addition* to the requirements of Section R318.1, an *approved* method of protecting the foam plastic and structure from subterranean termite damage is used.

3. On the interior side of *basement walls*.

SECTION R319
SITE ADDRESS

R319.1 Address identification. Buildings shall be provided with *approved* address identification. The address identification shall be legible and placed in a position that is visible from the street or road fronting the property. Address identification characters shall contrast with their background. Address numbers shall be Arabic numbers or alphabetical letters. Numbers shall not be spelled out. Each character shall be not less than 4 inches (102 mm) in height with a stroke width of not less than 0.5 inch (12.7 mm). Where required by the fire code official, address identification shall be provided in additional *approved* locations to facilitate emergency response. Where access is by means of a private road and the building address cannot be viewed from the public way, a monument, pole or other sign or means shall be used to identify the structure. Address identification shall be maintained.

SECTION R320
ACCESSIBILITY

R320.1 Scope. Where there are four or more IRC-3 *dwelling units* or sleeping units in a single structure, the provisions for Group R-3 occupancies located in Minnesota Rules, Chapter 1341, *Minnesota Accessibility Code*, shall apply.

R320.1.1 Guestrooms. Deleted.

SECTION R321
ELEVATORS AND PLATFORM LIFTS

R321.1 Elevators, platform lifts. For elevator and platform lift requirements, see Minnesota Rules, Chapter 1307, Elevators and Related Devices.

R321.2 Platform lifts. Deleted.

R321.3 Accessibility. Deleted.

SECTION R322
FLOOD-RESISTANT CONSTRUCTION

R322.1 General. See Minnesota Rules, Chapter 1335.

SECTION R323
STORM SHELTERS

R323.1 General. Deleted.

SECTION 324
SOLAR ENERGY SYSTEMS

R324.1 General. Solar energy systems shall comply with the provisions of this section.

R324.2 Solar thermal systems. Solar thermal systems shall be designed and installed in accordance with Chapter 23 and the *International Fire Code*.

R324.3 Photovoltaic systems. Photovoltaic systems shall be designed and installed in accordance with Sections R324.3.1 through R324.7.1, NFPA 70 and the manufacturer's installation instructions.

R324.3.1 Equipment listings. Photovoltaic panels and modules shall be listed and labeled in accordance with UL 1703. Inverters shall be *listed* and *labeled* in accordance with UL 1741. Systems connected to the utility grid shall use inverters *listed* for utility interaction.

R324.4 Rooftop-mounted photovoltaic systems. Rooftop-mounted *photovoltaic panel systems* installed on or above the roof covering shall be designed and installed in accordance with this section.

R324.4.1 Structural requirements. Rooftop-mounted *photovoltaic panel systems* shall be designed to structurally support the system and withstand applicable gravity loads in accordance with Chapter 3. The roof on which these systems are installed shall be designed and constructed to support the loads imposed by such systems in accordance with Chapter 8.

R324.4.1.1 Roof load. Portions of roof structures not covered with *photovoltaic panel systems* shall be designed for dead loads and roof loads in accordance with Sections R301.4 and R301.6. Portions of roof structures covered with *photovoltaic panel systems* shall be designed for the following load cases:

1. Dead load (including *photovoltaic panel* weight) plus snow load in accordance with Table R301.2(1).

2. Dead load (excluding *photovoltaic panel* weight) plus roof live load or snow load, whichever is greater, in accordance with Section R301.6.

R324.4.1.2 Wind load. Rooftop-mounted *photovoltaic panel* or *module* systems and their supports shall be designed and installed to resist the component and cladding loads specified in Table R301.2(2), adjusted for height and exposure in accordance with Table R301.2(3).

R324.4.2 Fire classification. Rooftop-mounted *photovoltaic panel systems* shall have the same fire classification as the roof assembly required in Section R902.

R324.4.3 Roof penetrations. Roof penetrations shall be flashed and sealed in accordance with Chapter 9.

R324.5 Building-integrated photovoltaic systems. Building-integrated photovoltaic systems that serve as roof coverings shall be designed and installed in accordance with Section R905.

R324.5.1 Photovoltaic shingles. Photovoltaic shingles shall comply with Section R905.16.

R324.5.2 Fire classification. *Building-integrated photovoltaic systems* shall have a fire classification in accordance with Section R902.3.

R324.6 Roof access and pathways. Roof access, pathways and setback requirements shall be provided in accordance with Sections R324.6.1 through R324.6.2.1. Access and minimum spacing shall be required to provide emergency access to the roof, to provide pathways to specific areas of the roof, provide for smoke ventilation opportunity areas, and to provide emergency egress from the roof.

Exceptions:

1. Detached, nonhabitable structures, including but not limited to detached garages, parking shade structures, carports, solar trellises and similar structures, shall not be required to provide roof access.

2. Roof access, pathways and setbacks need not be provided where the code official has determined that rooftop operations will not be employed.

3. These requirements shall not apply to roofs with slopes of two units vertical in 12 units horizontal (17-percent slope) or less.

R324.6.1 Pathways. Not fewer than two pathways, on separate roof planes from lowest roof edge to ridge and not less than 36 inches (914 mm) wide, shall be provided on all buildings. Not fewer than one pathway shall be provided on the street or driveway side of the roof. For each roof plane with a photovoltaic array, a pathway not less than 36 inches wide (914 mm) shall be provided from the lowest roof edge to ridge on the same roof plane as the photovoltaic array, on an adjacent roof plane, or straddling the same and adjacent roof planes. Pathways shall be over areas capable of supporting fire fighters accessing the roof. Pathways shall be located in areas with minimal obstructions such as vent pipes, conduit, or mechanical equipment.

R324.6.2 Setback at ridge. For photovoltaic arrays occupying not more than 33 percent of the plan view total roof area, not less than an 18-inch (457 mm) clear setback is required on both sides of a horizontal ridge. For photovoltaic arrays occupying more than 33 percent of the plan view total roof area, not less than a 36-inch (914 mm) clear setback is required on both sides of a horizontal ridge.

R324.6.2.1 Alternative setback at ridge. Where an automatic sprinkler system is installed within the dwelling in accordance with NFPA 13D or Section P2904, setbacks at ridges shall comply with one of the following:

1. For photovoltaic arrays occupying not more than 66 percent of the plan view total roof area, not less than an 18-inch (457 mm) clear setback is required on both sides of a horizontal ridge.

2. For photovoltaic arrays occupying more than 66 percent of the plan view total roof area, not less than a 36-inch (914 mm) clear setback is required on both sides of a horizontal ridge.

R324.6.2.2 Emergency escape and rescue opening. Panels and modules installed on dwellings shall not be placed on the portion of a roof that is below an emergency escape and rescue opening. A pathway not less than 36 inches (914 mm) wide shall be provided to the emergency escape and rescue opening.

R324.7 Ground-mounted photovoltaic systems. Ground-mounted photovoltaic systems shall be designed and installed in accordance with Section R301.

R324.7.1 Fire separation distances. Ground-mounted photovoltaic systems shall be subject to the *fire separation distance* requirements determined by the local *jurisdiction*.

SECTION R325
MEZZANINES

R325.1 General. Mezzanines shall comply with Sections R325 through R325.5. *Habitable attics* shall comply with Section R325.6.

R325.2 Mezzanines. The clear height above and below mezzanine floor construction shall be not less than 7 feet (2134 mm).

R325.3 Area limitation. The aggregate area of a mezzanine or mezzanines shall be not greater than one-third of the floor area of the room or space in which they are located. The enclosed portion of a room shall not be included in a determination of the floor area of the room in which the *mezzanine* is located.

Exception: The aggregate area of a mezzanine located within a dwelling unit equipped with a fire sprinkler system in accordance with Section P2904 shall not be greater than one-half of the floor area of the room, provided that the mezzanine meets all of the following requirements:

1. Except for enclosed closets and bathrooms, the mezzanine is open to the room in which such mezzanine is located.

2. The opening to the room is unobstructed except for walls not more than 42 inches (1067 mm) in height, columns and posts.

3. The exceptions to Section R325.5 are not applied.

R325.4 Means of egress. The means of egress for mezzanines shall comply with the applicable provisions of Section R311.

R325.5 Openness. Mezzanines shall be open and unobstructed to the room in which they are located except for walls not more than 36 inches (914 mm) in height, columns and posts.

Exceptions:

1. Mezzanines or portions thereof are not required to be open to the room in which they are located, provided that the aggregate floor area of the enclosed space is not greater than 10 percent of the mezzanine area.

2. In buildings that are not more than two stories above *grade plane* and equipped throughout with an automatic sprinkler system in accordance with Section R313, a mezzanine shall not be required to be open to the room in which the mezzanine is located.

R325.6 Habitable attic. A habitable attic shall not be considered a story where complying with all of the following requirements:

1. The occupiable floor area is not less than 70 square feet (17 m^2), in accordance with Section R304.

2. The occupiable floor area has a ceiling height in accordance with Section R305.

3. The occupiable space is enclosed by the roof assembly above, knee walls (if applicable) on the sides and the floor-ceiling assembly below.

4. The floor of the occupiable space shall not extend beyond the exterior walls of the floor below.

SECTION R326
SWIMMING POOLS, SPAS AND HOT TUBS

> ᴹ ᴺ **R326.1 General.** Deleted.

SECTION R327
STATIONARY STORAGE BATTERY SYSTEMS

R327.1 General. *Stationary storage battery system* shall comply with the provisions of this section.

R327.2 Equipment listings. *Stationary storage battery systems* shall be *listed* and *labeled* for residential use in accordance with UL 9540.

Exceptions:

1. Where *approved*, repurposed unlisted battery systems from electric vehicles are allowed to be installed outdoors or in detached sheds located not less than 5 feet (1524 mm) from exterior walls, property lines and public ways.

2. *Battery systems* that are an integral part of an electric vehicle are allowed provided that the installation complies with Section 625.48 of NFPA 70.

3. Battery systems less than 1 kWh (3.6 megajoules).

R327.3 Installation. *Stationary storage battery systems* shall be installed in accordance with the manufacturer's instructions and their *listing*, if applicable, and shall not be installed within the habitable space of a dwelling unit.

R327.4 Electrical installation. *Stationary storage battery systems* shall be installed in accordance with NFPA 70. Inverters shall be *listed* and *labeled* in accordance with UL 1741 or provided as part of the UL 9540 listing. Systems connected to the utility grid shall use inverters listed for utility interaction.

R327.5 Ventilation. Indoor installations of *stationary storage battery systems* that include batteries that produce hydrogen or other flammable gases during charging shall be provided with ventilation in accordance with Section M1307.4.

R327.6 Protection from impact. *Stationary storage battery systems* installed in a location subject to vehicle damage shall be protected by approved barriers.

CHAPTER 4

FOUNDATIONS

User note:

About this chapter: Chapter 4 provides requirements for constructing footings and walls for foundations of wood, masonry, concrete and precast concrete. In addition to a foundation's ability to support the required design loads, this chapter addresses several other factors that can affect foundation performance. These include controlling surface water and subsurface drainage, requiring soil tests where conditions warrant and evaluating proximity to slopes and minimum depth requirements. This chapter also provides requirements to minimize adverse effects of moisture, decay and pests in basements and crawl spaces.

SECTION R401
GENERAL

R401.1 Application. The provisions of this chapter shall control the design and construction of the foundation and foundation spaces for buildings. In addition to the provisions of this chapter, the design and construction of foundations in flood hazard areas as established by Table R301.2(1) shall meet the provisions of Section R322. Wood foundations shall be designed and installed in accordance with AWC PWF.

> **Exception:** The provisions of this chapter shall be permitted to be used for wood foundations only in the following situations:
>
> 1. In buildings that have not more than two floors and a roof.
>
> 2. Where interior *basement* and foundation walls are constructed at intervals not exceeding 50 feet (15 240 mm).

Wood foundations in Seismic Design Category D_0, D_1 or D_2 shall be designed in accordance with accepted engineering practice.

R401.2 Requirements. Foundation construction shall be capable of accommodating all loads in accordance with Section R301 and of transmitting the resulting loads to the supporting soil. Fill soils that support footings and foundations shall be designed, installed and tested in accordance with accepted engineering practice.

R401.3 Drainage. Surface drainage shall be diverted to a storm sewer conveyance or other *approved* point of collection that does not create a hazard. *Lots* shall be graded to drain surface water away from foundation walls. The *grade* shall fall not fewer than 6 inches (152 mm) within the first 10 feet (3048 mm).

> **Exception:** Where *lot lines*, walls, slopes or other physical barriers prohibit 6 inches (152 mm) of fall within 10 feet (3048 mm), drains or swales shall be constructed to ensure drainage away from the structure. Impervious surfaces within 10 feet (3048 mm) of the building foundation shall be sloped not less than 2 percent away from the building.

R401.4 Soil tests. Where quantifiable data created by accepted soil science methodologies indicate *expansive soils*, *compressible soils*, shifting soils or other questionable soil characteristics are likely to be present, the *building official* shall determine whether to require a soil test to determine the soil's characteristics at a particular location. This test shall be done by an *approved agency* using an *approved* method.

R401.4.1 Geotechnical evaluation. In lieu of a complete geotechnical evaluation, the load-bearing values in Table R401.4.1 shall be assumed.

TABLE R401.4.1
PRESUMPTIVE LOAD-BEARING
VALUES OF FOUNDATION MATERIALS[a]

CLASS OF MATERIAL	LOAD-BEARING PRESSURE (pounds per square foot)
Crystalline bedrock	12,000
Sedimentary and foliated rock	4,000
Sandy gravel and/or gravel (GW and GP)	3,000
Sand, silty sand, clayey sand, silty gravel and clayey gravel (SW, SP, SM, SC, GM and GC)	2,000
Clay, sandy, silty clay, clayey silt, silt and sandy siltclay (CL, ML, MH and CH)	1,500[b]

For SI: 1 pound per square foot = 0.0479 kPa.

a. Where soil tests are required by Section R401.4, the allowable bearing capacities of the soil shall be part of the recommendations.

b. Where the building official determines that in-place soils with an allowable bearing capacity of less than 1,500 psf are likely to be present at the site, the allowable bearing capacity shall be determined by a soils investigation.

R401.4.2 Compressible or shifting soil. Instead of a complete geotechnical evaluation, where top or subsoils are compressible or shifting, they shall be removed to a depth and width sufficient to ensure stable moisture content in each active zone and shall not be used as fill or stabilized within each active zone by chemical, dewatering or presaturation.

SECTION R402
MATERIALS

R402.1 Wood foundations. Wood foundation systems shall be designed and installed in accordance with the provisions of this code.

R402.1.1 Fasteners. Fasteners used below *grade* to attach plywood to the exterior side of exterior *basement* or crawlspace wall studs, or fasteners used in knee wall construction, shall be of Type 304 or 316 stainless steel. Fasteners used above *grade* to attach plywood and all lumber-to-lumber fasteners except those used in knee wall construction shall be of Type 304 or 316 stainless steel, silicon bronze, copper, hot-dipped galvanized (zinc coated) steel nails, or hot-tumbled galvanized (zinc coated) steel nails. Electro-galvanized steel nails and galvanized (zinc coated) steel staples shall not be permitted.

R402.1.2 Wood treatment. Lumber and plywood shall be pressure-preservative treated and dried after treatment in accordance with AWPA U1 (Commodity Specification A, Special Requirement 4.2), and shall bear the *label* of an accredited agency. Where lumber or plywood is cut or drilled after treatment, the treated surface shall be field treated with copper naphthenate, the concentration of which shall contain not less than 2-percent copper metal, by repeated brushing, dipping or soaking until the wood cannot absorb more preservative.

R402.2 Concrete. Concrete shall have a minimum specified compressive strength of f'_c, as shown in Table R402.2. Concrete subject to moderate or severe weathering as indicated in Table R301.2(1) shall be air entrained as specified in Table R402.2. The maximum weight of fly ash, other pozzolans, silica fume, slag or blended cements that is included in concrete mixtures for garage floor slabs and for exterior porches, carport slabs and steps that will be exposed to deicing chemicals shall not exceed the percentages of the total weight of cementitious materials specified in Section 19.3.3.4 of ACI 318. Materials used to produce concrete and testing thereof shall comply with the applicable standards listed in Chapters 19 and 20 of ACI 318 or ACI 332.

R402.2.1 Materials for concrete. Materials for concrete shall comply with the requirements of Section R608.5.1.

R402.3 Precast concrete. Precast concrete foundations shall be designed in accordance with Section R404.5 and shall be installed in accordance with the provisions of this code and the manufacturer's instructions.

R402.3.1 Precast concrete foundation materials. Materials used to produce precast concrete foundations shall meet the following requirements.

1. All concrete used in the manufacture of precast concrete foundations shall have a minimum compressive strength of 5,000 psi (34 470 kPa) at 28 days. Concrete exposed to a freezing and thawing environment shall be air entrained with a minimum total air content of 5 percent.

2. Structural reinforcing steel shall meet the requirements of ASTM A615, A706 or A996. The minimum yield strength of reinforcing steel shall be 40,000 psi (Grade 40) (276 MPa). Steel reinforcement for precast concrete foundation walls shall have a minimum concrete cover of $^3/_4$ inch (19.1 mm).

3. Panel-to-panel connections shall be made with Grade II steel fasteners.

4. The use of nonstructural fibers shall conform to ASTM C1116.

5. Grout used for bedding precast foundations placed on concrete footings shall meet ASTM C1107.

R402.4 Masonry. Masonry systems shall be designed and installed in accordance with this chapter and shall have a minimum specified compressive strength of 1,500 psi (10.3 MPa).

SECTION R403
FOOTINGS

R403.1 General. All exterior walls shall be supported on continuous solid or fully grouted masonry or concrete footings, crushed stone footings, wood foundations, or other *approved* structural systems that shall be of sufficient design to accommodate all loads according to Section R301 and to transmit the resulting loads to the soil within the limitations

TABLE R402.2
MINIMUM SPECIFIED COMPRESSIVE STRENGTH OF CONCRETE

TYPE OR LOCATION OF CONCRETE CONSTRUCTION	MINIMUM SPECIFIED COMPRESSIVE STRENGTH[a] (f'_c)		
	Weathering Potential[b]		
	Negligible	Moderate	Severe
Footings[g, h]	5,000	5,000	5,000
Basement walls, foundations, and other concrete not exposed to the weather	2,500	2,500	2,500[c]
Basement slabs and interior slabs on grade, except garage floor slabs	2,500	2,500	2,500[c]
Basement walls, foundation walls, exterior walls, and other vertical concrete work exposed to the weather	2,500	3,000[d]	3,000[d]
Porches, carport slabs, and steps exposed to the weather, and garage floor slabs	2,500	3,000[d, e, f]	3,500[d, e, f]

For SI: 1 pound per square inch = 6.895 kPa.

a. Strength at 28 days psi.

b. See Table R301.2(1) for weathering potential.

c. Concrete in these locations that may be subject to freezing and thawing during construction shall be air-entrained concrete in accordance with Footnote d.

d. Concrete shall be air-entrained. Total air content (percent by volume of concrete) shall be not less than 5 percent or more than 7 percent.

e. See Section R402.2 for maximum cementitious materials content.

f. For garage floors with a steel-troweled finish, reduction of the total air content (percent by volume of concrete) to not less than 3 percent is permitted if the specified compressive strength of the concrete is increased to not less than 4,000 psi.

g. Compressive strength (f'_c) of 2,500 psi, with an approved admixture that provides a water and vapor resistance at least equivalent to 5,000 psi concrete.

h. Compressive strength (f'_c) of 5,000 psi, is not required for post footings for decks or porches, wood foundations, slab-on-grade foundation walls, and footings for floating slabs.

as determined from the character of the soil. Footings shall be supported on undisturbed natural soils or engineered fill. Concrete footing shall be designed and constructed in accordance with the provisions of Section R403 or in accordance with ACI 332.

R403.1.1 Minimum size. The minimum width, W, and thickness, T, for concrete footings shall be in accordance with Tables R403.1(1) through R403.1(3) and Figure R403.1(1) or R403.1.3, as applicable. The footing width shall be based on the load-bearing value of the soil in accordance with Table R401.4.1. Footing projections, P, shall be not less than 2 inches (51 mm) and shall not exceed the thickness of the footing. Footing thickness and projection for fireplaces shall be in accordance with Section R1001.2. The size of footings supporting piers and columns shall be based on the tributary load and allowable soil pressure in accordance with Table R401.4.1. Footings for wood foundations shall be in accordance with the details set forth in Section R403.2, and Figures R403.1(2) and R403.1(3). Footings for precast foundations shall be in accordance with the details set forth in Section R403.4, Table R403.4, and Figures R403.4(1) and R403.4(2).

R403.1.2 Continuous footing in Seismic Design Categories D_0, D_1 and D_2. Exterior walls of buildings located in Seismic Design Categories D_0, D_1 and D_2 shall be supported by continuous solid or fully grouted masonry or concrete footings. Other footing materials or systems shall be designed in accordance with accepted engineering practice. Required interior *braced wall panels* in buildings located in Seismic Design Categories D_0, D_1 and D_2 with plan dimensions greater than 50 feet (15 240 mm) shall be supported by continuous solid or fully grouted masonry or concrete footings in accordance with Section R403.1.3.4, except for two-story buildings in Seismic Design Category D_2, in which all *braced wall panels*, interior and exterior, shall be supported on continuous foundations.

Exception: Two-story buildings shall be permitted to have interior *braced wall panels* supported on continuous foundations at intervals not exceeding 50 feet (15 240 mm) provided that:

1. The height of cripple walls does not exceed 4 feet (1219 mm).

2. First-floor braced wall panels are supported on doubled floor joists, continuous blocking or floor beams.

3. The distance between bracing lines does not exceed twice the building width measured parallel to the braced wall line.

R403.1.3 Footing and stem wall reinforcing in Seismic Design Categories D_0, D_1, and D_2. Concrete footings located in Seismic Design Categories D_0, D_1 and D_2, as established in Table R301.2(1), shall have minimum reinforcement in accordance with this section and Figure R403.1.3. Reinforcement shall be installed with support and cover in accordance with Section R403.1.3.5.

R403.1.3.1 Concrete stem walls with concrete footings. In Seismic Design Categories D_0, D_1 and D_2 where a construction joint is created between a concrete footing and a concrete stem wall, not fewer than one No. 4 vertical bar shall be installed at not more than 4 feet (1219 mm) on center. The vertical bar shall have a standard hook and extend to the bottom of the footing and shall have support and cover as specified in Section R403.1.3.5.3 and extend not less than 14 inches (357 mm) into the stem wall. Standard hooks shall comply with Section R608.5.4.5. Not fewer than one No. 4 horizontal bar shall be installed within 12 inches (305 mm) of the top of the stem wall and one No. 4 horizontal bar shall be located 3 to 4 inches (76 mm to 102 mm) from the bottom of the footing.

R403.1.3.2 Masonry stem walls with concrete footings. In Seismic Design Categories D_0, D_1 and D_2 where a masonry stem wall is supported on a concrete footing, not fewer than one No. 4 vertical bar shall be installed at not more than 4 feet (1219 mm) on center. The vertical bar shall have a standard hook and extend to the bottom of the footing and shall have support and cover as specified in Section R403.1.3.5.3 and extend not less than 14 inches (357 mm) into the stem wall. Standard hooks shall comply with Section R608.5.4.5. Not fewer than one No. 4 horizontal bar shall be installed within 12 inches (305 mm) of the top of the wall and one No. 4 horizontal bar shall be located 3 to 4 inches (76 mm to 102 mm) from the bottom of the footing. Masonry stem walls shall be solid grouted.

R403.1.3.3 Slabs-on-ground with turned-down footings. In Seismic Design Categories D_0, D_1 and D_2, slabs-on-ground cast monolithically with turned-down footings shall have not fewer than one No. 4 bar at the top and the bottom of the footing or one No. 5 bar or two No. 4 bars in the middle third of the footing depth.

Where the slab is not cast monolithically with the footing, No. 3 or larger vertical dowels with standard hooks on each end shall be installed at not more than 4 feet (1219 mm) on center in accordance with Figure R403.1.3, Detail 2. Standard hooks shall comply with Section R608.5.4.5.

R403.1.3.4 Interior bearing and braced wall panel footings in Seismic Design Categories D_0, D_1 and D_2. In Seismic Design Categories D_0, D_1 and D_2, interior footings supporting bearing walls or *braced wall panels*, and cast monolithically with a slab on *grade*, shall extend to a depth of not less than 12 inches (305 mm) below the top of the slab.

R403.1.3.5 Reinforcement. Footing and stem wall reinforcement shall comply with Sections R403.1.3.5.1 through R403.1.3.5.4.

R403.1.3.5.1 Steel reinforcement. Steel reinforcement shall comply with the requirements of ASTM A615, A706 or A996. ASTM A996 bars produced from rail steel shall be Type R. The minimum yield strength of reinforcing steel shall be 40,000 psi (Grade 40) (276 MPa).

TABLE R403.1(1)
MINIMUM WIDTH AND THICKNESS FOR CONCRETE FOOTINGS FOR LIGHT-FRAME CONSTRUCTION (inches)[a, b]

SNOW LOAD OR ROOF LIVE LOAD	STORY AND TYPE OF STRUCTURE WITH LIGHT FRAME	LOAD-BEARING VALUE OF SOIL (psf)					
		1500	2000	2500	3000	3500	4000
20 psf	1 story—slab-on-grade	12 × 6	12 × 6	12 × 6	12 × 6	12 × 6	12 × 6
	1 story—with crawl space	12 × 6	12 × 6	12 × 6	12 × 6	12 × 6	12 × 6
	1 story—plus basement	18 × 6	14 × 6	12 × 6	12 × 6	12 × 6	12 × 6
	2 story—slab-on-grade	12 × 6	12 × 6	12 × 6	12 × 6	12 × 6	12 × 6
	2 story—with crawl space	16 × 6	12 × 6	12 × 6	12 × 6	12 × 6	12 × 6
	2 story—plus basement	22 × 6	16 × 6	13 × 6	12 × 6	12 × 6	12 × 6
	3 story—slab-on-grade	14 × 6	12 × 6	12 × 6	12 × 6	12 × 6	12 × 6
	3 story—with crawl space	19 × 6	14 × 6	12 × 6	12 × 6	12 × 6	12 × 6
	3 story—plus basement	25 × 8	19 × 6	15 × 6	13 × 6	12 × 6	12 × 6
30 psf	1 story—slab-on-grade	12 × 6	12 × 6	12 × 6	12 × 6	12 × 6	12 × 6
	1 story—with crawl space	13 × 6	12 × 6	12 × 6	12 × 6	12 × 6	12 × 6
	1 story—plus basement	19 × 6	14 × 6	12 × 6	12 × 6	12 × 6	12 × 6
	2 story—slab-on-grade	12 × 6	12 × 6	12 × 6	12 × 6	12 × 6	12 × 6
	2 story—with crawl space	17 × 6	13 × 6	12 × 6	12 × 6	12 × 6	12 × 6
	2 story—plus basement	23 × 6	17 × 6	14 × 6	12 × 6	12 × 6	12 × 6
	3 story—slab-on-grade	15 × 6	12 × 6	12 × 6	12 × 6	12 × 6	12 × 6
	3 story—with crawl space	20 × 6	15 × 6	12 × 6	12 × 6	12 × 6	12 × 6
	3 story—plus basement	26 × 8	20 × 6	16 × 6	13 × 6	12 × 6	12 × 6
50 psf	1 story—slab-on-grade	12 × 6	12 × 6	12 × 6	12 × 6	12 × 6	12 × 6
	1 story—with crawl space	16 × 6	12 × 6	12 × 6	12 × 6	12 × 6	12 × 6
	1 story—plus basement	21 × 6	16 × 6	13 × 6	12 × 6	12 × 6	12 × 6
	2 story—slab-on-grade	14 × 6	12 × 6	12 × 6	12 × 6	12 × 6	12 × 6
	2 story—with crawl space	19 × 6	14 × 6	12 × 6	12 × 6	12 × 6	12 × 6
	2 story—plus basement	25 × 7	19 × 6	15 × 6	12 × 6	12 × 6	12 × 6
	3 story—slab-on-grade	17 × 6	13 × 6	12 × 6	12 × 6	12 × 6	12 × 6
	3 story—with crawl space	22 × 6	17 × 6	13 × 6	12 × 6	12 × 6	12 × 6
	3 story—plus basement	28 × 9	21 × 6	17 × 6	14 × 6	12 × 6	12 × 6
70 psf	1 story—slab-on-grade	12 × 6	12 × 6	12 × 6	12 × 6	12 × 6	12 × 6
	1 story—with crawl space	18 × 6	13 × 6	12 × 6	12 × 6	12 × 6	12 × 6
	1 story—plus basement	24 × 7	18 × 6	14 × 6	12 × 6	12 × 6	12 × 6
	2 story—slab-on-grade	16 × 6	12 × 6	12 × 6	12 × 6	12 × 6	12 × 6
	2 story—with crawl space	21 × 6	16 × 6	13 × 6	12 × 6	12 × 6	12 × 6
	2 story—plus basement	27 × 9	20 × 6	16 × 6	14 × 6	12 × 6	12 × 6
	3 story—slab-on-grade	19 × 6	14 × 6	12 × 6	12 × 6	12 × 6	12 × 6
	3 story—with crawl space	25 × 7	18 × 6	15 × 6	12 × 6	12 × 6	12 × 6
	3 story—plus basement	30 × 10	23 × 6	18 × 6	15 × 6	13 × 6	12 × 6

For SI: 1 inch = 25.4 mm, 1 plf = 14.6 N/m, 1 pound per square foot = 47.9 N/m².

a. Interpolation allowed. Extrapolation is not allowed.

b. Based on 32-foot-wide house with load-bearing center wall that carries half of the tributary attic, and floor framing. For every 2 feet of adjustment to the width of the house, add or subtract 2 inches of footing width and 1 inch of footing thickness (but not less than 6 inches thick).

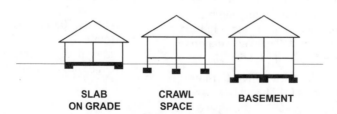

SLAB ON GRADE   CRAWL SPACE   BASEMENT

TABLE R403.1(2)
MINIMUM WIDTH AND THICKNESS FOR CONCRETE FOOTINGS FOR LIGHT-FRAME CONSTRUCTION WITH BRICK VENEER (inches)[a, b]

SNOW LOAD OR ROOF LIVE LOAD	STORY AND TYPE OF STRUCTURE WITH BRICK VENEER	LOAD-BEARING VALUE OF SOIL (psf)					
		1500	2000	2500	3000	3500	4000
20 psf	1 story—slab-on-grade	12 × 6	12 × 6	12 × 6	12 × 6	12 × 6	12 × 6
	1 story—with crawl space	15 × 6	12 × 6	12 × 6	12 × 6	12 × 6	12 × 6
	1 story—plus basement	21 × 6	15 × 6	12 × 6	12 × 6	12 × 6	12 × 6
	2 story—slab-on-grade	15 × 6	12 × 6	12 × 6	12 × 6	12 × 6	12 × 6
	2 story—with crawl space	20 × 6	15 × 6	12 × 6	12 × 6	12 × 6	12 × 6
	2 story—plus basement	26 × 8	20 × 6	16 × 6	13 × 6	12 × 6	12 × 6
	3 story—slab-on-grade	20 × 6	15 × 6	12 × 6	12 × 6	12 × 6	12 × 6
	3 story—with crawl space	26 × 8	19 × 6	15 × 6	13 × 6	12 × 6	12 × 6
	3 story—plus basement	32 × 11	24 × 7	19 × 6	16 × 6	14 × 6	12 × 6
30 psf	1 story—slab-on-grade	12 × 6	12 × 6	12 × 6	12 × 6	12 × 6	12 × 6
	1 story—with crawl space	16 × 6	12 × 6	12 × 6	12 × 6	12 × 6	12 × 6
	1 story—plus basement	22 × 6	16 × 6	13 × 6	12 × 6	12 × 6	12 × 6
	2 story—slab-on-grade	16 × 6	12 × 6	12 × 6	12 × 6	12 × 6	12 × 6
	2 story—with crawl space	22 × 6	16 × 6	13 × 6	12 × 6	12 × 6	12 × 6
	2 story—plus basement	27 × 9	21 × 6	16 × 6	14 × 6	12 × 6	12 × 6
	3 story—slab-on-grade	21 × 6	16 × 6	13 × 6	12 × 6	12 × 6	12 × 6
	3 story—with crawl space	27 × 8	20 × 6	16 × 6	13 × 6	12 × 6	12 × 6
	3 story—plus basement	33 × 11	24 × 7	20 × 6	16 × 6	14 × 6	12 × 6
50 psf	1 story—slab-on-grade	13 × 6	12 × 6	12 × 6	12 × 6	12 × 6	12 × 6
	1 story—with crawl space	18 × 6	14 × 6	12 × 6	12 × 6	12 × 6	12 × 6
	1 story—plus basement	24 × 7	18 × 6	14 × 6	12 × 6	12 × 6	12 × 6
	2 story—slab-on-grade	18 × 6	14 × 6	12 × 6	12 × 6	12 × 6	12 × 6
	2 story—with crawl space	24 × 7	18 × 6	14 × 6	12 × 6	12 × 6	12 × 6
	2 story—plus basement	29 × 10	22 × 6	18 × 6	15 × 6	13 × 6	12 × 6
	3 story—slab-on-grade	27 × 7	18 × 6	13 × 6	12 × 6	12 × 6	12 × 6
	3 story—with crawl space	29 × 9	22 × 6	17 × 6	14 × 6	12 × 6	12 × 6
	3 story—plus basement	35 × 12	26 × 8	21 × 6	17 × 6	15 × 6	13 × 6
70 psf	1 story—slab-on-grade	15 × 6	12 × 6	12 × 6	12 × 6	12 × 6	12 × 6
	1 story—with crawl space	20 × 6	15 × 6	12 × 6	12 × 6	12 × 6	12 × 6
	1 story—plus basement	26 × 8	20 × 6	16 × 6	13 × 6	12 × 6	12 × 6
	2 story—slab-on grade	20 × 6	15 × 6	12 × 6	12 × 6	12 × 6	12 × 6
	2 story—with crawl space	26 × 8	19 × 6	15 × 6	13 × 6	12 × 6	12 × 6
	2 story—plus basement	32 × 11	24 × 7	19 × 6	16 × 6	14 × 6	12 × 6
	3 story—slab-on-grade	26 × 8	19 × 6	15 × 6	13 × 6	12 × 6	12 × 6
	3 story—with crawl space	31 × 11	23 × 7	19 × 6	16 × 6	13 × 6	12 × 6
	3 story—plus basement	37 × 13	28 × 9	22 × 6	18 × 6	16 × 6	14 × 6

For SI: 1 inch = 25.4 mm, 1 plf = 14.6 N/m, 1 pound per square foot = 47.9 N/m².

a. Interpolation allowed. Extrapolation is not allowed.

b. Based on 32-foot-wide house with load-bearing center wall that carries half of the tributary attic, and floor framing. For every 2 feet of adjustment to the width of the house, add or subtract 2 inches of footing width and 1 inch of footing thickness (but not less than 6 inches thick).

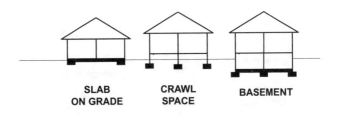

SLAB ON GRADE   CRAWL SPACE   BASEMENT

TABLE R403.1(3)
MINIMUM WIDTH AND THICKNESS FOR CONCRETE FOOTINGS
WITH CAST-IN-PLACE CONCRETE OR FULLY GROUTED MASONRY WALL CONSTRUCTION (inches)[a, b]

SNOW LOAD OR ROOF LIVE LOAD	STORY AND TYPE OF STRUCTURE WITH CMU	LOAD-BEARING VALUE OF SOIL (psf)					
		1500	2000	2500	3000	3500	4000
20 psf	1 story—slab-on-grade	14 × 6	12 × 6	12 × 6	12 × 6	12 × 6	12 × 6
	1 story—with crawl space	19 × 6	14 × 6	12 × 6	12 × 6	12 × 6	12 × 6
	1 story—plus basement	25 × 8	19 × 6	15 × 6	13 × 6	12 × 6	12 × 6
	2 story—slab-on-grade	23 × 7	18 × 6	14 × 6	12 × 6	12 × 6	12 × 6
	2 story—with crawl space	29 × 9	22 × 6	17 × 6	14 × 6	12 × 6	12 × 6
	2 story—plus basement	35 × 12	26 × 8	21 × 6	17 × 6	15 × 6	13 × 6
	3 story—slab-on-grade	32 × 11	24 × 7	19 × 6	16 × 6	14 × 6	12 × 6
	3 story—with crawl space	38 × 14	28 × 9	23 × 6	19 × 6	16 × 6	14 × 6
	3 story—plus basement	43 × 17	33 × 11	26 × 8	22 × 6	19 × 6	16 × 6
30 psf	1 story—slab-on-grade	15 × 6	12 × 6	12 × 6	12 × 6	12 × 6	12 × 6
	1 story—with crawl space	20 × 6	15 × 6	12 × 6	12 × 6	12 × 6	12 × 6
	1 story—plus basement	26 × 8	20 × 6	16 × 6	13 × 6	12 × 6	12 × 6
	2 story—slab-on-grade	24 × 7	18 × 6	15 × 6	12 × 6	12 × 6	12 × 6
	2 story—with crawl space	30 × 10	22 × 6	18 × 6	15 × 6	13 × 6	12 × 6
	2 story—plus basement	36 × 13	27 × 8	21 × 6	18 × 6	15 × 6	13 × 6
	3 story—slab-on-grade	33 × 12	25 × 7	20 × 6	17 × 6	14 × 6	12 × 6
	3 story—with crawl space	39 × 14	29 × 9	23 × 7	19 × 6	17 × 6	14 × 6
	3 story—plus basement	44 × 17	33 × 12	27 × 8	22 × 6	19 × 6	17 × 6
50 psf	1 story—slab-on-grade	17 × 6	13 × 6	12 × 6	12 × 6	12 × 6	12 × 6
	1 story—with crawl space	22 × 6	17 × 6	13 × 6	12 × 6	12 × 6	12 × 6
	1 story—plus basement	28 × 9	21 × 6	17 × 6	14 × 6	12 × 6	12 × 6
	2 story—slab-on-grade	27 × 8	20 × 6	16 × 6	13 × 6	12 × 6	12 × 6
	2 story—with crawl space	32 × 11	24 × 7	19 × 6	16 × 6	14 × 6	12 × 6
	2 story—plus basement	38 × 14	28 × 9	23 × 6	19 × 6	16 × 6	14 × 6
	3 story—slab-on-grade	35 × 13	27 × 8	21 × 6	18 × 6	15 × 6	13 × 6
	3 story—with crawl space	41 × 15	31 × 10	24 × 7	20 × 6	17 × 6	15 × 6
	3 story—plus basement	47 × 18	35 × 12	28 × 9	23 × 7	20 × 6	17 × 6
70 psf	1 story—slab-on-grade	19 × 6	14 × 6	12 × 6	12 × 6	12 × 6	12 × 6
	1 story—with crawl space	25 × 7	18 × 6	15 × 6	12 × 6	12 × 6	12 × 6
	1 story—plus basement	30 × 10	23 × 6	18 × 6	15 × 6	13 × 6	12 × 6
	2 story—slab-on-grade	29 × 9	22 × 6	17 × 6	14 × 6	12 × 6	12 × 6
	2 story—with crawl space	34 × 12	26 × 8	21 × 6	17 × 6	15 × 6	13 × 6
	2 story—plus basement	40 × 15	30 × 10	24 × 7	20 × 6	17 × 6	15 × 6
	3 story—slab-on-grade	38 × 14	28 × 9	23 × 6	19 × 6	16 × 6	14 × 6
	3 story—with crawl space	43 × 16	32 × 11	26 × 8	21 × 6	18 × 6	16 × 6
	3 story—plus basement	49 × 19	37 × 13	29 × 10	24 × 7	21 × 6	18 × 6

For SI: 1 inch = 25.4 mm, 1 plf = 14.6 N/m, 1 pound per square foot = 47.9 N/m².

a. Interpolation allowed. Extrapolation is not allowed.

b. Based on 32-foot-wide house with load-bearing center wall that carries half of the tributary attic, and floor framing. For every 2 feet of adjustment to the width of the house add or subtract 2 inches of footing width and 1 inch of footing thickness (but not less than 6 inches thick).

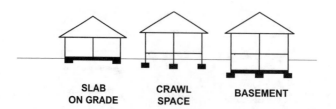

SLAB ON GRADE   CRAWL SPACE   BASEMENT

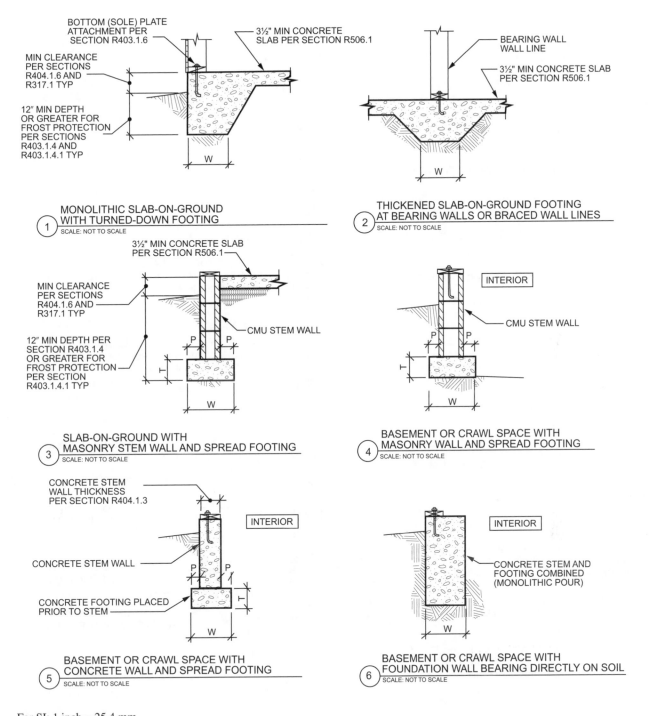

BOTTOM (SOLE) PLATE
ATTACHMENT PER
SECTION R403.1.6

MIN CLEARANCE
PER SECTIONS
R404.1.6 AND
R317.1 TYP

12" MIN DEPTH
OR GREATER FOR
FROST PROTECTION
PER SECTIONS
R403.1.4 AND
R403.1.4.1 TYP

3½" MIN CONCRETE
SLAB PER SECTION R506.1

W

MONOLITHIC SLAB-ON-GROUND
WITH TURNED-DOWN FOOTING
1 SCALE: NOT TO SCALE

BEARING WALL
WALL LINE

3½" MIN CONCRETE SLAB
PER SECTION R506.1

W

THICKENED SLAB-ON-GROUND FOOTING
AT BEARING WALLS OR BRACED WALL LINES
2 SCALE: NOT TO SCALE

3½" MIN CONCRETE SLAB
PER SECTION R506.1

MIN CLEARANCE
PER SECTIONS
R404.1.6 AND
R317.1 TYP

12" MIN DEPTH PER
SECTION R403.1.4
OR GREATER FOR
FROST PROTECTION
PER SECTION
R403.1.4.1 TYP

CMU STEM WALL

P   P

T

W

SLAB-ON-GROUND WITH
MASONRY STEM WALL AND SPREAD FOOTING
3 SCALE: NOT TO SCALE

INTERIOR

CMU STEM WALL

P   P

T

W

BASEMENT OR CRAWL SPACE WITH
MASONRY WALL AND SPREAD FOOTING
4 SCALE: NOT TO SCALE

CONCRETE STEM
WALL THICKNESS
PER SECTION R404.1.3

CONCRETE STEM WALL

CONCRETE FOOTING PLACED
PRIOR TO STEM

INTERIOR

P   P

T

W

BASEMENT OR CRAWL SPACE WITH
CONCRETE WALL AND SPREAD FOOTING
5 SCALE: NOT TO SCALE

INTERIOR

CONCRETE STEM AND
FOOTING COMBINED
(MONOLITHIC POUR)

W

BASEMENT OR CRAWL SPACE WITH
FOUNDATION WALL BEARING DIRECTLY ON SOIL
6 SCALE: NOT TO SCALE

For SI: 1 inch = 25.4 mm.

W = Width of footing, T = Thickness of footing and P = Projection per Section R403.1.1

NOTES:

a. See Section R404.3 for sill requirements.

b. See Section R403.1.6 for sill attachment.

c. See Section R506.2.3 for vapor barrier requirements.

d. See Section R403.1 for base.

e. See Figure R403.1.3 for additional footing requirements for structures in SDC D_0, D_1 and D_2 and townhouses in SDC C.

f. See Section R408 for under-floor ventilation and access requirements.

FIGURE R403.1(1)
PLAIN CONCRETE FOOTINGS WITH MASONRY AND CONCRETE STEM WALLS IN SDC A, B AND C[a, b, c, d, e, f]

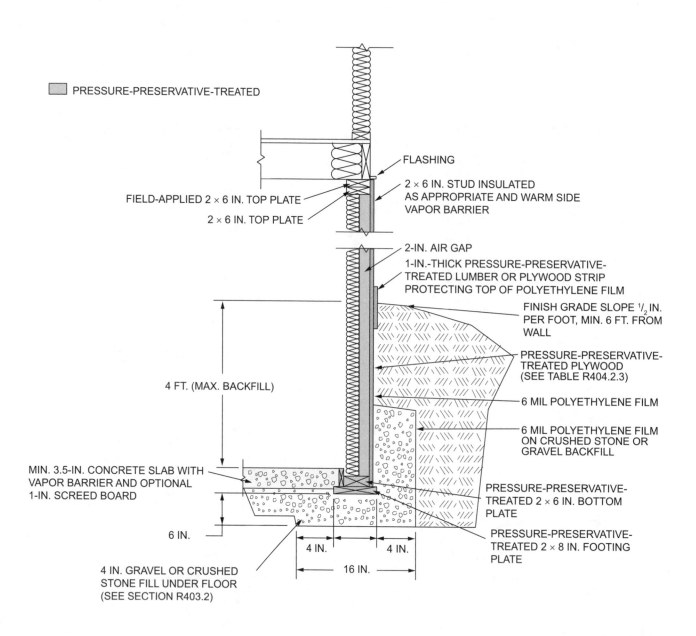

PRESSURE-PRESERVATIVE-TREATED

FLASHING

FIELD-APPLIED 2 × 6 IN. TOP PLATE

2 × 6 IN. TOP PLATE

2 × 6 IN. STUD INSULATED AS APPROPRIATE AND WARM SIDE VAPOR BARRIER

2-IN. AIR GAP

1-IN.-THICK PRESSURE-PRESERVATIVE-TREATED LUMBER OR PLYWOOD STRIP PROTECTING TOP OF POLYETHYLENE FILM

FINISH GRADE SLOPE $\frac{1}{2}$ IN. PER FOOT, MIN. 6 FT. FROM WALL

PRESSURE-PRESERVATIVE-TREATED PLYWOOD (SEE TABLE R404.2.3)

6 MIL POLYETHYLENE FILM

6 MIL POLYETHYLENE FILM ON CRUSHED STONE OR GRAVEL BACKFILL

4 FT. (MAX. BACKFILL)

MIN. 3.5-IN. CONCRETE SLAB WITH VAPOR BARRIER AND OPTIONAL 1-IN. SCREED BOARD

PRESSURE-PRESERVATIVE-TREATED 2 × 6 IN. BOTTOM PLATE

PRESSURE-PRESERVATIVE-TREATED 2 × 8 IN. FOOTING PLATE

6 IN.

4 IN.

4 IN.

16 IN.

4 IN. GRAVEL OR CRUSHED STONE FILL UNDER FLOOR (SEE SECTION R403.2)

For SI: 1 inch = 25.4 mm, 1 foot = 304.8 mm, 1 mil = 0.0254.

FIGURE R403.1(2)
PERMANENT WOOD FOUNDATION BASEMENT WALL SECTION

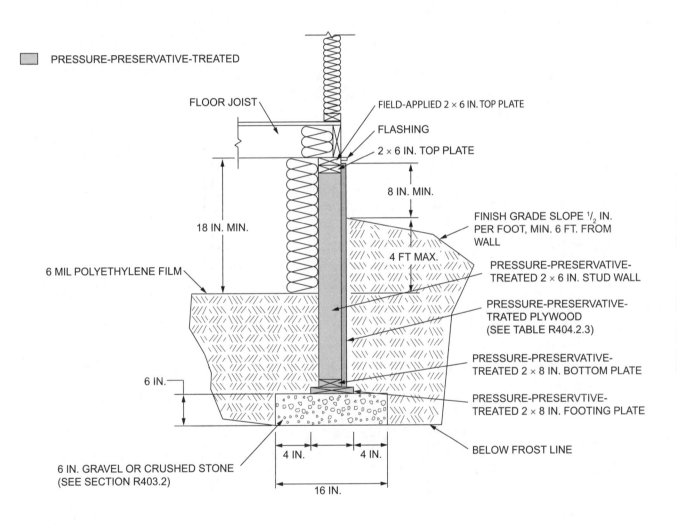

PRESSURE-PRESERVATIVE-TREATED

FLOOR JOIST

FIELD-APPLIED 2 × 6 IN. TOP PLATE

FLASHING

2 × 6 IN. TOP PLATE

8 IN. MIN.

18 IN. MIN.

FINISH GRADE SLOPE 1/2 IN. PER FOOT, MIN. 6 FT. FROM WALL

6 MIL POLYETHYLENE FILM

4 FT MAX.

PRESSURE-PRESERVATIVE-TREATED 2 × 6 IN. STUD WALL

PRESSURE-PRESERVATIVE-TRATED PLYWOOD (SEE TABLE R404.2.3)

PRESSURE-PRESERVATIVE-TREATED 2 × 8 IN. BOTTOM PLATE

6 IN.

PRESSURE-PRESERVTIVE-TREATED 2 × 8 IN. FOOTING PLATE

BELOW FROST LINE

6 IN. GRAVEL OR CRUSHED STONE (SEE SECTION R403.2)

4 IN.   4 IN.

16 IN.

For SI: 1 inch = 25.4 mm, 1 foot = 304.8 mm, 1 mil = 0.0254 mm.

FIGURE R403.1(3)
PERMANENT WOOD FOUNDATION CRAWL SPACE SECTION

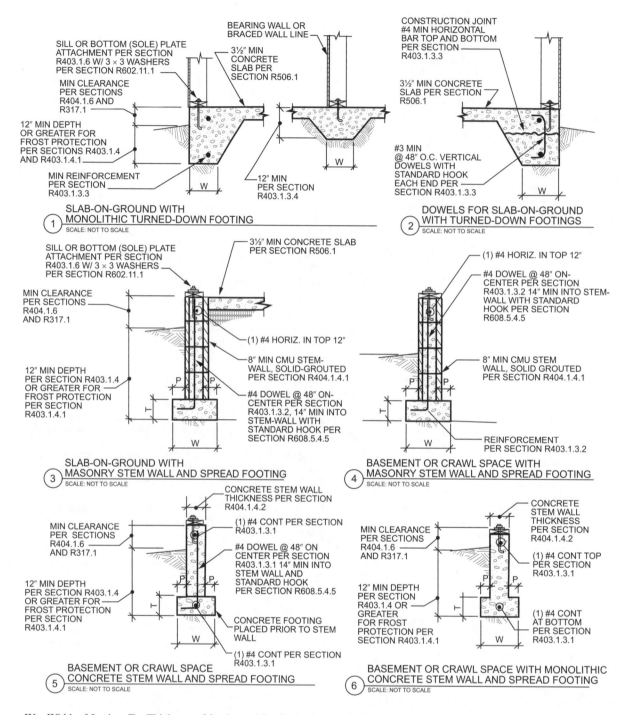

W = Width of footing, T = Thickness of footing and P = Projection per Section R403.1.1

NOTES:

a. See Section R404.3 for sill requirements.

b. See Section R403.1.6 for sill attachment.

c. See Section R506.2.3 for vapor barrier requirements.

d. See Section R403.1 for base.

e. See Section R408 for under-floor ventilation and access requirements.

f. See Section R403.1.3.5 for reinforcement requirements.

FIGURE R403.1.3

REINFORCED CONCRETE FOOTINGS AND MASONRY AND CONCRETE STEM WALLS IN SDC D$_0$, D$_1$ AND D$_2$[a, b, c, d, e, f]

R403.1.3.5.2 Location of reinforcement in wall. The center of vertical reinforcement in stem walls shall be located at the centerline of the wall. Horizontal and vertical reinforcement shall be located in footings and stem walls to provide the minimum cover required by Section R403.1.3.5.3.

R403.1.3.5.3 Support and cover. Reinforcement shall be secured in the proper location in the forms with tie wire or other bar support system to prevent displacement during the concrete placement operation. Steel reinforcement in concrete cast against the earth shall have a minimum cover of 3 inches (75 mm). Minimum cover for reinforcement in concrete cast in removable forms that will be exposed to the earth or weather shall be $1\frac{1}{2}$ inches (38 mm) for No. 5 bars and smaller, and 2 inches (50 mm) for No. 6 bars and larger. For concrete cast in removable forms that will not be exposed to the earth or weather, and for concrete cast in stay-in-place forms, minimum cover shall be $\frac{3}{4}$ inch (19 mm).

R403.1.3.5.4 Lap splices. Vertical and horizontal reinforcement shall be the longest lengths practical. Where splices are necessary in reinforcement, the length of lap splice shall be in accordance with Table R608.5.4.(1) and Figure R608.5.4(1). The maximum gap between noncontact parallel bars at a lap splice shall not exceed the smaller of one-fifth the required lap length and 6 inches (152 mm) [see Figure R608.5.4(1)].

R403.1.3.6 Isolated concrete footings. In detached one- and two-family dwellings that are three stories or less in height and constructed with stud bearing walls, isolated plain concrete footings supporting columns or pedestals are permitted.

R403.1.4 Minimum depth. Exterior footings shall be placed not less than 12 inches (305 mm) below the undisturbed ground surface. Where applicable, the depth of footings shall also conform to Sections R403.1.4.1 through R403.1.4.2.

R403.1.4.1 Frost protection. Footings shall not bear on frozen soil. Foundation walls, piers, and other permanent supports of buildings and structures not otherwise protected from frost shall be protected by one or more of the following methods:

1. Extended below the frost line specified in Table R301.2(1).

2. Constructing in accordance with Section R403.3.

3. Constructing in accordance with ASCE 32.

4. Erected on solid rock.

5. Constructing in accordance with Minnesota Rules, Chapter 1303.

R403.1.5 Slope. The top surface of footings shall be level. The bottom surface of footings shall not have a slope exceeding one unit vertical in 10 units horizontal (10-percent slope). Footings shall be stepped where it is necessary to change the elevation of the top surface of the footings or where the slope of the bottom surface of the footings will exceed one unit vertical in 10 units horizontal (10-percent slope).

R403.1.6 Foundation anchorage. Sill plates and walls supported directly on continuous foundations shall be anchored to the foundation in accordance with this section.

Wood sole plates at all exterior walls on monolithic slabs, wood sole plates of *braced wall panels* at building interiors on monolithic slabs, and all wood sill plates shall be anchored to the foundation with anchor bolts spaced a maximum of 6 feet (1829 mm) on center. Bolts shall be at least $\frac{1}{2}$-inch (12.7 mm) in diameter and shall extend a minimum of 7 inches (178 mm) into concrete or grouted cells of concrete masonry units. The bolts shall be located in the middle third of the width of the plate. A nut and washer shall be tightened on each bolt. There shall be a minimum of two bolts per plate section with one bolt located not more than 12 inches (305 mm) or less than seven bolt diameters from each end of the plate section. Interior bearing wall sole plates on monolithic slab foundation that are not part of a *braced wall panel* shall be positively anchored with *approved* fasteners. Sill plates and sole plates shall be protected against decay and termites where required by Sections R317 and R318. Cold-formed steel framing systems shall be fastened to the wood sill plates or anchored directly to the foundation as required in Section R505.3.1 or R603.1.1. When vertical reinforcing is required by other sections of this code, the foundation anchor bolts shall be within 8 inches (203 mm) of the vertical reinforcing. All anchor bolts installed in masonry shall be grouted in place with at least 1-inch (25 mm) of grout measured from the inside face of the masonry and the anchor bolt.

Exceptions:

1. Foundation anchor straps spaced as required to provide equivalent anchorage to $\frac{1}{2}$-inch diameter (12.7 mm) anchor bolts. When vertical reinforcing is required by other sections of this code, the foundation anchor straps shall align with the reinforcing.

2. Walls 24 inches (610 mm) total length or shorter connecting offset braced wall panels shall be anchored to the foundation with a minimum of one anchor bolt located in the center third of the plate section and shall be attached to adjacent braced wall panels according to Figure R602.10.5 at corners.

3. Walls 12 inches (305 mm) total length or shorter connecting offset *braced wall panels* shall be permitted to be connected to the foundation without anchor bolts. The wall shall be attached to adjacent braced wall panels according to Figure R602.10.5 at corners.

R403.1.6.1 Foundation anchorage in Seismic Design Categories C, D$_0$, D$_1$ and D$_2$. In addition to the requirements of Section R403.1.6, the following requirements shall apply to wood light-frame structures in Seismic Design Categories D_0, D_1 and D_2 and wood light-frame townhouses in Seismic Design Category C.

1. Plate washers conforming to Section R602.11.1 shall be provided for all anchor bolts over the full length of required *braced wall lines* except where *approved* anchor straps are used. Properly sized cut washers shall be permitted for anchor bolts in wall lines not containing *braced wall panels*.

2. Interior braced wall plates shall have anchor bolts spaced at not more than 6 feet (1829 mm) on center and located within 12 inches (305 mm) of the ends of each plate section where supported on a continuous foundation.

3. Interior bearing wall sole plates shall have anchor bolts spaced at not more than 6 feet (1829 mm) on center and located within 12 inches (305 mm) of the ends of each plate section where supported on a continuous foundation.

4. The maximum anchor bolt spacing shall be 4 feet (1219 mm) for buildings over two stories in height.

5. Stepped cripple walls shall conform to Section R602.11.2.

6. Where continuous wood foundations in accordance with Section R404.2 are used, the force transfer shall have a capacity equal to or greater than the connections required by Section R602.11.1 or the *braced wall panel* shall be connected to the wood foundations in accordance with the *braced wall panel*-to-floor fastening requirements of Table R602.3(1).

R403.1.7 Footings on or adjacent to slopes. The placement of buildings and structures on or adjacent to slopes steeper than one unit vertical in three units horizontal (33.3-percent slope) shall conform to Sections R403.1.7.1 through R403.1.7.4.

R403.1.7.1 Building clearances from ascending slopes. In general, buildings below slopes shall be set a sufficient distance from the slope to provide protection from slope drainage, erosion and shallow failures. Except as provided in Section R403.1.7.4 and Figure R403.1.7.1, the following criteria will be assumed to provide this protection. Where the existing slope is steeper than one unit vertical in one unit horizontal (100-percent slope), the toe of the slope shall be assumed to be at the intersection of a horizontal plane drawn from the top of the foundation and a plane drawn tangent to the slope at an angle of 45 degrees (0.79 rad) to the horizontal. Where a retaining wall is constructed at the toe of the slope, the height of the slope shall be measured from the top of the wall to the top of the slope.

R403.1.7.2 Footing setback from descending slope surfaces. Footings on or adjacent to slope surfaces shall be founded in material with an embedment and setback from the slope surface sufficient to provide vertical and lateral support for the footing without detrimental settlement. Except as provided for in Section R403.1.7.4 and Figure R403.1.7.1, the following setback is deemed adequate to meet the criteria. Where the slope is steeper than one unit vertical in one unit horizontal (100-percent slope), the required setback shall be measured from an imaginary plane 45 degrees (0.79 rad) to the horizontal, projected upward from the toe of the slope.

R403.1.7.3 Foundation elevation. On graded sites, the top of any exterior foundation shall extend above the elevation of the street gutter at point of discharge or the inlet of an *approved* drainage device not less than 12 inches (305 mm) plus 2 percent. Alternate elevations are permitted subject to the approval of the *building official*, provided that it can be demonstrated that required drainage to the point of discharge and away from the structure is provided at all locations on the site.

R403.1.7.4 Alternate setbacks and clearances. Alternate setbacks and clearances are permitted, subject to the approval of the *building official*. The *building official* is permitted to require an investigation and recommendation of a qualified engineer to demonstrate that the intent of this section has been satisfied. Such an investigation shall include consideration of material, height of slope, slope gradient, load intensity and erosion characteristics of slope material.

R403.1.8 Foundations on expansive soils. Foundation and floor slabs for buildings located on *expansive soils* shall be designed in accordance with Section 1808.6 of the *International Building Code*.

Exception: Slab-on-ground and other foundation systems that have performed adequately in soil conditions

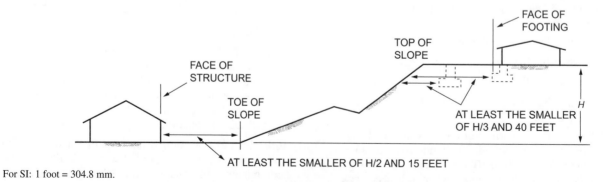

For SI: 1 foot = 304.8 mm.

FIGURE R403.1.7.1
FOUNDATION CLEARANCE FROM SLOPES

similar to those encountered at the building site are permitted subject to the approval of the *building official*.

R403.1.8.1 Expansive soils classifications. Soils meeting all of the following provisions shall be considered to be expansive, except that tests to show compliance with Items 1, 2 and 3 shall not be required if the test prescribed in Item 4 is conducted:

1. Plasticity Index (PI) of 15 or greater, determined in accordance with ASTM D4318.

2. More than 10 percent of the soil particles pass a No. 200 sieve (75 μm), determined in accordance with ASTM D422.

3. More than 10 percent of the soil particles are less than 5 micrometers in size, determined in accordance with ASTM D422.

4. Expansion Index greater than 20, determined in accordance with ASTM D4829.

R403.2 Footings for wood foundations. Footings for wood foundations shall be in accordance with Figures R403.1(2) and R403.1(3). Gravel shall be washed and well graded. The maximum size stone shall not exceed $^3/_4$ inch (19.1 mm). Gravel shall be free from organic, clayey or silty soils. Sand shall be coarse, not smaller than $^1/_{16}$-inch (1.6 mm) grains and shall be free from organic, clayey or silty soils. Crushed stone shall have a maximum size of $^1/_2$ inch (12.7 mm).

R403.3 Frost-protected shallow foundations. For buildings where the monthly mean temperature of the building is maintained at not less than 64°F (18°C), footings are not required to extend below the frost line where protected from frost by insulation in accordance with Figure R403.3(1) and Table R403.3(1). Foundations protected from frost in accordance with Figure R403.3(1) and Table R403.3(1) shall not be used for unheated spaces such as porches, utility rooms, garages and carports, and shall not be attached to *basements* or *crawl spaces* that are not maintained at a minimum monthly mean temperature of 64°F (18°C).

Materials used below *grade* for the purpose of insulating footings against frost shall be *labeled* as complying with ASTM C578.

R403.3.1 Foundations adjoining frost-protected shallow foundations. Foundations that adjoin frost-protected shallow foundations shall be protected from frost in accordance with Section R403.1.4.

R403.3.1.1 Attachment to unheated slab-on-ground structure. Vertical wall insulation and horizontal insulation of frost-protected shallow foundations that adjoin a slab-on-ground foundation that does not have a monthly mean temperature maintained at not less than 64°F (18°C) shall be in accordance with Figure R403.3(3) and Table R403.3(1). Vertical wall insulation shall extend between the frost-protected shallow foundation and the adjoining slab foundation. Required horizontal insulation shall be continuous under the adjoining slab foundation and through any foundation walls adjoining the frost- protected shallow foundation. Where insulation passes through a foundation wall, it

shall be either of a type complying with this section and having bearing capacity equal to or greater than the structural loads imposed by the building, or the building shall be designed and constructed using beams, lintels, cantilevers or other means of transferring building loads such that the structural loads of the building do not bear on the insulation.

R403.3.1.2 Attachment to heated structure. Where a frost-protected shallow foundation abuts a structure that has a monthly mean temperature maintained at not less than 64°F (18°C), horizontal insulation and vertical wall insulation shall not be required between the frost-protected shallow foundation and the adjoining structure. Where the frost-protected shallow foundation abuts the heated structure, the horizontal insulation and vertical wall insulation shall extend along the adjoining foundation in accordance with Figure R403.3(4) a distance of not less than Dimension A in Table R403.3(1).

> **Exception:** Where the frost-protected shallow foundation abuts the heated structure to form an inside corner, vertical insulation extending along the adjoining foundation is not required.

R403.3.2 Protection of horizontal insulation below ground. Horizontal insulation placed less than 12 inches (305 mm) below the ground surface or that portion of horizontal insulation extending outward more than 24 inches (610 mm) from the foundation edge shall be protected against damage by use of a concrete slab or asphalt paving on the ground surface directly above the insulation or by cementitious board, plywood rated for below-ground use, or other *approved* materials placed below ground, directly above the top surface of the insulation.

R403.3.3 Drainage. Final *grade* shall be sloped in accordance with Section R401.3. In other than Group I Soils, as detailed in Table R405.1, gravel or crushed stone beneath horizontal insulation below ground shall drain to daylight or into an *approved* sewer system.

R403.3.4 Termite protection. The use of foam plastic in areas of "very heavy" termite infestation probability shall be in accordance with Section R318.4.

R403.4 Footings for precast concrete foundations. Footings for precast concrete foundations shall comply with Section R403.4.

R403.4.1 Crushed stone footings. Clean crushed stone shall be free from organic, clayey or silty soils. Crushed stone shall be angular in nature and meet ASTM C33, with the maximum size stone not to exceed $^1/_2$ inch (12.7 mm) and the minimum stone size not to be smaller than $^1/_{16}$ inch (1.6 mm). Crushed stone footings for precast foundations shall be installed in accordance with Figure R403.4(1) and Table R403.4. Crushed stone footings shall be consolidated using a vibratory plate in not greater than 8-inch (203 mm) lifts. Crushed stone footings shall be limited to Seismic Design Categories A, B and C.

R403.4.2 Concrete footings. Concrete footings shall be installed in accordance with Section R403.1 and Figure R403.4(2).

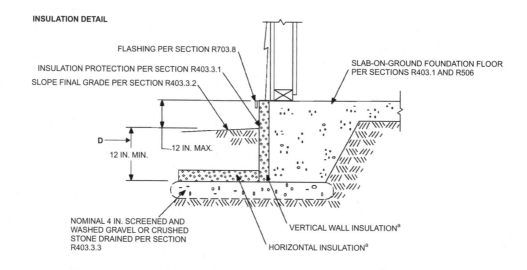

INSULATION DETAIL

FLASHING PER SECTION R703.8

INSULATION PROTECTION PER SECTION R403.3.1
SLOPE FINAL GRADE PER SECTION R403.3.2

SLAB-ON-GROUND FOUNDATION FLOOR
PER SECTIONS R403.1 AND R506

D

12 IN. MAX.

12 IN. MIN.

NOMINAL 4 IN. SCREENED AND
WASHED GRAVEL OR CRUSHED
STONE DRAINED PER SECTION
R403.3.3

VERTICAL WALL INSULATION[a]

HORIZONTAL INSULATION[a]

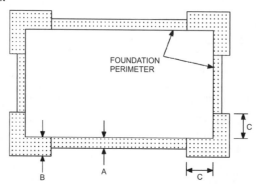

HORIZONTAL INSULATION PLAN

FOUNDATION
PERIMETER

C

B   A

C

For SI: 1 inch = 25.4 mm.

a. See Table R403.3(1) for required dimensions and *R*-values for vertical and horizontal insulation and minimum footing depth.

FIGURE R403.3(1)
INSULATION PLACEMENT FOR FROST-PROTECTED FOOTINGS IN HEATED BUILDINGS

TABLE R403.3(1)
MINIMUM FOOTING DEPTH AND INSULATION REQUIREMENTS FOR FROST-PROTECTED FOOTINGS IN HEATED BUILDINGS[a]

AIR FREEZING INDEX (°F-days)[b]	MINIMUM FOOTING DEPTH, D (inches)	VERTICAL INSULATION R-VALUE[c, d]	HORIZONTAL INSULATION R-VALUE[c, e]		HORIZONTAL INSULATION DIMENSIONS PER FIGURE R403.3(1) (inches)		
			Along walls	At corners	A	B	C
1,500 or less	12	4.5	Not required	Not required	Not required	Not required	Not required
2,000	14	5.6	Not required	Not required	Not required	Not required	Not required
2,500	16	6.7	1.7	4.9	12	24	40
3,000	16	7.8	6.5	8.6	12	24	40
3,500	16	9.0	8.0	11.2	24	30	60
4,000	16	10.1	10.5	13.1	24	36	60

For SI: 1 inch = 25.4 mm, °C = [(°F) - 32]/1.8.

a. Insulation requirements are for protection against frost damage in heated buildings. Greater values could be required to meet energy conservation standards.

b. See Figure R403.3(2) or Table R403.3(2) for Air Freezing Index values.

c. Insulation materials shall provide the stated minimum *R*-values under long-term exposure to moist, below-ground conditions in freezing climates. The following *R*-values shall be used to determine insulation thicknesses required for this application: Type II expanded polystyrene (EPS)-3.2 R per inch for vertical insulation and 2.6 R per inch for horizontal insulation; Type IX expanded polystyrene (EPS)-3.4 R per inch for vertical insulation and 2.8 R per inch for horizontal insulation; Types IV, V, VI, VII, and X extruded polystyrene (XPS)-4.5 R per inch for vertical insulation and 4.0 R per inch for horizontal insulation.

d. Vertical insulation shall be expanded polystyrene insulation or extruded polystyrene insulation.

e. Horizontal insulation shall be expanded polystyrene insulation or extruded polystyrene insulation.

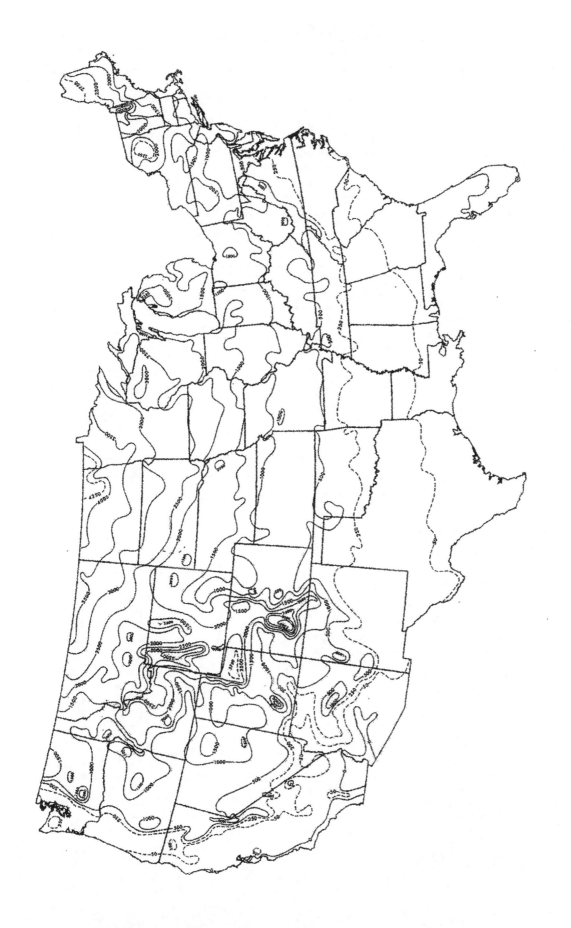

For SI: °C = [(°F) - 32]/1.8.

Note: The air-freezing index is defined as cumulative degree days below 32°F. It is used as a measure of the combined magnitude and duration of air temperature below freezing. The index was computed over a 12-month period (July-June) for each of the 3,044 stations used in the above analysis. Dates from the 1951-80 period were fitted to a Weibull probability distribution to produce an estimate of the 100-year return period.

FIGURE R403.3(2)
AIR-FREEZING INDEX AN ESTIMATE OF THE 100-YEAR RETURN PERIOD

TABLE R403.3(2)
AIR-FREEZING INDEX FOR U.S. LOCATIONS BY COUNTY

STATE	AIR-FREEZING INDEX					
	1500 or less	2000	2500	3000	3500	4000
Alabama	All counties	—	—	—	—	—
Alaska	Ketchikan Gateway, Prince of Wales-Outer Ketchikan (CA), Sitka, Wrangell-Petersburg (CA)	—	Aleutians West (CA), Haines, Juneau, Skagway-Hoonah-Angoon (CA), Yakutat	—	—	All counties not listed
Arizona	All counties	—	—	—	—	—
Arkansas	All counties	—	—	—	—	—
California	All counties not listed	Nevada, Sierra	—	—	—	—
Colorado	All counties not listed	Archuleta, Custer, Fremont, Huerfano, Las Animas, Ouray, Pitkin, San Miguel	Clear Creek, Conejos, Costilla, Dolores, Eagle, La Plata, Park, Routt, San Juan, Summit	Alamosa, Grand, Jackson, Larimer, Moffat, Rio Blanco, Rio Grande	Chaffee, Gunnison, Lake, Saguache	Hinsdale, Mineral
Connecticut	All counties not listed	Hartford, Litchfield	—	—	—	—
Delaware	All counties	—	—	—	—	—
District of Columbia	All counties	—	—	—	—	—
Florida	All counties	—	—	—	—	—
Georgia	All counties	—	—	—	—	—
Hawaii	All counties	—	—	—	—	—
Idaho	All counties not listed	Adams, Bannock, Blaine, Clearwater, Idaho, Lincoln, Oneida, Power, Valley, Washington	Bingham, Bonneville, Camas, Caribou, Elmore, Franklin, Jefferson, Madison, Teton	Bear Lake, Butte, Custer, Fremont, Lemhi	Clark	—
Illinois	All counties not listed	Boone, Bureau, Cook, Dekalb, DuPage, Fulton, Grundy, Henderson, Henry, Iroquois, Jo Daviess, Kane, Kankakee, Kendall, Knox, La Salle, Lake, Lee, Livingston, Marshall, Mason, McHenry, McLean, Mercer, Peoria, Putnam, Rock Island, Stark, Tazewell, Warren, Whiteside, Will, Woodford	Carroll, Ogle, Stephenson, Winnebago	—	—	—
Indiana	All counties not listed	Allen, Benton, Cass, Fountain, Fulton, Howard, Jasper, Kosciusko, La Porte, Lake, Marshall, Miami, Newton, Porter, Pulaski, Starke, Steuben, Tippecanoe, Tipton, Wabash, Warren, White	—	—	—	—

(continued)

TABLE R403.3(2)—continued
AIR-FREEZING INDEX FOR U.S. LOCATIONS BY COUNTY

STATE	AIR-FREEZING INDEX					
	1500 or less	2000	2500	3000	3500	4000
Iowa	Appanoose, Davis, Fremont, Lee, Van Buren	All counties not listed	Allamakee, Black Hawk, Boone, Bremer, Buchanan, Buena Vista, Butler, Calhoun, Cerro Gordo, Cherokee, Chickasaw, Clay, Clayton, Delaware, Dubuque, Fayette, Floyd, Franklin, Grundy, Hamilton, Hancock, Hardin, Humboldt, Ida, Jackson, Jasper, Jones, Linn, Marshall, Palo Alto, Plymouth, Pocahontas, Poweshiek, Sac, Sioux, Story, Tama, Webster, Winnebago, Woodbury, Worth, Wright	Dickinson, Emmet, Howard, Kossuth, Lyon, Mitchell, O'Brien, Osceola, Winneshiek	—	—
Kansas	All counties	—	—	—	—	—
Kentucky	All counties	—	—	—	—	—
Louisiana	All counties	—	—	—	—	—
Maine	York	Knox, Lincoln, Sagadahoc	Androscoggin, Cumberland, Hancock, Kennebec, Waldo, Washington	Aroostook, Franklin, Oxford, Penobscot, Piscataquis, Somerset	—	—
Maryland	All counties	—	—	—	—	—
Massachusetts	All counties not listed	Berkshire, Franklin, Hampden, Worcester	—	—	—	—
Michigan	Berrien, Branch, Cass, Kalamazoo, Macomb, Ottawa, St. Clair, St. Joseph	All counties not listed	Alger, Charlevoix, Cheboygan, Chippewa, Crawford, Delta, Emmet, Iosco, Kalkaska, Lake, Luce, Mackinac, Menominee, Missaukee, Montmorency, Ogemaw, Osceola, Otsego, Roscommon, Schoolcraft, Wexford	Baraga, Dickinson, Iron, Keweenaw, Marquette	Gogebic, Houghton, Ontonagon	—
Minnesota	—	—	Houston, Winona	All counties not listed	Aitkin, Big Stone, Carlton, Crow Wing, Douglas, Itasca, Kanabec, Lake, Morrison, Pine, Pope, Stearns, Stevens, Swift, Todd, Wadena	Becker, Beltrami, Cass, Clay, Clearwater, Grant, Hubbard, Kittson, Koochiching, Lake of the Woods, Mahnomen, Marshall, Norman, Otter Tail, Pennington, Polk, Red Lake, Roseau, St. Louis, Traverse, Wilkin

(continued)

TABLE R403.3(2)—continued
AIR-FREEZING INDEX FOR U.S. LOCATIONS BY COUNTY

STATE	AIR-FREEZING INDEX					
	1500 or less	2000	2500	3000	3500	4000
Mississippi	All counties	—	—	—	—	—
Missouri	All counties not listed	Atchison, Mercer, Nodaway, Putnam	—	—	—	—
Montana	Mineral	Broadwater, Golden Valley, Granite, Lake, Lincoln, Missoula, Ravalli, Sanders, Sweet Grass	Big Horn, Carbon, Jefferson, Judith Basin, Lewis and Clark, Meagher, Musselshell, Powder River, Powell, Silver Bow, Stillwater, Westland	Carter, Cascade, Deer Lodge, Falcon, Fergus, Flathead, Gallanting, Glacier, Madison, Park, Petroleum, Ponder, Rosebud, Teton, Treasure, Yellowstone	Beaverhead, Blaine, Chouteau, Custer, Dawson, Garfield, Liberty, McCone, Prairie, Toole, Wibaux	Daniels, Hill, Phillips, Richland, Roosevelt, Sheridan, Valley
Nebraska	Adams, Banner, Chase, Cheyenne, Clay, Deuel, Dundy, Fillmore, Franklin, Frontier, Furnas, Gage, Garden, Gosper, Harlan, Hayes, Hitchcock, Jefferson, Kimball, Morrill, Nemaha, Nuckolls, Pawnee, Perkins, Phelps, Red Willow, Richardson, Saline, Scotts Bluff, Seward, Thayer, Webster	All counties not listed	Boyd, Burt, Cedar, Cuming, Dakota, Dixon, Dodge, Knox, Thurston	—	—	—
Nevada	All counties not listed	Elko, Eureka, Nye, Washoe, White Pine	—	—	—	—
New Hampshire	—	All counties not listed	—	—	—	Carroll, Coos, Grafton
New Jersey	All counties	—	—	—	—	—
New Mexico	All counties not listed	Rio Arriba	Colfax, Mora, Taos	—	—	—
New York	Albany, Bronx, Cayuga, Columbia, Cortland, Dutchess, Genessee, Kings, Livingston, Monroe, Nassau, New York, Niagara, Onondaga, Ontario, Orange, Orleans, Putnam, Queens, Richmond, Rockland, Seneca, Suffolk, Wayne, Westchester, Yates	All counties not listed	Clinton, Essex, Franklin, Hamilton, Herkimer, Jefferson, Lewis, St. Lawrence, Warren	—	—	—
North Carolina	All counties	—	—	—	—	—

(continued)

TABLE R403.3(2)—continued
AIR-FREEZING INDEX FOR U.S. LOCATIONS BY COUNTY

STATE	AIR-FREEZING INDEX					
	1500 or less	2000	2500	3000	3500	4000
North Dakota	—	—	—	Billings, Bowman	Adams, Dickey, Golden Valley, Hettinger, LaMoure, Oliver, Ransom, Sargent, Sioux, Slope, Stark	All counties not listed
Ohio	All counties not listed	Ashland, Crawford, Defiance, Holmes, Huron, Knox, Licking, Morrow, Paulding, Putnam, Richland, Seneca, Williams	—	—	—	—
Oklahoma	All counties	—	—	—	—	—
Oregon	All counties not listed	Baker, Crook, Grant, Harney	—	—	—	—
Pennsylvania	All counties not listed	Berks, Blair, Bradford, Cambria, Cameron, Centre, Clarion, Clearfield, Clinton, Crawford, Elk, Forest, Huntingdon, Indiana, Jefferson, Lackawanna, Lycoming, McKean, Pike, Potter, Susquehanna, Tioga, Venango, Warren, Wayne, Wyoming	—	—	—	—
Rhode Island	All counties	—	—	—	—	—
South Carolina	All counties	—	—	—	—	—
South Dakota	—	Bennett, Custer, Fall River, Lawrence, Mellette, Shannon, Todd, Tripp	Bon Homme, Charles Mix, Davison, Douglas, Gregory, Jackson, Jones, Lyman	All counties not listed	Beadle, Brookings, Brown, Campbell, Codington, Corson, Day, Deuel, Edmunds, Faulk, Grant, Hamlin, Kingsbury, Marshall, McPherson, Perkins, Roberts, Spink, Walworth	—
Tennessee	All counties	—	—	—	—	—
Texas	All counties	—	—	—	—	—
Utah	All counties not listed	Box Elder, Morgan, Weber	Garfield, Salt Lake, Summit	Carbon, Daggett, Duchesne, Rich, Sanpete, Uintah, Wasatch	—	—

(continued)

TABLE R403.3(2)—continued
AIR-FREEZING INDEX FOR U.S. LOCATIONS BY COUNTY

STATE	AIR-FREEZING INDEX					
	1500 or less	2000	2500	3000	3500	4000
Vermont	—	Bennington, Grand Isle, Rutland, Windham	Addison, Chittenden, Franklin, Orange, Washington, Windsor	Caledonia, Essex, Lamoille, Orleans	—	—
Virginia	All counties	—	—	—	—	—
Washington	All counties not listed	Chelan, Douglas, Ferry, Okanogan	—	—	—	—
West Virginia	All counties	—	—	—	—	—
Wisconsin	—	Kenosha, Kewaunee, Racine, Sheboygan, Walworth	All counties not listed	Ashland, Barron, Burnett, Chippewa, Clark, Dunn, Eau Claire, Florence, Forest, Iron, Jackson, La Crosse, Langlade, Marathon, Monroe, Pepin, Polk, Portage, Price, Rust, St. Croix, Taylor, Trempealeau, Vilas, Wood	Bayfield, Douglas, Lincoln, Oneida, Sawyer, Washburn	—
Wyoming	Goshen, Platte	Converse, Crook, Laramie, Niobrara	Campbell, Carbon, Hot Springs, Johnson, Natrona, Sheridan, Uinta, Weston	Albany, Big Horn, Park, Washakie	Fremont, Teton	Lincoln, Sublette, Sweetwater

INSULATION DETAIL

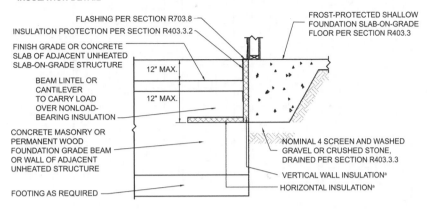

FLASHING PER SECTION R703.8

INSULATION PROTECTION PER SECTION R403.3.2

FINISH GRADE OR CONCRETE SLAB OF ADJACENT UNHEATED SLAB-ON-GRADE STRUCTURE

12" MAX.

BEAM LINTEL OR CANTILEVER TO CARRY LOAD OVER NONLOAD-BEARING INSULATION

12" MAX.

CONCRETE MASONRY OR PERMANENT WOOD FOUNDATION GRADE BEAM OR WALL OF ADJACENT UNHEATED STRUCTURE

FOOTING AS REQUIRED

FROST-PROTECTED SHALLOW FOUNDATION SLAB-ON-GRADE FLOOR PER SECTION R403.3

NOMINAL 4 SCREEN AND WASHED GRAVEL OR CRUSHED STONE, DRAINED PER SECTION R403.3.3

VERTICAL WALL INSULATION[a]

HORIZONTAL INSULATION[a]

HORIZONTAL INSULATION PLAN

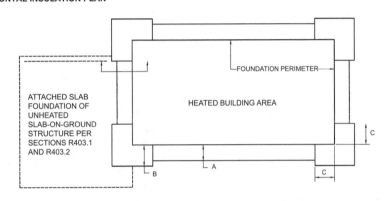

ATTACHED SLAB FOUNDATION OF UNHEATED SLAB-ON-GROUND STRUCTURE PER SECTIONS R403.1 AND R403.2

FOUNDATION PERIMETER

HEATED BUILDING AREA

C

A

B

C

For SI: 1 inch = 25.4 mm.

a. See Table R403.3(1) for required dimensions and *R*-values for vertical and horizontal insulation.

FIGURE R403.3(3)
INSULATION PLACEMENT FOR FROST-PROTECTED FOOTINGS ADJACENT TO UNHEATED SLAB-ON-GROUND STRUCTURE

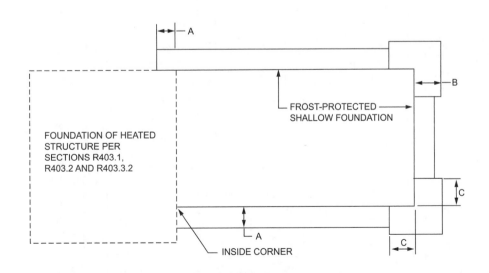

A

FOUNDATION OF HEATED STRUCTURE PER SECTIONS R403.1, R403.2 AND R403.3.2

FROST-PROTECTED SHALLOW FOUNDATION

B

C

A

C

INSIDE CORNER

FIGURE R403.3(4)
INSULATION PLACEMENT FOR FROST-PROTECTED FOOTINGS ADJACENT TO HEATED STRUCTURE

TABLE R403.4
MINIMUM DEPTH (D) AND WIDTH (W) OF CRUSHED STONE FOOTINGS[a,b] (inches)

NUMBER OF STORIES	UNIFORM WALL LOAD	DEPTH (D) AND WIDTH (W)	1500 MH, CH, CL, ML[c] — 8	10	12	2000 SC, GC, SM, GM, SP, SW[c] — 8	10	12	2500 — 8	10	12	3000 GP, GW[c] — 8	10	12	3500 — 8	10	12	4000 — 8	10	12
			Conventional light-frame construction																	
1-story	1100 plf	D	4	4	4	4	4	4	4	4	4	4	4	4	4	4	4	4	4	4
		W	13	15	17	13	15	17	13	15	17	13	15	17	13	15	17	13	15	17
2-story	1800 plf	D	6	4	4	4	4	4	4	4	4	4	4	4	4	4	4	4	4	4
		W	15	15	17	13	15	17	13	15	17	13	15	17	13	15	17	13	15	17
3-story	2900 plf	D	14	12	10	9	7	5	6	4	4	4	4	4	4	4	4	4	4	4
		W	25	24	24	19	19	18	15	15	17	13	15	17	13	15	17	13	15	17
			4-inch brick veneer over light-frame or 8-inch hollow concrete masonry																	
1-story	1500 plf	D	4	4	4	4	4	4	4	4	4	4	4	4	4	4	4	4	4	4
		W	13	15	17	13	15	17	13	15	17	13	15	17	13	15	17	13	15	17
2-story	2700 plf	D	12	11	9	8	6	4	5	4	4	4	4	4	4	4	4	4	4	4
		W	22	23	23	18	17	17	14	15	17	13	15	17	13	15	17	13	15	17
3-story	4000 plf	D	21	20	18	14	13	11	10	8	7	7	6	4	5	4	4	4	4	4
		W	33	34	33	25	26	25	20	20	21	17	17	17	14	15	17	13	15	17
			8-inch solid or fully grouted masonry																	
1-story	2000 plf	D	7	6	4	4	4	4	4	4	4	4	4	4	4	4	4	4	4	4
		W	17	17	17	13	15	17	13	15	17	13	15	17	13	15	17	13	15	17
2-story	3600 plf	D	19	17	15	12	11	9	9	7	5	6	4	4	4	4	4	4	4	4
		W	30	30	30	22	23	23	19	19	18	15	15	17	13	15	17	13	15	17
3-story	5300 plf	D	30	29	27	21	19	18	16	14	12	12	10	8	9	8	6	7	6	4
		W	43	44	44	33	32	33	27	27	26	22	22	22	19	20	19	17	17	17

Column groups under LOAD-BEARING VALUE OF SOIL (psf); Wall width (inches) = 8, 10, 12 within each value.

For SI: 1 inch = 25.4 mm, 1 plf = 14.6 N/m, 1 pound per square foot = 47.9 N/m^2.

a. Linear interpolation of stone depth between wall widths is permitted within each Load-Bearing Value of Soil (psf).

b. Crushed stone must be consolidated in 8-inch lifts with a plate vibrator.

c. Soil classes are in accordance with the Unified Soil Classification System. Refer to Table R405.1.

SECTION R404
FOUNDATION AND RETAINING WALLS

R404.1 Concrete and masonry foundation walls. Concrete foundation walls shall be selected and constructed in accordance with the provisions of Section R404.1.2. Masonry foundation walls shall be selected and constructed in accordance with the provisions of Section R404.1.3. Concrete and masonry foundation walls shall be laterally supported at the top and bottom. Foundation walls that meet all of the following shall be considered laterally supported:

1. Full basement floor shall be 3.5 inches (89 mm) thick concrete slab poured tight against the bottom of the foundation wall.

2. Floor joists and blocking shall be connected to the sill plate at the top of wall with an approved connector with listed capacity meeting the top of wall reaction in Table R404.1(1). Maximum spacing of floor joists shall be 24 inches on center. Spacing of blocking shall be in accordance with Table R404.1(1).

3. Bolt spacing for the sill plate shall be no greater than the requirements in Table R404.1(1).

4. The floor shall be blocked perpendicular to the floor joists. Blocking shall be installed in accordance with footnote f of Table R404.1(1).

   Exception: Cantilevered concrete and masonry foundation walls supporting unbalanced backfill that do not have permanent lateral support at the top of the foundation shall be constructed according to Table R404.1.1(5), Table R404.1.1(6), or Table R404.1.1(7).

R404.1.1 Design required. Concrete or masonry foundation walls shall be designed in accordance with accepted engineering practice where either of the following conditions exists:

1. Walls are subject to hydrostatic pressure from ground water.

2. Walls supporting more than 48 inches (1219 mm) of unbalanced backfill that do not have permanent lateral support at the top or bottom.

   Exception: Cantilevered concrete and masonry foundation walls constructed in accordance with Table R404.1.1(5), R404.1.1(6), or R404.1.1(7).

R404.1.2 Design of masonry foundation walls. Masonry foundation walls shall be designed and constructed in accordance with the provisions of this section or in accordance with the provisions of TMS 402. Where TMS 402 or the provisions of this section are used to design masonry foundation walls, project drawings, typical details and specifications are not required to bear the seal of the architect or engineer responsible for design, unless otherwise required by the state law of the jurisdiction having authority.

R404.1.2.1 Masonry foundation walls. Concrete masonry and clay masonry foundation walls shall be constructed as set forth in Table R404.1.1(1), R404.1.1(2), R404.1.1(3) or R404.1.1(4) and shall comply with applicable provisions of Section R606. In buildings assigned to Seismic Design Categories D_0, D_1 and D_2, concrete masonry and clay masonry foundation walls shall also comply with Section R404.1.4.1. Rubble stone masonry foundation walls shall be constructed in accordance with Sections R404.1.8 and R606.4.2. Rubble stone masonry walls shall not be used in Seismic Design Categories D_0, D_1 and D_2.

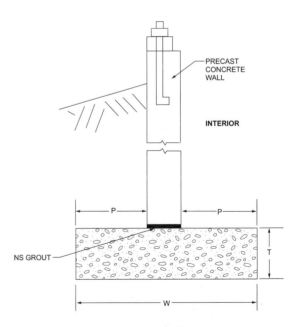

FIGURE R403.4(1)
BASEMENT OR CRAWL SPACE WITH PRECAST
FOUNDATION WALL BEARING ON CRUSHED STONE

FIGURE R403.4(2)
BASEMENT OR CRAWL SPACE WITH PRECAST
FOUNDATION WALL ON SPREAD FOOTING

TABLE R404.1(1)
MAXIMUM ANCHOR BOLT AND BLOCKING SPACING FOR SUPPORTED FOUNDATION WALL

MAX. WALL HEIGHT	MAX. UNBALANCED BACKFILL HEIGHT	SOIL CLASSES[a]	SOIL LOAD (pcf/ft)	TOP OF WALL REACTION (plf)[e]	1/2" DIAMETER ANCHOR BOLT SPACING (inches)[b, c, d]	SPACING OF BLOCKING PERPENDICULAR TO FLOOR JOISTS (inches)[f]
8'-0"	7'-6"	GW, GP, SW, & SP	30	260	72	72
		GM, GC, SM, SM-SC, & ML	45	400	72	72
		SC, MH, ML-CL, & I-CL	60	530	48	48
9'-0"	8'-6"	GW, GP, SW, & SP	30	340	72	72
		GM, GC, SM, SM-SC, & ML	45	510	48	48
		SC, MH, ML-CL, & I-CL	60	680	32	32
10'-0"	9'-6"	GW, GP, SW, & SP	30	430	64	64
		GM, GC, SM, SM-SC, & ML	45	640	40	40
		SC, MH, ML-CL, & I-CL	60	860	24	24

For SI: 1 inch = 25.4 mm, 1 foot = 304.8 mm.

a. Soil classes are in accordance with the Unified Soil Classification System. Refer to Table R405.1.

b. Anchor bolts shall be cast-in-place with a minimum 7-inch embed. Where vertical reinforcing is required by other sections of this code, the anchor bolts shall be within 8 inches of the vertical reinforcing and are to be spaced as required by this table. Anchor bolts installed in masonry shall be grouted in place with not less than 1 inch of grout measured from the inside face of the masonry and the anchor bolt.

c. The sill plate shall be 2 x 6 minimum. Anchor bolts shall be placed at least 2 1/2 inches from the edge of the sill plate and the edge of the foundation wall.

d. Anchor bolts shall have a 2 inch by 1/8 inch thick round or square washer tightened and countersunk 1/4 inch into the top of the sill plate. Use of standard and noncountersunk washers is permitted where anchor bolt spacing is half the spacing required by this table.

e. Minimum load to be used for the sizing of accepted anchors or fasteners if anchor bolts are not used.

f. Perpendicular blocking shall be 2-by the full depth joists or an approved alternative full depth joist material that is installed in the first three joists spaces adjacent to the foundation wall. The blocking shall be connected to the sill plate with an approved fastener sized in accordance with Footnote e. The floor sheathing shall be nailed to the blocking through the subfloor with a minimum of 8d common (2 1/2 x 0.131) nails at 3 inches on center or an equivalent connector. Blocking shall be installed within 8 inches of an anchor bolt location.

TABLE R404.1.1(1)
PLAIN MASONRY FOUNDATION WALLS[f]

MAXIMUM WALL HEIGHT (feet)	MAXIMUM UNBALANCED BACKFILL HEIGHT[c] (feet)	PLAIN MASONRY[a] MINIMUM NOMINAL WALL THICKNESS (inches)		
		Soil classes[b]		
		GW, GP, SW and SP	GM, GC, SM, SM-SC and ML	SC, MH, ML-CL and inorganic CL
5	4	6 solid[d] or 8	6 solid[d] or 8	6 solid[d] or 8
	5	6 solid[d] or 8	8	10
6	4	6 solid[d] or 8	6 solid[d] or 8	6 solid[d] or 8
	5	6 solid[d] or 8	8	10
	6	8	10	12
7	4	6 solid[d] or 8	8	8
	5	6 solid[d] or 8	10	10
	6	10	12	10 solid[d]
	7	12	10 solid[d]	12 solid[d]
8	4	6 solid[d] or 8	6 solid[d] or 8	8
	5	6 solid[d] or 8	10	12
	6	10	12	12 solid[d]
	7	12	12 solid[d]	Footnote e
	8	10 grout[d]	12 grout[d]	Footnote e
9	4	6 grout[d] or 8 solid[d] or 12	6 grout[d] or 8 solid[d]	8 grout[d] or 10 solid[d]
	5	6 grout[d] or 10 solid[d]	8 grout[d] or 12 solid[d]	8 grout[d]
	6	8 grout[d] or 12 solid[d]	10 grout[d]	10 grout[d]
	7	10 grout[d]	10 grout[d]	12 grout
	8	10 grout[d]	12 grout	Footnote e
	9	12 grout	Footnote e	Footnote e

For SI: 1 inch = 25.4 mm, 1 foot = 304.8 mm, 1 pound per square inch = 6.895 Pa.

a. Mortar shall be Type M or S and masonry shall be laid in running bond. Ungrouted hollow masonry units are permitted except where otherwise indicated.

b. Soil classes are in accordance with the Unified Soil Classification System. Refer to Table R405.1.

c. Unbalanced backfill height is the difference in height between the exterior finish ground level and the lower of the top of the concrete footing that supports the foundation wall or the interior finish ground level. Where an interior concrete slab-on-grade is provided and is in contact with the interior surface of the foundation wall, measurement of the unbalanced backfill height from the exterior finish ground level to the top of the interior concrete slab is permitted.

d. Solid indicates solid masonry unit; grout indicates grouted hollow units.

e. Wall construction shall be in accordance with either Table R404.1.1(2), Table R404.1.1(3), Table R404.1.1(4), or a design shall be provided.

f. The use of this table shall be prohibited for soil classifications not shown.

TABLE R404.1.1(2)
8-INCH MASONRY FOUNDATION WALLS WITH REINFORCING WHERE d ≥ 5 INCHES[a, c, f]

WALL HEIGHT	HEIGHT OF UNBALANCED BACKFILL[e]	MINIMUM VERTICAL REINFORCEMENT AND SPACING (INCHES)[b, c]		
		Soil classes and lateral soil load[d] (psf per foot below grade)		
		GW, GP, SW and SP soils 30	GM, GC, SM, SM-SC and ML soils 45	SC, ML-CL and inorganic CL soils 60
6 feet 8 inches	4 feet (or less)	#4 at 48	#4 at 48	#4 at 48
	5 feet	#4 at 48	#4 at 48	#4 at 48
	6 feet 8 inches	#4 at 48	#5 at 48	#6 at 48
7 feet 4 inches	4 feet (or less)	#4 at 48	#4 at 48	#4 at 48
	5 feet	#4 at 48	#4 at 48	#4 at 48
	6 feet	#4 at 48	#5 at 48	#5 at 48
	7 feet 4 inches	#5 at 48	#6 at 48	#6 at 40
8 feet	4 feet (or less)	#4 at 48	#4 at 48	#4 at 48
	5 feet	#4 at 48	#4 at 48	#4 at 48
	6 feet	#4 at 48	#5 at 48	#5 at 48
	7 feet	#5 at 48	#6 at 48	#6 at 40
	8 feet	#5 at 48	#6 at 48	#6 at 32
8 feet 8 inches	4 feet (or less)	#4 at 48	#4 at 48	#4 at 48
	5 feet	#4 at 48	#4 at 48	#5 at 48
	6 feet	#4 at 48	#5 at 48	#6 at 48
	7 feet	#5 at 48	#6 at 48	#6 at 40
	8 feet 8 inches	#6 at 48	#6 at 32	#6 at 24
9 feet 4 inches	4 feet (or less)	#4 at 48	#4 at 48	#4 at 48
	5 feet	#4 at 48	#4 at 48	#5 at 48
	6 feet	#4 at 48	#5 at 48	#6 at 48
	7 feet	#5 at 48	#6 at 48	#6 at 40
	8 feet	#6 at 48	#6 at 40	#6 at 24
	9 feet 4 inches	#6 at 40	#6 at 24	#6 at 16
10 feet	4 feet (or less)	#4 at 48	#4 at 48	#4 at 48
	5 feet	#4 at 48	#4 at 48	#5 at 48
	6 feet	#4 at 48	#5 at 48	#6 at 48
	7 feet	#5 at 48	#6 at 48	#6 at 32
	8 feet	#6 at 48	#6 at 32	#6 at 24
	9 feet	#6 at 40	#6 at 24	#6 at 16
	10 feet	#6 at 32	#6 at 16	#6 at 16

For SI: 1 inch = 25.4 mm, 1 foot = 304.8 mm, 1 pound per square foot per foot = 0.157 kPa/mm.

a. Mortar shall be Type M or S and masonry shall be laid in running bond.

b. Alternative reinforcing bar sizes and spacings having an equivalent cross-sectional area of reinforcement per lineal foot of wall shall be permitted provided the spacing of the reinforcement does not exceed 72 inches in Seismic Design Categories A, B and C, and 48 inches in Seismic Design Categories D_0, D_1 and D_2.

c. Vertical reinforcement shall be Grade 60 minimum. The distance, d, from the face of the soil side of the wall to the center of vertical reinforcement shall be not less than 5 inches.

d. Soil classes are in accordance with the Unified Soil Classification System and design lateral soil loads are for moist conditions without hydrostatic pressure. Refer to Table R405.1.

e. Unbalanced backfill height is the difference in height between the exterior finish ground level and the lower of the top of the concrete footing that supports the foundation wall or the interior finish ground level. Where an interior concrete slab-on-grade is provided and is in contact with the interior surface of the foundation wall, measurement of the unbalanced backfill height from the exterior finish ground level to the top of the interior concrete slab is permitted.

f. The use of this table shall be prohibited for soil classifications not shown.

TABLE R404.1.1(3)
10-INCH MASONRY FOUNDATION WALLS WITH REINFORCING WHERE d ≥ 6.75 INCHES[a, c, f]

WALL HEIGHT	HEIGHT OF UNBALANCED BACKFILL[e]	MINIMUM VERTICAL REINFORCEMENT AND SPACING (INCHES)[b, c]		
		Soil classes and later soil load[d] (psf per foot below grade)		
		GW, GP, SW and SP soils 30	GM, GC, SM, SM-SC and ML soils 45	SC, ML-CL and inorganic CL soils 60
6 feet 8 inches	4 feet (or less)	#4 at 56	#4 at 56	#4 at 56
	5 feet	#4 at 56	#4 at 56	#4 at 56
	6 feet 8 inches	#4 at 56	#5 at 56	#5 at 56
7 feet 4 inches	4 feet (or less)	#4 at 56	#4 at 56	#4 at 56
	5 feet	#4 at 56	#4 at 56	#4 at 56
	6 feet	#4 at 56	#4 at 56	#5 at 56
	7 feet 4 inches	#4 at 56	#5 at 56	#6 at 56
8 feet	4 feet (or less)	#4 at 56	#4 at 56	#4 at 56
	5 feet	#4 at 56	#4 at 56	#4 at 56
	6 feet	#4 at 56	#4 at 56	#5 at 56
	7 feet	#4 at 56	#5 at 56	#6 at 56
	8 feet	#5 at 56	#6 at 56	#6 at 48
8 feet 8 inches	4 feet (or less)	#4 at 56	#4 at 56	#4 at 56
	5 feet	#4 at 56	#4 at 56	#4 at 56
	6 feet	#4 at 56	#4 at 56	#5 at 56
	7 feet	#4 at 56	#5 at 56	#6 at 56
	8 feet 8 inches	#5 at 56	#6 at 48	#6 at 32
9 feet 4 inches	4 feet (or less)	#4 at 56	#4 at 56	#4 at 56
	5 feet	#4 at 56	#4 at 56	#4 at 56
	6 feet	#4 at 56	#5 at 56	#5 at 56
	7 feet	#4 at 56	#5 at 56	#6 at 56
	8 feet	#5 at 56	#6 at 56	#6 at 40
	9 feet 4 inches	#6 at 56	#6 at 40	#6 at 24
10 feet	4 feet (or less)	#4 at 56	#4 at 56	#4 at 56
	5 feet	#4 at 56	#4 at 56	#4 at 56
	6 feet	#4 at 56	#5 at 56	#5 at 56
	7 feet	#5 at 56	#6 at 56	#6 at 48
	8 feet	#5 at 56	#6 at 48	#6 at 40
	9 feet	#6 at 56	#6 at 40	#6 at 24
	10 feet	#6 at 48	#6 at 32	#6 at 24

For SI: 1 inch = 25.4 mm, 1 foot = 304.8 mm, 1 pound per square foot per foot = 0.157 kPa/mm.

a. Mortar shall be Type M or S and masonry shall be laid in running bond.

b. Alternative reinforcing bar sizes and spacings having an equivalent cross-sectional area of reinforcement per lineal foot of wall shall be permitted provided the spacing of the reinforcement does not exceed 72 inches in Seismic Design Categories A, B and C, and 48 inches in Seismic Design Categories D_0, D_1 and D_2.

c. Vertical reinforcement shall be Grade 60 minimum. The distance, d, from the face of the soil side of the wall to the center of vertical reinforcement shall be not less than 6.75 inches.

d. Soil classes are in accordance with the Unified Soil Classification System and design lateral soil loads are for moist conditions without hydrostatic pressure. Refer to Table R405.1.

e. Unbalanced backfill height is the difference in height between the exterior finish ground level and the lower of the top of the concrete footing that supports the foundation wall or the interior finish ground level. Where an interior concrete slab-on-grade is provided and is in contact with the interior surface of the foundation wall, measurement of the unbalanced backfill height from the exterior finish ground level to the top of the interior concrete slab is permitted.

f. The use of this table shall be prohibited for soil classifications not shown.

TABLE R404.1.1(4)
12-INCH MASONRY FOUNDATION WALLS WITH REINFORCING WHERE d ≥ 8.75 INCHES[a, c, f]

WALL HEIGHT	HEIGHT OF UNBALANCED BACKFILL[e]	MINIMUM VERTICAL REINFORCEMENT AND SPACING (INCHES)[b, c]		
		Soil classes and lateral soil load[d] (psf per foot below grade)		
		GW, GP, SW and SP soils 30	GM, GC, SM, SM-SC and ML soils 45	SC, ML-CL and inorganic CL soils 60
6 feet 8 inches	4 feet (or less)	#4 at 72	#4 at 72	#4 at 72
	5 feet	#4 at 72	#4 at 72	#4 at 72
	6 feet 8 inches	#4 at 72	#4 at 72	#5 at 72
7 feet 4 inches	4 feet (or less)	#4 at 72	#4 at 72	#4 at 72
	5 feet	#4 at 72	#4 at 72	#4 at 72
	6 feet	#4 at 72	#4 at 72	#5 at 72
	7 feet 4 inches	#4 at 72	#5 at 72	#6 at 72
8 feet	4 feet (or less)	#4 at 72	#4 at 72	#4 at 72
	5 feet	#4 at 72	#4 at 72	#4 at 72
	6 feet	#4 at 72	#4 at 72	#5 at 72
	7 feet	#4 at 72	#5 at 72	#6 at 72
	8 feet	#5 at 72	#6 at 72	#6 at 64
8 feet 8 inches	4 feet (or less)	#4 at 72	#4 at 72	#4 at 72
	5 feet	#4 at 72	#4 at 72	#4 at 72
	6 feet	#4 at 72	#4 at 72	#5 at 72
	7 feet	#4 at 72	#5 at 72	#6 at 72
	8 feet 8 inches	#5 at 72	#7 at 72	#6 at 48
9 feet 4 inches	4 feet (or less)	#4 at 72	#4 at 72	#4 at 72
	5 feet	#4 at 72	#4 at 72	#4 at 72
	6 feet	#4 at 72	#5 at 72	#5 at 72
	7 feet	#4 at 72	#5 at 72	#6 at 72
	8 feet	#5 at 72	#6 at 72	#6 at 56
	9 feet 4 inches	#6 at 72	#6 at 48	#6 at 40
10 feet	4 feet (or less)	#4 at 72	#4 at 72	#4 at 72
	5 feet	#4 at 72	#4 at 72	#4 at 72
	6 feet	#4 at 72	#5 at 72	#5 at 72
	7 feet	#4 at 72	#6 at 72	#6 at 72
	8 feet	#5 at 72	#6 at 72	#6 at 48
	9 feet	#6 at 72	#6 at 56	#6 at 40
	10 feet	#6 at 64	#6 at 40	#6 at 32

For SI: 1 inch = 25.4 mm, 1 foot = 304.8 mm, 1 pound per square foot per foot = 0.157 kPa/mm.

a. Mortar shall be Type M or S and masonry shall be laid in running bond.

b. Alternative reinforcing bar sizes and spacings having an equivalent cross-sectional area of reinforcement per lineal foot of wall shall be permitted provided the spacing of the reinforcement does not exceed 72 inches in Seismic Design Categories A, B and C, and 48 inches in Seismic Design Categories D_0, D_1 and D_2.

c. Vertical reinforcement shall be Grade 60 minimum. The distance, d, from the face of the soil side of the wall to the center of vertical reinforcement shall be not less than 8.75 inches.

d. Soil classes are in accordance with the Unified Soil Classification System and design lateral soil loads are for moist conditions without hydrostatic pressure. Refer to Table R405.1.

e. Unbalanced backfill height is the difference in height between the exterior finish ground level and the lower of the top of the concrete footing that supports the foundation wall or the interior finish ground levels. Where an interior concrete slab-on-grade is provided and in contact with the interior surface of the foundation wall, measurement of the unbalanced backfill height is permitted to be measured from the exterior finish ground level to the top of the interior concrete slab is permitted.

f. The use of this table shall be prohibited for soil classifications not shown.

TABLE R404.1.1(5)
CANTILEVERED CONCRETE AND MASONRY FOUNDATION WALLS

MAXIMUM WALL HEIGHT[j] (feet)	MAXIMUM UNBALANCED BACKFILL HEIGHT[e] (feet)	MINIMUM VERTICAL REINFORCEMENT SIZE AND SPACING FOR 8-INCH NOMINAL WALL THICKNESS[a, b, c, e, f, i, k]		
		Soil Classes[d]		
		GW, GP, SW, and SP	GM, GC, SM, SM-SC, and ML	SC, MH, ML-CL, and Inorganic CL
4	3	None required	None required	None required
	4	None required	None required	No. 4 @ 72 in. o.c.
5	3	None required	None required	None required
	4	No. 4 @ 72 in. o.c.	No. 4 @ 56 in. o.c.[h]	No. 4 @ 40 in. o.c.[g]
	5	No. 4 @ 72 in. o.c.	No. 4 @ 56 in. o.c.[h]	No. 4 @ 40 in. o.c.[g]

For SI: 1 foot = 304.8 mm, 1 inch = 25.4 mm.

a. Mortar shall be Type M or S and masonry shall be laid in running bond. Minimum unit compressive strength is 1,900 psi.

b. Alternative reinforcing bar sizes and spacings having an equivalent cross-sectional area of reinforcement per lineal foot of wall shall be permitted provided the spacing of the reinforcement does not exceed 72 inches.

c. Vertical reinforcement shall be Grade 60 minimum. The distance from the face of the soil side of the wall to the center of vertical reinforcement shall be no greater than 2.5 inches.

d. Soil classes are in accordance with the Unified Soil Classification System. Refer to Table R405.1.

e. Interior concrete floor slab-on-grade shall be placed tight to the wall. The exterior grade level shall be 6 inches minimum below the top of wall. Maximum height from top of slab-on-grade to bottom of floor joists is 10 feet, 0 inches. Unbalanced backfill height is the difference in height of the exterior finish ground levels and the top of the interior concrete slab-on-grade.

f. Minimum footing size of 20 inches by 8 inches shall be placed on soil with a bearing capacity of 2,000 psf. Minimum concrete compressive strength of footing shall be 3,000 psi.

g. Provide propped cantilever wall: top of footing shall be 16 inches below the bottom of the concrete floor slab minimum.

h. Provide #5 Grade 60 dowels, 1 foot, 6 inches long, to connect footing to wall. Embed dowel 5 inches into footing. Place dowels in center of wall thickness spaced at 32 inches on center maximum. No dowels are required where length of the foundation wall between perpendicular walls is two times the foundation wall height or less.

i. This table is applicable where the length of the foundation wall between perpendicular walls is 35 feet or less, or where the length of the foundation laterally supported on only one end by a perpendicular wall is 17 feet or less.

j. Maximum wall height is measured from top of the foundation wall to the bottom of the interior concrete slab-on-grade.

k. Install foundation anchorage per Section R403.1.6.

TABLE R404.1.1(6)
CANTILEVERED CONCRETE AND MASONRY FOUNDATION WALLS

MAXIMUM WALL HEIGHT[j] (feet)	MAXIMUM UNBALANCED BACKFILL HEIGHT[e] (feet)	MINIMUM VERTICAL REINFORCEMENT SIZE AND SPACING FOR 10-INCH NOMINAL WALL THICKNESS[a, b, c, e, f, i, k]		
		Soil Classes[d]		
		GW, GP, SW, and SP	GM, GC, SM, SM-SC, and ML	SC, MH, ML-CL, and Inorganic CL
4	3	None required	None required	None required
	4	None required	None required	None required
5	3	None required	None required	None required
	4	None required	No. 4 @ 72 in. o.c.	No. 4 @ 64 in. o.c.[g]
	5	No. 4 @ 72 in. o.c.	No. 4 @ 72 in. o.c.	No. 4 @ 56 in. o.c.[g]
6	3	None required	No. 4 @ 72 in. o.c.	No. 4 @ 72 in. o.c.
	4	No. 4 @ 72 in. o.c.	No. 4 @ 72 in. o.c.	No. 4 @ 64 in. o.c.[h]
	5	No. 4 @ 64 in. o.c.[h]	No. 4 @ 40 in. o.c.[g, h]	No. 5 @ 48 in. o.c.[g, h]
	6	No. 4 @ 64 in. o.c.[h]	No. 4 @ 40 in. o.c.[g, h]	No. 5 @ 48 in. o.c.[g, h]

For SI: 1 foot = 304.8 mm, 1 inch = 25.4 mm.

a. Mortar shall be Type M or S and masonry shall be laid in running bond. Minimum unit compressive strength is 1,900 psi.

b. Alternative reinforcing bar sizes and spacings having an equivalent cross-sectional area of reinforcement per lineal foot of wall shall be permitted provided the spacing of the reinforcement does not exceed 72 inches.

c. Vertical reinforcement shall be Grade 60 minimum. The distance from the face of the soil side of the wall to the center of vertical reinforcement shall be no greater than 2.5 inches.

d. Soil classes are in accordance with the Unified Soil Classification System. Refer to Table R405.1.

e. Interior concrete slab-on-grade shall be placed tight to the wall. The exterior grade level shall be 6 inches minimum below the top of wall. Maximum height from top of slab-on-grade to bottom of floor joists is 10 feet, 0 inches. Unbalanced backfill height is the difference in height of the exterior finish ground levels and the top of the interior concrete slab-on-grade.

f. Minimum footing size of 20 inches by 8 inches shall be placed on soil with a bearing capacity of 2,000 psf. Minimum concrete compressive strength of footing shall be 3,000 psi.

g. Provide propped cantilever wall: top of footing shall be 16 inches below the bottom of the concrete floor slab minimum.

h. Provide #5 Grade 60 dowels, 1 foot, 6 inches long, to connect footing to wall. Embed dowel 5 inches into footing. Place dowels in center of wall thickness spaced at 32 inches on center maximum. No dowels are required where length of the foundation wall between perpendicular walls is two times the foundation wall height or less.

i. This table is applicable where the length of the foundation wall between perpendicular walls is 35 feet or less, or where the length of the foundation laterally supported on only one end by a perpendicular wall is 17 feet or less.

j. Maximum wall height is measured from top of the foundation wall to the bottom of the interior concrete slab-on-grade.

k. Install foundation anchorage per Section R403.1.6.

TABLE R404.1.1(7)
CANTILEVERED CONCRETE AND MASONRY FOUNDATION WALLS

MAXIMUM WALL HEIGHT[i] (feet)	MAXIMUM UNBALANCED BACKFILL HEIGHT[e] (feet)	MINIMUM VERTICAL REINFORCEMENT SIZE AND SPACING FOR 12-INCH NOMINAL WALL THICKNESS[a, b, c, e, f, i, k]		
		Soil Classes[d]		
		GW, GP, SW, and SP	GM, GC, SM, SM-SC, and ML	SC, MH, ML-CL, and Inorganic CL
4	3	None required	None required	None required
	4	None required	None required	None required
5	3	None required	None required	None required
	4	None required	None required	No. 4 @ 72 in. o.c.
	5	No. 4 @ 72 in. o.c.	No. 4 @ 72 in. o.c.	No. 4 @ 72 in. o.c.
6	3	None required	None required	None required
	4	None required	None required	No. 4 @ 72 in. o.c.
	5	No. 4 @ 72 in. o.c.	No. 4 @ 56 in. o.c.[h]	No. 4 @ 40 in. o.c.[g]
	6	No. 4 @ 72 in. o.c.	No. 4 @ 56 in. o.c.[g]	No. 4 @ 32 in. o.c.[g, h]
7	3	None required	None required	None required
	4	None required	No. 4 @ 72 in. o.c.	No. 4 @ 72 in. o.c.
	5	No. 4 @ 72 in. o.c.	No. 4 @ 56 in. o.c.[h]	No. 4 @ 40 in. o.c.[g]
	6	No. 4 @ 48 in. o.c.[h]	No. 5 @ 48 in. o.c.[g, h]	No. 6 @ 48 in. o.c.[g, h]
	7	No. 4 @ 48 in. o.c.[h]	No. 5 @ 40 in. o.c.[g, h]	No. 6 @ 48 in. o.c.[g, h]

For SI: 1 foot = 304.8 mm, 1 inch = 25.4 mm.

a. Mortar shall be Type M or S and masonry shall be laid in running bond. Minimum unit compressive strength is 1,900 psi.

b. Alternative reinforcing bar sizes and spacings having an equivalent cross-sectional area of reinforcement per lineal foot of wall shall be permitted provided the spacing of the reinforcement does not exceed 72 inches.

c. Vertical reinforcement shall be Grade 60 minimum. The distance from the face of the soil side of the wall to the center of vertical reinforcement shall be no greater than 3 inches.

d. Soil classes are in accordance with the Unified Soil Classification System. Refer to Table R405.1.

e. Interior concrete slab-on-grade shall be placed tight to the wall. The exterior grade level shall be 6 inches minimum below the top of wall. Maximum height from top of slab-on-grade to bottom of floor joists is 10 feet, 0 inches. Unbalanced backfill height is the difference in height of the exterior finish ground levels and the top of the interior concrete slab-on-grade.

f. Minimum footing size of 20 inches by 8 inches shall be placed on soil with a bearing capacity of 2,000 psf. Minimum concrete compressive strength of footing shall be 3,000 psi.

g. Provide propped cantilever wall: top of footing shall be 16 inches below the bottom of the concrete floor slab minimum.

h. Provide #5 Grade 60 dowels, 1 foot, 6 inches long, to connect footing to wall. Embed dowel 5 inches into footing. Place dowels in center of wall thickness spaced at 32 inches on center maximum. No dowels are required where length of the foundation wall between perpendicular walls is two times the foundation wall height or less.

i. This table is applicable where the length of the foundation wall between perpendicular walls is 35 feet or less, or where the length of the foundation laterally supported on only one end by a perpendicular wall is 17 feet or less.

j. Maximum wall height is measured from top of the foundation wall to the bottom of the interior concrete slab-on-grade.

k. Install foundation anchorage per Section R403.1.6.

TABLE R404.1.2(1)
MINIMUM HORIZONTAL REINFORCEMENT FOR CONCRETE BASEMENT WALLS[a, b]

MAXIMUM UNSUPPORTED HEIGHT OF BASEMENT WALL (feet)	LOCATION OF HORIZONTAL REINFORCEMENT
≤ 8	One No. 4 bar within 12 inches of the top of the wall story and one No. 4 bar near mid-height of the wall story.
> 8	One No. 4 bar within 12 inches of the top of the wall story and one No. 4 bar near third points in the wall story.

For SI: 1 inch = 25.4 mm, 1 foot = 304.8 mm, 1 pound per square inch = 6.895 kPa.

a. Horizontal reinforcement requirements are for reinforcing bars with a minimum yield strength of 40,000 psi and concrete with a minimum concrete compressive strength of 2,500 psi.

b. See Section R404.1.3.2 for minimum reinforcement required for foundation walls supporting above-grade concrete walls.

TABLE R404.1.2(2)
MINIMUM VERTICAL REINFORCEMENT FOR 6-INCH NOMINAL FLAT CONCRETE BASEMENT WALLS[b, c, d, e, g, h, i, j, k]

MAXIMUM UNSUPPORTED WALL HEIGHT (feet)	MAXIMUM UNBALANCED BACKFILL HEIGHT[f] (feet)	MINIMUM VERTICAL REINFORCEMENT-BAR SIZE AND SPACING (inches)		
		Soil classes[a] and design lateral soil (psf per foot of depth)		
		GW, GP, SW, SP 30	GM, GC, SM, SM-SC and ML 45	SC, ML-CL and inorganic CL 60
8	4	NR	NR	NR
	5	NR	6 @ 39	6 @ 48
	6	5 @ 39	6 @ 48	6 @ 35
	7	6 @ 48	6 @ 34	6 @ 25
	8	6 @ 39	6 @ 25	6 @ 18
9	4	NR	NR	NR
	5	NR	5 @ 37	6 @ 48
	6	5 @ 36	6 @ 44	6 @ 32
	7	6 @ 47	6 @ 30	6 @ 22
	8	6 @ 34	6 @ 22	6 @ 16
	9	6 @ 27	6 @ 17	DR
10	4	NR	NR	NR
	5	NR	5 @ 35	6 @ 48
	6	6 @ 48	6 @ 41	6 @ 30
	7	6 @ 43	6 @ 28	6 @ 20
	8	6 @ 31	6 @ 20	DR
	9	6 @ 24	6 @ 15	DR
	10	6 @ 19	DR	DR

For SI: 1 inch = 25.4 mm; 1 foot = 304.8 mm; 1 pound per square foot per foot = 0.1571 kPa²/m, 1 pound per square inch = 6.895 kPa.

NR = Not Required.

DR = Design Required.

a. Soil classes are in accordance with the Unified Soil Classification System. Refer to Table R405.1.

b. Table values are based on reinforcing bars with a minimum yield strength of 60,000 psi concrete with a minimum specified compressive strength of 2,500 psi and vertical reinforcement being located at the centerline of the wall. See Section R404.1.3.3.7.2.

c. Vertical reinforcement with a yield strength of less than 60,000 psi and bars of a different size than specified in the table are permitted in accordance with Section R404.1.3.3.7.6 and Table R404.1.2(9).

d. Deflection criterion is L/240, where L is the height of the basement wall in inches.

e. Interpolation is not permitted.

f. Where walls will retain 4 feet or more of unbalanced backfill, they shall be laterally supported at the top and bottom before backfilling.

g. NR indicates vertical wall reinforcement is not required, except for 6-inch-nominal walls formed with stay-in-place forming systems in which case vertical reinforcement shall be No. 4@48 inches on center.

h. See Section R404.1.3.2 for minimum reinforcement required for basement walls supporting above-grade concrete walls.

i. See Table R608.3 for tolerance from nominal thickness permitted for flat walls.

j. DR means design is required in accordance with the applicable building code, or in the absence of a code, in accordance with ACI 318.

k. The use of this table shall be prohibited for soil classifications not shown.

MINIMUM VERTICAL REINFORCEMENT FOR 8-INCH (203 mm) NOMINAL FLAT CONCRETE BASEMENT WALLS[b, c, d, e, f, h, i, j]

MAXIMUM UNSUPPORTED WALL HEIGHT (feet)	MAXIMUM UNBALANCED BACKFILL HEIGHT[g] (feet)	MINIMUM VERTICAL REINFORCEMENT-BAR SIZE AND SPACING (inches)		
		Soil classes[a] and design lateral soil (psf per foot of depth)		
		GW, GP, SW, SP 30	GM, GC, SM, SM-SC and ML 45	SC, ML-CL and inorganic CL 60
8	4	NR	NR	NR
	5	NR	NR	NR
	6	NR	NR	6 @ 37
	7	NR	6 @ 36	6 @ 35
	8	6 @ 41	6 @ 35	6 @ 26
9	4	NR	NR	NR
	5	NR	NR	NR
	6	NR	NR	6 @ 35
	7	NR	6 @ 35	6 @ 32
	8	6 @ 36	6 @ 32	6 @ 23
	9	6 @ 35	6 @ 25	6 @ 18
10	4	NR	NR	NR
	5	NR	NR	NR
	6	NR	NR	6 @ 35
	7	NR	6 @ 35	6 @ 29
	8	6 @ 35	6 @ 29	6 @ 21
	9	6 @ 34	6 @ 22	6 @ 16
	10	6 @ 27	6 @ 17	6 @ 13

For SI: 1 inch = 25.4 mm; 1 foot = 304.8 mm; 1 pound per square foot per foot = 0.1571 kPa^2/m, 1 pound per square inch = 6.895 kPa.

NR = Not Required.

a. Soil classes are in accordance with the Unified Soil Classification System. Refer to Table R405.1.

b. Table values are based on reinforcing bars with a minimum yield strength of 60,000 psi, concrete with a minimum specified compressive strength of 2,500 psi and vertical reinforcement being located at the centerline of the wall. See Section R404.1.3.3.7.2.

c. Vertical reinforcement with a yield strength of less than 60,000 psi and bars of a different size than specified in the table are permitted in accordance with Section R404.1.3.3.7.6 and Table R404.1.2(9).

d. NR indicates vertical reinforcement is not required.

e. Deflection criterion is L/240, where L is the height of the basement wall in inches.

f. Interpolation is not permitted.

g. Where walls will retain 4 feet or more of unbalanced backfill, they shall be laterally supported at the top and bottom before backfilling.

h. See Section R404.1.3.2 for minimum reinforcement required for basement walls supporting above-grade concrete walls.

i. See Table R608.3 for tolerance from nominal thickness permitted for flat walls.

j. The use of this table shall be prohibited for soil classifications not shown.

TABLE R404.1.2(4)
MINIMUM VERTICAL REINFORCEMENT FOR 10-INCH NOMINAL FLAT CONCRETE BASEMENT WALLS[b, c, d, e, f, h, i, j]

MAXIMUM UNSUPPORTED WALL HEIGHT (feet)	MAXIMUM UNBALANCED BACKFILL HEIGHT[g] (feet)	MINIMUM VERTICAL REINFORCEMENT-BAR SIZE AND SPACING (inches)		
		Soil classes[a] and design lateral soil (psf per foot of depth)		
		GW, GP, SW, SP 30	GM, GC, SM, SM-SC and ML 45	SC, ML-CL and inorganic CL 60
8	4	NR	NR	NR
	5	NR	NR	NR
	6	NR	NR	NR
	7	NR	NR	NR
	8	6 @ 48	6 @ 35	6 @ 28
9	4	NR	NR	NR
	5	NR	NR	NR
	6	NR	NR	NR
	7	NR	NR	6 @ 31
	8	NR	6 @ 31	6 @ 28
	9	6 @ 37	6 @ 28	6 @ 24
10	4	NR	NR	NR
	5	NR	NR	NR
	6	NR	NR	NR
	7	NR	NR	6 @ 28
	8	NR	6 @ 28	6 @ 28
	9	6 @ 33	6 @ 28	6 @ 21
	10	6 @ 28	6 @ 23	6 @ 17

For SI: 1 inch = 25.4 mm; 1 foot = 304.8 mm; 1 pound per square foot per foot = 0.1571 kPa^2/m, 1 pound per square inch = 6.895 kPa.

NR = Not Required.

a. Soil classes are in accordance with the Unified Soil Classification System. Refer to Table R405.1.

b. Table values are based on reinforcing bars with a minimum yield strength of 60,000 psi concrete with a minimum specified compressive strength of 2,500 psi and vertical reinforcement being located at the centerline of the wall. See Section R404.1.3.3.7.2.

c. Vertical reinforcement with a yield strength of less than 60,000 psi and bars of a different size than specified in the table are permitted in accordance with Section R404.1.3.3.7.6 and Table R404.1.2(9).

d. NR indicates vertical reinforcement is not required.

e. Deflection criterion is $L/240$, where L is the height of the basement wall in inches.

f. Interpolation is not permitted.

g. Where walls will retain 4 feet or more of unbalanced backfill, they shall be laterally supported at the top and bottom before backfilling.

h. See Section R404.1.3.2 for minimum reinforcement required for basement walls supporting above-grade concrete walls.

i. See Table R608.3 for tolerance from nominal thickness permitted for flat walls.

j. The use of this table shall be prohibited for soil classifications not shown.

TABLE R404.1.2(5)
MINIMUM VERTICAL WALL REINFORCEMENT FOR 6-INCH WAFFLE-GRID BASEMENT WALLS[b, c, d, e, g, h, i, j]

MAXIMUM UNSUPPORTED WALL HEIGHT (feet)	MAXIMUM UNBALANCED BACKFILL HEIGHT[f] (feet)	MINIMUM VERTICAL REINFORCEMENT-BAR SIZE AND SPACING (inches)		
		Soil classes[a] and design lateral soil (psf per foot of depth)		
		GW, GP, SW, SP 30	GM, GC, SM, SM-SC and ML 45	SC, ML-CL and inorganic CL 60
8	4	4 @ 48	4 @ 46	6 @ 39
	5	4 @ 45	5 @ 46	6 @ 47
	6	5 @ 45	6 @ 40	DR
	7	6 @ 44	DR	DR
	8	6 @ 32	DR	DR
9	4	4 @ 48	4 @ 46	4 @ 37
	5	4 @ 42	5 @ 43	6 @ 44
	6	5 @ 41	6 @ 37	DR
	7	6 @ 39	DR	DR
	> 8	DR[i]	DR	DR
10	4	4 @ 48	4 @ 46	4 @ 35
	5	4 @ 40	5 @ 40	6 @ 41
	6	5 @ 38	6 @ 34	DR
	7	6 @ 36	DR	DR
	> 8	DR	DR	DR

For SI: 1 inch = 25.4 mm; 1 foot = 304.8 mm; 1 pound per square foot per foot = 0.1571 kPa^2/m, 1 pound per square inch = 6.895 kPa.

DR = Design Required.

a. Soil classes are in accordance with the Unified Soil Classification System. Refer to Table R405.1.

b. Table values are based on reinforcing bars with a minimum yield strength of 60,000 psi concrete with a minimum specified compressive strength of 2,500 psi and vertical reinforcement being located at the centerline of the wall. See Section R404.1.3.3.7.2.

c. Maximum spacings shown are the values calculated for the specified bar size. Where the bar used is Grade 60 and the size specified in the table, the actual spacing in the wall shall not exceed a whole-number multiple of 12 inches (12, 24, 36 and 48) that is less than or equal to the tabulated spacing. Vertical reinforcement with a yield strength of less than 60,000 psi and bars of a different size than specified in the table are permitted in accordance with Section R404.1.3.3.7.6 and Table R404.1.2(9).

d. Deflection criterion is $L/240$, where L is the height of the basement wall in inches.

e. Interpolation is not permitted.

f. Where walls will retain 4 feet or more of unbalanced backfill, they shall be laterally supported at the top and bottom before backfilling.

g. See Section R404.1.3.2 for minimum reinforcement required for basement walls supporting above-grade concrete walls.

h. See Table R608.3 for thicknesses and dimensions of waffle-grid walls.

i. DR means design is required in accordance with the applicable building code, or in the absence of a code, in accordance with ACI 318.

j. The use of this table shall be prohibited for soil classifications not shown.

TABLE R404.1.2(6)
MINIMUM VERTICAL REINFORCEMENT FOR 8-INCH WAFFLE-GRID BASEMENT WALLS[b, c, d, e, f, h, i, j, k]

MAXIMUM UNSUPPORTED WALL HEIGHT (feet)	MAXIMUM UNBALANCED BACKFILL HEIGHT[g] (feet)	MINIMUM VERTICAL REINFORCEMENT-BAR SIZE AND SPACING (inches)		
		Soil classes[a] and design lateral soil (psf per foot of depth)		
		GW, GP, SW, SP 30	GM, GC, SM, SM-SC and ML 45	SC, ML-CL and inorganic CL 60
8	4	NR	NR	NR
	5	NR	5 @ 48	5 @ 46
	6	5 @ 48	5 @ 43	6 @ 45
	7	5 @ 46	6 @ 43	6 @ 31
	8	6 @ 48	6 @ 32	6 @ 23
9	4	NR	NR	NR
	5	NR	5 @ 47	5 @ 46
	6	5 @ 46	5 @ 39	6 @ 41
	7	5 @ 42	6 @ 38	6 @ 28
	8	6 @ 44	6 @ 28	6 @ 20
	9	6 @ 34	6 @ 21	DR
10	4	NR	NR	NR
	5	NR	5 @ 46	5 @ 44
	6	5 @ 46	5 @ 37	6 @ 38
	7	5 @ 38	6 @ 35	6 @ 25
	8	6 @ 39	6 @ 25	DR
	9	6 @ 30	DR	DR
	10	6 @ 24	DR	DR

For SI: 1 inch = 25.4 mm; 1 foot = 304.8 mm; 1 pound per square foot per foot = 0.1571 kPa^2/m, 1 pound per square inch = 6.895 kPa.

NR = Not Required.

DR = Design Required.

a. Soil classes are in accordance with the Unified Soil Classification System. Refer to Table R405.1.

b. Table values are based on reinforcing bars with a minimum yield strength of 60,000 psi concrete with a minimum specified compressive strength of 2,500 psi and vertical reinforcement being located at the centerline of the wall. See Section R404.1.3.3.7.2.

c. Maximum spacings shown are the values calculated for the specified bar size. Where the bar used is Grade 60 (420 MPa) and the size specified in the table, the actual spacing in the wall shall not exceed a whole-number multiple of 12 inches (12, 24, 36 and 48) that is less than or equal to the tabulated spacing. Vertical reinforcement with a yield strength of less than 60,000 psi and bars of a different size than specified in the table are permitted in accordance with Section R404.1.3.3.7.6 and Table R404.1.2(9).

d. NR indicates vertical reinforcement is not required.

e. Deflection criterion is L/240, where L is the height of the basement wall in inches.

f. Interpolation shall not be permitted.

g. Where walls will retain 4 feet or more of unbalanced backfill, they shall be laterally supported at the top and bottom before backfilling.

h. See Section R404.1.3.2 for minimum reinforcement required for basement walls supporting above-grade concrete walls.

i. See Table R608.3 for thicknesses and dimensions of waffle-grid walls.

j. DR means design is required in accordance with the applicable building code, or in the absence of a code, in accordance with ACI 318.

k. The use of this table shall be prohibited for soil classifications not shown.

TABLE R404.1.2(7)
MINIMUM VERTICAL REINFORCEMENT FOR 6-INCH (152 mm) SCREEN-GRID BASEMENT WALLS[b, c, d, e, g, h, i, j]

MAXIMUM UNSUPPORTED WALL HEIGHT (feet)	MAXIMUM UNBALANCED BACKFILL HEIGHT[f] (feet)	MINIMUM VERTICAL REINFORCEMENT-BAR SIZE AND SPACING (inches)		
		Soil classes[a] and design lateral soil (psf per foot of depth)		
		GW, GP, SW, SP 30	GM, GC, SM, SM-SC and ML 45	SC, ML-CL and inorganic CL 60
8	4	4 @ 48	4 @ 48	5 @ 43
	5	4 @ 48	5 @ 48	5 @ 37
	6	5 @ 48	6 @ 45	6 @ 32
	7	6 @ 48	DR	DR
	8	6 @ 36	DR	DR
9	4	4 @ 48	4 @ 48	4 @ 41
	5	4 @ 48	5 @ 48	6 @ 48
	6	5 @ 45	6 @ 41	DR
	7	6 @ 43	DR	DR
	> 8	DR	DR	DR
10	4	4 @ 48	4 @ 48	4 @ 39
	5	4 @ 44	5 @ 44	6 @ 46
	6	5 @ 42	6 @ 38	DR
	7	6 @ 40	DR	DR
	> 8	DR	DR	DR

For SI: 1 inch = 25.4 mm; 1 foot = 304.8 mm; 1 pound per square foot per foot = 0.1571 kPa^2/m, 1 pound per square inch = 6.895 kPa.

DR = Design Required.

a. Soil classes are in accordance with the Unified Soil Classification System. Refer to Table R405.1.

b. Table values are based on reinforcing bars with a minimum yield strength of 60,000 psi, concrete with a minimum specified compressive strength of 2,500 psi and vertical reinforcement being located at the centerline of the wall. See Section R404.1.3.3.7.2.

c. Maximum spacings shown are the values calculated for the specified bar size. Where the bar used is Grade 60 and the size specified in the table, the actual spacing in the wall shall not exceed a whole-number multiple of 12 inches (12, 24, 36 and 48) that is less than or equal to the tabulated spacing. Vertical reinforcement with a yield strength of less than 60,000 psi and bars of a different size than specified in the table are permitted in accordance with Section R404.1.3.3.7.6 and Table R404.1.2(9).

d. Deflection criterion is L/240, where L is the height of the basement wall in inches.

e. Interpolation is not permitted.

f. Where walls will retain 4 feet or more of unbalanced backfill, they shall be laterally supported at the top and bottom before backfilling.

g. See Sections R404.1.3.2 for minimum reinforcement required for basement walls supporting above-grade concrete walls.

h. See Table R608.3 for thicknesses and dimensions of screen-grid walls.

i. DR means design is required in accordance with the applicable building code, or in the absence of a code, in accordance with ACI 318.

j. The use of this table shall be prohibited for soil classifications not shown.

TABLE R404.1.2(8)
MINIMUM VERTICAL REINFORCEMENT FOR 6-, 8-, 10- AND 12-INCH NOMINAL FLAT BASEMENT WALLS[b, c, d, e, f, h, i, k, n, o]

MAXIMUM WALL HEIGHT (feet)	MAXIMUM UNBALANCED BACKFILL HEIGHT[g] (feet)	MINIMUM VERTICAL REINFORCEMENT-BAR SIZE AND SPACING (inches)											
		Soil classes[a] and design lateral soil (psf per foot of depth)											
		GW, GP, SW, SP 30				GM, GC, SM, SM-SC and ML 45				SC, ML-CL and inorganic CL 60			
		Minimum nominal wall thickness (inches)											
		6	8	10	12	6	8	10	12	6	8	10	12
5	4	NR	NR	NR	NR	NR	NR	NR	NR	NR	NR	NR	NR
	5	NR	NR	NR	NR	NR	NR	NR	NR	NR	NR	NR	NR
6	4	NR	NR	NR	NR	NR	NR	NR	NR	NR	NR	NR	NR
	5	NR	NR	NR	NR	NR	NR[l]	NR	NR	4 @ 35	NR[l]	NR	NR
	6	NR	NR	NR	NR	5 @ 48	NR	NR	NR	5 @ 36	NR	NR	NR
7	4	NR	NR	NR	NR	NR	NR	NR	NR	NR	NR	NR	NR
	5	NR	NR	NR	NR	NR	NR	NR	NR	5 @ 47	NR	NR	NR
	6	NR	NR	NR	NR	5 @ 42	NR	NR	NR	6 @ 43	5 @ 48	NR[l]	NR
	7	5 @ 46	NR	NR	NR	6 @ 42	5 @ 46	NR[l]	NR	6 @ 34	6 @ 48	NR	NR
8	4	NR	NR	NR	NR	NR	NR	NR	NR	NR	NR	NR	NR
	5	NR	NR	NR	NR	4 @ 38	NR[l]	NR	NR	5 @ 43	NR	NR	NR
	6	4 @ 37	NR[l]	NR	NR	5 @ 37	NR	NR	NR	6 @ 37	5 @ 43	NR[l]	NR
	7	5 @ 40	NR	NR	NR	6 @ 37	5 @ 41	NR[l]	NR	6 @ 34	6 @ 43	NR	NR
	8	6 @ 43	5 @ 47	NR[l]	NR	6 @ 34	6 @ 43	NR	NR	6 @ 27	6 @ 32	6 @ 44	NR
9	4	NR	NR	NR	NR	NR	NR	NR	NR	NR	NR	NR	NR
	5	NR	NR	NR	NR	4 @ 35	NR[l]	NR	NR	5 @ 40	NR	NR	NR
	6	4 @ 34	NR[l]	NR	NR	6 @ 48	NR	NR	NR	6 @ 36	6 @ 39	NR[l]	NR
	7	5 @ 36	NR	NR	NR	6 @ 34	5 @ 37	NR	NR	6 @ 33	6 @ 38	5 @ 37	NR[l]
	8	6 @ 38	5 @ 41	NR[l]	NR	6 @ 33	6 @ 38	5 @ 37	NR[l]	6 @ 24	6 @ 29	6 @ 39	4 @ 48[m]
	9	6 @ 34	6 @ 46	NR	NR	6 @ 26	6 @ 30	6 @ 41	NR	6 @ 19	6 @ 23	6 @ 30	6 @ 39
10	4	NR	NR	NR	NR	NR	NR	NR	NR	NR	NR	NR	NR
	5	NR	NR	NR	NR	4 @ 33	NR[l]	NR	NR	5 @ 38	NR	NR	NR
	6	5 @ 48	NR[l]	NR	NR	6 @ 45	NR	NR	NR	6 @ 34	5 @ 37	NR	NR
	7	6 @ 47	NR	NR	NR	6 @ 34	6 @ 48	NR	NR	6 @ 30	6 @ 35	6 @ 48	NR[l]
	8	6 @ 34	5 @ 38	NR	NR	6 @ 30	6 @ 34	6 @ 47	NR[l]	6 @ 22	6 @ 26	6 @ 35	6 @ 45[m]
	9	6 @ 34	6 @ 41	4 @ 48	NR[l]	6 @ 23	6 @ 27	6 @ 35	4 @ 48[m]	DR	6 @ 22	6 @ 27	6 @ 34
	10	6 @ 28	6 @ 33	6 @ 45	NR	DR[j]	6 @ 23	6 @ 29	6 @ 38	DR	6 @ 22	6 @ 22	6 @ 28

For SI: 1 inch = 25.4 mm; 1 foot = 304.8 mm; 1 pound per square foot per foot = 0.1571 kPa^2/m, 1 pound per square inch = 6.895 kPa.

NR = Not Required.

DR = Design Required.

a. Soil classes are in accordance with the Unified Soil Classification System. Refer to Table R405.1.

b. Table values are based on reinforcing bars with a minimum yield strength of 60,000 psi.

c. Vertical reinforcement with a yield strength of less than 60,000 psi and bars of a different size than specified in the table are permitted in accordance with Section R404.1.3.3.7.6 and Table R404.1.2(9).

d. NR indicates vertical wall reinforcement is not required, except for 6-inch nominal walls formed with stay-in-place forming systems in which case vertical reinforcement shall be No. 4@48 inches on center.

e. Allowable deflection criterion is $L/240$, where L is the unsupported height of the basement wall in inches.

f. Interpolation is not permitted.

g. Where walls will retain 4 feet or more of unbalanced backfill, they shall be laterally supported at the top and bottom before backfilling.

h. Vertical reinforcement shall be located to provide a cover of $1\frac{1}{4}$ inches measured from the inside face of the wall. The center of the steel shall not vary from the specified location by more than the greater of 10 percent of the wall thickness or $\frac{3}{8}$ inch.

i. Concrete cover for reinforcement measured from the inside face of the wall shall be not less than $\frac{3}{4}$ inch. Concrete cover for reinforcement measured from the outside face of the wall shall be not less than $1\frac{1}{2}$ inches for No. 5 bars and smaller, and not less than 2 inches for larger bars.

j. DR means design is required in accordance with the applicable building code, or in the absence of a code, in accordance with ACI 318.

k. Concrete shall have a specified compressive strength, f'_c, of not less than 2,500 psi at 28 days, unless a higher strength is required by Footnote l or m.

l. The minimum thickness is permitted to be reduced 2 inches, provided that the minimum specified compressive strength of concrete, f'_c, is 4,000 psi.

m. A plain concrete wall with a minimum nominal thickness of 12 inches is permitted, provided that the minimum specified compressive strength of concrete, f'_c, is 3,500 psi.

n. See Table R608.3 for tolerance from nominal thickness permitted for flat walls.

o. The use of this table shall be prohibited for soil classifications not shown.

TABLE R404.1.2(9)
MINIMUM SPACING FOR ALTERNATE BAR SIZE AND ALTERNATE GRADE OF STEEL[a, b, c]

BAR SPACING FROM APPLICABLE TABLE IN SECTION R404.1.3.2 (inches)	BAR SIZE FROM APPLICABLE TABLE IN SECTION R404.1.3.2														
	#4					#5					#6				
	Alternate bar size and alternate grade of steel desired														
	Grade 60		Grade 40			Grade 60		Grade 40			Grade 60		Grade 40		
	#5	#6	#4	#5	#6	#4	#6	#4	#5	#6	#4	#5	#4	#5	#6
	Maximum spacing for alternate bar size and alternate grade of steel (inches)														
8	12	18	5	8	12	5	11	3	5	8	4	6	2	4	5
9	14	20	6	9	13	6	13	4	6	9	4	6	3	4	6
10	16	22	7	10	15	6	14	4	7	9	5	7	3	5	7
11	17	24	7	11	16	7	16	5	7	10	5	8	3	5	7
12	19	26	8	12	18	8	17	5	8	11	5	8	4	6	8
13	20	29	9	13	19	8	18	6	9	12	6	9	4	6	9
14	22	31	9	14	21	9	20	6	9	13	6	10	4	7	9
15	23	33	10	16	22	10	21	6	10	14	7	11	5	7	10
16	25	35	11	17	23	10	23	7	11	15	7	11	5	8	11
17	26	37	11	18	25	11	24	7	11	16	8	12	5	8	11
18	28	40	12	19	26	12	26	8	12	17	8	13	5	8	12
19	29	42	13	20	28	12	27	8	13	18	9	13	6	9	13
20	31	44	13	21	29	13	28	9	13	19	9	14	6	9	13
21	33	46	14	22	31	14	30	9	14	20	10	15	6	10	14
22	34	48	15	23	32	14	31	9	15	21	10	16	7	10	15
23	36	48	15	24	34	15	33	10	15	22	10	16	7	11	15
24	37	48	16	25	35	15	34	10	16	23	11	17	7	11	16
25	39	48	17	26	37	16	35	11	17	24	11	18	8	12	17
26	40	48	17	27	38	17	37	11	17	25	12	18	8	12	17
27	42	48	18	28	40	17	38	12	18	26	12	19	8	13	18
28	43	48	19	29	41	18	40	12	19	26	13	20	8	13	19
29	45	48	19	30	43	19	41	12	19	27	13	20	9	14	19
30	47	48	20	31	44	19	43	13	20	28	14	21	9	14	20
31	48	48	21	32	45	20	44	13	21	29	14	22	9	15	21
32	48	48	21	33	47	21	45	14	21	30	15	23	10	15	21
33	48	48	22	34	48	21	47	14	22	31	15	23	10	16	22
34	48	48	23	35	48	22	48	15	23	32	15	24	10	16	23
35	48	48	23	36	48	23	48	15	23	33	16	25	11	16	23
36	48	48	24	37	48	23	48	15	24	34	16	25	11	17	24
37	48	48	25	38	48	24	48	16	25	35	17	26	11	17	25
38	48	48	25	39	48	25	48	16	25	36	17	27	12	18	25
39	48	48	26	40	48	25	48	17	26	37	18	27	12	18	26
40	48	48	27	41	48	26	48	17	27	38	18	28	12	19	27
41	48	48	27	42	48	26	48	18	27	39	19	29	12	19	27
42	48	48	28	43	48	27	48	18	28	40	19	30	13	20	28
43	48	48	29	44	48	28	48	18	29	41	20	30	13	20	29
44	48	48	29	45	48	28	48	19	29	42	20	31	13	21	29
45	48	48	30	47	48	29	48	19	30	43	20	32	14	21	30
46	48	48	31	48	48	30	48	20	31	44	21	32	14	22	31
47	48	48	31	48	48	30	48	20	31	44	21	33	14	22	31
48	48	48	32	48	48	31	48	21	32	45	22	34	15	23	32

For SI: 1 inch = 25.4 mm, 1 pound per square inch = 6.895 kPa.

a. This table is for use with tables in Section R404.1.3.2 that specify the minimum bar size and maximum spacing of vertical wall reinforcement for foundation walls and above-grade walls. Reinforcement specified in tables in Section R404.1.3.2 is based on Grade 60 steel reinforcement.

b. Bar spacing shall not exceed 48 inches on center and shall be not less than one-half the nominal wall thickness.

c. For Grade 50 steel bars (ASTM A996, Type R), use spacing for Grade 40 bars or interpolate between Grades 40 and 60.

R404.1.3 Concrete foundation walls. Concrete foundation walls that support light-frame walls shall be designed and constructed in accordance with the provisions of this section, ACI 318, ACI 332 or PCA 100. Concrete foundation walls that support above-grade concrete walls that are within the applicability limits of Section R608.2 shall be designed and constructed in accordance with the provisions of this section, ACI 318, ACI 332 or PCA 100. Concrete foundation walls that support above-grade concrete walls that are not within the applicability limits of Section R608.2 shall be designed and constructed in accordance with the provisions of ACI 318, ACI 332 or PCA 100. Where ACI 318, ACI 332, PCA 100 or the provisions of this section are used to design concrete foundation walls, project drawings, typical details and specifications are not required to bear the seal of the architect or engineer responsible for design, unless otherwise required by the state law of the *jurisdiction* having authority.

R404.1.3.1 Concrete cross section. Concrete walls constructed in accordance with this code shall comply with the shapes and minimum concrete cross-sectional dimensions required by Table R608.3. Other types of forming systems resulting in concrete walls not in compliance with this section and Table R608.3 shall be designed in accordance with ACI 318.

R404.1.3.2 Reinforcement for foundation walls. Concrete foundation walls shall be laterally supported at the top and bottom. Horizontal reinforcement shall be provided in accordance with Table R404.1.2(1). Vertical reinforcement shall be provided in accordance with Table R404.1.2(2), R404.1.2(3), R404.1.2(4), R404.1.2(5), R404.1.2(6), R404.1.2(7) or R404.1.2(8). Vertical reinforcement for flat *basement* walls retaining 4 feet (1219 mm) or more of unbalanced backfill is permitted to be determined in accordance with Table R404.1.2(9). For *basement* walls supporting above-grade concrete walls, vertical reinforcement shall be the greater of that required by Tables R404.1.2(2) through R404.1.2(8) or by Section R608.6 for the above-grade wall. In buildings assigned to Seismic Design Category D_0, D_1 or D_2, concrete foundation walls shall also comply with Section R404.1.4.2.

R404.1.3.2.1 Concrete foundation stem walls supporting above-grade concrete walls. Foundation stem walls that support above-grade concrete walls shall be designed and constructed in accordance with this section.

1. Stem walls not laterally supported at top. Concrete stem walls that are not monolithic with slabs-on-ground or are not otherwise laterally supported by slabs-on-ground shall comply with this section. Where unbalanced backfill retained by the stem wall is less than or equal to 18 inches (457 mm), the stem wall and above-grade wall it supports shall be provided with vertical reinforcement in accordance with Section R608.6 and Table R608.6(1), R608.6(2) or R608.6(3) for above-grade walls. Where unbalanced backfill retained by the stem wall is

greater than 18 inches (457 mm), the stem wall and above-grade wall it supports shall be provided with vertical reinforcement in accordance with Section R608.6 and Table R608.6(4).

2. Stem walls laterally supported at top. Concrete stem walls that are monolithic with slabs-on-ground or are otherwise laterally supported by slabs-on-ground shall be vertically reinforced in accordance with Section R608.6 and Table R608.6(1), R608.6(2) or R608.6(3) for above-grade walls. Where the unbalanced backfill retained by the stem wall is greater than 18 inches (457 mm), the connection between the stem wall and the slab-on-ground, and the portion of the slab-on-ground providing lateral support for the wall shall be designed in accordance with PCA 100 or with accepted engineering practice. Where the unbalanced backfill retained by the stem wall is greater than 18 inches (457 mm), the minimum nominal thickness of the wall shall be 6 inches (152 mm).

R404.1.3.2.2 Concrete foundation stem walls supporting light-frame above-grade walls. Concrete foundation stem walls that support light-frame above-grade walls shall be designed and constructed in accordance with this section.

1. Stem walls not laterally supported at top. Concrete stem walls that are not monolithic with slabs-on-ground or are not otherwise laterally supported by slabs-on-ground and retain 48 inches (1219 mm) or less of unbalanced fill, measured from the top of the wall, shall be constructed in accordance with Section R404.1.3. Foundation stem walls that retain more than 48 inches (1219 mm) of unbalanced fill, measured from the top of the wall, shall be designed in accordance with Sections R404.1.4 and R404.4.

2. Stem walls laterally supported at top. Concrete stem walls that are monolithic with slabs-on-ground or are otherwise laterally supported by slabs-on-ground shall be constructed in accordance with Section R404.1.3. Where the unbalanced backfill retained by the stem wall is greater than 48 inches (1219 mm), the connection between the stem wall and the slab-on-ground, and the portion of the slab-on-ground providing lateral support for the wall, shall be designed in accordance with PCA 100 or in accordance with accepted engineering practice.

R404.1.3.3 Concrete, materials for concrete, and forms. Materials used in concrete, the concrete itself and forms shall conform to requirements of this section or ACI 318.

R404.1.3.3.1 Compressive strength. The minimum specified compressive strength of concrete, f'_c, shall comply with Section R402.2 and shall be not less than 2,500 psi (17.2 MPa) at 28 days in buildings assigned to Seismic Design Category A, B or C and 3000 psi (20.5 MPa) in buildings assigned to Seismic Design Category D_0, D_1 or D_2.

R404.1.3.3.2 Concrete mixing and delivery. Mixing and delivery of concrete shall comply with ASTM C94 or ASTM C685.

R404.1.3.3.3 Maximum aggregate size. The nominal maximum size of coarse aggregate shall not exceed one-fifth the narrowest distance between sides of forms, or three-fourths the clear spacing between reinforcing bars or between a bar and the side of the form.

Exception: Where *approved*, these limitations shall not apply where removable forms are used and workability and methods of consolidation permit concrete to be placed without honeycombs or voids.

R404.1.3.3.4 Proportioning and slump of concrete. Proportions of materials for concrete shall be established to provide workability and consistency to permit concrete to be worked readily into forms and around reinforcement under conditions of placement to be employed, without segregation or excessive bleeding. Slump of concrete placed in removable forms shall not exceed 6 inches (152 mm).

Exception: Where *approved*, the slump is permitted to exceed 6 inches (152 mm) for concrete mixtures that are resistant to segregation, and are in accordance with the form manufacturer's recommendations.

Slump of concrete placed in stay-in-place forms shall exceed 6 inches (152 mm). Slump of concrete shall be determined in accordance with ASTM C143.

R404.1.3.3.5 Consolidation of concrete. Concrete shall be consolidated by suitable means during placement and shall be worked around embedded items and reinforcement and into corners of forms. Where stay-in-place forms are used, concrete shall be consolidated by internal vibration.

Exception: Where *approved* for concrete to be placed in stay-in-place forms, self-consolidating concrete mixtures with slumps equal to or greater than 8 inches (203 mm) that are specifically designed for placement without internal vibration need not be internally vibrated.

R404.1.3.3.6 Form materials and form ties. Forms shall be made of wood, steel, aluminum, plastic, a composite of cement and foam insulation, a composite of cement and wood chips, or other *approved* material suitable for supporting and containing concrete. Forms shall provide sufficient strength to contain concrete during the concrete placement operation.

Form ties shall be steel, solid plastic, foam plastic, a composite of cement and wood chips, a composite of cement and foam plastic, or other suitable material capable of resisting the forces created by fluid pressure of fresh concrete.

R404.1.3.3.6.1 Stay-in-place forms. Stay-in-place concrete forms shall comply with this section.

1. Surface burning characteristics. The flame-spread index and smoke-developed index of forming material, other than foam plastic, left exposed on the interior shall comply with Section R302. The surface burning characteristics of foam plastic used in insulating concrete forms shall comply with Section R316.3.

2. Interior covering. Stay-in-place forms constructed of rigid foam plastic shall be protected on the interior of the building as required by Section R316. Where gypsum board is used to protect the foam plastic, it shall be installed with a mechanical fastening system. Use of adhesives in addition to mechanical fasteners is permitted.

3. Exterior wall covering. Stay-in-place forms constructed of rigid foam plastics shall be protected from sunlight and physical damage by the application of an approved exterior wall covering complying with this code. Exterior surfaces of other stay-in-place forming systems shall be protected in accordance with this code.

4. Termite protection. In areas where the probability of termite infestation is "very heavy" as indicated by Table R301.2(1) or Figure R301.2(7), foam plastic insulation shall be permitted below grade on foundation walls in accordance with Section R318.4.

5. Flat ICF wall system forms shall conform to ASTM E2634.

R404.1.3.3.7 Reinforcement.

R404.1.3.3.7.1 Steel reinforcement. Steel reinforcement shall comply with the requirements of ASTM A615, A706, or A996. ASTM A996 bars produced from rail steel shall be Type R. In buildings assigned to Seismic Design Category A, B or C, the minimum yield strength of reinforcing steel shall be 40,000 psi (Grade 40) (276 MPa). In buildings assigned to Seismic Design Category D_0, D_1 or D_2, reinforcing steel shall comply with the requirements of ASTM A706 for low-alloy steel with a minimum yield strength of 60,000 psi (Grade 60) (414 MPa).

R404.1.3.3.7.2 Location of reinforcement in wall. The center of vertical reinforcement in *basement* walls determined from Tables R404.1.2(2) through R404.1.2(7) shall be located at the centerline of the wall. Vertical reinforcement in *basement* walls determined from Table R404.1.2(8) shall be located to provide a maximum cover of $1^1/_4$ inches (32 mm) measured from the inside face of the wall. Regardless of the table used to determine vertical wall reinforcement, the center of the steel shall not vary from the specified location by more than the greater of 10 percent of the wall thickness and $^3/_8$ inch (10 mm). Horizontal and vertical reinforcement shall be located in foundation walls to provide the minimum cover required by Section R404.1.3.3.7.4.

R404.1.3.3.7.3 Wall openings. Vertical wall reinforcement required by Section R404.1.3.2 that is interrupted by wall openings shall have additional vertical reinforcement of the same size placed within 12 inches (305 mm) of each side of the opening.

R404.1.3.3.7.4 Support and cover. Reinforcement shall be secured in the proper location in the forms with tie wire or other bar support system to prevent displacement during the concrete placement operation. Steel reinforcement in concrete cast against the earth shall have a minimum cover of 3 inches (75 mm). Minimum cover for reinforcement in concrete cast in removable forms that will be exposed to the earth or weather shall be $1^1/_2$ inches (38 mm) for No. 5 bars and smaller, and 2 inches (50 mm) for No. 6 bars and larger. For concrete cast in removable forms that will not be exposed to the earth or weather, and for concrete cast in stay-in-place forms, minimum cover shall be $^3/_4$ inch (19 mm). The minus tolerance for cover shall not exceed the smaller of one-third the required cover or $^3/_8$ inch (10 mm).

R404.1.3.3.7.5 Lap splices. Vertical and horizontal wall reinforcement shall be the longest lengths practical. Where splices are necessary in reinforcement, the length of lap splice shall be in accordance with Table R608.5.4.(1) and Figure R608.5.4(1). The maximum gap between noncontact parallel bars at a lap splice shall not exceed the smaller of one-fifth the required lap length and 6 inches (152 mm) [See Figure R608.5.4(1)].

R404.1.3.3.7.6 Alternate grade of reinforcement and spacing. Where tables in Section R404.1.3.2 specify vertical wall reinforcement based on minimum bar size and maximum spacing, which are based on Grade 60 (414 MPa) steel reinforcement, different size bars or bars made from a different grade of steel are permitted provided that an equivalent area of steel per linear foot of wall is provided. Use of Table R404.1.2(9) is permitted to determine the maximum bar spacing for different bar sizes than specified in the tables or bars made from a different grade of steel. Bars shall not be spaced less

than one-half the wall thickness, or more than 48 inches (1219 mm) on center.

R404.1.3.3.7.7 Standard hooks. Where reinforcement is required by this code to terminate with a standard hook, the hook shall comply with Section R608.5.4.5 and Figure R608.5.4(3).

R404.1.3.3.7.8 Construction joint reinforcement. Construction joints in foundation walls shall be made and located to not impair the strength of the wall. Construction joints in plain concrete walls, including walls required to have not less than No. 4 bars at 48 inches (1219 mm) on center by Sections R404.1.3.2 and R404.1.4.2, shall be located at points of lateral support, and not fewer than one No. 4 bar shall extend across the construction joint at a spacing not to exceed 24 inches (610 mm) on center. Construction joint reinforcement shall have not less than 12 inches (305 mm) embedment on both sides of the joint. Construction joints in reinforced concrete walls shall be located in the middle third of the span between lateral supports, or located and constructed as required for joints in plain concrete walls.

> **Exception:** Use of vertical wall reinforcement required by this code is permitted in lieu of construction joint reinforcement provided that the spacing does not exceed 24 inches (610 mm), or the combination of wall reinforcement and No. 4 bars described in this section does not exceed 24 inches (610 mm).

R404.1.3.3.8 Exterior wall coverings. Requirements for installation of masonry veneer, stucco and other wall coverings on the exterior of concrete walls and other construction details not covered in this section shall comply with the requirements of this code.

R404.1.3.4 Requirements for Seismic Design Category C. Concrete foundation walls supporting above-grade concrete walls in townhouses assigned to Seismic Design Category C shall comply with ACI 318, ACI 332 or PCA 100 (see Section R404.1.3).

R404.1.4 Seismic Design Category D_0, D_1 or D_2.

R404.1.4.1 Masonry foundation walls. In buildings assigned to Seismic Design Category D_0, D_1 or D_2, as established in Table R301.2(1), masonry foundation walls shall comply with this section. In addition to the requirements of Table R404.1.1(1), plain masonry foundation walls shall comply with the following:

1. Wall height shall not exceed 8 feet (2438 mm).

2. Unbalanced backfill height shall not exceed 4 feet (1219 mm).

3. Minimum nominal thickness for plain masonry foundation walls shall be 8 inches (203 mm).

4. Masonry stem walls shall have a minimum vertical reinforcement of one No. 4 (No. 13) bar located not greater than 4 feet (1219 mm) on cen-

ter in grouted cells. Vertical reinforcement shall be tied to the horizontal reinforcement in the footings.

Foundation walls, supporting more than 4 feet (1219 mm) of unbalanced backfill or exceeding 8 feet (2438 mm) in height shall be constructed in accordance with Table R404.1.1(2), R404.1.1(3) or R404.1.1(4). Masonry foundation walls shall have two No. 4 (No. 13) horizontal bars located in the upper 12 inches (305 mm) of the wall.

R404.1.4.2 Concrete foundation walls. In buildings assigned to Seismic Design Category D_0, D_1 or D_2, as established in Table R301.2(1), concrete foundation walls that support light-frame walls shall comply with this section, and concrete foundation walls that support above-grade concrete walls shall comply with ACI 318, ACI 332 or PCA 100 (see Section R404.1.3). In addition to the horizontal reinforcement required by Table R404.1.2(1), plain concrete walls supporting light-frame walls shall comply with the following.

1. Wall height shall not exceed 8 feet (2438 mm).

2. Unbalanced backfill height shall not exceed 4 feet (1219 mm).

3. Minimum thickness for plain concrete foundation walls shall be 7.5 inches (191 mm) except that 6 inches (152 mm) is permitted where the maximum wall height is 4 feet, 6 inches (1372 mm).

Foundation walls less than 7.5 inches (191 mm) in thickness, supporting more than 4 feet (1219 mm) of unbalanced backfill or exceeding 8 feet (2438 mm) in height shall be provided with horizontal reinforcement in accordance with Table R404.1.2(1), and vertical reinforcement in accordance with Table R404.1.2(2), R404.1.2(3), R404.1.2(4), R404.1.2(5), R404.1.2(6), R404.1.2(7) or R404.1.2(8). Where Tables R404.1.2(2) through R404.1.2(8) permit plain concrete walls, not less than No. 4 (No. 13) vertical bars at a spacing not exceeding 48 inches (1219 mm) shall be provided.

R404.1.5 Foundation wall thickness based on walls supported. The thickness of masonry or concrete foundation walls shall be not less than that required by Section R404.1.5.1 or R404.1.5.2, respectively.

R404.1.5.1 Masonry wall thickness. Masonry foundation walls shall be not less than the thickness of the wall supported, except that masonry foundation walls of not less than 8-inch (203 mm) nominal thickness shall be permitted under brick veneered frame walls and under 10-inch-wide (254 mm) cavity walls where the total height of the wall supported, including gables, is not more than 20 feet (6096 mm), provided that the requirements of Section R404.1.1 are met.

R404.1.5.2 Concrete wall thickness. The thickness of concrete foundation walls shall be equal to or greater than the thickness of the wall in the *story* above. Concrete foundation walls with corbels, brackets or other projections built into the wall for support of masonry

veneer or other purposes are not within the scope of the tables in this section.

Where a concrete foundation wall is reduced in thickness to provide a shelf for the support of masonry veneer, the reduced thickness shall be equal to or greater than the thickness of the wall in the *story* above. Vertical reinforcement for the foundation wall shall be based on Table R404.1.2(8) and located in the wall as required by Section R404.1.3.3.7.2 where that table is used. Vertical reinforcement shall be based on the thickness of the thinner portion of the wall.

Exception: Where the height of the reduced thickness portion measured to the underside of the floor assembly or sill plate above is less than or equal to 24 inches (610 mm) and the reduction in thickness does not exceed 4 inches (102 mm), the vertical reinforcement is permitted to be based on the thicker portion of the wall.

R404.1.5.3 Pier and curtain wall foundations. Use of pier and curtain wall foundations shall be permitted to support light-frame construction not more than two stories in height, provided that the following requirements are met:

1. All load-bearing walls shall be placed on continuous concrete footings placed integrally with the exterior wall footings.

2. The minimum actual thickness of a load-bearing masonry wall shall be not less than 4 inches (102 mm) nominal or $3^3/_8$ inches (92 mm) actual thickness, and shall be bonded integrally with piers spaced in accordance with Section R606.6.4.

3. Piers shall be constructed in accordance with Sections R606.7 and R606.7.1, and shall be bonded into the load-bearing masonry wall in accordance with Section R606.13.1 or R606.13.1.1.

4. The maximum height of a 4-inch (102 mm) load-bearing masonry foundation wall supporting wood-frame walls and floors shall be not more than 4 feet (1219 mm).

5. Anchorage shall be in accordance with Section R403.1.6, Figure R404.1.5(1), or as specified by engineered design accepted by the *building official*.

6. The unbalanced fill for 4-inch (102 mm) foundation walls shall not exceed 24 inches (610 mm) for solid masonry or 12 inches (305 mm) for hollow masonry.

7. In Seismic Design Categories D_0, D_1 and D_2, prescriptive reinforcement shall be provided in the horizontal and vertical direction. Provide minimum horizontal joint reinforcement of two No. 9 gage wires spaced not less than 6 inches (152 mm) or one $1/_4$-inch-diameter (6.4 mm) wire at 10 inches (254 mm) on center vertically. Provide minimum vertical reinforcement of one No. 4 bar at 48 inches (1220 mm) on center horizontally grouted in place.

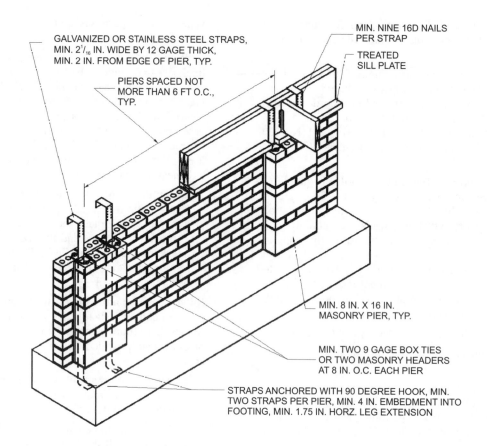

GALVANIZED OR STAINLESS STEEL STRAPS, MIN. 2$^1\!/_{16}$ IN. WIDE BY 12 GAGE THICK, MIN. 2 IN. FROM EDGE OF PIER, TYP.

PIERS SPACED NOT MORE THAN 6 FT O.C., TYP.

MIN. NINE 16D NAILS PER STRAP

TREATED SILL PLATE

MIN. 8 IN. X 16 IN. MASONRY PIER, TYP.

MIN. TWO 9 GAGE BOX TIES OR TWO MASONRY HEADERS AT 8 IN. O.C. EACH PIER

STRAPS ANCHORED WITH 90 DEGREE HOOK, MIN. TWO STRAPS PER PIER, MIN. 4 IN. EMBEDMENT INTO FOOTING, MIN. 1.75 IN. HORZ. LEG EXTENSION

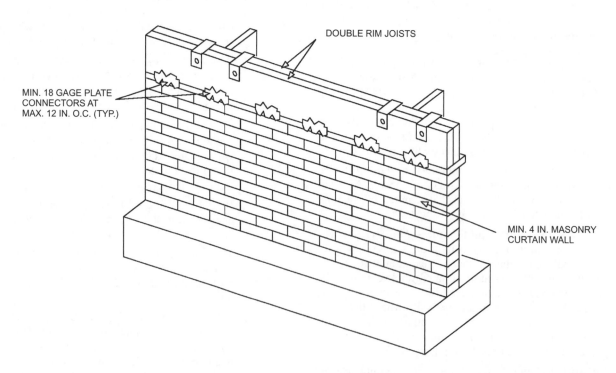

DOUBLE RIM JOISTS

MIN. 18 GAGE PLATE CONNECTORS AT MAX. 12 IN. O.C. (TYP.)

MIN. 4 IN. MASONRY CURTAIN WALL

For SI: 1 inch = 25.4 mm, 1 foot = 304.8 mm, 1 degree = 0.0175 rad.

FIGURE R404.1.5(1)
FOUNDATION WALL CLAY MASONRY CURTAIN WALL WITH CONCRETE MASONRY PIERS

R404.1.6 Height above finished grade. Concrete and masonry foundation walls shall extend above the finished *grade* adjacent to the foundation at all points not less than 4 inches (102 mm) where masonry veneer is used and not less than 6 inches (152 mm) elsewhere.

R404.1.7 Backfill placement. Backfill shall not be placed against the wall until the wall has sufficient strength and has been anchored to the floor above, or has been sufficiently braced to prevent damage by the backfill.

> **Exception:** Bracing is not required for walls supporting less than 4 feet (1219 mm) of unbalanced backfill.

R404.1.8 Rubble stone masonry. Rubble stone masonry foundation walls shall have a minimum thickness of 16 inches (406 mm), shall not support an unbalanced backfill exceeding 8 feet (2438 mm) in height, shall not support a soil pressure greater than 30 pounds per square foot per foot (4.71 kPa/m), and shall not be constructed in Seismic Design Categories D_0, D_1, D_2 or townhouses in Seismic Design Category C, as established in Figure R301.2(2).

R404.1.9 Isolated masonry piers. Isolated masonry piers shall be constructed in accordance with this section and the general masonry construction requirements of Section R606. Hollow masonry piers shall have a minimum nominal thickness of 8 inches (203 mm), with a nominal height not exceeding four times the nominal thickness and a nominal length not exceeding three times the nominal thickness. Where hollow masonry units are solidly filled with concrete or grout, piers shall be permitted to have a nominal height not exceeding ten times the nominal thickness. Footings for isolated masonry piers shall be sized in accordance with Section R403.1.1.

R404.1.9.1 Pier cap. Hollow masonry piers shall be capped with 4 inches (102 mm) of solid masonry or concrete, a masonry cap block, or shall have cavities of the top course filled with concrete or grout. Where required, termite protection for the pier cap shall be provided in accordance with Section R318.

R404.1.9.2 Masonry piers supporting floor girders. Masonry piers supporting wood girders sized in accordance with Tables R602.7(1) and R602.7(2) shall be permitted in accordance with this section. Piers supporting girders for interior bearing walls shall have a minimum nominal dimension of 12 inches (305 mm) and a maximum height of 10 feet (3048 mm) from top of footing to bottom of sill plate or girder. Piers supporting girders for exterior bearing walls shall have a minimum nominal dimension of 12 inches (305 mm) and a maximum height of 4 feet (1220 mm) from top of footing to bottom of sill plate or girder. Girders and sill plates shall be anchored to the pier or footing in accordance with Section R403.1.6 or Figure R404.1.5(1). Floor girder bearing shall be in accordance with Section R502.6.

R404.1.9.3 Masonry piers supporting braced wall panels. Masonry piers supporting *braced wall panels* shall be designed in accordance with accepted engineering practice.

R404.1.9.4 Seismic design of masonry piers. Masonry piers in *dwellings* located in Seismic Design Category D_0, D_1 or D_2, and townhouses in Seismic Design Category C, shall be designed in accordance with accepted engineering practice.

R404.1.9.5 Masonry piers in flood hazard areas. Masonry piers for *dwellings* in flood hazard areas shall be designed in accordance with Section R322.

R404.2 Wood foundation walls. Wood foundation walls shall be constructed in accordance with the provisions of Sections R404.2.1 through R404.2.6 and with the details shown in Figures R403.1(2) and R403.1(3).

R404.2.1 Identification. Load-bearing lumber shall be identified by the grade *mark* of a lumber grading or inspection agency that has been *approved* by an accreditation body that complies with DOC PS 20. In lieu of a grade *mark*, a certificate of inspection issued by a lumber grading or inspection agency meeting the requirements of this section shall be accepted. Wood structural panels shall conform to DOC PS 1 or DOC PS 2 and shall be identified by a grade *mark* or certificate of inspection issued by an *approved agency*.

R404.2.2 Stud size. The studs used in foundation walls shall be 2-inch by 6-inch (51 mm by 152 mm) members. Where spaced 16 inches (406 mm) on center, a wood species with an F_b value of not less than 1,250 pounds per square inch (8619 kPa) as listed in ANSI AWC NDS shall be used. Where spaced 12 inches (305 mm) on center, an F_b of not less than 875 psi (6033 kPa) shall be required.

R404.2.3 Height of backfill. For wood foundations that are not designed and installed in accordance with AWC PWF, the height of backfill against a foundation wall shall not exceed 4 feet (1219 mm). Where the height of fill is more than 12 inches (305 mm) above the interior *grade* of a *crawl space* or floor of a *basement*, the thickness of the plywood sheathing shall meet the requirements of Table R404.2.3.

R404.2.4 Backfilling. Wood foundation walls shall not be backfilled until the basement floor and first floor have been constructed or the walls have been braced. For *crawl space* construction, backfill or bracing shall be installed on the interior of the walls prior to placing backfill on the exterior.

R404.2.5 Drainage and dampproofing. Wood foundation basements shall be drained and dampproofed in accordance with Sections R405 and R406, respectively.

R404.2.6 Fastening. Wood structural panel foundation wall sheathing shall be attached to framing in accordance with Table R602.3(1) and Section R402.1.1.

R404.3 Wood sill plates. Wood sill plates shall be not less than 2-inch by 4-inch (51 mm by 102 mm) nominal lumber. Sill plate anchorage shall be in accordance with Sections R403.1.6 and R602.11.

R404.4 Retaining walls. Retaining walls that are not laterally supported at the top and that retain in excess of 48 inches (1219 mm) of unbalanced fill, or retaining walls exceeding 24 inches (610 mm) in height that resist lateral loads in addition

TABLE R404.2.3
PLYWOOD GRADE AND THICKNESS FOR WOOD FOUNDATION CONSTRUCTION (30 pcf equivalent-fluid weight soil pressure)

HEIGHT OF FILL (inches)	STUD SPACING (inches)	FACE GRAIN ACROSS STUDS			FACE GRAIN PARALLEL TO STUDS		
		Grade[a]	Minimum thickness (inches)	Span rating	Grade[a]	Minimum thickness (inches)[b, c]	Span rating
24	12	B	$^{15}/_{32}$	32/16	A	$^{15}/_{32}$	32/16
					B	$^{15}/_{32}$ [c]	32/16
	16	B	$^{15}/_{32}$	32/16	A	$^{15}/_{32}$ [c]	32/16
					B	$^{19}/_{32}$ [c] (4, 5 ply)	40/20
36	12	B	$^{15}/_{32}$	32/16	A	$^{15}/_{32}$	32/16
					B	$^{15}/_{32}$ [c] (4, 5 ply)	32/16
					B	$^{19}/_{32}$ (4, 5 ply)	40/20
	16	B	$^{15}/_{32}$ [c]	32/16	A	$^{19}/_{32}$	40/20
					B	$^{23}/_{32}$	48/24
48	12	B	$^{15}/_{32}$	32/16	A	$^{15}/_{32}$ [c]	32/16
					B	$^{19}/_{32}$ [c] (4, 5 ply)	40/20
	16	B	$^{19}/_{32}$	40/20	A	$^{19}/_{32}$ [c]	40/20
					A	$^{23}/_{32}$	48/24

For SI: 1 inch = 25.4 mm, 1 foot = 304.8 mm, 1 pound per cubic foot = 0.1572 kN/m³.

a. Plywood shall be of the following minimum grades in accordance with DOC PS 1 or DOC PS 2:
  1. DOC PS 1 Plywood grades marked:
    1.1. Structural I C-D (Exposure 1).
    1.2. C-D (Exposure 1).
  2. DOC PS 2 Plywood grades marked:
    2.1. Structural I Sheathing (Exposure 1).
    2.2. Sheathing (Exposure 1).
  3. Where a major portion of the wall is exposed above ground and a better appearance is desired, the following plywood grades marked exterior are suitable:
    3.1. Structural I A-C, Structural I B-C or Structural I C-C (Plugged) in accordance with DOC PS 1.
    3.2. A-C Group 1, B-C Group 1, C-C (Plugged) Group 1 or MDO Group 1 in accordance with DOC PS 1.
    3.3. Single Floor in accordance with DOC PS 1 or DOC PS 2.

b. Minimum thickness $^{15}/_{32}$ inch, except crawl space sheathing shall have not less than $^{3}/_{8}$ inch for face grain across studs 16 inches on center and maximum 2-foot depth of unequal fill.

c. For this fill height, thickness and grade combination, panels that are continuous over less than three spans (across less than three stud spacings) require blocking 16 inches above the bottom plate. Offset adjacent blocks and fasten through studs with two 16d corrosion-resistant nails at each end.

to soil, shall be designed in accordance with accepted engineering practice to ensure stability against overturning, sliding, excessive foundation pressure and water uplift. Retaining walls shall be designed for a safety factor of 1.5 against lateral sliding and overturning. This section shall not apply to foundation walls supporting buildings.

R404.5 Precast concrete foundation walls.

R404.5.1 Design. Precast concrete foundation walls shall be designed in accordance with accepted engineering practice. The design and manufacture of precast concrete foundation wall panels shall comply with the materials requirements of Section R402.3 or ACI 318. The panel design drawings shall be prepared by a registered design professional where required by the statutes of the *jurisdiction* in which the project is to be constructed in accordance with Section R106.1.

R404.5.2 Precast concrete foundation design drawings. Precast concrete foundation wall design drawings shall be submitted to the *building official* and *approved* prior to

installation. Drawings shall include, at a minimum, the following information:

1. Design loading as applicable.
2. Footing design and material.
3. Concentrated loads and their points of application.
4. Soil bearing capacity.
5. Maximum allowable total uniform load.
6. Seismic design category.
7. Basic wind speed.

R404.5.3 Identification. Precast concrete foundation wall panels shall be identified by a certificate of inspection *label* issued by an *approved* third-party inspection agency.

SECTION R405
FOUNDATION DRAINAGE

R405.1 Concrete or masonry foundations. Drains shall be provided around concrete or masonry foundations that retain earth and enclose habitable or usable spaces located below *grade*. Drainage tiles, gravel or crushed stone drains, perforated pipe or other *approved* systems or materials shall be installed at or below the top of the footing or below the bottom of the slab and shall discharge by gravity or mechanical means into an *approved* drainage system. Gravel or crushed stone drains shall extend not less than 1 foot (305 mm) beyond the outside edge of the footing and 6 inches (152 mm) above the top of the footing and be covered with an *approved* filter membrane material. The top of open joints of drain tiles shall be protected with strips of building paper. Except where otherwise recommended by the drain manufacturer, perforated drains shall be surrounded with an *approved* filter membrane or the filter membrane shall cover the washed gravel or crushed rock covering the drain. Drainage tiles or perforated pipe shall be placed on not less than 2 inches (51 mm) of washed gravel or crushed rock not less than one sieve size larger than the tile joint opening or perforation and covered with not less than 6 inches (152 mm) of the same material.

Exception: A drainage system is not required where the foundation is installed on well-drained ground or sand-gravel mixture soils according to the Unified Soil Classification System, Group I soils, as detailed in Table R405.1.

R405.1.1 Precast concrete foundation. Precast concrete walls that retain earth and enclose habitable or useable space located below-*grade* that rest on crushed stone foot-ings shall have a perforated drainage pipe installed below the base of the wall on either the interior or exterior side of the wall, not less than 1 foot (305 mm) beyond the edge of the wall. If the exterior drainage pipe is used, an *approved* filter membrane material shall cover the pipe. The drainage system shall discharge into an *approved* sewer system or to daylight.

R405.2 Wood foundations. Wood foundations enclosing habitable or usable spaces located below *grade* shall be adequately drained in accordance with Sections R405.2.1 through R405.2.3.

R405.2.1 Base. A porous layer of gravel, crushed stone or coarse sand shall be placed to a minimum thickness of 4 inches (102 mm) under the basement floor. Provision shall be made for automatic draining of this layer and the gravel or crushed stone wall footings.

R405.2.2 Vapor retarder. A 6-mil-thick (0.15 mm) polyethylene vapor retarder shall be applied over the porous layer with the basement floor constructed over the polyethylene.

R405.2.3 Drainage system. In other than Group I soils, a sump shall be provided to drain the porous layer and footings. The sump shall be not less than 24 inches (610 mm) in diameter or 20 inches square (0.0129 m²), shall extend not less than 24 inches (610 mm) below the bottom of the basement floor and shall be capable of positive gravity or

TABLE R405.1
PROPERTIES OF SOILS CLASSIFIED ACCORDING TO THE UNIFIED SOIL CLASSIFICATION SYSTEM

SOIL GROUP	UNIFIED SOIL CLASSIFICATION SYSTEM SYMBOL	SOIL DESCRIPTION	DRAINAGE CHARACTERISTICS[a]	FROST HEAVE POTENTIAL	VOLUME CHANGE POTENTIAL EXPANSION[b]
Group I	GW	Well-graded gravels, gravel sand mixtures, little or no fines	Good	Low	Low
	GP	Poorly graded gravels or gravel sand mixtures, little or no fines	Good	Low	Low
	SW	Well-graded sands, gravelly sands, little or no fines	Good	Low	Low
	SP	Poorly graded sands or gravelly sands, little or no fines	Good	Low	Low
	GM	Silty gravels, gravel-sand-silt mixtures	Good	Medium	Low
	SM	Silty sand, sand-silt mixtures	Good	Medium	Low
Group II	GC	Clayey gravels, gravel-sand-clay mixtures	Medium	Medium	Low
	SC	Clayey sands, sand-clay mixture	Medium	Medium	Low
	ML	Inorganic silts and very fine sands, rock flour, silty or clayey fine sands or clayey silts with slight plasticity	Medium	High	Low
	CL	Inorganic clays of low to medium plasticity, gravelly clays, sandy clays, silty clays, lean clays	Medium	Medium	Medium to Low
Group III	CH	Inorganic clays of high plasticity, fat clays	Poor	Medium	High
	MH	Inorganic silts, micaceous or diatomaceous fine sandy or silty soils, elastic silts	Poor	High	High
Group IV	OL	Organic silts and organic silty clays of low plasticity	Poor	Medium	Medium
	OH	Organic clays of medium to high plasticity, organic silts	Unsatisfactory	Medium	High
	Pt	Peat and other highly organic soils	Unsatisfactory	Medium	High

For SI: 1 inch = 25.4 mm.

a. The percolation rate for good drainage is over 4 inches per hour, medium drainage is 2 inches to 4 inches per hour, and poor is less than 2 inches per hour.

b. Soils with a low potential expansion typically have a plasticity index (PI) of 0 to 15, soils with a medium potential expansion have a PI of 10 to 35 and soils with a high potential expansion have a PI greater than 20.

mechanical drainage to remove any accumulated water. The drainage system shall discharge into an *approved* sewer system or to daylight.

SECTION R406
FOUNDATION WATERPROOFING AND DAMPPROOFING

R406.1 Concrete and masonry foundation dampproofing. Deleted.

R406.2 Concrete and masonry foundation waterproofing. Exterior foundation walls that retain earth and enclose below grade interior spaces, floors, and crawl spaces shall be waterproofed. Waterproofing shall be installed at a minimum from the top of the footing to the finished *grade* or in accordance with the manufacturer's installation instructions. Walls shall be waterproofed in accordance with one of the following:

1. Two-ply hot-mopped felts.

2. Fifty-five-pound (25 kg) roll roofing.

3. Six-mil (0.15 mm) polyvinyl chloride.

4. Six-mil (0.15 mm) polyethylene.

5. Forty-mil (1 mm) polymer-modified asphalt.

6. Sixty-mil (1.5 mm) flexible polymer cement.

7. One-eighth-inch (3 mm) cement-based, fiber-reinforced, waterproof coating.

8. Sixty-mil (1.5 mm) solvent-free liquid-applied synthetic rubber.

Exception: Organic-solvent-based products such as hydrocarbons, chlorinated hydrocarbons, ketones, and esters shall not be used for ICF walls with expanded polystyrene form material. Use of plastic roofing cements, acrylic coatings, latex coatings, mortars, and pargings to seal ICF walls is permitted. Cold-setting asphalt or hot asphalt shall conform to Type C of ASTM D449. Hot asphalt shall be applied at a temperature of less than 200°F (93°C).

All joints in membrane waterproofing shall be lapped and sealed with an adhesive compatible with the membrane.

R406.3 Dampproofing for wood foundations. Wood foundations enclosing habitable or usable spaces located below *grade* shall be dampproofed in accordance with Sections R406.3.1 through R406.3.4.

R406.3.1 Panel joint sealed. Plywood panel joints in the foundation walls shall be sealed full length with a caulking compound capable of producing a moistureproof seal under the conditions of temperature and moisture content at which it will be applied and used.

R406.3.2 Below-grade moisture barrier. A 6-mil-thick (0.15 mm) polyethylene film shall be applied over the below-*grade* portion of exterior foundation walls prior to backfilling. Joints in the polyethylene film shall be lapped 6 inches (152 mm) and sealed with adhesive. The top edge of the polyethylene film shall be bonded to the sheathing to form a seal. Film areas at *grade* level shall be protected from mechanical damage and exposure by a pressure-preservative treated lumber or plywood strip attached to the

wall several inches above finished *grade* level and extending approximately 9 inches (229 mm) below *grade*. The joint between the strip and the wall shall be caulked full length prior to fastening the strip to the wall. Where approved, other coverings appropriate to the architectural treatment shall be permitted to be used. The polyethylene film shall extend down to the bottom of the wood footing plate but shall not overlap or extend into the gravel or crushed stone footing.

R406.3.3 Porous fill. The space between the excavation and the foundation wall shall be backfilled with the same material used for footings, up to a height of 1 foot (305 mm) above the footing for well-drained sites, or one-half the total backfill height for poorly drained sites. The porous fill shall be covered with strips of 30-pound (13.6 kg) asphalt paper or 6-mil (0.15 mm) polyethylene to permit water seepage while avoiding infiltration of fine soils.

R406.3.4 Backfill. The remainder of the excavated area shall be backfilled with the same type of soil as was removed during the excavation.

R406.4 Precast concrete foundation system dampproofing. Except where required by Section R406.2 to be waterproofed, precast concrete foundation walls enclosing habitable or useable spaces located below *grade* shall be dampproofed in accordance with Section R406.1.

R406.4.1 Panel joints sealed. Precast concrete foundation panel joints shall be sealed full height with a sealant meeting ASTM C920, Type S or M, *Grade* NS, Class 25, Use NT, M or A. Joint sealant shall be installed in accordance with the manufacturer's instructions.

SECTION R407
COLUMNS

R407.1 Wood column protection. Wood columns shall be protected against decay as set forth in Section R317.

R407.2 Steel column protection. All surfaces (inside and outside) of steel columns shall be given a shop coat of rust-inhibitive paint, except for corrosion-resistant steel and steel treated with coatings to provide corrosion resistance.

R407.3 Structural requirements. The columns shall be restrained to prevent lateral displacement at the bottom end. Wood columns shall be not less in nominal size than 4 inches by 4 inches (102 mm by 102 mm). Steel columns shall be not less than 3-inch-diameter (76 mm) Schedule 40 pipe manufactured in accordance with ASTM A53 Grade B or *approved* equivalent.

Exception: In Seismic Design Categories A, B and C, columns not more than 48 inches (1219 mm) in height on a pier or footing are exempt from the bottom end lateral displacement requirement within under-floor areas enclosed by a continuous foundation.

SECTION R408
UNDER-FLOOR SPACE

R408.1 Ventilation. The under-floor space between the bottom of the floor joists and the earth under any building (except space occupied by a *basement*) shall have ventilation openings through foundation walls or exterior walls. The minimum net area of ventilation openings shall be not less than 1 square foot (0.0929 m^2) for each 150 square feet (14 m^2) of under-floor space area, unless the ground surface is covered by a Class 1 vapor retarder material. Where a Class 1 vapor retarder material is used, the minimum net area of ventilation openings shall be not less than 1 square foot (0.0929 m^2) for each 1,500 square feet (140 m^2) of under-floor space area. One such ventilating opening shall be within 3 feet (914 mm) of each corner of the building.

R408.2 Openings for under-floor ventilation. The minimum net area of ventilation openings shall be not less than 1 square foot (0.0929 m^2) for each 150 square feet (14 m^2) of under-floor area. One ventilation opening shall be within 3 feet (915 mm) of each corner of the building. Ventilation openings shall be covered for their height and width with any of the following materials provided that the least dimension of the covering shall not exceed $^1/_4$ inch (6.4 mm):

1. Perforated sheet metal plates not less than 0.070 inch (1.8 mm) thick.

2. Expanded sheet metal plates not less than 0.047 inch (1.2 mm) thick.

3. Cast-iron grill or grating.

4. Extruded load-bearing brick vents.

5. Hardware cloth of 0.035 inch (0.89 mm) wire or heavier.

6. Corrosion-resistant wire mesh, with the least dimension being $^1/_8$ inch (3.2 mm) thick.

Exception: The total area of ventilation openings shall be permitted to be reduced to $^1/_{1,500}$ of the under-floor area where the ground surface is covered with an *approved* Class I vapor retarder material and the required openings are placed to provide cross ventilation of the space. The installation of operable louvers shall not be prohibited.

R408.3 Unvented crawl space. Ventilation openings in under-floor spaces specified in Sections R408.1 and R408.2 shall not be required where the following items are provided:

1. Exposed earth is covered with a continuous Class I vapor retarder. Joints of the vapor retarder shall overlap by 6 inches (152 mm) and shall be sealed or taped. The edges of the vapor retarder shall extend not less than 6 inches (152 mm) up the stem wall and shall be attached and sealed to the stem wall or insulation.

2. One of the following is provided for the under-floor space:

    2.1. Continuously operated mechanical exhaust ventilation at a rate equal to 1 cubic foot per minute (0.47 L/s) for each 50 square feet (4.7 m^2) of *crawl space* floor area, including an air pathway to the common area (such as a duct or transfer grille), and perimeter walls insulated in accordance with Section N1102.2.11 of this code.

    2.2. *Conditioned air* supply sized to deliver at a rate equal to 1 cubic foot per minute (0.47 L/s) for each 50 square feet (4.7 m^2) of under-floor area,

including a return air pathway to the common area (such as a duct or transfer grille), and perimeter walls insulated in accordance with Section N1102.2.11 of this code.

    2.3. Plenum in existing structures complying with Section M1601.5, if under-floor space is used as a plenum.

    2.4. Dehumidification sized to provide 70 pints (33 liters) of moisture removal per day for every 1,000 square feet (93 m^2) of *crawl space* floor area.

R408.4 Access. Access shall be provided to all under-floor spaces. Access openings through the floor shall be not smaller than 18 inches by 24 inches (457 mm by 610 mm). Openings through a perimeter wall shall be not less than 16 inches by 24 inches (407 mm by 610 mm). Where any portion of the through-wall access is below *grade*, an areaway not less than 16 inches by 24 inches (407 mm by 610 mm) shall be provided. The bottom of the areaway shall be below the threshold of the access opening. Through wall access openings shall not be located under a door to the residence. See Section M1305.1.4 for access requirements where mechanical *equipment* is located under floors.

R408.5 Removal of debris. The under-floor *grade* shall be cleaned of all vegetation and organic material. Wood forms used for placing concrete shall be removed before a building is occupied or used for any purpose. Construction materials shall be removed before a building is occupied or used for any purpose.

R408.6 Finished grade. The finished *grade* of under-floor surface shall be permitted to be located at the bottom of the footings; however, where there is evidence that the groundwater table can rise to within 6 inches (152 mm) of the finished floor at the building perimeter or where there is evidence that the surface water does not readily drain from the building site, the *grade* in the under-floor space shall be as high as the outside finished *grade*, unless an *approved* drainage system is provided.

R408.7 Flood resistance. For buildings located in flood hazard areas as established in Table R301.2(1):

1. Walls enclosing the under-floor space shall be provided with flood openings in accordance with Section R322.2.2.

2. The finished ground level of the under-floor space shall be equal to or higher than the outside finished ground level on at least one side.

    Exception: Under-floor spaces that meet the requirements of FEMA TB 11-1.

CHAPTER 5

FLOORS

User note:

About this chapter: Chapter 5 provides the requirements for the design and construction of floor systems that will be capable of supporting minimum required design loads. This chapter covers wood floor framing, wood floors on the ground, cold-formed steel floor framing and concrete slabs on the ground. Allowable span tables are provided that greatly simplify the determination of joist, girder and sheathing sizes for raised floor systems of wood framing and cold-formed steel framing. This chapter also contains prescriptive requirements for wood-framed exterior decks and their attachment to the main building.

SECTION R501
GENERAL

R501.1 Application. The provisions of this chapter shall control the design and construction of the floors for buildings, including the floors of *attic* spaces used to house mechanical or plumbing fixtures and *equipment*.

R501.2 Requirements. Floor construction shall be capable of accommodating all loads in accordance with Section R301 and of transmitting the resulting loads to the supporting structural elements.

SECTION R502
WOOD FLOOR FRAMING

R502.1 General. Wood and wood-based products used for load-supporting purposes shall conform to the applicable provisions of this section.

R502.1.1 Sawn lumber. Sawn lumber shall be identified by a grade *mark* of an accredited lumber grading or inspection agency and have design values certified by an accreditation body that complies with DOC PS 20. In lieu of a grade *mark*, a certificate of inspection issued by a lumber grading or inspection agency meeting the requirements of this section shall be accepted.

R502.1.1.1 Preservative-treated lumber. Preservative treated dimension lumber shall be identified as required by Section R317.2.

R502.1.1.2 End-jointed lumber. *Approved* end-jointed lumber identified by a grade *mark* conforming to Section R502.1.1 shall be permitted to be used interchangeably with solid-sawn members of the same species and grade. End-jointed lumber used in an assembly required elsewhere in this code to have a fire-resistance rating shall have the designation "Heat-Resistant Adhesive" or "HRA" included in its grade mark.

R502.1.2 Prefabricated wood I-joists. Structural capacities and design provisions for prefabricated wood I-joists shall be established and monitored in accordance with ASTM D5055.

R502.1.3 Structural glued laminated timbers. Glued laminated timbers shall be manufactured and identified as required in ANSI A190.1, ANSI 117 and ASTM D3737.

R502.1.4 Structural log members. Structural log members shall comply with the provisions of ICC 400.

R502.1.5 Structural composite lumber. Structural capacities for structural composite lumber shall be established and monitored in accordance with ASTM D5456.

R502.1.6 Cross-laminated timber. Cross-laminated timber shall be manufactured and identified as required by ANSI/APA PRG 320.

R502.1.7 Engineered wood rim board. Engineered wood rim boards shall conform to ANSI/APA PRR 410 or shall be evaluated in accordance with ASTM D7672. Structural capacities shall be in accordance with ANSI/APA PRR 410 or established in accordance with ASTM D7672. Rim boards conforming to ANSI/APA PRR 410 shall be marked in accordance with that standard.

R502.2 Design and construction. Floors shall be designed and constructed in accordance with the provisions of this chapter, Figure R502.2 and Sections R317 and R318 or in accordance with ANSI AWC NDS.

R502.2.1 Framing at braced wall lines. A load path for lateral forces shall be provided between floor framing and *braced wall panels* located above or below a floor, as specified in Section R602.10.8.

R502.2.2 Blocking and subflooring. Blocking for fastening panel edges or fixtures shall be not less than utility grade lumber. Subflooring shall be not less than utility grade lumber, No. 4 common grade boards or wood structural panels as specified in Section R503.2. Fireblocking shall be of any grade lumber.

R502.3 Allowable joist spans. Spans for floor joists shall be in accordance with Tables R502.3.1(1) and R502.3.1(2). For other grades and species and for other loading conditions, refer to the AWC STJR.

R502.3.1 Sleeping areas and attic joists. Table R502.3.1(1) shall be used to determine the maximum allowable span of floor joists that support sleeping areas and *attics* that are accessed by means of a fixed stairway in accordance with Section R311.7 provided that the design live load does not exceed 30 pounds per square foot (1.44 kPa) and the design dead load does not exceed 20 pounds per square foot (0.96 kPa). The allowable span of ceiling joists that support *attics* used for limited storage or no storage shall be determined in accordance with Section R802.5.

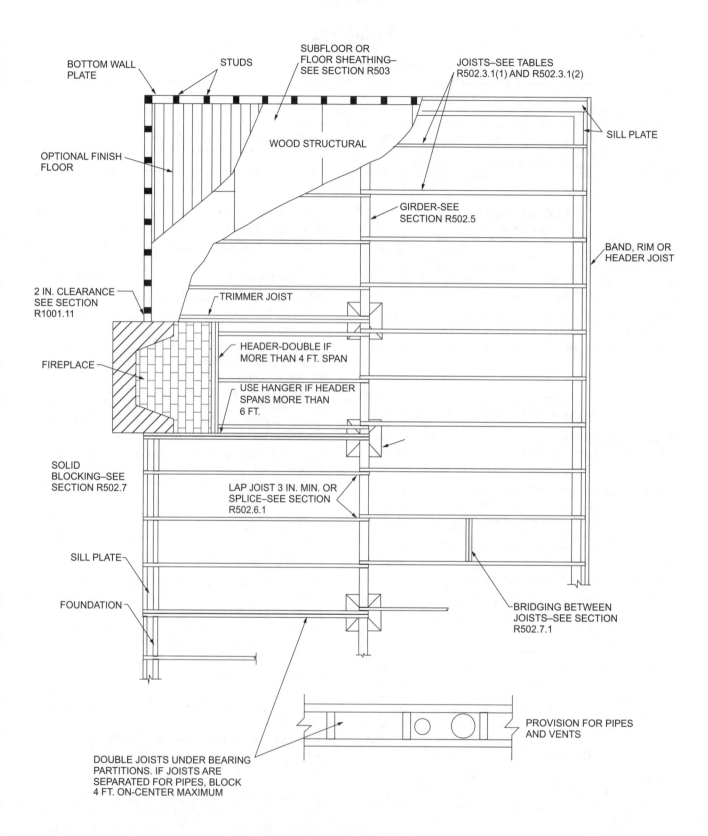

BOTTOM WALL PLATE

STUDS

SUBFLOOR OR FLOOR SHEATHING– SEE SECTION R503

JOISTS–SEE TABLES R502.3.1(1) AND R502.3.1(2)

SILL PLATE

OPTIONAL FINISH FLOOR

WOOD STRUCTURAL

GIRDER-SEE SECTION R502.5

BAND, RIM OR HEADER JOIST

2 IN. CLEARANCE SEE SECTION R1001.11

TRIMMER JOIST

HEADER-DOUBLE IF MORE THAN 4 FT. SPAN

FIREPLACE

USE HANGER IF HEADER SPANS MORE THAN 6 FT.

SOLID BLOCKING–SEE SECTION R502.7

LAP JOIST 3 IN. MIN. OR SPLICE–SEE SECTION R502.6.1

SILL PLATE

BRIDGING BETWEEN JOISTS–SEE SECTION R502.7.1

FOUNDATION

PROVISION FOR PIPES AND VENTS

DOUBLE JOISTS UNDER BEARING PARTITIONS. IF JOISTS ARE SEPARATED FOR PIPES, BLOCK 4 FT. ON-CENTER MAXIMUM

For SI: 1 inch = 25.4 mm, 1 foot = 304.8 mm.

**FIGURE R502.2
FLOOR CONSTRUCTION**

TABLE R502.3.1(1)
FLOOR JOIST SPANS FOR COMMON LUMBER SPECIES
(Residential sleeping areas, live load = 30 psf, L/Δ = 360)[a]

JOIST SPACING (inches)	SPECIES AND GRADE		DEAD LOAD = 10 psf				DEAD LOAD = 20 psf			
			2 × 6	2 × 8	2 × 10	2 × 12	2 × 6	2 × 8	2 × 10	2 × 12
			Maximum floor joist spans							
			(ft. - in.)	(ft. - in.)	(ft. - in.)	(ft. - in.)	(ft. - in.)	(ft. - in.)	(ft. - in.)	(ft. - in.)
12	Douglas fir-larch	SS	12-6	16-6	21-0	25-7	12-6	16-6	21-0	25-7
	Douglas fir-larch	#1	12-0	15-10	20-3	24-8	12-0	15-7	19-0	22-0
	Douglas fir-larch	#2	11-10	15-7	19-10	23-4	11-8	14-9	18-0	20-11
	Douglas fir-larch	#3	9-11	12-7	15-5	17-10	8-11	11-3	13-9	16-0
	Hem-fir	SS	11-10	15-7	19-10	24-2	11-10	15-7	19-10	24-2
	Hem-fir	#1	11-7	15-3	19-5	23-7	11-7	15-3	18-9	21-9
	Hem-fir	#2	11-0	14-6	18-6	22-6	11-0	14-4	17-6	20-4
	Hem-fir	#3	9-8	12-4	15-0	17-5	8-8	11-0	13-5	15-7
	Southern pine	SS	12-3	16-2	20-8	25-1	12-3	16-2	20-8	25-1
	Southern pine	#1	11-10	15-7	19-10	24-2	11-10	15-7	18-7	22-0
	Southern pine	#2	11-3	14-11	18-1	21-4	10-9	13-8	16-2	19-1
	Southern pine	#3	9-2	11-6	14-0	16-6	8-2	10-3	12-6	14-9
	Spruce-pine-fir	SS	11-7	15-3	19-5	23-7	11-7	15-3	19-5	23-7
	Spruce-pine-fir	#1	11-3	14-11	19-0	23-0	11-3	14-7	17-9	20-7
	Spruce-pine-fir	#2	11-3	14-11	19-0	23-0	11-3	14-7	17-9	20-7
	Spruce-pine-fir	#3	9-8	12-4	15-0	17-5	8-8	11-0	13-5	15-7
16	Douglas fir-larch	SS	11-4	15-0	19-1	23-3	11-4	15-0	19-1	23-3
	Douglas fir-larch	#1	10-11	14-5	18-5	21-4	10-8	13-6	16-5	19-1
	Douglas fir-larch	#2	10-9	14-2	17-5	20-3	10-1	12-9	15-7	18-1
	Douglas fir-larch	#3	8-7	10-11	13-4	15-5	7-8	9-9	11-11	13-10
	Hem-fir	SS	10-9	14-2	18-0	21-11	10-9	14-2	18-0	21-11
	Hem-fir	#1	10-6	13-10	17-8	21-1	10-6	13-4	16-3	18-10
	Hem-fir	#2	10-0	13-2	16-10	19-8	9-10	12-5	15-2	17-7
	Hem-fir	#3	8-5	10-8	13-0	15-1	7-6	9-6	11-8	13-6
	Southern pine	SS	11-2	14-8	18-9	22-10	11-2	14-8	18-9	22-10
	Southern pine	#1	10-9	14-2	18-0	21-4	10-9	13-9	16-1	19-1
	Southern pine	#2	10-3	13-3	15-8	18-6	9-4	11-10	14-0	16-6
	Southern pine	#3	7-11	10-0	11-1	14-4	7-1	8-11	10-10	12-10
	Spruce-pine-fir	SS	10-6	13-10	17-8	21-6	10-6	13-10	17-8	21-4
	Spruce-pine-fir	#1	10-3	13-6	17-2	19-11	9-11	12-7	15-5	17-10
	Spruce-pine-fir	#2	10-3	13-6	17-2	19-11	9-11	12-7	15-5	17-10
	Spruce-pine-fir	#3	8-5	10-8	13-0	15-1	7-6	9-6	11-8	13-6

(continued)

TABLE R502.3.1(1)—continued
FLOOR JOIST SPANS FOR COMMON LUMBER SPECIES
(Residential sleeping areas, live load = 30 psf, L/Δ = 360)[a]

JOIST SPACING (inches)	SPECIES AND GRADE		DEAD LOAD = 10 psf				DEAD LOAD = 20 psf			
			2 × 6	2 × 8	2 × 10	2 × 12	2 × 6	2 × 8	2 × 10	2 × 12
			Maximum floor joist spans							
			(ft.- in.)	(ft. - in.)	(ft. - in.)	(ft. - in.)	(ft. - in.)	(ft. - in.)	(ft. - in.)	(ft. - in.)
19.2	Douglas fir-larch	SS	10-8	14-1	18-0	21-10	10-8	14-1	18-0	21-4
	Douglas fir-larch	#1	10-4	13-7	16-9	19-6	9-8	12-4	15-0	17-5
	Douglas fir-larch	#2	10-1	13-0	15-11	18-6	9-3	11-8	14-3	16-6
	Douglas fir-larch	#3	7-10	10-0	12-2	14-1	7-0	8-11	10-11	12-7
	Hem-fir	SS	10-1	13-4	17-0	20-8	10-1	13-4	17-0	20-7
	Hem-fir	#1	9-10	13-0	16-7	19-3	9-7	12-2	14-10	17-2
	Hem-fir	#2	9-5	12-5	15-6	17-1	8-11	11-4	13-10	16-1
	Hem-fir	#3	7-8	9-9	11-10	13-9	6-10	8-8	10-7	12-4
	Southern pine	SS	10-6	13-10	17-8	21-6	10-6	13-10	17-8	21-6
	Southern pine	#1	10-1	13-4	16-5	19-6	9-11	12-7	14-8	17-5
	Southern pine	#2	9-6	12-1	14-4	16-10	8-6	10-10	12-10	15-1
	Southern pine	#3	7-3	9-1	11-0	13-1	6-5	8-2	9-10	11-8
	Spruce-pine-fir	SS	9-10	13-0	16-7	20-2	9-10	13-0	16-7	19-6
	Spruce-pine-fir	#1	9-8	12-9	15-8	18-3	9-1	11-6	14-1	16-3
	Spruce-pine-fir	#2	9-8	12-9	15-8	18-3	9-1	11-6	14-1	16-3
	Spruce-pine-fir	#3	7-8	9-9	11-10	13-9	6-10	8-8	10-7	12-4
24	Douglas fir-larch	SS	9-11	13-1	16-8	20-3	9-11	13-1	16-5	19-1
	Douglas fir-larch	#1	9-7	12-4	15-0	17-5	8-8	11-0	13-5	15-7
	Douglas fir-larch	#2	9-3	11-8	14-3	16-6	8-3	10-5	12-9	14-9
	Douglas fir-larch	#3	7-0	8-11	10-11	12-7	6-3	8-0	9-9	11-3
	Hem-fir	SS	9-4	12-4	15-9	19-2	9-4	12-4	15-9	18-5
	Hem-fir	#1	9-2	12-1	14-10	17-2	8-7	10-10	13-3	15-5
	Hem-fir	#2	8-9	11-4	13-10	16-1	8-0	10-2	12-5	14-4
	Hem-fir	#3	6-10	8-8	10-7	12-4	6-2	7-9	9-6	11-0
	Southern pine	SS	9-9	12-10	16-5	19-11	9-9	12-10	16-5	19-8
	Southern pine	#1	9-4	12-4	14-8	17-5	8-10	11-3	13-1	15-7
	Southern pine	#2	8-6	10-10	12-10	15-1	7-7	9-8	11-5	13-6
	Southern pine	#3	6-5	8-2	9-10	11-8	5-9	7-3	8-10	10-5
	Spruce-pine-fir	SS	9-2	12-1	15-5	18-9	9-2	12-1	15-0	17-5
	Spruce-pine-fir	#1	8-11	11-6	14-1	16-3	8-1	10-3	12-7	14-7
	Spruce-pine-fir	#2	8-11	11-6	14-1	16-3	8-1	10-3	12-7	14-7
	Spruce-pine-fir	#3	6-10	8-8	10-7	12-4	6-2	7-9	9-6	11-0

For SI: 1 inch = 25.4 mm, 1 foot = 304.8 mm, 1 pound per square foot = 0.0479 kPa.

Note: Check sources for availability of lumber in lengths greater than 20 feet.

a. Dead load limits for townhouses in Seismic Design Category C and all structures in Seismic Design Categories D_0, D_1 and D_2 shall be determined in accordance with Section R301.2.2.2.

TABLE R502.3.1(2)
FLOOR JOIST SPANS FOR COMMON LUMBER SPECIES
(Residential living areas, live load = 40 psf, L/Δ = 360)[b]

JOIST SPACING (inches)	SPECIES AND GRADE		DEAD LOAD = 10 psf				DEAD LOAD = 20 psf			
			2 × 6	2 × 8	2 × 10	2 × 12	2 × 6	2 × 8	2 × 10	2 × 12
			Maximum floor joist spans							
			(ft. - in.)	(ft. - in.)	(ft. - in.)	(ft. - in.)	(ft. - in.)	(ft. - in.)	(ft. - in.)	(ft. - in.)
12	Douglas fir-larch	SS	11-4	15-0	19-1	23-3	11-4	15-0	19-1	23-3
	Douglas fir-larch	#1	10-11	14-5	18-5	22-0	10-11	14-2	17-4	20-1
	Douglas fir-larch	#2	10-9	14-2	18-0	20-11	10-8	13-6	16-5	19-1
	Douglas fir-larch	#3	8-11	11-3	13-9	16-0	8-1	10-3	12-7	14-7
	Hem-fir	SS	10-9	14-2	18-0	21-11	10-9	14-2	18-0	21-11
	Hem-fir	#1	10-6	13-10	17-8	21-6	10-6	13-10	17-1	19-10
	Hem-fir	#2	10-0	13-2	16-10	20-4	10-0	13-1	16-0	18-6
	Hem-fir	#3	8-8	11-0	13-5	15-7	7-11	10-0	12-3	14-3
	Southern pine	SS	11-2	14-8	18-9	22-10	11-2	14-8	18-9	22-10
	Southern pine	#1	10-9	14-2	18-0	21-11	10-9	14-2	16-11	20-1
	Southern pine	#2	10-3	13-6	16-2	19-1	9-10	12-6	14-9	17-5
	Southern pine	#3	8-2	10-3	12-6	14-9	7-5	9-5	11-5	13-6
	Spruce-pine-fir	SS	10-6	13-10	17-8	21-6	10-6	13-10	17-8	21-6
	Spruce-pine-fir	#1	10-3	13-6	17-3	20-7	10-3	13-3	16-3	18-10
	Spruce-pine-fir	#2	10-3	13-6	17-3	20-7	10-3	13-3	16-3	18-10
	Spruce-pine-fir	#3	8-8	11-0	13-5	15-7	7-11	10-0	12-3	14-3
16	Douglas fir-larch	SS	10-4	13-7	17-4	21-1	10-4	13-7	17-4	21-1
	Douglas fir-larch	#1	9-11	13-1	16-5	19-1	9-8	12-4	15-0	17-5
	Douglas fir-larch	#2	9-9	12-9	15-7	18-1	9-3	11-8	14-3	16-6
	Douglas fir-larch	#3	7-8	9-9	11-11	13-10	7-0	8-11	10-11	12-7
	Hem-fir	SS	9-9	12-10	16-5	19-11	9-9	12-10	16-5	19-11
	Hem-fir	#1	9-6	12-7	16-0	18-10	9-6	12-2	14-10	17-2
	Hem-fir	#2	9-1	12-0	15-2	17-7	8-11	11-4	13-10	16-1
	Hem-fir	#3	7-6	9-6	11-8	13-6	6-10	8-8	10-7	12-4
	Southern pine	SS	10-2	13-4	17-0	20-9	10-2	13-4	17-0	20-9
	Southern pine	#1	9-9	12-10	16-1	19-1	9-9	12-7	14-8	17-5
	Southern pine	#2	9-4	11-10	14-0	16-6	8-6	10-10	12-10	15-1
	Southern pine	#3	7-1	8-11	10-10	12-10	6-5	8-2	9-10	11-8
	Spruce-pine-fir	SS	9-6	12-7	16-0	19-6	9-6	12-7	16-0	19-6
	Spruce-pine-fir	#1	9-4	12-3	15-5	17-10	9-1	11-6	14-1	16-3
	Spruce-pine-fir	#2	9-4	12-3	15-5	17-10	9-1	11-6	14-1	16-3
	Spruce-pine-fir	#3	7-6	9-6	11-8	13-6	6-10	8-8	10-7	12-4

(continued)

TABLE R502.3.1(2)—continued
FLOOR JOIST SPANS FOR COMMON LUMBER SPECIES
(Residential living areas, live load = 40 psf, L/Δ = 360)[b]

JOIST SPACING (inches)	SPECIES AND GRADE		DEAD LOAD = 10 psf				DEAD LOAD = 20 psf			
			2 × 6	2 × 8	2 × 10	2 × 12	2 × 6	2 × 8	2 × 10	2 × 12
			Maximum floor joist spans							
			(ft. - in.)	(ft. - in.)	(ft. - in.)	(ft. - in.)	(ft. - in.)	(ft. - in.)	(ft. - in.)	(ft. - in.)
19.2	Douglas fir-larch	SS	9-8	12-10	16-4	19-10	9-8	12-10	16-4	19-6
	Douglas fir-larch	#1	9-4	12-4	15-0	17-5	8-10	11-3	13-8	15-11
	Douglas fir-larch	#2	9-2	11-8	14-3	16-6	8-5	10-8	13-0	15-1
	Douglas fir-larch	#3	7-0	8-11	10-11	12-7	6-5	8-2	9-11	11-6
	Hem-fir	SS	9-2	12-1	15-5	18-9	9-2	12-1	15-5	18-9
	Hem-fir	#1	9-0	11-10	14-10	17-2	8-9	11-1	13-6	15-8
	Hem-fir	#2	8-7	11-3	13-10	16-1	8-2	10-4	12-8	14-8
	Hem-fir	#3	6-10	8-8	10-7	12-4	6-3	7-11	9-8	11-3
	Southern pine	SS	9-6	12-7	16-0	19-6	9-6	12-7	16-0	19-6
	Southern pine	#1	9-2	12-1	14-8	17-5	9-0	11-5	13-5	15-11
	Southern pine	#2	8-6	10-10	12-10	15-1	7-9	9-10	11-8	13-9
	Southern pine	#3	6-5	8-2	9-10	11-8	5-11	7-5	9-0	10-8
	Spruce-pine-fir	SS	9-0	11-10	15-1	18-4	9-0	11-10	15-1	17-9
	Spruce-pine-fir	#1	8-9	11-6	14-1	16-3	8-3	10-6	12-10	14-10
	Spruce-pine-fir	#2	8-9	11-6	14-1	16-3	8-3	10-6	12-10	14-10
	Spruce-pine-fir	#3	6-10	8-8	10-7	12-4	6-3	7-11	9-8	11-3
24	Douglas fir-larch	SS	9-0	11-11	15-2	18-5	9-0	11-11	15-0	17-5
	Douglas fir-larch	#1	8-8	11-0	13-5	15-7	7-11	10-0	12-3	14-3
	Douglas fir-larch	#2	8-3	10-5	12-9	14-9	7-6	9-6	11-8	13-6
	Douglas fir-larch	#3	6-3	8-0	9-9	11-3	5-9	7-3	8-11	10-4
	Hem-fir	SS	8-6	11-3	14-4	17-5	8-6	11-3	14-4	16-10[a]
	Hem-fir	#1	8-4	10-10	13-3	15-5	7-10	9-11	12-1	14-0
	Hem-fir	#2	7-11	10-2	12-5	14-4	7-4	9-3	11-4	13-1
	Hem-fir	#3	6-2	7-9	9-6	11-0	5-7	7-1	8-8	10-1
	Southern pine	SS	8-10	11-8	14-11	18-1	8-10	11-8	14-11	18-0
	Southern pine	#1	8-6	11-3	13-1	15-7	8-1	10-3	12-0	14-3
	Southern pine	#2	7-7	9-8	11-5	13-6	7-0	8-10	10-5	12-4
	Southern pine	#3	5-9	7-3	8-10	10-5	5-3	6-8	8-1	9-6
	Spruce-pine-fir	SS	8-4	11-0	14-0	17-0	8-4	11-0	13-8	15-11
	Spruce-pine-fir	#1	8-1	10-3	12-7	14-7	7-5	9-5	11-6	13-4
	Spruce-pine-fir	#2	8-1	10-3	12-7	14-7	7-5	9-5	11-6	13-4
	Spruce-pine-fir	#3	6-2	7-9	9-6	11-0	5-7	7-1	8-8	10-1

For SI: 1 inch = 25.4 mm, 1 foot = 304.8 mm, 1 pound per square foot = 0.0479 kPa.

Note: Check sources for availability of lumber in lengths greater than 20 feet.

a. End bearing length shall be increased to 2 inches.

b. Dead load limits for townhouses in Seismic Design Category C and all structures in Seismic Design Categories D_0, D_1, and D_2 shall be determined in accordance with Section R301.2.2.2.

R502.3.2 Other floor joists. Table R502.3.1(2) shall be used to determine the maximum allowable span of floor joists that support other areas of the building, other than sleeping rooms and *attics*, provided that the design live load does not exceed 40 pounds per square foot (1.92 kPa) and the design dead load does not exceed 20 pounds per square foot (0.96 kPa).

R502.3.3 Floor cantilevers. Floor cantilever spans shall not exceed the nominal depth of the wood floor joist. Floor cantilevers constructed in accordance with Table R502.3.3(1) shall be permitted where supporting a light-frame bearing wall and roof only. Floor cantilevers supporting an exterior balcony are permitted to be constructed in accordance with Table R502.3.3(2).

R502.4 Joists under bearing partitions. Joists under parallel bearing partitions shall be of adequate size to support the load. Double joists, sized to adequately support the load, that are separated to permit the installation of piping or vents shall be full-depth solid blocked with lumber not less than 2 inches (51 mm) in nominal thickness spaced not more than 4 feet (1219 mm) on center. Bearing partitions perpendicular to joists shall not be offset from supporting girders, walls or partitions more than the joist depth unless such joists are of sufficient size to carry the additional load.

R502.5 Allowable girder and header spans. The allowable spans of girders and headers fabricated of dimension lumber shall not exceed the values set forth in Tables R602.7(1), R602.7(2) and R602.7(3).

R502.6 Bearing. The ends of each joist, beam or girder shall have not less than 1$^1/_2$ inches (38 mm) of bearing on wood or metal, have not less than 3 inches of bearing (76 mm) on masonry or concrete or be supported by *approved* joist hangers. Alternatively, the ends of joists shall be supported on a 1-inch by 4-inch (25 mm by 102 mm) ribbon strip and shall be nailed to the adjacent stud. The bearing on masonry or concrete shall be direct, or a sill plate of 2-inch-minimum (51 mm) nominal thickness shall be provided under the joist, beam or girder. The sill plate shall provide a minimum nominal bearing area of 48 square inches (30 865 mm^2).

R502.6.1 Floor systems. Joists framing from opposite sides over a bearing support shall lap not less than 3 inches (76 mm) and shall be nailed together with a minimum three 10d face nails. A wood or metal splice with strength equal to or greater than that provided by the nailed lap is permitted.

R502.6.2 Joist framing. Joists framing into the side of a wood girder shall be supported by *approved* framing anchors or on ledger strips not less than nominal 2 inches by 2 inches (51 mm by 51 mm).

R502.7 Lateral restraint at supports. Joists shall be supported laterally at the ends by full-depth solid blocking not less than 2 inches (51 mm) nominal in thickness; or by attachment to a full-depth header, band or rim joist, or to an adjoining stud or shall be otherwise provided with lateral support to prevent rotation.

Exceptions:

1. Trusses, structural composite lumber, structural glued-laminated members and I-joists shall be supported laterally as required by the manufacturer's recommendations.

2. In Seismic Design Categories D$_0$, D$_1$ and D$_2$, lateral restraint shall be provided at each intermediate support.

R502.7.1 Bridging. Joists exceeding a nominal 2 inches by 12 inches (51 mm by 305 mm) shall be supported laterally by solid blocking, diagonal bridging (wood or metal), or a continuous 1-inch by 3-inch (25 mm by 76 mm) strip nailed across the bottom of joists perpendicular to joists at intervals not exceeding 8 feet (2438 mm).

Exception: Trusses, structural composite lumber, structural glued-laminated members and I-joists shall be supported laterally as required by the manufacturer's recommendations.

R502.8 Cutting, drilling and notching. Structural floor members shall not be cut, bored or notched in excess of the limitations specified in this section. See Figure R502.8.

R502.8.1 Sawn lumber. Notches in solid lumber joists, rafters and beams shall not exceed one-sixth of the depth of the member, shall not be longer than one-third of the depth of the member and shall not be located in the middle one-third of the span. Notches at the ends of the member shall not exceed one-fourth the depth of the member. The tension side of members 4 inches (102 mm) or greater in nominal thickness shall not be notched except at the ends of the members. The diameter of holes bored or cut into members shall not exceed one-third the depth of the member. Holes shall not be closer than 2 inches (51 mm) to the top or bottom of the member, or to any other hole located in the member. Where the member is notched, the hole shall not be closer than 2 inches (51 mm) to the notch.

R502.8.2 Engineered wood products. Cuts, notches and holes bored in trusses, structural composite lumber, structural glue-laminated members, cross-laminated timber members or I-joists are prohibited except where permitted by the manufacturer's recommendations or where the effects of such alterations are specifically considered in the design of the member by a *registered design professional*.

R502.9 Fastening. Floor framing shall be nailed in accordance with Table R602.3(1). Where posts and beam or girder construction is used to support floor framing, positive connections shall be provided to ensure against uplift and lateral displacement.

TABLE R502.3.3(1)
CANTILEVER SPANS FOR FLOOR JOISTS SUPPORTING LIGHT-FRAME EXTERIOR BEARING WALL AND ROOF ONLY[a, b, c, f, g, h]
(Floor Live Load ≤ 40 psf, Roof Live Load ≤ 20 psf)

MEMBER & SPACING	MAXIMUM CANTILEVER SPAN (uplift force at backspan support in lbs.)[d, e]											
	Ground Snow Load											
	≤ 20 psf			30 psf			50 psf			70 psf		
	Roof Width			Roof Width			Roof Width			Roof Width		
	24 ft	32 ft	40 ft	24 ft	32 ft	40 ft	24 ft	32 ft	40 ft	24 ft	32 ft	40 ft
2 × 8 @ 12″	20″ (177)	15″ (227)	—	18″ (209)	—	—	—	—	—	—	—	—
2 × 10 @ 16″	29″ (228)	21″ (297)	16″ (364)	26″ (271)	18″ (354)	—	20″ (375)	—	—	—	—	—
2 × 10 @ 12″	36″ (166)	26″ (219)	20″ (270)	34″ (198)	22″ (263)	16″ (324)	26″ (277)	—	—	19″ (356)	—	—
2 × 12 @ 16″	—	32″ (287)	25″ (356)	36″ (263)	29″ (345)	21″ (428)	29″ (367)	20″ (484)	—	23″ (471)	—	—
2 × 12 @ 12″	—	42″ (209)	31″ (263)	—	37″ (253)	27″ (317)	36″ (271)	27″ (358)	17″ (447)	31″ (348)	19″ (462)	—
2 × 12 @ 8″	—	48″ (136)	45″ (169)	—	48″ (164)	38″ (206)	—	40″ (233)	26″ (294)	36″ (230)	29″ (304)	18″ (379)

For SI: 1 inch = 25.4 mm, 1 foot = 304.8 mm, 1 pound per square foot = 0.0479 kPa.

a. Tabulated values are for clear-span roof supported solely by exterior bearing walls.

b. Spans are based on No. 2 Grade lumber of Douglas fir-larch, hem-fir, and spruce-pine-fir for repetitive (three or more) members. No.1 or better shall be used for Southern pine.

c. Ratio of backspan to cantilever span shall be not less than 3:1.

d. Connections capable of resisting the indicated uplift force shall be provided at the backspan support.

e. Uplift force is for a backspan to cantilever span ratio of 3:1. Tabulated uplift values are permitted to be reduced by multiplying by a factor equal to 3 divided by the actual backspan ratio provided (3/backspan ratio).

f. See Section R301.2.2.6, Item 1, for additional limitations on cantilevered floor joists for detached one- and two-family dwellings in Seismic Design Category D_0, D_1, or D_2 and townhouses in Seismic Design Category C, D_0, D_1 or D_2.

g. A full-depth rim joist shall be provided at the unsupported end of the cantilever joists. Solid blocking shall be provided at the supported end. Where the cantilever length is 24 inches or less and the building is assigned to Seismic Design Category A, B or C, solid blocking at the support for the cantilever shall not be required.

h. Linear interpolation shall be permitted for building widths and ground snow loads other than shown.

TABLE R502.3.3(2)
CANTILEVER SPANS FOR FLOOR JOISTS SUPPORTING EXTERIOR BALCONY[a, b, e, f]

MEMBER SIZE	SPACING	MAXIMUM CANTILEVER SPAN (uplift force at backspan support in lbs.)[c, d]		
		Ground Snow Load		
		≤ 30 psf	50 psf	70 psf
2 × 8	12″	42″ (139)	39″ (156)	34″ (165)
2 × 8	16″	36″ (151)	34″ (171)	29″ (180)
2 × 10	12″	61″ (164)	57″ (189)	49″ (201)
2 × 10	16″	53″ (180)	49″ (208)	42″ (220)
2 × 10	24″	43″ (212)	40″ (241)	34″ (255)
2 × 12	16″	72″ (228)	67″ (260)	57″ (268)
2 × 12	24″	58″ (279)	54″ (319)	47″ (330)

For SI: 1 inch = 25.4 mm, 1 pound per square foot = 0.0479 kPa.

a. Spans are based on No. 2 Grade lumber of Douglas fir-larch, hem-fir, and spruce-pine-fir for repetitive (three or more) members. No.1 or better shall be used for Southern pine.

b. Ratio of backspan to cantilever span shall be not less than 2:1.

c. Connections capable of resisting the indicated uplift force shall be provided at the backspan support.

d. Uplift force is for a backspan to cantilever span ratio of 2:1. Tabulated uplift values are permitted to be reduced by multiplying by a factor equal to 2 divided by the actual backspan ratio provided (2/backspan ratio).

e. A full-depth rim joist shall be provided at the unsupported end of the cantilever joists. Solid blocking shall be provided at the supported end. Where the cantilever length is 24 inches or less and the building is assigned to Seismic Design Category A, B or C, solid blocking at the support for the cantilever shall not be required.

f. Linear interpolation shall be permitted for ground snow loads other than shown.

R502.10 Framing of openings. Openings in floor framing shall be framed with header and trimmer joists. Where the header joist span does not exceed 4 feet (1219 mm), the header joist shall be a single member the same size as the floor joist. Single trimmer joists shall be used to carry a single header joist that is located within 3 feet (914 mm) of the trimmer joist bearing. Where the header joist span exceeds 4 feet (1219 mm), the trimmer joists and the header joist shall be doubled and of sufficient cross section to support the floor joists framing into the header.

R502.11 Wood trusses.

R502.11.1 Design. Wood trusses shall be designed in accordance with *approved* engineering practice. The design and manufacture of metal-plate-connected wood trusses shall comply with ANSI/TPI 1. The truss design drawings

shall be prepared by a registered professional where required by the statutes of the *jurisdiction* in which the project is to be constructed in accordance with Section R106.1.

R502.11.2 Bracing. Trusses shall be braced to prevent rotation and provide lateral stability in accordance with the requirements specified in the *construction documents* for the building and on the individual truss design drawings. In the absence of specific bracing requirements, trusses shall be braced in accordance with accepted industry practices, such as, the SBCA *Building Component Safety Information (BCSI) Guide to Good Practice for Handling, Installing & Bracing of Metal Plate Connected Wood Trusses.*

R502.11.3 Alterations to trusses. Truss members and components shall not be cut, notched, spliced or otherwise altered in any way without the approval of a registered

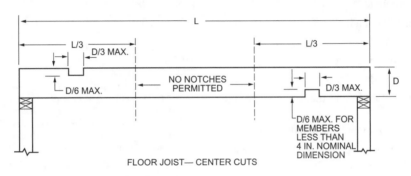

FLOOR JOIST— CENTER CUTS

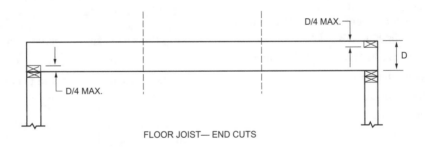

FLOOR JOIST— END CUTS

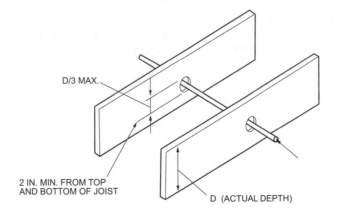

For SI: 1 inch = 25.4 mm.

FIGURE R502.8
CUTTING, NOTCHING AND DRILLING

design professional. Alterations resulting in the addition of load that exceeds the design load for the truss, shall not be permitted without verification that the truss is capable of supporting the additional loading.

R502.11.4 Truss design drawings. Truss design drawings, prepared in compliance with Section R502.11.1, shall be submitted to the *building official* and *approved* prior to installation. Truss design drawings shall be provided with the shipment of trusses delivered to the job site. Truss design drawings shall include, at a minimum, the information specified as follows:

1. Slope or depth, span and spacing.

2. Location of all joints.

3. Required bearing widths.

4. Design loads as applicable:

    4.1. Top chord live load.

    4.2. Top chord dead load.

    4.3. Bottom chord live load.

    4.4. Bottom chord dead load.

    4.5. Concentrated loads and their points of application.

    4.6. Controlling wind and earthquake loads.

5. Adjustments to lumber and joint connector design values for conditions of use.

6. Each reaction force and direction.

7. Joint connector type and description, such as size, thickness or gage, and the dimensioned location of each joint connector except where symmetrically located relative to the joint interface.

8. Lumber size, species and grade for each member.

9. Connection requirements for:

    9.1. Truss-to-girder-truss.

    9.2. Truss ply-to-ply.

    9.3. Field splices.

10. Calculated deflection ratio, maximum description for live and total load, or both.

11. Maximum axial compression forces in the truss members to enable the building designer to design the size, connections and anchorage of the permanent continuous lateral bracing. Forces shall be shown on the truss drawing or on supplemental documents.

12. Required permanent truss member bracing location.

R502.12 Draftstopping required. Draftstopping shall be provided in accordance with Section R302.12.

R502.13 Fireblocking required. Fireblocking shall be provided in accordance with Section R302.11.

SECTION R503
FLOOR SHEATHING

R503.1 Lumber sheathing. Maximum allowable spans for lumber used as floor sheathing shall conform to Tables R503.1, R503.2.1.1(1) and R503.2.1.1(2).

TABLE R503.1
MINIMUM THICKNESS OF LUMBER FLOOR SHEATHING

JOIST OR BEAM SPACING (inches)	MINIMUM NET THICKNESS	
	Perpendicular to joist	Diagonal to joist
24	$^{11}/_{16}$	$^{3}/_{4}$
16	$^{5}/_{8}$	$^{5}/_{8}$
48[a]		
54[b]	$1^{1}/_{2}$ T & G	N/A
60[c]		

For SI: 1 inch = 25.4 mm, 1 pound per square inch = 6.895 kPa.

N/A = Not Applicable.

a. For this support spacing, lumber sheathing shall have a minimum F_b of 675 and minimum E of 1,100,000 (see ANSI AWC NDS).

b. For this support spacing, lumber sheathing shall have a minimum F_b of 765 and minimum E of 1,400,000 (see ANSI AWC NDS).

c. For this support spacing, lumber sheathing shall have a minimum F_b of 855 and minimum E of 1,700,000 (see ANSI AWC NDS).

R503.1.1 End joints. End joints in lumber used as subflooring shall occur over supports unless end-matched lumber is used, in which case each piece shall bear on not less than two joists. Subflooring shall be permitted to be omitted where joist spacing does not exceed 16 inches (406 mm) and a 1-inch (25 mm) nominal tongue-and-groove wood strip flooring is applied perpendicular to the joists.

R503.2 Wood structural panel sheathing.

R503.2.1 Identification and grade. Wood structural panel sheathing used for structural purposes shall conform to CSA O325, CSA O437 DOC PS 1 or DOC PS 2. Panels shall be identified for grade, bond classification and Performance Category by a grade mark or certificate of inspection issued by an approved agency. The Performance Category value shall be used as the "nominal panel thickness" or "panel thickness" wherever referenced in this code

R503.2.1.1 Subfloor and combined subfloor underlayment. Where used as subflooring or combination subfloor underlayment, wood structural panels shall be of one of the grades specified in Table R503.2.1.1(1). Where sanded plywood is used as combination subfloor underlayment, the grade, bond classification, and Performance Category shall be as specified in Table R503.2.1.1(2).

TABLE R503.2.1.1(2)
ALLOWABLE SPANS FOR SANDED
PLYWOOD COMBINATION SUBFLOOR UNDERLAYMENT[a]

IDENTIFICATION	SPACING OF JOISTS (inches)		
	16	20	24
Species group[b]	—	—	—
1	$^1/_2$	$^5/_8$	$^3/_4$
2, 3	$^5/_8$	$^3/_4$	$^7/_8$
4	$^3/_4$	$^7/_8$	1

For SI: 1 inch = 25.4 mm, 1 pound per square foot = 0.0479 kPa.

a. Plywood continuous over two or more spans and face grain perpendicular to supports. Unsupported edges shall be tongue-and-groove or blocked except where nominal $^1/_4$-inch-thick wood panel-type underlayment, fiber-cement underlayment or $^3/_4$-inch wood finish floor is used. Fiber-cement underlayment shall comply with ASTM C1288 or ISO 8336 Category C.

Allowable uniform live load at maximum span based on deflection of $^1/_{360}$ of span is 100 psf.

b. Applicable to all grades of sanded exterior-type plywood.

R503.2.2 Allowable spans. The maximum allowable span for wood structural panels used as subfloor or combination subfloor underlayment shall be as set forth in Table R503.2.1.1(1), or APA E30. The maximum span for sanded plywood combination subfloor underlayment shall be as set forth in Table R503.2.1.1(2).

R503.2.3 Installation. Wood structural panels used as subfloor or combination subfloor underlayment shall be attached to wood framing in accordance with Table R602.3(1) and shall be attached to cold-formed steel framing in accordance with Table R505.3.1(2).

TABLE R503.2.1.1(1)
ALLOWABLE SPANS AND LOADS FOR WOOD STRUCTURAL PANELS FOR ROOF AND
SUBFLOOR SHEATHING AND COMBINATION SUBFLOOR UNDERLAYMENT[a, b, c]

SPAN RATING	MINIMUM NOMINAL PANEL THICKNESS (inch)	ALLOWABLE LIVE LOAD (psf)[h, l]		MAXIMUM SPAN (inches)		LOAD (pounds per square foot, at maximum span)		MAXIMUM SPAN (inches)
		SPAN @ 16" o.c.	SPAN @ 24" o.c.	With edge support[d]	Without edge support	Total load	Live load	
Sheathing[e]				Roof[f]				Subfloor[j]
16/0	$^3/_8$	30	—	16	16	40	30	0
20/0	$^3/_8$	50	—	20	20	40	30	0
24/0	$^3/_8$	100	30	24	20[g]	40	30	0
24/16	$^7/_{16}$	100	40	24	24	50	40	16
32/16	$^{15}/_{32}, ^1/_2$	180	70	32	28	40	30	16[h]
40/20	$^{19}/_{32}, ^5/_8$	305	130	40	32	40	30	20[h, i]
48/24	$^{23}/_{32}, ^3/_4$	—	175	48	36	45	35	24
60/32	$^7/_8$	—	305	60	48	45	35	32
Underlayment, C-C plugged, single floor[e]				Roof[f]				Combination subfloor underlayment[k]
16 o.c.	$^{19}/_{32}, ^5/_8$	100	40	24	24	50	40	16[i]
20 o.c.	$^{19}/_{32}, ^5/_8$	150	60	32	32	40	30	20[i, j]
24 o.c.	$^{23}/_{32}, ^3/_4$	240	100	48	36	35	25	24
32 o.c.	$^7/_8$	—	185	48	40	50	40	32
48 o.c.	$1^3/_{32}, 1^1/_8$	—	290	60	48	50	40	48

For SI: 1 inch = 25.4 mm, 1 pound per square foot = 0.0479 kPa.

a. The allowable total loads were determined using a dead load of 10 psf. If the dead load exceeds 10 psf, then the live load shall be reduced accordingly.

b. Panels continuous over two or more spans with long dimension (strength axis) perpendicular to supports. Spans shall be limited to values shown because of possible effect of concentrated loads.

c. Applies to panels 24 inches or wider.

d. Lumber blocking, panel edge clips (one midway between each support, except two equally spaced between supports where span is 48 inches), tongue-and-groove panel edges, or other approved type of edge support.

e. Includes Structural I panels in these grades.

f. Uniform load deflection limitation: $^1/_{180}$ of span under live load plus dead load, $^1/_{240}$ of span under live load only.

g. Maximum span 24 inches for $^{15}/_{32}$- and $^1/_2$-inch panels.

h. Maximum span 24 inches where $^3/_4$-inch wood finish flooring is installed at right angles to joists.

i. Maximum span 24 inches where 1.5 inches of lightweight concrete or approved cellular concrete is placed over the subfloor.

j. Unsupported edges shall have tongue-and-groove joints or shall be supported with blocking unless minimum nominal $^1/_4$-inch-thick wood panel-type underlayment, fiber-cement underlayment with end and edge joints offset not less than 2 inches or $1^1/_2$ inches of lightweight concrete or approved cellular concrete is placed over the subfloor, or $^3/_4$-inch wood finish flooring is installed at right angles to the supports. Fiber-cement underlayment shall comply with ASTM C1288 or ISO 8336 Category C. Allowable uniform live load at maximum span, based on deflection of $^1/_{360}$ of span, is 100 psf.

k. Unsupported edges shall have tongue-and-groove joints or shall be supported by blocking unless nominal $^1/_4$-inch-thick wood panel-type underlayment, fiber-cement underlayment with end and edge joints offset not less than 2 inches or $^3/_4$-inch wood finish flooring is installed at right angles to the supports. Fiber-cement underlayment shall comply with ASTM C1288 or ISO 8336 Category C. Allowable uniform live load at maximum span, based on deflection of $^1/_{360}$ of span, is 100 psf, except panels with a span rating of 48 on center are limited to 65 psf total uniform load at maximum span.

l. Allowable live load values at spans of 16 inches on center and 24 inches on center taken from reference standard APA E30, APA Engineered Wood Construction Guide. Refer to reference standard for allowable spans not listed in the table.

R503.3 Particleboard.

R503.3.1 Identification and grade. Particleboard shall conform to ANSI A208.1 and shall be so identified by a grade *mark* or certificate of inspection issued by an *approved agency*.

R503.3.2 Floor underlayment. Particleboard floor underlayment shall conform to Type PBU and shall be not less than $^1/_4$ inch (6.4 mm) in thickness.

R503.3.3 Installation. Particleboard underlayment shall be installed in accordance with the recommendations of the manufacturer and attached to framing in accordance with Table R602.3(1).

SECTION R504
PRESSURE PRESERVATIVE-TREATED WOOD FLOORS (ON GROUND)

R504.1 General. Pressure preservative-treated wood *basement* floors and floors on ground shall be designed to withstand axial forces and bending moments resulting from lateral soil pressures at the base of the exterior walls and floor live and dead loads. Floor framing shall be designed to meet joist deflection requirements in accordance with Section R301.

R504.1.1 Unbalanced soil loads. Unless special provision is made to resist sliding caused by unbalanced lateral soil loads, wood *basement* floors shall be limited to applications where the differential depth of fill on opposite exterior foundation walls is 2 feet (610 mm) or less.

R504.1.2 Construction. Joists in wood *basement* floors shall bear tightly against the narrow face of studs in the foundation wall or directly against a band joist that bears on the studs. Plywood subfloor shall be continuous over lapped joists or over butt joints between in-line joists. Sufficient blocking shall be provided between joists to transfer lateral forces at the base of the end walls into the floor system.

R504.1.3 Uplift and buckling. Where required, resistance to uplift or restraint against buckling shall be provided by interior bearing walls or properly designed stub walls anchored in the supporting soil below.

R504.2 Site preparation. The area within the foundation walls shall have all vegetation, topsoil and foreign material removed, and any fill material that is added shall be free of vegetation and foreign material. The fill shall be compacted to ensure uniform support of the pressure preservative-treated wood floor sleepers.

R504.2.1 Base. A minimum 4-inch-thick (102 mm) granular base of gravel having a maximum size of $^3/_4$ inch (19.1 mm) or crushed stone having a maximum size of $^1/_2$ inch (12.7 mm) shall be placed over the compacted earth.

R504.2.2 Moisture barrier. Polyethylene sheeting of minimum 6-mil (0.15 mm) thickness shall be placed over the granular base. Joints shall be lapped 6 inches (152 mm) and left unsealed. The polyethylene membrane shall be placed over the pressure preservative-treated wood sleepers and shall not extend beneath the footing plates of the exterior walls.

R504.3 Materials. Framing materials, including sleepers, joists, blocking and plywood subflooring, shall be pressure-preservative treated and dried after treatment in accordance with AWPA U1 (Commodity Specification A, Special Requirement 4.2), and shall bear the *label* of an accredited agency.

SECTION R505
COLD-FORMED STEEL FLOOR FRAMING

R505.1 Cold-formed steel floor framing. Elements shall be straight and free of any defects that would significantly affect structural performance. Cold-formed steel floor framing members shall be in accordance with the requirements of this section.

R505.1.1 Applicability limits. The provisions of this section shall control the construction of cold-formed steel floor framing for buildings not greater than 60 feet (18 288 mm) in length perpendicular to the joist span, not greater than 40 feet (12 192 mm) in width parallel to the joist span and less than or equal to three stories above grade plane. Cold-formed steel floor framing constructed in accordance with the provisions of this section shall be limited to sites where the ultimate design wind speed is less than 140 miles per hour (63 m/s), Exposure Category B or C, and the ground snow load is less than or equal to 70 pounds per square foot (3.35 kPa).

R505.1.2 In-line framing. Where supported by cold-formed steel-framed walls in accordance with Section R603, cold-formed steel floor framing shall be constructed with floor joists located in-line with load-bearing studs located below the joists in accordance with Figure R505.1.2 and the tolerances specified as follows:

1. The maximum tolerance shall be $^3/_4$ inch (19.1 mm) between the centerline of the horizontal framing member and the centerline of the vertical framing member.

2. Where the centerline of the horizontal framing member and bearing stiffener are located to one side of the centerline of the vertical framing member, the maximum tolerance shall be $^1/_8$ inch (3 mm) between the web of the horizontal framing member and the edge of the vertical framing member.

R505.1.3 Floor trusses. Cold-formed steel trusses shall be designed, braced and installed in accordance with AISI S240. In the absence of specific bracing requirements, trusses shall be braced in accordance with accepted industry practices, such as the SBCA *Cold-Formed Steel Building Component Safety Information (CFSBCSI), Guide to Good Practice for Handling, Installing & Bracing of Cold-Formed Steel Trusses.* Truss members shall not be notched, cut or altered in any manner without an *approved* design.

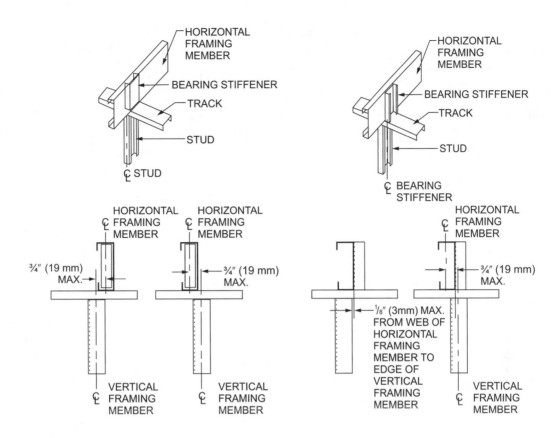

For SI: 1 inch = 25.4 mm.

FIGURE R505.1.2
IN-LINE FRAMING

R505.2 Structural framing. Load-bearing cold-formed steel floor framing members shall be in accordance with this section.

R505.2.1 Material. Load-bearing cold-formed steel framing members shall be cold formed to shape from structural quality sheet steel complying with the requirements of ASTM A1003: Structural Grades 33 Type H and 50 Type H.

R505.2.2 Corrosion protection. Load-bearing cold-formed steel framing shall have a metallic coating complying with ASTM A1003 and one of the following:

1. Not less than G 60 in accordance with ASTM A653.

2. Not less than AZ 50 in accordance with ASTM A792.

R505.2.3 Dimension, thickness and material grade. Load-bearing cold-formed steel floor framing members shall comply with Figure R505.2.3(1) and with the dimensional and thickness requirements specified in Table R505.2.3. Additionally, all C-shaped sections shall have a minimum flange width of 1.625 inches (41 mm) and a maximum flange width of 2 inches (51 mm). The minimum lip size for C-shaped sections shall be $^1/_2$ inch (12.7 mm). Track sections shall comply with Figure R505.2.3(2) and shall have a minimum flange width of $1^1/_4$ inch (32

mm). Minimum Grade 33 ksi steel shall be used wherever 33 mil and 43 mil thicknesses are specified. Minimum Grade 50 ksi steel shall be used wherever 54 and 68 mil thicknesses are specified.

R505.2.4 Identification. Load-bearing cold-formed steel framing members shall have a legible *label*, stencil, stamp or embossment with the following information as a minimum:

1. Manufacturer's identification.

2. Minimum base steel thickness in inches (mm).

3. Minimum coating designation.

4. Minimum yield strength, in kips per square inch (ksi) (MPa).

R505.2.5 Fastening. Screws for steel-to-steel connections shall be installed with a minimum edge distance and center-to-center spacing of $^1/_2$ inch (12.7 mm), shall be self-drilling tapping, and shall conform to ASTM C1513. Floor sheathing shall be attached to cold-formed steel joists with minimum No. 8 self-drilling tapping screws that conform to ASTM C1513. Screws attaching floor sheathing to cold-formed steel joists shall have a minimum head diameter of 0.292 inch (7.4 mm) with countersunk heads and shall be installed with a minimum edge distance of $^3/_8$ inch (9.5 mm). Gypsum board ceilings shall be attached to cold-

TABLE R505.2.3
COLD-FORMED STEEL JOIST SIZES AND THICKNESS

MEMBER DESIGNATION[a]	WEB DEPTH (inches)	MINIMUM BASE STEEL THICKNESS mil (inches)
550S162-t	5.5	33 (0.0329), 43 (0.0428), 54 (0.0538), 68 (0.0677)
800S162-t	8	33 (0.0329), 43 (0.0428), 54 (0.0538), 68 (0.0677)
1000S162-t	10	43 (0.0428), 54 (0.0538), 68 (0.0677)
1200S162-t	12	43 (0.0428), 54 (0.0538), 68 (0.0677)

For SI: 1 inch = 25.4 mm, 1 mil = 0.0254 mm.

a. The member designation is defined by the first number representing the member depth in 0.01 inch, the letter "S" representing a stud or joist member, the second number representing the flange width in 0.01 inch, and the letter "t" shall be a number representing the minimum base metal thickness in mils.

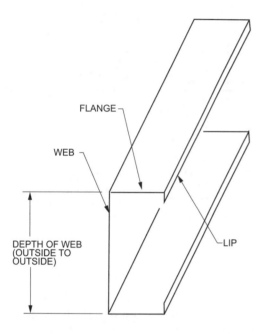

FIGURE R505.2.3(1)
C-SHAPED SECTION

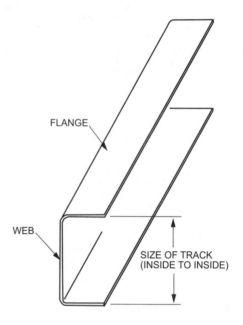

FIGURE R505.2.3(2)
TRACK SECTION

formed steel joists with minimum No. 6 screws conforming to ASTM C954 or ASTM C1513 with a bugle-head style and shall be installed in accordance with Section R702. For all connections, screws shall extend through the steel not fewer than three exposed threads. Fasteners shall have a rust-inhibitive coating suitable for the installation in which they are being used, or be manufactured from material not susceptible to corrosion.

R505.2.6 Web holes, web hole reinforcing and web hole patching. Web holes, web hole reinforcing, and web hole patching shall be in accordance with this section.

R505.2.6.1 Web holes. Web holes in floor joists shall comply with all of the following conditions:

1. Holes shall conform to Figure R505.2.6.1.

2. Holes shall be permitted only along the centerline of the web of the framing member.

3. Holes shall have a center-to-center spacing of not less than 24 inches (610 mm).

4. Holes shall have a web hole width not greater than 0.5 times the member depth, or $2^1/_2$ inches (64.5 mm).

5. Holes shall have a web hole length not exceeding $4^1/_2$ inches (114 mm).

6. Holes shall have a minimum distance between the edge of the bearing surface and the edge of the web hole of not less than 10 inches (254 mm).

Framing members with web holes not conforming to these requirements shall be reinforced in accordance with Section R505.2.6.2, patched in accordance with Section R505.2.6.3 or designed in accordance with accepted engineering practices.

R505.2.6.2 Web hole reinforcing. Reinforcement of web holes in floor joists not conforming to the requirements of Section R505.2.6.1 shall be permitted if the hole is located fully within the center 40 percent of the span and the depth and length of the hole does not exceed 65 percent of the flat width of the web. The reinforcing shall

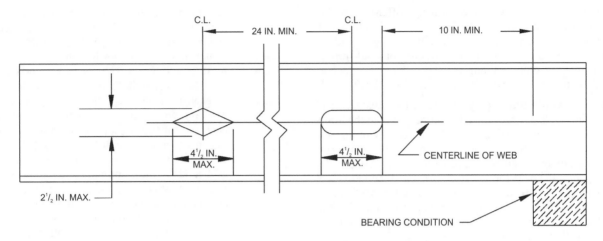

For SI: 1 inch = 25.4 mm.

FIGURE R505.2.6.1
FLOOR JOIST WEB HOLES

be a steel plate or C-shaped section with a hole that does not exceed the web hole size limitations of Section R505.2.6.1 for the member being reinforced. The steel reinforcing shall be not thinner than the thickness of the receiving member and shall extend not less than 1 inch (25 mm) beyond all edges of the hole. The steel reinforcing shall be fastened to the web of the receiving member with No. 8 screws spaced not more than 1 inch (25 mm) center-to-center along the edges of the patch with minimum edge distance of $^1/_2$ inch (12.7 mm).

R505.2.6.3 Hole patching. Patching of web holes in floor joists not conforming to the requirements in Section R505.2.6.1 shall be permitted in accordance with either of the following methods:

1. Framing members shall be replaced or designed in accordance with accepted engineering practices where web holes exceed the following size limits:

   1.1. The depth of the hole, measured across the web, exceeds 70 percent of the flat width of the web.

   1.2. The length of the hole, measured along the web, exceeds 10 inches (254 mm) or the depth of the web, whichever is greater.

2. Web holes not exceeding the dimensional requirements in Section R505.2.6.3, Item 1, shall be patched with a solid steel plate, stud section or track section in accordance with Figure R505.2.6.3. The steel patch shall, as a minimum, be of the same thickness as the receiving member and shall extend not less than 1 inch (25 mm) beyond all edges of the hole. The steel patch shall be fastened to the web of the receiving member with No. 8 screws spaced not more than 1 inch (25 mm) center-to-center along the edges of the patch with minimum edge distance of $^1/_2$ inch (12.7 mm).

R505.3 Floor construction. Cold-formed steel floors shall be constructed in accordance with this section.

R505.3.1 Floor-to-foundation or load-bearing wall connections. Cold-formed steel-framed floors shall be anchored to foundations, wood sills or load-bearing walls in accordance with Table R505.3.1(1) and Figure R505.3.1(1), R505.3.1(2), R505.3.1(3), R505.3.1(4), R505.3.1(5) or R505.3.1(6). Anchor bolts shall be located not more than 12 inches (305 mm) from corners or the termination of bottom tracks. Continuous cold-formed steel joists supported by interior load-bearing walls shall be constructed in accordance with Figure R505.3.1(7). Lapped cold-formed steel joists shall be constructed in accordance with Figure R505.3.1(8). End floor joists constructed on foundation walls parallel to the joist span shall

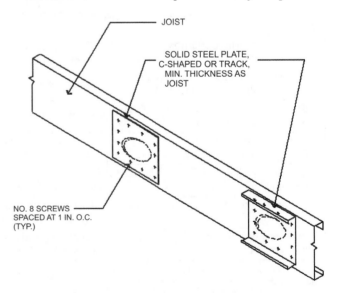

For SI: 1 inch = 25.4 mm.

FIGURE R505.2.6.3
FLOOR JOIST WEB HOLE PATCH

be doubled unless a C-shaped bearing stiffener, sized in accordance with Section R505.3.4, is installed web-to-web with the floor joist beneath each supported wall stud, as shown in Figure R505.3.1(9). Fastening of cold-formed steel joists to other framing members shall be in accordance with Section R505.2.5 and Table R505.3.1(2).

R505.3.2 Minimum floor joist sizes. Floor joist size and thickness shall be determined in accordance with the limits set forth in Table R505.3.2 for single or continuous spans. Where continuous joist members are used, the interior bearing supports shall be located within 2 feet (610 mm) of midspan of the cold-formed steel joists, and the individual spans shall not exceed the spans in Table R505.3.2. Floor joists shall have a bearing support length of not less than $1^1/_2$ inches (38 mm) for exterior wall supports and $3^1/_2$ inches (89 mm) for interior wall supports. Tracks shall be not less than 33 mils (0.84 mm) thick except where used as part of a floor header or trimmer in accordance with Section R505.3.8. Bearing stiffeners shall be installed in accordance with Section R505.3.4.

R505.3.3 Joist bracing and blocking. Joist bracing and blocking shall be in accordance with this section.

R505.3.3.1 Joist top flange bracing. The top flanges of cold-formed steel joists shall be laterally braced by the application of floor sheathing fastened to the joists in accordance with Section R505.2.5 and Table R505.3.1(2).

R505.3.3.2 Joist bottom flange bracing/blocking. Floor joists with spans that exceed 12 feet (3658 mm) shall have the bottom flanges laterally braced in accordance with one of the following:

1. Gypsum board installed with minimum No. 6 screws in accordance with Section R702.

2. Continuous steel straps installed in accordance with Figure R505.3.3.2(1). Steel straps shall be spaced at not greater than 12 feet (3658 mm) on center and shall be not less than $1^1/_2$ inches (38 mm) in width and 33 mils (0.84 mm) in thickness. Straps shall be fastened to the bottom flange of each joist with one No. 8 screw, fastened to blocking with two No. 8 screws, and fastened at each end (of strap) with two No. 8 screws. Blocking in accordance with Figure R505.3.3.2(1) or R505.3.3.2(2) shall be installed between joists at each end of the continuous strapping and at a maximum spacing of 12 feet (3658 mm) measured along the continuous strapping (perpendicular to the joist run). Blocking shall also be located at the termination of all straps. As an alternative to blocking at the ends, anchoring the strap to a stable building component with two No. 8 screws shall be permitted.

R505.3.3.3 Blocking at interior bearing supports. Blocking is not required for continuous back-to-back floor joists at bearing supports. Blocking shall be installed between every other joist for single continuous floor joists across bearing supports in accordance with Figure R505.3.1(7). Blocking shall consist of C-shaped or track section with a minimum thickness of 33 mils (0.84 mm). Blocking shall be fastened to each adjacent joist through a 33-mil (0.84 mm) clip angle, bent web of blocking or flanges of web stiffeners with two No. 8 screws on each side. The minimum depth of the blocking shall be equal to the depth of the joist minus 2 inches (51 mm). The minimum length of the angle shall be equal to the depth of the joist minus 2 inches (51 mm).

TABLE R505.3.1(1)
FLOOR-TO-FOUNDATION OR BEARING WALL CONNECTION REQUIREMENTS[a, b]

FRAMING CONDITION	BASIC ULTIMATE WIND SPEED (mph) AND EXPOSURE	
	110 mph Exposure Category C or less than 139 mph Exposure Category B	Less than 139 mph Exposure Category C
Floor joist to wall track of exterior wall in accordance with Figure R505.3.1(1)	2-No. 8 screws	3-No. 8 screws
Rim track or end joist to load-bearing wall top track in accordance with Figure R505.3.1(1)	1-No. 8 screw at 24 inches o.c.	1-No. 8 screw at 24 inches o.c.
Rim track or end joist to wood sill in accordance with Figure R505.3.1(2)	Steel plate spaced at 4 feet o.c. with 4-No. 8 screws and 4-10d or 6-8d common nails	Steel plate spaced at 2 feet o.c. with 4-No. 8 screws and 4-10d or 6-8d common nails
Rim track or end joist to foundation in accordance with Figure R505.3.1(3)	$1/_2$-inch minimum diameter anchor bolt and clip angle spaced at 6 feet o.c. with 8-No. 8 screws	$1/_2$-inch minimum diameter anchor bolt and clip angle spaced at 4 feet o.c. with 8-No. 8 screws
Cantilevered joist to foundation in accordance with Figure R505.3.1(4)	$1/_2$-inch minimum diameter anchor bolt and clip angle spaced at 6 feet o.c. with 8-No. 8 screws	$1/_2$-inch minimum diameter anchor bolt and clip angle spaced at 4 feet o.c. with 8-No. 8 screws
Cantilevered joist to wood sill in accordance with Figure R505.3.1(5)	Steel plate spaced at 4 feet o.c. with 4-No. 8 screws and 4-10d or 6-8d common nails	Steel plate spaced at 2 feet o.c. with 4-No. 8 screws and 4-10d or 6-8d common nails
Cantilevered joist to exterior load-bearing wall track in accordance with Figure R505.3.1(6)	2-No. 8 screws	3-No. 8 screws

For SI: 1 inch = 25.4 mm, 1 pound per square foot = 0.0479 kPa, 1 mile per hour = 0.447 m/s, 1 foot = 304.8 mm.

a. Anchor bolts are to be located not more than 12 inches from corners or the termination of bottom tracks such as at door openings or corners. Bolts extend not less than 15 inches into masonry or 7 inches into concrete. Anchor bolts connecting cold-formed steel framing to the foundation structure are to be installed so that the distance from the center of the bolt hole to the edge of the connected member is not less than one and one-half bolt diameters.

b. All screw sizes shown are minimum.

TABLE R505.3.1(2)
FLOOR FASTENING SCHEDULE[a]

DESCRIPTION OF BUILDING ELEMENTS	NUMBER AND SIZE OF FASTENERS	SPACING OF FASTENERS
Floor joist to track of an interior load-bearing wall in accordance with Figures R505.3.1(7) and R505.3.1(8)	2 No. 8 screws	Each joist
Floor joist to track at end of joist	2 No. 8 screws	One per flange or two per bearing stiffener
Subfloor to floor joists	No. 8 screws	6 in. o.c. on edges and 12 in. o.c. at intermediate supports

For SI: 1 inch = 25.4 mm.

a. All screw sizes shown are minimum.

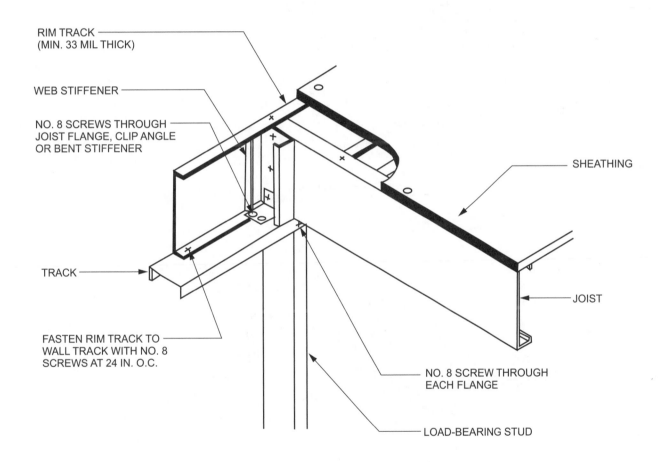

For SI: 1 mil = 0.0254 mm, 1 inch = 25.4 mm.

FIGURE R505.3.1(1)
FLOOR-TO-EXTERIOR LOAD-BEARING WALL STUD CONNECTION

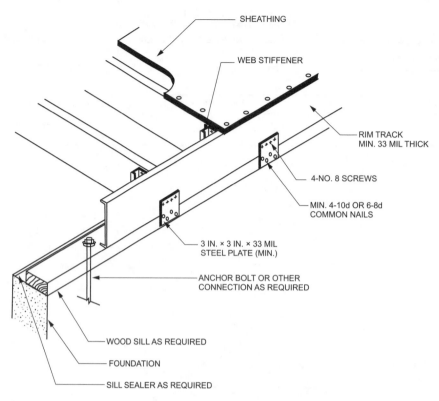

For SI: 1 mil = 0.0254 mm, 1 inch = 25.4 mm.

FIGURE R505.3.1(2)
FLOOR-TO-WOOD-SILL CONNECTION

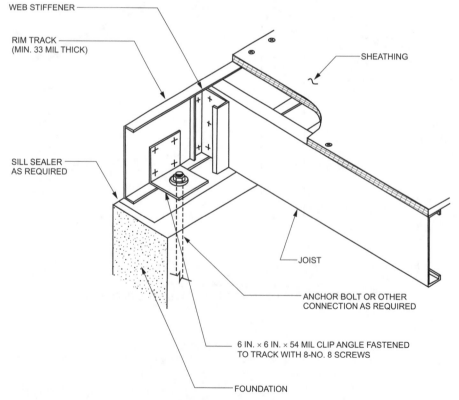

For SI: 1 mil = 0.0254 mm, 1 inch = 25.4 mm.

FIGURE R505.3.1(3)
FLOOR-TO-FOUNDATION CONNECTION

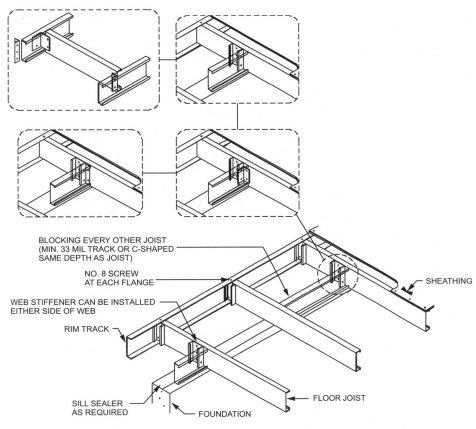

For SI: 1 mil = 0.0254 mm.

FIGURE R505.3.1(4)
CANTILEVERED FLOOR-TO-FOUNDATION CONNECTION

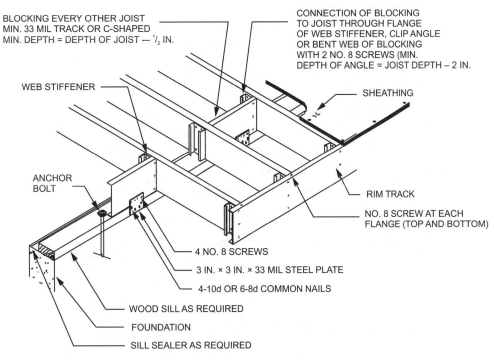

For SI: 1 mil = 0.0254 mm, 1 inch = 25.4 mm.

FIGURE R505.3.1(5)
CANTILEVERED FLOOR-TO-WOOD-SILL CONNECTION

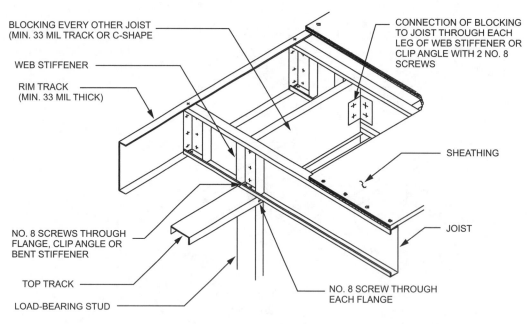

BLOCKING EVERY OTHER JOIST
(MIN. 33 MIL TRACK OR C-SHAPE

WEB STIFFENER

RIM TRACK
(MIN. 33 MIL THICK)

CONNECTION OF BLOCKING
TO JOIST THROUGH EACH
LEG OF WEB STIFFENER OR
CLIP ANGLE WITH 2 NO. 8
SCREWS

SHEATHING

NO. 8 SCREWS THROUGH
FLANGE, CLIP ANGLE OR
BENT STIFFENER

TOP TRACK

LOAD-BEARING STUD

JOIST

NO. 8 SCREW THROUGH
EACH FLANGE

For SI: 1 mil = 0.0254 mm.

FIGURE R505.3.1(6)
CANTILEVERED FLOOR TO EXTERIOR LOAD-BEARING WALL CONNECTION

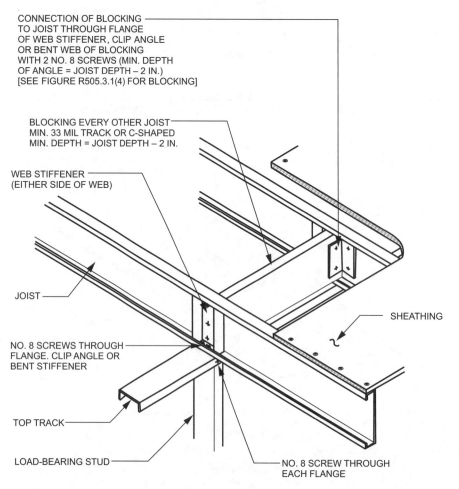

CONNECTION OF BLOCKING
TO JOIST THROUGH FLANGE
OF WEB STIFFENER, CLIP ANGLE
OR BENT WEB OF BLOCKING
WITH 2 NO. 8 SCREWS (MIN. DEPTH
OF ANGLE = JOIST DEPTH – 2 IN.)
[SEE FIGURE R505.3.1(4) FOR BLOCKING]

BLOCKING EVERY OTHER JOIST
MIN. 33 MIL TRACK OR C-SHAPED
MIN. DEPTH = JOIST DEPTH – 2 IN.

WEB STIFFENER
(EITHER SIDE OF WEB)

JOIST

SHEATHING

NO. 8 SCREWS THROUGH
FLANGE. CLIP ANGLE OR
BENT STIFFENER

TOP TRACK

LOAD-BEARING STUD

NO. 8 SCREW THROUGH
EACH FLANGE

For SI: 1 mil = 0.0254 mm, 1 inch = 25.4 mm.

FIGURE R505.3.1(7)
CONTINUOUS SPAN JOIST SUPPORTED ON INTERIOR LOAD-BEARING WALL

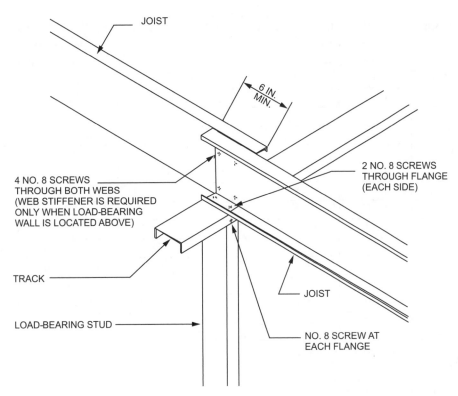

For SI: 1 inch = 25.4 mm.

FIGURE R505.3.1(8)
LAPPED JOISTS SUPPORTED ON INTERIOR LOAD-BEARING WALL

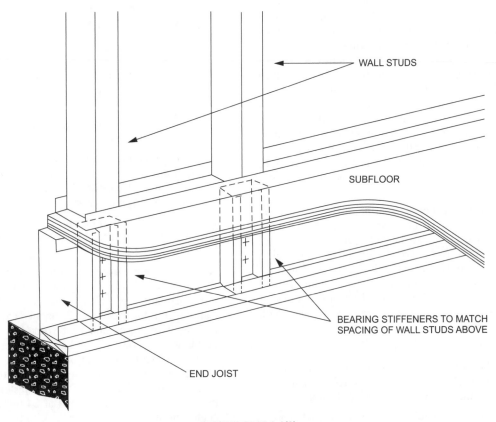

FIGURE R505.3.1(9)
BEARING STIFFENERS FOR END JOISTS

TABLE R505.3.2
ALLOWABLE SPANS FOR COLD-FORMED STEEL JOISTS—SINGLE OR CONTINUOUS SPANS[a, b, c, d, e, f]

JOIST DESIGNATION	30 PSF LIVE LOAD				40 PSF LIVE LOAD			
	Spacing (inches)				Spacing (inches)			
	12	16	19.2	24	12	16	19.2	24
550S162-33	11'-8"	10'-4"	9'-5"	8'-5"	10'-7"	9'-2"	8'-5"	7'-6"
550S162-43	12'-8"	11'-6"	10'-8"	10'-5"	11'-6"	10'-4"	9'-10"	9'-3"
550S162-54	13'-7"	12'-4"	11'-7"	10'-9"	12'-4"	11'-3"	10'-7"	9'-10"
550S162-68	14'-7"	13'-3"	12'-6"	11'-7"	13'-3"	12'-0"	11'-4"	10'-6"
800S162-33	14'-6"	12'-6"	11'-5"	10'-3"	12'-10"	11'-1"	10'-2"	9'-1"
800S162-43	17'-0"	15'-1"	13'-9"	12'-4"	15'-5"	13'-5"	12'-3"	10'-11"
800S162-54	18'-3"	16'-7"	15'-8"	14'-6"	16'-7"	15'-1"	14'-2"	13'-2"
800S162-68	19'-9"	17'-11"	16'-11"	15'-8"	17'-11"	16'-3"	15'-4"	14'-3"
1000S162-43	19'-4"	16'-9"	15'-3"	13'-8"	17'-2"	14'-10"	13'-7"	12'-2"
1000S162-54	21'-9"	19'-9"	18'-7"	17'-3"	19'-9"	18'-0"	16'-11"	15'-8"
1000S162-68	23'-7"	21'-5"	20'-2"	18'-9"	21'-5"	19'-6"	18'-4"	17'-0"
1200S162-54	25'-1"	22'-10"	21'-6"	19'-9"	22'-10"	20'-9"	19'-6"	17'-6"
1200S162-68	27'-3"	24'-9"	23'-4"	21'-8"	24'-9"	22'-6"	21'-2"	19'-8"

For SI: 1 inch = 25.4 mm, 1 foot = 304.8 mm, 1 pound per square foot = 0.0479 kPa, 1 mil = 0.0254 mm.

a. Deflection criteria: L/480 for live loads, L/240 for total loads.
b. Floor dead load = 10 psf.
c. Table provides the maximum clear span in feet and inches.
d. Bearing stiffeners are to be installed at all support points and concentrated loads.
e. Minimum Grade 33 ksi steel shall be used for 33 mil and 43 mil thickness. Minimum Grade 50 ksi steel shall be used for 54 and 68 mil thickness.
f. Table R505.3.2 is not applicable for 800S162-33 and 1000S162-43 continuous joist members.

R505.3.3.4 Blocking at cantilevers. Blocking shall be installed between every other joist over cantilever bearing supports in accordance with Figure R505.3.1(4), R505.3.1(5) or R505.3.1(6). Blocking shall consist of C-shaped or track section with minimum thickness of 33 mils (0.84 mm). Blocking shall be fastened to each adjacent joist through bent web of blocking, 33 mil clip angle or flange of web stiffener with two No. 8 screws at each end. The depth of the blocking shall be equal to the depth of the joist. The minimum length of the angle shall be equal to the depth of the joist minus 2 inches (51 mm). Blocking shall be fastened through the floor sheathing and to the support with three No. 8 screws (top and bottom).

R505.3.4 Bearing stiffeners. Bearing stiffeners shall be installed at each joist bearing location in accordance with this section, except for joists lapped over an interior support not carrying a load-bearing wall above. Floor joists supporting jamb studs with multiple members shall have two bearing stiffeners in accordance with Figure R505.3.4(1). Bearing stiffeners shall be fabricated from a C-shaped, track or clip angle member in accordance with the one of following:

1. C-shaped bearing stiffeners:

    1.1. Where the joist is not carrying a load-bearing wall above, the bearing stiffener shall be a minimum 33 mil (0.84 mm) thickness.

    1.2. Where the joist is carrying a load-bearing wall above, the bearing stiffener shall be not

less than the same designation thickness as the wall stud above.

2. Track bearing stiffeners:

    2.1. Where the joist is not carrying a load-bearing wall above, the bearing stiffener shall be a minimum 43 mil (1.09 mm) thickness.

    2.2. Where the joist is carrying a load-bearing wall above, the bearing stiffener shall be not less than one designation thickness greater than the wall stud above.

The minimum length of a bearing stiffener shall be the depth of member being stiffened minus $3/8$ inch (9.5 mm). Each bearing stiffener shall be fastened to the web of the member it is stiffening as shown in Figure R505.3.4(2).

R505.3.5 Cutting and notching. Flanges and lips of load-bearing cold-formed steel floor framing members shall not be cut or notched.

R505.3.6 Floor cantilevers. Floor cantilevers for the top floor of a two- or three-story building or the first floor of a one-story building shall not exceed 24 inches (610 mm). Cantilevers, not exceeding 24 inches (610 mm) and supporting two stories and roof (first floor of a two-story building), shall be permitted provided that all cantilevered joists are doubled (nested or back-to-back). The doubled cantilevered joists shall extend not less than 6 feet (1829 mm) toward the inside and shall be fastened with not less than two No. 8 screws spaced at 24 inches (610 mm) on center through the webs (for back-to-back) or flanges (for nested joists).

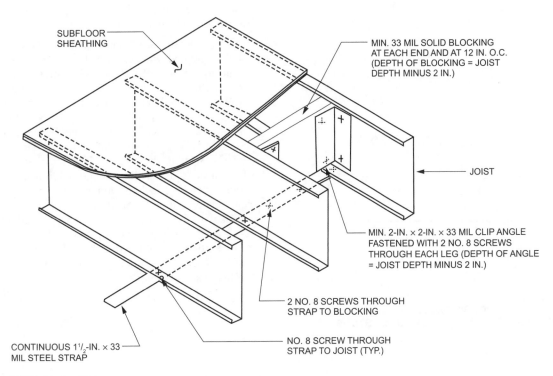

SUBFLOOR
SHEATHING

MIN. 33 MIL SOLID BLOCKING
AT EACH END AND AT 12 IN. O.C.
(DEPTH OF BLOCKING = JOIST
DEPTH MINUS 2 IN.)

JOIST

MIN. 2-IN. × 2-IN. × 33 MIL CLIP ANGLE
FASTENED WITH 2 NO. 8 SCREWS
THROUGH EACH LEG (DEPTH OF ANGLE
= JOIST DEPTH MINUS 2 IN.)

2 NO. 8 SCREWS THROUGH
STRAP TO BLOCKING

NO. 8 SCREW THROUGH
STRAP TO JOIST (TYP.)

CONTINUOUS 1½-IN. × 33
MIL STEEL STRAP

For SI: 1 mil = 0.0254, 1 inch = 25.4 mm.

FIGURE R505.3.3.2(1)
JOIST BLOCKING (SOLID)

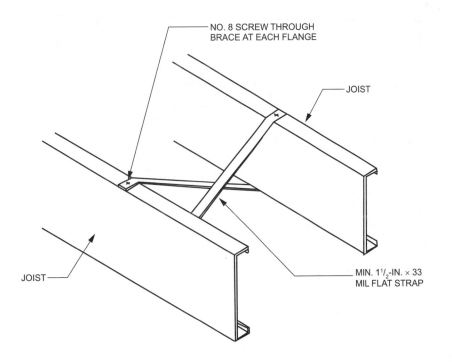

NO. 8 SCREW THROUGH
BRACE AT EACH FLANGE

JOIST

JOIST

MIN. 1½-IN. × 33
MIL FLAT STRAP

For SI: 1 mil = 0.0254, 1 inch = 25.4 mm.

FIGURE R505.3.3.2(2)
JOIST BLOCKING (STRAP)

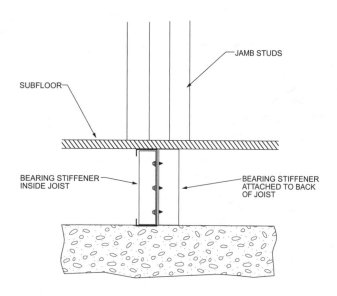

FIGURE R505.3.4(1)
BEARING STIFFENERS UNDER JAMB STUDS

R505.3.7 Splicing. Joists and other structural members shall not be spliced without an *approved* design. Splicing of tracks shall conform to Figure R505.3.7.

R505.3.8 Framing of floor openings. Openings in floors shall be framed with header and trimmer joists. Header joist spans shall not exceed 6 feet (1829 mm) or 8 feet (2438 mm) in length in accordance with Figure R505.3.8(1) or R505.3.8(2), respectively. Header and trimmer joists shall be fabricated from joist and track members, having a minimum size and thickness at least equivalent to the adjacent floor joists, and shall be installed in accordance with Figures R505.3.8(1), R505.3.8(2), R505.3.8(3) and R505.3.8(4). Each header joist shall be connected to trimmer joists with four 2-inch by 2-inch (51-mm by 51-mm) clip angles. Each clip angle shall be fastened to both the header and trimmer joists with four No. 8 screws, evenly spaced, through each leg of the clip angle. The clip angles shall have a thickness not less than that of the floor joist. Each track section for a built-up header or trimmer joist shall extend the full length of the joist (continuous).

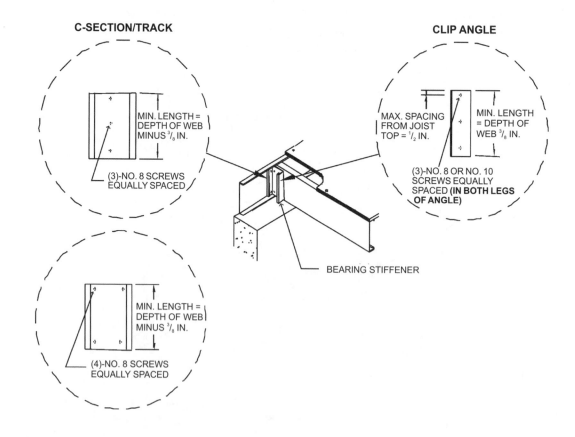

For SI: 1 inch = 25.4 mm.

FIGURE R505.3.4(2)
BEARING STIFFENER

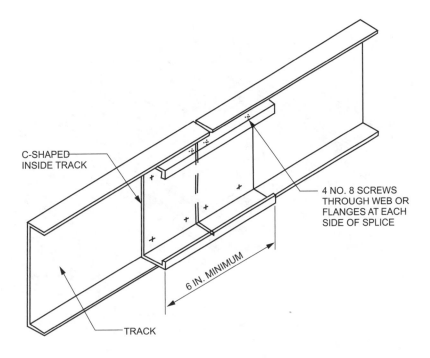

For SI: 1 inch = 25.4 mm.

FIGURE R505.3.7
TRACK SPLICE

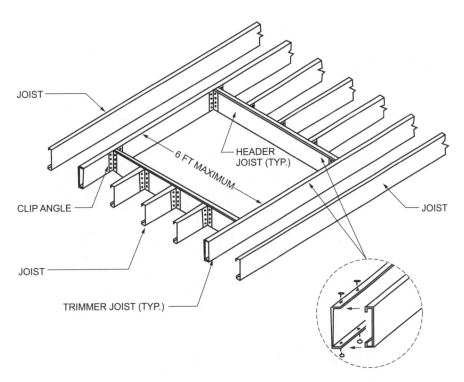

For SI: 1 foot = 304.8 mm.

FIGURE R505.3.8(1)
COLD-FORMED STEEL FLOOR CONSTRUCTION—6-FOOT FLOOR OPENING

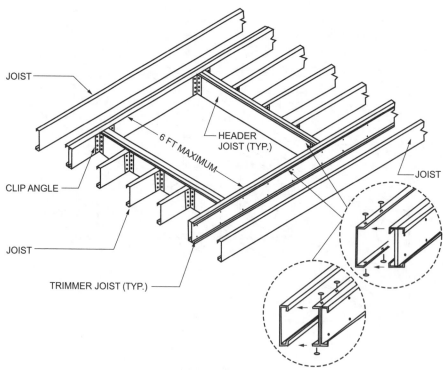

JOIST

HEADER
JOIST (TYP.)

6 FT MAXIMUM

CLIP ANGLE

JOIST

JOIST

TRIMMER JOIST (TYP.)

For SI: 1 foot = 304.8 mm.

FIGURE R505.3.8(2)
COLD-FORMED STEEL FLOOR CONSTRUCTION—8-FOOT FLOOR OPENING

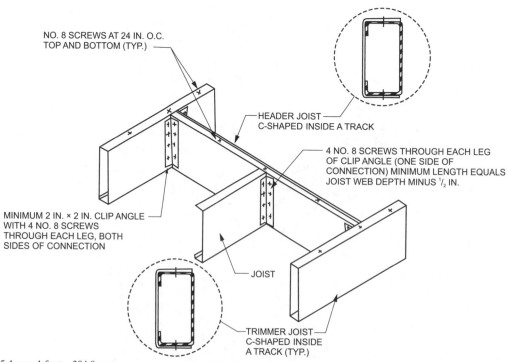

NO. 8 SCREWS AT 24 IN. O.C.
TOP AND BOTTOM (TYP.)

HEADER JOIST
C-SHAPED INSIDE A TRACK

4 NO. 8 SCREWS THROUGH EACH LEG
OF CLIP ANGLE (ONE SIDE OF
CONNECTION) MINIMUM LENGTH EQUALS
JOIST WEB DEPTH MINUS $^{1}/_{2}$ IN.

MINIMUM 2 IN. × 2 IN. CLIP ANGLE
WITH 4 NO. 8 SCREWS
THROUGH EACH LEG, BOTH
SIDES OF CONNECTION

JOIST

TRIMMER JOIST
C-SHAPED INSIDE
A TRACK (TYP.)

For SI: 1 inch = 25.4 mm, 1 foot = 304.8 mm.

FIGURE R505.3.8(3)
COLD-FORMED STEEL FLOOR CONSTRUCTION: FLOOR HEADER TO TRIMMER CONNECTION—6-FOOT OPENING

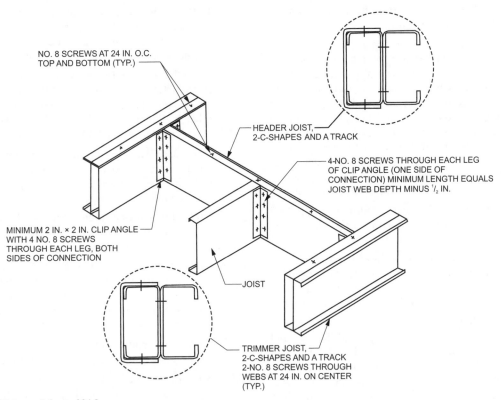

NO. 8 SCREWS AT 24 IN. O.C.
TOP AND BOTTOM (TYP.)

HEADER JOIST,
2-C-SHAPES AND A TRACK

4-NO. 8 SCREWS THROUGH EACH LEG
OF CLIP ANGLE (ONE SIDE OF
CONNECTION) MINIMUM LENGTH EQUALS
JOIST WEB DEPTH MINUS $^1/_2$ IN.

MINIMUM 2 IN. × 2 IN. CLIP ANGLE
WITH 4 NO. 8 SCREWS
THROUGH EACH LEG, BOTH
SIDES OF CONNECTION

JOIST

TRIMMER JOIST,
2-C-SHAPES AND A TRACK
2-NO. 8 SCREWS THROUGH
WEBS AT 24 IN. ON CENTER
(TYP.)

For SI: 1 inch = 25.4 mm, 1 foot = 304.8 mm.

FIGURE R505.3.8(4)
COLD-FORMED STEEL FLOOR CONSTRUCTION: FLOOR HEADER TO TRIMMER CONNECTION—8-FOOT OPENING

SECTION R506
CONCRETE FLOORS (ON GROUND)

R506.1 General. Concrete slab-on-ground floors shall be designed and constructed in accordance with the provisions of this section or ACI 332. Floors shall be a minimum $3^1/_2$ inches (89 mm) thick (for expansive soils, see Section R403.1.8). The specified compressive strength of concrete shall be as set forth in Section R402.2.

R506.2 Site preparation. The area within the foundation walls shall have all vegetation, top soil and foreign material removed.

R506.2.1 Fill. Fill material shall be free of vegetation and foreign material. The fill shall be compacted to ensure uniform support of the slab, and except where *approved*, the fill depths shall not exceed 24 inches (610 mm) for clean sand or gravel and 8 inches (203 mm) for earth.

R506.2.2 Base. A 4-inch-thick (102 mm) base course consisting of clean graded sand, gravel, crushed stone, crushed concrete or crushed blast-furnace slag passing a 2-inch (51 mm) sieve shall be placed on the prepared subgrade where the slab is below *grade*.

Exception: A base course is not required where the concrete slab is installed on well-drained or sand-gravel mixture soils classified as Group I according to the United Soil Classification System in accordance with Table R405.1.

R506.2.3 Vapor retarder. A 6-mil (0.006 inch; 152 μm) polyethylene or *approved* vapor retarder with joints lapped not less than 6 inches (152 mm) shall be placed between the concrete floor slab and the base course or the prepared subgrade where a base course does not exist.

Exception: The vapor retarder is not required for the following:

1. Garages, utility buildings and other unheated *accessory structures*.

2. For unheated storage rooms having an area of less than 70 square feet (6.5 m²) and carports.

3. Driveways, walks, patios and other flatwork not likely to be enclosed and heated at a later date.

4. Where *approved* by the *building official*, based on local site conditions.

R506.2.4 Reinforcement support. Where provided in slabs-on-ground, reinforcement shall be supported to remain in place from the center to upper one-third of the slab for the duration of the concrete placement.

SECTION R507
EXTERIOR DECKS

R507.1 Decks. Wood-framed decks shall be in accordance with this section. For decks using materials and conditions not prescribed in this section, refer to Section R301.

R507.2 Materials. Materials used for the construction of decks shall comply with this section.

R507.2.1 Wood materials. Wood materials shall be No. 2 grade or better lumber, preservative-treated in accordance with Section R317, or *approved*, naturally durable lumber, and termite protected where required in accordance with Section R318. Where design in accordance with Section R301 is provided, wood structural members shall be designed using the wet service factor defined in AWC NDS. Cuts, notches and drilled holes of preservative-treated wood members shall be treated in accordance with Section R317.1.1. All preservative-treated wood products in contact with the ground shall be labeled for such usage.

R507.2.1.1 Engineered wood products. Engineered wood products shall be in accordance with Section R502.

R507.2.2 Plastic composite deck boards, stair treads, guards, or handrails. Plastic composite exterior deck boards, stair treads, guards and handrails shall comply with the requirements of ASTM D7032 and this section.

R507.2.2.1 Labeling. Plastic composite deck boards and stair treads, or their packaging, shall bear a label that indicates compliance with ASTM D7032 and includes the allowable load and maximum allowable span determined in accordance with ASTM D7032. Plastic or composite handrails and guards, or their packaging, shall bear a label that indicates compliance with ASTM D7032 and includes the maximum allowable span determined in accordance with ASTM D7032.

R507.2.2.2 Flame spread index. Plastic composite deck boards, stair treads, guards, and handrails shall exhibit a flame spread index not exceeding 200 when tested in accordance with ASTM E84 or UL 723 with the test specimen remaining in place during the test.

Exception: Plastic composites determined to be noncombustible.

R507.2.2.3 Decay resistance. Plastic composite deck boards, stair treads, guards and handrails containing wood, cellulosic or other biodegradable materials shall be decay resistant in accordance with ASTM D7032.

R507.2.2.4 Termite resistance. Where required by Section 318, plastic composite deck boards, stair treads, guards and handrails containing wood, cellulosic or other biodegradable materials shall be termite resistant in accordance with ASTM D7032.

R507.2.2.5 Installation of plastic composites. Plastic composite deck boards, stair treads, guards and handrails shall be installed in accordance with this code and the manufacturer's instructions.

R507.2.3 Fasteners and connectors. Metal fasteners and connectors used for all decks shall be in accordance with Section R317.3 and Table R507.2.3.

R507.2.4 Flashing. Flashing shall be corrosion-resistant metal of nominal thickness not less than 0.019 inch (0.48 mm) or *approved* nonmetallic material that is compatible with the substrate of the structure and the decking materials.

R507.2.5 Alternate materials. Alternative materials, including glass and metals, shall be permitted.

R507.3 Footings. Decks shall be supported on concrete footings or other approved structural systems designed to accommodate all loads in accordance with Section R301. Deck footings shall be sized to carry the imposed loads from the deck structure to the ground as shown in Figure R507.3. The footing depth shall be in accordance with Section R403.1.4.

Exception: Free-standing decks consisting of joists directly supported on grade over their entire length.

R507.3.1 Minimum size. The minimum size of concrete footings shall be in accordance with Table R507.3.1, based on the tributary area and allowable soil-bearing pressure in accordance with Table R401.4.1.

TABLE R507.2.3
FASTENER AND CONNECTOR SPECIFICATIONS FOR DECKS[a, b]

ITEM	MATERIAL	MINIMUM FINISH/COATING	ALTERNATE FINISH/COATING[e]
Nails and timber rivets	In accordance with ASTM F1667	Hot-dipped galvanized per ASTM A153	Stainless steel, silicon bronze or copper
Bolts[c] Lag screws[d] (including nuts and washers)	In accordance with ASTM A307 (bolts), ASTM A563 (nuts), ASTM F844 (washers)	Hot-dipped galvanized per ASTM A153, Class C (Class D for $^3/_8$-inch diameter and less) or mechanically galvanized per ASTM B695, Class 55 or 410 stainless steel	Stainless steel, silicon bronze or copper
Metal connectors	Per manufacturer's specification	ASTM A653 type G185 zinc coated galvanized steel or post hot-dipped galvanized per ASTM A123 providing a minimum average coating weight of 2.0 oz./ft^2 (total both sides)	Stainless steel

For SI: 1 inch = 25.4 mm, 1 foot = 304.8 mm.

a. Equivalent materials, coatings and finishes shall be permitted.

b. Fasteners and connectors exposed to salt water or located within 300 feet of a salt water shoreline shall be stainless steel.

c. Holes for bolts shall be drilled a minimum $^1/_{32}$ inch and a maximum $^1/_{16}$ inch larger than the bolt.

d. Lag screws $^1/_2$ inch and larger shall be predrilled to avoid wood splitting per the National Design Specification (NDS) for Wood Construction.

e. Stainless-steel-driven fasteners shall be in accordance with ASTM F1667.

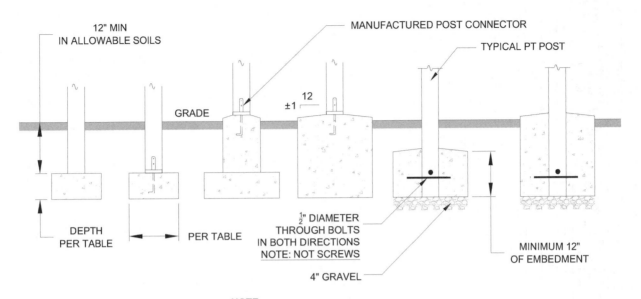

For SI: 1 inch = 25.4 mm.

FIGURE R507.3
DECK POSTS TO DECK FOOTING CONNECTION

R507.3.2 Minimum depth. Deck footings shall extend below the frost line specified in Table R301.2(1) in accordance with Section R403.1.4.1.

Exceptions:

1. Free-standing decks that meet all of the following criteria:

   1.1. The joists bear directly on precast concrete pier blocks at grade without support by beams or posts.

   1.2. The area of the deck does not exceed 200 square feet (18.9 m²).

   1.3. The walking surface is not more than 20 inches (616 mm) above grade at any point within 36 inches (914 mm) measured horizontally from the edge.

2. Free-standing decks need not be provided with footings that extend below the frost line.

R507.4 Deck posts. For single-level wood-framed decks with beams sized in accordance with Table R507.5, deck post size shall be in accordance with Table R507.4.

TABLE R507.4
DECK POST HEIGHT[a]

DECK POST SIZE	MAXIMUM HEIGHT[a, b] (feet-inches)
4 × 4	6-9[c]
4 × 6	8
6 × 6	14
8 × 8	14

For SI: 1 inch = 25.4 mm, 1 foot = 304.8 mm, 1 pound per square foot = 0.0479 kPa.

a. Measured to the underside of the beam.

b. Based on 40 psf live load.

c. The maximum permitted height is 8 feet for one-ply and two-ply beams. The maximum permitted height for three-ply beams on post cap is 6 feet 9 inches.

R507.4.1 Deck post to deck footing connection. Where posts bear on concrete footings in accordance with Section R403 and Figure R507.4.1, lateral restraint shall be provided by manufactured connectors or a minimum post embedment of 12 inches (305 mm) in surrounding soils or concrete piers. Other footing systems shall be permitted.

Exception: Where expansive, compressible, shifting or other questionable soils are present, surrounding soils shall not be relied on for lateral support.

TABLE R507.3.1
MINIMUM FOOTING SIZE FOR DECKS[a, c, d]

LIVE LOAD[b] (psf)	TRIBUTARY AREA (sq. ft.)	LOAD BEARING VALUE OF SOILS[a, c, d] (psf)											
		1500[e]			2000[e]			2500[e]			≥ 3000[e]		
		Side of a square footing (inches)	Diameter of a round footing (inches)	Thickness (inches)	Side of a square footing (inches)	Diameter of a round footing (inches)	Thickness (inches)	Side of a square footing (inches)	Diameter of a round footing (inches)	Thickness (inches)	Side of a square footing (inches)	Diameter of a round footing (inches)	Thickness (inches)
40	20	12	14	6	12	14	6	12	14	6	12	14	6
	40	14	16	6	12	14	6	12	14	6	12	14	6
	60	17	19	6	15	17	6	13	15	6	12	14	6
	80	20	22	7	17	19	6	15	17	6	14	16	6
	100	22	25	8	19	21	7	17	19	6	15	17	6
	120	24	27	9	21	23	8	19	21	7	17	19	6
	140	26	29	10	22	25	8	20	23	8	18	21	7
	160	28	31	11	24	27	9	21	24	8	20	22	7

For SI: 1 inch = 25.4 mm, 1 square foot = 0.0929 m², 1 pound per square foot = 0.0479 kPa.

a. Interpolation permitted, extrapolation not permitted.

b. Live load = 40 psf, dead load = 10 psf.

c. Assumes minimum square footing to be 12 inches x 12 inches for 6 x 6 post.

d. If the support is a brick or CMU pier, the footing shall have a minimum 2-inch projection on all sides.

e. Area, in square feet, of deck surface supported by post and footings.

R507.5 Deck Beams. Maximum allowable spans for wood deck beams, as shown in Figure R507.5, shall be in accordance with Table R507.5. Beam plies shall be fastened with two rows of 10d (3-inch × 0.128-inch) nails minimum at 16 inches (406 mm) on center along each edge. Beams shall be permitted to cantilever at each end up to one-fourth of the allowable beam span. Deck beams of other materials shall be permitted where designed in accordance with accepted engineering practices.

R507.5.1 Deck beam bearing. The ends of beams shall have not less than $1^1/_2$ inches (38 mm) of bearing on wood or metal and not less than 3 inches (76 mm) of bearing on concrete or masonry for the entire width of the beam. Where multiple-span beams bear on intermediate posts, each ply must have full bearing on the post in accordance with Figures R507.5.1(1) and R507.5.1(2).

R507.5.2 Deck beam connection to supports. Deck beams shall be attached to supports in a manner capable of transferring vertical loads and resisting horizontal displacement. Deck beam connections to wood posts shall be in accordance with Figures R507.5.1(1) and R507.5.1(2). Manufactured post-to-beam connectors shall be sized for the post and beam sizes. Bolts shall have washers under the head and nut.

R507.6 Deck joists. Maximum allowable spans for wood deck joists, as shown in Figure R507.6, shall be in accordance with Table R507.6. The maximum joist spacing shall be limited by the decking materials in accordance with Table R507.7. The maximum joist cantilever shall be limited to one-fourth of the joist span or the maximum cantilever length specified in Table R507.6, whichever is less.

R507.6.1 Deck joist bearing. The ends of joists shall have not less than $1^1/_2$ inches (38 mm) of bearing on wood or metal and not less than 3 inches (76 mm) of bearing on concrete or masonry over its entire width. Joists bearing on top of a multiple-ply beam or ledger shall be fastened in accordance with Table R602.3(1). Joists bearing on top of a single-ply beam or ledger shall be attached by a mechanical connector. Joist framing into the side of a beam or ledger board shall be supported by approved joist hangers.

R507.6.2 Deck joist lateral restraint. Joist ends and bearing locations shall be provided with lateral resistance to prevent rotation. Where lateral restraint is provided by joist hangers or blocking between joists, their depth shall equal not less than 60 percent of the joist depth. Where lateral restraint is provided by rim joists, they shall be secured to the end of each joist with not fewer than three 10d (3-inch by 0.128-inch) (76 mm by 3.3 mm) nails or three No. 10x 3-inch (76 mm) long wood screws.

R507.7 Decking. Maximum allowable spacing for joists supporting decking shall be in accordance with Table R507.7. Wood decking shall be attached to each supporting member with not less than two 8d threaded nails or two No. 8 wood screws. Other approved decking or fastener systems shall be installed in accordance with the manufacturer's installation requirements.

R507.8 Vertical and lateral supports. Where supported by attachment to an exterior wall, decks shall be positively anchored to the primary structure and designed for both vertical and lateral loads. Such attachment shall not be accomplished by the use of toenails or nails subject to withdrawal. For decks with cantilevered framing members, connection to exterior walls or other framing members shall be designed and constructed to resist uplift resulting from the full live load specified in Table R301.5 acting on the cantilevered portion of the deck. Where positive connection to the primary building structure cannot be verified during inspection, decks shall be self-supporting.

R507.9 Vertical and lateral supports at band joist. Vertical and lateral supports for decks shall comply with this section.

R507.9.1 Vertical supports. Vertical loads shall be transferred to band joists with ledgers in accordance with this section.

R507.9.1.1 Ledger details. Deck ledgers shall be a minimum 2-inch by 8-inch (51 mm by 203 mm) nominal, pressure-preservative-treated Southern pine, incised pressure-preservative-treated hem-fir, or approved, naturally durable, No. 2 grade or better lumber. Deck ledgers shall not support concentrated loads from beams or girders. Deck ledgers shall not be supported on stone or masonry veneer.

R507.9.1.2 Band joist details. Band joists supporting a ledger shall be a minimum 2-inch-nominal (51 mm), solid-sawn, spruce-pine-fir or better lumber or a minimum 1-inch by $9^1/_2$-inch (25 mm × 241 mm) dimensional, Douglas fir or better, laminated veneer lumber. Band joists shall bear fully on the primary structure capable of supporting all required loads.

R507.9.1.3 Ledger to band joist details. Fasteners used in deck ledger connections in accordance with Table R507.9.1.3(1) shall be hot-dipped galvanized or stainless steel and shall be installed in accordance with Table R507.9.1.3(2) and Figures R507.9.1.3(1) and R507.9.1.3(2).

R507.9.1.4 Alternate ledger details. Alternate framing configurations supporting a ledger constructed to meet the load requirements of Section R301.5 shall be permitted.

R507.9.2 Lateral connection. Lateral loads shall be transfered to the ground or to a structure capable of transmitting them to the ground. Where the lateral load connection is provided in accordance with Figure R507.9.2(1), holddown tension devices shall be installed in not less than two locations per deck, within 24 inches (610 mm) of each end of the deck. Each device shall have an allowable stress design capacity of not less than 1,500 pounds (6672 N). Where the lateral load connections are provided in accordance with Figure R507.9.2(2), the hold-down tension devices shall be installed in not less than four locations per deck, and each device shall have an allowable stress design capacity of not less than 750 pounds (3336 N).

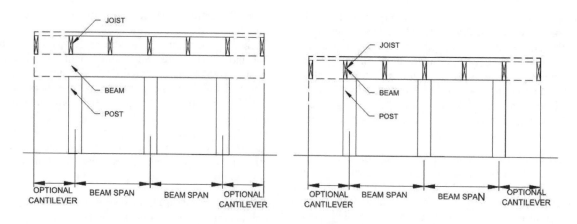

DROPPED BEAM

FLUSH BEAM

FIGURE R507.5
TYPICAL DECK JOIST SPANS

TABLE R507.5
DECK BEAM SPAN LENGTHS[a, b, g] (feet - inches)

SPECIES[c]	SIZE[d]	DECK JOIST SPAN LESS THAN OR EQUAL TO: (feet)						
		6	8	10	12	14	16	18
Southern pine	1 – 2 × 6	4-11	4-0	3-7	3-3	3-0	2-10	2-8
	1 – 2 × 8	5-11	5-1	4-7	4-2	2-10	3-7	3-5
	1 – 2 × 10	7-0	6-0	5-5	4-11	4-7	4-3	4-0
	1 – 2 × 12	8-3	7-1	6-4	5-10	5-5	5-0	4-9
	2 – 2 × 6	6-11	5-11	5-4	4-10	4-6	4-3	4-0
	2 – 2 × 8	8-9	7-7	6-9	6-2	5-9	5-4	5-0
	2 – 2 × 10	10-4	9-0	8-0	7-4	6-9	6-4	6-0
	2 – 2 × 12	12-2	10-7	9-5	8-7	8-0	7-6	7-0
	3 – 2 × 6	8-2	7-5	6-8	6-1	5-8	5-3	5-0
	3 – 2 × 8	10-10	9-6	8-6	7-9	7-2	6-8	6-4
	3 – 2 × 10	13-0	11-3	10-0	9-2	8-6	7-11	7-6
	3 – 2 × 12	15-3	13-3	11-10	10-9	10-0	9-4	8-10
Douglas fir-larch[e], hem-fir[e], spruce-pine-fir[e], redwood, western cedars, ponderosa pine[f], red pine[f]	3 × 6 or 2 – 2 × 6	5-5	4-8	4-2	3-10	3-6	3-1	2-9
	3 × 8 or 2 – 2 × 8	6-10	5-11	5-4	4-10	4-6	4-1	3-8
	3 × 10 or 2 – 2 × 10	8-4	7-3	6-6	5-11	5-6	5-1	4-8
	3 × 12 or 2 – 2 × 12	9-8	8-5	7-6	6-10	6-4	5-11	5-7
	4 × 6	6-5	5-6	4-11	4-6	4-2	3-11	3-8
	4 × 8	8-5	7-3	6-6	5-11	5-6	5-2	4-10
	4 × 10	9-11	8-7	7-8	7-0	6-6	6-1	5-8
	4 × 12	11-5	9-11	8-10	8-1	7-6	7-0	6-7
	3 – 2 × 6	7-4	6-8	6-0	5-6	5-1	4-9	4-6
	3 – 2 × 8	9-8	8-6	7-7	6-11	6-5	6-0	5-8
	3 – 2 × 10	12-0	10-5	9-4	8-6	7-10	7-4	6-11
	3 – 2 × 12	13-11	12-1	10-9	9-10	9-1	8-6	8-1

For SI: 1 inch = 25.4 mm, 1 foot = 304.8 mm, 1 pound per square foot = 0.0479 kPa, 1 pound = 0.454 kg.

a. Live load = 40 psf, dead load = 10 psf, L/Δ = 360 at main span, L/Δ = 180 at cantilever with a 220-pound point load applied at the end.

b. Beams supporting deck joists from one side only.

c. No. 2 grade, wet service factor.

d. Beam depth shall be greater than or equal to depth of joists with a flush beam condition.

e. Includes incising factor.

f. Northern species. Incising factor not included.

g. Beam cantilevers are limited to the adjacent beam's span divided by 4.

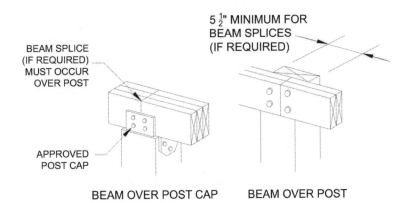

5 ½" MINIMUM FOR
BEAM SPLICES
(IF REQUIRED)

BEAM SPLICE
(IF REQUIRED)
MUST OCCUR
OVER POST

APPROVED
POST CAP

BEAM OVER POST CAP   BEAM OVER POST

For SI: 1 inch = 25.4 mm.

**FIGURE R507.5.1(1)
DECK BEAM TO DECK POST**

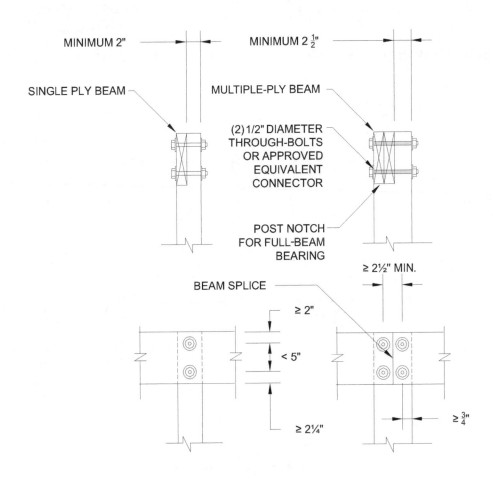

MINIMUM 2"   MINIMUM 2 ½"

SINGLE PLY BEAM   MULTIPLE-PLY BEAM

(2) 1/2" DIAMETER
THROUGH-BOLTS
OR APPROVED
EQUIVALENT
CONNECTOR

POST NOTCH
FOR FULL-BEAM
BEARING

BEAM SPLICE

≥ 2½" MIN.

≥ 2"

< 5"

≥ 2¼"   ≥ ¾"

For SI: 1 inch = 25.4 mm.

**FIGURE R507.5.1(2)
NOTCHED POST-TO-BEAM CONNECTION**

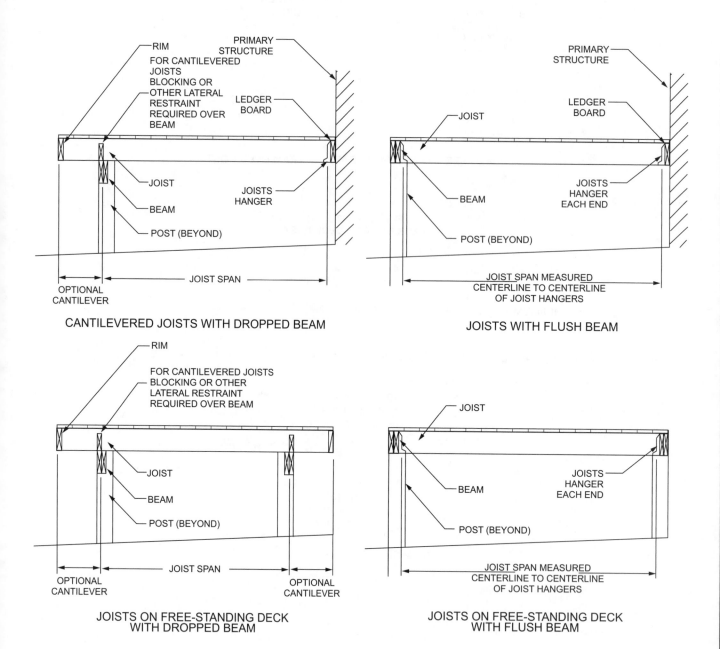

CANTILEVERED JOISTS WITH DROPPED BEAM

JOISTS WITH FLUSH BEAM

JOISTS ON FREE-STANDING DECK
WITH DROPPED BEAM

JOISTS ON FREE-STANDING DECK
WITH FLUSH BEAM

FIGURE R507.6
TYPICAL DECK JOIST SPANS

TABLE R507.6
DECK JOIST SPANS FOR COMMON LUMBER SPECIES (ft. - in.)

SPECIES[a]	SIZE	ALLOWABLE JOIST SPAN[b]			MAXIMUM CANTILEVER[c, f]		
		SPACING OF DECK JOISTS (inches)			SPACING OF DECK JOISTS WITH CANTILEVERS[c] (inches)		
		12	16	24	12	16	24
Southern pine	2 × 6	9-11	9-0	7-7	1-3	1-4	1-6
	2 × 8	13-1	11-10	9-8	2-1	2-3	2-5
	2 × 10	16-2	14-0	11-5	3-4	3-6	2-10
	2 × 12	18-0	16-6	13-6	4-6	4-2	3-4
Douglas fir-larch[d], hem-fir[d] spruce-pine-fir[d],	2 × 6	9-6	8-8	7-2	1-2	1-3	1-5
	2 × 8	12-6	11-1	9-1	1-11	2-1	2-3
	2 × 10	15-8	13-7	11-1	3-1	3-5	2-9
	2 × 12	18-0	15-9	12-10	4-6	3-11	3-3
Redwood, western cedars, ponderosa pine[e], red pine[e]	2 × 6	8-10	8-0	7-0	1-0	1-1	1-2
	2 × 8	11-8	10-7	8-8	1-8	1-10	2-0
	2 × 10	14-11	13-0	10-7	2-8	2-10	2-8
	2 × 12	17-5	15-1	12-4	3-10	3-9	3-1

For SI: 1 inch = 25.4 mm, 1 foot = 304.8 mm, 1 pound per square foot = 0.0479 kPa, 1 pound = 0.454 kg.

a. No. 2 grade with wet service factor.

b. Live load = 40 psf, dead load = 10 psf, L/Δ = 360.

c. Live load = 40 psf, dead load = 10 psf, L/Δ = 360 at main span, L/Δ = 180 at cantilever with a 220-pound point load applied to end.

d. Includes incising factor.

e. Northern species with no incising factor.

f. Cantilevered spans not exceeding the nominal depth of the joist are permitted.

TABLE R507.7
MAXIMUM JOIST SPACING FOR DECKING

DECKING MATERIAL TYPE AND NOMINAL SIZE	MAXIMUM ON-CENTER JOIST SPACING	
	Decking perpendicular to joist	Decking diagonal to joist[a]
1¼-inch-thick wood	16 inches	12 inches
2-inch-thick wood	24 inches	16 inches
Plastic composite	In accordance with Section R507.2	In accordance with Section R507.2

For SI: 1 inch = 25.4 mm, 1 foot = 304.8 mm, 1 degree = 0.01745 rad.

a. Maximum angle of 45 degrees from perpendicular for wood deck boards.

TABLE R507.9.1.3(1)
DECK LEDGER CONNECTION TO BAND JOIST[a]
(Deck live load = 40 psf, deck dead load = 10 psf

CONNECTION DETAILS	JOIST SPAN						
	6' and less	6'1" to 8'	8'1" to 10'	10'1" to 12'	12'1" to 14'	14'1" to 16'	16'1" to 18'
	On-center spacing of fasteners						
$^1/_2$-inch diameter lag screw with $^1/_2$-inch maximum sheathing[b, c]	30	23	18	15	13	11	10
$^1/_2$-inch diameter bolt with $^1/_2$-inch maximum sheathing[c]	36	36	34	29	24	21	19
$^1/_2$-inch diameter bolt with 1-inch maximum sheathing[d]	36	36	29	24	21	18	16

For SI: 1 inch = 25.4 mm, 1 foot = 304.8 mm, 1 pound per square foot = 0.0479 kPa.

a. Ledgers shall be flashed in accordance with Section R703.4 to prevent water from contacting the house band joist.

b. The tip of the lag screw shall fully extend beyond the inside face of the band joist.

c. Sheathing shall be wood structural panel or solid sawn lumber.

d. Sheathing shall be permitted to be wood structural panel, gypsum board, fiberboard, lumber, or foam sheathing. Up to $^1/_2$-inch thickness of stacked washers shall be permitted to substitute for up to $^1/_2$ inch of allowable sheathing thickness where combined with wood structural panel or lumber sheathing.

TABLE R507.9.1.3(2)
PLACEMENT OF LAG SCREWS AND BOLTS IN DECK LEDGERS AND BAND JOISTS

	MINIMUM END AND EDGE DISTANCES AND SPACING BETWEEN ROWS			
	TOP EDGE	BOTTOM EDGE	ENDS	ROW SPACING
Ledger[a]	2 inches[d]	$^3/_4$ inch	2 inches[b]	$1^5/_8$ inches[b]
Band Joist[c]	$^3/_4$ inch	2 inches	2 inches[b]	$1^5/_8$ inches[b]

For SI: 1 inch = 25.4 mm.

a. Lag screws or bolts shall be staggered from the top to the bottom along the horizontal run of the deck ledger in accordance with Figure R507.9.1.3(1).

b. Maximum 5 inches.

c. For engineered rim joists, the manufacturer's recommendations shall govern.

d. The minimum distance from bottom row of lag screws or bolts to the top edge of the ledger shall be in accordance with Figure R507.9.1.3(1).

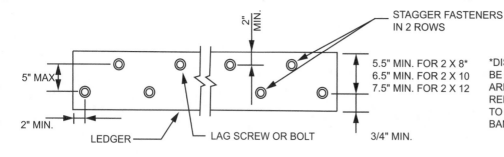

For SI: 1 inch = 25.4 mm.

FIGURE R507.9.1.3(1)
PLACEMENT OF LAG SCREWS AND BOLTS IN LEDGERS

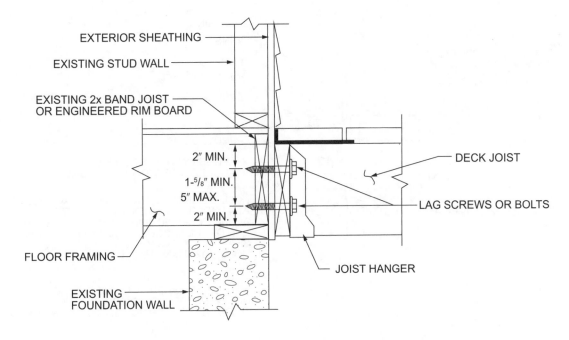

For SI: 1 inch = 25.4 mm.

FIGURE R507.9.1.3(2)
PLACEMENT OF LAG SCREWS AND BOLTS IN BAND JOISTS

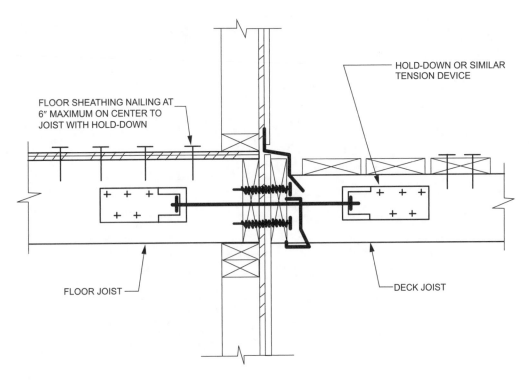

For SI: 1 inch = 25.4 mm.

FIGURE R507.9.2(1)
DECK ATTACHMENT FOR LATERAL LOADS

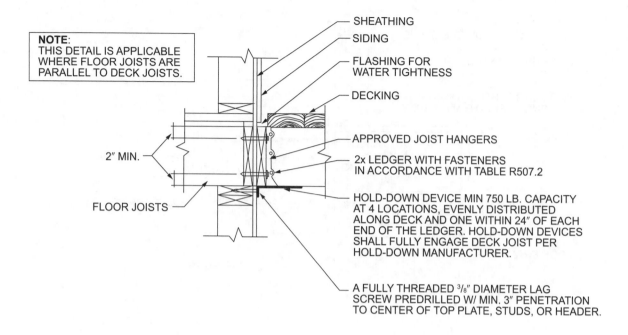

NOTE:
THIS DETAIL IS APPLICABLE
WHERE FLOOR JOISTS ARE
PARALLEL TO DECK JOISTS.

SHEATHING

SIDING

FLASHING FOR
WATER TIGHTNESS

DECKING

APPROVED JOIST HANGERS

2x LEDGER WITH FASTENERS
IN ACCORDANCE WITH TABLE R507.2

HOLD-DOWN DEVICE MIN 750 LB. CAPACITY
AT 4 LOCATIONS, EVENLY DISTRIBUTED
ALONG DECK AND ONE WITHIN 24″ OF EACH
END OF THE LEDGER. HOLD-DOWN DEVICES
SHALL FULLY ENGAGE DECK JOIST PER
HOLD-DOWN MANUFACTURER.

A FULLY THREADED ³/₈″ DIAMETER LAG
SCREW PREDRILLED W/ MIN. 3″ PENETRATION
TO CENTER OF TOP PLATE, STUDS, OR HEADER.

2″ MIN.

FLOOR JOISTS

For SI: 1 inch = 25.4 mm, 1 foot = 304.8 mm.

**FIGURE R507.9.2(2)
DECK ATTACHMENT FOR LATERAL LOADS**

CHAPTER 6

WALL CONSTRUCTION

SECTION R601
GENERAL

R601.1 Application. The provisions of this chapter shall control the design and construction of walls and partitions for buildings.

R601.2 Requirements. Wall construction shall be capable of accommodating all loads imposed in accordance with Section R301 and of transmitting the resulting loads to the supporting structural elements.

R601.2.1 Compressible floor-covering materials. Compressible floor-covering materials that compress more than $^1/_{32}$ inch (0.8 mm) when subjected to 50 pounds (23 kg) applied over 1 inch square (645 mm) of material and are greater than $^1/_8$ inch (3.2 mm) in thickness in the uncompressed state shall not extend beneath walls, partitions or columns, which are fastened to the floor.

SECTION R602
WOOD WALL FRAMING

R602.1 General. Wood and wood-based products used for load-supporting purposes shall conform to the applicable provisions of this section.

R602.1.1 Sawn lumber. Sawn lumber shall be identified by a grade mark of an accredited lumber grading or inspection agency and have design values certified by an accreditation body that complies with DOC PS 20. In lieu of a grade mark, a certification of inspection issued by a lumber grading or inspection agency meeting the requirements of this section shall be accepted.

R602.1.2 End-jointed lumber. Approved end-jointed lumber identified by a grade mark conforming to Section R602.1 shall be permitted to be used interchangeably with solid-sawn members of the same species and grade. End-jointed lumber used in an assembly required elsewhere in this code to have a fire-resistance rating shall have the designation "Heat Resistant Adhesive" or "HRA" included in its grade mark.

R602.1.3 Structural glued-laminated timbers. Glued-laminated timbers shall be manufactured and identified as required in ANSI A190.1, ANSI 117 and ASTM D3737.

R602.1.4 Structural log members. Structural log members shall comply with the provisions of ICC 400.

R602.1.5 Structural composite lumber. Structural capacities for structural composite lumber shall be established and monitored in accordance with ASTM D5456.

R602.1.6 Cross-laminated timber. Cross-laminated timber shall be manufactured and identified as required by ANSI/APA PRG 320.

R602.1.7 Engineered wood rim board. Engineered wood rim boards shall conform to ANSI/APA PRR 410 or shall be evaluated in accordance with ASTM D7672. Structural capacities shall be in accordance with either ANSI/APA PRR 410 or established in accordance with ASTM D7672. Rim boards conforming to ANSI/APA PRR 410 shall be marked in accordance with that standard.

R602.1.8 Wood structural panels. Wood structural panel sheathing shall conform to DOC PS 1, DOC PS 2 or, when manufactured in Canada, CSA O325 or CSA O437. Panels shall be identified for grade, bond classification, and performance category by a grade mark or certificate of inspection issued by an approved agency.

R602.1.9 Particleboard. Particleboard shall conform to ANSI A208.1. Particleboard shall be identified by the grade mark or certificate of inspection issued by an approved agency.

R602.1.10 Fiberboard. Fiberboard shall conform to ASTM C208. Fiberboard sheathing, where used structurally, shall be identified by an approved agency as conforming to ASTM C208.

R602.1.11 Structural insulated panels. *Structural insulated panels* shall be manufactured and identified in accordance with ANSI/APA PRS 610.1.

R602.2 Grade. Studs shall be a minimum No. 3, standard or stud grade lumber.

Exception: Bearing studs not supporting floors and nonbearing studs shall be permitted to be utility grade lumber, provided that the studs are spaced in accordance with Table R602.3(5).

R602.3 Design and construction. Exterior walls of wood-frame construction shall be designed and constructed in accordance with the provisions of this chapter and Figures R602.3(1) and R602.3(2), or in accordance with AWC NDS. Components of exterior walls shall be fastened in accordance with Tables R602.3(1) through R602.3(4). Wall sheathing shall be fastened directly to framing members and, where placed on the exterior side of an exterior wall, shall be capa-

TABLE R602.3(1)
FASTENING SCHEDULE

ITEM	DESCRIPTION OF BUILDING ELEMENTS	NUMBER AND TYPE OF FASTENER[a, b, c]	SPACING AND LOCATION
	Roof		
1	Blocking between ceiling joists or rafters to top plate	4-8d box ($2^1/_2'' \times 0.113''$) or 3-8d common ($2^1/_2'' \times 0.131''$); or 3-10d box ($3'' \times 0.128''$); or 3-$3'' \times 0.131''$ nails	Toe nail
2	Ceiling joists to top plate	4-8d box ($2^1/_2'' \times 0.113''$); or 3-8d common ($2^1/_2'' \times 0.131''$); or 3-10d box ($3'' \times 0.128''$); or 3-$3'' \times 0.131''$ nails	Per joist, toe nail
3	Ceiling joist not attached to parallel rafter, laps over partitions (see Section R802.5.2 and Table R802.5.2)	4-10d box ($3'' \times 0.128''$); or 3-16d common ($3^1/_2'' \times 0.162''$); or 4-$3'' \times 0.131''$ nails	Face nail
4	Ceiling joist attached to parallel rafter (heel joint) (see Section R802.5.2 and Table R802.5.2)	Table R802.5.2	Face nail
5	Collar tie to rafter, face nail or $1^1/_4''\times$ 20 ga. ridge strap to rafter	4-10d box ($3'' \times 0.128''$); or 3-10d common ($3'' \times 0.148''$); or 4-$3'' \times 0.131''$ nails	Face nail each rafter
6	Rafter or roof truss to plate	3-16d box nails ($3^1/_2'' \times 0.135''$); 3-10d common nails ($3'' \times 0.148''$); or 4-10d box ($3'' \times 0.128''$); or 4-$3'' \times 0.131''$ nails	2 toe nails on one side and 1 toe nail on opposite side of each rafter or truss[i]
7	Roof rafters to ridge, valley or hip rafters or roof rafter to minimum 2″ ridge beam	4-16d ($3^1/_2'' \times 0.135''$); or 3-10d common ($3'' \times 0.148''$); or 4-10d box ($3'' \times 0.128''$); or 4-$3'' \times 0.131''$ nails	Toe nail
		3-16d box $3^1/_2'' \times 0.135''$); or 2-16d common ($3^1/_2'' \times 0.162''$); or 3-10d box ($3'' \times 0.128''$); or 3-$3'' \times 0.131''$ nails	End nail
	Wall		
8	Stud to stud (not at braced wall panels)	16d common ($3^1/_2'' \times 0.162''$)	24″ o.c. face nail
		10d box ($3'' \times 0.128''$); or $3'' \times 0.131''$ nails	16″ o.c. face nail
9	Stud to stud and abutting studs at intersecting wall corners (at braced wall panels)	16d box ($3^1/_2'' \times 0.135''$); or $3'' \times 0.131''$ nails	12″ o.c. face nail
		16d common ($3^1/_2'' \times 0.162''$)	16″ o.c. face nail
10	Built-up header (2″ to 2″ header with $^1/_2''$ spacer)	16d common ($3^1/_2'' \times 0.162''$)	16″ o.c. each edge face nail
		16d box ($3^1/_2'' \times 0.135''$)	12″ o.c. each edge face nail
11	Continuous header to stud	5-8d box ($2^1/_2'' \times 0.113''$); or 4-8d common ($2^1/_2'' \times 0.131''$); or 4-10d box ($3'' \times 0.128''$)	Toe nail
12	Top plate to top plate	16d common ($3^1/_2'' \times 0.162''$)	16″ o.c. face nail
		10d box ($3'' \times 0.128''$); or $3'' \times 0.131''$ nails	12″ o.c. face nail
13	Double top plate splice	8-16d common ($3^1/_2'' \times 0.162''$); or 12-16d box ($3^1/_2'' \times 0.135''$); or 12-10d box ($3'' \times 0.128''$); or 12-$3'' \times 0.131''$ nails	Face nail on each side of end joint (minimum 24″ lap splice length each side of end joint)

(continued)

TABLE R602.3(1)—continued
FASTENING SCHEDULE

ITEM	DESCRIPTION OF BUILDING ELEMENTS	NUMBER AND TYPE OF FASTENER[a, b, c]	SPACING AND LOCATION
14	Bottom plate to joist, rim joist, band joist or blocking (not at braced wall panels)	16d common ($3^1/_2'' \times 0.162''$)	16″ o.c. face nail
		16d box ($3^1/_2'' \times 0.135''$); or $3'' \times 0.131''$ nails	12″ o.c. face nail
15	Bottom plate to joist, rim joist, band joist or blocking (at braced wall panel)	3-16d box ($3^1/_2'' \times 0.135''$); or 2-16d common ($3^1/_2'' \times 0.162''$); or 4-$3'' \times 0.131''$ nails	3 each 16″ o.c. face nail 2 each 16″ o.c. face nail 4 each 16″ o.c. face nail
16	Top or bottom plate to stud	4-8d box ($2^1/_2'' \times 0.113''$); or 3-16d box ($3^1/_2'' \times 0.135''$); or 4-8d common ($2^1/_2'' \times 0.131''$); or 4-10d box ($3'' \times 0.128''$); or 4-$3'' \times 0.131''$ nails	Toe nail
		3-16d box ($3^1/_2'' \times 0.135''$); or 2-16d common ($3^1/_2'' \times 0.162''$); or 3-10d box ($3'' \times 0.128''$); or 3-$3'' \times 0.131''$ nails	End nail
17	Top plates, laps at corners and intersections	3-10d box ($3'' \times 0.128''$); or 2-16d common ($3^1/_2'' \times 0.162''$); or 3-$3'' \times 0.131''$ nails	Face nail
18	1″ brace to each stud and plate	3-8d box ($2^1/_2'' \times 0.113''$); or 2-8d common ($2^1/_2'' \times 0.131''$); or 2-10d box ($3'' \times 0.128''$); or 2 staples $1^3/_4''$	Face nail
19	1″ × 6″ sheathing to each bearing	3-8d box ($2^1/_2'' \times 0.113''$); or 2-8d common ($2^1/_2'' \times 0.131''$); or 2-10d box ($3'' \times 0.128''$); or 2 staples, 1″ crown, 16 ga., $1^3/_4''$ long	Face nail
20	1″ × 8″ and wider sheathing to each bearing	3-8d box ($2^1/_2'' \times 0.113''$); or 3-8d common ($2^1/_2'' \times 0.131''$); or 3-10d box ($3'' \times 0.128''$); or 3 staples, 1″ crown, 16 ga., $1^3/_4''$ long	Face nail
		Wider than 1″ × 8″ 4-8d box ($2^1/_2'' \times 0.113''$); or 3-8d common ($2^1/_2'' \times 0.131''$); or 3-10d box ($3'' \times 0.128''$); or 4 staples, 1″ crown, 16 ga., $1^3/_4''$ long	
Floor			
21	Joist to sill, top plate or girder	4-8d box ($2^1/_2'' \times 0.113''$); or 3-8d common ($2^1/_2'' \times 0.131''$); or 3-10d box ($3'' \times 0.128''$); or 3-$3'' \times 0.131''$ nails	Toe nail
22	Rim joist, band joist or blocking to sill or top plate (roof applications also)	8d box ($2^1/_2'' \times 0.113''$)	4″ o.c. toe nail
		8d common ($2^1/_2'' \times 0.131''$); or 10d box ($3'' \times 0.128''$); or $3'' \times 0.131''$ nails	6″ o.c. toe nail
23	1″ × 6″ subfloor or less to each joist	3-8d box ($2^1/_2'' \times 0.113''$); or 2-8d common ($2^1/_2'' \times 0.131''$); or 3-10d box ($3'' \times 0.128''$); or 2 staples, 1″ crown, 16 ga., $1^3/_4''$ long	Face nail

(continued)

TABLE 602.3(1)
FASTENING SCHEDULE—continued

ITEM	DESCRIPTION OF BUILDING ELEMENTS	NUMBER AND TYPE OF FASTENER[a, b, c]	SPACING AND LOCATION
	Floor		
24	2″ subfloor to joist or girder	3-16d box ($3^1/_2$″ × 0.135″); or 2-16d common ($3^1/_2$″ × 0.162″)	Blind and face nail
25	2″ planks (plank & beam—floor & roof)	3-16d box ($3^1/_2$″ × 0.135″); or 2-16d common ($3^1/_2$″ × 0.162″)	At each bearing, face nail
26	Band or rim joist to joist	3-16d common ($3^1/_2$″ × 0.162″) 4-10 box (3″ × 0.128″), or 4-3″ × 0.131″ nails; or 4-3″ × 14 ga. staples, $^7/_{16}$″ crown	End nail
27	Built-up girders and beams, 2-inch lumber layers	20d common (4″ × 0.192″); or	Nail each layer as follows: 32″ o.c. at top and bottom and staggered.
		10d box (3″ × 0.128″); or 3″ × 0.131″ nails	24″ o.c. face nail at top and bottom staggered on opposite sides
		And: 2-20d common (4″ × 0.192″); or 3-10d box (3″ × 0.128″); or 3-3″ × 0.131″ nails	Face nail at ends and at each splice
28	Ledger strip supporting joists or rafters	4-16d box ($3^1/_2$″ × 0.135″); or 3-16d common ($3^1/_2$″ × 0.162″); or 4-10d box (3″ × 0.128″); or 4-3″ × 0.131″ nails	At each joist or rafter, face nail
29	Bridging or blocking to joist	2-10d box (3″ × 0.128″), or 2-8d common ($2^1/_2$″ × 0.131″; or 2-3″ × 0.131″) nails	Each end, toe nail

ITEM	DESCRIPTION OF BUILDING ELEMENTS	NUMBER AND TYPE OF FASTENER[a, b, c]	SPACING OF FASTENERS	
			Edges (inches)[h]	Intermediate supports[c, e] (inches)
	Wood structural panels, subfloor, roof and interior wall sheathing to framing and particleboard wall sheathing to framing **[see Table R602.3(3) for wood structural panel *exterior* wall sheathing to wall framing]**			
30	$^3/_8$″ – $^1/_2$″	6d common (2″ × 0.113″) nail (subfloor, wall)[i] 8d common ($2^1/_2$″ × 0.131″) nail (roof); or RSRS-01 ($2^3/_8$″ × 0.113″) nail (roof)[j]	6	12[f]
31	$^{19}/_{32}$″ – 1″	8d common nail ($2^1/_2$″ × 0.131″); or RSRS-01; ($2^3/_8$″ × 0.113″) nail (roof)[j]	6	12[f]
32	$1^1/_8$″ – $1^1/_4$″	10d common (3″ × 0.148″) nail; or 8d ($2^1/_2$″ × 0.131″) deformed nail	6	12
	Other wall sheathing[g]			
33	$^1/_2$″ structural cellulosic fiberboard sheathing	$1^1/_2$″ galvanized roofing nail, $^7/_{16}$″ head diameter, or $1^1/_4$″ long 16 ga. staple with $^7/_{16}$″ or 1″ crown	3	6
34	$^{25}/_{32}$″ structural cellulosic fiberboard sheathing	$1^3/_4$″ galvanized roofing nail, $^7/_{16}$″ head diameter, or $1^1/_2$″ long 16 ga. staple with $^7/_{16}$″ or 1″ crown	3	6
35	$^1/_2$″ gypsum sheathing[d]	$1^1/_2$″ galvanized roofing nail; staple galvanized, $1^1/_2$″ long; $1^1/_4$″ screws, Type W or S	7	7
36	$^5/_8$″ gypsum sheathing[d]	$1^3/_4$″ galvanized roofing nail; staple galvanized, $1^5/_8$″ long; $1^5/_8$″ screws, Type W or S	7	7
	Wood structural panels, combination subfloor underlayment to framing			
37	$^3/_4$″ and less	6d deformed (2″ × 0.120″) nail; or 8d common ($2^1/_2$″ × 0.131″) nail	6	12
38	$^7/_8$″ – 1″	8d common ($2^1/_2$″ × 0.131″) nail; or 8d deformed ($2^1/_2$″ × 0.120″) nail	6	12
39	$1^1/_8$″ – $1^1/_4$″	10d common (3″ × 0.148″) nail; or 8d deformed ($2^1/_2$″ × 0.120″) nail	6	12

For SI: 1 inch = 25.4 mm, 1 foot = 304.8 mm, 1 mile per hour = 0.447 m/s; 1 ksi = 6.895 MPa.

(continued)

a. Nails are smooth-common, box or deformed shanks except where otherwise stated. Nails used for framing and sheathing connections shall have minimum average bending yield strengths as shown: 80 ksi for shank diameter of 0.192 inch (20d common nail), 90 ksi for shank diameters larger than 0.142 inch but not larger than 0.177 inch, and 100 ksi for shank diameters of 0.142 inch or less.

b. Staples are 16 gage wire and have a minimum $^7/_{16}$-inch on diameter crown width.

c. Nails shall be spaced at not more than 6 inches on center at all supports where spans are 48 inches or greater.

d. Four-foot by 8-foot or 4-foot by 9-foot panels shall be applied vertically.

e. Spacing of fasteners not included in this table shall be based on Table R602.3(2).

f. For wood structural panel roof sheathing attached to gable end roof framing and to intermediate supports within 48 inches of roof edges and ridges, nails shall be spaced at 6 inches on center where the ultimate design wind speed is less than 130 mph and shall be spaced 4 inches on center where the ultimate design wind speed is 130 mph or greater but less than 140 mph.

g. Gypsum sheathing shall conform to ASTM C1396 and shall be installed in accordance with GA 253. Fiberboard sheathing shall conform to ASTM C208.

h. Spacing of fasteners on floor sheathing panel edges applies to panel edges supported by framing members and required blocking and at floor perimeters only. Spacing of fasteners on roof sheathing panel edges applies to panel edges supported by framing members and required blocking. Blocking of roof or floor sheathing panel edges perpendicular to the framing members need not be provided except as required by other provisions of this code. Floor perimeter shall be supported by framing members or solid blocking.

i. Where a rafter is fastened to an adjacent parallel ceiling joist in accordance with this schedule, provide two toe nails on one side of the rafter and toe nails from the ceiling joist to top plate in accordance with this schedule. The toe nail on the opposite side of the rafter shall not be required.

j. RSRS-01 is a Roof Sheathing Ring Shank nail meeting the specifications in ASTM F1667.

ble of resisting the wind pressures listed in Table R301.2(2) adjusted for height and exposure using Table R301.2(3) and shall conform to the requirements of Table R602.3(3). Wall sheathing used only for exterior wall covering purposes shall comply with Section R703.

Studs shall be continuous from support at the sole plate to a support at the top plate to resist loads perpendicular to the wall. The support shall be a foundation or floor, ceiling or roof diaphragm or shall be designed in accordance with accepted engineering practice.

Exception: Jack studs, trimmer studs and cripple studs at openings in walls that comply with Tables R602.7(1) and R602.7(2).

R602.3.1 Stud size, height and spacing. The size, height and spacing of studs shall be in accordance with Table R602.3(5).

Exceptions:

1. Utility grade studs shall not be spaced more than 16 inches (406 mm) on center, shall not support more than a roof and ceiling, and shall not exceed 8 feet (2438 mm) in height for exterior walls and load-bearing walls or 10 feet (3048 mm) for interior nonload-bearing walls.

2. Where snow loads are less than or equal to 25 pounds per square foot (1.2 kPa), and the ultimate design wind speed is less than or equal to 130 mph (58.1 m/s), 2-inch by 6-inch (38 mm by 140 mm) studs supporting a roof load with not more than 6 feet (1829 mm) of tributary length shall have a maximum height of 18 feet (5486 mm) where spaced at 16 inches (406 mm) on center, or 20 feet (6096 mm) where spaced at 12 inches (305 mm) on center. Studs shall be No. 2 grade lumber or better.

3. Exterior load-bearing studs not exceeding 12 feet (3658 mm) in height provided in accordance with Table R602.3(6). The minimum number of full-height studs adjacent to openings shall be in accordance with Section R602.7.5. The building shall be located in Exposure B, the roof live load shall not exceed 20 psf (0.96 kPa), and the ground snow load shall not exceed 30 psf (1.4 kPa). Studs and plates shall be No. 2 grade lumber or better.

R602.3.2 Top plate. Wood stud walls shall be capped with a double top plate installed to provide overlapping at corners and intersections with bearing partitions. End joints in top plates shall be offset not less than 24 inches (610 mm). Joints in plates need not occur over studs. Plates shall be not less than 2-inches (51 mm) nominal thickness and have a width not less than the width of the studs.

Exception: A single top plate used as an alternative to a double top plate shall comply with the following:

1. The single top plate shall be tied at corners, intersecting walls, and at in-line splices in straight wall lines in accordance with Table R602.3.2.

2. The rafters or joists shall be centered over the studs with a tolerance of not more than 1 inch (25 mm).

3. Omission of the top plate is permitted over headers where the headers are adequately tied to adjacent wall sections in accordance with Table R602.3.2.

R602.3.3 Bearing studs. Where joists, trusses or rafters are spaced more than 16 inches (406 mm) on center and the bearing studs below are spaced 24 inches (610 mm) on center, such members shall bear within 5 inches (127 mm) of the studs beneath.

Exceptions:

1. The top plates are two 2-inch by 6-inch (38 mm by 140 mm) or two 3-inch by 4-inch (64 mm by 89 mm) members.

2. A third top plate is installed.

3. Solid blocking equal in size to the studs is installed to reinforce the double top plate.

R602.3.4 Bottom (sole) plate. Studs shall have full bearing on a nominal 2-by (51 mm) or larger plate or sill having a width not less than to the width of the studs.

TABLE R602.3.1
MAXIMUM ALLOWABLE LENGTH OF WOOD WALL STUDS EXPOSED TO WIND SPEEDS OF 115 MPH OR LESS[b, c, d, e, f, g, h, i, j]
Where conditions are not within the parameters of footnotes b, c, d, e, f, g, h, i, and j design is required.

ROOF SPANS UP TO 22' SUPPORTING A ROOF ONLY					
Maximum Wall Height (feet)	Exposure Category[h, i]	On-Center Spacing (inches)			
		24	16	12	8
10	B	2x6	2x4	2x4	2x4
	C	2x6	2x6	2x4	2x4
12	B	2x6	2x6	2x4	2x4
	C	2x6	2x6	2x6	2x4
14	B	2x6	2x6	2x6	2x4
	C	2x6	2x6	2x6	2x6
16	B	2x8	2x6	2x6	2x6
	C	2x8	2x6	2x6	2x6
18	B	2x8	2x8	2x6	2x6
	C	2x8	2x8	2x6	2x6
20	B	2x8	2x8	2x8	2x6
	C	NA[a]	2x8	2x8	2x6
24	B	NA[a]	2x8	2x8	2x8
	C	NA[a]	NA[a]	2x8	2x8

ROOF SPANS GREATER THAN 22' AND UP TO 26' SUPPORTING A ROOF ONLY					
Maximum Wall Height (feet)	Exposure Category[h, i]	On-Center Spacing (inches)			
		24	16	12	8
10	B	2x6	2x6	2x4	2x4
	C	2x6	2x6	2x6	2x4
12	B	2x6	2x6	2x6	2x4
	C	2x8	2x6	2x6	2x6
14	B	2x6	2x6	2x6	2x6
	C	2x8	2x8	2x6	2x6
16	B	2x8	2x6	2x6	2x6
	C	2x8	2x8	2x6	2x6
18	B	2x8	2x8	2x6	2x6
	C	NA[a]	2x8	2x8	2x6
20	B	NA[a]	2x8	2x8	2x6
	C	NA[a]	NA[a]	2x8	2x8
24	B	NA[a]	NA[a]	2x8	2x8
	C	NA[a]	NA[a]	NA[a]	2x8

(continued)

TABLE R602.3.1—continued
MAXIMUM ALLOWABLE LENGTH OF WOOD WALL STUDS EXPOSED TO WIND SPEEDS OF 115 MPH OR LESS[b, c, d, e, f, g, h, i, j]
Where conditions are not within the parameters of footnotes b, c, d, e, f, g, h, i, and j design is required.

| Maximum Wall Height (feet) | Exposure Category[h, i] | ROOF SPANS GREATER THAN 26′ AND UP TO 30′ SUPPORTING A ROOF ONLY | | | |
| | | On-Center Spacing (inches) | | | |
		24	16	12	8
10	B	2x6	2x6	2x4	2x4
10	C	2x6	2x6	2x6	2x4
12	B	2x6	2x6	2x6	2x4
12	C	2x8	2x6	2x6	2x6
14	B	2x8	2x6	2x6	2x6
14	C	2x8	2x8	2x6	2x6
16	B	2x8	2x6	2x6	2x6
16	C	2x8	2x8	2x8	2x6
18	B	2x8	2x8	2x6	2x6
18	C	NA[a]	2x8	2x8	2x8
20	B	NA[a]	2x8	2x8	2x6
20	C	NA[a]	NA[a]	2x8	2x8
24	B	NA[a]	NA[a]	2x8	2x8
24	C	NA[a]	NA[a]	NA[a]	2x8

| Maximum Wall Height (feet) | Exposure Category[h, i] | ROOF SPANS GREATER THAN 30′ AND UP TO 34′ SUPPORTING A ROOF ONLY | | | |
| | | On-Center Spacing (inches) | | | |
		24	16	12	8
10	B	2x6	2x6	2x4	2x4
10	C	2x6	2x6	2x6	2x4
12	B	2x6	2x6	2x6	2x4
12	C	2x8	2x6	2x6	2x6
14	B	2x8	2x6	2x6	2x6
14	C	2x8	2x8	2x6	2x6
16	B	2x8	2x8	2x6	2x6
16	C	NA[a]	2x8	2x8	2x6
18	B	2x8	2x8	2x6	2x6
18	C	NA[a]	NA[a]	2x8	2x8
20	B	NA[a]	2x8	2x8	2x6
20	C	NA[a]	NA[a]	2x8	2x8
24	B	NA[a]	NA[a]	2x8	2x8
24	C	NA[a]	NA[a]	NA[a]	2x8

For SI: 1 inch = 25.4 mm, 1 foot = 304.8 mm, 1 pound per square foot = 0.0479 kPa, 1 pound per square inch = 6.895 kPa, 1 mile = 0.447 m/s.

a. Design required.

b. Applicability of these tables assumes the following: SPF#2 or better, Ground snow = 60 psf, Roof snow = 42 psf, Component and Cladding Zone 4–50 square feet (Exposure B = 14.3 psf, Exposure C = 18.4 psf), eaves not greater than 2.0 feet in dimension.

c. The exterior of the wall shall be continuously sheathed in accordance with one of the materials listed in items 30 to 36 in Table R602.3(1), including the prescribed fastening. All wall bracing requirements shall be in accordance with section R602.10.

d. Studs shall be continuous full height. Where studs do not extend full height due to a wall opening, full height studs shall be provided on each side of the opening, equal in number to the spacing of the required full height studs multiplied by half the width of the opening, plus one stud. Where multiple openings occur adjacent to one another, framing between openings shall include the total of all full height studs required for both openings combined.

e. Full depth blocking is required at 10-foot spacing maximum.

f. Utility, standard, stud, and No. 3 grade lumber of any species are not permitted.

g. This table is based on a maximum allowable deflection limit of L/120.

h. Where the sill plate of the frame wall bears on the supporting foundation and the frame wall is up to 12 feet in height, anchor the sill plate to the supporting foundation wall with $1/2$-inch diameter anchor bolts spaced a maximum of 6 feet on center. For frame walls more than 12 feet but not exceeding 24 feet in height, anchor the sill plate to the supporting foundation wall with $1/2$-inch diameter anchor bolts spaced a maximum of 3 feet on center.

i. Where the sill plate of the frame wall bears on the supporting floor framing, it shall be fastened to the rim board through the subfloor using 8d common ($3^1/_2$ by 0.131) nails or equivalent fastening spaced at 6 inches on center.

j. For frame walls up to 20 feet in height, fasten the studs to the top and sole plates in accordance with Table R602.3(1). For frame walls that are more than 20 feet in height, fasten the studs to the top plate and sole plate using fastening or an approved fastener that is capable of supporting at least 450 pounds.

R602.3.5 Braced wall panel uplift load path. Braced wall panels located at exterior walls that support roof rafters or trusses (including stories below top story) shall have the framing members connected in accordance with one of the following:

1. Fastening in accordance with Table R602.3(1) where:

    1.1. The ultimate design wind speed does not exceed 115 mph (51 m/s), the wind exposure category is B, the roof pitch is 5:12 or greater, and the roof span is 32 feet (9754 mm) or less.

    1.2. The net uplift value at the top of a wall does not exceed 100 plf (146 N/mm). The net uplift value shall be determined in accordance with Section R802.11 and shall be permitted to be reduced by 60 plf (86 N/mm) for each full wall above.

2. Where the net uplift value at the top of a wall exceeds 100 plf (146 N/mm), installing approved uplift framing connectors to provide a continuous load path from the top of the wall to the foundation or to a point where the uplift force is 100 plf (146 N/mm) or less. The net uplift value shall be as determined in Item 1.2.

3. Wall sheathing and fasteners designed to resist combined uplift and shear forces in accordance with accepted engineering practice.

R602.4 Interior load-bearing walls. Interior load-bearing walls shall be constructed, framed and fireblocked as specified for exterior walls.

R602.5 Interior nonbearing walls. Interior nonbearing walls shall be permitted to be constructed with 2-inch by 3-inch (51 mm by 76 mm) studs spaced 24 inches (610 mm) on center or, where not part of a *braced wall line*, 2-inch by 4-inch (51 mm by 102 mm) flat studs spaced at 16 inches (406 mm) on center. Interior nonbearing walls shall be capped with not less than a single top plate. Interior nonbearing walls shall be fireblocked in accordance with Section R602.8.

R602.6 Drilling and notching of studs. Drilling and notching of studs shall be in accordance with the following:

1. Notching. Any stud in an exterior wall or bearing partition shall be permitted to be cut or notched to a depth not exceeding 25 percent of its width. Studs in nonbearing partitions shall be permitted to be notched to a depth not to exceed 40 percent of a single stud width.

2. Drilling. Any stud shall be permitted to be bored or drilled, provided that the diameter of the resulting hole is not more than 60 percent of the stud width, the edge of the hole is not more than $^5/_8$ inch (16 mm) to the edge of the stud, and the hole is not located in the same section as a cut or notch. Studs located in exterior walls or bearing partitions drilled over 40 percent and up to 60 percent shall be doubled with not more than two successive doubled studs bored. See Figures R602.6(1) and R602.6(2).

    Exception: Use of *approved* stud shoes is permitted where they are installed in accordance with the manufacturer's recommendations.

R602.6.1 Drilling and notching of top plate. Where piping or ductwork is placed in or partly in an exterior wall or interior load-bearing wall, necessitating cutting, drilling or notching of the top plate by more than 50 percent of its width, a galvanized metal tie not less than 0.054 inch thick (1.37 mm) (16 ga) and $1^1/_2$ inches (38 mm) wide shall be fastened across and to the plate at each side of the opening with not less than eight 10d (0.148 inch diameter) nails having a minimum length of $1^1/_2$ inches (38 mm) at each side or equivalent. The metal tie must extend not less than 6 inches past the opening. See Figure R602.6.1.

Exception: Where the entire side of the wall with the notch or cut is covered by wood structural panel sheathing.

R602.7 Headers. For header spans, see Tables R602.7(1), R602.7(2) and R602.7(3).

R602.7.1 Single member headers. Single headers shall be framed with a single flat 2-inch-nominal (51 mm) member or wall plate not less in width than the wall studs on the top and bottom of the header in accordance with Figures R602.7.1(1) and R602.7.1(2) and face nailed to the top and bottom of the header with 10d box nails (3 inches × 0.128 inches) spaced 12 inches on center.

R602.7.2 Rim board headers. Rim board header size, material and span shall be in accordance with Table R602.7(1). Rim board headers shall be constructed in accordance with Figure R602.7.2 and shall be supported at each end by full-height studs. The number of full-height studs at each end shall be not less than the number of studs displaced by half of the header span based on the maximum stud spacing in accordance with Table R602.3(5). Rim board headers supporting concentrated loads shall be designed in accordance with accepted engineering practice.

TABLE R602.3.2
SINGLE TOP-PLATE SPLICE CONNECTION DETAILS

CONDITION	TOP-PLATE SPLICE LOCATION			
	Corners and intersecting walls		Butt joints in straight walls	
	Splice plate size	Minimum nails each side of joint	Splice plate size	Minimum nails each side of joint
Structures in SDC A-C; and in SDC D_0, D_1 and D_2 with braced wall line spacing less than 25 feet	3″ × 6″ × 0.036″ galvanized steel plate or equivalent	(6) 8d box ($2^1/_2$″ × 0.113″) nails	3″ × 12″ × 0.036″ galvanized steel plate or equivalent	(12) 8d box ($2^1/_2$″ × 0.113″) nails
Structures in SDC D_0, D_1 and D_2, with braced wall line spacing greater than or equal to 25 feet	3″ × 8″ by 0.036″ galvanized steel plate or equivalent	(9) 8d box ($2^1/_2$″ × 0.113″) nails	3″ × 16″ × 0.036″ galvanized steel plate or equivalent	(18) 8d box ($2^1/_2$″ × 0.113″) nails

For SI: 1 inch = 25.4 mm, 1 foot = 304.8 mm.

TABLE R602.3(2)
ALTERNATE ATTACHMENTS TO TABLE R602.3(1)

NOMINAL MATERIAL THICKNESS (inches)	DESCRIPTION[a, b] OF FASTENER AND LENGTH (inches)	SPACING[c] OF FASTENERS	
		Edges (inches)	Intermediate supports (inches)
Wood structural panels subfloor, roof[g] and wall sheathing to framing and particleboard wall sheathing to framing[f]			
Up to $^1/_2$	Staple 15 ga. $1^3/_4$	4	8
	0.097 - 0.099 Nail $2^1/_4$	3	6
	Staple 16 ga. $1^3/_4$	3	6
$^{19}/_{32}$ and $^5/_8$	0.113 Nail 2	3	6
	Staple 15 and 16 ga. 2	4	8
	0.097 - 0.099 Nail $2^1/_4$	4	8
$^{23}/_{32}$ and $^3/_4$	Staple 14 ga. 2	4	8
	Staple 15 ga. $1^3/_4$	3	6
	0.097 - 0.099 Nail $2^1/_4$	4	8
	Staple 16 ga. 2	4	8
1	Staple 14 ga. $2^1/_4$	4	8
	0.113 Nail $2^1/_4$	3	6
	Staple 15 ga. $2^1/_4$	4	8
	0.097 - 0.099 Nail $2^1/_2$	4	8

NOMINAL MATERIAL THICKNESS (inches)	DESCRIPTION[a, b] OF FASTENER AND LENGTH (inches)	SPACING[c] OF FASTENERS	
		Edges (inches)	Body of panel[d] (inches)
Floor underlayment; plywood-hardboard-particleboard[f]-fiber-cement[h]			
Fiber-cement			
$^1/_4$	3d, corrosion-resistant, ring shank nails (finished flooring other than tile)	3	6
	Staple 18 ga., $^7/_8$ long, $^1/_4$ crown (finished flooring other than tile)	3	6
	$1^1/_4$ long × .121 shank × .375 head diameter corrosion-resistant (galvanized or stainless steel) roofing nails (for tile finish)	8	8
	$1^1/_4$ long, No. 8 × .375 head diameter, ribbed wafer-head screws (for tile finish)	8	8
Plywood			
$^1/_4$ and $^5/_{16}$	$1^1/_4$ ring or screw shank nail-minimum $12^1/_2$ ga. (0.099″) shank diameter	3	6
	Staple 18 ga., $^7/_8$, $^3/_{16}$ crown width	2	5
$^{11}/_{32}$, $^3/_8$, $^{15}/_{32}$, and $^1/_2$	$1^1/_4$ ring or screw shank nail-minimum $12^1/_2$ ga. (0.099″) shank diameter	6	8[e]
$^{19}/_{32}$, $^5/_8$, $^{23}/_{32}$ and $^3/_4$	$1^1/_2$ ring or screw shank nail-minimum $12^1/_2$ ga. (0.099″) shank diameter	6	8
	Staple 16 ga. $1^1/_2$	6	8
Hardboard[f]			
0.200	$1^1/_2$ long ring-grooved underlayment nail	6	6
	4d cement-coated sinker nail	6	6
	Staple 18 ga., $^7/_8$ long (plastic coated)	3	6
Particleboard			
$^1/_4$	4d ring-grooved underlayment nail	3	6
	Staple 18 ga., $^7/_8$ long, $^3/_{16}$ crown	3	6
$^3/_8$	6d ring-grooved underlayment nail	6	10
	Staple 16 ga., $1^1/_8$ long, $^3/_8$ crown	3	6
$^1/_2$, $^5/_8$	6d ring-grooved underlayment nail	6	10
	Staple 16 ga., $1^5/_8$ long, $^3/_8$ crown	3	6

(continued)

TABLE R602.3(2)—continued
ALTERNATE ATTACHMENTS TO TABLE R602.3(1)

For SI: 1 inch = 25.4 mm.

a. Nail is a general description and shall be permitted to be T-head, modified round head or round head.

b. Staples shall have a minimum crown width of $^7/_{16}$-inch on diameter except as noted.

c. Nails or staples shall be spaced at not more than 6 inches on center at all supports where spans are 48 inches or greater. Nails or staples shall be spaced at not more than 12 inches on center at intermediate supports for floors.

d. Fasteners shall be placed in a grid pattern throughout the body of the panel.

e. For 5-ply panels, intermediate nails shall be spaced not more than 12 inches on center each way.

f. Hardboard underlayment shall conform to CPA/ANSI A135.4

g. Specified alternate attachments for roof sheathing shall be permitted where the ultimate design wind speed is less than 130 mph. Fasteners attaching wood structural panel roof sheathing to gable end wall framing shall be installed using the spacing listed for panel edges.

h. Fiber-cement underlayment shall conform to ASTM C1288 or ISO 8336, Category C.

TABLE R602.3(3)
REQUIREMENTS FOR WOOD STRUCTURAL PANEL WALL SHEATHING USED TO RESIST WIND PRESSURES[a, b, c]

MINIMUM NAIL		MINIMUM WOOD STRUCTURAL PANEL SPAN RATING	MINIMUM NOMINAL PANEL THICKNESS (inches)	MAXIMUM WALL STUD SPACING (inches)	PANEL NAIL SPACING		ULTIMATE DESIGN WIND SPEED V$_{ult}$ (mph)		
Size	Penetration (inches)				Edges (inches o.c.)	Field (inches o.c.)	Wind exposure category		
							B	C	D
6d Common (2.0" × 0.113")	1.5	24/0	$^3/_8$	16	6	12	140	115	110
8d Common (2.5" × 0.131")	1.75	24/16	$^7/_{16}$	16	6	12	170	140	135
				24	6	12	140	115	110

For SI: 1 inch = 25.4 mm, 1 mile per hour = 0.447 m/s.

a. Panel strength axis parallel or perpendicular to supports. Three-ply plywood sheathing with studs spaced more than 16 inches on center shall be applied with panel strength axis perpendicular to supports.

b. Table is based on wind pressures acting toward and away from building surfaces in accordance with Section R301.2. Lateral bracing requirements shall be in accordance with Section R602.10.

c. Wood structural panels with span ratings of Wall-16 or Wall-24 shall be permitted as an alternate to panels with a 24/0 span rating. Plywood siding rated 16 o.c. or 24 o.c. shall be permitted as an alternate to panels with a 24/16 span rating. Wall-16 and Plywood siding 16 o.c. shall be used with studs spaced not

TABLE R602.3(4)
ALLOWABLE SPANS FOR PARTICLEBOARD WALL SHEATHING[a]

THICKNESS (inch)	GRADE	STUD SPACING (inches)	
		Where siding is nailed to studs	Where siding is nailed to sheathing
$^3/_8$	M-1 Exterior glue	16	—
$^1/_2$	M-2 Exterior glue	16	16

For SI: 1 inch = 25.4 mm.

a. Wall sheathing not exposed to the weather. If the panels are applied horizontally, the end joints of the panel shall be offset so that four panel corners will not meet. Panel edges must be supported. Leave a $^1/_{16}$-inch gap between panels and nail not less than $^3/_8$ inch from panel edges.

TABLE R602.3(5)
SIZE, HEIGHT AND SPACING OF WOOD STUDS[a]

STUD SIZE (inches)	BEARING WALLS					NONBEARING WALLS	
	Laterally unsupported stud height[a] (feet)	Maximum spacing where supporting a roof-ceiling assembly or a habitable attic assembly, only (inches)	Maximum spacing where supporting one floor, plus a roof-ceiling assembly or a habitable attic assembly (inches)	Maximum spacing where supporting two floors, plus a roof-ceiling assembly or a habitable attic assembly (inches)	Maximum spacing where supporting one floor height[a] (inches)	Laterally unsupported stud height[a] (feet)	Maximum spacing (inches)
2 × 3[b]	—	—	—	—	—	10	16
2 × 4	10	24[c]	16[c]	—	24	14	24
3 × 4	10	24	24	16	24	14	24
2 × 5	10	24	24	—	24	16	24
2 × 6	10	24	24	16	24	20	24

For SI: 1 inch = 25.4 mm, 1 foot = 304.8 mm.

a. Listed heights are distances between points of lateral support placed perpendicular to the plane of the wall. Bearing walls shall be sheathed on not less than one side or bridging shall be installed not greater than 4 feet apart measured vertically from either end of the stud. Increases in unsupported height are permitted where in compliance with Exception 2 of Section R602.3.1 or designed in accordance with accepted engineering practice.

b. Shall not be used in exterior walls.

c. A habitable attic assembly supported by 2 × 4 studs is limited to a roof span of 32 feet. Where the roof span exceeds 32 feet, the wall studs shall be increased

TABLE R602.3(6)
ALTERNATE WOOD BEARING WALL STUD SIZE, HEIGHT AND SPACING

STUD HEIGHT	SUPPORTING	STUD SPACING[a]	ULTIMATE DESIGN WIND SPEED					
			115 mph		130 mph[b]		140 mph[b]	
			Maximum roof/floor span[c]		Maximum roof/floor span[c]		Maximum roof/floor span[c]	
			12 ft.	24 ft.	12 ft.	24 ft.	12 ft.	24 ft.
11 ft.	Roof Only	12 in.	2 × 4	2 × 4	2 × 4	2 × 4	2 × 4	2 × 4
		16 in.	2 × 4	2 × 4	2 × 4	2 × 6	2 × 4	2 × 6
		24 in.	2 × 6	2 × 6	2 × 6	2 × 6	2 × 6	2 × 6
	Roof and One Floor	12 in.	2 × 4	2 × 6	2 × 4	2 × 6	2 × 4	2 × 6
		16 in.	2 × 6	2 × 6	2 × 6	2 × 6	2 × 6	2 × 6
		24 in.	2 × 6	2 × 6	2 × 6	2 × 6	2 × 6	2 × 6
12 ft.	Roof Only	12 in	2 × 4	2 × 4	2 × 4	2 × 6	2 × 4	2 × 6
		16 in.	2 × 4	2 × 6	2 × 6	2 × 6	2 × 6	2 × 6
		24 in.	2 × 6	2 × 6	2 × 6	2 × 6	2 × 6	2 × 6
	Roof and One Floor	12 in	2 × 4	2 × 6	2 × 6	2 × 6	2 × 6	2 × 6
		16 in.	2 × 6	2 × 6	2 × 6	2 × 6	2 × 6	2 × 6
		24 in.	2 × 6	2 × 6	2 × 6	2 × 6	2 × 6	DR

For SI: 1 inch = 25.4mm, 1 foot = 304.8 mm, 1 mph = 0.447 m/s, 1 pound = 4.448 N.

DR = Design Required.

a. Wall studs not exceeding 16 inches on center shall be sheathed with minimum $1/2$-inch gypsum board on the interior and $3/8$-inch wood structural panel sheathing on the exterior. Wood structural panel sheathing shall be attached with 8d (2.5" x 0.131") nails not greater than 6 inches on center along panel edges and 12 inches on center at intermediate supports, and all panel joints shall occur over studs or blocking.

b. Where the ultimate design wind speed exceeds 115 mph, studs shall be attached to top and bottom plates with connectors having a minimum 300-pound lateral capacity.

c. The maximum span is applicable to both single- and multiple-span roof and floor conditions. The roof assembly shall not contain a habitable attic.

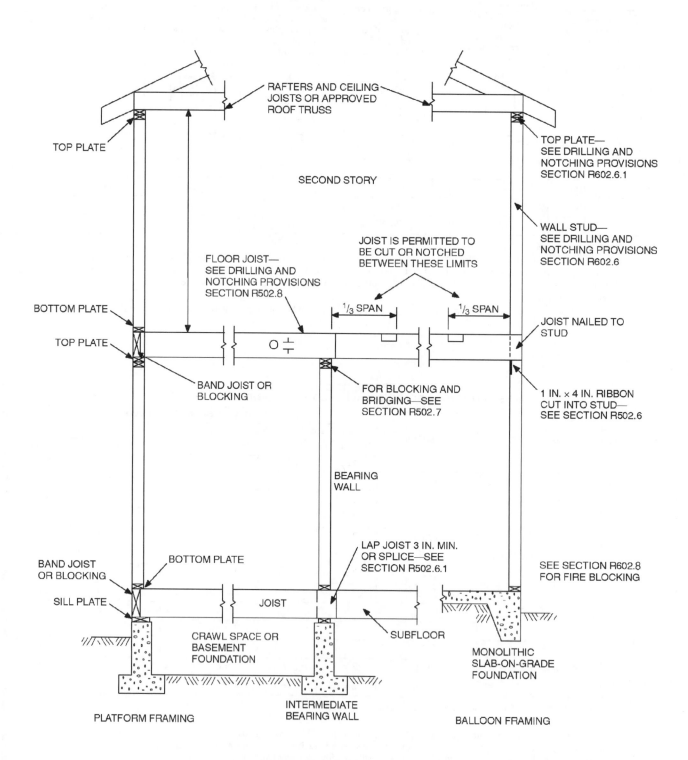

RAFTERS AND CEILING JOISTS OR APPROVED ROOF TRUSS

TOP PLATE

TOP PLATE— SEE DRILLING AND NOTCHING PROVISIONS SECTION R602.6.1

SECOND STORY

WALL STUD— SEE DRILLING AND NOTCHING PROVISIONS SECTION R602.6

JOIST IS PERMITTED TO BE CUT OR NOTCHED BETWEEN THESE LIMITS

FLOOR JOIST— SEE DRILLING AND NOTCHING PROVISIONS SECTION R502.8

BOTTOM PLATE

$\frac{1}{3}$ SPAN $\frac{1}{3}$ SPAN

TOP PLATE

JOIST NAILED TO STUD

BAND JOIST OR BLOCKING

FOR BLOCKING AND BRIDGING—SEE SECTION R502.7

1 IN. × 4 IN. RIBBON CUT INTO STUD— SEE SECTION R502.6

BEARING WALL

BAND JOIST OR BLOCKING

BOTTOM PLATE

LAP JOIST 3 IN. MIN. OR SPLICE—SEE SECTION R502.6.1

SEE SECTION R602.8 FOR FIRE BLOCKING

SILL PLATE

JOIST

SUBFLOOR

CRAWL SPACE OR BASEMENT FOUNDATION

MONOLITHIC SLAB-ON-GRADE FOUNDATION

PLATFORM FRAMING

INTERMEDIATE BEARING WALL

BALLOON FRAMING

For SI: 1 inch = 25.4 mm, 1 foot = 304.8 mm.

FIGURE R602.3(1)
TYPICAL WALL, FLOOR AND ROOF FRAMING

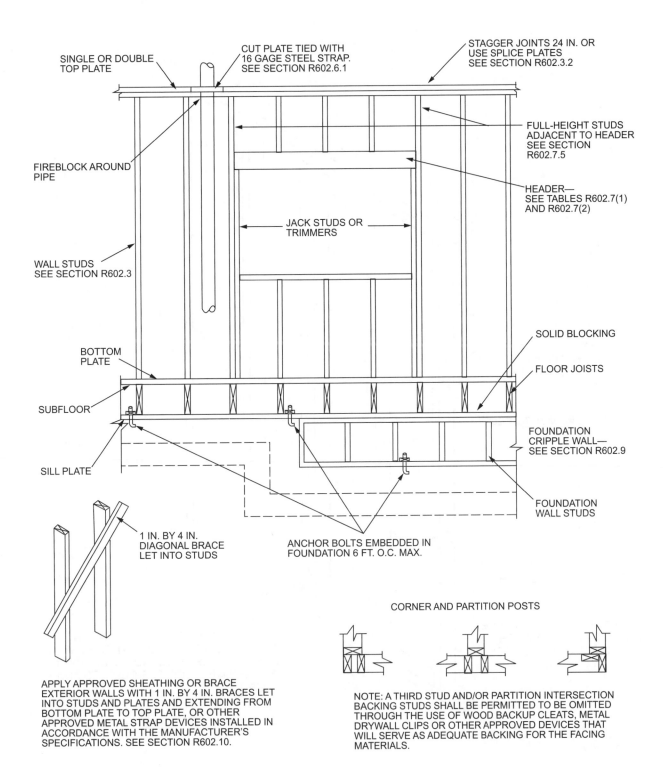

SINGLE OR DOUBLE TOP PLATE

CUT PLATE TIED WITH 16 GAGE STEEL STRAP. SEE SECTION R602.6.1

STAGGER JOINTS 24 IN. OR USE SPLICE PLATES SEE SECTION R602.3.2

FULL-HEIGHT STUDS ADJACENT TO HEADER SEE SECTION R602.7.5

FIREBLOCK AROUND PIPE

HEADER— SEE TABLES R602.7(1) AND R602.7(2)

JACK STUDS OR TRIMMERS

WALL STUDS SEE SECTION R602.3

SOLID BLOCKING

BOTTOM PLATE

FLOOR JOISTS

SUBFLOOR

FOUNDATION CRIPPLE WALL— SEE SECTION R602.9

SILL PLATE

FOUNDATION WALL STUDS

1 IN. BY 4 IN. DIAGONAL BRACE LET INTO STUDS

ANCHOR BOLTS EMBEDDED IN FOUNDATION 6 FT. O.C. MAX.

APPLY APPROVED SHEATHING OR BRACE EXTERIOR WALLS WITH 1 IN. BY 4 IN. BRACES LET INTO STUDS AND PLATES AND EXTENDING FROM BOTTOM PLATE TO TOP PLATE, OR OTHER APPROVED METAL STRAP DEVICES INSTALLED IN ACCORDANCE WITH THE MANUFACTURER'S SPECIFICATIONS. SEE SECTION R602.10.

CORNER AND PARTITION POSTS

NOTE: A THIRD STUD AND/OR PARTITION INTERSECTION BACKING STUDS SHALL BE PERMITTED TO BE OMITTED THROUGH THE USE OF WOOD BACKUP CLEATS, METAL DRYWALL CLIPS OR OTHER APPROVED DEVICES THAT WILL SERVE AS ADEQUATE BACKING FOR THE FACING MATERIALS.

For SI: 1 inch = 25.4 mm, 1 foot = 304.8 mm.

FIGURE R602.3(2)
FRAMING DETAILS

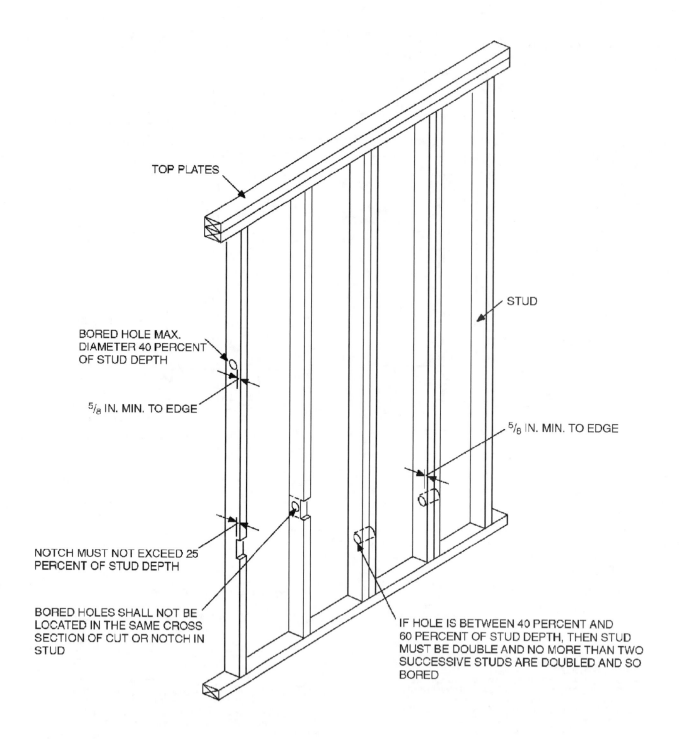

TOP PLATES

STUD

BORED HOLE MAX.
DIAMETER 40 PERCENT
OF STUD DEPTH

5/8 IN. MIN. TO EDGE

5/8 IN. MIN. TO EDGE

NOTCH MUST NOT EXCEED 25
PERCENT OF STUD DEPTH

BORED HOLES SHALL NOT BE
LOCATED IN THE SAME CROSS
SECTION OF CUT OR NOTCH IN
STUD

IF HOLE IS BETWEEN 40 PERCENT AND
60 PERCENT OF STUD DEPTH, THEN STUD
MUST BE DOUBLE AND NO MORE THAN TWO
SUCCESSIVE STUDS ARE DOUBLED AND SO
BORED

For SI: 1 inch = 25.4 mm.
Note: Condition for exterior and bearing walls.

FIGURE R602.6(1)
NOTCHING AND BORED HOLE LIMITATIONS FOR EXTERIOR WALLS AND BEARING WALLS

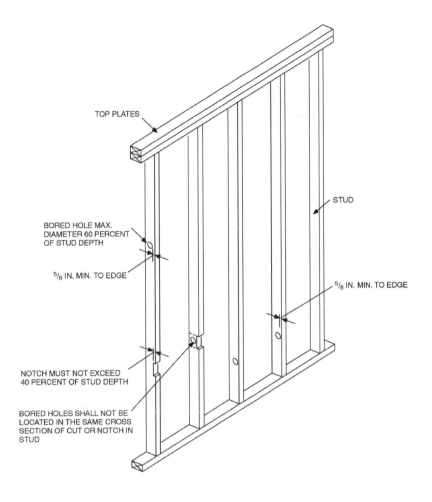

For SI: 1 inch = 25.4 mm.

FIGURE R602.6(2)
NOTCHING AND BORED HOLE LIMITATIONS FOR INTERIOR NONBEARING WALLS

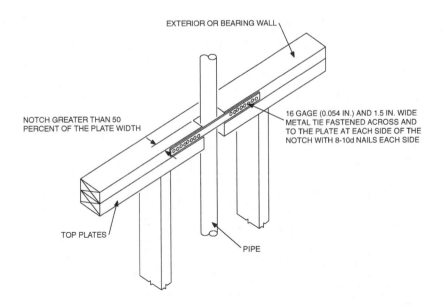

For SI: 1 inch = 25.4 mm.

FIGURE R602.6.1
TOP PLATE FRAMING TO ACCOMMODATE PIPING

TABLE R602.7(1)
GIRDER SPANS[a] AND HEADER SPANS[a] FOR EXTERIOR BEARING WALLS
(Maximum spans for Douglas fir-larch, hem-fir, Southern pine and spruce-pine-fir[b] and required number of jack studs)

GIRDERS AND HEADERS SUPPORTING	SIZE	GROUND SNOW LOAD (psf)[e]																
		30						50						70					
		Building width[c] (feet)																	
		12		24		36		12		24		36		12		24		36	
		Span[f]	NJ[d]	Span[f]	NJ[d]	Span[f]	NJ[d]	Span[f]	NJ[d]	Span[f]	NJ[d]	Span[f]	NJ[d]	Span[f]	NJ[d]	Span[f]	NJ[d]	Span[f]	NJ[d]
ROOF AND CEILING (HEADER, TYP)	1-2 × 6	4-0	1	3-1	2	2-7	2	3-5	1	2-8	2	2-3	2	3-0	2	2-4	2	2-0	2
	1-2 × 8	5-1	2	3-11	2	3-3	2	4-4	2	3-4	2	2-10	2	3-10	2	3-0	2	2-6	3
	1-2 × 10	6-0	2	4-8	2	3-11	2	5-2	2	4-0	2	3-4	3	4-7	2	3-6	3	3-0	3
	1-2 × 12	7-1	2	5-5	2	4-7	3	6-1	2	4-8	3	3-11	3	5-5	2	4-2	3	3-6	3
	2-2 × 4	4-0	1	3-1	1	2-7	1	3-5	1	2-7	1	2-2	1	3-0	1	2-4	1	2-0	1
	2-2 × 6	6-0	1	4-7	1	3-10	1	5-1	1	3-11	1	3-3	2	4-6	1	3-6	2	2-11	2
	2-2 × 8	7-7	1	5-9	1	4-10	2	6-5	1	5-0	2	4-2	2	5-9	1	4-5	2	3-9	2
	2-2 × 10	9-0	1	6-10	2	5-9	2	7-8	2	5-11	2	4-11	2	6-9	2	5-3	2	4-5	2
	2-2 × 12	10-7	2	8-1	2	6-10	2	9-0	2	6-11	2	5-10	2	8-0	2	6-2	2	5-2	3
	3-2 × 8	9-5	1	7-3	1	6-1	1	8-1	1	6-3	1	5-3	2	7-2	1	5-6	2	4-8	2
	3-2 × 10	11-3	1	8-7	1	7-3	2	9-7	1	7-4	2	6-2	2	8-6	1	6-7	2	5-6	2
	3-2 × 12	13-2	1	10-1	2	8-6	2	11-3	2	8-8	2	7-4	2	10-0	2	7-9	2	6-6	2
	4-2 × 8	10-11	1	8-4	1	7-0	1	9-4	1	7-2	1	6-0	1	8-3	1	6-4	1	5-4	2
	4-2 × 10	12-11	1	9-11	1	8-4	1	11-1	1	8-6	1	7-2	2	9-10	1	7-7	2	6-4	2
	4-2 × 12	15-3	1	11-8	1	9-10	2	13-0	1	10-0	2	8-5	2	11-7	1	8-11	2	7-6	2
ROOF, CEILING AND ONE FLOOR (CENTER BEARING)	1-2 × 6	3-3	1	2-7	2	2-2	2	3-0	2	2-4	2	2-0	2	2-9	2	2-2	2	1-10	2
	1-2 × 8	4-1	2	3-3	2	2-9	2	3-9	2	3-0	2	2-6	3	3-6	2	2-9	2	2-4	3
	1-2 × 10	4-11	2	3-10	2	3-3	3	4-6	2	3-6	3	3-0	3	4-1	2	3-3	3	2-9	3
	1-2 × 12	5-9	2	4-6	3	3-10	3	5-3	2	4-2	3	3-6	3	4-10	3	3-10	3	3-3	4
	2-2 × 4	3-3	1	2-6	1	2-2	1	3-0	1	2-4	1	2-0	1	2-8	1	2-2	1	1-10	1
	2-2 × 6	4-10	1	3-9	1	3-3	2	4-5	1	3-6	2	3-0	2	4-1	1	3-3	2	2-9	2
	2-2 × 8	6-1	1	4-10	2	4-1	2	5-7	2	4-5	2	3-9	2	5-2	2	4-1	2	3-6	2
	2-2 × 10	7-3	2	5-8	2	4-10	2	6-8	2	5-3	2	4-5	2	6-1	2	4-10	2	4-1	2
	2-2 × 12	8-6	2	6-8	2	5-8	2	7-10	2	6-2	2	5-3	3	7-2	2	5-8	2	4-10	3
	3-2 × 8	7-8	1	6-0	1	5-1	1	7-0	1	5-6	2	4-8	2	6-5	1	5-1	2	4-4	2
	3-2 × 10	9-1	1	7-2	2	6-1	2	8-4	1	6-7	2	5-7	2	7-8	2	6-1	2	5-2	2
	3-2 × 12	10-8	2	8-5	2	7-2	2	9-10	2	7-8	2	6-7	2	9-0	2	7-1	2	6-1	2
	4-2 × 8	8-10	1	6-11	1	5-11	1	8-1	1	6-4	1	5-5	2	7-5	1	5-11	1	5-0	2
	4-2 × 10	10-6	1	8-3	2	7-0	2	9-8	1	7-7	2	6-5	2	8-10	1	7-0	2	6-0	2
	4-2 × 12	12-4	1	9-8	2	8-3	2	11-4	2	8-11	2	7-7	2	10-4	2	8-3	2	7-0	2
ROOF, CEILING AND ONE FLOOR (CLEAR SPAN)	1-2 × 6	2-11	2	2-3	2	1-11	2	2-9	2	2-1	2	1-9	2	2-7	2	2-0	2	1-8	2
	1-2 × 8	3-9	2	2-10	2	2-5	3	3-6	2	2-8	2	2-3	3	3-3	2	2-6	3	2-2	3
	1-2 × 10	4-5	2	3-5	3	2-10	3	4-2	2	3-2	3	2-8	3	3-11	2	3-0	3	2-6	3
	1-2 × 12	5-2	2	4-0	3	3-4	3	4-10	3	3-9	3	3-2	4	4-7	3	3-6	3	3-0	4
	2-2 × 4	2-11	1	2-3	1	1-10	1	2-9	1	2-1	1	1-9	1	2-7	1	2-0	1	1-8	1
	2-2 × 6	4-4	1	3-4	2	2-10	2	4-1	1	3-2	2	2-8	2	3-10	1	3-0	2	2-6	2
	2-2 × 8	5-6	2	4-3	2	3-7	2	5-2	2	4-0	2	3-4	2	4-10	2	3-9	2	3-2	2
	2-2 × 10	6-7	2	5-0	2	4-2	2	6-1	2	4-9	2	4-0	2	5-9	2	4-5	2	3-9	3
	2-2 × 12	7-9	2	5-11	2	4-11	3	7-2	2	5-7	2	4-8	3	6-9	2	5-3	3	4-5	3
	3-2 × 8	6-11	1	5-3	2	4-5	2	6-5	1	5-0	2	4-2	2	6-1	1	4-8	2	4-0	2
	3-2 × 10	8-3	2	6-3	2	5-3	2	7-8	2	5-11	2	5-0	2	7-3	2	5-7	2	4-8	2
	3-2 × 12	9-8	2	7-5	2	6-2	2	9-0	2	7-0	2	5-10	2	8-6	2	6-7	2	5-6	3
	4-2 × 8	8-0	1	6-1	1	5-1	2	7-5	1	5-9	2	4-10	2	7-0	1	5-5	2	4-7	2
	4-2 × 10	9-6	1	7-3	2	6-1	2	8-10	1	6-10	2	5-9	2	8-4	1	6-5	2	5-5	2
	4-2 × 12	11-2	2	8-6	2	7-2	2	10-5	2	8-0	2	6-9	2	9-10	2	7-7	2	6-5	2

(continued)

TABLE R602.7(1)—continued
GIRDER SPANS[a] AND HEADER SPANS[a] FOR EXTERIOR BEARING WALLS
(Maximum spans for Douglas fir-larch, hem-fir, Southern pine and spruce-pine-fir[b] and required number of jack studs)

GIRDERS AND HEADERS SUPPORTING	SIZE	GROUND SNOW LOAD (psf)[e]																	
		30						50						70					
		Building width[c] (feet)																	
		20		24		36		20		24		36		20		24		36	
		Span[f]	NJ[d]	Span[f]	NJ[d]	Span[f]	NJ[d]	Span[f]	NJ[d]	Span[f]	NJ[d]	Span[f]	NJ[d]	Span[f]	NJ[d]	Span[f]	NJ[d]	Span[f]	NJ[d]
Roof, ceiling and two center-... ROOF, CEILING AND TWO FLOORS (CENTER BEARING)	1-2 × 6	2-8	2	2-1	2	1-10	2	2-7	2	2-0	2	1-9	2	2-5	2	1-11	2	1-8	2
	1-2 × 8	3-5	2	2-8	2	2-4	3	3-3	2	2-7	2	2-2	3	3-1	2	2-5	3	2-1	3
	1-2 × 10	4-0	2	3-2	3	2-9	3	3-10	2	3-1	3	2-7	3	3-8	2	2-11	3	2-5	3
	1-2 × 12	4-9	3	3-9	3	3-2	4	4-6	3	3-7	3	3-1	4	4-3	3	3-5	3	2-11	4
	2-2 × 4	2-8	1	2-1	1	1-9	1	2-6	1	2-0	1	1-8	1	2-5	1	1-11	1	1-7	1
	2-2 × 6	4-0	1	3-2	2	2-8	2	3-9	1	3-0	2	2-7	2	3-7	1	2-10	2	2-5	2
	2-2 × 8	5-0	2	4-0	2	3-5	2	4-10	2	3-10	2	3-3	2	4-7	2	3-7	2	3-1	2
	2-2 × 10	6-0	2	4-9	2	4-0	2	5-8	2	4-6	2	3-10	3	5-5	2	4-3	2	3-8	3
	2-2 × 12	7-0	2	5-7	2	4-9	3	6-8	2	5-4	3	4-6	3	6-4	2	5-0	3	4-3	3
	3-2 × 8	6-4	1	5-0	2	4-3	2	6-0	1	4-9	2	4-1	2	5-8	2	4-6	2	3-10	2
	3-2 × 10	7-6	2	5-11	2	5-1	2	7-1	2	5-8	2	4-10	2	6-9	2	5-4	2	4-7	2
	3-2 × 12	8-10	2	7-0	2	5-11	2	8-5	2	6-8	2	5-8	3	8-0	2	6-4	2	5-4	3
	4-2 × 8	7-3	1	5-9	1	4-11	1	6-11	1	5-6	2	4-8	2	6-7	1	5-2	2	4-5	2
	4-2 × 10	8-8	1	6-10	2	5-10	2	8-3	2	6-6	2	5-7	2	7-10	2	6-2	2	5-3	2
	4-2 × 12	10-2	2	8-1	2	6-10	2	9-8	2	7-8	2	6-7	2	9-2	2	7-3	2	6-2	2
Roof, ceiling, and two clear-... ROOF, CEILING AND TWO FLOORS (CLEAR SPAN)	1-2 × 6	2-3	2	1-9	2	1-5	2	2-3	2	1-9	2	1-5	3	2-2	2	1-8	2	1-5	3
	1-2 × 8	2-10	2	2-2	3	1-10	3	2-10	2	2-2	3	1-10	3	2-9	2	2-1	3	1-10	3
	1-2 × 10	3-4	2	2-7	3	2-2	3	3-4	3	2-7	3	2-2	4	3-3	3	2-6	3	2-2	4
	1-2 × 12	4-0	3	3-0	3	2-7	4	4-0	3	3-0	4	2-7	4	3-10	3	3-0	4	2-6	4
	2-2 × 4	2-3	1	1-8	1	1-4	1	2-3	1	1-8	1	1-4	1	2-2	1	1-8	1	1-4	2
	2-2 × 6	3-4	1	2-6	2	2-2	2	3-4	2	2-6	2	2-2	2	3-3	2	2-6	2	2-1	2
	2-2 × 8	4-3	2	3-3	2	2-8	2	4-3	2	3-3	2	2-8	2	4-1	2	3-2	2	2-8	3
	2-2 × 10	5-0	2	3-10	2	3-2	3	5-0	2	3-10	2	3-2	3	4-10	2	3-9	3	3-2	3
	2-2 × 12	5-11	2	4-6	3	3-9	3	5-11	2	4-6	3	3-9	3	5-8	2	4-5	3	3-9	3
	3-2 × 8	5-3	1	4-0	2	3-5	2	5-3	2	4-0	2	3-5	2	5-1	2	3-11	2	3-4	2
	3-2 × 10	6-3	2	4-9	2	4-0	2	6-3	2	4-9	2	4-0	2	6-1	2	4-8	2	4-0	3
	3-2 × 12	7-5	2	5-8	2	4-9	3	7-5	2	5-8	2	4-9	3	7-2	2	5-6	3	4-8	3
	4-2 × 8	6-1	1	4-8	2	3-11	2	6-1	1	4-8	2	3-11	2	5-11	1	4-7	2	3-10	2
	4-2 × 10	7-3	2	5-6	2	4-8	2	7-3	2	5-6	2	4-8	2	7-0	2	5-5	2	4-7	2
	4-2 × 12	8-6	2	6-6	2	5-6	2	8-6	2	6-6	2	5-6	2	8-3	2	6-4	2	5-4	3

For SI: 1 inch = 25.4 mm, 1 pound per square foot = 0.0479 kPa.

a. Spans are given in feet and inches.

b. Spans are based on minimum design properties for No. 2 grade lumber of Douglas fir-larch, hem-fir, Southern pine, and spruce-pine-fir.

c. Building width is measured perpendicular to the ridge. For widths between those shown, spans are permitted to be interpolated.

d. NJ = Number of jack studs required to support each end. Where the number of required jack studs equals one, the header is permitted to be supported by an approved framing anchor attached to the full-height wall stud and to the header.

e. Use 30 psf ground snow load for cases in which ground snow load is less than 30 psf and the roof live load is equal to or less than 20 psf.

f. Spans are calculated assuming the top of the header or girder is laterally braced by perpendicular framing. Where the top of the header or girder is not laterally braced (for example, cripple studs bearing on the header), tabulated spans for headers consisting of 2 × 8, 2 × 10, or 2 × 12 sizes shall be multiplied by 0.70 or the header or girder shall be designed.

TABLE R602.7(2)
GIRDER SPANS[a] AND HEADER SPANS[a] FOR INTERIOR BEARING WALLS
(Maximum spans for Douglas fir-larch, hem-fir, southern pine and spruce-pine-fir[b] and required number of jack studs)

HEADERS AND GIRDERS SUPPORTING	SIZE	BUILDING Width[c] (feet)					
		12		24		36	
		Span[e]	NJ[d]	Span[e]	NJ[d]	Span[e]	NJ[d]
One floor only	2-2 × 4	4-1	1	2-10	1	2-4	1
	2-2 × 6	6-1	1	4-4	1	3-6	1
	2-2 × 8	7-9	1	5-5	1	4-5	2
	2-2 × 10	9-2	1	6-6	2	5-3	2
	2-2 × 12	10-9	1	7-7	2	6-3	2
	3-2 × 8	9-8	1	6-10	1	5-7	1
	3-2 × 10	11-5	1	8-1	1	6-7	2
	3-2 × 12	13-6	1	9-6	2	7-9	2
	4-2 × 8	11-2	1	7-11	1	6-5	1
	4-2 × 10	13-3	1	9-4	1	7-8	1
	4-2 × 12	15-7	1	11-0	1	9-0	2
Two floors	2-2 × 4	2-7	1	1-11	1	1-7	1
	2-2 × 6	3-11	1	2-11	2	2-5	2
	2-2 × 8	5-0	1	3-8	2	3-1	2
	2-2 × 10	5-11	2	4-4	2	3-7	2
	2-2 × 12	6-11	2	5-2	2	4-3	3
	3-2 × 8	6-3	1	4-7	2	3-10	2
	3-2 × 10	7-5	1	5-6	2	4-6	2
	3-2 × 12	8-8	2	6-5	2	5-4	2
	4-2 × 8	7-2	1	5-4	1	4-5	2
	4-2 × 10	8-6	1	6-4	2	5-3	2
	4-2 × 12	10-1	1	7-5	2	6-2	2

For SI: 1 inch = 25.4 mm, 1 foot = 304.8 mm.

a. Spans are given in feet and inches.

b. Spans are based on minimum design properties for No. 2 grade lumber of Douglas fir-larch, hem-fir, Southern pine, and spruce-pine-fir.

c. Building width is measured perpendicular to the ridge. For widths between those shown, spans are permitted to be interpolated.

d. NJ = Number of jack studs required to support each end. Where the number of required jack studs equals one, the header is permitted to be supported by an approved framing anchor attached to the full-height wall stud and to the header.

e. Spans are calculated assuming the top of the header or girder is laterally braced by perpendicular framing. Where the top of the header or girder is not laterally braced (for example, cripple studs bearing on the header), tabulated spans for headers consisting of 2 × 8, 2 × 10, or 2 × 12 sizes shall be multiplied by 0.70 or the header or girder shall be designed.

TABLE R602.7(3)
GIRDER AND HEADER SPANS[a] FOR OPEN PORCHES
(Maximum span for Douglas fir-larch, hem-fir, Southern pine and spruce-pine-fir[b])

SIZE	SUPPORTING ROOF						SUPPORTING FLOOR	
	GROUND SNOW LOAD (psf)							
	30		50		70			
	DEPTH OF PORCH[c] (feet)							
	8	14	8	14	8	14	8	14
2-2 × 6	7-6	5-8	6-2	4-8	5-4	4-0	6-4	4-9
2-2 × 8	10-1	7-7	8-3	6-2	7-1	5-4	8-5	6-4
2-2 × 10	12-4	9-4	10-1	7-7	8-9	6-7	10-4	7-9
2-2 × 12	14-4	10-10	11-8	8-10	10-1	7-8	11-11	9-0

For SI: 1 inch = 25.4 mm, 1 foot = 304.8 mm, 1 pound per square foot = 0.0479 kPa.

a. Spans are given in feet and inches.

b. Tabulated values assume No. 2 grade lumber, wet service and incising for refractory species. Use 30 psf ground snow load for cases in which ground snow load is less than 30 psf and the roof live load is equal to or less than 20 psf.

c. Porch depth is measured horizontally from building face to centerline of the header. For depths between those shown, spans are permitted to be interpolated.

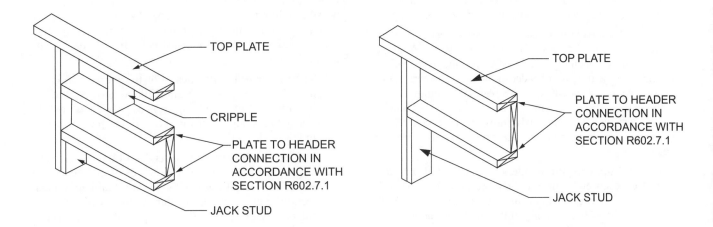

FIGURE R602.7.1(1)
SINGLE-MEMBER HEADER IN EXTERIOR BEARING WALL

FIGURE R602.7.1(2)
ALTERNATIVE SINGLE-MEMBER HEADER WITHOUT CRIPPLE

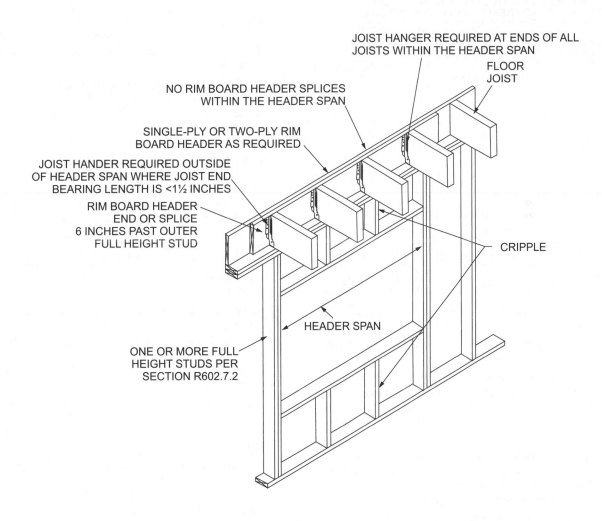

For SI: 25.4 mm = 1 inch.

FIGURE R602.7.2
RIM BOARD HEADER CONSTRUCTION

R602.7.3 Wood structural panel box headers. Wood structural panel box headers shall be constructed in accordance with Figure R602.7.3 and Table R602.7.3.

R602.7.4 Nonbearing walls. Load-bearing headers are not required in interior or exterior nonbearing walls. A single flat 2-inch by 4-inch (51 mm by 102 mm) member shall be permitted to be used as a header in interior or exterior nonbearing walls for openings up to 8 feet (2438 mm) in width if the vertical distance to the parallel nailing surface above is not more than 24 inches (610 mm). For such nonbearing headers, cripples or blocking are not required above the header.

R602.7.5 Supports for headers. Headers shall be supported on each end with one or more jack studs or with approved framing anchors in accordance with Table R602.7(1) or R602.7(2). The full-height stud adjacent to each end of the header shall be end nailed to each end of the header with four-16d nails (3.5 inches × 0.135 inches). The minimum number of full-height studs at each end of a header shall be in accordance with Table R602.7.5.

TABLE R602.7.5
MINIMUM NUMBER OF FULL-HEIGHT STUDS
AT EACH END OF HEADERS IN EXTERIOR WALLS[a]

MAXIMUM HEADER SPAN (feet)	ULTIMATE DESIGN WIND SPEED AND EXPOSURE CATEGORY	
	< 140 mph, Exposure B or < 130 mph, Exposure C	≤ 115 mph, Exposure B[b]
4	1	1
6	2	1
8	2	1
10	3	2
12	3	2
14	3	2
16	4	2
18	4	2

For SI: 1 foot = 304.8 mm, 1 mile per hour = 0.447 m/s.

a. For header spans between those given, use the minimum number of full-height studs associated with the larger header span.

b. The tabulated minimum number of full-height studs is applicable where jack studs are provided to support the header at each end in accordance with Table R602.7(1). Where a framing anchor is used to support the header in lieu of a jack stud in accordance with Note d of Table R602.7(1), the minimum number of full-height studs at each end of a header shall be in accordance with requirements for wind speed < 140 mph, Exposure B.

R602.8 Fireblocking required. Fireblocking shall be provided in accordance with Section R302.11.

R602.9 Cripple walls. Foundation cripple walls shall be framed of studs not smaller than the studding above. Where exceeding 4 feet (1219 mm) in height, such walls shall be framed of studs having the size required for an additional *story*.

Cripple walls with a stud height less than 14 inches (356 mm) shall be continuously sheathed on one side with wood structural panels fastened to both the top and bottom plates in accordance with Table R602.3(1), or the cripple walls shall be constructed of solid blocking.

Cripple walls shall be supported on continuous foundations.

R602.10 Wall bracing. Buildings shall be braced in accordance with this section or, when applicable, Section R602.12. Where a building, or portion thereof, does not comply with one or more of the bracing requirements in this section, those portions shall be designed and constructed in accordance with Section R301.1.

R602.10.1 Braced wall lines. For the purpose of determining the amount and location of bracing required in each story level of a building, *braced wall lines* shall be designated as straight lines in the building plan placed in accordance with this section.

R602.10.1.1 Length of a braced wall line. The length of a *braced wall line* shall be the distance between its ends. The end of a *braced wall line* shall be the intersection with a perpendicular *braced wall line*, an angled *braced wall line* as permitted in Section R602.10.1.4 or an exterior wall as shown in Figure R602.10.1.1.

R602.10.1.2 Offsets along a braced wall line. Exterior walls parallel to a *braced wall line* shall be offset not more than 4 feet (1219 mm) from the designated *braced wall line* location as shown in Figure R602.10.1.1. Interior walls used as bracing shall be offset not more than 4 feet (1219 mm) from a *braced wall line* through the interior of the building as shown in Figure R602.10.1.1.

R602.10.1.3 Spacing of braced wall lines. The spacing between parallel *braced wall lines* shall be in accordance with Table R602.10.1.3. Intermediate *braced wall lines* through the interior of the building shall be permitted.

R602.10.1.4 Angled walls. Any portion of a wall along a *braced wall line* shall be permitted to angle out of plane for a maximum diagonal length of 8 feet (2438 mm). Where the angled wall occurs at a corner, the length of the *braced wall line* shall be measured from the projected corner as shown in Figure R602.10.1.4. Where the diagonal length is greater than 8 feet (2438 mm), it shall be considered to be a separate *braced wall line* and shall be braced in accordance with Section R602.10.1.

R602.10.2 Braced wall panels. *Braced wall panels* shall be full-height sections of wall that shall not have vertical or horizontal offsets. *Braced wall panels* shall be constructed and placed along a *braced wall line* in accordance with this section and the bracing methods specified in Section R602.10.4.

R602.10.2.1 Braced wall panel uplift load path. The bracing lengths in Table R602.10.3(1) apply only when uplift loads are resisted in accordance with Section R602.3.5.

R602.10.2.2 Locations of braced wall panels. A *braced wall panel* shall begin within 10 feet (3810 mm) from each end of a *braced wall line* as determined in Section R602.10.1.1. The distance between adjacent edges of *braced wall panels* along a *braced wall line* shall be not greater than 20 feet (6096 mm) as shown in Figure R602.10.2.2.

TABLE R602.7.3
MAXIMUM SPANS FOR WOOD STRUCTURAL PANEL BOX HEADERS[a]

HEADER CONSTRUCTION[b]	HEADER DEPTH (inches)	HOUSE DEPTH (feet)				
		24	26	28	30	32
Wood structural panel–one side	9	4	4	3	3	—
	15	5	5	4	3	3
Wood structural panel–both sides	9	7	5	5	4	3
	15	8	8	7	7	6

For SI: 1 inch = 25.4 mm, 1 foot = 304.8 mm.

a. Spans are based on single story with clear-span trussed roof or two story with floor and roof supported by interior-bearing walls.

b. See Figure R602.7.3 for construction details.

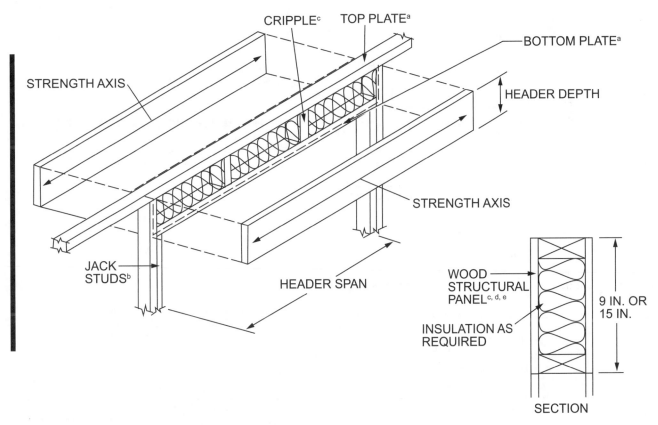

For SI: 1 inch = 25.4 mm, 1 foot = 304.8 mm.

NOTES:

a. The top and bottom plates shall be continuous at header location.

b. Jack studs shall be used for spans over 4 feet.

c. Cripple spacing shall be the same as for studs.

d. Wood structural panel faces shall be single pieces of $^{15}/_{32}$-inch-thick Exposure 1 (exterior glue) or thicker, installed on the interior or exterior or both sides of the header.

e. Wood structural panel faces shall be nailed to framing and cripples with 8d common or galvanized box nails spaced 3 inches on center, staggering alternate nails $^{1}/_{2}$ inch. Galvanized nails shall be hot-dipped or tumbled.

FIGURE R602.7.3
TYPICAL WOOD STRUCTURAL PANEL BOX HEADER CONSTRUCTION

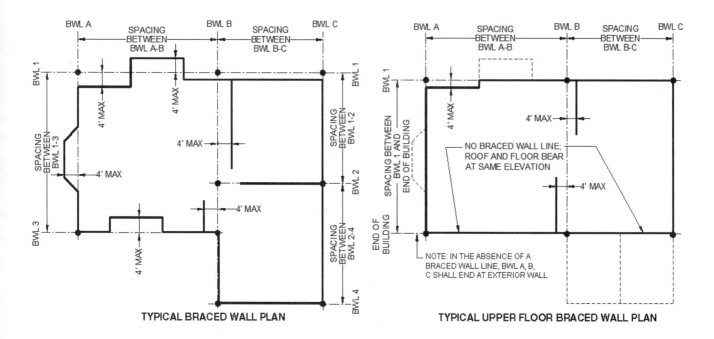

For SI: 1 foot = 304.8 mm.

FIGURE R602.10.1.1
BRACED WALL LINES

TABLE R602.10.1.3
BRACED WALL LINE SPACING

APPLICATION	CONDITION	BUILDING TYPE	BRACED WALL LINE SPACING CRITERIA	
			Maximum Spacing	Exception to Maximum Spacing
Wind bracing	Ultimate design wind speed 100 mph to < 140 mph	Detached, townhouse	60 feet	None
Seismic bracing	SDC A – C	Detached	Use wind bracing	
	SDC A – B	Townhouse	Use wind bracing	
	SDC C	Townhouse	35 feet	Up to 50 feet when length of required bracing per Table R602.10.3(3) is adjusted in accordance with Table R602.10.3(4).
	SDC D_0, D_1, D_2	Detached, townhouses, one- and two-story only	25 feet	Up to 35 feet to allow for a single room not to exceed 900 square feet. Spacing of all other braced wall lines shall not exceed 25 feet.
	SDC D_0, D_1, D_2	Detached, townhouse	25 feet	Up to 35 feet when length of required bracing per Table R602.10.3(3) is adjusted in accordance with Table R602.10.3(4).

For SI: 1 foot = 304.8 mm, 1 square foot = 0.0929 m^2, 1 mile per hour = 0.447 m/s.

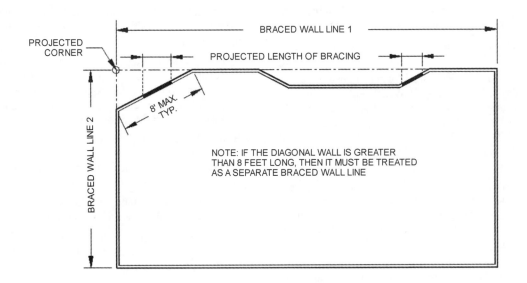

For SI: 1 foot = 304.8 mm.

FIGURE R602.10.1.4
ANGLED WALLS

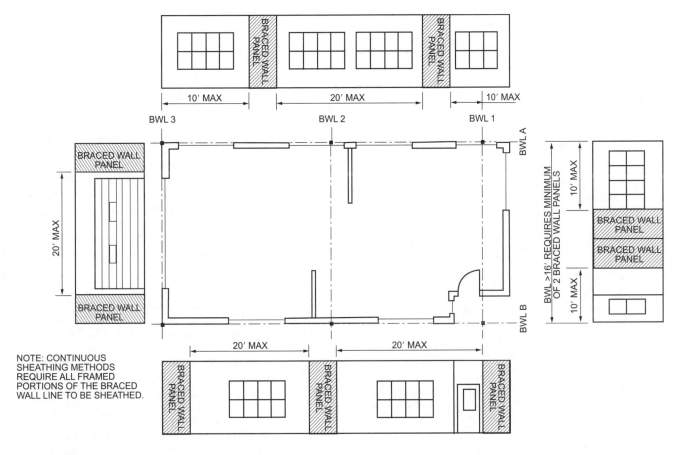

NOTE: CONTINUOUS
SHEATHING METHODS
REQUIRE ALL FRAMED
PORTIONS OF THE BRACED
WALL LINE TO BE SHEATHED.

For SI: 1 foot = 304.8 mm.

FIGURE R602.10.2.2
LOCATION OF BRACED WALL PANELS

R602.10.2.2.1 Location of braced wall panels in Seismic Design Categories D$_0$, D$_1$ and D$_2$. Braced wall panels shall be located at each end of a braced wall line.

> **Exception:** Braced wall panels constructed of Method WSP or BV-WSP and continuous sheathing methods as specified in Section R602.10.4 shall be permitted to begin not more than 10 feet (3048 mm) from each end of a braced wall line provided that each end complies with one of the following:
>
> 1. A minimum 24-inch-wide (610 mm) panel for Methods WSP, CS-WSP, CS-G and CS-PF is applied to each side of the building corner as shown in End Condition 4 of Figure R602.10.7.
>
> 2. The end of each braced wall panel closest to the end of the braced wall line shall have an 1,800 lb (8 kN) hold-down device fastened to the stud at the edge of the braced wall panel closest to the corner and to the foundation or framing below as shown in End Condition 5 of Figure R602.10.7.

R602.10.2.3 Minimum number of braced wall panels. *Braced wall lines* with a length of 16 feet (4877 mm) or less shall have not less than two *braced wall panels* of any length or one *braced wall panel* equal to 48 inches (1219 mm) or more. *Braced wall lines* greater than 16 feet (4877 mm) shall have not less than two *braced wall panels*.

R602.10.3 Required length of bracing. The required length of bracing along each *braced wall line* shall be determined as follows:

1. All buildings in Seismic Design Categories A and B shall use Table R602.10.3(1) and the applicable adjustment factors in Table R602.10.3(2).

2. Detached buildings in Seismic Design Category C shall use Table R602.10.3(1) and the applicable adjustment factors in Table R602.10.3(2).

3. Townhouses in Seismic Design Category C shall use the greater value determined from Table R602.10.3(1) or R602.10.3(3) and the applicable adjustment factors in Table R602.10.3(2) or R602.10.3(4), respectively.

4. All buildings in Seismic Design Categories D$_0$, D$_1$ and D$_2$ shall use the greater value determined from Table R602.10.3(1) or R602.10.3(3) and the applicable adjustment factors in Table R602.10.3(2) or R602.10.3(4), respectively.

Only *braced wall panels* parallel to the *braced wall line* shall contribute toward the required length of bracing of that *braced wall line*. *Braced wall panels* along an angled wall meeting the minimum length requirements of Tables R602.10.5 and R602.10.5.2 shall be permitted to contribute its projected length toward the minimum required length of bracing for the *braced wall line* as shown in Figure R602.10.1.4. Any *braced wall panel* on an angled wall

at the end of a *braced wall line* shall contribute its projected length for only one of the *braced wall lines* at the projected corner.

Exception: The length of wall bracing for dwellings in Seismic Design Categories D$_0$, D$_1$ and D$_2$ with stone or masonry veneer installed in accordance with Section R703.8 and exceeding the first-story height shall be in accordance with Section R602.10.6.5.

R602.10.4 Construction methods for braced wall panels. Intermittent and continuously sheathed *braced wall panels* shall be constructed in accordance with this section and the methods listed in Table R602.10.4.

R602.10.4.1 Mixing methods. Mixing of bracing methods shall be permitted as follows:

1. Mixing intermittent bracing and continuous sheathing methods from story to story shall be permitted.

2. Mixing intermittent bracing methods from *braced wall line* to *braced wall line* within a story shall be permitted. In regions within Seismic Design Categories A, B and C where the ultimate design wind speed is less than or equal to 130 mph (58m/s), mixing of intermittent bracing and continuous sheathing methods from braced wall line to braced wall line within a story shall be permitted.

3. Mixing intermittent bracing methods along a *braced wall line* shall be permitted in Seismic Design Categories A and B, and detached dwellings in Seismic Design Category C, provided that the length of required bracing in accordance with Table R602.10.3(1) or R602.10.3(3) is the highest value of all intermittent bracing methods used.

4. Mixing of continuous sheathing methods CS-WSP, CS-G and CS-PF along a *braced wall line* shall be permitted. Intermittent methods ABW, PFH and PFG shall be permitted to be used along a *braced wall line* with continuous sheathed methods, provided that the length of required bracing for that braced wall line is determined in accordance with Table R602.10.3(1) or R602.10.3(3) using the highest value of the bracing methods used.

5. In Seismic Design Categories A and B, and for detached one- and two-family dwellings in Seismic Design Category C, mixing of intermittent bracing methods along the interior portion of a *braced wall line* with continuous sheathing methods CS-WSP, CS-G and CS-PF along the exterior portion of the same braced wall line shall be permitted. The length of required bracing shall be the highest value of all intermittent bracing methods used in accordance with Table R602.10.3(1) or R602.10.3(3) as adjusted by Tables R602.10.3(2) and R602.10.3(4), respectively. The requirements of Section R602.10.7 shall apply to each end of the continuously sheathed portion of the braced wall line.

TABLE R602.10.3(1)
BRACING REQUIREMENTS BASED ON WIND SPEED

• EXPOSURE CATEGORY B • 30-FOOT MEAN ROOF HEIGHT • 10-FOOT WALL HEIGHT • 2 BRACED WALL LINES			MINIMUM TOTAL LENGTH (FEET) OF BRACED WALL PANELS REQUIRED ALONG EACH BRACED WALL LINE[a]			
Ultimate Design Wind Speed (mph)	Story Location	Braced Wall Line Spacing[c] (feet)	Method LIB[b]	Method GB	Methods DWB, WSP, SFB, PBS, PCP, HPS, BV-WSP, ABW, PFH, PFC, CS-SFB	Methods CS-WSP, CS-G, CS-PF
≤ 110		10	3.5	3.5	2.0	1.5
		20	6.0	6.0	3.5	3.0
		30	8.5	8.5	5.0	4.5
		40	11.5	11.5	6.5	5.5
		50	14.0	14.0	8.0	7.0
		60	16.5	16.5	9.5	8.0
		10	6.5	6.5	3.5	3.0
		20	11.5	11.5	6.5	5.5
		30	16.5	16.5	9.5	8.0
		40	21.5	21.5	12.5	10.5
		50	26.5	26.5	15.5	13.0
		60	31.5	31.5	18.0	15.5
		10	NP	9.5	5.5	4.5
		20	NP	17.0	10.0	8.5
		30	NP	24.5	14.0	12.0
		40	NP	32.0	18.5	15.5
		50	NP	39.5	22.5	19.0
		60	NP	46.5	26.5	23.0
≤ 115		10	3.5	3.5	2.0	2.0
		20	6.5	6.5	3.5	3.5
		30	9.5	9.5	5.5	4.5
		40	12.5	12.5	7.0	6.0
		50	15.0	15.0	9.0	7.5
		60	18.0	18.0	10.5	9.0
		10	7.0	7.0	4.0	3.5
		20	12.5	12.5	7.5	6.5
		30	18.0	18.0	10.5	9.0
		40	23.5	23.5	13.5	11.5
		50	29.0	29.0	16.5	14.0
		60	34.5	34.5	20.0	17.0
		10	NP	10.0	6.0	5.0
		20	NP	18.5	11.0	9.0
		30	NP	27.0	15.5	13.0
		40	NP	35.0	20.0	17.0
		50	NP	43.0	24.5	21.0
		60	NP	51.0	29.0	25.0

(continued)

TABLE R602.10.3(1)—continued
BRACING REQUIREMENTS BASED ON WIND SPEED

			MINIMUM TOTAL LENGTH (FEET) OF BRACED WALL PANELS REQUIRED ALONG EACH BRACED WALL LINE[a]			

- EXPOSURE CATEGORY B
- 30-FOOT MEAN ROOF HEIGHT
- 10-FOOT WALL HEIGHT
- 2 BRACED WALL LINES

Ultimate Design Wind Speed (mph)	Story Location	Braced Wall Line Spacing[c] (feet)	Method LIB[b]	Method GB	Methods DWB, WSP, SFB, PBS, PCP, HPS, BV-WSP, ABW, PFH, PFG, CS-SFB	Methods CS-WSP, CS-G, CS-PF
≤ 120		10	4.0	4.0	2.5	2.0
		20	7.0	7.0	4.0	3.5
		30	10.5	10.5	6.0	5.0
		40	13.5	13.5	8.0	6.5
		50	16.5	16.5	9.5	8.0
		60	19.5	19.5	11.5	9.5
		10	7.5	7.5	4.5	3.5
		20	14.0	14.0	8.0	7.0
		30	20.0	20.0	11.5	9.5
		40	25.5	25.5	15.0	12.5
		50	31.5	31.5	18.0	15.5
		60	37.5	37.5	21.5	18.5
		10	NP	11.0	6.5	5.5
		20	NP	20.5	11.5	10.0
		30	NP	29.0	17.0	14.5
		40	NP	38.0	22.0	18.5
		50	NP	47.0	27.0	23.0
		60	NP	55.5	32.0	27.0
≤ 130		10	4.5	4.5	2.5	2.5
		20	8.5	8.5	5.0	4.0
		30	12.0	12.0	7.0	6.0
		40	15.5	15.5	9.0	7.5
		50	19.5	19.5	11.0	9.5
		60	23.0	23.0	13.0	11.0
		10	8.5	8.5	5.0	4.5
		20	16.0	16.0	9.5	8.0
		30	23.0	23.0	13.5	11.5
		40	30.0	30.0	17.5	15.0
		50	37.0	37.0	21.5	18.0
		60	44.0	44.0	25.0	21.5
		10	NP	13.0	7.5	6.5
		20	NP	24.0	13.5	11.5
		30	NP	34.5	19.5	17.0
		40	NP	44.5	25.5	22.0
		50	NP	55.0	31.5	26.5
		60	NP	65.0	37.5	31.5

(continued)

TABLE R602.10.3(1)—continued
BRACING REQUIREMENTS BASED ON WIND SPEED

• EXPOSURE CATEGORY B • 30-FOOT MEAN ROOF HEIGHT • 10-FOOT WALL HEIGHT • 2 BRACED WALL LINES			MINIMUM TOTAL LENGTH (FEET) OF BRACED WALL PANELS REQUIRED ALONG EACH BRACED WALL LINE[a]			
Ultimate Design Wind Speed (mph)	Story Location	Braced Wall Line Spacing[c] (feet)	Method LIB[b]	Method GB	Methods DWB, WSP, SFB, PBS, PCP, HPS, BV-WSP, ABW, PFH, PFG, CS-SFB	Methods CS-WSP, CS-G, CS-PF
< 140		10	5.5	5.5	3.0	2.5
		20	10.0	10.0	5.5	5.0
		30	14.0	14.0	8.0	7.0
		40	18.0	18.0	10.5	9.0
		50	22.5	22.5	13.0	11.0
		60	26.5	26.5	15.0	13.0
		10	10.0	10.0	6.0	5.0
		20	18.5	18.5	11.0	9.0
		30	27.0	27.0	15.5	13.0
		40	35.0	35.0	20.0	17.0
		50	43.0	43.0	24.5	21.0
		60	51.0	51.0	29.0	25.0
		10	NP	15.0	8.5	7.5
		20	NP	27.5	16.0	13.5
		30	NP	39.5	23.0	19.5
		40	NP	51.5	29.5	25.0
		50	NP	63.5	36.5	31.0
		60	NP	75.5	43.0	36.5

For SI: 1 inch = 25.4 mm, 1 foot = 304.8 mm, 1 mile per hour = 0.447 m/s.

NP = Not Permitted.

a. Linear interpolation shall be permitted.

b. Method LIB shall have gypsum board fastened to not less than one side with nails or screws in accordance with Table R602.3(1) for exterior sheathing or Table R702.3.5 for interior gypsum board. Spacing of fasteners at panel edges shall not exceed 8 inches.

c. Where three or more parallel braced wall lines are present and the distances between adjacent braced wall lines are different, the average dimension shall be permitted to be used for braced wall line spacing.

TABLE R602.10.3(2)
WIND ADJUSTMENT FACTORS TO THE REQUIRED LENGTH OF WALL BRACING

ITEM NUMBER	ADJUSTMENT BASED ON	STORY/SUPPORTING	CONDITION	ADJUSTMENT FACTOR[a, b] [multiply length from Table R602.10.3(1) by this factor]	APPLICABLE METHODS
1	Exposure category[d]	One-story structure	B	1.00	All methods
			C	1.20	
			D	1.50	
		Two-story structure	B	1.00	
			C	1.30	
			D	1.60	
		Three-story structure	B	1.00	
			C	1.40	
			D	1.70	
2	Roof eave-to-ridge height	Roof only	≤ 5 feet	0.70	
			10 feet	1.00	
			15 feet	1.30	
			20 feet	1.60	
		Roof + 1 floor	≤ 5 feet	0.85	
			10 feet	1.00	
			15 feet	1.15	
			20 feet	1.30	
		Roof + 2 floors	≤ 5 feet	0.90	
			10 feet	1.00	
			15 feet	1.10	
			20 feet	Not permitted	
3	Story height (Section R301.3)	Any story	8 feet	0.90	
			9 feet	0.95	
			10 feet	1.00	
			11 feet	1.05	
			12 feet	1.10	
4	Number of braced wall lines (per plan direction)[c]	Any story	2	1.00	
			3	1.30	
			4	1.45	
			≥ 5	1.60	
5	Additional 800-pound hold-down device	Top story only	Fastened to the end studs of each braced wall panel and to the foundation or framing below	0.80	DWB, WSP, SFB, PBS, PCP, HPS
6	Interior gypsum board finish (or equivalent)	Any story	Omitted from inside face of braced wall panels	1.40	DWB, WSP, SFB, PBS, PCP, HPS, CS-WSP, CS-G, CS-SFB
7	Gypsum board fastening	Any story	4 inches o.c. at panel edges, including top and bottom plates, and all horizontal joints blocked	0.7	GB
8	Horizontal blocking	Any story	Horizontal block is omitted	2.0	WSP, CS-WSP

For SI: 1 inch = 25.4 mm, 1 foot = 304.8 mm, 1 pound = 4.48 N.

a. Linear interpolation shall be permitted.

b. The total adjustment factor is the product of all applicable adjustment factors.

c. The adjustment factor is permitted to be 1.0 when determining bracing amounts for intermediate braced wall lines provided the bracing amounts on adjacent braced wall lines are based on a spacing and number that neglects the intermediate braced wall line.

d. The same adjustment factor shall be applied to all braced wall lines on all floors of the structure, based on the worst-case exposure category.

TABLE R602.10.3(3)
BRACING REQUIREMENTS BASED ON SEISMIC DESIGN CATEGORY

- SOIL CLASS D[b]
- WALL HEIGHT = 10 FEET
- 10 PSF FLOOR DEAD LOAD
- 15 PSF ROOF/CEILING DEAD LOAD
- BRACED WALL LINE SPACING ≤ 25 FEET

MINIMUM TOTAL LENGTH (FEET) OF BRACED WALL PANELS REQUIRED ALONG EACH BRACED WALL LINE[a, f]

Seismic Design Category	Story Location	Braced Wall Line Length (feet)[c]	Method LIB[d]	Method GB	Methods DWB, SFB, PBS, PCP, HPS, CS-SFB[e]	Method WSP	Methods CS-WSP, CS-G, CS-PF
C (townhouses only)		10	2.5	2.5	2.5	1.6	1.4
		20	5.0	5.0	5.0	3.2	2.7
		30	7.5	7.5	7.5	4.8	4.1
		40	10.0	10.0	10.0	6.4	5.4
		50	12.5	12.5	12.5	8.0	6.8
		10	NP	4.5	4.5	3.0	2.6
		20	NP	9.0	9.0	6.0	5.1
		30	NP	13.5	13.5	9.0	7.7
		40	NP	18.0	18.0	12.0	10.2
		50	NP	22.5	22.5	15.0	12.8
		10	NP	6.0	6.0	4.5	3.8
		20	NP	12.0	12.0	9.0	7.7
		30	NP	18.0	18.0	13.5	11.5
		40	NP	24.0	24.0	18.0	15.3
		50	NP	30.0	30.0	22.5	19.1
D_0		10	NP	2.8	2.8	1.8	1.6
		20	NP	5.5	5.5	3.6	3.1
		30	NP	8.3	8.3	5.4	4.6
		40	NP	11.0	11.0	7.2	6.1
		50	NP	13.8	13.8	9.0	7.7
		10	NP	5.3	5.3	3.8	3.2
		20	NP	10.5	10.5	7.5	6.4
		30	NP	15.8	15.8	11.3	9.6
		40	NP	21.0	21.0	15.0	12.8
		50	NP	26.3	26.3	18.8	16.0
		10	NP	7.3	7.3	5.3	4.5
		20	NP	14.5	14.5	10.5	9.0
		30	NP	21.8	21.8	15.8	13.4
		40	NP	29.0	29.0	21.0	17.9
		50	NP	36.3	36.3	26.3	22.3

(continued)

TABLE R602.10.3(3)—continued
BRACING REQUIREMENTS BASED ON SEISMIC DESIGN CATEGORY

• SOIL CLASS D[b] • WALL HEIGHT = 10 FEET • 10 PSF FLOOR DEAD LOAD • 15 PSF ROOF/CEILING DEAD LOAD • BRACED WALL LINE SPACING ≤ 25 FEET			MINIMUM TOTAL LENGTH (FEET) OF BRACED WALL PANELS REQUIRED ALONG EACH BRACED WALL LINE[a, f]				
Seismic Design Category	Story Location	Braced Wall Line Length (feet)[c]	Method LIB[d]	Method GB	Methods DWB, SFB, PBS, PCP, HPS, CS-SFB[e]	Method WSP	Methods CS-WSP, CS-G, CS-PF
D₁		10	NP	3.0	3.0	2.0	1.7
		20	NP	6.0	6.0	4.0	3.4
		30	NP	9.0	9.0	6.0	5.1
		40	NP	12.0	12.0	8.0	6.8
		50	NP	15.0	15.0	10.0	8.5
		10	NP	6.0	6.0	4.5	3.8
		20	NP	12.0	12.0	9.0	7.7
		30	NP	18.0	18.0	13.5	11.5
		40	NP	24.0	24.0	18.0	15.3
		50	NP	30.0	30.0	22.5	19.1
		10	NP	8.5	8.5	6.0	5.1
		20	NP	17.0	17.0	12.0	10.2
		30	NP	25.5	25.5	18.0	15.3
		40	NP	34.0	34.0	24.0	20.4
		50	NP	42.5	42.5	30.0	25.5
D₂		10	NP	4.0	4.0	2.5	2.1
		20	NP	8.0	8.0	5.0	4.3
		30	NP	12.0	12.0	7.5	6.4
		40	NP	16.0	16.0	10.0	8.5
		50	NP	20.0	20.0	12.5	10.6
		10	NP	7.5	7.5	5.5	4.7
		20	NP	15.0	15.0	11.0	9.4
		30	NP	22.5	22.5	16.5	14.0
		40	NP	30.0	30.0	22.0	18.7
		50	NP	37.5	37.5	27.5	23.4
		10	NP	NP	NP	NP	NP
		20	NP	NP	NP	NP	NP
		30	NP	NP	NP	NP	NP
		40	NP	NP	NP	NP	NP
		50	NP	NP	NP	NP	NP
	Cripple wall below one- or two-story dwelling	10	NP	NP	NP	7.5	6.4
		20	NP	NP	NP	15.0	12.8
		30	NP	NP	NP	22.5	19.1
		40	NP	NP	NP	30.0	25.5
		50	NP	NP	NP	37.5	31.9

For SI: 1 inch = 25.4 mm, 1 foot = 304.8 mm, 1 pound per square foot = 0.0479 kPa.

NP = Not Permitted.

a. Linear interpolation shall be permitted.

b. Wall bracing lengths are based on a soil site class "D." Interpolation of bracing length between the S_{ds} values associated with the seismic design categories shall be permitted when a site-specific S_{ds} value is determined in accordance with Section 1613.2 of the *International Building Code*.

c. Where the braced wall line length is greater than 50 feet, braced wall lines shall be permitted to be divided into shorter segments having lengths of 50 feet or less, and the amount of bracing within each segment shall be in accordance with this table.

d. Method LIB shall have gypsum board fastened to not less than one side with nails or screws in accordance with Table R602.3(1) for exterior sheathing or Table R702.3.5 for interior gypsum board. Spacing of fasteners at panel edges shall not exceed 8 inches.

e. Methods PFG and CS-SFB do not apply in Seismic Design Categories D₀, D₁ and D₂.

f. Where more than one bracing method is used, mixing methods shall be in accordance with Section R602.10.4.1.

TABLE R602.10.3(4)
SEISMIC ADJUSTMENT FACTORS TO THE REQUIRED LENGTH OF WALL BRACING

ITEM NUMBER	ADJUSTMENT BASED ON	STORY	CONDITION	ADJUSTMENT FACTOR[a, b] [Multiply length from Table R602.10.3(3) by this factor]	APPLICABLE METHODS
1	Story height (Section 301.3)	Any story	≤ 10 feet	1.0	All methods
			> 10 feet and ≤ 12 feet	1.2	
2	Braced wall line spacing, townhouses in SDC C	Any story	≤ 35 feet	1.0	
			> 35 feet and ≤ 50 feet	1.43	
3	Braced wall line spacing, in SDC D_0, D_1, D_2[c]	Any story	> 25 feet and ≤ 30 feet	1.2	
			> 30 feet and ≤ 35 feet	1.4	
4	Wall dead load	Any story	> 8 psf and < 15 psf	1.0	
			< 8 psf	0.85	
5	Roof/ceiling dead load for wall supporting	1-, 2- or 3-story building	≤15 psf	1.0	
		2- or 3-story building	> 15 psf and ≤ 25 psf	1.1	
		1-story building or top story	> 15 psf and ≤ 25 psf	1.2	
6	Walls with stone or masonry veneer, townhouses in SDC C[d, e]			1.0	All methods
				1.5	
				1.5	
7	Walls with stone or masonry veneer, detached one- and two-family dwellings in SDC $D_0 – D_2$[d, f]	Any story	See Table R602.10.6.5		BV-WSP
8	Walls with stone or masonry veneer, detached one- and two-family dwellings in SDC $D_0 – D_2$[d, f]	First and second story of two-story dwelling	See Table R602.10.6.5	1.2	WSP, CS-WSP
9	Interior gypsum board finish (or equivalent)	Any story	Omitted from inside face of braced wall panels	1.5	DWB, WSP, SFB, PBS, PCP, HPS, CS-WSP, CS-G, CS-SFB
10	Horizontal blocking	Any story	Horizontal blocking omitted	2.0	WSP, CS-WSP

For SI: 1 foot = 304.8 mm, 1 pound per square foot = 0.0479 kPa.

a. Linear interpolation shall be permitted.

b. The total length of bracing required for a given wall line is the product of all applicable adjustment factors.

c. The length-to-width ratio for the floor/roof diaphragm shall not exceed 3:1.

d. Applies to stone or masonry veneer exceeding the first story height.

e. The adjustment factor for stone or masonry veneer shall be applied to all exterior braced wall lines and all braced wall lines on the interior of the building, backing or perpendicular to and laterally supporting veneered walls.

f. See Section R602.10.6.5 for requirements where stone or masonry veneer does not exceed the first-story height.

TABLE R602.10.4
BRACING METHODS

METHODS, MATERIAL		MINIMUM THICKNESS	FIGURE	CONNECTION CRITERIA[a]	
				Fasteners	Spacing
Intermittent Bracing Methods	**LIB** Let-in-bracing	1 × 4 wood or approved metal straps at 45° to 60° angles for maximum 16″ stud spacing		Wood: 2-8d common nails or 3-8d ($2^1/_2$″ long x 0.113″ dia.) nails	Wood: per stud and top and bottom plates
				Metal strap: per manufacturer	Metal: per manufacturer
	DWB Diagonal wood boards	$^3/_4$″ (1″ nominal) for maximum 24″ stud spacing		2-8d ($2^1/_2$″ long × 0.113″ dia.) nails or 2 - $1^3/_4$″ long staples	Per stud
	WSP Wood structural panel (See Section R604)	$^3/_8$″		Exterior sheathing per Table R602.3(3)	6″ edges 12″ field
				Interior sheathing per Table R602.3(1) or R602.3(2)	Varies by fastener
	BV-WSP[e] Wood structural panels with stone or masonry veneer (See Section R602.10.6.5)	$^7/_{16}$″	See Figure R602.10.6.5	8d common ($2^1/_2$″ × 0.131) nails	4″ at panel edges 12″ at intermediate supports 4″ at braced wall panel end posts
	SFB Structural fiberboard sheathing	$^1/_2$″ or $^{25}/_{32}$″ for maximum 16″ stud spacing		$1^1/_2$″ long × 0.12″ dia. (for $^1/_2$″ thick sheathing) $1^3/_4$″ long × 0.12″ dia. (for $^{25}/_{32}$″ thick sheathing) galvanized roofing nails	3″ edges 6″ field
	GB Gypsum board	$^1/_2$″		Nails or screws per Table R602.3(1) for exterior locations	For all braced wall panel locations: 7″ edges (including top and bottom plates) 7″ field
				Nails or screws per Table R702.3.5 for interior locations	
	PBS Particleboard sheathing (See Section R605)	$^3/_8$″ or $^1/_2$″ for maximum 16″ stud spacing		For $^3/_8$″, 6d common (2″ long × 0.113″ dia.) nails For $^1/_2$″, 8d common ($2^1/_2$″ long × 0.131″ dia.) nails	3″ edges 6″ field
	PCP Portland cement plaster	See Section R703.7 for maximum 16″ stud spacing		$1^1/_2$″ long, 11 gage, $^7/_{16}$″ dia. head nails or $^7/_8$″ long, 16 gage staples	6″ o.c. on all framing members
	HPS Hardboard panel siding	$^7/_{16}$″ for maximum 16″ stud spacing		0.092″ dia., 0.225″ dia. head nails with length to accommodate $1^1/_2$″ penetration into studs	4″ edges 8″ field
	ABW Alternate braced wall	$^3/_8$″		See Section R602.10.6.1	See Section R602.10.6.1

(continued)

TABLE R602.10.4—continued
BRACING METHODS

METHODS, MATERIAL		MINIMUM THICKNESS	FIGURE	CONNECTION CRITERIA[a]	
				Fasteners	Spacing
Intermittent Bracing Methods	**PFH** Portal frame with hold-downs	$^3/_8$″		See Section R602.10.6.2	See Section R602.10.6.2
	PFG Portal frame at garage	$^7/_{16}$″		See Section R602.10.6.3	See Section R602.10.6.3
Continuous Sheathing Methods	**CS-WSP** Continuously sheathed wood structural panel	$^3/_8$″		Exterior sheathing per Table R602.3(3)	6″ edges 12″ field
				Interior sheathing per Table R602.3(1) or R602.3(2)	Varies by fastener
	CS-G[b, c] Continuously sheathed wood structural panel adjacent to garage openings	$^3/_8$″		See Method CS-WSP	See Method CS-WSP
	CS-PF Continuously sheathed portal frame	$^7/_{16}$″		See Section R602.10.6.4	See Section R602.10.6.4
	CS-SFB[d] Continuously sheathed structural fiberboard	$^1/_2$″ or $^{25}/_{32}$″ for maximum 16″ stud spacing		$1^1/_2$″ long × 0.12″ dia. (for $^1/_2$″ thick sheathing) $1^3/_4$″ long × 0.12″ dia. (for $^{25}/_{32}$″ thick sheathing) galvanized roofing nails	3″ edges 6″ field

For SI: 1 inch = 25.4 mm, 1 foot = 304.8 mm, 1 degree = 0.0175 rad, 1 pound per square foot = 47.8 N/m², 1 mile per hour = 0.447 m/s.

a. Adhesive attachment of wall sheathing, including Method GB, shall not be permitted in Seismic Design Categories C, D_0, D_1 and D_2.

b. Applies to panels next to garage door opening where supporting gable end wall or roof load only. Shall only be used on one wall of the garage. In Seismic Design Categories D_0, D_1 and D_2, roof covering dead load shall not exceed 3 psf.

c. Garage openings adjacent to a Method CS-G panel shall be provided with a header in accordance with Table R602.7(1). A full-height clear opening shall not be permitted adjacent to a Method CS-G panel.

d. Method CS-SFB does not apply in Seismic Design Categories D_0, D_1 and D_2.

e. Method applies to detached one- and two-family dwellings in Seismic Design Categories D_0 through D_2 only.

R602.10.4.2 Continuous sheathing methods. Continuous sheathing methods require structural panel sheathing to be used on all sheathable surfaces on one side of a *braced wall line* including areas above and below openings and gable end walls and shall meet the requirements of Section R602.10.7.

R602.10.4.3 Braced wall panel interior finish material. *Braced wall panels* shall have gypsum wall board installed on the side of the wall opposite the bracing material. Gypsum wall board shall be not less than $^1/_2$ inch (12.7 mm) in thickness and be fastened with nails or screws in accordance with Table R602.3(1) for exterior sheathing or Table R702.3.5 for interior gypsum wall board. Spacing of fasteners at panel edges for gypsum wall board opposite Method LIB bracing shall not exceed 8 inches (203 mm). Interior finish material shall not be glued in Seismic Design Categories D_0, D_1 and D_2.

Exceptions:

1. Interior finish material is not required opposite wall panels that are braced in accordance with Methods GB, BV-WSP, ABW, PFH, PFG and CS-PF, unless otherwise required by Section R302.6.

2. An approved interior finish material with an in-plane shear resistance equivalent to gypsum board shall be permitted to be substituted, unless otherwise required by Section R302.6.

3. Except for Method LIB, gypsum wall board is permitted to be omitted provided that the required length of bracing in Tables R602.10.3(1) and R602.10.3(3) is multiplied by the appropriate adjustment factor in Tables R602.10.3(2) and R602.10.3(4), respectively, unless otherwise required by Section R302.6.

R602.10.4.4 Panel joints. Vertical joints of panel sheathing shall occur over and be fastened to common studs. Horizontal joints of panel sheathing in *braced wall panels* shall occur over and be fastened to common blocking of a thickness of $1^1/_2$ inches (38 mm) or greater.

Exceptions:

1. For methods WSP and CS-WSP, blocking of horizontal joints is permitted to be omitted when adjustment factor No. 8 of Table R602.10.3(2) or No. 9 of Table R602.10.3(4) is applied.

2. Vertical joints of panel sheathing shall be permitted to occur over double studs, where adjoining panel edges are attached to separate studs with the required panel edge fastening schedule, and the adjacent studs are attached together with two rows of 10d box nails [3 inches by 0.128 inch (76.2 mm by 3.25 mm)] at 10 inches o.c. (254 mm).

3. Blocking at horizontal joints shall not be required in wall segments that are not counted as *braced wall panels*.

4. Where Method GB panels are installed horizontally, blocking of horizontal joints is not required.

R602.10.5 Minimum length of a braced wall panel. The minimum length of a *braced wall panel* shall comply with Table R602.10.5. For Methods CS-WSP and CS-SFB, the minimum panel length shall be based on the adjacent clear opening height in accordance with Table R602.10.5 and Figure R602.10.5. Where a panel has an opening on either side of differing heights, the taller opening height shall be used to determine the panel length.

R602.10.5.1 Contributing length. For purposes of computing the required length of bracing in Tables R602.10.3(1) and R602.10.3(3), the contributing length of each *braced wall panel* shall be as specified in Table R602.10.5.

R602.10.5.2 Partial credit. For Methods DWB, WSP, SFB, PBS, PCP and HPS in Seismic Design Categories A, B and C, panels between 36 inches and 48 inches (914 mm and 1219 mm) in length shall be considered a *braced wall panel* and shall be permitted to partially contribute toward the required length of bracing in Tables R602.10.3(1) and R602.10.3(3), and the contributing length shall be determined from Table R602.10.5.2.

R602.10.6 Construction of Methods ABW, PFH, PFG, CS-PF and BV-WSP. Methods ABW, PFH, PFG, CS-PF and BV-WSP shall be constructed as specified in Sections R602.10.6.1 through R602.10.6.5.

R602.10.6.1 Method ABW: Alternate braced wall panels. Method ABW *braced wall panels* shall be constructed in accordance with Figure R602.10.6.1. The hold-down force shall be in accordance with Table R602.10.6.1.

R602.10.6.2 Method PFH: Portal frame with hold-downs. Method PFH *braced wall panels* shall be constructed in accordance with Figure R602.10.6.2.

R602.10.6.3 Method PFG: Portal frame at garage door openings in Seismic Design Categories A, B and C. Where supporting a roof or one story and a roof, a Method PFG *braced wall panel* constructed in accordance with Figure R602.10.6.3 shall be permitted on either side of garage door openings.

R602.10.6.4 Method CS-PF: Continuously sheathed portal frame. Continuously sheathed portal frame *braced wall panels* shall be constructed in accordance with Figure R602.10.6.4 and Table R602.10.6.4. The number of continuously sheathed portal frame panels in a single *braced wall line* shall not exceed four.

TABLE R602.10.5
MINIMUM LENGTH OF BRACED WALL PANELS

METHOD (See Table R602.10.4)		MINIMUM LENGTH[a] (inches) Wall Height					CONTRIBUTING LENGTH (inches)
		8 feet	9 feet	10 feet	11 feet	12 feet	
DWB, WSP, SFB, PBS, PCP, HPS, BV-WSP		48	48	48	53	58	Actual[b]
GB		48	48	48	53	58	Double sided = Actual Single sided = 0.5 × Actual
LIB		55	62	69	NP	NP	Actual[b]
ABW	SDC A, B and C, ultimate design wind speed < 140 mph	28	32	34	38	42	48
	SDC D$_0$, D$_1$ and D$_2$, ultimate design wind speed < 140 mph	32	32	34	NP	NP	
CS-G		24	27	30	33	36	Actual[b]
CS-WSP, CS-SFB	Adjacent clear opening height (inches)						
	≤ 64	24	27	30	33	36	Actual[b]
	68	26	27	30	33	36	
	72	27	27	30	33	36	
	76	30	29	30	33	36	
	80	32	30	30	33	36	
	84	35	32	32	33	36	
	88	38	35	33	33	36	
	92	43	37	35	35	36	
	96	48	41	38	36	36	
	100	—	44	40	38	38	
	104	—	49	43	40	39	
	108	—	54	46	43	41	
	112	—	—	50	45	43	
	116	—	—	55	48	45	
	120	—	—	60	52	48	
	124	—	—	—	56	51	
	128	—	—	—	61	54	
	132	—	—	—	66	58	
	136	—	—	—	—	62	
	140	—	—	—	—	66	
	144	—	—	—	—	72	

METHOD (See Table R602.10.4)		Portal header height					
		8 feet	9 feet	10 feet	11 feet	12 feet	
PFH	Supporting roof only	16	16	16	Note c	Note c	48
	Supporting one story and roof	24	24	24	Note c	Note c	
PFG		24	27	30	Note d	Note d	1.5 × Actual[b]
CS-PF	SDC A, B and C	16	18	20	Note e	Note e	1.5 × Actual[b]
	SDC D$_0$, D$_1$ and D$_2$	16	18	20	Note e	Note e	Actual[b]

For SI: 1 inch = 25.4 mm, 1 foot = 304.8 mm, 1 mile per hour = 0.447 m/s.

NP = Not Permitted.

a. Linear interpolation shall be permitted.

b. Use the actual length where it is greater than or equal to the minimum length.

c. Maximum header height for PFH is 10 feet in accordance with Figure R602.10.6.2, but wall height shall be permitted to be increased to 12 feet with pony wall.

d. Maximum header height for PFG is 10 feet in accordance with Figure R602.10.6.3, but wall height shall be permitted to be increased to 12 feet with pony wall.

e. Maximum header height for CS-PF is 10 feet in accordance with Figure R602.10.6.4, but wall height shall be permitted to be increased to 12 feet with pony wall.

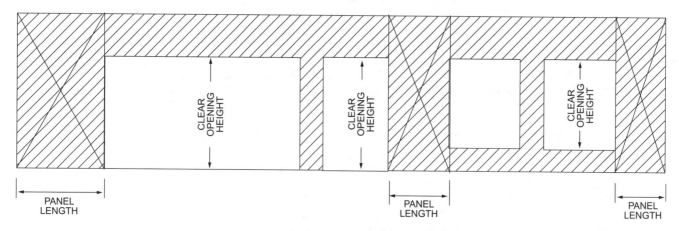

FIGURE R602.10.5
BRACED WALL PANELS WITH CONTINUOUS SHEATHING

TABLE R602.10.5.2
PARTIAL CREDIT FOR BRACED WALL PANELS LESS THAN 48 INCHES IN ACTUAL LENGTH

ACTUAL LENGTH OF BRACED WALL PANEL (inches)	CONTRIBUTING LENGTH OF BRACED WALL PANEL (inches)[a]	
	8-foot Wall Height	9-foot Wall Height
48	48	48
42	36	36
36	27	NA

For SI: 1 inch = 25.4 mm, 1 foot = 304.8 mm.

NA = Not Applicable.

a. Linear interpolation shall be permitted.

TABLE R602.10.6.1
MINIMUM HOLD-DOWN FORCES FOR METHOD ABW BRACED WALL PANELS

SEISMIC DESIGN CATEGORY AND WIND SPEED	SUPPORTING/STORY	HOLD-DOWN FORCE (pounds)				
		Height of Braced Wall Panel				
		8 feet	9 feet	10 feet	11 feet	12 feet
SDC A, B and C Ultimate design wind speed < 140 mph	One story	1,800	1,800	1,800	2,000	2,200
	First of two stories	3,000	3,000	3,000	3,300	3,600
SDC D_0, D_1 and D_2 Ultimate design wind speed <140 mph	One story	1,800	1,800	1,800	NP	NP
	First of two stories	3,000	3,000	3,000	NP	NP

For SI: 1 inch = 25.4 mm, 1 foot = 304.8 mm, 1 pound = 4.45 N, 1 mile per hour = 0.447 m/s.

NP = Not Permitted.

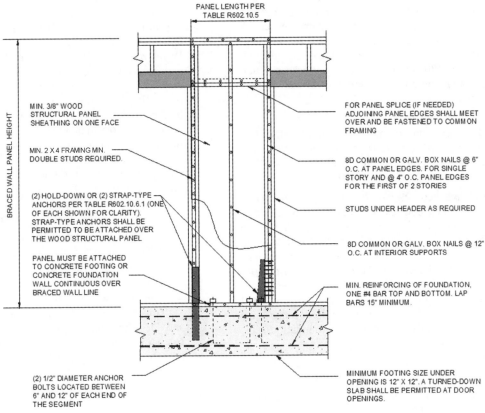

PANEL LENGTH PER
TABLE R602.10.5

BRACED WALL PANEL HEIGHT

MIN. 3/8" WOOD
STRUCTURAL PANEL
SHEATHING ON ONE FACE

MIN. 2 X 4 FRAMING MIN.
DOUBLE STUDS REQUIRED.

(2) HOLD-DOWN OR (2) STRAP-TYPE
ANCHORS PER TABLE R602.10.6.1 (ONE
OF EACH SHOWN FOR CLARITY).
STRAP-TYPE ANCHORS SHALL BE
PERMITTED TO BE ATTACHED OVER
THE WOOD STRUCTURAL PANEL

PANEL MUST BE ATTACHED
TO CONCRETE FOOTING OR
CONCRETE FOUNDATION
WALL CONTINUOUS OVER
BRACED WALL LINE

FOR PANEL SPLICE (IF NEEDED)
ADJOINING PANEL EDGES SHALL MEET
OVER AND BE FASTENED TO COMMON
FRAMING

8D COMMON OR GALV. BOX NAILS @ 6"
O.C. AT PANEL EDGES. FOR SINGLE
STORY AND @ 4" O.C. PANEL EDGES
FOR THE FIRST OF 2 STORIES

STUDS UNDER HEADER AS REQUIRED

8D COMMON OR GALV. BOX NAILS @ 12"
O.C. AT INTERIOR SUPPORTS

MIN. REINFORCING OF FOUNDATION,
ONE #4 BAR TOP AND BOTTOM. LAP
BARS 15" MINIMUM.

(2) 1/2" DIAMETER ANCHOR
BOLTS LOCATED BETWEEN
6" AND 12" OF EACH END OF
THE SEGMENT

MINIMUM FOOTING SIZE UNDER
OPENING IS 12" X 12". A TURNED-DOWN
SLAB SHALL BE PERMITTED AT DOOR
OPENINGS.

For SI: 1 inch = 25.4 mm.

FIGURE R602.10.6.1
METHOD ABW—ALTERNATE BRACED WALL PANEL

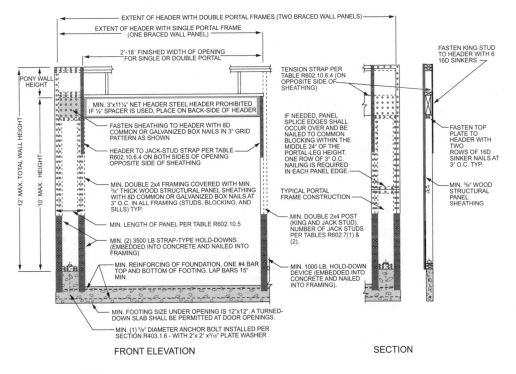

EXTENT OF HEADER WITH DOUBLE PORTAL FRAMES (TWO BRACED WALL PANELS)

EXTENT OF HEADER WITH SINGLE PORTAL FRAME
(ONE BRACED WALL PANEL)

2'-18' FINISHED WIDTH OF OPENING
FOR SINGLE OR DOUBLE PORTAL

PONY WALL
HEIGHT

12' MAX. TOTAL WALL HEIGHT

10' MAX. HEIGHT

MIN. 3"x11¼" NET HEADER STEEL HEADER PROHIBITED
IF ½" SPACER IS USED, PLACE ON BACK-SIDE OF HEADER

FASTEN SHEATHING TO HEADER WITH 8D
COMMON OR GALVANIZED BOX NAILS IN 3" GRID
PATTERN AS SHOWN

HEADER TO JACK-STUD STRAP PER TABLE
R602.10.6.4 ON BOTH SIDES OF OPENING
OPPOSITE SIDE OF SHEATHING

MIN. DOUBLE 2x4 FRAMING COVERED WITH MIN.
³⁄₈" THICK WOOD STRUCTURAL PANEL SHEATHING
WITH 8D COMMON OR GALVANIZED BOX NAILS AT
3" O.C. IN ALL FRAMING (STUDS, BLOCKING, AND
SILLS) TYP.

MIN. LENGTH OF PANEL PER TABLE R602.10.5

MIN. (2) 3500 LB STRAP-TYPE HOLD-DOWNS
(EMBEDDED INTO CONCRETE AND NAILED INTO
FRAMING)

MIN. REINFORCING OF FOUNDATION, ONE #4 BAR
TOP AND BOTTOM OF FOOTING. LAP BARS 15"
MIN.

MIN. FOOTING SIZE UNDER OPENING IS 12"x12". A TURNED-
DOWN SLAB SHALL BE PERMITTED AT DOOR OPENINGS.

MIN. (1) ⁵⁄₈" DIAMETER ANCHOR BOLT INSTALLED PER
SECTION R403.1.6 - WITH 2"x 2" x³⁄₁₆" PLATE WASHER

TENSION STRAP PER
TABLE R602.10.6.4 (ON
OPPOSITE SIDE OF
SHEATHING)

IF NEEDED, PANEL
SPLICE EDGES SHALL
OCCUR OVER AND BE
NAILED TO COMMON
BLOCKING WITHIN THE
MIDDLE 24" OF THE
PORTAL-LEG HEIGHT.
ONE ROW OF 3" O.C.
NAILING IS REQUIRED
IN EACH PANEL EDGE.

TYPICAL PORTAL
FRAME CONSTRUCTION

MIN. DOUBLE 2x4 POST
(KING AND JACK STUD).
NUMBER OF JACK STUDS
PER TABLES R602.7(1) &
(2).

MIN. 1000 LB. HOLD-DOWN
DEVICE (EMBEDDED INTO
CONCRETE AND NAILED
INTO FRAMING).

FASTEN KING STUD
TO HEADER WITH 6
16D SINKERS

FASTEN TOP
PLATE TO
HEADER WITH
TWO
ROWS OF 16D
SINKER NAILS AT
3" O.C. TYP.

MIN. ³⁄₈" WOOD
STRUCTURAL
PANEL
SHEATHING

FRONT ELEVATION

SECTION

For SI: 1 inch = 25.4 mm, 1 foot = 304.8 mm.

FIGURE R602.10.6.2
METHOD PFH—PORTAL FRAME WITH HOLD-DOWNS

R602.10.6.5 Wall bracing for dwellings with stone and masonry veneer in Seismic Design Categories D_0, D_1 and D_2. Where stone and masonry veneer are installed in accordance with Section R703.8, wall bracing on exterior *braced wall lines* and *braced wall lines* on the interior of the building, backing or perpendicular to and laterally supporting veneered walls shall comply with this section.

Where dwellings in Seismic Design Categories D_0, D_1 and D_2 have stone or masonry veneer installed in accordance with Section R703.8, and the veneer does not exceed the first-story height, wall bracing shall be in accordance with Section R602.10.3.

Where detached one- or two-family dwellings in Seismic Design Categories D_0, D_1 and D_2 have stone or masonry veneer installed in accordance with Section R703.8, and the veneer exceeds the first-*story height*, wall bracing at exterior *braced wall lines* and *braced wall lines* on the interior of the building shall be constructed using Method BV-WSP in accordance with this section and Figure R602.10.6.5. Cripple walls shall not be permitted, and required interior *braced wall lines* shall be supported on continuous foundations.

Where detached one- or two-family *dwellings* in Seismic Design Categories D_0, D_1 and D_2 have exterior veneer installed in accordance with Section R703.8 and are braced in accordance with Method WSP or CS-WSP, veneer shall be permitted in the second story in accordance with Item 1 or 2, provided that the *dwelling* does not extend more than two stories above grade plane, the veneer does not exceed 5 inches (127 mm) in thickness, the height of veneer on gable-end walls does not extend more than 8 feet (2438 mm) above the bearing wall top plate elevation, and the total length of *braced wall panel* specified by Table R602.10.3(3) is multiplied by 1.2 for each first- and second-story *braced wall line*.

1. The total area of the veneer on the second-story exterior walls shall be permitted to extend up to 25 percent of the occupied second floor area.

2. The veneer on the second-story exterior walls shall be permitted to cover one side of the *dwelling*, including walls on bay windows and similar appurtenances within the one dwelling side.

Townhouses in Seismic Design Categories D_0, D_1 and D_2 with stone or masonry veneer exceeding the first-story height shall be designed in accordance with accepted engineering practice.

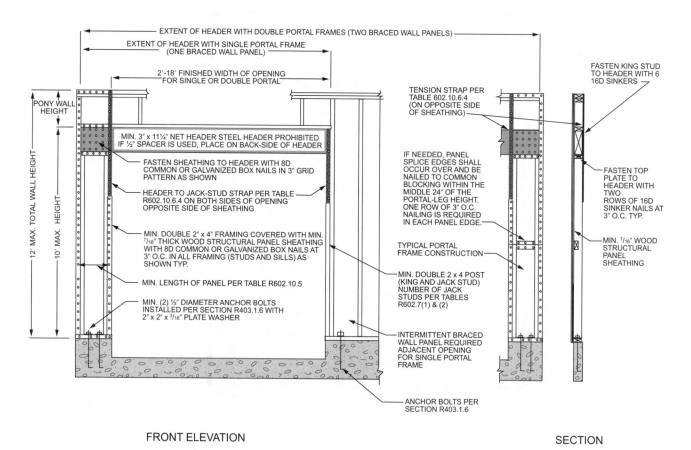

FRONT ELEVATION

SECTION

For SI: 1 inch = 25.4 mm, 1 foot = 304.8 mm.

FIGURE R602.10.6.3
METHOD PFG—PORTAL FRAME AT GARAGE DOOR OPENINGS IN SEISMIC DESIGN CATEGORIES A, B AND C

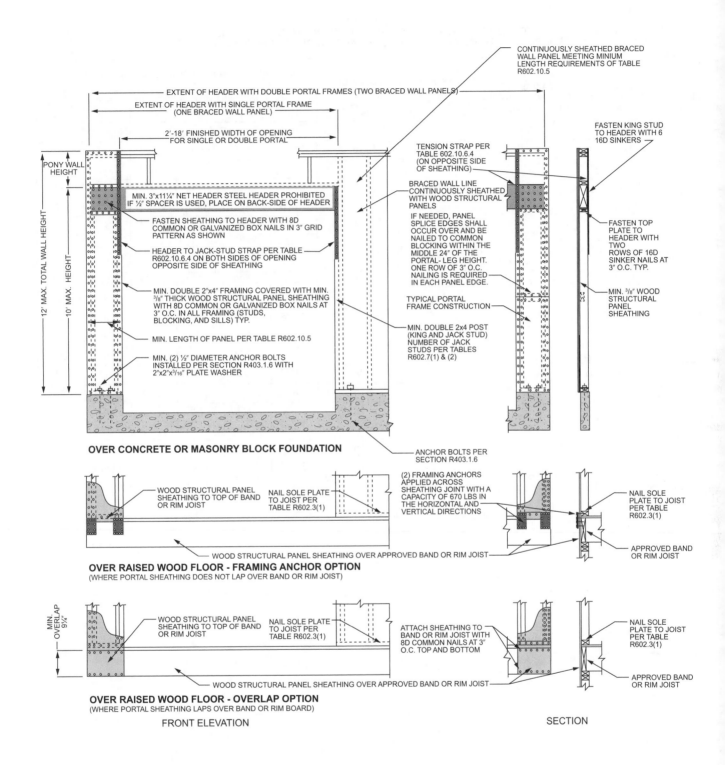

CONTINUOUSLY SHEATHED BRACED WALL PANEL MEETING MINIUM LENGTH REQUIREMENTS OF TABLE R602.10.5

EXTENT OF HEADER WITH DOUBLE PORTAL FRAMES (TWO BRACED WALL PANELS)

EXTENT OF HEADER WITH SINGLE PORTAL FRAME (ONE BRACED WALL PANEL)

2'-18' FINISHED WIDTH OF OPENING FOR SINGLE OR DOUBLE PORTAL

FASTEN KING STUD TO HEADER WITH 6 16D SINKERS

PONY WALL HEIGHT

12' MAX. TOTAL WALL HEIGHT

10' MAX. HEIGHT

TENSION STRAP PER TABLE 602.10.6.4 (ON OPPOSITE SIDE OF SHEATHING)

MIN. 3"x11¼" NET HEADER STEEL HEADER PROHIBITED IF ½" SPACER IS USED, PLACE ON BACK-SIDE OF HEADER

FASTEN SHEATHING TO HEADER WITH 8D COMMON OR GALVANIZED BOX NAILS IN 3" GRID PATTERN AS SHOWN

HEADER TO JACK-STUD STRAP PER TABLE R602.10.6.4 ON BOTH SIDES OF OPENING OPPOSITE SIDE OF SHEATHING

MIN. DOUBLE 2"x4" FRAMING COVERED WITH MIN. ³/₈" THICK WOOD STRUCTURAL PANEL SHEATHING WITH 8D COMMON OR GALVANIZED BOX NAILS AT 3" O.C. IN ALL FRAMING (STUDS, BLOCKING, AND SILLS) TYP.

MIN. LENGTH OF PANEL PER TABLE R602.10.5

MIN. (2) ½" DIAMETER ANCHOR BOLTS INSTALLED PER SECTION R403.1.6 WITH 2"x2"x³/₁₆" PLATE WASHER

BRACED WALL LINE CONTINUOUSLY SHEATHED WITH WOOD STRUCTURAL PANELS

IF NEEDED, PANEL SPLICE EDGES SHALL OCCUR OVER AND BE NAILED TO COMMON BLOCKING WITHIN THE MIDDLE 24" OF THE PORTAL- LEG HEIGHT. ONE ROW OF 3" O.C. NAILING IS REQUIRED IN EACH PANEL EDGE.

TYPICAL PORTAL FRAME CONSTRUCTION

MIN. DOUBLE 2x4 POST (KING AND JACK STUD) NUMBER OF JACK STUDS PER TABLES R602.7(1) & (2)

FASTEN TOP PLATE TO HEADER WITH TWO ROWS OF 16D SINKER NAILS AT 3" O.C. TYP.

MIN. ³/₈" WOOD STRUCTURAL PANEL SHEATHING

OVER CONCRETE OR MASONRY BLOCK FOUNDATION

ANCHOR BOLTS PER SECTION R403.1.6

WOOD STRUCTURAL PANEL SHEATHING TO TOP OF BAND OR RIM JOIST

NAIL SOLE PLATE TO JOIST PER TABLE R602.3(1)

(2) FRAMING ANCHORS APPLIED ACROSS SHEATHING JOINT WITH A CAPACITY OF 670 LBS IN THE HORIZONTAL AND VERTICAL DIRECTIONS

NAIL SOLE PLATE TO JOIST PER TABLE R602.3(1)

APPROVED BAND OR RIM JOIST

WOOD STRUCTURAL PANEL SHEATHING OVER APPROVED BAND OR RIM JOIST

OVER RAISED WOOD FLOOR - FRAMING ANCHOR OPTION
(WHERE PORTAL SHEATHING DOES NOT LAP OVER BAND OR RIM JOIST)

MIN. OVERLAP 9¼"

WOOD STRUCTURAL PANEL SHEATHING TO TOP OF BAND OR RIM JOIST

NAIL SOLE PLATE TO JOIST PER TABLE R602.3(1)

ATTACH SHEATHING TO BAND OR RIM JOIST WITH 8D COMMON NAILS AT 3" O.C. TOP AND BOTTOM

NAIL SOLE PLATE TO JOIST PER TABLE R602.3(1)

APPROVED BAND OR RIM JOIST

WOOD STRUCTURAL PANEL SHEATHING OVER APPROVED BAND OR RIM JOIST

OVER RAISED WOOD FLOOR - OVERLAP OPTION
(WHERE PORTAL SHEATHING LAPS OVER BAND OR RIM BOARD)

FRONT ELEVATION

SECTION

For SI: 1 inch = 25.4 mm, 1 foot = 304.8 mm.

FIGURE R602.10.6.4
METHOD CS-PF—CONTINUOUSLY SHEATHED PORTAL FRAME PANEL CONSTRUCTION

TABLE R602.10.6.4
TENSION STRAP CAPACITY FOR RESISTING WIND PRESSURES
PERPENDICULAR TO METHODS PFH, PFG AND CS-PF BRACED WALL PANELS[a]

MINIMUM WALL STUD FRAMING NOMINAL SIZE AND GRADE	MAXIMUM PONY WALL HEIGHT (feet)	MAXIMUM TOTAL WALL HEIGHT (feet)	MAXIMUM OPENING WIDTH (feet)	TENSION STRAP CAPACITY REQUIRED (pounds)[a]					
				Ultimate Design Wind Speed V_{ult} (mph)					
				110	115	130	110	115	130
				Exposure B			Exposure C		
2 × 4 No. 2 Grade	0	10	18	1,000	1,000	1,000	1,000	1,000	1,050
	1	10	9	1,000	1,000	1,000	1,000	1,000	1,750
			16	1,000	1,025	2,050	2,075	2,500	3,950
			18	1,000	1,275	2,375	2,400	2,850	DR
	2	10	9	1,000	1,000	1,475	1,500	1,875	3,125
			16	1,775	2,175	3,525	3,550	4,125	DR
			18	2,075	2,500	3,950	3,975	DR	DR
	2	12	9	1,150	1,500	2,650	2,675	3,175	DR
			16	2,875	3,375	DR	DR	DR	DR
			18	3,425	3,975	DR	DR	DR	DR
	4	12	9	2,275	2,750	DR	DR	DR	DR
			12	3,225	3,775	DR	DR	DR	DR
2 × 6 Stud Grade	2	12	9	1,000	1,000	1,700	1,700	2,025	3,050
			16	1,825	2,150	3,225	3,225	3,675	DR
			18	2,200	2,550	3,725	3,750	DR	DR
	4	12	9	1,450	1,750	2,700	2,725	3,125	DR
			16	2,050	2,400	DR	DR	DR	DR
			18	3,350	3,800	DR	DR	DR	DR

For SI: 1 inch = 25.4 mm, 1 foot = 304.8 mm, 1 mile per hour = 0.447 m/s.

DR = Design Required.

a. Straps shall be installed in accordance with manufacturer's recommendations.

TABLE R602.10.6.5
METHOD BV-WSP WALL BRACING REQUIREMENTS

| SEISMIC DESIGN CATEGORY | STORY | BRACED WALL LINE LENGTH (FEET) | | | | | SINGLE-STORY HOLD-DOWN FORCE (pounds)[a] | CUMULATIVE HOLD-DOWN FORCE (pounds)[b] |
| | | 10 | 20 | 30 | 40 | 50 | | |
		Minimum Total Length (feet) of Braced Wall Panels Required Along each Braced Wall Line						
D₀		4.0	7.0	10.5	14.0	17.5	NA	—
		4.0	7.0	10.5	14.0	17.5	1900	—
		4.5	9.0	13.5	18.0	22.5	3500	5400
		6.0	12.0	18.0	24.0	30.0	3500	8900
D₁		4.5	9.0	13.5	18.0	22.5	2100	—
		4.5	9.0	13.5	18.0	22.5	3700	5800
		6.0	12.0	18.0	24.0	30.0	3700	9500
D₂		5.5	11.0	16.5	22.0	27.5	2300	—
		5.5	11.0	16.5	22.0	27.5	3900	6200
		NP	NP	NP	NP	NP	NA	NA

For SI: 1 inch = 25.4 mm, 1 foot = 304.8 mm, 1 pound per square foot = 0.479 kPa, 1 pound-force = 4.448 N.

NP = Not Permitted.

NA = Not Applicable.

a. Hold-down force is minimum allowable stress design load for connector providing uplift tie from wall framing at end of braced wall panel at the noted story to wall framing at end of braced wall panel at the story below, or to foundation or foundation wall. Use single-story hold-down force where edges of braced wall panels do not align; a continuous load path to the foundation shall be maintained.

b. Where hold-down connectors from stories above align with stories below, use cumulative hold-down force to size middle- and bottom-story hold-down connectors.

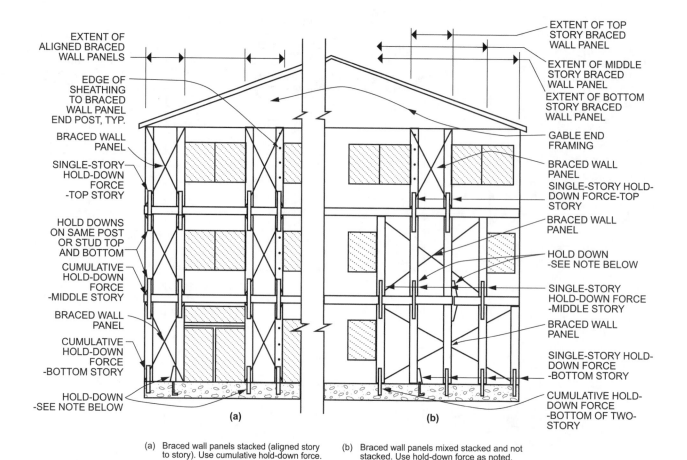

EXTENT OF ALIGNED BRACED WALL PANELS

EDGE OF SHEATHING TO BRACED WALL PANEL END POST, TYP.

BRACED WALL PANEL

SINGLE-STORY HOLD-DOWN FORCE -TOP STORY

HOLD DOWNS ON SAME POST OR STUD TOP AND BOTTOM

CUMULATIVE HOLD-DOWN FORCE -MIDDLE STORY

BRACED WALL PANEL

CUMULATIVE HOLD-DOWN FORCE -BOTTOM STORY

HOLD-DOWN -SEE NOTE BELOW

EXTENT OF TOP STORY BRACED WALL PANEL

EXTENT OF MIDDLE STORY BRACED WALL PANEL

EXTENT OF BOTTOM STORY BRACED WALL PANEL

GABLE END FRAMING

BRACED WALL PANEL

SINGLE-STORY HOLD-DOWN FORCE-TOP STORY

BRACED WALL PANEL

HOLD DOWN -SEE NOTE BELOW

SINGLE-STORY HOLD-DOWN FORCE -MIDDLE STORY

BRACED WALL PANEL

SINGLE-STORY HOLD-DOWN FORCE -BOTTOM STORY

CUMULATIVE HOLD-DOWN FORCE -BOTTOM OF TWO-STORY

(a)

(b)

(a) Braced wall panels stacked (aligned story to story). Use cumulative hold-down force.

(b) Braced wall panels mixed stacked and not stacked. Use hold-down force as noted.

Note: Hold downs should be strap ties, tension ties, or other approved hold-down devices and shall be installed in accordance with the manufacturer's instructions.

FIGURE R602.10.6.5
METHOD BV-WSP—WALL BRACING FOR DWELLINGS WITH STONE AND MASONRY VENEER IN SEISMIC DESIGN CATEGORIES D$_0$, D$_1$ and D$_2$

R602.10.6.5.1 Length of bracing. The length of bracing along each *braced wall line* shall be the greater of that required by the ultimate design wind speed and *braced wall line* spacing in accordance with Table R602.10.3(1) as adjusted by the factors in Table R602.10.3(2) or the seismic design category and *braced wall line* length in accordance with Table R602.10.6.5. Angled walls shall be permitted to be counted in accordance with Section R602.10.1.4, and *braced wall panel* location shall be in accordance with Section R602.10.2.2. Spacing between *braced wall lines* shall be in accordance with Table R602.10.1.3. The seismic adjustment factors in Table R602.10.3(4) shall not be applied to the length of bracing determined using Table R602.10.6.5, except that the bracing amount increase for *braced wall line* spacing greater than 25 feet (7620 mm) in accordance with Table R602.10.1.3 shall be required. The minimum total length of bracing in a *braced wall line,* after all adjustments have been taken, shall be not less than 48 inches (1219 mm) total.

R602.10.7 Ends of braced wall lines with continuous sheathing. Each end of a *braced wall line* with continuous sheathing shall have one of the conditions shown in Figure R602.10.7.

R602.10.8 Braced wall panel connections. *Braced wall panels* shall be connected to floor framing or foundations as follows:

1. Where joists are perpendicular to a *braced wall panel* above or below, a rim joist, band joist or blocking shall be provided along the entire length of the *braced wall panel* in accordance with Figure R602.10.8(1). Fastening of top and bottom wall plates to framing, rim joist, band joist or blocking shall be in accordance with Table R602.3(1).

2. Where joists are parallel to a *braced wall panel* above or below, a rim joist, end joist or other parallel framing member shall be provided directly above and below the *braced wall panel* in accordance with Figure R602.10.8(2). Where a parallel framing member cannot be located directly above and below

the panel, full-depth blocking at 16-inch (406 mm) spacing shall be provided between the parallel framing members to each side of the *braced wall panel* in accordance with Figure R602.10.8(2). Fastening of blocking and wall plates shall be in accordance with Table R602.3(1) and Figure R602.10.8(2).

3. Connections of *braced wall panels* to concrete or masonry shall be in accordance with Section R403.1.6.

R602.10.8.1 Braced wall panel connections for Seismic Design Categories D$_0$, D$_1$ and D$_2$. *Braced wall panels* shall be fastened to required foundations in accordance with Section R602.11.1, and top plate lap

splices shall be face-nailed with not less than eight 16d nails on each side of the splice.

R602.10.8.2 Connections to roof framing. Top plates of exterior *braced wall panels* shall be attached to rafters or roof trusses above in accordance with Table R602.3(1) and this section. Where required by this section, blocking between rafters or roof trusses shall be attached to top plates of *braced wall panels* and to rafters and roof trusses in accordance with Table R602.3(1). A continuous band, rim or header joist or roof truss parallel to the *braced wall panels* shall be permitted to replace the blocking required by this section. Blocking shall not be required over openings in continuously sheathed *braced wall lines*. In addition to

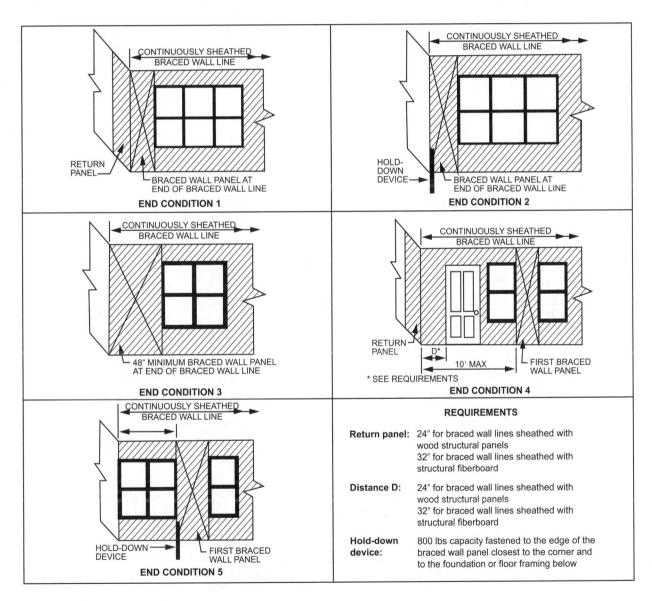

For SI: 1 inch = 25.4 mm, 1 foot = 304.8 mm, 1 pound = 4.45 N.

FIGURE R602.10.7
END CONDITIONS FOR BRACED WALL LINES WITH CONTINUOUS SHEATHING

the requirements of this section, lateral support shall be provided for rafters and ceiling joists in accordance with Section R802.8 and for trusses in accordance with Section R802.10.3. Roof ventilation shall be provided in accordance with Section R806.1.

1. For Seismic Design Categories A, B and C where the distance from the top of the braced wall panel to the top of the rafters or roof trusses above is $9^{1}/_{4}$ inches (235 mm) or less, blocking between rafters or roof trusses shall not be required. Where the distance from the top of the braced wall panel to the top of the rafters or roof trusses above is between $9^{1}/_{4}$ inches (235 mm) and $15^{1}/_{4}$ inches (387 mm), blocking between rafters or roof trusses shall be provided above the braced wall panel in accordance with Figure R602.10.8.2(1).

   Exception: Where the outside edge of truss vertical web members aligns with the outside face of the wall studs below, wood structural panel sheathing extending above the top plate as shown in Figure R602.10.8.2(3) shall be permitted to be fastened to each truss web with three-8d nails ($2^{1}/_{2}$ inches × 0.131 inch) and blocking between the trusses shall not be required.

2. For Seismic Design Categories D_0, D_1 and D_2, where the distance from the top of the braced wall panel to the top of the rafters or roof trusses is $15^{1}/_{4}$ inches (387 mm) or less, blocking between rafters or roof trusses shall be provided above the braced wall panel in accordance with Figure R602.10.8.2(1).

3. Where the distance from the top of the braced wall panel to the top of rafters or roof trusses exceeds $15^{1}/_{4}$ inches (387 mm), the top plates of the braced wall panel shall be connected to perpendicular rafters or roof trusses above in accordance with one or more of the following methods:

   3.1. Soffit blocking panels constructed in accordance with Figure R602.10.8.2(2).

   3.2. Vertical blocking panels constructed in accordance with Figure R602.10.8.2(3).

   3.3. Blocking panels provided by the roof truss manufacturer and designed in accordance with Section R802.

   3.4. Blocking, blocking panels or other methods of lateral load transfer designed in accordance with the AWC WFCM or accepted engineering practice.

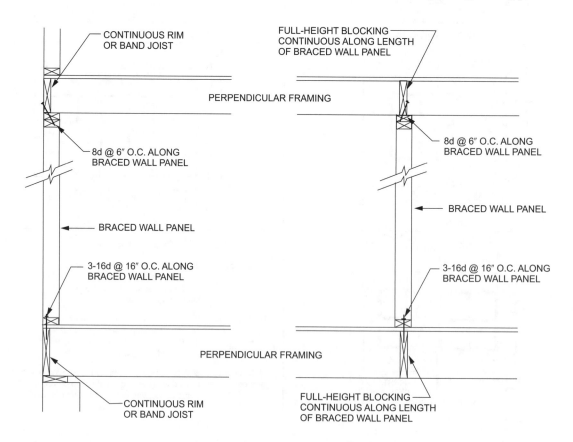

For SI: 1 inch = 25.4 mm.

FIGURE R602.10.8(1)
BRACED WALL PANEL CONNECTION WHEN PERPENDICULAR TO FLOOR/CEILING FRAMING

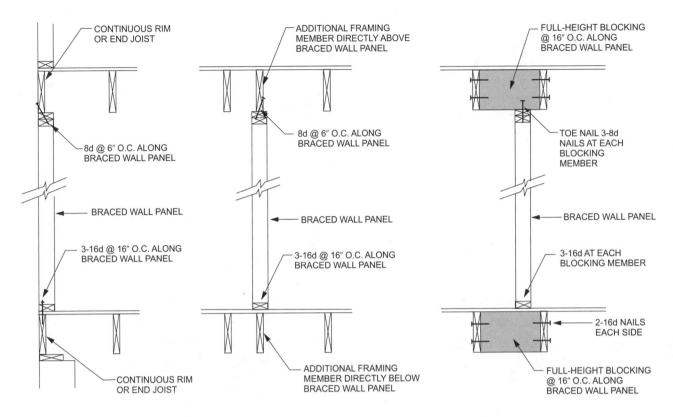

For SI: 1 inch = 25.4 mm.

FIGURE R602.10.8(2)
BRACED WALL PANEL CONNECTION WHEN PARALLEL TO FLOOR/CEILING FRAMING

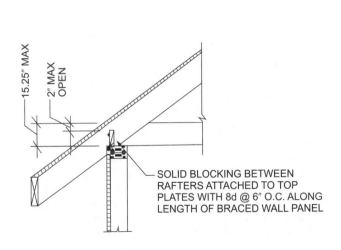

For SI: 1 inch = 25.4 mm.

FIGURE R602.10.8.2(1)
BRACED WALL PANEL CONNECTION
TO PERPENDICULAR RAFTERS

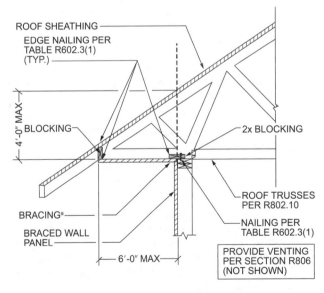

For SI: 1 inch = 25.4 mm, 1 foot = 304.8 mm.

a. Methods of bracing shall be as described in Section R602.10.4.

FIGURE R602.10.8.2(2)
BRACED WALL PANEL CONNECTION OPTION TO
PERPENDICULAR RAFTERS OR ROOF TRUSSES

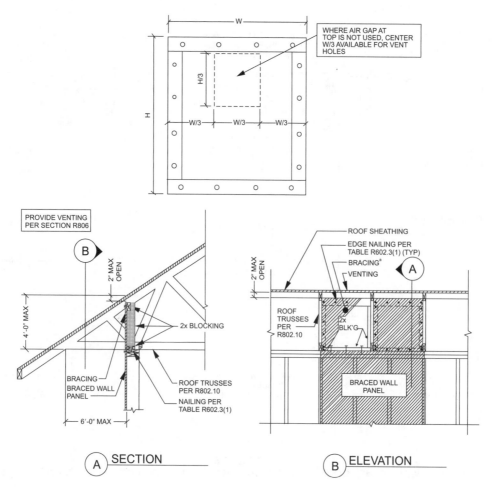

For SI: 1 inch = 25.4 mm, 1 foot =304.8 mm

a. Methods of bracing shall be as described in Section R602.10.4.

FIGURE R602.10.8.2(3)
BRACED WALL PANEL CONNECTION OPTION TO PERPENDICULAR RAFTERS OR ROOF TRUSSES

R602.10.9 Braced wall panel support. *Braced wall panel* support shall be provided as follows:

1. Cantilevered floor joists complying with Section R502.3.3 shall be permitted to support *braced wall panels*.

2. Raised floor system post or pier foundations supporting *braced wall panels* shall be designed in accordance with accepted engineering practice.

3. Masonry stem walls with a length of 48 inches (1219 mm) or less supporting *braced wall panels* shall be reinforced in accordance with Figure R602.10.9. Masonry stem walls with a length greater than 48 inches (1219 mm) supporting *braced wall panels* shall be constructed in accordance with Section R403.1 Methods ABW and PFH shall not be permitted to attach to masonry stem walls.

4. Concrete stem walls with a length of 48 inches (1219 mm) or less, greater than 12 inches (305 mm) tall and less than 6 inches (152 mm) thick shall have

reinforcement sized and located in accordance with Figure R602.10.9.

R602.10.9.1 Braced wall panel support for Seismic Design Categories D$_0$, D$_1$ and D$_2$. In Seismic Design Categories D$_0$, D$_1$ and D$_2$, braced wall panel footings shall be as specified in Section R403.1.2.

R602.10.10 Cripple wall bracing. Cripple walls shall be constructed in accordance with Section R602.9 and braced in accordance with this section. Cripple walls shall be braced with the length and method of bracing used for the wall above in accordance with Tables R602.10.3(1) and R602.10.3(3), and the applicable adjustment factors in Table R602.10.3(2) or R602.10.3(4), respectively, except that the length of cripple wall bracing shall be multiplied by a factor of 1.15. Where gypsum wall board is not used on the inside of the cripple wall bracing, the length adjustments for the elimination of the gypsum wallboard, or equivalent, shall be applied as directed in Tables R602.10.3(2) and R602.10.3(4) to the length of cripple wall bracing required. This adjustment shall be taken in addition to the 1.15 increase.

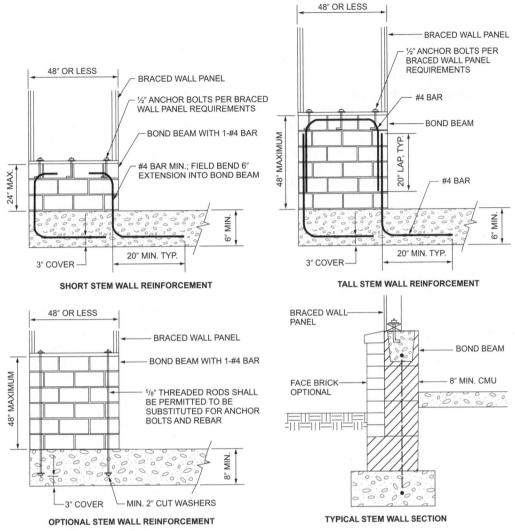

For SI: 1 inch = 25.4 mm.

FIGURE R602.10.9
MASONRY STEM WALLS SUPPORTING BRACED WALL PANELS

R602.10.10.1 Cripple wall bracing for Seismic Design Categories D_0 and D_1 and townhouses in Seismic Design Category C. In addition to the requirements in Section R602.10.10, the distance between adjacent edges of *braced wall panels* for cripple walls along a *braced wall line* shall be 14 feet (4267 mm) maximum.

Where *braced wall lines* at interior walls are not supported on a continuous foundation below, the adjacent parallel cripple walls, where provided, shall be braced with Method WSP or Method CS-WSP in accordance with Section R602.10.4. The length of bracing required in accordance with Table R602.10.3(3) for the cripple walls shall be multiplied by 1.5. Where the cripple walls do not have sufficient length to provide the required bracing, the spacing of panel edge fasteners shall be reduced to 4 inches (102 mm) on center and

the required bracing length adjusted by 0.7. If the required length can still not be provided, the cripple wall shall be designed in accordance with accepted engineering practice.

R602.10.10.2 Cripple wall bracing for Seismic Design Category D_2. In Seismic Design Category D_2, cripple walls shall be braced in accordance with Tables R602.10.3(3) and R602.10.3(4).

R602.10.10.3 Redesignation of cripple walls. Where all cripple wall segments along a *braced wall line* do not exceed 48 inches (1219 mm) in height, the cripple walls shall be permitted to be redesignated as a first-*story* wall for purposes of determining wall bracing requirements. Where any cripple wall segment in a *braced wall line* exceeds 48 inches (1219 mm) in height, the entire cripple wall shall be counted as an additional *story*. If the cripple walls are redesignated, the stories above the redesignated *story* shall be counted as the second and third stories, respectively.

R602.11 Wall anchorage. *Braced wall line* sills shall be anchored to concrete or masonry foundations in accordance with Sections R403.1.6 and R602.11.1.

R602.11.1 Wall anchorage for all buildings in Seismic Design Categories D₀, D₁ and D₂ and townhouses in Seismic Design Category C. Plate washers, not less than 0.229 inch by 3 inches by 3 inches (5.8 mm by 76 mm by 76 mm) in size, shall be provided between the foundation sill plate and the nut except where *approved* anchor straps are used. The hole in the plate washer is permitted to be diagonally slotted with a width of up to $^3/_{16}$ inch (5 mm) larger than the bolt diameter and a slot length not to exceed $1^3/_4$ inches (44 mm), provided a standard cut washer is placed between the plate washer and the nut.

R602.11.2 Stepped foundations in Seismic Design Categories D₀, D₁ and D₂. In all buildings located in Seismic Design Categories D₀, D₁ or D₂, where the height of a required *braced wall line* that extends from foundation to floor above varies more than 4 feet (1219 mm), the *braced wall line* shall be constructed in accordance with the following:

1. Where the lowest floor framing rests directly on a sill bolted to a foundation not less than 8 feet (2440 mm) in length along a line of bracing, the line shall be considered as braced. The double plate of the cripple stud wall beyond the segment of footing that extends to the lowest framed floor shall be spliced by extending the upper top plate not less than 4 feet (1219 mm) along the foundation. Anchor bolts shall

be located not more than 1 foot and 3 feet (305 and 914 mm) from the step in the foundation. See Figure R602.11.2.

2. Where cripple walls occur between the top of the foundation and the lowest floor framing, the bracing requirements of Sections R602.10.10, R602.10.10.1 and R602.10.10.2 shall apply.

3. Where only the bottom of the foundation is stepped and the lowest floor framing rests directly on a sill bolted to the foundations, the requirements of Sections R403.1.6 and R602.11.1 shall apply.

R602.12 Simplified wall bracing. Buildings meeting all of the following conditions shall be permitted to be braced in accordance with this section as an alternative to the requirements of Section R602.10. The entire building shall be braced in accordance with this section; the use of other bracing provisions of Section R602.10, except as specified herein, shall not be permitted.

1. There shall be not more than three stories above the top of a concrete or masonry foundation or basement wall. Permanent wood foundations shall not be permitted.

2. Floors shall not cantilever more than 24 inches (607 mm) beyond the foundation or bearing wall below.

3. Wall height shall not be greater than 10 feet (3048 mm).

4. The building shall have a roof eave-to-ridge height of 15 feet (4572 mm) or less.

5. Exterior walls shall have gypsum board with a minimum thickness of $^1/_2$ inch (12.7 mm) installed on the interior side fastened in accordance with Table R702.3.5.

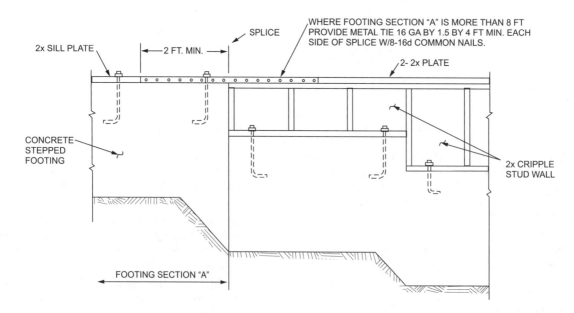

For SI: 1 inch = 25.4 mm, 1 foot = 304.8 mm.

Note: Where footing Section "A" is less than 8 feet long in a 25-foot-long wall, install bracing at cripple stud wall.

FIGURE R602.11.2
STEPPED FOUNDATION CONSTRUCTION

6. The structure shall be located where the ultimate design wind speed is less than or equal to 130 mph (58 m/s), and the exposure category is B or C.

7. The structure shall be located in Seismic Design Category A, B or C for detached one- and two-family dwellings or Seismic Design Category A or B for townhouses.

8. Cripple walls shall not be permitted in three-story buildings.

R602.12.1 Circumscribed rectangle. The bracing required for each building shall be determined by circumscribing a rectangle around the entire building on each floor as shown in Figure R602.12.1. The rectangle shall surround all enclosed offsets and projections such as sunrooms and attached garages. Open structures, such as carports and decks, shall be permitted to be excluded. The rectangle shall not have a side greater than 60 feet (18 288 mm), and the ratio between the long side and short side shall be not greater than 3:1.

R602.12.2 Sheathing materials. The following sheathing materials installed on the exterior side of exterior walls shall be used to construct a bracing unit as defined in Section R602.12.3. Mixing materials is prohibited.

1. Wood structural panels with a minimum thickness of $^3/_8$ inch (9.5 mm) fastened in accordance with Table R602.3(3).

2. Structural fiberboard sheathing with a minimum thickness of $^1/_2$ inch (12.7 mm) fastened in accordance with Table R602.3(1).

R602.12.3 Bracing unit. A bracing unit shall be a full-height sheathed segment of the exterior wall without openings or vertical or horizontal offsets and a minimum length as specified herein. Interior walls shall not contribute toward the amount of required bracing. Mixing of Items 1 and 2 is prohibited on the same story.

1. Where all framed portions of all exterior walls are sheathed in accordance with Section R602.12.2, including wall areas between bracing units, above and below openings and on gable end walls, the minimum length of a bracing unit shall be 3 feet (914 mm).

2. Where the exterior walls are braced with sheathing panels in accordance with Section R602.12.2 and areas between bracing units are covered with other materials, the minimum length of a bracing unit shall be 4 feet (1219 mm).

R602.12.3.1 Multiple bracing units. Segments of wall compliant with Section R602.12.3 and longer than the minimum bracing unit length shall be considered as multiple bracing units. The number of bracing units shall be determined by dividing the wall segment length by the minimum bracing unit length. Full-height sheathed segments of wall narrower than the minimum bracing unit length shall not contribute toward a bracing unit except as specified in Section R602.12.6.

R602.12.4 Number of bracing units. Each side of the circumscribed rectangle, as shown in Figure R602.12.1, shall have, at a minimum, the number of bracing units in accordance with Table R602.12.4 placed on the parallel exterior walls facing the side of the rectangle. Bracing units shall then be placed using the distribution requirements specified in Section R602.12.5.

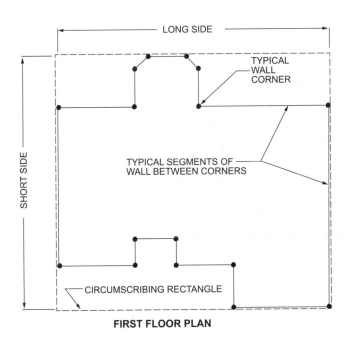

FIRST FLOOR PLAN

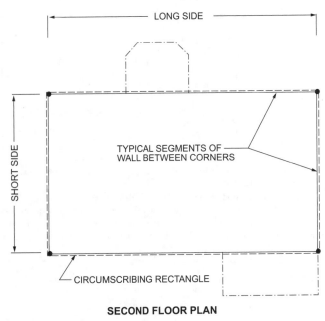

SECOND FLOOR PLAN

FIGURE R602.12.1
RECTANGLE CIRCUMSCRIBING AN ENCLOSED BUILDING

TABLE R602.12.4
MINIMUM NUMBER OF BRACING UNITS ON EACH SIDE OF THE CIRCUMSCRIBED RECTANGLE

ULTIMATE DESIGN WIND SPEED (mph)	STORY LEVEL	EAVE-TO-RIDGE HEIGHT (feet)	MINIMUM NUMBER OF BRACING UNITS ON EACH LONG SIDE[a,b,d] Length of short side (feet)[c]						MINIMUM NUMBER OF BRACING UNITS ON EACH SHORT SIDE[a,b,d] Length of long side (feet)[c]					
			10	20	30	40	50	60	10	20	30	40	50	60
115	Three stories	10	1	2	2	2	3	3	1	2	2	2	3	3
	Two stories		2	3	3	4	5	6	2	3	3	4	5	6
	One story		2	3	4	6	7	8	2	3	4	6	7	8
	Three stories	15	1	2	3	3	4	4	1	2	3	3	4	4
	Two stories		2	3	4	5	6	7	2	3	4	5	6	7
	One story		2	4	5	6	7	9	2	4	5	6	7	9
130	Three stories	10	1	2	2	3	3	4	1	2	2	3	3	4
	Two stories		2	3	4	5	6	7	2	3	4	5	6	7
	One story		2	4	5	7	8	10	2	4	5	7	8	10
	Three stories	15	2	3	3	4	4	6	2	3	3	4	4	6
	Two stories		3	4	6	7	8	10	3	4	6	7	8	10
	One story		3	6	7	10	11	13	3	6	7	10	11	13

For SI: 1 inch = 25.4 mm, 1 foot = 304.8 mm, 1 mile per hour = 0.447m/s.

a. Interpolation shall not be permitted.

b. Cripple walls or wood-framed basement walls in a walk-out condition shall be designated as the first story and the stories above shall be redesignated as the second and third stories, respectively, and shall be prohibited in a three-story structure.

c. Actual lengths of the sides of the circumscribed rectangle shall be rounded to the next highest unit of 10 when using this table.

d. For Exposure Category C, multiply bracing units by a factor of 1.20 for a one-story building, 1.30 for a two-story building and 1.40 for a three-story building.

R602.12.5 Distribution of bracing units. The placement of bracing units on exterior walls shall meet all of the following requirements as shown in Figure R602.12.5.

1. A bracing unit shall begin not more than 12 feet (3658 mm) from any wall corner.

2. The distance between adjacent edges of bracing units shall be not greater than 20 feet (6096 mm).

3. Segments of wall greater than 8 feet (2438 mm) in length shall have not less than one bracing unit.

R602.12.6 Narrow panels. The bracing methods referenced in Section R602.10 and specified in Sections R602.12.6.1 through R602.12.6.3 shall be permitted where using simplified wall bracing.

R602.12.6.1 Method CS-G. *Braced wall panels* constructed as Method CS-G in accordance with Tables R602.10.4 and R602.10.5 shall be permitted for one-story garages where all framed portions of all exterior walls are sheathed with wood structural panels. Each CS-G panel shall be equivalent to 0.5 of a bracing unit. Segments of wall that include a Method CS-G panel shall meet the requirements of Section R602.10.4.2.

R602.12.6.2 Method CS-PF. Braced wall panels constructed as Method CS-PF in accordance with Section R602.10.6.4 shall be permitted where all framed portions of all exterior walls are sheathed with wood structural panels. Each CS-PF panel shall equal 0.75 bracing units. Not more than four CS-PF panels shall be permitted on all segments of walls parallel to each side of the circumscribed rectangle. Segments of wall that include a Method CS-PF panel shall meet the requirements of Section R602.10.4.2.

R602.12.6.3 Methods ABW, PFH and PFG. Braced wall panels constructed as Method ABW, PFH and PFG shall be permitted where bracing units are constructed using wood structural panels applied either continuously or intermittently. Each ABW and PFH panel shall equal one bracing unit and each PFG panel shall be equal to 0.75 bracing unit.

R602.12.7 Lateral support. For bracing units located along the eaves, the vertical distance from the outside edge of the top wall plate to the roof sheathing above shall not exceed 9.25 inches (235 mm) at the location of a bracing

unit unless lateral support is provided in accordance with Section R602.10.8.2.

R602.12.8 Stem walls. Masonry stem walls with a height and length of 48 inches (1219 mm) or less supporting a bracing unit or a Method CS-G, CS-PF or PFG *braced wall panel* shall be constructed in accordance with Figure R602.10.9. Concrete stem walls with a length of 48 inches (1219 mm) or less, greater than 12 inches (305 mm) tall and less than 6 inches (152 mm) thick shall be reinforced sized and located in accordance with Figure R602.10.9.

SECTION R603
COLD-FORMED STEEL WALL FRAMING

R603.1 General. Elements shall be straight and free of any defects that would significantly affect structural performance. Cold-formed steel wall framing members shall be in accordance with the requirements of this section.

R603.1.1 Applicability limits. The provisions of this section shall control the construction of exterior cold-formed steel wall framing and interior load-bearing cold-formed steel wall framing for buildings not more than 60 feet (18 288 mm) long perpendicular to the joist or truss span, not more than 40 feet (12 192 mm) wide parallel to the joist or truss span, and less than or equal to three stories above grade plane. Exterior walls installed in accordance with the provisions of this section shall be considered as load-bearing walls. Cold-formed steel walls constructed in accordance with the provisions of this section shall be limited to sites where the ultimate design wind speed is less than 140 miles per hour (63 m/s), Exposure Category B or C, and the ground snow load is less than or equal to 70 pounds per square foot (3.35 kPa).

R603.1.2 In-line framing. Load-bearing cold-formed steel studs constructed in accordance with Section R603 shall be located in-line with joists, trusses and rafters in accordance with Figure R603.1.2 and the tolerances specified as follows:

1. The maximum tolerance shall be $^3/_4$ inch (19 mm) between the centerline of the horizontal framing member and the centerline of the vertical framing member.

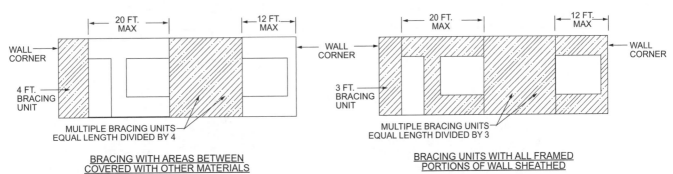

For SI: 1 foot = 304.8 mm.

FIGURE R602.12.5
BRACING UNIT DISTRIBUTION

2. Where the centerline of the horizontal framing member and bearing stiffener is located to one side of the centerline of the vertical framing member, the maximum tolerance shall be $^1/_8$ inch (3 mm) between the web of the horizontal framing member and the edge of the vertical framing member.

R603.2 Structural framing. Load-bearing cold-formed steel wall framing members shall be in accordance with this section.

R603.2.1 Material. Load-bearing cold-formed steel framing members shall be cold formed to shape from structural-quality sheet steel complying with the requirements of ASTM A1003: Structural Grades 33 Type H and 50 Type H.

R603.2.2 Corrosion protection. Load-bearing cold-formed steel framing shall have a metallic coating complying with ASTM A1003 and one of the following:

1. Not less than G 60 in accordance with ASTM A653.

2. Not less than AZ 50 in accordance with ASTM A792.

R603.2.3 Dimension, thickness and material grade. Load-bearing cold-formed steel wall framing members shall comply with Figure R603.2.3(1) and with the dimensional and thickness requirements specified in Table R603.2.3. Additionally, C-shaped sections shall have a minimum flange width of $1^5/_8$ inches (41 mm) and a maximum flange width of 2 inches (51 mm). The minimum lip size for C-shaped sections shall be $^1/_2$ inch (12.7 mm).

Track sections shall comply with Figure R603.2.3(2) and shall have a minimum flange width of $1^1/_4$ inches (32 mm). Minimum Grade 33 ksi steel shall be used wherever 33 mil and 43 mil thicknesses are specified. Minimum Grade 50 ksi steel shall be used wherever 54 and 68 mil thicknesses are specified.

R603.2.4 Identification. Load-bearing cold-formed steel framing members shall have a legible label, stencil, stamp or embossment with the following information as a minimum:

1. Manufacturer's identification.

2. Minimum base steel thickness in inches (mm).

3. Minimum coating designation.

4. Minimum yield strength, in kips per square inch (ksi) (MPa).

R603.2.5 Fastening. Screws for steel-to-steel connections shall be installed with a minimum edge distance and center-to-center spacing of $^1/_2$ inch (12.7 mm), shall be self-drilling tapping and shall conform to ASTM C1513. Structural sheathing shall be attached to cold-formed steel studs with minimum No. 8 self-drilling tapping screws that conform to ASTM C1513. Screws for attaching structural sheathing to cold-formed steel wall framing shall have a minimum head diameter of 0.292 inch (7.4 mm) with countersunk heads and shall be installed with a minimum

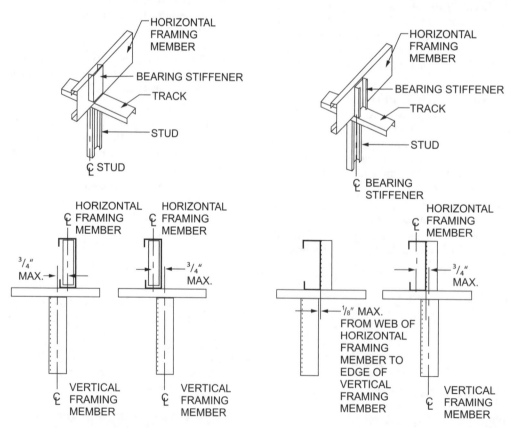

For SI: 1 inch = 25.4 mm,

FIGURE R603.1.2
IN-LINE FRAMING

edge distance of $^3/_8$ inch (9.5 mm). Gypsum board shall be attached to cold-formed steel wall framing with minimum No. 6 screws conforming to ASTM C954 or ASTM C1513 with a bugle-head style and shall be installed in accordance with Section R702. For connections, screws shall extend through the steel not fewer than three exposed threads. Fasteners shall have rust-inhibitive coating suitable for the installation in which they are being used, or be manufactured from material not susceptible to corrosion.

R603.2.6 Web holes, web hole reinforcing and web hole patching. Web holes, web hole reinforcing and web hole patching shall be in accordance with this section.

R603.2.6.1 Web holes. Web holes in wall studs and other structural members shall comply with all of the following conditions:

1. Holes shall conform to Figure R603.2.6.1.

2. Holes shall be permitted only along the centerline of the web of the framing member.

3. Holes shall have a center-to-center spacing of not less than 24 inches (610 mm).

4. Holes shall have a web hole width not greater than 0.5 times the member depth, or $1^1/_2$ inches (38 mm).

5. Holes shall have a web hole length not exceeding $4^1/_2$ inches (114 mm).

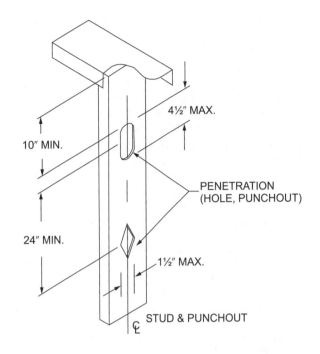

For SI: 1 inch = 25.4 mm.

FIGURE R603.2.6.1
WALL STUD WEB HOLES

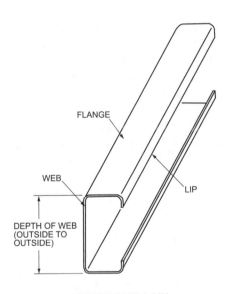

FIGURE R603.2.3(1)
C-SHAPED SECTION

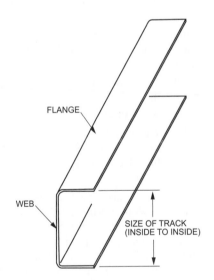

FIGURE R603.2.3(2)
TRACK SECTION

TABLE R603.2.3
LOAD-BEARING COLD-FORMED STEEL STUD SIZES AND THICKNESSES

MEMBER DESIGNATION[a]	WEB DEPTH (inches)	MINIMUM BASE STEEL THICKNESS mil (inches)
350S162-t	3.5	33 (0.0329), 43 (0.0428), 54 (0.0538)
550S162-t	5.5	33 (0.0329), 43 (0.0428), 54 (0.0538), 68 (0.0677)

For SI: 1 inch = 25.4 mm; 1 mil = 0.0254 mm.

a. The member designation is defined by the first number representing the member depth in hundredths of an inch, "S" representing a stud or joist member, the second number representing the flange width in hundredths of an inch, and the letter "t" shall be a number representing the minimum base metal thickness in mils.

6. Holes shall have a minimum distance between the edge of the bearing surface and the edge of the web hole of not less than 10 inches (254 mm).

Framing members with web holes not conforming to the above requirements shall be reinforced in accordance with Section R603.2.6.2, patched in accordance with Section R603.2.6.3 or designed in accordance with accepted engineering practice.

R603.2.6.2 Web hole reinforcing. Web holes in gable endwall studs not conforming to the requirements of Section R603.2.6.1 shall be permitted to be reinforced if the hole is located fully within the center 40 percent of the span and the depth and length of the hole does not exceed 65 percent of the flat width of the web. The reinforcing shall be a steel plate or C-shaped section with a hole that does not exceed the web hole size limitations of Section R603.2.6.1 for the member being reinforced. The steel reinforcing shall be the same thickness as the receiving member and shall extend not less than 1 inch (25 mm) beyond all edges of the hole. The steel reinforcing shall be fastened to the web of the receiving member with No. 8 screws spaced not more than 1 inch (25 mm) center-to-center along the edges of the patch with minimum edge distance of $^1/_2$ inch (12.7 mm).

R603.2.6.3 Hole patching. Web holes in wall studs and other structural members not conforming to the requirements in Section R603.2.6.1 shall be permitted to be patched in accordance with either of the following methods:

1. Framing members shall be replaced or designed in accordance with accepted engineering practice where web holes exceed the following size limits:

    1.1. The depth of the hole, measured across the web, exceeds 70 percent of the flat width of the web.

    1.2. The length of the hole measured along the web exceeds 10 inches (254 mm) or the depth of the web, whichever is greater.

2. Web holes not exceeding the dimensional requirements in Section R603.2.6.3, Item 1, shall be patched with a solid steel plate, stud section or track section in accordance with Figure R603.2.6.3. The steel patch shall, as a minimum, be the same thickness as the receiving member and shall extend not less than 1 inch (25 mm) beyond all edges of the hole. The steel patch shall be fastened to the web of the receiving member with No. 8 screws spaced not more than 1 inch (25 mm) center-to-center along the edges of the patch with a minimum edge distance of $^1/_2$ inch (12.7 mm).

R603.3 Wall construction. Exterior cold-formed steel framed walls and interior load-bearing cold-formed steel framed walls shall be constructed in accordance with the provisions of this section.

R603.3.1 Wall to foundation or floor connection. Cold-formed steel framed walls shall be anchored to founda-

tions or floors in accordance with Table R603.3.1 and Figure R603.3.1(1), R603.3.1(2), R603.3.1(3) or R603.3.1(4). Anchor bolts shall be located not more than 12 inches (305 mm) from corners or the termination of bottom tracks. Anchor bolts shall extend not less than 15 inches (381 mm) into masonry or 7 inches (178 mm) into concrete. Foundation anchor straps shall be permitted, in lieu of anchor bolts, if spaced as required to provide equivalent anchorage to the required anchor bolts and installed in accordance with manufacturer's requirements.

R603.3.1.1 Gable endwalls. Gable endwalls with heights greater than 10 feet (3048 mm) shall be anchored to foundations or floors in accordance with Table R603.3.1.1(1) or R603.3.1.1(2).

R603.3.2 Minimum stud sizes. Cold-formed steel walls shall be constructed in accordance with Figure R603.3.1(1), R603.3.1(2) or R603.3.1(3), as applicable. Exterior wall stud size and thickness shall be determined in accordance with the limits set forth in Tables R603.3.2(2) through R603.3.2(16). Interior load-bearing wall stud size and thickness shall be determined in accordance with the limits set forth in Tables R603.3.2(2) through R603.3.2(16) based on an ultimate design wind speed of 115 miles per hour (51 m/s), Exposure Category B, and the building width, stud spacing and snow load, as appropriate. Fastening requirements shall be in accordance with Section R603.2.5 and Table R603.3.2(1). Top and bottom tracks shall have the same minimum thickness as the wall studs.

Exterior wall studs shall be permitted to be reduced to the next thinner size, as shown in Tables R603.3.2(2) through R603.3.2(16), but not less than 33 mils (0.84 mm), where both of the following conditions exist:

1. Minimum of $^1/_2$-inch (12.7 mm) gypsum board is installed and fastened on the interior surface in accordance with Section R702.

2. Wood structural sheathing panels of minimum $^7/_{16}$-inch-thick (11.1 mm) oriented strand board or $^{15}/_{32}$-inch-thick (12 mm) plywood are installed and fas-

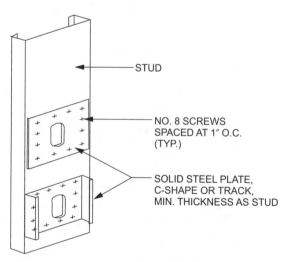

STUD

NO. 8 SCREWS SPACED AT 1" O.C. (TYP.)

SOLID STEEL PLATE, C-SHAPE OR TRACK, MIN. THICKNESS AS STUD

For SI: 1 inch = 25.4 mm.

FIGURE R603.2.6.3
WALL STUD WEB HOLE PATCH

tened in accordance with Section R603.9.1 and Table R603.3.2(1) on the outside surface.

Interior load-bearing walls shall be permitted to be reduced to the next thinner size, as shown in Tables R603.3.2(2) through R603.3.2(16), but not less than 33 mils (0.84 mm), where not less than $^1/_2$-inch (12.7 mm) gypsum board is installed and fastened in accordance with Section R702 on both sides of the wall. The tabulated stud thickness for load-bearing walls shall be used where the attic load is 10 pounds per square foot (480 Pa) or less. A limited attic storage load of 20 pounds per square foot (960 Pa) shall be permitted provided that the next higher snow load column is used to select the stud size from Tables R603.3.2(2) through R603.3.2(16).

For two-story buildings, the tabulated stud thickness for walls supporting one floor, roof and ceiling shall be used where the second-floor live load is 30 pounds per square foot (1440 Pa). Second-floor live loads of 40 psf (1920 Pa)

shall be permitted provided that the next higher snow load column is used to select the stud size from Tables R603.3.2(2) through R603.3.2(11).

For three-story buildings, the tabulated stud thickness for walls supporting one or two floors, roof and ceiling shall be used where the third-floor live load is 30 pounds per square foot (1440 Pa). Third-floor live loads of 40 pounds per square foot (1920 Pa) shall be permitted provided that the next higher snow load column is used to select the stud size from Tables R603.3.2(12) through R603.3.2(16).

R603.3.2.1 Gable endwalls. The size and thickness of gable endwall studs with heights less than or equal to 10 feet (3048 mm) shall be permitted in accordance with the limits set forth in Table R603.3.2.1(1). The size and thickness of gable endwall studs with heights greater than 10 feet (3048 mm) shall be determined in accordance with the limits set forth in Table R603.3.2.1(2).

TABLE R603.3.1
WALL TO FOUNDATION OR FLOOR CONNECTION REQUIREMENTS[a, b]

FRAMING CONDITION			ULTIMATE WIND SPEED AND EXPOSURE CATEGORY (mph)					
			115 B	120 B	130 B or 115 C	< 140 B or 120 C	130 C	< 140 C
Wall bottom track to floor per Figure R603.3.1(1)			1-No. 8 screw at 12″ o.c.	1-No. 8 screw at 8″ o.c.	2-No. 8 screws at 8″ o.c.	2-No. 8 screws at 6″ o.c.	3-No. 8 screws at 8″ o.c.	3-No. 8 screws at 6″ o.c.
Wall bottom track to foundation per Figure R603.3.1(2)[d]			$^1/_2$″ minimum diameter anchor bolt at 6′ o.c.	$^1/_2$″ minimum diameter anchor bolt at 6′ o.c.	$^1/_2$″ minimum diameter anchor bolt at 4′ o.c.	$^1/_2$″ minimum diameter anchor bolt at 4′ o.c.	$^1/_2$″ minimum diameter anchor bolt at 3′-4″ o.c.	$^1/_2$″ minimum diameter anchor bolt at 2′-8″ o.c.
Wall bottom track to wood sill per Figure R603.3.1(3)			Steel plate spaced at 4′ o.c., with 4-No. 8 screws and 4-10d or 6-8d common nails	Steel plate spaced at 4′ o.c., with 4-No. 8 screws and 4-10d or 6-8d common nails	Steel plate spaced at 3′ o.c., with 4-No. 8 screws and 4-10d or 6-8d common nails	Steel plate spaced at 3′ o.c., with 4-No. 8 screws and 4-10d or 6-8d common nails	Steel plate spaced at 2′ o.c., with 4-No. 8 screws and 4-10d or 6-8d common nails	Steel plate spaced at 1′-4″ o.c., with 4-No. 8 screws and 4-10d or 6-8d common nails
	Stud Spacing (inches)	Roof Span (feet)						
Wind uplift connector strength (lbs)[c, e]	16	24	NR	NR	NR	NR	NR	NR
		28	NR	NR	NR	NR	NR	339
		32	NR	NR	NR	NR	NR	382
		36	NR	NR	NR	NR	333	426
		40	NR	NR	NR	NR	368	470
	24	24	NR	NR	NR	NR	343	443
		28	NR	NR	NR	NR	395	508
		32	NR	NR	NR	330	447	573
		36	NR	NR	NR	371	500	639
		40	NR	NR	345	411	552	704

For SI: 1 inch = 25.4 mm, 1 mile per hour = 0.447 m/s, 1 foot = 304.8 mm, 1 pound = 4.45 N.

a. Anchor bolts are to be located not more than 12 inches from corners or the termination of bottom tracks, such as at door openings or corners. Bolts are to extend not less than 15 inches into masonry or 7 inches into concrete.

b. All screw sizes shown are minimum.

c. NR = Uplift connector not required.

d. Foundation anchor straps are permitted in place of anchor bolts, if spaced as required to provide equivalent anchorage to the required anchor bolts and installed in accordance with manufacturer's requirements.

e. See Figure R603.3.1(4) for details.

TABLE R603.3.1.1(1)
GABLE ENDWALL TO FLOOR CONNECTION REQUIREMENTS[a, b, c]

ULTIMATE WIND SPEED (mph)		WALL BOTTOM TRACK TO FLOOR JOIST OR TRACK CONNECTION		
Exposure Category		Stud height, h (feet)		
B	C	$10 < h \le 14$	$14 < h \le 18$	$18 < h \le 22$
115	—	1-No. 8 screw @ 12″ o.c.	1-No. 8 screw @ 12″ o.c.	1-No. 8 screw @ 12″ o.c.
120	—	1-No. 8 screw @ 12″ o.c.	1-No. 8 screw @ 12″ o.c.	1-No. 8 screw @ 12″ o.c.
130	115	1-No. 8 screw @ 12″ o.c.	1-No. 8 screw @ 12″ o.c.	2-No. 8 screws @ 12″ o.c.
< 140	120	1-No. 8 screw @ 12″ o.c.	1-No. 8 screw @ 12″ o.c.	2-No. 8 screws @ 12″ o.c.
—	130	2-No. 8 screws @ 12″ o.c.	1-No. 8 screw @ 8″ o.c.	2-No. 8 screws @ 8″ o.c.
—	< 140	2-No. 8 screws @ 12″ o.c.	1-No. 8 screw @ 8″ o.c.	2-No. 8 screws @ 8″ o.c.

For SI: 1 inch = 25.4 mm, 1 mile per hour = 0.447 m/s, 1 foot = 304.8 mm.

a. Refer to Table R603.3.1.1(2) for gable endwall bottom track to foundation connections.

b. Where attachment is not given, special design is required.

c. Stud height, h, is measured from wall bottom track to wall top track or brace connection height.

TABLE R603.3.1.1(2)
GABLE ENDWALL BOTTOM TRACK TO FOUNDATION CONNECTION REQUIREMENTS[a, b, c]

ULTIMATE WIND SPEED (mph)		MINIMUM SPACING FOR $\frac{1}{2}$-INCH-DIAMETER ANCHOR BOLTS[d]		
Exposure Category		Stud height, h (feet)		
B	C	$10 < h \le 14$	$14 < h \le 18$	$18 < h \le 22$
115	—	6′- 0″ o.c.	6′- 0″ o.c.	6′- 0″ o.c.
120	—	6′- 0″ o.c.	5′- 7″ o.c.	6′- 0″ o.c.
130	115	5′- 0″ o.c.	6′- 0″ o.c.	6′- 0″ o.c.
< 140	120	6′- 0″ o.c.	5′- 6″ o.c.	6′- 0″ o.c.
—	130	5′- 3″ o.c.	6′- 0″ o.c.	6′- 0″ o.c.
—	< 140	3′- 0″ o.c.	3′- 0″ o.c.	3′- 0″ o.c.

For SI: 1 inch = 25.4 mm, 1 mile per hour = 0.447 m/s, 1 foot = 304.8 mm.

a. Refer to Table R603.3.1.1(1) for gable endwall bottom track to floor joist or track connection connections.

b. Where attachment is not given, special design is required.

c. Stud height, h, is measured from wall bottom track to wall top track or brace connection height.

d. Foundation anchor straps are permitted in place of anchor bolts if spaced as required to provide equivalent anchorage to the required anchor bolts and installed in accordance with manufacturer's requirements.

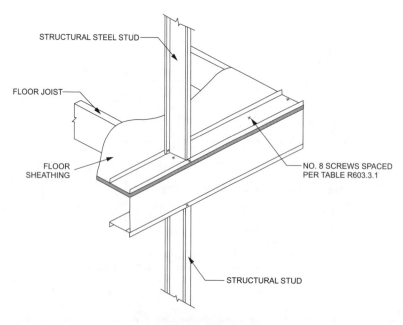

STRUCTURAL STEEL STUD

FLOOR JOIST

FLOOR SHEATHING

NO. 8 SCREWS SPACED PER TABLE R603.3.1

STRUCTURAL STUD

FIGURE R603.3.1(1)
WALL TO FLOOR CONNECTION

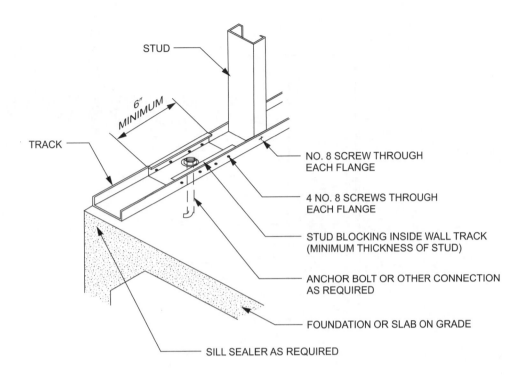

STUD

6" MINIMUM

TRACK

NO. 8 SCREW THROUGH
EACH FLANGE

4 NO. 8 SCREWS THROUGH
EACH FLANGE

STUD BLOCKING INSIDE WALL TRACK
(MINIMUM THICKNESS OF STUD)

ANCHOR BOLT OR OTHER CONNECTION
AS REQUIRED

FOUNDATION OR SLAB ON GRADE

SILL SEALER AS REQUIRED

For SI: 1 inch = 25.4 mm.

FIGURE R603.3.1(2)
WALL TO FOUNDATION CONNECTION

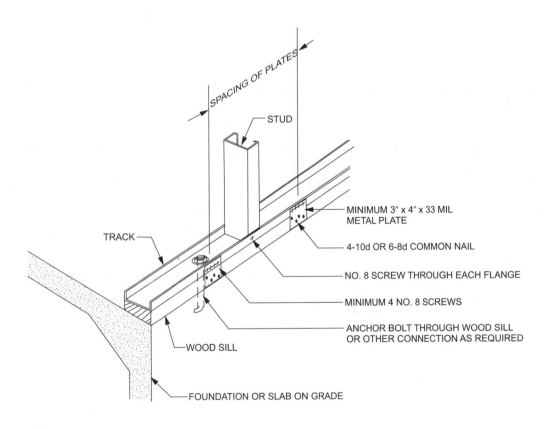

SPACING OF PLATES

STUD

TRACK

MINIMUM 3" x 4" x 33 MIL
METAL PLATE

4-10d OR 6-8d COMMON NAIL

NO. 8 SCREW THROUGH EACH FLANGE

MINIMUM 4 NO. 8 SCREWS

ANCHOR BOLT THROUGH WOOD SILL
OR OTHER CONNECTION AS REQUIRED

WOOD SILL

FOUNDATION OR SLAB ON GRADE

For SI: 1 mil = 0.0254 mm, 1 inch = 25.4 mm.

FIGURE R603.3.1(3)
WALL TO WOOD SILL CONNECTION

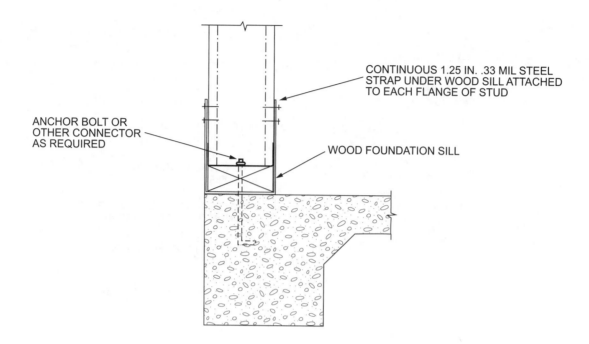

For SI: 1 mil = 0.0254 mm, 1 inch = 25.4 mm.

FIGURE R603.3.1(4)
WIND UPLIFT CONNECTOR

TABLE R603.3.2(1)
WALL FASTENING SCHEDULE[a]

DESCRIPTION OF BUILDING ELEMENT	NUMBER AND SIZE OF FASTENERS[a]	SPACING OF FASTENERS
Wall stud to top or bottom track	2-No. 8 screws	Each end of stud, one per flange
Structural sheathing to wall studs	No. 8 screws[b]	6″ o.c. on edges and 12″ o.c. at intermediate supports
$^1/_2$″ gypsum board to framing	No. 6 screws	12″ o.c.

For SI: 1 inch = 25.4 mm.

a. All screw sizes shown are minimum.

b. Screws for attachment of structural sheathing panels are to be bugle-head, flat-head, or similar head styles with a minimum head diameter of 0.29 inch.

TABLE R603.3.2(2)
24-FOOT-WIDE BUILDING SUPPORTING ROOF AND CEILING ONLY[a, b, c, d]

ULTIMATE WIND SPEED AND EXPOSURE CATEGORY (mph)		MEMBER SIZE	STUD SPACING (inches)	MINIMUM STUD THICKNESS (mils)											
				8-foot Studs				9-foot Studs				10-foot Studs			
				Ground Snow Load (psf)											
Exp. B	Exp. C			20	30	50	70	20	30	50	70	20	30	50	70
115	—	350S162	16	33	33	33	33	33	33	33	33	33	33	33	33
			24	33	33	33	43	33	33	33	43	33	33	43	43
		550S162	16	33	33	33	33	33	33	33	33	33	33	33	33
			24	33	33	33	33	33	33	33	33	33	33	33	43
120	—	350S162	16	33	33	33	33	33	33	33	33	33	33	33	33
			24	33	33	33	43	33	33	33	43	43	43	43	43
		550S162	16	33	33	33	33	33	33	33	33	33	33	33	33
			24	33	33	33	43	33	33	33	33	33	33	33	43
130	115	350S162	16	33	33	33	33	33	33	33	33	33	33	33	33
			24	33	33	43	43	43	43	43	43	43	43	43	54
		550S162	16	33	33	33	33	33	33	33	33	33	33	33	33
			24	33	33	33	43	33	33	33	43	33	33	33	43
< 140	120	350S162	16	33	33	33	33	33	33	33	33	33	33	33	43
			24	33	33	43	43	43	43	43	43	54	54	54	54
		550S162	16	33	33	33	33	33	33	33	33	33	33	33	33
			24	33	33	33	43	33	33	33	43	43	43	43	43
—	130	350S162	16	33	33	33	33	33	33	33	33	43	43	43	43
			24	43	43	43	43	54	54	54	54	54	54	54	54
		550S162	16	33	33	33	33	33	33	33	33	33	33	33	33
			24	33	33	33	43	43	43	43	43	43	43	43	43
—	< 140	350S 162	16	33	33	33	33	43	43	43	43	43	43	43	43
			24	43	43	43	54	54	54	54	54	54	54	54	54
		550S 162	16	33	33	33	33	33	33	33	33	33	33	33	33
			24	43	43	43	43	43	43	43	43	43	43	43	43

For SI: 1 inch = 25.4 mm, 1 foot = 304.8 mm, 1 mil = 0.0254 mm, 1 mile per hour = 0.447 m/s, 1 pound per square foot = 0.0479 kPa, 1 ksi = 1,000 psi = 6.895 MPa.

a. Deflection criterion: $L/240$.

b. Design load assumptions:
   Second-floor dead load is 10 psf.
   Second-floor live load is 30 psf.
   Roof/ceiling dead load is 12 psf.
   Attic live load is 10 psf.

c. Building width is in the direction of horizontal framing members supported by the wall studs.

d. Minimum Grade 33 ksi steel shall be used for 33 mil and 43 mil thicknesses. Minimum Grade 50 ksi steel shall be used for 54 and 68 mil thicknesses.

TABLE R603.3.2(3)
28-FOOT-WIDE BUILDING SUPPORTING ROOF AND CEILING ONLY[a, b, c, d]

ULTIMATE WIND SPEED AND EXPOSURE CATEGORY (mph)		MEMBER SIZE	STUD SPACING (inches)	MINIMUM STUD THICKNESS (mils)											
				8-foot Studs				9-foot Studs				10-foot Studs			
				Ground Snow Load (psf)											
Exp. B	Exp. C			20	30	50	70	20	30	50	70	20	30	50	70
115	—	350S162	16	33	33	33	33	33	33	33	33	33	33	33	33
			24	33	33	43	43	33	33	43	43	33	33	43	54
		550S162	16	33	33	33	33	33	33	33	33	33	33	33	33
			24	33	33	33	43	33	33	33	43	33	33	33	43
120	—	350S162	16	33	33	33	33	33	33	33	33	33	33	33	33
			24	33	33	43	43	33	33	43	43	43	43	43	54
		550S162	16	33	33	33	33	33	33	33	33	33	33	33	33
			24	33	33	33	43	33	33	33	43	33	33	33	43
130	115	350S162	16	33	33	33	33	33	33	33	33	33	33	33	43
			24	33	33	43	54	43	43	43	54	43	43	43	54
		550S162	16	33	33	33	33	33	33	33	33	33	33	33	33
			24	33	33	33	43	33	33	33	43	33	33	33	43
< 140	120	350S162	16	33	33	33	33	33	33	33	33	33	33	33	43
			24	33	33	43	54	43	43	43	54	54	54	54	54
		550S162	16	33	33	33	33	33	33	33	33	33	33	33	33
			24	33	33	33	43	33	33	33	43	43	43	43	43
—	130	350S162	16	33	33	33	33	33	33	33	43	43	43	43	43
			24	43	43	43	54	54	54	54	54	54	54	54	54
		550S162	16	33	33	33	33	33	33	33	33	33	33	33	33
			24	33	33	33	43	43	43	43	43	43	43	43	43
—	< 140	350S 162	16	33	33	33	43	43	43	43	43	43	43	43	43
			24	43	43	43	54	54	54	54	54	54	54	54	54
		550S162	16	33	33	33	33	33	33	33	33	33	33	33	33
			24	43	43	43	43	43	43	43	43	43	43	43	43

For SI: 1 inch = 25.4 mm, 1 foot = 304.8 mm, 1 mil = 0.0254 mm, 1 mile per hour = 0.447 m/s, 1 pound per square foot = 0.0479 kPa,
   1 ksi = 1,000 psi = 6.895 MPa.

a. Deflection criterion: L/240.
b. Design load assumptions:
   Second-floor dead load is 10 psf.
   Second-floor live load is 30 psf.
   Roof/ceiling dead load is 12 psf.
   Attic live load is 10 psf.
c. Building width is in the direction of horizontal framing members supported by the wall studs.
d. Minimum Grade 33 ksi steel shall be used for 33 mil and 43 mil thicknesses. Minimum Grade 50 ksi steel shall be used for 54 and 68 mil thicknesses.

TABLE R603.3.2(4)
32-FOOT-WIDE BUILDING SUPPORTING ROOF AND CEILING ONLY[a, b, c, d]

ULTIMATE WIND SPEED AND EXPOSURE CATEGORY (mph)		MEMBER SIZE	STUD SPACING (inches)	MINIMUM STUD THICKNESS (mils)											
				8-foot Studs				9-foot Studs				10-foot Studs			
				Ground Snow Load (psf)											
Exp. B	Exp. C			20	30	50	70	20	30	50	70	20	30	50	70
115	—	350S162	16	33	33	33	33	33	33	33	33	33	33	33	43
			24	33	33	43	54	33	33	43	54	43	43	43	54
		550S162	16	33	33	33	33	33	33	33	33	33	33	33	33
			24	33	33	33	43	33	33	33	43	33	33	33	43
120	—	350S162	16	33	33	33	33	33	33	33	33	33	33	33	43
			24	33	33	43	54	33	33	43	54	43	43	43	54
		550S162	16	33	33	33	33	33	33	33	33	33	33	33	33
			24	33	33	33	43	33	33	33	43	33	33	43	43
130	115	350S162	16	33	33	33	43	33	33	33	43	33	33	33	43
			24	33	33	43	54	43	43	43	54	43	43	54	54
		550S162	16	33	33	33	33	33	33	33	33	33	33	33	33
			24	33	33	43	43	33	33	33	43	33	33	43	43
< 140	120	350S162	16	33	33	33	43	33	33	33	43	33	33	33	43
			24	33	33	43	54	43	43	43	54	54	54	54	54
		550S162	16	33	33	33	33	33	33	33	33	33	33	33	33
			24	33	33	43	43	33	33	33	43	43	43	43	43
—	130	350S162	16	33	33	33	43	33	33	33	43	43	43	43	43
			24	43	43	43	54	54	54	54	54	54	54	54	54
		550S162	16	33	33	33	33	33	33	33	33	33	33	33	33
			24	33	33	43	43	43	43	43	43	43	43	43	43
—	< 140	350S162	16	33	33	33	43	43	43	43	43	43	43	43	43
			24	43	43	54	54	54	54	54	54	54	54	54	54
		550S162	16	33	33	33	33	33	33	33	33	33	33	33	33
			24	43	43	43	43	43	43	43	43	43	43	43	43

For SI: 1 inch = 25.4 mm, 1 foot = 304.8 mm, 1 mil = 0.0254 mm, 1 mile per hour = 0.447 m/s, 1 pound per square foot = 0.0479 kPa, 1 ksi = 1,000 psi = 6.895 MPa.

a. Deflection criterion: $L/240$.
b. Design load assumptions:
   Second-floor dead load is 10 psf.
   Second-floor live load is 30 psf.
   Roof/ceiling dead load is 12 psf.
   Attic live load is 10 psf.
c. Building width is in the direction of horizontal framing members supported by the wall studs.
d. Minimum Grade 33 ksi steel shall be used for 33 mil and 43 mil thicknesses. Minimum Grade 50 ksi steel shall be used for 54 and 68 mil thicknesses.

TABLE R603.3.2(5)
36-FOOT-WIDE BUILDING SUPPORTING ROOF AND CEILING ONLY[a, b, c, d]

ULTIMATE WIND SPEED AND EXPOSURE CATEORY (mph)		MEMBER SIZE	STUD SPACING (inches)	MINIMUM STUD THICKNESS (mils)											
				8-foot Studs				9-foot Studs				10-foot Studs			
				Ground Snow Load (psf)											
Exp. B	Exp. C			20	30	50	70	20	30	50	70	20	30	50	70
115	—	350S162	16	33	33	33	43	33	33	33	43	33	33	33	43
			24	33	33	43	54	33	33	43	54	43	43	54	54
		550S162	16	33	33	33	33	33	33	33	33	33	33	33	33
			24	33	33	43	43	33	33	43	43	33	33	43	43
120	—	350S162	16	33	33	33	43	33	33	33	43	33	33	33	43
			24	33	33	43	54	33	33	43	54	43	43	54	54
		550S162	16	33	33	33	33	33	33	33	33	33	33	33	33
			24	33	33	43	43	33	33	43	43	33	33	43	43
130	115	350S162	16	33	33	33	43	33	33	33	43	33	33	43	43
			24	33	43	43	54	43	43	43	54	43	43	54	54
		550S162	16	33	33	33	33	33	33	33	33	33	33	33	33
			24	33	33	43	43	33	33	43	43	33	33	43	43
< 140	120	350S162	16	33	33	33	43	33	33	33	33	33	33	43	43
			24	43	43	43	54	43	43	43	54	54	54	54	54
		550S162	16	33	33	33	33	33	33	33	33	33	33	33	33
			24	33	33	43	43	33	33	43	43	43	43	43	54
—	130	350S162	16	33	33	33	43	33	33	33	43	43	43	43	43
			24	43	43	54	54	54	54	54	54	54	54	54	54
		550S162	16	33	33	33	33	33	33	33	33	33	33	33	43
			24	33	33	43	54	43	43	43	43	43	43	43	54
—	< 140	350S162	16	33	33	33	43	43	43	43	43	43	43	43	54
			24	43	43	54	54	54	54	54	54	54	54	54	68
		550S162	16	33	33	33	33	33	33	33	33	33	33	33	43
			24	43	43	43	54	43	43	43	43	43	43	43	54

For SI: 1 inch = 25.4 mm, 1 foot = 304.8 mm, 1 mil = 0.0254 mm, 1 mile per hour = 0.447 m/s, 1 pound per square foot = 0.0479 kPa, 1 ksi = 1,000 psi = 6.895 MPa.

a. Deflection criterion: $L/240$.
b. Design load assumptions:
  Second-floor dead load is 10 psf.
  Second-floor live load is 30 psf.
  Roof/ceiling dead load is 12 psf.
  Attic live load is 10 psf.
c. Building width is in the direction of horizontal framing members supported by the wall studs.
d. Minimum Grade 33 ksi steel shall be used for 33 mil and 43 mil thicknesses. Minimum Grade 50 ksi steel shall be used for 54 and 68 mil thicknesses.

TABLE R603.3.2(6)
40-FOOT-WIDE BUILDING SUPPORTING ROOF AND CEILING ONLY[a, b, c, d]

ULTIMATE WIND SPEED AND EXPOSURE CATEGORY (mph)		MEMBER SIZE	STUD SPACING (inches)	MINIMUM STUD THICKNESS (mils)											
				8-foot Studs				9-foot Studs				10-foot Studs			
				Ground Snow Load (psf)											
Exp. B	Exp. C			20	30	50	70	20	30	50	70	20	30	50	70
115	—	350S162	16	33	33	33	43	33	33	33	43	33	33	43	43
			24	33	33	43	54	33	43	43	54	43	43	54	54
		550S162	16	33	33	33	43	33	33	33	33	33	33	33	33
			24	33	33	43	54	33	33	43	43	33	33	43	54
120	—	350S162	16	33	33	33	43	33	33	33	43	33	33	43	43
			24	33	43	43	54	33	43	43	54	43	43	54	54
		550S162	16	33	33	33	43	33	33	33	33	33	33	33	43
			24	33	33	43	54	33	33	43	43	33	33	43	54
130	115	350S162	16	33	33	33	43	33	33	33	43	33	33	43	43
			24	43	43	54	54	43	43	54	54	43	54	54	54
		550S162	16	33	33	33	43	33	33	33	33	33	33	33	43
			24	33	33	43	54	33	33	43	54	33	33	43	54
< 140	120	350S162	16	33	33	33	43	33	33	33	43	33	33	43	43
			24	43	43	54	54	43	43	54	54	54	54	54	54
		550S162	16	33	33	33	43	33	33	33	33	33	33	33	43
			24	33	33	43	54	33	33	43	54	43	43	43	54
—	130	350S162	16	33	33	43	43	33	33	43	43	43	43	43	54
			24	43	43	54	54	54	54	54	54	54	54	54	68
		550S162	16	33	33	33	43	33	33	33	43	33	33	33	43
			24	33	33	43	54	43	43	43	54	43	43	43	54
—	< 140	350S162	16	33	33	43	43	43	43	43	43	43	43	43	54
			24	43	43	54	54	54	54	54	54	54	54	54	68
		550S162	16	33	33	33	43	33	33	33	43	33	33	33	43
			24	43	43	43	54	43	43	43	54	43	43	43	54

For SI: 1 inch = 25.4 mm, 1 foot = 304.8 mm, 1 mil = 0.0254 mm, 1 mile per hour = 0.447 m/s, 1 pound per square foot = 0.0479 kPa,
1 ksi = 1,000 psi = 6.895 MPa.

a. Deflection criterion: L/240.
b. Design load assumptions:
   Second-floor dead load is 10 psf.
   Second-floor live load is 30 psf.
   Roof/ceiling dead load is 12 psf.
   Attic live load is 10 psf.
c. Building width is in the direction of horizontal framing members supported by the wall studs.
d. Minimum Grade 33 ksi steel shall be used for 33 mil and 43 mil thicknesses. Minimum Grade 50 ksi steel shall be used for 54 and 68 mil thicknesses.

TABLE R603.3.2(7)
24-FOOT-WIDE BUILDING SUPPORTING ONE FLOOR, ROOF AND CEILING[a, b, c, d]

ULTIMATE WIND SPEED AND EXPOSURE CATEGORY (mph)		MEMBER SIZE	STUD SPACING (inches)	MINIMUM STUD THICKNESS (mils)											
				8-foot Studs				9-foot Studs				10-foot Studs			
				Ground Snow Load (psf)											
Exp. B	Exp. C			20	30	50	70	20	30	50	70	20	30	50	70
115	—	350S162	16	33	33	33	33	33	33	33	33	33	33	33	43
			24	33	33	43	43	43	43	43	43	43	43	43	54
		550S162	16	33	33	33	33	33	33	33	33	33	33	33	33
			24	33	33	33	43	33	33	33	43	33	33	33	43
120	—	350S162	16	33	33	33	33	33	33	33	33	33	33	33	43
			24	43	43	43	43	43	43	43	43	43	43	54	54
		550S162	16	33	33	33	33	33	33	33	33	33	33	33	33
			24	33	33	33	43	33	33	33	43	33	33	33	43
130	115	350S162	16	33	33	33	43	33	33	33	43	43	43	43	43
			24	43	43	43	54	43	43	54	54	54	54	54	54
		550S162	16	33	33	33	33	33	33	33	33	33	33	33	33
			24	33	33	33	43	33	33	33	43	33	33	43	43
< 140	120	350S162	16	33	33	33	43	33	33	43	43	43	43	43	43
			24	43	43	43	54	43	54	54	54	54	54	54	54
		550S162	16	33	33	33	33	33	33	33	33	33	33	33	33
			24	33	33	43	43	33	33	33	43	43	43	43	43
—	130	350S162	16	33	33	33	43	43	43	43	43	43	43	43	54
			24	43	43	54	54	54	54	54	54	54	54	54	54
		550S162	16	33	33	33	33	33	33	33	33	33	33	33	33
			24	33	33	43	43	43	43	43	43	43	43	43	43
—	< 140	350S162	16	43	43	43	43	43	43	43	43	54	54	54	54
			24	54	54	54	54	54	54	54	54	54	54	54	54
		550S162	16	33	33	33	33	33	33	33	33	33	33	33	33
			24	43	43	43	43	43	43	43	43	43	43	43	43

For SI: 1 inch = 25.4 mm, 1 foot = 304.8 mm, 1 mil = 0.0254 mm, 1 mile per hour = 0.447 m/s, 1 pound per square foot = 0.0479 kPa, 1 ksi = 1,000 psi = 6.895 MPa.

a. Deflection criterion: $L/240$.
b. Design load assumptions:
   Second-floor dead load is 10 psf.
   Second-floor live load is 30 psf.
   Roof/ceiling dead load is 12 psf.
   Attic live load is 10 psf.
c. Building width is in the direction of horizontal framing members supported by the wall studs.
d. Minimum Grade 33 ksi steel shall be used for 33 mil and 43 mil thicknesses. Minimum Grade 50 ksi steel shall be used for 54 and 68 mil thicknesses.

TABLE R603.3.2(8)
28-FOOT-WIDE BUILDING SUPPORTING ONE FLOOR, ROOF AND CEILING[a, b, c, d]

ULTIMATE WIND SPEED AND EXPOSURE CATEGORY (mph)		MEMBER SIZE	STUD SPACING (inches)	MINIMUM STUD THICKNESS (mils)											
				8-foot Studs				9-foot Studs				10-foot Studs			
				Ground Snow Load (psf)											
Exp. B	Exp. C			20	30	50	70	20	30	50	70	20	30	50	70
115	—	350S162	16	33	33	33	43	33	33	33	43	33	33	43	43
			24	43	43	43	54	43	43	43	54	43	43	54	54
		550S162	16	33	33	33	33	33	33	33	33	33	33	33	33
			24	33	33	43	43	33	33	43	43	33	33	43	43
120	—	350S162	16	33	33	33	43	33	33	33	43	33	33	43	43
			24	43	43	43	54	43	43	43	54	54	54	54	54
		550S162	16	33	33	33	33	33	33	33	33	33	33	33	33
			24	33	33	43	43	33	33	43	43	33	33	43	43
130	115	350S162	16	33	33	33	43	33	33	43	43	43	43	43	43
			24	43	43	43	54	43	54	54	54	54	54	54	54
		550S162	16	33	33	33	33	33	33	33	33	33	33	33	33
			24	33	33	43	43	33	33	43	43	43	43	43	43
< 140	120	350S162	16	33	33	33	43	43	43	43	43	43	43	43	43
			24	43	43	54	54	54	54	54	54	54	54	54	54
		550S162	16	33	33	33	33	33	33	33	33	33	33	33	33
			24	33	33	43	43	33	33	43	43	43	43	43	43
—	130	350S162	16	33	33	43	43	43	43	43	43	43	43	54	54
			24	54	54	54	54	54	54	54	54	54	54	54	54
		550S162	16	33	33	33	33	33	33	33	33	33	33	33	43
			24	33	33	43	43	43	43	43	43	43	43	43	43
—	< 140	350S162	16	43	43	43	43	43	43	43	43	54	54	54	54
			24	54	54	54	54	54	54	54	54	54	54	54	54
		550S162	16	33	33	33	33	33	33	33	33	33	33	33	43
			24	43	43	43	43	43	43	43	43	43	43	43	54

For SI: 1 inch = 25.4 mm, 1 foot = 304.8 mm, 1 mil = 0.0254 mm, 1 mile per hour = 0.447 m/s, 1 pound per square foot = 0.0479 kPa, 1 ksi = 1,000 psi = 6.895 MPa.

a. Deflection criterion: $L/240$.

b. Design load assumptions:
   Second-floor dead load is 10 psf.
   Second-floor live load is 30 psf.
   Roof/ceiling dead load is 12 psf.
   Attic live load is 10 psf.

c. Building width is in the direction of horizontal framing members supported by the wall studs.

d. Minimum Grade 33 ksi steel shall be used for 33 mil and 43 mil thicknesses. Minimum Grade 50 ksi steel shall be used for 54 and 68 mil thicknesses.

TABLE R603.3.2(9)
32-FOOT-WIDE BUILDING SUPPORTING ONE FLOOR, ROOF AND CEILING[a, b, c, d]

ULTIMATE WIND SPEED AND EXPOSURE CATEGORY (mph)		MEMBER SIZE	STUD SPACING (inches)	MINIMUM STUD THICKNESS (mils)											
				8-foot Studs				9-foot Studs				10-foot Studs			
				Ground Snow Load (psf)											
Exp. B	Exp. C			20	30	50	70	20	30	50	70	20	30	50	70
115	—	350S162	16	33	33	33	43	33	33	33	43	33	43	43	43
			24	43	43	43	54	43	43	43	54	54	54	54	54
		550S162	16	33	33	33	43	33	33	33	33	33	33	33	43
			24	33	43	43	54	33	33	43	43	33	33	43	43
120	—	350S162	16	33	33	33	43	33	33	33	43	43	43	43	43
			24	43	43	43	54	43	43	43	54	54	54	54	54
		550S162	16	33	33	33	43	33	33	33	33	33	33	33	43
			24	33	43	43	54	33	33	43	43	33	33	43	54
130	115	350S162	16	33	33	43	43	43	43	43	43	43	43	43	43
			24	43	43	54	54	54	54	54	54	54	54	54	54
		550S162	16	33	33	33	43	33	33	33	33	33	33	33	43
			24	33	43	43	54	33	33	43	43	43	43	43	54
< 140	120	350S162	16	33	33	43	43	43	43	43	43	43	43	43	54
			24	43	54	54	54	54	54	54	54	54	54	54	54
		550S162	16	33	33	33	43	33	33	33	43	33	33	33	43
			24	33	43	43	54	33	43	43	43	43	43	43	54
—	130	350S162	16	43	43	43	43	43	43	43	43	43	54	54	54
			24	54	54	54	54	54	54	54	54	54	54	54	54
		550S162	16	33	33	33	43	33	33	33	43	33	33	33	43
			24	43	43	43	54	43	43	43	54	43	43	43	54
—	< 140	350S162	16	43	43	43	43	43	43	43	54	54	54	54	54
			24	54	54	54	54	54	54	54	54	54	54	54	68
		550S162	16	33	33	33	43	33	33	33	43	33	33	33	43
			24	43	43	43	54	43	43	43	54	43	43	43	54

For SI: 1 inch = 25.4 mm, 1 foot = 304.8 mm, 1 mil = 0.0254 mm, 1 mile per hour = 0.447 m/s, 1 pound per square foot = 0.0479 kPa, 1 ksi = 1,000 psi = 6.895 MPa.

a. Deflection criterion: $L/240$.

b. Design load assumptions:
   Second-floor dead load is 10 psf.
   Second-floor live load is 30 psf.
   Roof/ceiling dead load is 12 psf.
   Attic live load is 10 psf.

c. Building width is in the direction of horizontal framing members supported by the wall studs.

d. Minimum Grade 33 ksi steel shall be used for 33 mil and 43 mil thicknesses. Minimum Grade 50 ksi steel shall be used for 54 and 68 mil thicknesses.

TABLE R603.3.2(10)
36-FOOT-WIDE BUILDING SUPPORTING ONE FLOOR, ROOF AND CEILING[a, b, c, d]

ULTIMATE WIND SPEED AND EXPOSURE CATEGORY (mph)		MEMBER SIZE	STUD SPACING (inches)	MINIMUM STUD THICKNESS (mils)											
				8-foot Studs				9-foot Studs				10-foot Studs			
				Ground Snow Load (psf)											
Exp. B	Exp. C			20	30	50	70	20	30	50	70	20	30	50	70
115	—	350S162	16	33	33	43	43	33	33	43	43	43	43	43	43
			24	43	43	54	54	43	43	54	54	54	54	54	54
		550S162	16	33	33	33	43	33	33	33	43	33	33	33	43
			24	43	43	43	54	43	43	43	54	43	43	43	54
120	—	350S162	16	33	33	43	43	33	33	43	43	43	43	43	43
			24	43	43	54	54	43	43	54	54	54	54	54	54
		550S162	16	33	33	33	43	33	33	33	43	33	33	33	43
			24	43	43	43	54	43	43	43	54	43	43	43	54
130	115	350S162	16	33	33	43	43	43	43	43	43	43	43	43	54
			24	43	54	54	54	54	54	54	54	54	54	54	68
		550S162	16	33	33	33	43	33	33	33	43	33	33	33	43
			24	43	43	43	54	43	43	43	54	43	43	43	54
< 140	120	350S162	16	43	43	43	43	43	43	43	43	43	43	54	54
			24	54	54	54	54	54	54	54	54	54	54	54	68
		550S162	16	33	33	33	43	33	33	33	43	33	33	33	43
			24	43	43	43	54	43	43	43	54	43	43	43	54
—	130	350S162	16	43	43	43	43	43	43	43	43	54	54	54	54
			24	54	54	54	54	54	54	54	54	54	54	54	68
		550S162	16	33	33	33	43	33	33	33	43	33	33	33	43
			24	43	43	43	54	43	43	43	54	43	43	43	54
—	< 140	350S162	16	43	43	43	54	43	43	54	54	54	54	54	54
			24	54	54	54	54	54	54	54	54	54	54	54	68
		550S162	16	33	33	33	43	33	33	33	43	33	33	43	43
			24	43	43	43	54	43	43	43	54	43	43	54	54

For SI: 1 inch = 25.4 mm, 1 foot = 304.8 mm, 1 mil = 0.0254 mm, 1 mile per hour = 0.447 m/s, 1 pound per square foot = 0.0479 kPa, 1 ksi = 1,000 psi = 6.895 MPa.

a. Deflection criterion: L/240.

b. Design load assumptions:
   Second-floor dead load is 10 psf.
   Second-floor live load is 30 psf.
   Roof/ceiling dead load is 12 psf.
   Attic live load is 10 psf.

c. Building width is in the direction of horizontal framing members supported by the wall studs.

d. Minimum Grade 33 ksi steel shall be used for 33 mil and 43 mil thicknesses. Minimum Grade 50 ksi steel shall be used for 54 and 68 mil thicknesses.

TABLE R603.3.2(11)
40-FOOT-WIDE BUILDING SUPPORTING ONE FLOOR, ROOF AND CEILING[a, b, c, d]

ULTIMATE WIND SPEED AND EXPOSURE CATEGORY (mph)		MEMBER SIZE	STUD SPACING (inches)	MINIMUM STUD THICKNESS (mils)											
				8-foot Studs				9-foot Studs				10-foot Studs			
				Ground Snow Load (psf)											
Exp. B	Exp. C			20	30	50	70	20	30	50	70	20	30	50	70
115	—	350S162	16	33	33	43	43	33	33	43	43	43	43	43	54
			24	43	43	54	54	43	43	54	54	54	54	54	68
		550S162	16	33	33	33	43	33	33	33	43	33	33	33	43
			24	43	43	54	54	43	43	43	54	43	43	43	54
120	—	350S162	16	33	33	43	43	33	33	43	43	43	43	43	54
			24	43	43	54	54	54	54	54	54	54	54	54	68
		550S162	16	33	33	33	43	33	33	33	43	33	33	33	43
			24	43	43	54	54	43	43	43	54	43	43	43	54
130	115	350S162	16	43	43	43	54	43	43	43	43	43	43	54	54
			24	54	54	54	54	54	54	54	54	54	54	54	68
		550S162	16	33	33	43	43	33	33	33	43	33	33	43	43
			24	43	43	54	54	43	43	43	54	43	43	54	54
< 140	120	350S162	16	43	43	43	54	43	43	43	54	43	43	54	54
			24	54	54	54	54	54	54	54	54	54	54	54	68
		550S162	16	33	33	43	43	33	33	33	43	33	33	43	43
			24	43	43	54	54	43	43	43	54	43	43	54	54
—	130	350S162	16	43	43	43	54	43	43	43	54	54	54	54	54
			24	54	54	54	68	54	54	54	54	54	54	68	68
		550S162	16	33	33	43	43	33	33	33	43	33	33	43	43
			24	43	43	54	54	43	43	43	54	43	43	54	54
—	< 140	350S162	16	43	43	43	54	43	43	54	54	54	54	54	54
			24	54	54	54	68	54	54	54	68	54	54	68	68
		550S162	16	33	33	43	43	33	33	43	43	33	43	43	43
			24	43	43	54	54	43	43	43	54	43	43	54	54

For SI: 1 inch = 25.4 mm, 1 foot = 304.8 mm, 1 mil = 0.0254 mm, 1 mile per hour = 0.447 m/s, 1 pound per square foot = 0.0479 kPa, 1 ksi = 1,000 psi = 6.895 MPa.

a. Deflection criterion: $L/240$.
b. Design load assumptions:
   Second-floor dead load is 10 psf.
   Second-floor live load is 30 psf.
   Roof/ceiling dead load is 12 psf.
   Attic live load is 10 psf.
c. Building width is in the direction of horizontal framing members supported by the wall studs.
d. Minimum Grade 33 ksi steel shall be used for 33 mil and 43 mil thicknesses. Minimum Grade 50 ksi steel shall be used for 54 and 68 mil thicknesses.

TABLE R603.3.2(12)
24-FOOT-WIDE BUILDING SUPPORTING TWO FLOORS, ROOF AND CEILING[a, b, c, d]

ULTIMATE WIND SPEED AND EXPOSURE CATEGORY (mph)		MEMBER SIZE	STUD SPACING (inches)	MINIMUM STUD THICKNESS (mils)											
				8-foot Studs				9-foot Studs				10-foot Studs			
				Ground Snow Load (psf)											
Exp. B	Exp. C			20	30	50	70	20	30	50	70	20	30	50	70
115	—	350S162	16	43	43	43	43	33	33	33	43	43	43	43	43
			24	54	54	54	54	54	54	54	54	54	54	54	54
		550S162	16	33	33	43	43	33	33	33	33	33	33	33	43
			24	43	43	54	54	43	43	43	43	43	43	43	54
120	—	350S162	16	43	43	43	43	33	33	43	43	43	43	43	43
			24	54	54	54	54	54	54	54	54	54	54	54	54
		550S162	16	33	33	43	43	33	33	33	33	33	33	33	43
			24	43	43	54	54	43	43	43	43	43	43	43	54
130	115	350S162	16	43	43	43	43	43	43	43	43	43	43	43	54
			24	54	54	54	54	54	54	54	54	54	54	54	54
		550S162	16	33	33	43	43	33	33	33	33	33	33	33	43
			24	43	43	54	54	43	43	43	43	43	43	43	54
< 140	120	350S162	16	43	43	43	43	43	43	43	43	43	43	54	54
			24	54	54	54	54	54	54	54	54	54	54	54	54
		550S162	16	33	33	43	43	33	33	33	33	33	33	33	43
			24	43	43	54	54	43	43	43	43	43	43	43	54
—	130	350S162	16	43	43	43	43	43	43	43	43	54	54	54	54
			24	54	54	54	54	54	54	54	54	54	54	68	68
		550S162	16	33	33	43	43	33	33	33	33	33	33	33	43
			24	43	43	54	54	43	43	43	43	43	43	43	54
—	< 140	350S162	16	43	43	43	43	43	43	54	54	54	54	54	54
			24	54	54	54	54	54	54	54	54	54	54	68	68
		550S162	16	33	33	43	43	33	33	33	33	33	33	43	43
			24	43	43	54	54	43	43	43	43	54	54	54	54

For SI: 1 inch = 25.4 mm, 1 foot = 304.8 mm, 1 mil = 0.0254 mm, 1 mile per hour = 0.447 m/s, 1 pound per square foot = 0.0479 kPa,
   1 ksi = 1,000 psi = 6.895 MPa.

a. Deflection criterion: $L/240$.
b. Design load assumptions:
   Top- and middle-floor dead load is 10 psf.
   Top-floor live load is 30 psf.
   Middle-floor live load is 40 psf.
   Roof/ceiling dead load is 12 psf.
   Attic live load is 10 psf.
c. Building width is in the direction of horizontal framing members supported by the wall studs.
d. Minimum Grade 33 ksi steel shall be used for 33 mil and 43 mil thicknesses. Minimum Grade 50 ksi steel shall be used for 54 and 68 mil thicknesses.

TABLE R603.3.2(13)
28-FOOT-WIDE BUILDING SUPPORTING TWO FLOORS, ROOF AND CEILING[a, b, c, d]

ULTIMATE WIND SPEED AND EXPOSURE CATEGORY (mph) Exp. B	Exp. C	MEMBER SIZE	STUD SPACING (inches)	MINIMUM STUD THICKNESS (mils) 8-foot Studs Ground Snow Load (psf) 20	30	50	70	9-foot Studs 20	30	50	70	10-foot Studs 20	30	50	70
115	—	350S162	16	43	43	43	43	43	43	43	43	43	43	43	43
			24	54	54	54	54	54	54	54	54	54	54	54	54
		550S162	16	43	43	43	43	43	43	43	43	43	43	43	43
			24	54	54	54	54	54	54	54	54	54	54	54	54
120	—	350S162	16	43	43	43	43	43	43	43	43	43	43	43	43
			24	54	54	54	54	54	54	54	54	54	54	54	54
		550S162	16	43	43	43	43	43	43	43	43	43	43	43	43
			24	54	54	54	54	54	54	54	54	54	54	54	54
130	115	350S162	16	43	43	43	43	43	43	43	43	43	43	54	54
			24	54	54	54	54	54	54	54	54	54	54	54	68
		550S162	16	43	43	43	43	43	43	43	43	43	43	43	43
			24	54	54	54	54	54	54	54	54	54	54	54	54
< 140	120	350S162	16	43	43	43	43	43	43	43	43	54	54	54	54
			24	54	54	54	54	54	54	54	54	54	54	68	68
		550S162	16	43	43	43	43	43	43	43	43	43	43	43	43
			24	54	54	54	54	54	54	54	54	54	54	54	54
—	130	350S162	16	43	43	43	43	43	43	43	54	54	54	54	54
			24	54	54	54	54	54	54	54	54	68	68	68	68
		550S162	16	43	43	43	43	43	43	43	43	43	43	43	43
			24	54	54	54	54	54	54	54	54	54	54	54	54
—	< 140	350S162	16	43	43	43	54	54	54	54	54	54	54	54	54
			24	54	54	54	54	54	54	54	68	68	68	68	68
		550S162	16	43	43	43	43	43	43	43	43	43	43	43	43
			24	54	54	54	54	54	54	54	54	54	54	54	54

For SI: 1 inch = 25.4 mm, 1 foot = 304.8 mm, 1 mil = 0.0254 mm, 1 mile per hour = 0.447 m/s, 1 pound per square foot = 0.0479 kPa, 1 ksi = 1,000 psi = 6.895 MPa.

a. Deflection criterion: $L/240$.
b. Design load assumptions:
   Top- and middle-floor dead load is 10 psf.
   Top-floor live load is 30 psf.
   Middle-floor live load is 40 psf.
   Roof/ceiling dead load is 12 psf.
   Attic live load is 10 psf.
c. Building width is in the direction of horizontal framing members supported by the wall studs.
d. Minimum Grade 33 ksi steel shall be used for 33 mil and 43 mil thicknesses. Minimum Grade 50 ksi steel shall be used for 54 and 68 mil thicknesses.

TABLE R603.3.2(14)
32-FOOT-WIDE BUILDING SUPPORTING TWO FLOORS, ROOF AND CEILING[a, b, c, d]

ULTIMATE WIND SPEED AND EXPOSURE CATEGORY (mph)		MEMBER SIZE	STUD SPACING (inches)	MINIMUM STUD THICKNESS (mils)											
				8-foot Studs				9-foot Studs				10-foot Studs			
				Ground Snow Load (psf)											
Exp. B	Exp. C			20	30	50	70	20	30	50	70	20	30	50	70
115	—	350S162	16	43	43	43	54	43	43	43	43	43	43	43	54
			24	54	54	54	68	54	54	54	54	54	54	54	68
		550S162	16	43	43	43	43	43	43	43	43	43	43	43	43
			24	54	54	54	54	54	54	54	54	54	54	54	54
120	—	350S162	16	43	43	43	54	43	43	43	43	43	43	43	54
			24	54	54	54	68	54	54	54	54	54	54	54	68
		550S162	16	43	43	43	43	43	43	43	43	43	43	43	43
			24	54	54	54	54	54	54	54	54	54	54	54	54
130	115	350S162	16	43	43	43	54	43	43	43	43	54	54	54	54
			24	54	54	54	68	54	54	54	54	54	68	68	68
		550S162	16	43	43	43	43	43	43	43	43	43	43	43	43
			24	54	54	54	54	54	54	54	54	54	54	54	54
< 140	120	350S162	16	43	43	43	54	43	43	43	54	54	54	54	54
			24	54	54	54	68	54	54	54	54	68	68	68	68
		550S162	16	43	43	43	43	43	43	43	43	43	43	43	43
			24	54	54	54	54	54	54	54	54	54	54	54	54
—	130	350S162	16	43	43	43	54	43	54	54	54	54	54	54	54
			24	54	54	54	68	54	54	54	68	68	68	68	68
		550S162	16	43	43	43	43	43	43	43	43	43	43	43	43
			24	54	54	54	54	54	54	54	54	54	54	54	54
—	< 140	350S162	16	43	43	54	54	54	54	54	54	54	54	54	54
			24	54	54	54	68	54	68	68	68	68	68	68	68
		550S162	16	43	43	43	43	43	43	43	43	43	43	43	43
			24	54	54	54	54	54	54	54	54	54	54	54	54

For SI: 1 inch = 25.4 mm, 1 foot = 304.8 mm, 1 mil = 0.0254 mm, 1 mile per hour = 0.447 m/s, 1 pound per square foot = 0.0479 kPa, 1 ksi = 1,000 psi = 6.895 MPa.

a. Deflection criterion: $L/240$.
b. Design load assumptions:

  Top- and middle-floor dead load is 10 psf.

  Top-floor live load is 30 psf.

  Middle-floor live load is 40 psf.

  Roof/ceiling dead load is 12 psf.

  Attic live load is 10 psf.

c. Building width is in the direction of horizontal framing members supported by the wall studs.

d. Minimum Grade 33 ksi steel shall be used for 33 mil and 43 mil thicknesses. Minimum Grade 50 ksi steel shall be used for 54 and 68 mil thicknesses.

TABLE R603.3.2(15)
36-FOOT-WIDE BUILDING SUPPORTING TWO FLOORS, ROOF AND CEILING[a, b, c, d]

ULTIMATE WIND SPEED AND EXPOSURE CATEGORY (mph)		MEMBER SIZE	STUD SPACING (inches)	MINIMUM STUD THICKNESS (mils)											
				8-foot Studs				9-foot Studs				10-foot Studs			
				Ground Snow Load (psf)											
Exp. B	Exp. C			20	30	50	70	20	30	50	70	20	30	50	70
115	—	350S162	16	54	54	54	54	43	43	43	54	54	54	54	54
			24	68	68	68	68	54	54	54	68	68	68	68	68
		550S162	16	43	43	43	54	43	43	43	43	43	43	43	43
			24	54	54	54	54	54	54	54	54	54	54	54	54
120	—	350S162	16	54	54	54	54	43	43	43	54	54	54	54	54
			24	68	68	68	68	54	54	54	68	68	68	68	68
		550S162	16	43	43	43	54	43	43	43	43	43	43	43	43
			24	54	54	54	54	54	54	54	54	54	54	54	54
130	115	350S162	16	54	54	54	54	43	43	43	54	54	54	54	54
			24	68	68	68	68	54	54	54	68	68	68	68	68
		550S162	16	43	43	43	54	43	43	43	43	43	43	43	43
			24	54	54	54	54	54	54	54	54	54	54	54	54
< 140	120	350S162	16	54	54	54	54	43	43	54	54	54	54	54	54
			24	68	68	68	68	54	54	54	68	68	68	68	68
		550S162	16	43	43	43	54	43	43	43	43	43	43	43	43
			24	54	54	54	54	54	54	54	54	54	54	54	54
—	130	350S162	16	54	54	54	54	54	54	54	54	54	54	54	54
			24	68	68	68	68	54	54	68	68	68	68	68	68
		550S162	16	43	43	43	54	43	43	43	43	43	43	43	43
			24	54	54	54	54	54	54	54	54	54	54	54	54
—	< 140	350S162	16	54	54	54	54	54	54	54	54	54	54	54	54
			24	68	68	68	68	68	68	68	68	68	68	68	68
		550S162	16	43	43	43	54	43	43	43	43	43	43	43	43
			24	54	54	54	54	54	54	54	54	54	54	54	54

For SI: 1 inch = 25.4 mm, 1 foot = 304.8 mm, 1 mil = 0.0254 mm, 1 mile per hour = 0.447 m/s, 1 pound per square foot = 0.0479 kPa, 1 ksi = 1,000 psi = 6.895 MPa.

a. Deflection criterion: $L/240$.
b. Design load assumptions:
   Top- and middle-floor dead load is 10 psf.
   Top-floor live load is 30 psf.
   Middle-floor live load is 40 psf.
   Roof/ceiling dead load is 12 psf.
   Attic live load is 10 psf.
c. Building width is in the direction of horizontal framing members supported by the wall studs.
d. Minimum Grade 33 ksi steel shall be used for 33 mil and 43 mil thicknesses. Minimum Grade 50 ksi steel shall be used for 54 and 68 mil thicknesses.

TABLE R603.3.2(16)
40-FOOT-WIDE BUILDING SUPPORTING TWO FLOORS, ROOF AND CEILING[a, b, c, d]

ULTIMATE WIND SPEED AND EXPOSURE CATEGORY (mph)		MEMBER SIZE	STUD SPACING (inches)	MINIMUM STUD THICKNESS (mils)											
				8-foot Studs				9-foot Studs				10-foot Studs			
				Ground Snow Load (psf)											
Exp. B	Exp. C			20	30	50	70	20	30	50	70	20	30	50	70
115	—	350S162	16	54	54	54	54	54	54	54	54	54	54	54	54
			24	68	68	68	68	68	68	68	68	68	68	68	68
		550S162	16	54	54	54	54	43	43	54	54	43	43	54	54
			24	54	54	54	68	54	54	54	54	54	54	54	54
120	—	350S162	16	54	54	54	54	54	54	54	54	54	54	54	54
			24	68	68	68	68	68	68	68	68	68	68	68	68
		550S162	16	54	54	54	54	43	43	54	54	43	43	54	54
			24	54	54	54	68	54	54	54	54	54	54	54	54
130	115	350S162	16	54	54	54	54	54	54	54	54	54	54	54	54
			24	68	68	68	68	68	68	68	68	68	68	68	68
		550S162	16	54	54	54	54	43	43	54	54	43	43	54	54
			24	54	54	54	68	54	54	54	54	54	54	54	54
< 140	120	350S162	16	54	54	54	54	54	54	54	54	54	54	54	54
			24	68	68	68	68	68	68	68	68	68	68	68	68
		550S162	16	54	54	54	54	43	43	54	54	43	43	54	54
			24	54	54	54	68	54	54	54	54	54	54	54	54
—	130	350S162	16	54	54	54	54	54	54	54	54	54	54	54	54
			24	68	68	68	68	68	68	68	68	68	68	68	68
		550S162	16	54	54	54	54	43	43	54	54	43	43	54	54
			24	54	54	54	68	54	54	54	54	54	54	54	54
—	< 140	350S162	16	54	54	54	54	54	54	54	54	54	54	54	54
			24	68	68	68	68	68	68	68	68	68	68	68	68
		550S162	16	54	54	54	54	43	43	54	54	43	43	54	54
			24	54	54	54	68	54	54	54	54	54	54	54	54

For SI: 1 inch = 25.4 mm, 1 foot = 304.8 mm, 1 mil = 0.0254 mm, 1 mile per hour = 0.447 m/s, 1 pound per square foot = 0.0479 kPa, 1 ksi = 1,000 psi = 6.895 MPa.

a. Deflection criterion: $L/240$.

b. Design load assumptions:

 Top- and middle-floor dead load is 10 psf.

 Top-floor live load is 30 psf.

 Middle-floor live load is 40 psf.

 Roof/ceiling dead load is 12 psf.

 Attic live load is 10 psf.

c. Building width is in the direction of horizontal framing members supported by the wall studs.

d. Minimum Grade 33 ksi steel shall be used for 33 mil and 43 mil thicknesses. Minimum Grade 50 ksi steel shall be used for 54 and 68 mil thicknesses.

R603.3.3 Stud bracing. The flanges of cold-formed steel studs shall be laterally braced in accordance with one of the following:

1. Gypsum board on both sides, structural sheathing on both sides, or gypsum board on one side and structural sheathing on the other side of load-bearing walls with gypsum board installed with minimum No. 6 screws in accordance with Section R702 and structural sheathing installed in accordance with Section R603.9 and Table R603.3.2(1).

2. Horizontal steel straps fastened in accordance with Figure R603.3.3(1) on both sides at mid-height for 8-foot (2438 mm) walls, and at one-third points for 9-foot and 10-foot (2743 mm and 3048 mm) walls. Horizontal steel straps shall be not less than $1^1/_2$ inches in width and 33 mils in thickness (38 mm by 0.84 mm). Straps shall be attached to the flanges of studs with one No. 8 screw. In-line blocking shall be installed between studs at the termination of straps and at 12-foot (3658 mm) intervals along the strap. Straps shall be fastened to the blocking with two No. 8 screws.

3. Sheathing on one side and strapping on the other side fastened in accordance with Figure R603.3.3(2). Sheathing shall be installed in accordance with Item 1. Steel straps shall be installed in accordance with Item 2.

TABLE R603.3.2.1(1)
ALL BUILDING WIDTHS GABLE ENDWALLS 8, 9 OR 10 FEET IN HEIGHT[a, b, c, d]

ULTIMATE WIND SPEED AND EXPOSURE CATEGORY (mph)		MEMBER SIZE	STUD SPACING (inches)	MINIMUM STUD THICKNESS (mils)		
Exp. B	Exp. C			8-foot Studs	9-foot Studs	10-foot Studs
115	—	350S162	16	33	33	33
			24	33	33	33
		550S162	16	33	33	33
			24	33	33	33
120	—	350S162	16	33	33	33
			24	33	33	43
		550S162	16	33	33	33
			24	33	33	33
130	115	350S162	16	33	33	33
			24	33	43	43
		550S162	16	33	33	33
			24	33	33	33
< 140	120	350S162	16	33	33	43
			24	33	43	54
		550S162	16	33	33	33
			24	33	33	33
—	130	350S162	16	33	33	43
			24	43	43	54
		550S162	16	33	33	33
			24	33	43	43
—	< 140	350S162	16	33	43	43
			24	43	54	54
		550S162	16	33	33	33
			24	43	43	43

For SI: 1 inch = 25.4 mm, 1 foot = 304.8 mm, 1 mil = 0.0254 mm, 1 mile per hour = 0.447 m/s, 1 pound per square foot = 0.0479 kPa, 1 ksi = 1,000 psi = 6.895 MPa.

a. Deflection criterion *L*/240.

b. Design load assumptions:
   Ground snow load is 70 psf.
   Roof/ceiling dead load is 12 psf.
   Floor dead load is 10 psf.
   Floor live load is 40 psf.
   Attic dead load is 10 psf.

c. Building width is in the direction of horizontal framing members supported by the wall studs.

d. Minimum Grade 33 ksi steel shall be used for 33 mil and 43 mil thicknesses. Minimum Grade 50 ksi steel shall be used for 54 and 68 mil thicknesses.

TABLE R603.3.2.1(2)
ALL BUILDING WIDTHS GABLE ENDWALLS OVER 10 FEET IN HEIGHT[a, b, c, d]

ULTIMATE WIND SPEED AND EXPOSURE CATEGORY (mph)		MEMBER SIZE	STUD SPACING (inches)	MINIMUM STUD THICKNESS (mils)					
				Stud Height, h (feet)					
Exp. B	Exp. C			$10 < h \le 12$	$12 < h \le 14$	$14 < h \le 16$	$16 < h \le 18$	$18 < h \le 20$	$20 < h \le 22$
115	—	350S162	16	33	43	68	97	—	—
			24	43	68	—	—	—	—
		550S162	16	33	33	33	43	43	54
			24	33	43	43	54	68	97
120	—	350S162	16	43	54	97	—	—	—
			24	54	97	—	—	—	—
		550S162	16	33	33	43	43	54	68
			24	33	43	54	54	68	97
130	115	350S162	16	43	54	97	—	—	—
			24	54	97	—	—	—	—
		550S162	16	33	33	43	54	54	97
			24	43	43	54	68	97	97
< 140	120	350S162	16	43	68	—	—	—	—
			24	68	—	—	—	—	—
		550S162	16	33	43	43	54	68	97
			24	43	54	54	68	97	—
—	130	350S162	16	54	97	—	—	—	—
			24	97	—	—	—	—	—
		550S162	16	33	43	54	68	97	—
			24	43	54	54	97	—	—
—	< 140	350S162	16	54	97	—	—	—	—
			24	97	—	—	—	—	—
		550S162	16	43	43	54	97	97	—
			24	54	54	68	—	—	—

For SI: 1 inch = 25.4 mm, 1 foot = 304.8 mm, 1 mil = 0.0254 mm, 1 mile per hour = 0.447 m/s, 1 pound per square foot = 0.0479 kPa, 1 ksi = 1,000 psi = 6.895 MPa.

a. Deflection criterion $L/240$.
b. Design load assumptions:
    Ground snow load is 70 psf.
    Roof/ceiling dead load is 12 psf.
    Floor dead load is 10 psf.
    Floor live load is 40 psf.
    Attic dead load is 10 psf.
c. Building width is in the direction of horizontal framing members supported by the wall studs.
d. Minimum Grade 33 ksi steel shall be used for 33 mil and 43 mil thicknesses. Minimum Grade 50 ksi steel shall be used for 54 and 68 mil thicknesses.

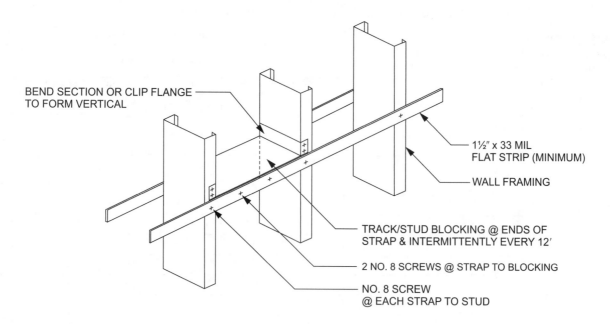

BEND SECTION OR CLIP FLANGE
TO FORM VERTICAL

1½″ x 33 MIL
FLAT STRIP (MINIMUM)

WALL FRAMING

TRACK/STUD BLOCKING @ ENDS OF
STRAP & INTERMITTENTLY EVERY 12′

2 NO. 8 SCREWS @ STRAP TO BLOCKING

NO. 8 SCREW
@ EACH STRAP TO STUD

For SI: 1 mil = 0.0254 mm, 1 inch = 25.4 mm, 1 foot = 304.8 mm.

FIGURE R603.3.3(1)
STUD BRACING WITH STRAPPING ONLY

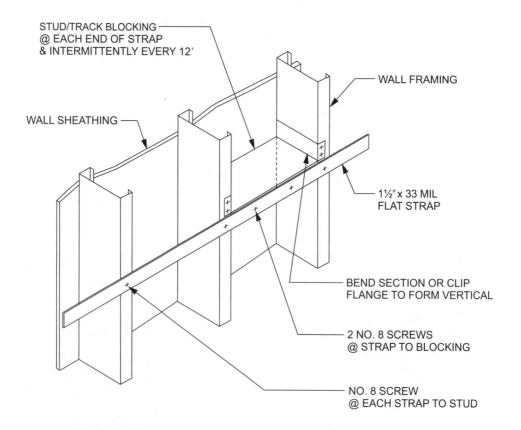

STUD/TRACK BLOCKING
@ EACH END OF STRAP
& INTERMITTENTLY EVERY 12′

WALL FRAMING

WALL SHEATHING

1½″ x 33 MIL
FLAT STRAP

BEND SECTION OR CLIP
FLANGE TO FORM VERTICAL

2 NO. 8 SCREWS
@ STRAP TO BLOCKING

NO. 8 SCREW
@ EACH STRAP TO STUD

For SI: 1 mil = 0.0254 mm, 1 inch = 25.4 mm, 1 foot = 304.8 mm.

FIGURE R603.3.3(2)
STUD BRACING WITH STRAPPING AND SHEATHING MATERIAL

R603.3.4 Cutting and notching. Flanges and lips of cold-formed steel studs and headers shall not be cut or notched.

R603.3.5 Splicing. Steel studs and other structural members shall not be spliced without an *approved* design. Tracks shall be spliced in accordance with Figure R603.3.5.

R603.4 Corner framing. In exterior walls, corner studs and the top tracks shall be installed in accordance with Figure R603.4.

R603.5 Exterior wall covering. The method of attachment of exterior wall covering materials to cold-formed steel stud wall framing shall conform to the manufacturer's installation instructions.

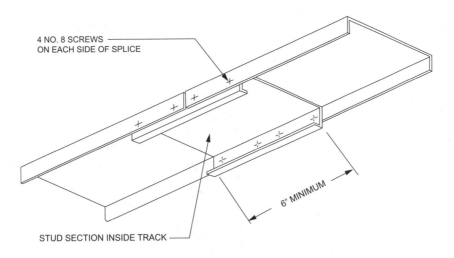

For SI: 1 inch = 25.4 mm.

FIGURE R603.3.5
TRACK SPLICE

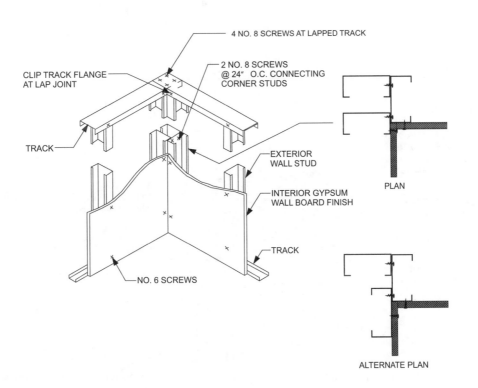

For SI: 1 inch = 25.4 mm.

FIGURE R603.4
CORNER FRAMING

R603.6 Headers. Headers shall be installed above all wall openings in exterior walls and interior load-bearing walls. Box beam headers and back-to-back headers each shall be formed from two equal sized C-shaped members in accordance with Figures R603.6(1) and R603.6(2), respectively, and Tables R603.6(1) through R603.6(6). L-shaped headers shall be permitted to be constructed in accordance with AISI S230. Alternately, headers shall be permitted to be designed and constructed in accordance with AISI S240.

R603.6.1 Headers in gable endwalls. Box beam and back-to-back headers in gable endwalls shall be permitted to be constructed in accordance with Section R603.6 or with the header directly above the opening in accordance with Figures R603.6.1(1) and R603.6.1(2) and the following provisions:

1. Two 362S162-33 for openings less than or equal to 4 feet (1219 mm).

2. Two 600S162-43 for openings greater than 4 feet (1219 mm) but less than or equal to 6 feet (1829 mm).

3. Two 800S162-54 for openings greater than 6 feet (1829 mm) but less than or equal to 9 feet (2743 mm).

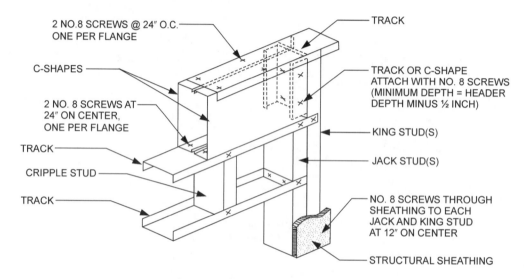

For SI: 1 inch = 25.4 mm.

FIGURE R603.6(1)
BOX BEAM HEADER

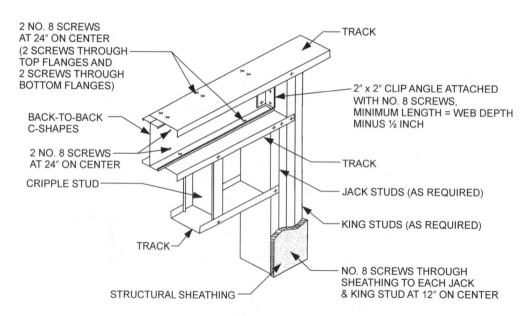

For SI: 1 inch = 25.4 mm.

FIGURE R603.6(2)
BACK-TO-BACK HEADER

TABLE R603.6(1)
BOX-BEAM AND BACK-TO-BACK HEADER SPANS
Headers Supporting Roof and Ceiling Only[a, b, d]

MEMBER DESIGNATION	GROUND SNOW LOAD (20 psf)					GROUND SNOW LOAD (30 psf)				
	Building width[c] (feet)					Building width[c] (feet)				
	24	28	32	36	40	24	28	32	36	40
2-350S162-33	3'-3"	2'-8"	2'-2"	—	—	2'-8"	2'-2"	—	—	—
2-350S162-43	4'-2"	3'-9"	3'-4"	2'-11"	2'-7"	3'-9"	3'-4"	2'-11"	2'-7"	2'-2"
2-350S162-54	6'-2"	5'-10"	5'-8"	5'-3"	4'-10"	5'-11"	5'-8"	5'-2"	4'-10"	4'-6"
2-350S162-68	6'-7"	6'-3"	6'-0"	5'-10"	5'-8"	6'-4"	6'-1"	5'-10"	5'-8"	5'-6"
2-550S162-33	4'-8"	4'-0"	3'-6"	3'-0"	2'-6"	4'-1"	3'-6"	3'-0"	2'-6"	—
2-550S162-43	6'-0"	5'-4"	4'-10"	4'-4"	3'-11"	5'-5"	4'-10"	4'-4"	3'-10"	3'-5"
2-550S162-54	8'-9"	8'-5"	8'-1"	7'-9"	7'-3"	8'-6"	8'-1"	7'-8"	7'-2"	6'-8"
2-550S162-68	9'-5"	9'-0"	8'-8"	8'-4"	8'-1"	9'-1"	8'-8"	8'-4"	8'-1"	7'-10"
2-800S162-33	4'-5"	3'-11"	3'-5"	3'-1"	2'-10"	3'-11"	3'-6"	3'-1"	2'-9"	2'-3"
2-800S162-43	7'-3"	6'-7"	5'-11"	5'-4"	4'-10"	6'-7"	5'-11"	5'-4"	4'-9"	4'-3"
2-800S162-54	10'-10"	10'-2"	9'-7"	9'-0"	8'-5"	10'-2"	9'-7"	8'-11"	8'-4"	7'-9"
2-800S162-68	12'-8"	11'-10"	11'-2"	10'-7"	10'-1"	11'-11"	11'-2"	10'-7"	10'-0"	9'-6"
2-1000S162-43	7'-10"	6'-10"	6'-1"	5'-6"	5'-0"	6'-11"	6'-1"	5'-5"	4'-11"	4'-6"
2-1000S162-54	12'-3"	11'-5"	10'-9"	10'-2"	9'-6"	11'-6"	10'-9"	10'-1"	9'-5"	8'-9"
2-1000S162-68	14'-5"	13'-5"	12'-8"	12'-0"	11'-6"	13'-6"	12'-8"	12'-0"	11'-5"	10'-10"
2-1200S162-54	12'-11"	11'-3"	10'-0"	9'-0"	8'-2"	11'-5"	10'-0"	9'-0"	8'-1"	7'-4"
2-1200S162-68	15'-11"	14'-10"	14'-0"	13'-4"	12'-8"	15'-0"	14'-0"	13'-3"	12'-7"	11'-11"

For SI: 1 mil = 0.0254 mm, 1 inch = 25.4 mm, 1 foot = 304.8 mm, 1 pound per square foot = 0.0479 kPa, 1 pound per square inch = 6.895 kPa,
    1 ksi = 1,000 psi = 6.895 MPa.

a. Deflection criteria: $L/360$ for live loads, $L/240$ for total loads.
b. Design load assumptions:
    Roof/ceiling dead load is 12 psf.
    Attic dead load is 10 psf.
c. Building width is in the direction of horizontal framing members supported by the header.
d. Minimum Grade 33 ksi steel shall be used for 33 mil and 43 mil thicknesses. Minimum Grade 50 ksi steel shall be used for 54 and 68 mil thicknesses.

TABLE R603.6(2)
BOX-BEAM AND BACK-TO-BACK HEADER SPANS
Headers Supporting Roof and Ceiling Only[a, b, d]

MEMBER DESIGNATION	GROUND SNOW LOAD (50 psf)					GROUND SNOW LOAD (70 psf)				
	Building width[c] (feet)					Building width[c] (feet)				
	24	28	32	36	40	24	28	32	36	40
2-350S162-33	—	—	—	—	—	—	—	—	—	—
2-350S162-43	2'-4"	—	—	—	—	—	—	—	—	—
2-350S162-54	4'-8"	4'-2"	3'-9"	3'-5"	3'-1"	3'-7"	3'-2"	2'-9"	2'-5"	2'-0"
2-350S162-68	5'-7"	5'-2"	4'-9"	4'-4"	3'-11"	4'-7"	4'-1"	3'-7"	3'-2"	2'-10"
2-550S162-33	2'-2"	—	—	—	—	—	—	—	—	—
2-550S162-43	3'-8"	3'-1"	2'-6"	—	—	2'-3"	—	—	—	—
2-550S162-54	6'-11"	6'-3"	5'-9"	5'-3"	4'-9"	5'-6"	4'-11"	4'-5"	3'-11"	3'-5"
2-550S162-68	8'-0"	7'-6"	6'-11"	6'-5"	5'-11"	6'-9"	6'-1"	5'-6"	5'-0"	4'-7"
2-800S162-33	2'-7"	—	—	—	—	—	—	—	—	—
2-800S162-43	4'-6"	3'-9"	3'-1"	2'-5"	—	2'-10"	—	—	—	—
2-800S162-54	8'-0"	7'-3"	6'-8"	6'-1"	5'-7"	6'-5"	5'-9"	5'-1"	4'-7"	4'-0"
2-800S162-68	9'-9"	9'-0"	8'-3"	7'-8"	7'-1"	8'-0"	7'-3"	6'-7"	6'-0"	5'-6"
2-1000S162-43	4'-8"	4'-1"	3'-6"	2'-9"	—	3'-3"	2'-2"	—	—	—
2-1000S162-54	9'-1"	8'-2"	7'-3"	6'-7"	6'-0"	7'-0"	6'-2"	5'-6"	5'-0"	4'-6"
2-1000S162-68	11'-1"	10'-2"	9'-5"	8'-8"	8'-1"	9'-1"	8'-3"	7'-6"	6'-10"	6'-3"
2-1200S162-54	7'-8"	6'-9"	6'-1"	5'-6"	5'-0"	5'-10"	5'-1"	4'-7"	4'-1"	3'-9"
2-1200S162-68	12'-3"	11'-3"	10'-4"	9'-7"	8'-11"	10'-1"	9'-1"	8'-3"	7'-6"	6'-10"

For SI: 1 mil = 0.0254 mm, 1 inch = 25.4 mm, 1 foot = 304.8 mm, 1 pound per square foot = 0.0479 kPa, 1 pound per square inch = 6.895 kPa, 1 ksi = 1,000 psi = 6.895 MPa.

a. Deflection criteria: $L/360$ for live loads, $L/240$ for total loads.
b. Design load assumptions:
   Roof/ceiling dead load is 12 psf.
   Attic dead load is 10 psf.
c. Building width is in the direction of horizontal framing members supported by the header.
d. Minimum Grade 33 ksi steel shall be used for 33 mil and 43 mil thicknesses. Minimum Grade 50 ksi steel shall be used for 54 and 68 mil thicknesses.

TABLE R603.6(3)
BOX-BEAM AND BACK-TO-BACK HEADER SPANS
Headers Supporting One Floor, Roof and Ceiling[a, b, d]

MEMBER DESIGNATION	GROUND SNOW LOAD (20 psf)					GROUND SNOW LOAD (30 psf)				
	Building width[c] (feet)					Building width[c] (feet)				
	24	28	32	36	40	24	28	32	36	40
2-350S162-33	—	—	—	—	—	—	—	—	—	—
2-350S162-43	2'-2"	—	—	—	—	2'-1"	—	—	—	—
2-350S162-54	4'-4"	3'-10"	3'-5"	3'-1"	2'-9"	4'-3"	2'-9"	3'-4"	3'-0"	2'-8"
2-350S162-68	5'-0"	4'-9"	4'-7"	4'-2"	3'-9"	4'-11"	4'-8"	4'-6"	4'-1"	3'-9"
2-550S162-33	—	—	—	—	—	—	—	—	—	—
2-550S162-43	3'-5"	2'-9"	2'-1"	—	—	3'-3"	2'-7"	—	—	—
2-550S162-54	6'-6"	5'-10"	5'-3"	4'-9"	4'-4"	6'-4"	5'-9"	5'-2"	4'-8"	4'-3"
2-550S162-68	7'-2"	6'-10"	6'-5"	5'-11"	5'-6"	7'-0"	6'-9"	6'-4"	5'-10"	5'-4"
2-800S162-33	2'-1"	—	—	—	—	—	—	—	—	—
2-800S162-43	4'-2"	3'-4"	2'-7"	—	—	4'-0"	3'-3"	2'-5"	—	—
2-800S162-54	7'-6"	6'-9"	6'-2"	5'-7"	5'-0"	7'-5"	6'-8"	6'-0"	5'-5"	4'-11"
2-800S162-68	9'-3"	8'-5"	7'-8"	7'-1"	6'-6"	9'-1"	8'-3"	7'-7"	7'-0"	6'-5"
2-1000S162-43	4'-4"	3'-9"	2'-11"	—	—	4'-3"	3'-8"	2'-9"	—	—
2-1000S162-54	8'-6"	7'-6"	6'-8"	6'-0"	5'-5"	8'-4"	7'-4"	6'-6"	5'-10"	5'-4"
2-1000S162-68	10'-6"	9'-7"	8'-9"	8'-0"	7'-5"	10'-4"	9'-5"	8'-7"	7'-11"	7'-3"
2-1200S162-54	7'-1"	6'-2"	5'-6"	5'-0"	4'-6"	6'-11"	6'-1"	5'-5"	4'-10"	4'-5"
2-1200S162-68	11'-7"	10'-7"	9'-8"	8'-11"	8'-2"	11'-5"	10'-5"	9'-6"	8'-9"	8'-0"

For SI: 1 inch = 25.4 mm, 1 foot = 304.8 mm, 1 pound per square foot = 0.0479 kPa, 1 pound per square inch = 6.895 kPa.

a. Deflection criteria: $L/360$ for live loads, $L/240$ for total loads.

b. Design load assumptions:
   Second-floor dead load is 10 psf.
   Roof/ceiling dead load is 12 psf.
   Second-floor live load is 30 psf.
   Attic dead load is 10 psf.

c. Building width is in the direction of horizontal framing members supported by the header.

d. Minimum Grade 33 ksi steel shall be used for 33 mil and 43 mil thicknesses. Minimum Grade 50 ksi steel shall be used for 54 and 68 mil thicknesses.

TABLE R603.6(4)
BOX-BEAM AND BACK-TO-BACK HEADER SPANS
Headers Supporting One Floor, Roof and Ceiling[a, b, d]

MEMBER DESIGNATION	GROUND SNOW LOAD (50 psf)					GROUND SNOW LOAD (70 psf)				
	Building width[c] (feet)					Building width[c] (feet)				
	24	28	32	36	40	24	28	32	36	40
2-350S162-33	—	—	—	—	—	—	—	—	—	—
2-350S162-43	—	—	—	—	—	—	—	—	—	—
2-350S162-54	3'-5"	3'-0"	2'-7"	2'-2"	—	2'-8"	2'-2"	—	—	—
2-350S162-68	4'-6"	4'-1"	3'-8"	3'-3"	2'-11"	3'-9"	3'-3"	2'-10"	2'-5"	2'-1"
2-550S162-33	—	—	—	—	—	—	—	—	—	—
2-550S162-43	2'-0"	—	—	—	—	—	—	—	—	—
2-550S162-54	5'-3"	3'-8"	4'-1"	3'-8"	3'-2"	4'-3"	3'-8"	3'-1"	2'-7"	2'-0"
2-550S162-68	6'-5"	5'-10"	5'-3"	4'-9"	4'-4"	5'-5"	4'-9"	4'-3"	3'-9"	3'-4"
2-800S162-33	—	—	—	—	—	—	—	—	—	—
2-800S162-43	2'-6"	—	—	—	—	—	—	—	—	—
2-800S162-54	6'-1"	5'-5"	4'-10"	4'-3"	3'-9"	4'-11"	4'-3"	3'-8"	3'-0"	2'-5"
2-800S162-68	7'-8"	6'-11"	6'-3"	5'-9"	5'-2"	6'-5"	5'-9"	5'-1"	4'-6"	4'-0"
2-1000S162-43	2'-10"	—	—	—	—	—	—	—	—	—
2-1000S162-54	6'-7"	5'-10"	5'-3"	4'-9"	4'-3"	5'-4"	4'-9"	4'-1"	3'-5"	2'-9"
2-1000S162-68	8'-8"	7'-10"	7'-2"	6'-6"	5'-11"	7'-4"	6'-6"	5'-9"	5'-1"	4'-6"
2-1200S162-54	5'-6"	4'-10"	4'-4"	3'-11"	3'-7"	4'-5"	3'-11"	3'-6"	3'-2"	2'-11"
2-1200S162-68	9'-7"	8'-8"	7'-11"	7'-2"	6'-6"	8'-1"	7'-2"	6'-4"	5'-8"	5'-0"

For SI: 1 mil = 0.0254 mm, 1 inch = 25.4 mm, 1 foot = 304.8 mm, 1 pound per square foot = 0.0479 kPa, 1 pound per square inch = 6.895 kPa, 1 ksi = 1,000 psi = 6.895 MPa.

a. Deflection criteria: $L/360$ for live loads, $L/240$ for total loads.

b. Design load assumptions:
   Second-floor dead load is 10 psf.
   Roof/ceiling dead load is 12 psf.
   Second-floor live load is 30 psf.
   Attic dead load is 10 psf.

c. Building width is in the direction of horizontal framing members supported by the header.

d. Minimum Grade 33 ksi steel shall be used for 33 mil and 43 mil thicknesses. Minimum Grade 50 ksi steel shall be used for 54 and 68 mil thicknesses.

TABLE R603.6(5)
BOX-BEAM AND BACK-TO-BACK HEADER SPANS
Headers Supporting Two Floors, Roof and Ceiling[a, b, d]

MEMBER DESIGNATION	GROUND SNOW LOAD (20 psf)					GROUND SNOW LOAD (30 psf)				
	Building width[c] (feet)					Building width[c] (feet)				
	24	28	32	36	40	24	28	32	36	40
2-350S162-33	—	—	—	—	—	—	—	—	—	—
2-350S162-43	—	—	—	—	—	—	—	—	—	—
2-350S162-54	2'-5"	—	—	—	—	2'-4"	—	—	—	—
2-350S162-68	3'-6"	3'-0"	2'-6"	2'-1"	—	3'-5"	2'-11"	2'-6"	2'-0"	—
2-550S162-33	—	—	—	—	—	—	—	—	—	—
2-550S162-43	—	—	—	—	—	—	—	—	—	—
2-550S162-54	3'-11"	3'-3"	2'-8"	2'-0"	—	3'-10"	3'-3"	2'-7"	—	—
2-550S162-68	5'-1"	4'-5"	3'-10"	3'-3"	2'-9"	5'-0"	4'-4"	3'-9"	3'-3"	2'-9"
2-800S162-33	—	—	—	—	—	—	—	—	—	—
2-800S162-43	—	—	—	—	—	—	—	—	—	—
2-800S162-54	4'-7"	3'-10"	3'-1"	2'-5"	—	4'-6"	3'-9"	3'-0"	2'-4"	—
2-800S162-68	6'-0"	5'-3"	4'-7"	3'-11"	3'-4"	6'-0"	5'-2"	4'-6"	3'-11"	3'-3"
2-1000S162-43	—	—	—	—	—	—	—	—	—	—
2-1000S162-54	5'-0"	4'-4"	3'-6"	2'-9"	—	4'-11"	4'-3"	3'-5"	2'-7"	—
2-1000S162-68	6'-10"	6'-0"	5'-3"	4'-6"	3'-10"	6'-9"	5'-11"	5'-2"	4'-5"	3'-9"
2-1200S162-54	4'-2"	3'-7"	3'-3"	2'-11"	—	4'-1"	3'-7"	3'-2"	2'-10"	—
2-1200S162-68	7'-7"	6'-7"	5'-9"	5'-0"	4'-2"	7'-6"	6'-6"	5'-8"	4'-10"	4'-1"

For SI: 1 mil = 0.0254 mm, 1 inch = 25.4 mm, 1 foot = 304.8 mm, 1 pound per square foot = 0.0479 kPa, 1 pound per square inch = 6.895 kPa,
    1 ksi = 1,000 psi = 6.895 MPa.

a. Deflection criteria: L/360 for live loads, L/240 for total loads.
b. Design load assumptions:
    Second-floor dead load is 10 psf.
    Roof/ceiling dead load is 12 psf.
    Second-floor live load is 40 psf
    Third-floor live load is 30 psf.
    Attic live load is 10 psf.
c. Building width is in the direction of horizontal framing members supported by the header.
d. Minimum Grade 33 ksi steel shall be used for 33 mil and 43 mil thicknesses. Minimum Grade 50 ksi steel shall be used for 54 and 68 mil thicknesses.

TABLE R603.6(6)
BOX-BEAM AND BACK-TO-BACK HEADER SPANS
Headers Supporting Two Floors, Roof and Ceiling[a, b, d]

MEMBER DESIGNATION	GROUND SNOW LOAD (50 psf)					GROUND SNOW LOAD (70 psf)				
	Building width[c] (feet)					Building width[c] (feet)				
	24	28	32	36	40	24	28	32	36	40
2-350S162-33	—	—	—	—	—	—	—	—	—	—
2-350S162-43	—	—	—	—	—	—	—	—	—	—
2-350S162-54	2'-2"	—	—	—	—	—	—	—	—	—
2-350S162-68	3'-3"	2'-9"	2'-3"	—	—	2'-11"	2'-5"	—	—	—
2-550S162-33	—	—	—	—	—	—	—	—	—	—
2-550S162-43	—	—	—	—	—	—	—	—	—	—
2-550S162-54	3'-7"	2'-11"	2'-3"	—	—	3'-3"	2'-7"	—	—	—
2-550S162-68	4'-9"	2'-1"	3'-6"	3'-0"	2'-5"	4'-4"	3'-9"	3'-2"	2'-8"	2'-1"
2-800S162-33	—	—	—	—	—	—	—	—	—	—
2-800S162-43	—	—	—	—	—	—	—	—	—	—
2-800S162-54	4'-3"	3'-5"	2'-8"	—	—	3'-9"	3'-0"	2'-3"	—	—
2-800S162-68	5'-8"	4'-11"	4'-2"	3'-7"	2'-11"	5'-3"	4'-6"	3'-10"	3'-3"	2'-7"
2-1000S162-43	—	—	—	—	—	—	—	—	—	—
2-1000S162-54	4'-8"	3'-11"	3'-1"	2'-2"	—	4'-3"	3'-5"	2'-7"	—	—
2-1000S162-68	6'-5"	5'-7"	4'-9"	4'-1"	3'-4"	5'-11"	5'-1"	4'-5"	3'-8"	2'-11"
2-1200S162-54	3'-11"	3'-5"	3'-0"	2'-4"	—	3'-7"	3'-2"	2'-10"	—	—
2-1200S162-68	7'-1"	6'-2"	5'-3"	4'-6"	3'-8"	6'-6"	5'-8"	4'-10"	4'-0"	3'-3"

For SI: 1 mil = 0.0254 mm, 1 inch = 25.4 mm, 1 foot = 304.8 mm, 1 pound per square foot = 0.0479 kPa, 1 pound per square inch = 6.895 kPa,
　　1 ksi = 1,000 psi = 6.895 MPa.
a. Deflection criteria: $L/360$ for live loads, $L/240$ for total loads.
b. Design load assumptions:
　Second-floor dead load is 10 psf.
　Roof/ceiling dead load is 12 psf.
　Second-floor live load is 40 psf
　Third-floor live load is 30 psf.
　Attic live load is 10 psf.
c. Building width is in the direction of horizontal framing members supported by the header.
d. Minimum Grade 33 ksi steel shall be used for 33 mil and 43 mil thicknesses. Minimum Grade 50 ksi steel shall be used for 54 and 68 mil thicknesses.

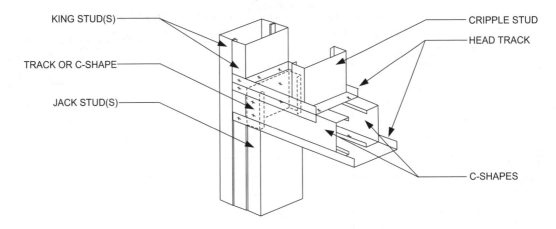

FIGURE R603.6.1(1)
BOX BEAM HEADER IN GABLE ENDWALL

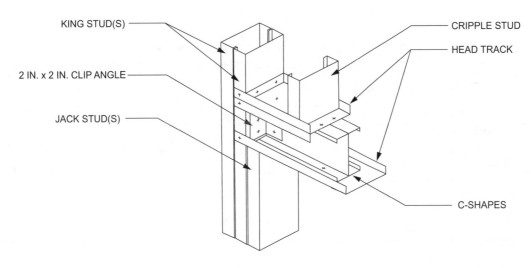

For SI: 1 inch = 25.4 mm.

FIGURE R603.6.1(2)
BACK-TO-BACK HEADER IN GABLE ENDWALL

R603.7 Jack and king studs. The number of jack and king studs installed on each side of a header shall comply with Table R603.7(1). King, jack and cripple studs shall be of the same dimension and thickness as the adjacent wall studs. Headers shall be connected to king studs in accordance with Table R603.7(2) and the following provisions:

1. For box beam headers, one-half of the total number of required screws shall be applied to the header and one-half to the king stud by use of C-shaped or track member in accordance with Figure R603.6(1). The track or C-shaped sections shall extend the depth of the header minus $^1/_2$ inch (12.7 mm) and shall have a minimum thickness not less than that of the wall studs.

2. For back-to-back headers, one-half the total number of screws shall be applied to the header and one-half to the king stud by use of a minimum 2-inch by 2-inch (51 mm by 51 mm) clip angle in accordance with Figure R603.6(2). The clip angle shall extend the depth of the header minus $^1/_2$ inch (12.7 mm) and shall have a minimum thickness not less than that of the wall studs. Jack and king studs shall be interconnected with structural sheathing in accordance with Figures R603.6(1) and R603.6(2).

R603.8 Head and sill track. Head track spans above door and window openings and sill track spans beneath window openings shall comply with Table R603.8. For openings less than 4 feet (1219 mm) in height that have both a head track and a sill track, multiplying the spans by 1.75 shall be permitted in Table R603.8. For openings less than or equal to 6 feet (1829 mm) in height that have both a head track and a sill track, multiplying the spans in Table R603.8 by 1.50 shall be permitted.

R603.9 Structural sheathing. Structural sheathing shall be installed in accordance with Figure R603.9 and this section on all sheathable exterior wall surfaces, including areas above and below openings.

TABLE R603.7(1)
TOTAL NUMBER OF JACK AND KING STUDS REQUIRED AT EACH END OF AN OPENING

SIZE OF OPENING (feet-inches)	24-INCH O.C. STUD SPACING		16-INCH O.C. STUD SPACING	
	No. of jack studs	No. of king studs	No. of jack studs	No. of king studs
Up to 3'-6"	1	1	1	1
> 3'-6" to 5'-0"	1	2	1	2
> 5'-0" to 5'-6"	1	2	2	2
> 5'-6" to 8'-0"	1	2	2	2
> 8'-0" to 10'-6"	2	2	2	3
> 10'-6" to 12'-0"	2	2	3	3
> 12'-0" to 13'-0"	2	3	3	3
> 13'-0" to 14'-0"	2	3	3	4
> 14'-0" to 16'-0"	2	3	3	4
> 16'-0" to 18'-0"	3	3	4	4

For SI: 1 inch = 25.4 mm, 1 foot = 304.8 mm.

TABLE R603.7(2)
HEADER TO KING STUD CONNECTION REQUIREMENTS[a, b, c, d]

HEADER SPAN (feet)	ULTIMATE WIND SPEED (mph), EXPOSURE CATEGORY					
	115 B	120 B	130 B / 115 C	<140 B / 120 C	130 C	<140 C
≤ 4	4-No. 8 screws	4-No. 8 screws	4-No. 8 screws	4-No. 8 screws	6-No. 8 screws	6-No. 8 screws
> 4 to 8	4-No. 8 screws	4-No. 8 screws	4-No. 8 screws	6-No. 8 screws	8-No. 8 screws	8-No. 8 screws
> 8 to 12	4-No. 8 screws	6-No. 8 screws	6-No. 8 screws	8-No. 8 screws	10-No. 8 screws	12-No. 8 screws
> 12 to 16	4-No. 8 screws	6-No. 8 screws	8-No. 8 screws	10-No. 8 screws	12-No. 8 screws	14-No. 8 screws

For SI: 1 inch = 25.4 mm, 1 foot = 304.8 mm, 1 mile per hour = 0.447 m/s, 1 pound = 4.448 N.

a. All screw sizes shown are minimum.

b. For headers located on the first floor of a two-story building or the first or second floor of a three-story building, the total number of screws is permitted to be reduced by 2 screws, but the total number of screws shall be not less than four.

c. For roof slopes of 6:12 or greater, the required number of screws shall be permitted to be reduced by half, but the total number of screws shall be not less than four.

d. Screws can be replaced by an uplift connector that has a capacity of the number of screws multiplied by 164 pounds.

TABLE R603.8
HEAD AND SILL TRACK SPAN

ULTIMATE WIND SPEED AND EXPOSURE CATEGORY (mph)		ALLOWABLE HEAD AND SILL TRACK SPAN[a, b, c] (feet-inches)					
		TRACK DESIGNATION[d]					
B	C	350T125-33	350T125-43	350T125-54	550T125-33	550T125-43	550T125-54
115	—	5'-9"	6'-9"	9'-3"	7'-3"	9'-1"	12'-5"
120	—	5'-6"	6'-6"	8'-11"	7'-0"	8'-9"	11'-11"
130	115	4'-10"	5'-9"	7'-10"	6'-2"	7'-8"	10'-6"
< 140	120	4'-8"	5'-6"	7'-6"	5'-11"	7'-4"	10'-1"
—	130	4'-3"	5'-1"	6'-11"	5'-6"	6'-9"	9'-4"
—	< 140	4'-0"	4'-9"	6'-5"	5'-1"	6'-4"	8'-8"

For SI: 1 mil = 0.0254 mm, 1 inch = 25.4 mm, 1 foot = 304.8 mm, 1 mile per hour = 0.447 m/s, 1 ksi = 1,000 psi = 6.895 MPa.

a. Deflection limit: $L/240$.

b. Head and sill track spans are based on components and cladding wind pressures and 48-inch tributary span.

c. For openings less than 4 feet in height that have both a head track and sill track, the spans are permitted to be multiplied by 1.75. For openings less than or equal to 6 feet in height that have both a head track and a sill track, the spans are permitted to be multiplied by a factor of 1.5.

d. Minimum Grade 33 ksi steel shall be used for 33 mil and 43 mil thicknesses. Minimum Grade 50 ksi steel shall be used for 54 and 68 mil thicknesses.

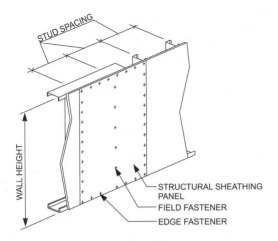

FIGURE R603.9
STRUCTURAL SHEATHING FASTENING PATTERN

R603.9.1 Sheathing materials. Structural sheathing panels shall consist of minimum $^7/_{16}$-inch-thick (11 mm) oriented strand board or $^{15}/_{32}$-inch-thick (12 mm) plywood.

R603.9.2 Determination of minimum length of full-height sheathing. The minimum length of full-height sheathing on each *braced wall line* shall be determined by multiplying the length of the *braced wall line* by the percentage obtained from Table R603.9.2(1) and by the plan aspect-ratio adjustment factors obtained from Table R603.9.2(2). The minimum length of full-height sheathing shall be not less than 20 percent of the *braced wall line* length.

To be considered full-height sheathing, structural sheathing shall extend from the bottom to the top of the wall without interruption by openings. Only sheathed, full-height wall sections, uninterrupted by openings, which are not less than 48 inches (1219 mm) wide, shall be counted toward meeting the minimum percentages in Table R603.9.2(1). In addition, structural sheathing shall comply with all of the following requirements:

1. Be installed with the long dimension parallel to the stud framing and shall cover the full vertical height of wall from the bottom of the bottom track to the top of the top track of each *story*. Installing the long dimension perpendicular to the stud framing or using shorter segments shall be permitted provided that the horizontal joint is blocked as described in Item 2.

2. Be blocked where the long dimension is installed perpendicular to the stud framing. Blocking shall be not less than 33 mil (0.84 mm) thickness. Each horizontal structural sheathing panel shall be fastened with No. 8 screws spaced at 6 inches (152 mm) on center to the blocking at the joint.

3. Be applied to each end (corners) of each of the exterior walls with a minimum 48-inch-wide (1219 mm) panel.

Exception: Where stone or masonry veneer is installed, the required length of full-height sheathing and overturning anchorage required shall be determined in accordance with Section R603.9.5.

R603.9.2.1 Full height sheathing. The minimum percentage of full-height structural sheathing shall be multiplied by 1.10 for 9-foot-high (2743 mm) walls and multiplied by 1.20 for 10-foot-high (3048 mm) walls.

R603.9.2.2 Full-height sheathing in lowest story. In the lowest *story* of a *dwelling*, multiplying the percentage of full-height sheathing required in Table R603.9.2(1) by 0.6 shall be permitted where hold-down anchors are provided in accordance with Section R603.9.4.2.

R603.9.3 Structural sheathing fastening. Edges and interior areas of structural sheathing panels shall be fastened to framing members and tracks in accordance with Figure R603.9 and Table R603.3.2(1). Screws for attachment of structural sheathing panels shall be bugle-head, flat-head, or similar head style with a minimum head diameter of 0.29 inch (8 mm).

For continuously sheathed *braced wall lines* using wood structural panels installed with No. 8 screws spaced 4 inches (102 mm) on center at all panel edges and 12 inches (304.8 mm) on center on intermediate framing members, the following shall apply:

1. Multiplying the percentages of full-height sheathing in Table R603.9.2(1) by 0.72 shall be permitted.

2. For bottom track attached to foundations or framing below, the bottom track anchor or screw connection spacing in Tables R505.3.1(1) and R603.3.1 shall be multiplied by two-thirds

R603.9.4 Uplift connection requirements. Uplift connections shall be provided in accordance with this section.

R603.9.4.1 Ultimate design wind speeds greater than 130 mph. Where ultimate design wind speeds exceed 130 miles per hour (58 m/s), Exposure Category C walls shall be provided with direct uplift connections in accordance with AISI S230, Section E13.3, and AISI S230, Section F8.2, as required for 140 miles per hour (63 m/s), Exposure Category C.

R603.9.4.2 Hold-down anchor. Where the percentage of full-height sheathing is adjusted in accordance with Section R603.9.2.2, a hold-down anchor, with a strength of 4,300 pounds (19 kN), shall be provided at each end of each full-height sheathed wall section used to meet the minimum percent sheathing requirements of Section R603.9.2. Hold-down anchors shall be attached to back-to-back studs; structural sheathing panels shall have edge fastening to the studs, in accordance with Section R603.9.3 and AISI S230, Table E11-1.

A single hold-down anchor, installed in accordance with Figure R603.9.4.2, shall be permitted at the corners of buildings.

R603.9.5 Structural sheathing for stone and masonry veneer. Where stone and masonry veneer are installed in accordance with Section R703.8, the length of full-height sheathing for exterior and interior wall lines backing or perpendicular to and laterally supporting walls with veneer shall comply with this section.

TABLE R603.9.2(1)
MINIMUM PERCENTAGE OF FULL-HEIGHT STRUCTURAL SHEATHING ON EXTERIOR WALLS[a, b]

WALL SUPPORTING	ROOF SLOPE	ULTIMATE WIND SPEED AND EXPOSURE (mph)					
		115 B	120 B	130 B / 115 C	< 140 B / 120 C	< 130 C	< 140 C
Roof and ceiling only (one story or top floor of two- or three-story building)	3:12	9	11	11	13	17	20
	6:12	13	15	17	22	28	35
	9:12	23	27	29	33	53	59
	12:12	32	39	40	44	70	76
One story, roof and ceiling (first floor of a two-story building or second floor of a three-story building)	3:12	26	32	34	39	53	67
	6:12	27	33	34	44	61	75
	9:12	38	45	46	61	78	92
	12:12	43	53	57	72	106	116
Two stories, roof and ceiling (first floor of a three-story building)	3:12	43	53	57	64	89	113
	6:12	41	51	51	67	95	114
	9:12	53	63	63	89	104	126
	12:12	54	67	74	100	142	157

For SI: 1 mph = 0.447 m/s.

a. Linear interpolation is permitted.

b. For hip-roofed homes the minimum percentage of full-height sheathing, based on wind, is permitted to be multiplied by a factor of 0.95 for roof slopes not exceeding 7:12 and a factor of 0.9 for roof slopes greater than 7:12.

TABLE R603.9.2(2)
FULL-HEIGHT SHEATHING LENGTH ADJUSTMENT FACTORS

PLAN ASPECT RATIO	LENGTH ADJUSTMENT FACTORS	
	Short wall	Long wall
1:1	1.0	1.0
1.5:1	1.5	0.67
2:1	2.0	0.50
3:1	3.0	0.33
4:1	4.0	0.25

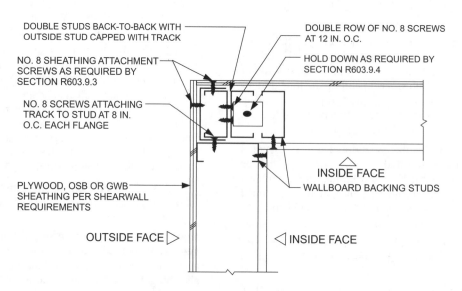

For SI: 1 inch = 25.4 mm.

FIGURE R603.9.4.2
CORNER STUD HOLD-DOWN DETAIL

TABLE R603.9.5(1)
REQUIRED LENGTH OF FULL-HEIGHT SHEATHING AND ASSOCIATED OVERTURNING ANCHORAGE FOR WALLS SUPPORTING WALLS WITH STONE OR MASONRY VENEER AND USING 33-MIL COLD-FORMED STEEL FRAMING AND 6-INCH SCREW SPACING ON THE PERIMETER OF EACH PANEL OF STRUCTURAL SHEATHING

SEISMIC DESIGN CATEGORY	STORY	BRACED WALL LINE LENGTH (feet)						SINGLE-STORY HOLD-DOWN FORCE (pounds)	CUMULATIVE HOLD-DOWN FORCE (pounds)
		10	20	30	40	50	60		
		Minimum total length of braced wall panels required along each braced wall line (feet)							
D_0		3.3	4.7	6.1	7.4	8.8	10.2	3,360	—
		5.3	8.7	12.1	15.4	18.8	22.2	3,360	6,720
		7.3	12.7	18.0	23.4	28.8	34.2	3,360	10,080
D_1		4.1	5.8	7.5	9.2	10.9	12.7	3,360	—
		6.6	10.7	14.9	19.1	23.3	27.5	3,360	6,720
		9.0	15.7	22.4	29.0	35.7	42.2	3,360	10,080
D_2		5.7	8.2	10.6	13.0	15.4	17.8	3,360	—
		9.2	15.1	21.1	27.0	32.9	38.8	3,360	6,720
		12.7	22.1	31.5	40.9	50.3	59.7	3,360	10,080

For SI: 1 mil = 0.0254 mm, 1 inch = 25.4 mm, 1 foot = 304.8 mm, 1 pound-force = 4.448 N.

TABLE R603.9.5(2)
REQUIRED LENGTH OF FULL-HEIGHT SHEATHING AND ASSOCIATED OVERTURNING ANCHORAGE FOR WALLS SUPPORTING WALLS WITH STONE OR MASONRY VENEER AND USING 43-MIL COLD-FORMED STEEL FRAMING AND 6-INCH SCREW SPACING ON THE PERIMETER OF EACH PANEL OF STRUCTURAL SHEATHING

SEISMIC DESIGN CATEGORY	STORY	BRACED WALL LINE LENGTH (feet)						SINGLE-STORY HOLD-DOWN FORCE (pounds)	CUMULATIVE HOLD-DOWN FORCE (pounds)
		10	20	30	40	50	60		
		Minimum total length of braced wall panels required along each braced wall line (feet)							
D_0		2.8	4.0	5.1	6.3	7.5	8.7	3,960	—
		4.5	7.4	10.2	13.1	16.0	18.8	3,960	7,920
		6.2	10.7	15.3	19.9	24.4	29.0	3,960	11,880
D_1		3.5	4.9	6.4	7.8	9.3	10.7	3,960	—
		5.6	9.1	12.7	16.2	19.8	23.3	3,960	7,920
		7.7	13.3	19.0	24.6	30.3	35.9	3,960	11,880
D_2		4.9	6.9	9.0	11.0	13.1	15.1	3,960	—
		7.8	12.9	17.9	22.9	27.9	32.9	3,960	7,920
		10.8	18.8	26.7	34.7	42.7	50.7	3,960	11,880

For SI: 1 mil = 0.0254 mm, 1 inch = 25.4 mm, 1 foot = 304.8 mm, 1 pound-force = 4.448 N.

TABLE R603.9.5(3)
REQUIRED LENGTH OF FULL-HEIGHT SHEATHING AND ASSOCIATED OVERTURNING ANCHORAGE FOR WALLS SUPPORTING WALLS WITH STONE OR MASONRY VENEER AND USING 33-MIL COLD-FORMED STEEL FRAMING AND 4-INCH SCREW SPACING ON THE PERIMETER OF EACH PANEL OF STRUCTURAL SHEATHING

SEISMIC DESIGN CATEGORY	STORY	BRACED WALL LINE LENGTH (feet)						SINGLE-STORY HOLD-DOWN FORCE (pounds)	CUMULATIVE HOLD-DOWN FORCE (pounds)
		10	20	30	40	50	60		
		Minimum total length of braced wall panels required along each braced wall line (feet)							
D_0	(1st of 3)	2.5	3.6	4.6	5.7	6.8	7.8	4,392	—
	(2nd of 3)	4.0	6.6	9.2	11.8	14.4	17.0	4,392	8,784
	(3rd of 3)	5.6	9.7	13.8	17.9	22.0	26.2	4,392	13,176
D_1	(1st of 3)	3.1	4.4	5.7	7.1	8.4	9.7	4,392	—
	(2nd of 3)	5.0	8.2	11.4	14.6	17.8	21.0	4,392	8,784
	(3rd of 3)	6.9	12.0	17.1	22.2	27.3	32.4	4,392	13,176
D_2	(1st of 3)	4.4	6.2	8.1	10.0	11.8	13.7	4,392	—
	(2nd of 3)	7.1	11.6	16.1	20.6	25.1	29.7	4,392	8,784
	(3rd of 3)	9.7	16.9	24.1	31.3	38.5	45.7	4,392	13,176

For SI: 1 mil = 0.0254 mm, 1 inch = 25.4 mm, 1 foot = 304.8 mm, 1 pound-force = 4.448 N.

TABLE R603.9.5(4)
REQUIRED LENGTH OF FULL-HEIGHT SHEATHING AND ASSOCIATED OVERTURNING ANCHORAGE FOR WALLS SUPPORTING WALLS WITH STONE OR MASONRY VENEER AND USING 43-MIL COLD-FORMED STEEL FRAMING AND 4-INCH SCREW SPACING ON THE PERIMETER OF EACH PANEL OF STRUCTURAL SHEATHING

SEISMIC DESIGN CATEGORY	STORY	BRACED WALL LINE LENGTH (feet)						SINGLE-STORY HOLD-DOWN FORCE (pounds)	CUMULATIVE HOLD-DOWN FORCE (pounds)
		10	20	30	40	50	60		
		Minimum total length of braced wall panels required along each braced wall line (feet)							
D_0		1.9	2.7	3.4	4.2	5.0	5.8	5,928	—
		3.0	4.9	6.8	8.8	10.7	12.6	5,928	11,856
D_1		2.3	3.3	4.3	5.2	6.2	7.2	5,928	—
		3.7	6.1	8.5	10.8	13.2	15.6	5,928	11,856
D_2		3.3	4.6	6.0	7.4	8.7	10.1	5,928	—
		5.2	8.6	11.9	15.3	18.6	22.0	5,928	11,856

For SI: 1 mil = 0.0254 mm, 1 inch = 25.4 mm, 1 foot = 304.8 mm, 1 pound-force = 4.448 N.

R603.9.5.1 Seismic Design Category C. In Seismic Design Category C, the length of structural sheathing for walls supporting one *story*, roof and ceiling shall be the greater of the amounts required by Section R603.9.2, except Section R603.9.2.2 shall be permitted.

R603.9.5.2 Seismic Design Categories D_0, D_1 and D_2. In Seismic Design Categories D_0, D_1 and D_2, the required length of structural sheathing and overturning anchorage shall be determined in accordance with Tables R603.9.5(1), R603.9.5(2), R603.9.5(3), and R603.9.5(4). Overturning anchorage shall be installed on the doubled studs at the end of each full-height wall segment.

SECTION R604
WOOD STRUCTURAL PANELS

R604.1 Identification and grade. Wood structural panels shall conform to DOC PS 1, DOC PS 2 or ANSI/APA PRP 210, CSA O325 or CSA O437. Panels shall be identified by a grade mark or certificate of inspection issued by an *approved* agency.

R604.2 Allowable spans. The maximum allowable spans for wood structural panel wall sheathing shall not exceed the values set forth in Table R602.3(3).

R604.3 Installation. Wood structural panel wall sheathing shall be attached to framing in accordance with Table R602.3(1) or R602.3(3).

SECTION R605
PARTICLEBOARD

R605.1 Identification and grade. Particleboard shall conform to ANSI A208.1 and shall be so identified by a grade mark or certificate of inspection issued by an *approved* agency. Particleboard shall comply with the grades specified in Table R602.3(4).

SECTION R606
GENERAL MASONRY CONSTRUCTION

R606.1 General. Masonry construction shall be designed and constructed in accordance with the provisions of this section, TMS 402, TMS 403, or TMS 404.

R606.1.1 Professional registration not required. Where the empirical design provisions of Appendix A of TMS 402, the provisions of TMS 403, or the provisions of this section are used to design masonry, project drawings, typical details and specifications are not required to bear the seal of the architect or engineer responsible for design, unless otherwise required by the state law of the *jurisdiction* having authority.

R606.2 Masonry construction materials.

R606.2.1 Concrete masonry units. Concrete masonry units shall conform to the following standards: ASTM C55 for concrete brick; ASTM C73 for calcium silicate face brick; ASTM C90 for load-bearing concrete masonry units; ASTM C744 for prefaced concrete and calcium silicate masonry units; or ASTM C1634 for concrete facing brick.

R606.2.2 Clay or shale masonry units. Clay or shale masonry units shall conform to the following standards: ASTM C34 for structural clay *load-bearing wall* tile; ASTM C56 for structural clay nonload-bearing wall tile; ASTM C62 for building brick (solid masonry units made from clay or shale); ASTM C126 for ceramic-glazed structural clay facing tile, facing brick and solid masonry units; ASTM C212 for structural clay facing tile; ASTM C216 for facing brick (solid masonry units made from clay or shale); ASTM C652 for hollow brick (hollow masonry units made from clay or shale); ASTM C1088 for solid units of thin veneer brick; or ASTM C1405 for glazed brick (single-fired solid brick units).

> **Exception:** Structural clay tile for nonstructural use in fireproofing of structural members and in wall furring shall not be required to meet the compressive strength specifications. The fire-resistance rating shall be determined in accordance with ASTM E119 or UL 263 and shall comply with the requirements of Section R302.

R606.2.3 AAC masonry. AAC masonry units shall conform to ASTM C1691 and ASTM C1693 for the strength class specified.

R606.2.4 Stone masonry units. Stone masonry units shall conform to the following standards: ASTM C503 for marble building stone (exterior); ASTM C568 for limestone building stone; ASTM C615 for granite building stone; ASTM C616 for sandstone building stone; or ASTM C629 for slate building stone.

R606.2.5 Architectural cast stone. Architectural cast stone shall conform to ASTM C1364.

R606.2.6 Adhered manufactured stone masonry veneer units. Adhered manufactured stone masonry veneer units shall conform to ASTM C1670.

R606.2.7 Second-hand units. Second-hand masonry units shall not be reused unless they conform to the requirements of new units. The units shall be of whole, sound materials and free from cracks and other defects that will interfere with proper laying or use. Old mortar shall be cleaned from the unit before reuse.

R606.2.8 Mortar. Except for mortars listed in Sections R606.2.9, R606.2.10 and R606.2.11, mortar for use in masonry construction shall meet the proportion specifications of Table R606.2.8 or the property specifications of ASTM C270. The type of mortar shall be in accordance with Sections R606.2.8.1, R606.2.8.2 and R606.2.8.3.

> **R606.2.8.1 Foundation walls.** Mortar for masonry foundation walls constructed as set forth in Tables R404.1.1(1) through R404.1.1(4) shall be Type M or S mortar.

> **R606.2.8.2 Masonry in Seismic Design Categories A, B and C.** Mortar for masonry serving as the lateral force-resisting system in Seismic Design Categories A, B and C shall be Type M, S or N mortar.

TABLE R606.2.8
MORTAR PROPORTIONS[a, b]

MORTAR	TYPE	Portland cement or blended cement	Mortar cement			Masonry cement			Hydrated lime[c] or lime putty	Aggregate ratio (measured in damp, loose conditions)
			M	S	N	M	S	N		
Cement-lime	M	1	—	—	—	—	—	—	$1/4$	
	S	1	—	—	—	—	—	—	over $1/4$ to $1/2$	
	N	1	—	—	—	—	—	—	over $1/2$ to $1^1/4$	
	O	1	—	—	—	—	—	—	over $1^1/4$ to $2^1/2$	
Mortar cement	M	1	—	—	1	—	—	—	—	Not less than $2^1/4$ and not more than 3 times the sum of separate volumes of lime, if used, and cement
	M	—	1	—	—	—	—	—		
	S	$1/2$	—	—	1	—	—	—		
	S	—	—	1	—	—	—	—		
	N	—	—	—	1	—	—	—		
	O	—	—	—	1	—	—	—		
Masonry cement	M	1	—	—	—	—	—	1	—	
	M	—	—	—	—	1	—	—		
	S	$1/2$	—	—	—	—	—	1		
	S	—	—	—	—	—	1	—		
	N	—	—	—	—	—	—	1		
	O	—	—	—	—	—	—	1		

For SI: 1 cubic foot = 0.0283 m³, 1 pound = 0.454 kg.

a. For the purpose of these specifications, the weight of 1 cubic foot of the respective materials shall be considered to be as follows:

Portland cement	94 pounds	Masonry cement	Weight printed on bag
Mortar cement	Weight printed on bag	Hydrated lime	40 pounds
Lime putty (Quicklime)	80 pounds	Sand, damp and loose	80 pounds of dry sand

b. Two air-entraining materials shall not be combined in mortar.

c. Hydrated lime conforming to the requirements of ASTM C207.

R606.2.8.3 Masonry in Seismic Design Categories D_0, D_1 and D_2. Mortar for masonry serving as the lateral-force-resisting system in Seismic Design Categories D_0, D_1 and D_2 shall be Type M or S Portland cement-lime or mortar cement.

R606.2.9 Surface-bonding mortar. Surface-bonding mortar shall comply with ASTM C887. Surface bonding of concrete masonry units shall comply with ASTM C946.

R606.2.10 Mortar for AAC masonry. Thin-bed mortar for AAC masonry shall comply with Article 2.1 C.1 of TMS 602. Mortar used for the leveling courses of AAC masonry shall comply with Article 2.1 C.2 of TMS 602.

R606.2.11 Mortar for adhered masonry veneer. Mortar for use with adhered masonry veneer shall conform to ASTM C270 Type S or Type N or shall comply with ANSI A118.4 for latex-modified Portland cement mortar.

R606.2.12 Grout. Grout shall consist of cementitious material and aggregate in accordance with ASTM C476 or the proportion specifications of Table R606.2.12. Type M or Type S mortar to which sufficient water has been added to produce pouring consistency shall be permitted to be used as grout.

R606.2.13 Metal reinforcement and accessories. Metal reinforcement and accessories shall conform to Article 2.4 of TMS 602.

R606.3 Construction requirements.

R606.3.1 Bed and head joints. Unless otherwise required or indicated on the project drawings, head and bed joints shall be $^3/_8$ inch (9.5 mm) thick, except that the thickness of the bed joint of the starting course placed over foundations shall be not less than $^1/_4$ inch (6.4 mm) and not more than $^3/_4$ inch (19.1 mm). Mortar joint thickness for load-bearing masonry shall be within the following tolerances from the specified dimensions:

1. Bed joint: + $^1/_8$ inch (3.2 mm).
2. Head joint: - $^1/_4$ inch (6.4 mm), + $^3/_8$ inch (9.5 mm).
3. Collar joints: - $^1/_4$ inch (6.4 mm), + $^3/_8$ inch (9.5 mm).

R606.3.2 Masonry unit placement. The mortar shall be sufficiently plastic and units shall be placed with sufficient pressure to extrude mortar from the joint and produce a tight joint. Deep furrowing of bed joints that produces voids shall not be permitted. Any units disturbed to the extent that initial bond is broken after initial placement shall be removed and relaid in fresh mortar. Surfaces to be in contact with mortar shall be clean and free of deleterious materials.

R606.3.2.1 Solid masonry. *Solid masonry* units shall be laid with full head and bed joints and all interior vertical joints that are designed to receive mortar shall be filled.

R606.3.2.2 Hollow masonry. For hollow masonry units, head and bed joints shall be filled solidly with mortar for a distance in from the face of the unit not less than the thickness of the face shell.

R606.3.3 Installation of wall ties. The installation of wall ties shall be as follows:

1. The ends of wall ties shall be embedded in mortar joints. Wall ties shall have not less than $^5/_8$-inch (15.9 mm) mortar coverage from the exposed face.

2. Wall ties shall not be bent after being embedded in grout or mortar.

3. For solid masonry units, solid grouted hollow units, or hollow units in anchored masonry veneer, wall ties shall be embedded in mortar bed not less than $1^1/_2$ inches (38 mm).

4. For hollow masonry units in other than anchored masonry veneer, wall ties shall engage outer face shells by not less than $^1/_2$ inch (13 mm).

R606.3.4 Protection for reinforcement. Bars shall be completely embedded in mortar or grout. Joint reinforcement embedded in horizontal mortar joints shall not have less than $^5/_8$-inch (15.9 mm) mortar coverage from the exposed face. Other reinforcement shall have a minimum coverage of one bar diameter over all bars, but not less than $^3/_4$ inch (19 mm), except where exposed to weather or soil, in which case the minimum coverage shall be 2 inches (51 mm).

R606.3.4.1 Corrosion protection. Minimum corrosion protection of joint reinforcement, anchor ties and wire fabric for use in masonry wall construction shall conform to Table R606.3.4.1.

TABLE R606.2.12
GROUT PROPORTIONS BY VOLUME FOR MASONRY CONSTRUCTION

TYPE	PORTLAND CEMENT OR BLENDED CEMENT SLAG CEMENT	HYDRATED LIME OR LIME PUTTY	AGGREGATE MEASURED IN A DAMP, LOOSE CONDITION	
			Fine	Coarse
Fine	1	0 to 1/10	$2^1/_4$ to 3 times the sum of the volume of the cementitious materials	—
Coarse	1	0 to 1/10	$2^1/_4$ to 3 times the sum of the volume of the cementitious materials	1 to 2 times the sum of the volumes of the cementitious materials

TABLE R606.3.4.1
MINIMUM CORROSION PROTECTION

MASONRY METAL ACCESSORY	STANDARD
Joint reinforcement, interior walls	ASTM A641, Class 1
Wire ties or anchors in exterior walls completely embedded in mortar or grout	ASTM A641, Class 3
Wire ties or anchors in exterior walls not completely embedded in mortar or grout	ASTM A153, Class B-2
Joint reinforcement in exterior walls or interior walls exposed to moist environment	ASTM A153, Class B-2
Sheet metal ties or anchors exposed to weather	ASTM A153, Class B-2
Sheet metal ties or anchors completely embedded in mortar or grout	ASTM A653, Coating Designation G60
Stainless steel hardware for any exposure	ASTM A167, Type 304

R606.3.5 Grouting requirements.

R606.3.5.1 Grout placement. Grout shall be a plastic mix suitable for pumping without segregation of the constituents and shall be mixed thoroughly. Grout shall be placed by pumping or by an approved alternate method and shall be placed before any initial set occurs and not more than $1^1/_2$ hours after water has been added. Grout shall be consolidated by puddling or mechanical vibrating during placing and reconsolidated after excess moisture has been absorbed but before plasticity is lost. Grout shall not be pumped through aluminum pipes.

Maximum pour heights and the minimum dimensions of spaces provided for grout placement shall conform to Table R606.3.5.1. Grout shall be poured in lifts with a maximum height of 8 feet (2438 mm). Where a total grout pour exceeds 8 feet (2438 mm) in height, the grout shall be placed in lifts not exceeding 64 inches (1626 mm) and special inspection during grouting shall be required. If the work is stopped for 1 hour or longer, the horizontal construction joints shall be formed by stopping all tiers at the same elevation and with the grout 1 inch (25 mm) below the top.

R606.3.5.2 Cleanouts. Provisions shall be made for cleaning the space to be grouted. Mortar that projects more than $1/_2$ inch (12.7 mm) into the grout space and any other foreign matter shall be removed from the grout space prior to inspection and grouting. Where required by the building official, cleanouts shall be provided in the bottom course of masonry for each grout pour where the grout pour height exceeds 64 inches (1626 mm). In solid grouted masonry, cleanouts shall be spaced horizontally not more than 32 inches (813 mm) on center. The cleanouts shall be sealed before grouting and after inspection.

R606.3.5.3 Construction. Requirements for grouted masonry construction shall be as follows:

1. Masonry shall be built to preserve the unobstructed vertical continuity of the cells or spaces to be filled. In partially grouted construction, cross webs forming cells to be filled shall be full-bedded in mortar to prevent leakage of grout. Head and end joints shall be solidly filled with mortar for a distance in from the face of the wall or unit not less than the thickness of the longitudinal face shells.

2. Vertical reinforcement shall be held in position at top and bottom and at intervals not exceeding 200 diameters of the reinforcement.

3. Cells containing reinforcement shall be filled solidly with grout.

4. The thickness of grout or mortar between masonry units and reinforcement shall be not less than $1/_4$ inch (6.4 mm), except that $1/_4$-inch (6.4 mm) bars shall be permitted to be laid in horizontal mortar joints not less than $1/_2$ inch (12.7 mm) thick, and steel wire reinforcement shall be permitted to be laid in horizontal mortar joints not less than twice the thickness of the wire diameter.

TABLE R606.3.5.1
GROUT SPACE DIMENSIONS AND POUR HEIGHTS

GROUT TYPE	GROUT POUR MAXIMUM HEIGHT (feet)	MINIMUM WIDTH OF GROUT SPACES[a, b] (inches)	MINIMUM GROUT[b, c] SPACE DIMENSIONS FOR GROUTING CELLS OF HOLLOW UNITS (inches × inches)
Fine	1	0.75	1.5 × 2
	5	2	2 × 3
	12	2.5	2.5 × 3
	24	3	3 × 3
Coarse	1	1.5	1.5 × 3
	5	2	2.5 × 3
	12	2.5	3 × 3
	24	3	3 × 4

For SI: 1 inch = 25.4 mm, 1 foot = 304.8 mm.

a. For grouting between masonry wythes.

b. Grout space dimension is the clear dimension between any masonry protrusion and shall be increased by the horizontal projection of the diameters of the horizontal bars within the cross section of the grout space.

R606.3.6 Grouted multiple-wythe masonry. Grouted multiple-wythe masonry shall conform to all the requirements specified in Section R606.3.5 and the requirements of this section.

R606.3.6.1 Bonding of backup wythe. Where all interior vertical spaces are filled with grout in multiple-wythe construction, masonry headers shall not be permitted. Metal wall ties shall be used in accordance with Section R606.13.2 to prevent spreading of the wythes and to maintain the vertical alignment of the wall. Wall ties shall be installed in accordance with Section R606.13.2 where the backup wythe in multiple-wythe construction is fully grouted.

R606.3.6.2 Grout barriers. Vertical grout barriers or dams shall be built of *solid masonry* across the grout space the entire height of the wall to control the flow of the grout horizontally. Grout barriers shall be not more than 25 feet (7620 mm) apart. The grouting of any section of a wall between control barriers shall be completed in one day without interruptions greater than 1 hour.

R606.3.7 Masonry bonding pattern. Masonry laid in running and stack bond shall conform to Sections R606.3.7.1 and R606.3.7.2.

R606.3.7.1 Masonry laid in running bond. In each wythe of masonry laid in running bond, head joints in successive courses shall be offset by not less than one-fourth the unit length, or the masonry walls shall be reinforced longitudinally as required in Section R606.3.7.2.

R606.3.7.2 Masonry laid in stack bond. Where unit masonry is laid with less head joint offset than in Section R606.3.7.1, the minimum area of horizontal reinforcement placed in mortar bed joints or in bond beams spaced not more than 48 inches (1219 mm) apart shall be 0.0007 times the vertical cross-sectional area of the wall.

R606.4 Thickness of masonry. The nominal thickness of masonry walls shall conform to the requirements of Sections R606.4.1 through R606.4.4.

R606.4.1 Minimum thickness. The minimum thickness of masonry bearing walls more than one story high shall be 8 inches (203 mm). *Solid masonry* walls of one-story dwellings and garages shall be not less than 6 inches (152 mm) in thickness where not greater than 9 feet (2743 mm) in height, provided that where gable construction is used, an additional 6 feet (1829 mm) is permitted to the peak of the gable. Masonry walls shall be laterally supported in either the horizontal or vertical direction at intervals as required by Section R606.6.4.

R606.4.2 Rubble stone masonry wall. The minimum thickness of rough, random or coursed rubble stone masonry walls shall be 16 inches (406 mm).

R606.4.3 Change in thickness. Where walls of masonry of hollow units or masonry-bonded hollow walls are decreased in thickness, a course of solid masonry or masonry units filled with mortar or grout shall be constructed between the wall below and the thinner wall above, or special units or construction shall be used to transmit the loads from face shells or wythes above to those below.

R606.4.4 Parapet walls. Unreinforced solid masonry parapet walls shall be not less than 8 inches (203 mm) thick and their height shall not exceed four times their thickness. Unreinforced hollow unit masonry parapet walls shall be not less than 8 inches (203 mm) thick, and their height shall not exceed three times their thickness. Masonry parapet walls in areas subject to wind loads of 30 pounds per square foot (1.44 kPa) located in Seismic Design Category D_0, D_1 or D_2, or on townhouses in Seismic Design Category C shall be reinforced in accordance with Section R606.12.

R606.5 Corbeled masonry. Corbeled masonry shall be in accordance with Sections R606.5.1 through R606.5.3.

R606.5.1 Units. *Solid masonry* units or masonry units filled with mortar or grout shall be used for corbeling.

R606.5.2 Corbel projection. The maximum projection of one unit shall not exceed one-half the height of the unit or one-third the thickness at right angles to the wall. The maximum corbeled projection beyond the face of the wall shall not exceed:

1. One-half of the wall thickness for multiple-wythe walls bonded by mortar or grout and wall ties or masonry headers.

2. One-half the wythe thickness for single wythe walls, masonry-bonded hollow walls, multiple-wythe walls with open collar joints and veneer walls.

R606.5.3 Corbeled masonry supporting floor or roof-framing members. Where corbeled masonry is used to support floor or roof-framing members, the top course of the corbel shall be a header course or the top course bed joint shall have ties to the vertical wall.

R606.6 Support conditions. Bearing and support conditions shall be in accordance with Sections R606.6.1 through R606.6.4.

R606.6.1 Bearing on support. Each masonry wythe shall be supported by not less than two-thirds of the wythe thickness.

R606.6.2 Support at foundation. Cavity wall or masonry veneer construction shall be permitted to be supported on an 8-inch (203 mm) foundation wall, provided the 8-inch (203 mm) wall is corbeled to the width of the wall system above with masonry constructed of solid masonry units or masonry units filled with mortar or grout. The total horizontal projection of the corbel shall not exceed 2 inches (51 mm) with individual corbels projecting not more than one-third the thickness of the unit or one-half the height of the unit. The hollow space behind the corbeled masonry shall be filled with mortar or grout.

R606.6.3 Beam supports. Beams, girders or other concentrated loads supported by a wall or column shall have a bearing of not less than 3 inches (76 mm) in length measured parallel to the beam on *solid masonry* not less than 4 inches (102 mm) in thickness, or on a metal bearing plate of adequate design and dimensions to distribute the load safely, or on a continuous reinforced masonry member projecting not less than 4 inches (102 mm) from the face of the wall.

R606.6.3.1 Joist bearing. Joists shall have a bearing of not less than $1^1/_2$ inches (38 mm), except as provided in Section R606.6.3, and shall be supported in accordance with Figure R606.11(1).

R606.6.4 Lateral support. Masonry walls shall be laterally supported in either the horizontal or the vertical direction. The maximum spacing between lateral supports shall not exceed the distances in Table R606.6.4. Lateral support shall be provided by cross walls, pilasters, buttresses or structural frame members where the limiting distance is taken horizontally, or by floors or roofs where the limiting distance is taken vertically.

TABLE R606.6.4
SPACING OF LATERAL SUPPORT FOR MASONRY WALLS

CONSTRUCTION	MAXIMUM WALL LENGTH TO THICKNESS OR WALL HEIGHT TO THICKNESS[a, b]
Bearing walls:	
Solid or solid grouted	20
All other	18
Nonbearing walls:	
Exterior	18
Interior	36

For SI: 1 foot = 304.8 mm.

a. Except for cavity walls and cantilevered walls, the thickness of a wall shall be its nominal thickness measured perpendicular to the face of the wall. For cavity walls, the thickness shall be determined as the sum of the nominal thicknesses of the individual wythes. For cantilever walls, except for parapets, the ratio of height to nominal thickness shall not exceed 6 for solid masonry, or 4 for hollow masonry. For parapets, see Section R606.4.4.

b. An additional unsupported height of 6 feet is permitted for gable end walls.

R606.6.4.1 Horizontal lateral support. Lateral support in the horizontal direction provided by intersecting masonry walls shall be provided by one of the methods in Section R606.6.4.1.1 or R606.6.4.1.2.

R606.6.4.1.1 Bonding pattern. Fifty percent of the units at the intersection shall be laid in an overlapping masonry bonding pattern, with alternate units having a bearing of not less than 3 inches (76 mm) on the unit below.

R606.6.4.1.2 Metal reinforcement. Interior non-load-bearing walls shall be anchored at their intersections, at vertical intervals of not more than 16 inches (406 mm) with joint reinforcement of not less than 9 gage [0.148 inch (4 mm)], or $1/_4$-inch (6 mm) galvanized mesh hardware cloth. Intersecting masonry walls, other than interior nonload-bearing walls, shall be anchored at vertical intervals of not more than 8 inches (203 mm) with joint reinforcement of not less than 9 gage (4 mm) and shall extend not less than 30 inches (762 mm) in each direction at the intersection. Other metal ties, joint reinforcement or anchors, if used, shall be spaced to provide equivalent area of anchorage to that required by this section.

R606.6.4.2 Vertical lateral support. Vertical lateral support of masonry walls in Seismic Design Category A, B or C shall be provided in accordance with one of the methods in Section R606.6.4.2.1 or R606.6.4.2.2.

R606.6.4.2.1 Roof structures. Masonry walls shall be anchored to roof structures with metal strap anchors spaced in accordance with the manufacturer's instructions, $1/_2$-inch (13 mm) bolts spaced not more than 6 feet (1829 mm) on center, or other *approved* anchors. Anchors shall be embedded not less than 16 inches (406 mm) into the masonry, or be hooked or welded to bond beam reinforcement placed not less than 6 inches (152 mm) from the top of the wall.

R606.6.4.2.2 Floor diaphragms. Masonry walls shall be anchored to floor *diaphragm* framing by metal strap anchors spaced in accordance with the manufacturer's instructions, $1/_2$-inch-diameter (13 mm) bolts spaced at intervals not to exceed 6 feet (1829 mm) and installed as shown in Figure R606.11(1), or by other *approved* methods.

R606.7 Piers. The unsupported height of masonry piers shall not exceed 10 times their least dimension. Where structural clay tile or hollow concrete masonry units are used for isolated piers to support beams and girders, the cellular spaces shall be filled solidly with grout or Type M or S mortar, except that unfilled hollow piers shall be permitted to be used if their unsupported height is not more than four times their least dimension. Where hollow masonry units are solidly filled with grout or Type M, S or N mortar, the allowable compressive stress shall be permitted to be increased as provided in Table R606.9.

R606.7.1 Pier cap. Hollow piers shall be capped with 4 inches (102 mm) of *solid masonry* or concrete, a masonry cap block, or shall have cavities of the top course filled with concrete or grout.

R606.8 Chases. Chases and recesses in masonry walls shall not be deeper than one-third the wall thickness. The maximum length of a horizontal chase or horizontal projection shall not exceed 4 feet (1219 mm) and shall have not less than 8 inches (203 mm) of masonry in back of the chases and recesses and between adjacent chases or recesses and the jambs of openings. Chases and recesses in masonry walls shall be designed and constructed so as not to reduce the required strength or required fire resistance of the wall and shall not be permitted within the required area of a pier. Masonry directly above chases or recesses wider than 12 inches (305 mm) shall be supported on noncombustible lintels.

R606.9 Allowable stresses. Allowable compressive stresses in masonry shall not exceed the values prescribed in Table R606.9. In determining the stresses in masonry, the effects of all loads and conditions of loading and the influence of all forces affecting the design and strength of the several parts shall be taken into account.

R606.9.1 Combined units. In walls or other structural members composed of different kinds or grades of units, materials or mortars, the maximum stress shall not exceed the allowable stress for the weakest of the combination of units, materials and mortars of which the member is composed. The net thickness of any facing unit that is used to resist stress shall be not less than $1^1/_2$ inches (38 mm).

R606.10 Lintels. Masonry over openings shall be supported by steel lintels, reinforced concrete or masonry lintels or masonry arches, designed to support load imposed.

TABLE R606.9
ALLOWABLE COMPRESSIVE STRESSES FOR
EMPIRICAL DESIGN OF MASONRY

CONSTRUCTION; COMPRESSIVE STRENGTH OF UNIT, GROSS AREA	ALLOWABLE COMPRESSIVE STRESSES[a] GROSS CROSS-SECTIONAL AREA[b]	
	Type M or S mortar	Type N mortar
Solid masonry of brick and other solid units of clay or shale; sand-lime or concrete brick:		
8,000 + psi	350	300
4,500 psi	225	200
2,500 psi	160	140
1,500 psi	115	100
Grouted[c] masonry, of clay or shale; sand-lime or concrete:		
4,500 + psi	225	200
2,500 psi	160	140
1,500 psi	115	100
Solid masonry of solid concrete masonry units:		
3,000 + psi	225	200
2,000 psi	160	140
1,200 psi	115	100
Masonry of hollow load-bearing units:		
2,000 + psi	140	120
1,500 psi	115	100
1,000 psi	75	70
700 psi	60	55
Hollow walls (cavity or masonry bonded[d]) solid units:		
2,500 + psi	160	140
1,500 psi	115	100
Hollow units	75	70
Stone ashlar masonry:		
Granite	720	640
Limestone or marble	450	400
Sandstone or cast stone	360	320
Rubble stone masonry:		
Coarse, rough or random	120	100

For SI: 1 pound per square inch = 6.895 kPa.

a. Linear interpolation shall be used for determining allowable stresses for masonry units having compressive strengths that are intermediate between those given in the table.

b. Gross cross-sectional area shall be calculated on the actual rather than nominal dimensions.

c. See Section R606.13.

d. Where floor and roof loads are carried on one wythe, the gross cross-sectional area is that of the wythe under load; if both wythes are loaded, the gross cross-sectional area is that of the wall minus the area of the cavity between the wythes. Walls bonded with metal ties shall be considered as cavity walls unless the collar joints are filled with mortar or grout.

R606.11 Anchorage. Masonry walls shall be anchored to floor and roof systems in accordance with the details shown in Figure R606.11(1), R606.11(2) or R606.11(3). Footings shall be permitted to be considered as points of lateral support.

R606.12 Seismic requirements. The seismic requirements of this section shall apply to the design of masonry and the construction of masonry building elements located in Seismic Design Category D_0, D_1 or D_2. Townhouses in Seismic Design Category C shall comply with the requirements of Section R606.12.2. These requirements shall not apply to glass unit masonry conforming to Section R610, anchored masonry veneer conforming to Section R703.8 or adhered masonry veneer conforming to Section R703.12.

R606.12.1 General. Masonry structures and masonry elements shall comply with the requirements of Sections R606.12.2 through R606.12.4 based on the seismic design category established in Table R301.2(2). Masonry structures and masonry elements shall comply with the requirements of Section R606.12 and Figures R606.11(1), R606.11(2) and R606.11(3) or shall be designed in accordance with TMS 402 or TMS 403.

R606.12.1.1 Floor and roof diaphragm construction. Floor and roof *diaphragms* shall be constructed of wood structural panels attached to wood framing in accordance with Table R602.3(1) or to cold-formed steel floor framing in accordance with Table R505.3.1(2) or to cold-formed steel roof framing in accordance with Table R804.3. Additionally, sheathing panel edges perpendicular to framing members shall be backed by blocking, and sheathing shall be connected to the blocking with fasteners at the edge spacing. For Seismic Design Categories C, D_0, D_1 and D_2, where the width-to-thickness dimension of the *diaphragm* exceeds 2-to-1, edge spacing of fasteners shall be 4 inches (102 mm) on center.

R606.12.2 Seismic Design Category C. Townhouses located in Seismic Design Category C shall comply with the requirements of this section.

R606.12.2.1 Minimum length of wall without openings. Table R606.12.2.1 shall be used to determine the minimum required solid wall length without openings at each masonry exterior wall. The provided percentage of solid wall length shall include only those wall segments that are 3 feet (914 mm) or longer. The maximum clear distance between wall segments included in determining the solid wall length shall not exceed 18 feet (5486 mm). Shear wall segments required to meet the minimum wall length shall be in accordance with Section R606.12.2.2.3.

R606.12.2.2 Design of elements not part of the lateral force-resisting system.

R606.12.2.2.1 Load-bearing frames or columns. Elements not part of the lateral force-resisting system shall be analyzed to determine their effect on the response of the system. The frames or columns shall be adequate for vertical load-carrying capacity and induced moment caused by the design *story* drift.

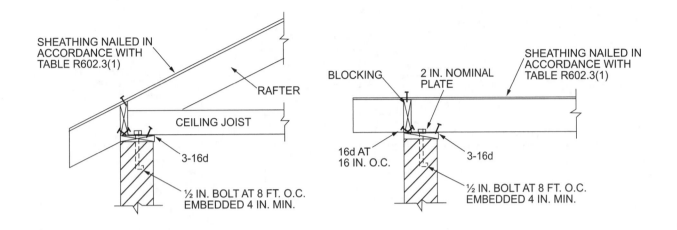

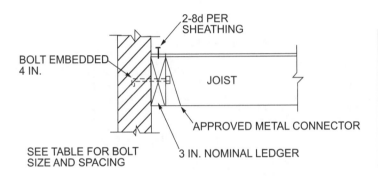

**LEDGER BOLT
SIZE AND SPACING**

JOIST SPAN	BOLT SIZE AND SPACING	
	ROOF	FLOOR
10 FT.	$^1/_2$ AT 2 FT. 6 IN. $^7/_8$ AT 3 FT. 6 IN.	$^1/_2$ AT 2 FT. 0 IN. $^7/_8$ AT 2 FT. 9 IN.
10—15 FT.	$^1/_2$ AT 1 FT. 9 IN. $^7/_8$ AT 2 FT. 6 IN.	$^1/_2$ AT 1 FT. 4 IN. $^7/_8$ AT 2 FT. 0 IN.
15—20 FT.	$^1/_2$ AT 1 FT. 3 IN. $^7/_8$ AT 2 FT. 0 IN.	$^1/_2$ AT 1 FT. 0 IN. $^7/_8$ AT 1 FT. 6 IN.

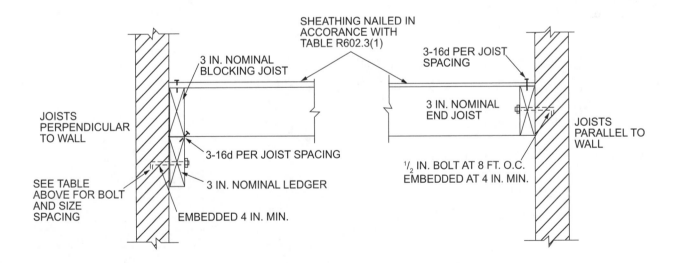

For SI: 1 inch = 25.4 mm, 1 foot = 304.8 mm, 1 pound per square foot = 0.0479 kPa.

Note: Where bolts are located in hollow masonry, the cells in the courses receiving the bolt shall be grouted solid.

**FIGURE R606.11(1)
ANCHORAGE REQUIREMENTS FOR MASONRY WALLS LOCATED IN SEISMIC
DESIGN CATEGORY A, B OR C AND WHERE WIND LOADS ARE LESS THAN 30 PSF**

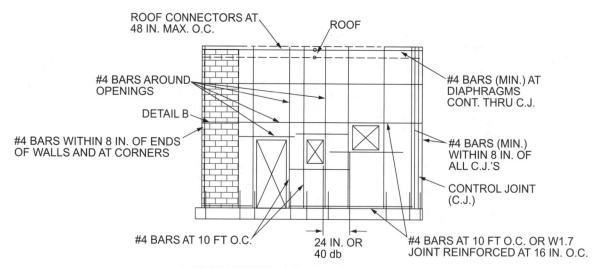

ROOF CONNECTORS AT 48 IN. MAX. O.C.

ROOF

#4 BARS AROUND OPENINGS

#4 BARS (MIN.) AT DIAPHRAGMS CONT. THRU C.J.

DETAIL B

#4 BARS WITHIN 8 IN. OF ENDS OF WALLS AND AT CORNERS

#4 BARS (MIN.) WITHIN 8 IN. OF ALL C.J.'S

CONTROL JOINT (C.J.)

#4 BARS AT 10 FT O.C.

24 IN. OR 40 db

#4 BARS AT 10 FT O.C. OR W1.7 JOINT REINFORCED AT 16 IN. O.C.

MINIMUM REINFORCEMENT FOR MASONRY WALLS

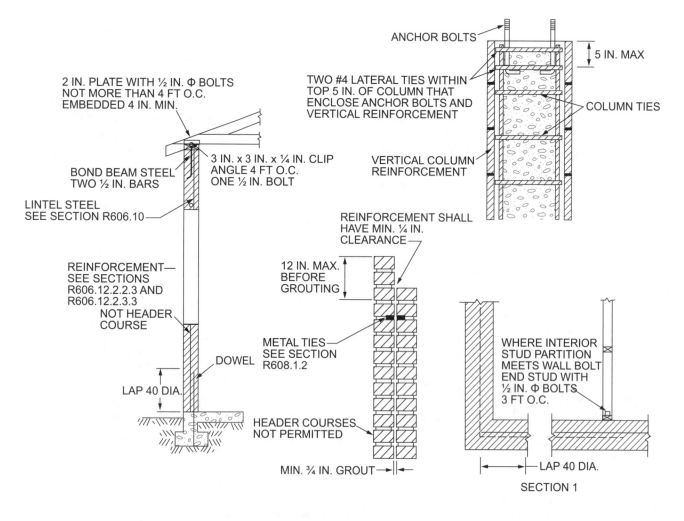

ANCHOR BOLTS

5 IN. MAX

2 IN. PLATE WITH ½ IN. Φ BOLTS NOT MORE THAN 4 FT O.C. EMBEDDED 4 IN. MIN.

TWO #4 LATERAL TIES WITHIN TOP 5 IN. OF COLUMN THAT ENCLOSE ANCHOR BOLTS AND VERTICAL REINFORCEMENT

COLUMN TIES

3 IN. x 3 IN. x ¼ IN. CLIP ANGLE 4 FT O.C. ONE ½ IN. BOLT

BOND BEAM STEEL TWO ½ IN. BARS

VERTICAL COLUMN REINFORCEMENT

LINTEL STEEL SEE SECTION R606.10

REINFORCEMENT SHALL HAVE MIN. ¼ IN. CLEARANCE

REINFORCEMENT— SEE SECTIONS R606.12.2.2.3 AND R606.12.2.3.3

12 IN. MAX. BEFORE GROUTING

NOT HEADER COURSE

METAL TIES SEE SECTION R608.1.2

DOWEL

WHERE INTERIOR STUD PARTITION MEETS WALL BOLT END STUD WITH ½ IN. Φ BOLTS 3 FT O.C.

LAP 40 DIA.

HEADER COURSES NOT PERMITTED

MIN. ¾ IN. GROUT

LAP 40 DIA.

SECTION 1

For SI: 1 inch = 25.4 mm, 1 foot = 304.8 mm.

FIGURE R606.11(2)
REQUIREMENTS FOR REINFORCED GROUTED MASONRY CONSTRUCTION IN SEISMIC DESIGN CATEGORY C

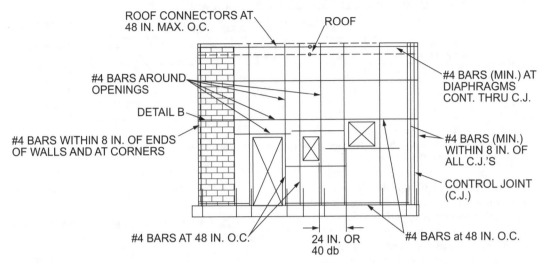

ROOF CONNECTORS AT 48 IN. MAX. O.C.

ROOF

#4 BARS AROUND OPENINGS

DETAIL B

#4 BARS WITHIN 8 IN. OF ENDS OF WALLS AND AT CORNERS

#4 BARS (MIN.) AT DIAPHRAGMS CONT. THRU C.J.

#4 BARS (MIN.) WITHIN 8 IN. OF ALL C.J.'S

CONTROL JOINT (C.J.)

#4 BARS AT 48 IN. O.C.

24 IN. OR 40 db

#4 BARS at 48 IN. O.C.

MINIMUM REINFORCEMENT FOR MASONRY WALLS

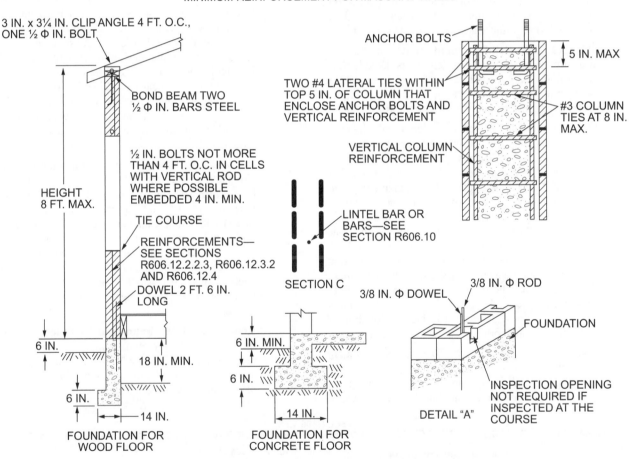

3 IN. x 3¼ IN. CLIP ANGLE 4 FT. O.C., ONE ½ Φ IN. BOLT

BOND BEAM TWO ½ Φ IN. BARS STEEL

½ IN. BOLTS NOT MORE THAN 4 FT. O.C. IN CELLS WITH VERTICAL ROD WHERE POSSIBLE EMBEDDED 4 IN. MIN.

HEIGHT 8 FT. MAX.

TIE COURSE

REINFORCEMENTS— SEE SECTIONS R606.12.2.2.3, R606.12.3.2 AND R606.12.4

DOWEL 2 FT. 6 IN. LONG

6 IN.

18 IN. MIN.

6 IN.

14 IN.

FOUNDATION FOR WOOD FLOOR

ANCHOR BOLTS

5 IN. MAX

TWO #4 LATERAL TIES WITHIN TOP 5 IN. OF COLUMN THAT ENCLOSE ANCHOR BOLTS AND VERTICAL REINFORCEMENT

#3 COLUMN TIES AT 8 IN. MAX.

VERTICAL COLUMN REINFORCEMENT

LINTEL BAR OR BARS—SEE SECTION R606.10

SECTION C

6 IN. MIN.

6 IN.

14 IN.

FOUNDATION FOR CONCRETE FLOOR

3/8 IN. Φ DOWEL

3/8 IN. Φ ROD

FOUNDATION

INSPECTION OPENING NOT REQUIRED IF INSPECTED AT THE COURSE

DETAIL "A"

For SI: 1 inch = 25.4 mm, 1 foot = 304.8 mm.

Note: A full bed joint must be provided. Cells containing vertical bars are to be filled to the top of wall and provide inspection opening as shown on detail "A." Horizontal bars are to be laid as shown on detail "B." Lintel bars are to be laid as shown on Section C.

FIGURE R606.11(3)
REQUIREMENTS FOR REINFORCED MASONRY CONSTRUCTION IN SEISMIC DESIGN CATEGORY D_0, D_1 OR D_2

TABLE R606.12.2.1
MINIMUM SOLID WALL LENGTH ALONG EXTERIOR WALL LINES

SESIMIC DESIGN CATEGORY	MINIMUM SOLID WALL LENGTH (percent)[a]		
	One story or top story of two story	Wall supporting light-framed second story and roof	Wall supporting masonry second story and roof
Townhouses in C	20	25	35
D_0 or D_1	25	NP	NP
D_2	30	NP	NP

NP = Not Permitted, except with design in accordance with the *International Building Code.*

a. For all walls, the minimum required length of solid walls shall be based on the table percent multiplied by the dimension, parallel to the wall direction under consideration, of a rectangle inscribing the overall building plan.

R606.12.2.2.2 Masonry partition walls. Masonry partition walls, masonry screen walls and other masonry elements that are not designed to resist vertical or lateral loads, other than those induced by their own weight, shall be isolated from the structure so that vertical and lateral forces are not imparted to these elements. Isolation joints and connectors between these elements and the structure shall be designed to accommodate the design *story* drift.

R606.12.2.2.3 Reinforcement requirements for masonry elements. Masonry elements listed in Section R606.12.2.2.2 shall be reinforced in either the horizontal or vertical direction as shown in Figure R606.11(2) and in accordance with the following:

1. Horizontal reinforcement. Horizontal joint reinforcement shall consist of not less than two longitudinal W1.7 wires spaced not more than 16 inches (406 mm) for walls greater than 4 inches (102 mm) in width and not less than one longitudinal W1.7 wire spaced not more than 16 inches (406 mm) for walls not exceeding 4 inches (102 mm) in width; or not less than one No. 4 bar spaced not more than 48 inches (1219 mm). Where two longitudinal wires of joint reinforcement are used, the space between these wires shall be the widest that the mortar joint will accommodate. Horizontal reinforcement shall be provided within 16 inches (406 mm) of the top and bottom of these masonry elements.

2. Vertical reinforcement. Vertical reinforcement shall consist of not less than one No. 4 bar spaced not more than 48 inches (1219 mm). Vertical reinforcement shall be located within

16 inches (406 mm) of the ends of masonry walls.

R606.12.2.3 Design of elements part of the lateral force-resisting system.

R606.12.2.3.1 Connections to masonry shear walls. Connectors shall be provided to transfer forces between masonry walls and horizontal elements in accordance with the requirements of Section 4.1.4 of TMS 402. Connectors shall be designed to transfer horizontal design forces acting either perpendicular or parallel to the wall, but not less than 200 pounds per linear foot (2919 N/m) of wall. The maximum spacing between connectors shall be 4 feet (1219 mm). Such anchorage mechanisms shall not induce tension stresses perpendicular to grain in ledgers or nailers.

R606.12.2.3.2 Connections to masonry columns. Connectors shall be provided to transfer forces between masonry columns and horizontal elements in accordance with the requirements of Section 4.1.4 of TMS 402. Where anchor bolts are used to connect horizontal elements to the tops of columns, the bolts shall be placed within lateral ties. Lateral ties shall enclose both the vertical bars in the column and the anchor bolts. There shall be not less than two No. 4 lateral ties provided in the top 5 inches (127 mm) of the column.

R606.12.2.3.3 Minimum reinforcement requirements for masonry shear walls. Vertical reinforcement of not less than one No. 4 bar shall be provided at corners, within 16 inches (406 mm) of each side of openings, within 8 inches (203 mm) of each side of movement joints, within 8 inches (203 mm) of the

TABLE R606.12.3.2
MINIMUM DISTRIBUTED WALL REINFORCEMENT FOR BUILDINGS ASSIGNED TO SEISMIC DESIGN CATEGORY D_0 or D_1

NOMINAL WALL THICKNESS (inches)	MINIMUM SUM OF THE VERTICAL AND HORIZONTAL REINFORCEMENT AREAS[a] (square inches per foot)	MINIMUM REINFORCEMENT AS DISTRIBUTED IN BOTH HORIZONTAL AND VERTICAL DIRECTIONS[b] (square inches per foot)	MINUMUM BAR SIZE FOR REINFORCEMENT SPACED AT 48 INCHES
6	0.135	0.047	#4
8	0.183	0.064	#5
10	0.231	0.081	#6
12	0.279	0.098	#6

For SI: 1 inch = 25.4 mm, 1 foot = 304.8 mm, 1 square inch per foot = 2064 mm²/m.

a. Based on the minimum reinforcing ratio of 0.002 times the gross cross-sectional area of the wall.

b. Based on the minimum reinforcing ratio each direction of 0.0007 times the gross cross-sectional area of the wall.

ends of walls, and at a maximum spacing of 10 feet (3048 mm).

Horizontal joint reinforcement shall consist of not less than two wires of W1.7 spaced not more than 16 inches (406 mm); or bond beam reinforcement of not less than one No. 4 bar spaced not more than 10 feet (3048 mm) shall be provided. Horizontal reinforcement shall be provided at the bottom and top of wall openings and shall extend not less than 24 inches (610 mm) nor less than 40 bar diameters past the opening; continuously at structurally connected roof and floor levels; and within 16 inches (406 mm) of the top of walls.

R606.12.3 Seismic Design Category D₀ or D₁. Structures in Seismic Design Category D_0 or D_1 shall comply with the requirements of Seismic Design Category C and the additional requirements of this section. AAC masonry shall not be used for the design of masonry elements that are part of the lateral force-resisting system.

R606.12.3.1 Design requirements. Masonry elements other than those covered by Section R606.12.2.2.2 shall be designed in accordance with the requirements of Chapters 1 through 7 and Sections 8.1 and 8.3 of TMS 402, ACI 530/ASCE 5 and shall meet the minimum reinforcement requirements contained in Sections R606.12.3.2 and R606.12.3.2.1. Otherwise, masonry shall be designed in accordance with TMS 403.

Exception: Masonry walls limited to one *story* in height and 9 feet (2743 mm) between lateral supports need not be designed provided they comply with the minimum reinforcement requirements of Sections R606.12.3.2 and R606.12.3.2.1.

R606.12.3.2 Minimum reinforcement requirements for masonry walls. Masonry walls other than those covered by Section R606.12.2.2.3 shall be reinforced in both the vertical and horizontal direction. The sum of the cross-sectional area of horizontal and vertical reinforcement shall be not less than 0.002 times the gross cross-sectional area of the wall, and the minimum cross-sectional area in each direction shall be not less than 0.0007 times the gross cross-sectional area of the wall. Reinforcement shall be uniformly distributed. Table R606.12.3.2 shows the minimum reinforcing bar sizes required for varying thicknesses of masonry walls. The maximum spacing of reinforcement shall be 48 inches (1219 mm) provided that the walls are solid grouted and constructed of hollow open-end units, hollow units laid with full head joints or two wythes of solid units. The maximum spacing of reinforcement shall be 24 inches (610 mm) for all other masonry.

R606.12.3.2.1 Shear wall reinforcement requirements. The maximum spacing of vertical and horizontal reinforcement shall be the smaller of one-third the length of the shear wall, one-third the height of the shear wall, or 48 inches (1219 mm). The minimum cross-sectional area of vertical reinforcement shall be one-third of the required shear reinforcement. Shear reinforcement shall be

anchored around vertical reinforcing bars with a standard hook.

R606.12.3.3 Minimum reinforcement for masonry columns. Lateral ties in masonry columns shall be spaced not more than 8 inches (203 mm) on center and shall be not less than $^3/_8$-inch (9.5 mm) diameter. Lateral ties shall be embedded in grout.

R606.12.3.4 Material restrictions. Type N mortar or masonry cement shall not be used as part of the lateral force-resisting system.

R606.12.3.5 Lateral tie anchorage. Standard hooks for lateral tie anchorage shall be either a 135-degree (2.4 rad) standard hook or a 180-degree (3.2 rad) standard hook.

R606.12.4 Seismic Design Category D₂. Structures in Seismic Design Category D_2 shall comply with the requirements of Seismic Design Category D_1 and to the additional requirements of this section.

R606.12.4.1 Design of elements not part of the lateral force-resisting system. Stack bond masonry that is not part of the lateral force-resisting system shall have a horizontal cross-sectional area of reinforcement of not less than 0.0015 times the gross cross-sectional area of masonry. Table R606.12.4.1 shows minimum reinforcing bar sizes for masonry walls. The maximum spacing of horizontal reinforcement shall be 24 inches (610 mm). These elements shall be solidly grouted and shall be constructed of hollow open-end units or two wythes of solid units.

TABLE R606.12.4.1
MINIMUM REINFORCING FOR STACKED BONDED MASONRY WALLS IN SEISMIC DESIGN CATEGORY D₂

NOMINAL WALL THICKNESS (inches)	MINIMUM BAR SIZE SPACED AT 24 INCHES
6	#4
8	#5
10	#5
12	#6

For SI: 1 inch = 25.4 mm.

R606.12.4.2 Design of elements part of the lateral force-resisting system. Stack bond masonry that is part of the lateral force-resisting system shall have a horizontal cross-sectional area of reinforcement of not less than 0.0025 times the gross cross-sectional area of masonry. Table R606.12.4.2 shows minimum reinforcing bar sizes for masonry walls. The maximum spacing of horizontal reinforcement shall be 16 inches (406 mm). These elements shall be solidly grouted and shall be constructed of hollow open-end units or two wythes of solid units.

TABLE R606.12.4.2
MINIMUM REINFORCING FOR STACKED BONDED MASONRY WALLS IN SEISMIC DESIGN CATEGORY D₂

NOMINAL WALL THICKNESS (inches)	MINIMUM BAR SIZE SPACED AT 16 INCHES
6	#4
8	#5
10	#5
12	#6

For SI: 1 inch = 25.4 mm.

R606.13 Multiple-wythe masonry. The facing and backing of multiple-wythe masonry walls shall be bonded in accordance with Section R606.13.1, R606.13.2 or R606.13.3. In cavity walls, neither the facing nor the backing shall be less than 3 inches (76 mm) nominal in thickness and the cavity shall be not more than 4 inches (102 mm) nominal in width. The backing shall not be less than the thickness of the facing.

Exception: Cavities shall be permitted to exceed the 4-inch (102 mm) nominal dimension provided that tie size and tie spacing have been established by calculation.

R606.13.1 Bonding with masonry headers. Bonding with solid or hollow masonry headers shall comply with Sections R606.13.1.1 and R606.13.1.2.

R606.13.1.1 Solid units. Where the facing and backing (adjacent wythes) of *solid masonry* construction are bonded by means of masonry headers, not less than 4 percent of the wall surface of each face shall be composed of headers extending not less than 3 inches (76 mm) into the backing. The distance between adjacent full-length headers shall not exceed 24 inches (610 mm) either vertically or horizontally. In walls in which a single header does not extend through the wall, headers from the opposite sides shall overlap not less than 3 inches (76 mm), or headers from opposite sides shall be covered with another header course overlapping the header below not less than 3 inches (76 mm).

R606.13.1.2 Hollow units. Where two or more hollow units are used to make up the thickness of a wall, the stretcher courses shall be bonded at vertical intervals not exceeding 34 inches (864 mm) by lapping not less than 3 inches (76 mm) over the unit below, or by lapping at vertical intervals not exceeding 17 inches (432 mm) with units that are not less than 50 percent thicker than the units below.

R606.13.2 Bonding with wall ties or joint reinforcement. Bonding with wall ties or joint reinforcement shall comply with Section R606.13.2.3.

R606.13.2.1 Bonding with wall ties. Bonding with wall ties, except as required by Section R607, where the facing and backing (adjacent wythes) of masonry walls are bonded with $^3/_{16}$-inch-diameter (5 mm) wall ties embedded in the horizontal mortar joints, there shall be not less than one metal tie for each $4^1/_2$ square feet (0.418 m^2) of wall area. Ties in alternate courses shall be staggered. The maximum vertical distance between ties shall not exceed 24 inches (610 mm), and the maximum horizontal distance shall not exceed 36 inches (914 mm). Rods or ties bent to rectangular shape shall be used with hollow masonry units laid with the cells vertical. In other walls, the ends of ties shall be bent to 90-degree (0.79 rad) angles to provide hooks not less than 2 inches (51 mm) long. Additional bonding ties shall be provided at all openings, spaced not more than 3 feet (914 mm) apart around the perimeter and within 12 inches (305 mm) of the opening.

R606.13.2.2 Bonding with adjustable wall ties. Where the facing and backing (adjacent wythes) of masonry are bonded with adjustable wall ties, there shall be not less than one tie for each 2.67 square feet (0.248 m^2) of wall area. Neither the vertical nor the horizontal spacing of the adjustable wall ties shall exceed 24 inches (610 mm). The maximum vertical offset of bed joints from one wythe to the other shall be 1.25 inches (32 mm). The maximum clearance between connecting parts of the ties shall be $^1/_{16}$ inch (2 mm). Where pintle legs are used, ties shall have not less than two $^3/_{16}$-inch-diameter (5 mm) legs.

R606.13.2.3 Bonding with prefabricated joint reinforcement. Where the facing and backing (adjacent wythes) of masonry are bonded with prefabricated joint reinforcement, there shall be not less than one cross wire serving as a tie for each 2.67 square feet (0.248 m^2) of wall area. The vertical spacing of the joint reinforcement shall not exceed 16 inches (406 mm). Cross wires on prefabricated joint reinforcement shall not be smaller than No. 9 gage. The longitudinal wires shall be embedded in the mortar.

R606.13.3 Bonding with natural or cast stone. Bonding with natural and cast stone shall conform to Sections R606.13.3.1 and R606.13.3.2.

R606.13.3.1 Ashlar masonry. In ashlar masonry, bonder units, uniformly distributed, shall be provided to the extent of not less than 10 percent of the wall area. Such bonder units shall extend not less than 4 inches (102 mm) into the backing wall.

R606.13.3.2 Rubble stone masonry. Rubble stone masonry 24 inches (610 mm) or less in thickness shall have bonder units with a maximum spacing of 3 feet (914 mm) vertically and 3 feet (914 mm) horizontally, and if the masonry is of greater thickness than 24 inches (610 mm), shall have one bonder unit for each 6 square feet (0.557 m^2) of wall surface on both sides.

R606.14 Anchored and adhered masonry veneer.

R606.14.1 Anchored veneer. Anchored masonry veneer installed over a backing of wood or cold-formed steel shall meet the requirements of Section R703.8.

R606.14.2 Adhered veneer. Adhered masonry veneer shall be installed in accordance with the requirements of Section R703.12.

SECTION R607
GLASS UNIT MASONRY

R607.1 General. Panels of glass unit masonry located in load-bearing and nonload-bearing exterior and interior walls shall be constructed in accordance with this section.

R607.2 Materials. Hollow glass units shall be partially evacuated and have a minimum average glass face thickness of $^3/_{16}$ inch (5 mm). The surface of units in contact with mortar shall be treated with a polyvinyl butyral coating or latex-based paint. The use of reclaimed units is prohibited.

R607.3 Units. Hollow or solid glass block units shall be standard or thin units.

R607.3.1 Standard units. The specified thickness of standard units shall be not less than $3^7/_8$ inches (98 mm).

R607.3.2 Thin units. The specified thickness of thin units shall be not less than $3\frac{1}{8}$ inches (79 mm) for hollow units and not less than 3 inches (76 mm) for solid units.

R607.4 Isolated panels. Isolated panels of glass unit masonry shall conform to the requirements of this section.

R607.4.1 Exterior standard-unit panels. The maximum area of each individual standard-unit panel shall be 144 square feet (13.4 m²) where the design wind pressure is 20 pounds per square foot (958 Pa). The maximum area of such panels subjected to design wind pressures other than 20 pounds per square foot (958 Pa) shall be in accordance with Figure R607.4.1. The maximum panel dimension between structural supports shall be 25 feet (7620 mm) in width or 20 feet (6096 mm) in height.

R607.4.2 Exterior thin-unit panels. The maximum area of each individual thin-unit panel shall be 85 square feet (7.9 m²). The maximum dimension between structural supports shall be 15 feet (4572 mm) in width or 10 feet (3048 mm) in height. Thin units shall not be used in applications where the design wind pressure as stated in Table R301.2(2) exceeds 20 pounds per square foot (958 Pa).

R607.4.3 Interior panels. The maximum area of each individual standard-unit panel shall be 250 square feet (23.2 m²). The maximum area of each thin-unit panel shall be 150 square feet (13.9 m²). The maximum dimension between structural supports shall be 25 feet (7620 mm) in width or 20 feet (6096 mm) in height.

R607.4.4 Curved panels. The width of curved panels shall conform to the requirements of Sections R607.4.1, R607.4.2 and R607.4.3, except additional structural supports shall be provided at locations where a curved section joins a straight section, and at inflection points in multiple-curve walls.

R607.5 Panel support. Glass unit masonry panels shall conform to the support requirements of this section.

R607.5.1 Deflection. The maximum total deflection of structural members that support glass unit masonry shall not exceed $\frac{1}{600}$.

R607.5.2 Lateral support. Glass unit masonry panels shall be laterally supported along the top and sides of the panel. Lateral supports for glass unit masonry panels shall be designed to resist not less than 200 pounds per lineal feet (2918 N/m) of panel, or the actual applied loads, whichever is greater. Except for single-unit panels, lateral support shall be provided by panel anchors along the top and sides spaced not greater than 16 inches (406 mm) on center or by channel-type restraints. Single-unit panels shall be supported by channel-type restraints.

Exceptions:

1. Lateral support is not required at the top of panels that are one unit wide.

2. Lateral support is not required at the sides of panels that are one unit high.

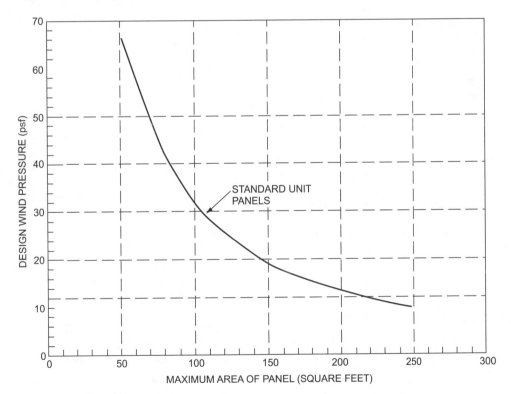

For SI: 1 square foot = 0.0929 m², 1 pound per square foot = 0.0479 kPa.

FIGURE R607.4.1
GLASS UNIT MASONRY DESIGN WIND LOAD RESISTANCE

R607.5.2.1 Panel anchor restraints. Panel anchors shall be spaced not greater than 16 inches (406 mm) on center in both jambs and across the head. Panel anchors shall be embedded not less than 12 inches (305 mm) and shall be provided with two fasteners so as to resist the loads specified in Section R607.5.2.

R607.5.2.2 Channel-type restraints. Glass unit masonry panels shall be recessed not less than 1 inch (25 mm) within channels and chases. Channel-type restraints shall be oversized to accommodate expansion material in the opening, packing and sealant between the framing restraints, and the glass unit masonry perimeter units.

R607.6 Sills. Before the bedding of glass units, the sill area shall be covered with a water-base asphaltic emulsion coating. The coating shall be not less than $^1/_8$ inch (3 mm) thick.

R607.7 Expansion joints. Glass unit masonry panels shall be provided with expansion joints along the top and sides at all structural supports. Expansion joints shall be not less than $^3/_8$ inch (10 mm) in thickness and shall have sufficient thickness to accommodate displacements of the supporting structure. Expansion joints shall be entirely free of mortar and other debris and shall be filled with resilient material.

R607.8 Mortar. Glass unit masonry shall be laid with Type S or N mortar. Mortar shall not be retempered after initial set. Mortar unused within $1^1/_2$ hours after initial mixing shall be discarded.

R607.9 Reinforcement. Glass unit masonry panels shall have horizontal joint reinforcement spaced not greater than 16 inches (406 mm) on center located in the mortar bed joint. Horizontal joint reinforcement shall extend the entire length of the panel but shall not extend across expansion joints. Longitudinal wires shall be lapped not less than 6 inches (152 mm) at splices. Joint reinforcement shall be placed in the bed joint immediately below and above openings in the panel. The reinforcement shall have not less than two parallel longitudinal wires of size W1.7 or greater, and have welded cross wires of size W1.7 or greater.

R607.10 Placement. Glass units shall be placed so head and bed joints are filled solidly. Mortar shall not be furrowed. Head and bed joints of glass unit masonry shall be $^1/_4$ inch (6.4 mm) thick, except that vertical joint thickness of radial panels shall be not less than $^1/_8$ inch (3 mm) or greater than $^5/_8$ inch (16 mm). The bed joint thickness tolerance shall be minus $^1/_{16}$ inch (1.6 mm) and plus $^1/_8$ inch (3 mm). The head joint thickness tolerance shall be plus or minus $^1/_8$ inch (3 mm).

SECTION R608
EXTERIOR CONCRETE WALL CONSTRUCTION

R608.1 General. Exterior concrete walls shall be designed and constructed in accordance with the provisions of this section or in accordance with the provisions of PCA 100 or ACI 318. Where PCA 100, ACI 318 or the provisions of this section are used to design concrete walls, project drawings, typical details and specifications are not required to bear the seal of the architect or engineer responsible for design, unless otherwise required by the state law of the jurisdiction having authority.

R608.1.1 Interior construction. These provisions are based on the assumption that interior walls and partitions, both load-bearing and nonload-bearing, floors and roof/ceiling assemblies are constructed of *light-framed construction* complying with the limitations of this code and the additional limitations of Section R608.2. Design and construction of light-framed assemblies shall be in accordance with the applicable provisions of this code. Where second-story exterior walls are of *light-framed construction*, they shall be designed and constructed as required by this code.

Aspects of concrete construction not specifically addressed by this code, including interior concrete walls, shall comply with ACI 318.

R608.1.2 Other concrete walls. Exterior concrete walls constructed in accordance with this code shall comply with the shapes and minimum concrete cross-sectional dimensions of Table R608.3. Other types of forming systems resulting in concrete walls not in compliance with this section shall be designed in accordance with ACI 318.

R608.2 Applicability limits. The provisions of this section shall apply to the construction of exterior concrete walls for buildings not greater than 60 feet (18 288 mm) in plan dimensions, floors with clear spans not greater than 32 feet (9754 mm) and roofs with clear spans not greater than 40 feet (12 192 mm). Buildings shall not exceed 35 feet (10 668 mm) in mean roof height or two stories in height above grade. Floor/ceiling dead loads shall not exceed 10 pounds per square foot (479 Pa), roof/ceiling dead loads shall not exceed 15 pounds per square foot (718 Pa) and *attic* live loads shall not exceed 20 pounds per square foot (958 Pa). Roof overhangs shall not exceed 2 feet (610 mm) of horizontal projection beyond the exterior wall and the dead load of the overhangs shall not exceed 8 pounds per square foot (383 Pa).

Walls constructed in accordance with the provisions of this section shall be limited to buildings subjected to a maximum design wind speed of 160 mph (72 m/s) Exposure B, 136 mph (61 m/s) Exposure C and 125 mph (56 m/s) Exposure D. Walls constructed in accordance with the provisions of this section shall be limited to detached one- and two-family *dwellings* and townhouses assigned to Seismic Design Category A or B, and detached one- and two-family *dwellings* assigned to Seismic Design Category C.

Buildings that are not within the scope of this section shall be designed in accordance with PCA 100 or ACI 318.

R608.3 Concrete wall systems. Concrete walls constructed in accordance with these provisions shall comply with the shapes and minimum concrete cross-sectional dimensions of Table R608.3.

R608.3.1 Flat wall systems. Flat concrete wall systems shall comply with Table R608.3 and Figure R608.3(1) and have a minimum nominal thickness of 4 inches (102 mm).

R608.3.2 Waffle-grid wall systems. Waffle-grid wall systems shall comply with Table R608.3 and Figure R608.3(2) and shall have a minimum nominal thickness of 6 inches (152 mm) for the horizontal and vertical concrete members (cores). The core and web dimensions shall comply with Table R608.3. The maximum weight of waffle-grid walls shall comply with Table R608.3.

TABLE R608.3
DIMENSIONAL REQUIREMENTS FOR WALLS[a]

WALL TYPE AND NOMINAL THICKNESS	MAXIMUM WALL WEIGHT[b] (psf)	MINIMUM WIDTH, W, OF VERTICAL CORES (inches)	MINIMUM THICKNESS, T, OF VERTICAL CORES (inches)	MAXIMUM SPACING OF VERTICAL CORES (inches)	MAXIMUM SPACING OF HORIZONTAL CORES (inches)	MINIMUM WEB THICKNESS (inches)
4″ Flat[c]	50	NA	NA	NA	NA	NA
6″ Flat[c]	75	NA	NA	NA	NA	NA
8″ Flat[c]	100	NA	NA	NA	NA	NA
10″ Flat[c]	125	NA	NA	NA	NA	NA
6″ Waffle-grid	56	8[d]	5.5[d]	12	16	2
8″ Waffle-grid	76	8[e]	8[e]	12	16	2
6″ Screen-grid	53	6.25[f]	6.25[f]	12	12	NA

For SI: 1 inch = 25.4 mm; 1 pound per square foot = 0.0479 kPa, 1 pound per cubic foot = 2402.77 kg/m^3, 1 square inch = 645.16 mm^2, 1 inch^4 = 42 cm^4.

NA = Not Applicable.

a. Width "W," thickness "T," spacing and web thickness, refer to Figures R608.3(2) and R608.3(3).

b. Wall weight is based on a unit weight of concrete of 150 pcf. For flat walls the weight is based on the nominal thickness. The tabulated values do not include any allowance for interior and exterior finishes.

c. Nominal wall thickness. The actual as-built thickness of a flat wall shall not be more than $^1/_2$ inch less or more than $^1/_4$ inch more than the nominal dimension indicated.

d. Vertical core is assumed to be elliptical-shaped. Another shape of core is permitted provided the minimum thickness is 5 inches, the moment of inertia, I, about the centerline of the wall (ignoring the web) is not less than 65 inch^4, and the area, A, is not less than 31.25 square inches. The width used to calculate A and I shall not exceed 8 inches.

e. Vertical core is assumed to be circular. Another shape of core is permitted provided the minimum thickness is 7 inches, the moment of inertia, I, about the centerline of the wall (ignoring the web) is not less than 200 inch^4, and the area, A, is not less than 49 square inches. The width used to calculate A and I shall not exceed 8 inches.

f. Vertical core is assumed to be circular. Another shape of core is permitted provided the minimum thickness is 5.5 inches, the moment of inertia, I, about the centerline of the wall is not less than 76 inch^4, and the area, A, is not less than 30.25 square inches. The width used to calculate A and I shall not exceed 6.25 inches.

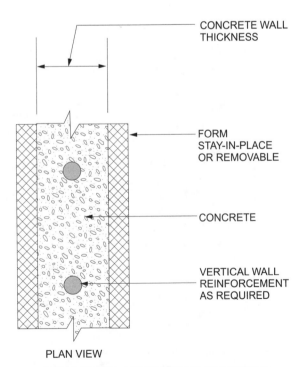

PLAN VIEW

SEE TABLE 608.3 FOR MINIMUM DIMENSIONS

FIGURE R608.3(1)
FLAT WALL SYSTEM

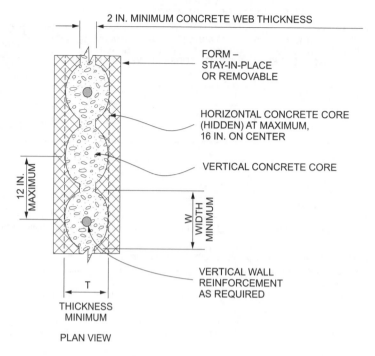

2 IN. MINIMUM CONCRETE WEB THICKNESS

FORM –
STAY-IN-PLACE
OR REMOVABLE

HORIZONTAL CONCRETE CORE
(HIDDEN) AT MAXIMUM,
16 IN. ON CENTER

VERTICAL CONCRETE CORE

12 IN.
MAXIMUM

W
WIDTH
MINIMUM

VERTICAL WALL
REINFORCEMENT
AS REQUIRED

T

THICKNESS
MINIMUM

PLAN VIEW

SEE TABLE R608.3 FOR MINIMUM DIMENSIONS

For SI: 1 inch = 25.4 mm.

FIGURE R608.3(2)
WAFFLE-GRID WALL SYSTEM

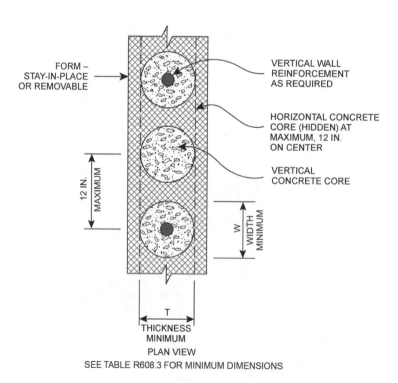

FORM –
STAY-IN-PLACE
OR REMOVABLE

VERTICAL WALL
REINFORCEMENT
AS REQUIRED

HORIZONTAL CONCRETE
CORE (HIDDEN) AT
MAXIMUM, 12 IN.
ON CENTER

VERTICAL
CONCRETE CORE

12 IN.
MAXIMUM

W
WIDTH
MINIMUM

T
THICKNESS
MINIMUM

PLAN VIEW

SEE TABLE R608.3 FOR MINIMUM DIMENSIONS

For SI: 1 inch = 25.4 mm.

FIGURE R608.3(3)
SCREEN-GRID WALL SYSTEM

R608.3.3 Screen-grid wall systems. Screen-grid systems shall comply with Table R608.3 and Figure R608.3(3) and shall have a minimum nominal thickness of 6 inches (152 mm) for the horizontal and vertical concrete members (cores). The core dimensions shall comply with Table R608.3. The maximum weight of screen-grid walls shall comply with Table R608.3.

R608.4 Stay-in-place forms. Stay-in-place concrete forms shall comply with this section.

R608.4.1 Surface burning characteristics. The flame spread index and smoke-developed index of forming material, other than foam plastic, left exposed on the interior shall comply with Section R302.9. The surface burning characteristics of foam plastic used in insulating concrete forms shall comply with Section R316.3.

R608.4.2 Interior covering. Stay-in-place forms constructed of rigid foam plastic shall be protected on the interior of the building as required by Sections R316.4 and R702.3.4. Where gypsum board is used to protect the foam plastic, it shall be installed with a mechanical fastening system. Use of adhesives is permitted in addition to mechanical fasteners.

R608.4.3 Exterior wall covering. Stay-in-place forms constructed of rigid foam plastics shall be protected from sunlight and physical damage by the application of an *approved* exterior wall covering complying with this code. Exterior surfaces of other stay-in-place forming systems shall be protected in accordance with this code.

Requirements for installation of masonry veneer, stucco and other finishes on the exterior of concrete walls and other construction details not covered in this section shall comply with the requirements of this code.

R608.4.4 Flat ICF wall systems. Flat ICF wall system forms shall conform to ASTM E2634.

R608.5 Materials. Materials used in the construction of concrete walls shall comply with this section.

R608.5.1 Concrete and materials for concrete. Materials used in concrete, and the concrete itself, shall conform to requirements of this section, PCA 100 or ACI 318.

R608.5.1.1 Cements. The following standards as referenced in Chapter 44 shall be permitted to be used.

1. ASTM C150
2. ASTM C595
3. ASTM C1157

R608.5.1.2 Concrete mixing and delivery. Mixing and delivery of concrete shall comply with ASTM C94 or ASTM C685.

R608.5.1.3 Maximum aggregate size. The nominal maximum size of coarse aggregate shall not exceed one-fifth the narrowest distance between sides of forms, or three-fourths the clear spacing between reinforcing bars or between a bar and the side of the form.

Exception: When *approved*, these limitations shall not apply where removable forms are used and

workability and methods of consolidation permit concrete to be placed without honeycombs or voids.

R608.5.1.4 Proportioning and slump of concrete. Proportions of materials for concrete shall be established to provide workability and consistency to permit concrete to be worked readily into forms and around reinforcement under conditions of placement to be employed, without segregation or excessive bleeding. Slump of concrete placed in removable forms shall not exceed 6 inches (152 mm).

Exception: When *approved*, the slump is permitted to exceed 6 inches (152 mm) for concrete mixtures that are resistant to segregation, and are in accordance with the form manufacturer's recommendations.

Slump of concrete placed in stay-in-place forms shall exceed 6 inches (152 mm). Slump of concrete shall be determined in accordance with ASTM C143.

R608.5.1.5 Compressive strength. The minimum specified compressive strength of concrete, f'_c, shall comply with Section R402.2 and shall be not less than 2,500 pounds per square inch (17.2 MPa) at 28 days.

R608.5.1.6 Consolidation of concrete. Concrete shall be consolidated by suitable means during placement and shall be worked around embedded items and reinforcement and into corners of forms. Where stay-in-place forms are used, concrete shall be consolidated by internal vibration.

Exception: When *approved*, self-consolidating concrete mixtures with slumps equal to or greater than 8 inches (203 mm) that are specifically designed for placement without internal vibration need not be internally vibrated.

R608.5.2 Steel reinforcement and anchor bolts.

R608.5.2.1 Steel reinforcement. Steel reinforcement shall comply with ASTM A615, ASTM A706, or ASTM A996. ASTM A996 bars produced from rail steel shall be Type R.

R608.5.2.2 Anchor bolts. Anchor bolts for use with connection details in accordance with Figures R608.9(1) through R608.9(12) shall be bolts with heads complying with ASTM A307 or ASTM F1554. ASTM A307 bolts shall be Grade A with heads. ASTM F1554 bolts shall be Grade 36 minimum. Instead of bolts with heads, it is permissible to use rods with threads on both ends fabricated from steel complying with ASTM A36. The threaded end of the rod to be embedded in the concrete shall be provided with a hex or square nut.

R608.5.2.3 Sheet steel angles and tension tie straps. Angles and tension tie straps for use with connection details in accordance with Figures R608.9(1) through R608.9(12) shall be fabricated from sheet steel complying with ASTM A653 SS, ASTM A792 SS, or ASTM A875 SS. The steel shall be minimum Grade 33 unless a higher grade is required by the applicable figure.

R608.5.3 Form materials and form ties. Forms shall be made of wood, steel, aluminum, plastic, a composite of cement and foam insulation, a composite of cement and wood chips, or other *approved* material suitable for supporting and containing concrete. Forms shall provide sufficient strength to contain concrete during the concrete placement operation.

Form ties shall be steel, solid plastic, foam plastic, a composite of cement and wood chips, a composite of cement and foam plastic, or other suitable material capable of resisting the forces created by fluid pressure of fresh concrete.

R608.5.4 Reinforcement installation details.

R608.5.4.1 Support and cover. Reinforcement shall be secured in the proper location in the forms with tie wire or other bar support system such that displacement will not occur during the concrete placement operation. Steel reinforcement in concrete cast against the earth shall have a minimum cover of 3 inches (76 mm). Minimum cover for reinforcement in concrete cast in removable forms that will be exposed to the earth or weather shall be $1^{1}/_{2}$ inches (38 mm) for No. 5 bars and smaller, and 2 inches (50 mm) for No. 6 bars and larger. For concrete cast in removable forms that will not be exposed to the earth or weather, and for concrete cast in stay-in-place forms, minimum cover shall be $^{3}/_{4}$ inch (19 mm). The minus tolerance for cover shall not exceed the smaller of one-third the required cover and $^{3}/_{8}$ inch (10 mm). See Section R608.5.4.4 for cover requirements for hooks of bars developed in tension.

TABLE R608.5.4(1)
LAP SPLICE AND TENSION DEVELOPMENT LENGTHS

	BAR SIZE NO.	YIELD STRENGTH OF STEEL, f_y - psi (MPa)	
		40,000 (280)	60,000 (420)
		Splice length or tension development length (inches)	
Lap splice length-tension	4	20	30
	5	25	38
	6	30	45
Tension development length for straight bar	4	15	23
	5	19	28
	6	23	34
Tension development length for: a. 90-degree and 180-degree standard hooks with not less than $2^{1}/_{2}$ inches of side cover perpendicular to plane of hook, and b. 90-degree standard hooks with not less than 2 inches of cover on the bar extension beyond the hook.	4	6	9
	5	7	11
	6	8	13
Tension development length for bar with 90-degree or 180-degree standard hook having less cover than required in Items a and b.	4	8	12
	5	10	15
	6	12	18

For SI: 1 inch = 25.4 mm, 1 degree = 0.0175 rad, 1 pound per square inch = 6.895 kPa.

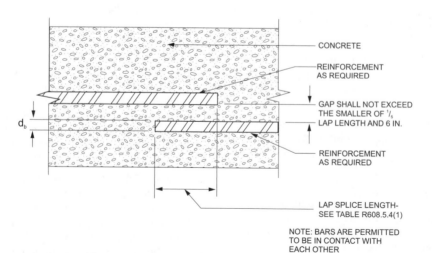

For SI: 1 inch = 25.4 mm.

FIGURE R608.5.4(1)
LAP SPLICES

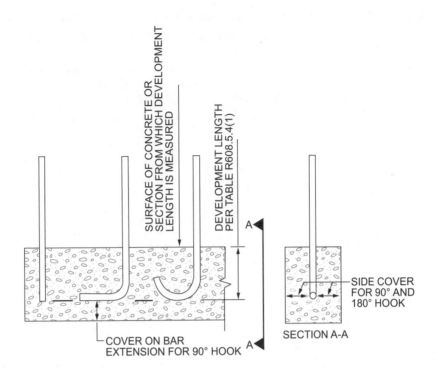

For SI: 1 degree = 0.0175 rad.

FIGURE R608.5.4(2)
DEVELOPMENT LENGTH AND COVER FOR HOOKS AND BAR EXTENSION

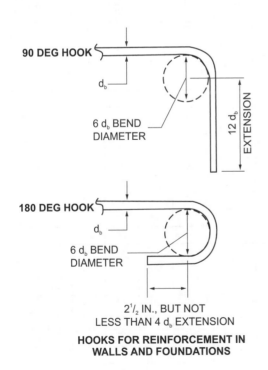

HOOKS FOR REINFORCEMENT IN
WALLS AND FOUNDATIONS

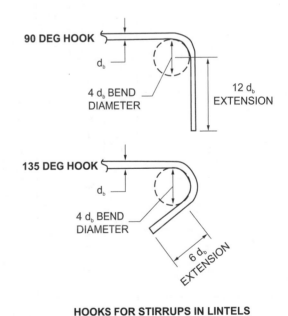

HOOKS FOR STIRRUPS IN LINTELS

For SI: 1 inch = 25.4 mm, 1 degree = 0.0175 rad.

FIGURE R608.5.4(3)
STANDARD HOOKS

TABLE R608.5.4(2)
MAXIMUM SPACING FOR ALTERNATIVE BAR SIZE AND ALTERNATIVE GRADE OF STEEL[a, b, c]

BAR SPACING FROM APPLICABLE TABLE IN SECTION R608.6 (inches)	#4					#5					#6				
	Grade 60		Grade 40			Grade 60		Grade 40			Grade 60		Grade 40		
	#5	#6	#4	#5	#6	#4	#6	#4	#5	#6	#4	#5	#4	#5	#6
	Maximum spacing for alternate bar size and alternate grade of steel (inches)														
8	12	18	5	8	12	5	11	3	5	8	4	6	2	4	5
9	14	20	6	9	13	6	13	4	6	9	4	6	3	4	6
10	16	22	7	10	15	6	14	4	7	9	5	7	3	5	7
11	17	24	7	11	16	7	16	5	7	10	5	8	3	5	7
12	19	26	8	12	18	8	17	5	8	11	5	8	4	6	8
13	20	29	9	13	19	8	18	6	9	12	6	9	4	6	9
14	22	31	9	14	21	9	20	6	9	13	6	10	4	7	9
15	23	33	10	16	22	10	21	6	10	14	7	11	5	7	10
16	25	35	11	17	23	10	23	7	11	15	7	11	5	8	11
17	26	37	11	18	25	11	24	7	11	16	8	12	5	8	11
18	28	40	12	19	26	12	26	8	12	17	8	13	5	8	12
19	29	42	13	20	28	12	27	8	13	18	9	13	6	9	13
20	31	44	13	21	29	13	28	9	13	19	9	14	6	9	13
21	33	46	14	22	31	14	30	9	14	20	10	15	6	10	14
22	34	48	15	23	32	14	31	9	15	21	10	16	7	10	15
23	36	48	15	24	34	15	33	10	15	22	10	16	7	11	15
24	37	48	16	25	35	15	34	10	16	23	11	17	7	11	16
25	39	48	17	26	37	16	35	11	17	24	11	18	8	12	17
26	40	48	17	27	38	17	37	11	17	25	12	18	8	12	17
27	42	48	18	28	40	17	38	12	18	26	12	19	8	13	18
28	43	48	19	29	41	18	40	12	19	26	13	20	8	13	19
29	45	48	19	30	43	19	41	12	19	27	13	20	9	14	19
30	47	48	20	31	44	19	43	13	20	28	14	21	9	14	20
31	48	48	21	32	45	20	44	13	21	29	14	22	9	15	21
32	48	48	21	33	47	21	45	14	21	30	15	23	10	15	21
33	48	48	22	34	48	21	47	14	22	31	15	23	10	16	22
34	48	48	23	35	48	22	48	15	23	32	15	24	10	16	23
35	48	48	23	36	48	23	48	15	23	33	16	25	11	16	23
36	48	48	24	37	48	23	48	15	24	34	16	25	11	17	24
37	48	48	25	38	48	24	48	16	25	35	17	26	11	17	25
38	48	48	25	39	48	25	48	16	25	36	17	27	12	18	25
39	48	48	26	40	48	25	48	17	26	37	18	27	12	18	26
40	48	48	27	41	48	26	48	17	27	38	18	28	12	19	27
41	48	48	27	42	48	26	48	18	27	39	19	29	12	19	27
42	48	48	28	43	48	27	48	18	28	40	19	30	13	20	28
43	48	48	29	44	48	28	48	18	29	41	20	30	13	20	29
44	48	48	29	45	48	28	48	19	29	42	20	31	13	21	29
45	48	48	30	47	48	29	48	19	30	43	20	32	14	21	30
46	48	48	31	48	48	30	48	20	31	44	21	32	14	22	31
47	48	48	31	48	48	30	48	20	31	44	21	33	14	22	31
48	48	48	32	48	48	31	48	21	32	45	22	34	15	23	32

For SI: 1 inch = 25.4 mm.

a. This table is for use with tables in Section R608.6 that specify the minimum bar size and maximum spacing of vertical wall reinforcement for foundation walls and above-grade walls. Reinforcement specified in tables in Section R608.6 is based on Grade 60 (420 MPa) steel reinforcement.

b. Bar spacing shall not exceed 48 inches on center and shall be not less than one-half the nominal wall thickness.

c. For Grade 50 (350 MPa) steel bars (ASTM A996, Type R), use spacing for Grade 40 (280 MPa) bars or interpolate between Grade 40 (280 MPa) and Grade 60 (420 MPa).

R608.5.4.2 Location of reinforcement in walls. For location of reinforcement in foundation walls and above-grade walls, see Sections R404.1.3.3.7.2 and R608.6.5, respectively.

R608.5.4.3 Lap splices. Vertical and horizontal wall reinforcement required by Sections R608.6 and R608.7 shall be the longest lengths practical. Where splices are necessary in reinforcement, the length of lap splices shall be in accordance with Table R608.5.4(1) and Figure R608.5.4(1). The maximum gap between noncontact parallel bars at a lap splice shall not exceed the smaller of one-fifth the required lap length and 6 inches (152 mm). See Figure R608.5.4(1).

R608.5.4.4 Development of bars in tension. Where bars are required to be developed in tension by other provisions of this code, development lengths and cover for hooks and bar extensions shall comply with Table R608.5.4(1) and Figure R608.5.4(2). The development lengths shown in Table R608.5.4(1) shall apply to bundled bars in lintels installed in accordance with Section R608.8.2.2.

R608.5.4.5 Standard hooks. Where reinforcement is required by this code to terminate with a standard hook, the hook shall comply with Figure R608.5.4(3).

R608.5.4.6 Webs of waffle-grid walls. Reinforcement, including stirrups, shall not be placed in webs of waffle-grid walls, including lintels. Webs are permitted to have form ties.

R608.5.4.7 Alternate grade of reinforcement and spacing. Where tables in Sections R404.1.3 and R608.6 specify vertical wall reinforcement based on minimum bar size and maximum spacing, which are based on Grade 60 (420 MPa) steel reinforcement, different size bars or bars made from a different grade of steel are permitted provided an equivalent area of steel per linear foot of wall is provided. Use of Table R608.5.4(2) is permitted to determine the maximum bar spacing for different bar sizes than specified in the tables and bars made from a different grade of steel. Bars shall not be spaced less than one-half the wall thickness, or more than 48 inches (1219 mm) on center.

R608.5.5 Construction joints in walls. Construction joints shall be made and located to not impair the strength of the wall. Construction joints in plain concrete walls, including walls required to have not less than No. 4 bars at 48 inches (1219 mm) on center by Section R608.6, shall be located at points of lateral support, and not less than one No. 4 bar shall extend across the construction joint at a spacing not to exceed 24 inches (610 mm) on center. Construction joint reinforcement shall have not less than 12 inches (305 mm) of embedment on both sides of the joint. Construction joints in reinforced concrete walls shall be located in the middle third of the span between lateral supports, or located and constructed as required for joints in plain concrete walls.

Exception: Vertical wall reinforcement required by this code is permitted to be used in lieu of construction joint reinforcement, provided the spacing does not exceed 24 inches (610 mm), or the combination of wall reinforcement and No. 4 bars described in Section R608.5.5 does not exceed 24 inches (610 mm).

R608.6 Above-grade wall requirements.

R608.6.1 General. The minimum thickness of load-bearing and nonload-bearing above-grade walls and reinforcement shall be as set forth in the appropriate table in this section based on the type of wall form to be used. The wall shall be designed in accordance with ACI 318 where the wall or building is not within the limitations of Section R608.2, where design is required by the tables in this section or where the wall is not within the scope of the tables in this section.

Above-grade concrete walls shall be constructed in accordance with this section and Figure R608.6(1), R608.6(2), R608.6(3) or R608.6(4). Above-grade concrete walls that are continuous with stem walls and not laterally supported by the slab-on-ground shall be designed and constructed in accordance with this section. Concrete walls shall be supported on continuous foundation walls or slabs-on-ground that are monolithic with the footing in accordance with Section R403. The minimum length of solid wall without openings shall be in accordance with Section R608.7. Reinforcement around openings, including lintels, shall be in accordance with Section R608.8. Lateral support for above-grade walls in the out-of-plane direction shall be provided by connections to the floor framing system, if applicable, and to ceiling and roof framing systems in accordance with Section R608.9. The wall thickness shall be equal to or greater than the thickness of the wall in the *story* above.

R608.6.2 Wall reinforcement for wind. Vertical wall reinforcement for resistance to out-of-plane wind forces shall be determined from Table R608.6(1), R608.6(2), R608.6(3) or R608.6(4). For the design of nonload-bearing walls, in Tables R608.6(1), R608.6(2) and R608.6(3) use the appropriate column labeled "Top." (see Sections R608.7.2.2.2 and R608.7.2.2.3). There shall be a vertical bar at corners of exterior walls. Unless more horizontal reinforcement is required by Section R608.7.2.2.1, the minimum horizontal reinforcement shall be four No. 4 bars [Grade 40 (280 MPa)] placed as follows: top bar within 12 inches (305 mm) of the top of the wall, bottom bar within 12 inches (305 mm) of the finish floor and one bar each at approximately one-third and two-thirds of the wall height.

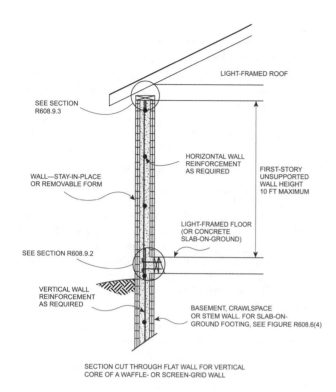

For SI: 1 foot = 304.8 mm.

FIGURE R608.6(1)
ABOVE-GRADE CONCRETE WALL CONSTRUCTION ONE STORY

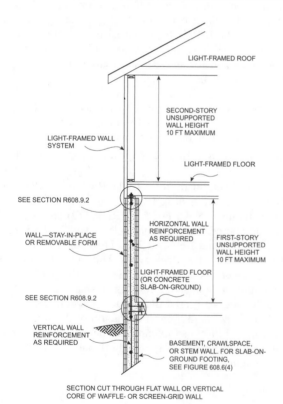

For SI: 1 foot = 304.8 mm.

FIGURE R608.6(2)
ABOVE-GRADE CONCRETE WALL CONSTRUCTION CONCRETE FIRST STORY AND LIGHT-FRAMED SECOND STORY

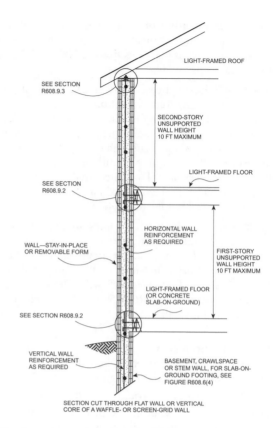

For SI: 1 foot = 304.8 mm.

FIGURE R608.6(3)
ABOVE-GRADE CONCRETE WALL CONSTRUCTION TWO-STORY

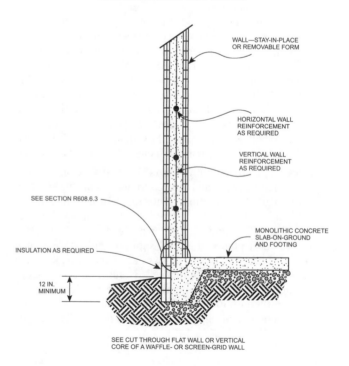

For SI: 1 inch = 25.4 mm.

FIGURE R608.6(4)
ABOVE-GRADE CONCRETE WALL SUPPORTED ON MONOLITHIC SLAB-ON-GROUND FOOTING

TABLE R608.6(1)
MINIMUM VERTICAL REINFORCEMENT FOR FLAT ABOVE-GRADE WALLS[a, b, c, d, e]

MAXIMUM WIND SPEED (mph)			MAXIMUM UNSUPPORTED WALL HEIGHT PER STORY (feet)	MINIMUM VERTICAL REINFORCEMENT-BAR SIZE AND SPACING (inches)[f, g]							
Exposure Category				Nominal[h] wall thickness (inches)							
B	C	D		4		6		8		10	
				Top[i]	Side[i]	Top[i]	Side[i]	Top[i]	Side[i]	Top[i]	Side[i]
115			8	4@48	4@48	4@48	4@48	4@48	4@48	4@48	4@48
			9	4@48	4@39	4@48	4@48	4@48	4@48	4@48	4@48
			10	4@41	4@34	4@48	4@48	4@48	4@48	4@48	4@48
120			8	4@48	4@43	4@48	4@48	4@48	4@48	4@48	4@48
			9	4@48	4@36	4@48	4@48	4@48	4@48	4@48	4@48
			10	4@37	4@34	4@48	4@48	4@48	4@48	4@48	4@48
130	110		8	4@48	4@38	4@48	4@48	4@48	4@48	4@48	4@48
			9	4@39	4@34	4@48	4@48	4@48	4@48	4@48	4@48
			10	4@34	4@34	4@48	4@48	4@48	4@48	4@48	4@48
140	119	110	8	4@43	4@34	4@48	4@48	4@48	4@48	4@48	4@48
			9	4@34	4@34	4@48	4@48	4@48	4@48	4@48	4@48
			10	4@34	4@31	4@48	4@48	4@48	4@48	4@48	4@48
150	127	117	8	4@37	4@34	4@48	4@48	4@48	4@48	4@48	4@48
			9	4@34	4@33	4@48	4@48	4@48	4@48	4@48	4@48
			10	4@31	4@27	4@48	4@48	4@48	4@48	4@48	4@48
160	136	125	8	4@34	4@34	4@48	4@48	4@48	4@48	4@48	4@48
			9	4@34	4@29	4@48	4@48	4@48	4@48	4@48	4@48
			10	4@27	4@24	4@48	4@48	4@48	4@48	4@48	4@48

For SI: 1 inch = 25.4 mm, 1 foot = 304.8 mm, 1 mile per hour = 0.447 m/s, 1 pound per square inch = 1.895 kPa, 1 square foot = 0.0929 m².

a. Table is based on ASCE 7 components and cladding wind pressures for an enclosed building using a mean roof height of 35 feet, interior wall area 4, an effective wind area of 10 square feet, topographic factor, K_{zt}, equal to 1.0, and Risk Category II.

b. Table is based on concrete with a minimum specified compressive strength of 2,500 psi.

c. See Section R608.6.5 for location of reinforcement in wall.

d. Deflection criterion is $L/240$, where L is the unsupported height of the wall in inches.

e. Interpolation is not permitted.

f. Where No. 4 reinforcing bars at a spacing of 48 inches are specified in the table as indicated by shaded cells, use of bars with a minimum yield strength of 40,000 psi or 60,000 psi is permitted.

g. Other than for No. 4 bars spaced at 48 inches on center, table values are based on reinforcing bars with a minimum yield strength of 60,000 psi. Vertical reinforcement with a yield strength of less than 60,000 psi or bars of a different size than specified in the table are permitted in accordance with Section R608.5.4.7 and Table R608.5.4(2).

h. See Table R608.3 for tolerances on nominal thicknesses.

i. "Top" means gravity load from roof or floor construction bears on top of wall. "Side" means gravity load from floor construction is transferred to wall from a wood ledger or cold-formed steel track bolted to side of wall. For nonload-bearing walls where floor framing members span parallel to the wall, use of the "Top" bearing condition is permitted.

TABLE R608.6(2)
MINIMUM VERTICAL REINFORCEMENT FOR WAFFLE-GRID ABOVE-GRADE WALLS[a, b, c, d, e]

MAXIMUM WIND SPEED (mph)			MAXIMUM UNSUPPORTED WALL HEIGHT PER STORY (feet)	MINIMUM VERTICAL REINFORCEMENT-BAR SIZE AND SPACING (inches)[f, g]			
Exposure Category				Nominal[h] wall thickness (inches)			
				6		8	
B	C	D		Top[i]	Side[i]	Top[i]	Side[i]
115			8	4@48	4@48	4@48	4@48
			9	4@48	5@43	4@48	4@48
			10	5@47	5@37	4@48	4@48
120			8	4@48	5@48	4@48	4@48
			9	4@48	5@40	4@48	4@48
			10	5@43	5@37	4@48	4@48
130	110		8	4@48	5@42	4@48	4@48
			9	5@45	5@37	4@48	4@48
			10	5@37	5@37	4@48	4@48
140	119	110	8	4@48	5@38	4@48	4@48
			9	5@39	5@37	4@48	4@48
			10	5@37	5@35	4@48	4@48
150	127	117	8	5@43	5@37	4@48	4@48
			9	5@37	5@37	4@48	4@48
			10	5@36	6@44	4@48	4@48
160	136	125	8	5@38	5@37	4@48	4@48
			9	5@37	6@47	4@48	4@48
			10	6@45	6@39	4@48	6@46

For SI: 1 inch = 25.4 mm, 1 foot = 304.8 mm, 1 mile per hour = 0.447 m/s, 1 pound per square inch = 6.895 kPa, 1 square foot = 0.0929 m².

a. Table is based on ASCE 7 components and cladding wind pressures for an enclosed building using a mean roof height of 35 feet, interior wall area 4, an effective wind area of 10 square feet, topographic factor, K_{zt}, equal to 1.0, and Risk Category II.

b. Table is based on concrete with a minimum specified compressive strength of 2,500 psi.

c. See Section R608.6.5 for location of reinforcement in wall.

d. Deflection criterion is $L/240$, where L is the unsupported height of the wall in inches.

e. Interpolation is not permitted.

f. Where No. 4 reinforcing bars at a spacing of 48 inches are specified in the table as indicated by shaded cells, use of bars with a minimum yield strength of 40,000 psi or 60,000 psi is permitted.

g. Other than for No. 4 bars spaced at 48 inches on center, table values are based on reinforcing bars with a minimum yield strength of 60,000 psi. Maximum spacings shown are the values calculated for the specified bar size. Where the bar used is Grade 60 and the size specified in the table, the actual spacing in the wall shall not exceed a whole-number multiple of 12 inches such as, 12, 24, 36 and 48, that is less than or equal to the tabulated spacing. Vertical reinforcement with a yield strength of less than 60,000 psi or bars of a different size than specified in the table are permitted in accordance with Section R608.5.4.7 and Table R608.5.4(2).

h. See Table R608.3 for minimum core dimensions and maximum spacing of horizontal and vertical cores.

i. "Top" means gravity load from roof or floor construction bears on top of wall. "Side" means gravity load from floor construction is transferred to wall from a wood ledger or cold-formed steel track bolted to side of wall. For nonload-bearing walls and where floor framing members span parallel to the wall, the "top" bearing condition is permitted to be used.

TABLE R608.6(3)
MINIMUM VERTICAL REINFORCEMENT FOR 6-INCH SCREEN-GRID ABOVE-GRADE WALLS[a, b, c, d, e]

MAXIMUM WIND SPEED (mph)			MAXIMUM UNSUPPORTED WALL HEIGHT PER STORY (feet)	MINIMUM VERTICAL REINFORCEMENT-BAR SIZE AND SPACING (inches)[f, g]	
Exposure Category				Nominal[h] wall thickness (inches)	
				6	
B	C	D		Top[i]	Side[i]
115			8	4@48	4@48
			9	4@48	5@41
			10	4@48	6@48
120			8	4@48	4@48
			9	4@48	5@38
			10	5@42	6@48
130	110		8	4@48	5@41
			9	5@44	6@48
			10	5@35	6@48
140	119	110	8	4@48	5@36
			9	5@38	6@48
			10	6@48	6@48
150	127	117	8	5@42	6@48
			9	6@48	6@48
			10	6@48	6@42
160	136	125	8	5@37	6@48
			9	6@48	6@45
			10	6@44	6@38

For SI: 1 inch = 25.4 mm, 1 foot = 304.8 mm, 1 mile per hour = 0.447 m/s, 1 pound per square inch = 6.895 kPa, 1 square foot = 0.0929 m^2.

a. Table is based on ASCE 7 components and cladding wind pressures for an enclosed building using a mean roof height of 35 feet, interior wall area 4, an effective wind area of 10 square feet, topographic factor, K_{zt}, equal to 1.0, and Risk Category II.

b. Table is based on concrete with a minimum specified compressive strength of 2,500 psi.

c. See Section R608.6.5 for location of reinforcement in wall.

d. Deflection criterion is $L/240$, where L is the unsupported height of the wall in inches.

e. Interpolation is not permitted.

f. Where No. 4 reinforcing bars at a spacing of 48 inches are specified in the table as indicated by shaded cells, use of bars with a minimum yield strength of 40,000 psi or 60,000 psi is permitted.

g. Other than for No. 4 bars spaced at 48 inches on center, table values are based on reinforcing bars with a minimum yield strength of 60,000 psi. Maximum spacings shown are the values calculated for the specified bar size. Where the bar used is Grade 60 and the size specified in the table, the actual spacing in the wall shall not exceed a whole-number multiple of 12 inches such as, 12, 24, 36 and 48, that is less than or equal to the tabulated spacing. Vertical reinforcement with a yield strength of less than 60,000 psi or bars of a different size than specified in the table are permitted in accordance with Section R608.5.4.7 and Table R608.5.4(2).

h. See Table R608.3 for minimum core dimensions and maximum spacing of horizontal and vertical cores.

i. "Top" means gravity load from roof or floor construction bears on top of wall. "Side" means gravity load from floor construction is transferred to wall from a wood ledger or cold-formed steel track bolted to side of wall. For nonload-bearing wall and where floor framing members span parallel to the wall, use of the "Top" bearing condition is permitted.

TABLE R608.6(4)
MINIMUM VERTICAL REINFORCEMENT FOR FLAT, WAFFLE- AND SCREEN-GRID
ABOVE-GRADE WALLS DESIGNED CONTINUOUS WITH FOUNDATION STEM WALLS[a, b, c, d, e, k]

MAXIMUM WIND SPEED (mph) Exposure Category			HEIGHT OF STEM WALL[h, i] (feet)	MAXIMUM DESIGN LATERAL SOIL LOAD (psf/ft)	MAXIMUM UNSUPPORTED HEIGHT OF ABOVE-GRADE WALL (feet)	MINIMUM VERTICAL REINFORCEMENT-BAR SIZE AND SPACING (inches)[f, g] Wall type and nominal thickness[j] (inches)						
						Flat				Waffle		Screen
B	C	D				4	6	8	10	6	8	6
115			3	30	8	4@30	4@48	4@48	4@48	4@22	4@26	4@21
					10	4@23	5@43	4@48	4@48	4@17	4@20	4@16
				60	10	4@19	5@37	4@48	4@48	4@14	4@17	4@14
			6	30	10	DR	5@21	6@35	4@48	DR	4@10	DR
				60	10	DR	5@12	6@25	6@28	DR	DR	DR
120			3	30	8	4@28	4@48	4@48	4@48	4@21	4@48	4@20
					10	4@22	5@41	4@48	4@48	4@16	4@19	4@15
				60	10	4@18	5@35	4@48	4@48	4@14	4@17	4@13
			6	30	10	DR	5@21	6@35	4@48	DR	4@10	DR
				60	10	DR	5@12	6@25	6@28	DR	DR	DR
130	110		3	30	8	4@25	4@48	4@48	4@48	4@18	4@22	4@18
					10	4@19	5@36	4@48	4@48	4@14	4@17	4@13
				60	10	4@16	5@34	4@48	4@48	4@12	4@17	4@12
			6	30	10	DR	5@19	6@35	4@48	DR	4@9	DR
				60	10	DR	5@12	6@24	6@28	DR	DR	DR
140	119	110	3	30	8	4@22	5@42	4@48	4@48	4@16	4@20	4@16
					10	4@17	5@34	4@48	4@48	4@21	4@17	4@12
				60	10	4@15	5@34	4@48	4@48	4@11	4@17	4@10
			6	30	10	DR	5@18	6@35	6@35	DR	4@48	DR
				60	10	DR	5@11	6@23	6@28	DR	DR	DR
150	127	117	3	30	8	4@20	5@37	4@48	4@48	4@15	4@18	4@14
					10	4@15	5@34	4@48	4@48	4@11	4@17	4@11
				60	10	4@13	5@34	4@48	4@48	4@10	4@16	4@9
			6	30	10	DR	5@17	6@33	6@32	DR	4@8	DR
				60	10	DR	DR	6@22	6@28	DR	DR	DR
160	136	125	3	30	8	4@18	5@34	4@48	4@48	4@13	4@17	4@13
					10	4@13	5@34	4@48	4@48	4@10	4@16	4@9
				60	10	4@11	5@31	6@45	4@48	4@9	4@14	4@8
			6	30	10	DR	5@15	6@31	6@30	DR	4@7	DR
				60	10	DR	DR	6@21	6@27	DR	DR	DR

For SI: 1 inch = 25.4 mm, 1 foot = 304.8 mm, 1 mile per hour = 0.447 m/s, 1 pound per square inch = 6.895 kPa, 1 square foot = 0.0929 m^2.

DR = Design Required.

a. Table is based on ASCE 7 components and cladding wind pressures for an enclosed building using a mean roof height of 35 feet, interior wall area 4, an effective wind area of 10 square feet, topographic factor, K_{zt}, equal to 1.0, and Risk Category II.

b. Table is based on concrete with a minimum specified compressive strength of 2,500 psi.

c. See Section R608.6.5 for location of reinforcement in wall.

d. Deflection criterion is $L/240$, where L is the height of the wall in inches from the exterior finish ground level to the top of the above-grade wall.

e. Interpolation is not permitted. For intermediate values of basic wind speed, heights of stem wall and above-grade wall, and design lateral soil load, use next higher value.

f. Where No. 4 reinforcing bars at a spacing of 48 inches are specified in the table as indicated by shaded cells, use of bars with a minimum yield strength of 40,000 psi or 60,000 psi is permitted.

g. Other than for No. 4 bars spaced at 48 inches on center, table values are based on reinforcing bars with a minimum yield strength of 60,000 psi. Maximum spacings shown are the values calculated for the specified bar size. In waffle and screen-grid walls where the bar used is Grade 60 and the size specified in the table, the actual spacing in the wall shall not exceed a whole-number multiple of 12 inches such as, 12, 24, 36 and 48, that is less than or equal to the tabulated spacing. Vertical reinforcement with a yield strength of less than 60,000 psi and bars of a different size than specified in the table are permitted in accordance with Section R608.5.4.7 and Table R608.5.4(2).

h. Height of stem wall is the distance from the exterior finish ground level to the top of the slab-on-ground.

i. Where the distance from the exterior finish ground level to the top of the slab-on-ground is equal to or greater than 4 feet, the stem wall shall be laterally supported at the top and bottom before backfilling. Where the wall is designed and constructed to be continuous with the above-grade wall, temporary supports bracing the top of the stem wall shall remain in place until the above-grade wall is laterally supported at the top by floor or roof construction.

j. See Table R608.3 for tolerances on nominal thicknesses, and minimum core dimensions and maximum spacing of horizontal and vertical cores for waffle- and screen-grid walls.

k. Tabulated values are applicable to construction where gravity loads bear on top of wall, and conditions where gravity loads from floor construction are transferred to wall from a wood ledger or cold-formed steel track bolted to side of wall. See Tables R608.6(1), R608.6(2) and R608.6(3).

R608.6.3 Continuity of wall reinforcement between stories. Vertical reinforcement required by this section shall be continuous between elements providing lateral support for the wall. Reinforcement in the wall of the *story* above shall be continuous with the reinforcement in the wall of the *story* below, or the foundation wall, if applicable. Lap splices, where required, shall comply with Section R608.5.4.3 and Figure R608.5.4(1). Where the above-grade wall is supported by a monolithic slab-on-ground and footing, dowel bars with a size and spacing to match the vertical above-grade concrete wall reinforcement shall be embedded in the monolithic slab-on-ground and footing the distance required to develop the dowel bar in tension in accordance with Section R608.5.4.4 and Figure R608.5.4(2) and lap-spliced with the above-grade wall reinforcement in accordance with Section R608.5.4.3 and Figure R608.5.4(1).

Where a construction joint in the wall is located below the level of the floor and less than the distance required to develop the bar in tension, the distance required to develop the bar in tension shall be measured from the top of the concrete below the joint. See Section R608.5.5.

Exception: Where reinforcement in the wall above cannot be made continuous with the reinforcement in the wall below, the bottom of the reinforcement in the wall above shall be terminated in accordance with one of the following:

1. Extend below the top of the floor the distance required to develop the bar in tension in accordance with Section R608.5.4.4 and Figure R608.5.4(2).

2. Lap-spliced in accordance with Section R608.5.4.3 and Figure R608.5.4(1) with a dowel bar that extends into the wall below the distance required to develop the bar in tension in accordance with Section R608.5.4.4 and Figure R608.5.4(2).

R608.6.4 Termination of reinforcement. Where indicated in Items 1 through 3, vertical wall reinforcement in the top-most *story* with concrete walls shall be terminated with a 90-degree (1.57 rad) standard hook complying with Section R608.5.4.5 and Figure R608.5.4(3).

1. Vertical bars adjacent to door and window openings required by Section R608.8.1.2.

2. Vertical bars at the ends of required solid wall segments (see Section R608.7.2.2.2).

3. Vertical bars (other than end bars, see Item 2) used as shear reinforcement in required solid wall segments where the reduction factor for design strength, R_3, used is based on the wall having horizontal and vertical shear reinforcement (see Section R608.7.2.2.3).

The bar extension of the hook shall be oriented parallel to the horizontal wall reinforcement and be within 4 inches (102 mm) of the top of the wall.

Horizontal reinforcement shall be continuous around the building corners by bending one of the bars and lap-splicing it with the bar in the other wall in accordance with Section R608.5.4.3 and Figure R608.5.4(1).

In required solid wall segments where the reduction factor for design strength, R_3, is based on the wall having horizontal and vertical shear reinforcement in accordance with Section R608.7.2.2.1, horizontal wall reinforcement shall be terminated with a standard hook complying with Section R608.5.4.5 and Figure R608.5.4(3) or in a lap-splice, except at corners where the reinforcement shall be continuous as required.

Exception: In lieu of bending horizontal reinforcement at corners, separate bent reinforcing bars shall be permitted provided that the bent bar is lap-spliced with the horizontal reinforcement in both walls in accordance with Section R608.5.4.3 and Figure R608.5.4(1).

R608.6.5 Location of reinforcement in wall. Except for vertical reinforcement at the ends of required solid wall segments, which shall be located as required by Section R608.7.2.2.2, the location of the vertical reinforcement shall not vary from the center of the wall by more than the greater of 10 percent of the wall thickness and $^3/_8$-inch (10 mm). Horizontal and vertical reinforcement shall be located to provide not less than the minimum cover required by Section R608.5.4.1.

R608.7 Solid walls for resistance to lateral forces.

R608.7.1 Length of solid wall. Each exterior wall line in each *story* shall have a total length of solid wall required by Section R608.7.1.1. A solid wall is a section of flat, waffle-grid or screen-grid wall, extending the full *story height* without openings or penetrations, except those permitted by Section R608.7.2. Solid wall segments that contribute to the total length of solid wall shall comply with Section R608.7.2.

R608.7.1.1 Length of solid wall for wind. Buildings shall have solid walls in each exterior endwall line (the side of a building that is parallel to the span of the roof or floor framing) and sidewall line (the side of a building that is perpendicular to the span of the roof or floor framing) to resist lateral in-plane wind forces. The site-appropriate basic wind speed and exposure category shall be used in Tables R608.7(1A) through (1C) to determine the unreduced total length, *UR*, of solid wall required in each exterior endwall line and sidewall line. For buildings with a mean roof height of less than 35 feet (10 668 mm), the unreduced values determined from Tables R608.7(1A) though (1C) are permitted to be reduced by multiplying by the applicable factor, R_1, from Table R608.7(2); however, reduced values shall be not less than the minimum values in Tables R608.7(1A) through (1C). Where the floor-to-ceiling height of a *story* is less than 10 feet (3048 mm), the unreduced values determined from Tables R608.7(1A) through (1C), including minimum values, are permitted to be reduced by multiplying by the applicable factor, R_2, from Table R608.7(3). To account for different design strengths than assumed in determining the values in Tables R608.7(1A) through (1C), the unreduced lengths determined from Tables R608.7(1A) through (1C), including minimum values, are permitted to be reduced by multiplying by the applicable factor, R_3, from Table R608.7(4). The reductions permitted by Tables R608.7(2), R608.7(3) and R608.7(4) are cumulative.

The total length of solid wall segments, *TL*, in a wall line that comply with the minimum length requirements of Section R608.7.2.1 [see Figure R608.7(1)] shall be equal to or greater than the product of the unreduced length of solid wall from Tables R608.7(1A) through (1C), *UR* and the applicable reduction factors, if any, from Tables R608.7(2), R608.7(3) and R608.7(4) as indicated by Equation R6-1.

$$TL \geq R_1 \times R_2 \times R_3 \times UR \qquad \text{(Equation R6-1)}$$

where:

TL = Total length of solid wall segments in a wall line that comply with Section R608.7.2.1 [see Figure R608.7(1)].

R_1 = 1.0 or reduction factor for mean roof height from Table R608.7(2).

R_2 = 1.0 or reduction factor for floor-to-ceiling wall height from Table R608.7(3).

R_3 = 1.0 or reduction factor for design strength from Table R608.7(4).

UR = Unreduced length of solid wall from Tables R608.7(1A) through (1C).

The total length of solid wall in a wall line, *TL*, shall be not less than that provided by two solid wall segments complying with the minimum length requirements of Section R608.7.2.1.

To facilitate determining the required wall thickness, wall type, number and *grade* of vertical bars at each end of each solid wall segment, and whether shear reinforcement is required, use of Equation R6-2 is permitted.

$$R \leq \frac{TL}{R_1 \times R_2 \times UR} \qquad \text{(Equation R6-2)}$$

After determining the maximum permitted value of the reduction factor for design strength, R_3, in accordance with Equation R6-2, select a wall type from Table R608.7(4) with R_3 less than or equal to the value calculated.

R608.7.2 Solid wall segments. Solid wall segments that contribute to the required length of solid wall shall comply with this section. Reinforcement shall be provided in accordance with Section R608.7.2.2 and Table R608.7(4). Solid wall segments shall extend the full story-height without openings, other than openings for the utilities and other building services passing through the wall. In flat walls and waffle-grid walls, such openings shall have an area of less than 30 square inches (19 355 mm^2) without any dimension exceeding $6^1/_4$ inches (159 mm), and shall not be located within 6 inches (152 mm) of the side edges of the solid wall segment. In screen-grid walls, such openings shall be located in the portion of the solid wall segment between horizontal and vertical cores of concrete and

opening size and location are not restricted provided there is not any concrete removed.

R608.7.2.1 Minimum length of solid wall segment and maximum spacing. Only solid wall segments equal to or greater than 24 inches (610 mm) in length shall be included in the total length of solid wall required by Section R608.7.1. In addition, not more than two solid wall segments equal to or greater than 24 inches (610 mm) in length and less than 48 inches (1219 mm) in length shall be included in the required total length of solid wall. The maximum clear opening width shall be 18 feet (5486 mm). See Figure R608.7(1).

R608.7.2.2 Reinforcement in solid wall segments.

R608.7.2.2.1 Horizontal shear reinforcement. Where reduction factors for design strength, R_3, from Table R608.7(4) based on horizontal and vertical shear reinforcement being provided are used, solid wall segments shall have horizontal reinforcement consisting of minimum No. 4 bars. Horizontal shear reinforcement shall be the same grade of steel required for the vertical reinforcement at the ends of solid wall segments by Section R608.7.2.2.2.

The spacing of horizontal reinforcement shall not exceed the smaller of one-half the length of the solid wall segment, minus 2 inches (51 mm), and 18 inches (457 mm). Horizontal shear reinforcement shall terminate in accordance with Section R608.6.4.

R608.7.2.2.2 Vertical reinforcement. Vertical reinforcement applicable to the reduction factor(s) for design strength, R_3, from Table R608.7(4) that is used, shall be located at each end of each solid wall segment in accordance with the applicable detail in Figure R608.7(2). The No. 4 vertical bar required on each side of an opening by Section R608.8.1.2 is permitted to be used as reinforcement at the ends of solid wall segments where installed in accordance with the applicable detail in Figure R608.7(2). There shall be not less than two No. 4 bars at each end of solid wall segments located as required by the applicable detail in Figure R608.7(2). One of the bars at each end of solid wall segments shall be deemed to meet the requirements for vertical wall reinforcement required by Section R608.6.

The vertical wall reinforcement at each end of each solid wall segment shall be developed below the bottom of the adjacent wall opening [see Figure R608.7(3)] by one of the following methods:

1. Where the wall height below the bottom of the adjacent opening is equal to or greater than 22 inches (559 mm) for No. 4 or 28 inches (711 mm) for No. 5 vertical wall reinforcement, reinforcement around openings in accordance with Section R608.8.1 shall be sufficient.

2. Where the wall height below the bottom of the adjacent opening is less than required by Item 1, the vertical wall reinforcement adjacent to the opening shall extend into the footing far

TABLE R608.7(1A)
UNREDUCED LENGTH, *UR*, OF SOLID WALL REQUIRED IN EACH EXTERIOR ENDWALL
FOR WIND PERPENDICULAR TO RIDGE ONE STORY OR TOP STORY OF TWO STORY[a, c, d, e, f, g]

SIDEWALL LENGTH (feet)	ENDWALL LENGTH (feet)	ROOF SLOPE	UNREDUCED LENGTH, *UR*, OF SOLID WALL REQUIRED IN ENDWALLS FOR WIND PERPENDICULAR TO RIDGE (feet)						
			Basic Wind Speed (mph) Exposure						
			115B	120B	130B	140B	150B	160B	Minimum[b]
			—	—	110C	119C	127C	136C	
			—	—	—	110D	117D	125D	
15	15	< 1:12	1.03	1.12	1.32	1.53	1.76	2.00	0.92
		5:12	1.43	1.56	1.83	2.12	2.43	2.77	1.15
		7:12	2.00	2.18	2.56	2.97	3.41	3.88	1.25
		12:12	3.20	3.48	4.09	4.74	5.44	6.19	1.54
	30	< 1:12	1.03	1.12	1.32	1.53	1.76	2.00	0.98
		5:12	1.43	1.56	1.83	2.12	2.43	2.77	1.43
		7:12	2.78	3.03	3.56	4.13	4.74	5.39	1.64
		12:12	5.17	5.63	6.61	7.67	8.80	10.01	2.21
	45	< 1:12	1.03	1.12	1.32	1.53	1.76	2.00	1.04
		5:12	1.43	1.56	1.83	2.12	2.43	2.77	1.72
		7:12	3.57	3.88	4.56	5.28	6.07	6.90	2.03
		12:12	7.15	7.78	9.13	10.59	12.16	13.84	2.89
	60	< 1:12	1.03	1.12	1.32	1.53	1.76	2.00	1.09
		5:12	1.43	1.56	1.83	2.12	2.43	2.77	2.01
		7:12	4.35	4.73	5.55	6.44	7.39	8.41	2.42
		12:12	9.12	9.93	11.66	13.52	15.52	17.66	3.57
30	15	< 1:12	1.84	2.01	2.35	2.73	3.13	3.57	1.82
		5:12	2.56	2.78	3.27	3.79	4.35	4.95	2.23
		7:12	3.61	3.93	4.61	5.34	6.13	6.98	2.42
		12:12	5.61	6.10	7.16	8.31	9.54	10.85	2.93
	30	< 1:12	1.84	2.01	2.35	2.73	3.13	3.57	1.93
		5:12	2.56	2.78	3.27	3.79	4.35	4.95	2.75
		7:12	4.92	5.35	6.28	7.29	8.37	9.52	3.12
		12:12	8.92	9.71	11.39	13.22	15.17	17.26	4.14
	45	< 1:12	1.84	2.01	2.35	2.73	3.13	3.57	2.03
		5:12	2.56	2.78	3.27	3.79	4.35	4.95	3.26
		7:12	6.23	6.78	7.96	9.23	10.60	12.06	3.82
		12:12	12.23	13.31	15.63	18.12	20.80	23.67	5.36
	60	< 1:12	1.84	2.01	2.35	2.73	3.13	3.57	2.14
		5:12	2.56	2.78	3.27	3.79	4.35	4.95	3.78
		7:12	7.54	8.21	9.64	11.17	12.83	14.60	4.52
		12:12	15.54	16.92	19.86	23.03	26.44	30.08	6.57

(continued)

TABLE R608.7(1A)—continued
UNREDUCED LENGTH, *UR*, OF SOLID WALL REQUIRED IN EACH EXTERIOR ENDWALL FOR WIND PERPENDICULAR TO RIDGE ONE STORY OR TOP STORY OF TWO STORY[a, c, d, e, f, g]

SIDEWALL LENGTH (feet)	ENDWALL LENGTH (feet)	ROOF SLOPE	UNREDUCED LENGTH, *UR*, OF SOLID WALL REQUIRED IN ENDWALLS FOR WIND PERPENDICULAR TO RIDGE (feet)						
			Basic Wind Speed (mph) Exposure						
			115B	120B	130B	140B	150B	160B	Minimum[b]
			—	—	110C	119C	127C	136C	
			—	—	—	110D	117D	125D	
60	15	< 1:12	3.42	3.72	4.36	5.06	5.81	6.61	3.63
		5:12	4.75	5.17	6.06	7.03	8.07	9.19	4.40
		7:12	6.76	7.36	8.64	10.02	11.51	13.09	4.75
		12:12	10.35	11.27	13.23	15.34	17.61	20.04	5.71
	30	< 1:12	3.42	3.72	4.36	5.06	5.81	6.61	3.83
		5:12	4.75	5.17	6.06	7.03	8.07	9.19	5.37
		7:12	9.12	9.93	11.66	13.52	15.52	17.66	6.07
		12:12	16.30	17.75	20.83	24.16	27.73	31.55	8.00
	45	< 1:12	3.55	3.87	4.54	5.27	6.05	6.88	4.03
		5:12	4.94	5.37	6.31	7.31	8.40	9.55	6.34
		7:12	11.71	12.75	14.97	17.36	19.93	22.67	7.39
		12:12	22.70	24.71	29.00	33.64	38.62	43.94	10.29
	60	< 1:12	3.68	4.01	4.71	5.46	6.27	7.13	4.23
		5:12	5.11	5.57	6.54	7.58	8.70	9.90	7.31
		7:12	14.38	15.66	18.37	21.31	24.46	27.83	8.71
		12:12	29.30	31.90	37.44	43.42	49.85	56.72	12.57

For SI: 1 inch = 25.4 mm, 1 foot = 304.8 mm, 1 mile per hour = 0.447 m/s, 1 pound-force per linear foot = 0.146 kN/m, 1 pound per square foot = 47.88 Pa.

a. Tabulated lengths were derived by calculating design wind pressures in accordance with Figure 28.4-1 of ASCE 7 for a building with a mean roof height of 35 feet, topographic factor, K_{zt}, equal to 1.0, and Risk Category II. For wind perpendicular to the ridge, the effects of a 2-foot overhang on each endwall are included. The design pressures were used to calculate forces to be resisted by solid wall segments in each. The forces to be resisted by each wall line were then divided by the default design strength of 840 pounds per linear foot of length to determine the unreduced length, *UR*, of solid wall length required in each endwall. The actual mean roof height of the building shall not exceed the least horizontal dimension of the building.

b. Tabulated lengths in the "minimum" column are based on the requirement of Section 28.4.4 of ASCE 7 that the main windforce-resisting system be designed for a minimum pressure of 16 psf multiplied by the wall area of the building and 8 psf multiplied by the roof area of the building projected onto a vertical plane normal to the assumed wind direction. Tabulated lengths in shaded cells are less than the "minimum" value. Where the minimum controls, it is permitted to be reduced in accordance with Notes c, d and e. See Section R608.7.1.1.

c. For buildings with a mean roof height of less than 35 feet, tabulated lengths are permitted to be reduced by multiplying by the appropriate factor, R_1, from Table R608.7(2). The reduced length shall be not less than the "minimum" value shown in the table.

d. Tabulated lengths for "one story or top story of two story" are based on a floor-to-ceiling height of 10 feet. Tabulated lengths for "first story of two story" are based on floor-to-ceiling heights of 10 feet each for the first and second story. For floor-to-ceiling heights less than assumed, use the lengths in this table or Table R608.7 (1B) or (1C), or multiply the value in the table by the reduction factor, R_2, from Table R608.7(3).

e. Tabulated lengths are based on the default design shear strength of 840 pounds per linear foot of solid wall segment. The tabulated lengths are permitted to be reduced by multiplying by the applicable reduction factor for design strength, R_3, from Table R608.7(4).

f. The reduction factors, R_1, R_2 and R_3, in Tables R608.7(2), R608.7(3), and R608.7(4), respectively, are permitted to be compounded, subject to the limitations of Note b. However, the minimum number and minimum length of solid wall segments in each wall line shall comply with Sections R608.7.1 and R608.7.2.1, respectively.

g. For intermediate values of sidewall length, endwall length, roof slope and basic wind speed, use the next higher value, or determine by interpolation.

TABLE R608.7(1B)
UNREDUCED LENGTH, *UR*, OF SOLID WALL REQUIRED IN EACH EXTERIOR ENDWALL
FOR WIND PERPENDICULAR TO RIDGE FIRST STORY OF TWO STORY[a, c, d, e, f, g]

SIDEWALL LENGTH (feet)	ENDWALL LENGTH (feet)	ROOF SLOPE	UNREDUCED LENGTH, *UR*, OF SOLID WALL REQUIRED IN ENDWALLS FOR WIND PERPENDICULAR TO RIDGE (feet)						
			Basic Wind Speed (mph) Exposure						
			115B	120B	130B	140B	150B	160B	
			—	—	110C	119C	127C	136C	Minimum[b]
			—	—	—	110D	117D	125D	
15	15	< 1:12	2.98	3.25	3.81	4.42	5.07	5.77	2.54
		5:12	4.13	4.50	5.28	6.12	7.03	8.00	2.76
		7:12	4.31	4.70	5.51	6.39	7.34	8.35	2.87
		12:12	5.51	6.00	7.04	8.16	9.37	10.66	3.15
	30	< 1:12	2.98	3.25	3.81	4.42	5.07	5.77	2.59
		5:12	4.13	4.50	5.28	6.12	7.03	8.00	3.05
		7:12	5.09	5.55	6.51	7.55	8.67	9.86	3.26
		12:12	7.48	8.15	9.56	11.09	12.73	14.49	3.83
	45	< 1:12	2.98	3.25	3.81	4.42	5.07	5.77	2.65
		5:12	4.13	4.50	5.28	6.12	7.03	8.00	3.34
		7:12	5.88	6.40	7.51	8.71	10.00	11.37	3.65
		12:12	9.46	10.30	12.09	14.02	16.09	18.31	4.51
	60	< 1:12	2.98	3.25	3.81	4.42	5.07	5.77	2.71
		5:12	4.13	4.50	5.28	6.12	7.03	8.00	3.63
		7:12	6.66	7.25	8.51	9.87	11.32	12.89	4.04
		12:12	11.43	12.45	14.61	16.94	19.45	22.13	5.19
30	15	< 1:12	5.32	5.79	6.80	7.89	9.05	10.30	5.06
		5:12	7.39	8.04	9.44	10.95	12.57	14.30	5.47
		7:12	7.94	8.65	10.15	11.77	13.51	15.37	5.65
		12:12	9.94	10.82	12.70	14.73	16.91	19.24	6.17
	30	< 1:12	5.32	5.79	6.80	7.89	9.05	10.30	5.16
		5:12	7.39	8.04	9.44	10.95	12.57	14.30	5.98
		7:12	9.25	10.07	11.82	13.71	15.74	17.91	6.35
		12:12	13.25	14.43	16.93	19.64	22.54	25.65	7.38
	45	< 1:12	5.32	5.79	6.80	7.89	9.05	10.30	5.27
		5:12	7.39	8.04	9.44	10.95	12.57	14.30	6.50
		7:12	10.56	11.50	13.50	15.65	17.97	20.45	7.06
		12:12	16.56	18.03	21.16	24.55	28.18	32.06	8.60
	60	< 1:12	5.32	5.79	6.80	7.89	9.05	10.30	5.38
		5:12	7.39	8.04	9.44	10.95	12.57	14.30	7.01
		7:12	11.87	12.93	15.17	17.60	20.20	22.98	7.76
		12:12	19.87	21.64	25.40	29.45	33.81	38.47	9.81

(continued)

TABLE R608.7(1B)—continued
UNREDUCED LENGTH, *UR*, OF SOLID WALL REQUIRED IN EACH EXTERIOR ENDWALL
FOR WIND PERPENDICULAR TO RIDGE FIRST STORY OF TWO STORY[a, c, d, e, f, g]

SIDEWALL LENGTH (feet)	ENDWALL LENGTH (feet)	ROOF SLOPE	UNREDUCED LENGTH, *UR*, OF SOLID WALL REQUIRED IN ENDWALLS FOR WIND PERPENDICULAR TO RIDGE (feet)						
			Basic Wind Speed (mph) Exposure						
			115B	120B	130B	140B	150B	160B	
			—	—	110C	119C	127C	136C	Minimum[b]
			—	—	—	110D	117D	125D	
60	15	< 1:12	9.87	10.74	12.61	14.62	16.79	19.10	10.10
		5:12	13.71	14.93	17.52	20.32	23.33	26.54	10.87
		7:12	15.08	16.42	19.27	22.35	25.66	29.20	11.22
		12:12	18.67	20.33	23.86	27.67	31.77	36.14	12.19
	30	< 1:12	9.87	10.74	12.61	14.62	16.79	19.10	10.30
		5:12	13.71	14.93	17.52	20.32	23.33	26.54	11.85
		7:12	17.44	18.99	22.29	25.85	29.67	33.76	12.54
		12:12	24.62	26.81	31.46	36.49	41.89	47.66	14.48
	45	< 1:12	10.27	11.18	13.12	15.21	17.47	19.87	10.50
		5:12	14.26	15.52	18.22	21.13	24.26	27.60	12.82
		7:12	20.21	22.01	25.83	29.95	34.39	39.12	13.86
		12:12	31.20	33.97	39.87	46.23	53.07	60.39	16.76
	60	< 1:12	10.64	11.59	13.60	15.77	18.11	20.60	10.70
		5:12	14.77	16.09	18.88	21.90	25.14	28.60	13.79
		7:12	23.05	25.09	29.45	34.15	39.21	44.61	15.18
		12:12	37.97	41.34	48.52	56.27	64.60	73.49	19.05

For SI: 1 inch = 25.4 mm, 1 foot = 304.8 mm, 1 mile per hour = 0.447 m/s, 1 pound force per linear foot = 0.146 kN/m, 1 pound per square foot = 47.88 Pa.

a. Tabulated lengths were derived by calculating design wind pressures in accordance with Figure 28.4-1 of ASCE 7 for a building with a mean roof height of 35 feet, topographic factor, K_{zt}, equal to 1.0, and Risk Category II. For wind perpendicular to the ridge, the effects of a 2-foot overhang on each endwall are included. The design pressures were used to calculate forces to be resisted by solid wall segments in each endwall. The forces to be resisted by each wall line were then divided by the default design strength of 840 pounds per linear foot of length to determine the unreduced length, *UR*, of solid wall length required in each endwall. The actual mean roof height of the building shall not exceed the least horizontal dimension of the building.

b. Tabulated lengths in the "minimum" column are based on the requirement of Section 28.4.4 of ASCE 7 that the main windforce-resisting system be designed for a minimum pressure of 1016 psf multiplied by the wall area of the building and 8 psf multiplied by the roof area of the building projected onto a vertical plane normal to the assumed wind direction. Tabulated lengths in shaded cells are less than the "minimum" value. Where the minimum controls, it is permitted to be reduced in accordance with Notes c, d and e. See Section R608.7.1.1.

c. For buildings with a mean roof height of less than 35 feet, tabulated lengths are permitted to be reduced by multiplying by the appropriate factor, R_1, from Table R608.7(2). The reduced length shall be not less than the "minimum" value shown in the table.

d. Tabulated lengths for "one story or top story of two story" are based on a floor-to-ceiling height of 10 feet. Tabulated lengths for "first story of two story" are based on floor-to-ceiling heights of 10 feet each for the first and second story. For floor-to-ceiling heights less than assumed, use the lengths in this table or Table R608.7(1A) or (1C), or multiply the value in the table by the reduction factor, R_2, from Table R608.7(3).

e. Tabulated lengths are based on the default design shear strength of 840 pounds per linear foot of solid wall segment. The tabulated lengths are permitted to be reduced by multiplying by the applicable reduction factor for design strength, R_3, from Table R608.7(4).

f. The reduction factors, R_1, R_2 and R_3, in Tables R608.7(2), R608.7(3), and R608.7(4), respectively, are permitted to be compounded, subject to the limitations of Note b. However, the minimum number and minimum length of solid wall segments in each wall line shall comply with Sections R608.7.1 and R608.7.2.1, respectively.

g. For intermediate values of sidewall length, endwall length, roof slope and basic wind speed, use the next higher value, or determine by interpolation.

TABLE R608.7(1C)
UNREDUCED LENGTH, *UR*, OF SOLID WALL REQUIRED IN EACH
EXTERIOR SIDEWALL FOR WIND PARALLEL TO RIDGE[a, c, d, e, f, g]

SIDEWALL LENGTH (feet)	ENDWALL LENGTH (feet)	ROOF SLOPE	UNREDUCED LENGTH, *UR*, OF SOLID WALL REQUIRED IN SIDEWALLS FOR WIND PARALLEL TO RIDGE (feet)						
			Basic Wind Speed (mph) Exposure						
			115B	120B	130B	140B	150B	160B	
			—	—	110C	119C	127C	136C	Minimum[b]
			—	—	—	110D	117D	125D	
			One story or top story of two story						
< 30	15	< 1:12	1.08	1.18	1.39	161	1.84	2.10	0.90
		5:12	1.29	1.40	1.65	1.91	2.19	2.49	1.08
		7:12	1.38	1.50	1.76	2.04	2.35	2.67	1.17
		12:12	1.63	1.78	2.09	2.42	2.78	3.16	1.39
	30	< 1:12	2.02	2.20	2.59	3.00	3.44	3.92	1.90
		5:12	2.73	2.97	3.48	4.04	4.64	5.28	2.62
		7:12	3.05	3.32	3.89	4.51	5.18	5.89	2.95
		12:12	3.93	4.27	5.02	5.82	6.68	7.60	3.86
	45	< 1:12	3.03	3.30	3.87	4.49	5.15	5.86	2.99
		5:12	4.55	4.96	5.82	6.75	7.74	8.81	4.62
		7:12	5.24	5.71	6.70	7.77	8.92	10.15	5.36
		12:12	7.16	7.79	9.14	10.61	12.17	13.85	7.39
	60	< 1:12	4.11	4.47	5.25	6.09	6.99	7.96	4.18
		5:12	6.78	7.39	8.67	10.05	11.54	13.13	7.07
		7:12	8.00	8.71	10.22	11.85	13.61	15.48	8.38
		12:12	11.35	12.36	14.51	16.82	19.31	21.97	12.00
60	45	< 1:12	3.17	3.46	4.06	4.70	5.40	6.14	2.99
		5:12	4.75	5.18	6.07	7.04	8.09	9.20	4.62
		7:12	5.47	5.96	6.99	8.11	9.31	10.59	5.36
		12:12	7.45	8.11	9.52	11.04	12.68	14.43	7.39
	60	< 1:12	4.41	4.81	5.64	6.54	7.51	8.54	4.18
		5:12	7.22	7.86	9.23	10.70	12.29	13.98	7.07
		7:12	8.50	9.25	10.86	12.59	14.46	16.45	8.38
		12:12	12.02	13.09	15.36	17.81	20.45	23.27	12.00

(continued)

TABLE R608.7(1C)—continued
UNREDUCED LENGTH, *UR*, OF SOLID WALL REQUIRED IN EACH
EXTERIOR SIDEWALL FOR WIND PARALLEL TO RIDGE[a, c, d, e, f, g]

SIDEWALL LENGTH (feet)	ENDWALL LENGTH (feet)	ROOF SLOPE	UNREDUCED LENGTH, *UR*, OF SOLID WALL REQUIRED IN SIDEWALLS FOR WIND PARALLEL TO RIDGE (feet)						Minimum[b]
			Basic Wind Speed Exposure (mph)						
			115B	120B	130B	140B	150B	160B	
			—	—	110C	119C	127C	136C	
			—	—	—	110D	117D	125D	
			First story of two story						
< 30	15	< 1:12	3.03	3.30	3.88	4.49	5.16	5.87	2.52
		5:12	3.24	3.52	4.14	4.80	5.51	6.26	2.70
		7:12	3.33	3.62	4.25	4.93	5.66	6.44	2.79
		12:12	3.58	3.90	4.58	5.31	6.10	6.94	3.01
	30	< 1:12	5.50	5.99	7.03	8.16	9.36	10.65	5.14
		5:12	6.21	6.76	7.93	9.20	10.56	12.01	5.86
		7:12	6.52	7.10	8.34	9.67	11.10	12.63	6.19
		12:12	7.41	8.06	9.46	10.97	12.60	14.33	7.10
	45	< 1:12	8.00	8.71	10.22	11.85	13.61	15.48	7.85
		5:12	9.52	10.37	12.17	14.11	16.20	18.43	9.48
		7:12	10.21	11.12	13.05	15.14	17.38	19.77	10.21
		12:12	12.13	13.20	15.50	17.97	20.63	23.47	12.25
	60	< 1:12	10.56	11.50	13.50	15.65	17.97	20.44	10.65
		5:12	13.24	14.41	16.91	19.62	22.52	25.62	13.54
		7:12	14.45	15.73	18.46	21.41	24.58	27.97	14.85
		12:12	17.80	19.38	22.75	26.38	30.29	34.46	18.48
60	45	< 1:12	8.39	9.14	10.72	12.44	14.28	16.25	7.85
		5:12	9.97	10.86	12.74	14.78	16.97	19.30	9.48
		7:12	10.69	11.64	13.66	15.84	18.19	20.69	10.21
		12:12	12.67	13.80	16.19	18.78	21.56	24.53	12.25
	60	< 1:12	11.37	12.38	14.53	16.85	19.35	22.01	10.65
		5:12	14.18	15.44	18.12	21.02	24.13	27.45	13.54
		7:12	15.46	16.83	19.75	22.91	26.29	29.92	14.85
		12:12	18.98	20.66	24.25	28.13	32.29	36.74	18.48

For SI: 1 inch = 25.4 mm, 1 foot = 304.8 mm, 1 mile per hour = 0.447 m/s, 1 pound-force per linear foot = 0.146 kN/m, 1 pound per square foot = 47.88 Pa.

a. Tabulated lengths were derived by calculating design wind pressures in accordance with Figure 28.4-1 of ASCE 7 for a building with a mean roof height of 35 feet, topographic factor, K_{zt}, equal to 1.0, and Risk Category II. The design pressures were used to calculate forces to be resisted by solid wall segments in each sidewall. The forces to be resisted by each wall line were then divided by the default design strength of 840 pounds per linear foot of length to determine the unreduced length, *UR*, of solid wall length required in each sidewall. The actual mean roof height of the building shall not exceed the least horizontal dimension of the building.

b. Tabulated lengths in the "minimum" column are based on the requirement of Section 28.4.4 of ASCE 7 that the main windforce-resisting system be designed for a minimum pressure of 16 psf multiplied by the wall area of the building and 8 psf multiplied by the roof area of the building projected onto a vertical plane normal to the assumed wind direction. Tabulated lengths in shaded cells are less than the "minimum" value. Where the minimum controls, it is permitted to be reduced in accordance with Notes c, d and e. See Section R608.7.1.1.

c. For buildings with a mean roof height of less than 35 feet, tabulated lengths are permitted to be reduced by multiplying by the appropriate factor, R_1, from Table R608.7(2). The reduced length shall be not less than the "minimum" value shown in the table.

d. Tabulated lengths for "one story or top story of two story" are based on a floor-to-ceiling height of 10 feet. Tabulated lengths for "first story of two story" are based on floor-to-ceiling heights of 10 feet each for the first and second story. For floor-to-ceiling heights less than assumed, use the lengths in this table or Table R608.7(1A) or (1B), or multiply the value in the table by the reduction factor, R_2, from Table R608.7(3).

e. Tabulated lengths are based on the default design shear strength of 840 pounds per linear foot of solid wall segment. The tabulated lengths are permitted to be reduced by multiplying by the applicable reduction factor for design strength, R_3, from Table R608.7(4).

f. The reduction factors, R_1, R_2 and R_3, in Tables R608.7(2), R608.7(3), and R608.7(4), respectively, are permitted to be compounded, subject to the limitations of Note b. However, the minimum number and minimum length of solid walls segments in each wall line shall comply with Sections R608.7.1 and R608.7.2.1, respectively.

g. For intermediate values of sidewall length, endwall length, roof slope and basic wind speed, use the next higher value, or determine by interpolation.

TABLE R608.7(2)
REDUCTION FACTOR, R_1, FOR BUILDINGS WITH MEAN ROOF HEIGHT LESS THAN 35 FEET[a]

MEAN ROOF HEIGHT[b, c] (feet)	REDUCTION FACTOR R_1, FOR MEAN ROOF HEIGHT		
	Exposure category		
	B	C	D
< 15	0.96	0.84	0.87
20	0.96	0.89	0.91
25	0.96	0.93	0.94
30	0.96	0.97	0.98
35	1.00	1.00	1.00

For SI: 1 foot = 304.8 mm, 1 degree = 0.0175 rad.

a. See Section R608.7.1.1 and Note c to Table R608.7(1A) for application of reduction factors in this table. This reduction is not permitted for "minimum" values.

b. For intermediate values of mean roof height, use the factor for the next greater height, or determine by interpolation.

c. Mean roof height is the average of the roof eave height and height of the highest point on the roof surface, except that for roof slopes of less than or equal to $2^1/_8$:12 (10 degrees), the mean roof height is permitted to be taken as the roof eave height.

TABLE R608.7(3)
REDUCTION FACTOR, R_2, FOR FLOOR-TO-CEILING WALL HEIGHTS LESS THAN 10 FEET[a, b]

STORY UNDER CONSIDERATION	FLOOR-TO-CEILING HEIGHT[c] (feet)	ENDWALL LENGTH (feet)	ROOF SLOPE	REDUCTION FACTOR, R_2
Endwalls—for wind perpendicular to ridge				
One story or top story of two story	8	15	< 5:12	0.83
			7:12	0.90
			12:12	0.94
		60	< 5:12	0.83
			7:12	0.95
			12:12	0.98
First story of two story	16 combined first and second story	15	< 5:12	0.83
			7:12	0.86
			12:12	0.89
		60	< 5:12	0.83
			7:12	0.91
			12:12	0.95
Sidewalls—for wind parallel to ridge				
One story or top story of two story	8	15	< 1:12	0.84
			5:12	0.87
			7:12	0.88
			12:12	0.89
		60	< 1:12	0.86
			5:12	0.92
			7:12	0.93
			12:12	0.95
First story of two story	16 combined first and second story	15	< 1:12	0.83
			5:12	0.84
			7:12	0.85
			12:12	0.86
		60	< 1:12	0.84
			5:12	0.87
			7:12	0.88
			12:12	0.90

For SI: 1 foot = 304.8 mm.

a. See Section R608.7.1.1 and Note d to Table R608.7(1A) for application of reduction factors in this table.

b. For intermediate values of endwall length and roof slope, use the next higher value or determine by interpolation.

c. Tabulated values in Table R608.7(1A) and (1C) for "one story or top story of two story" are based on a floor-to-ceiling height of 10 feet. Tabulated values in Table R608.7(1B) and (1C) for "first story of two story" are based on floor-to-ceiling heights of 10 feet each for the first and second story. For floor-to-ceiling heights between those shown in this table and those assumed in Table R608.7(1A), (1B) or (1C), use the solid wall lengths in Table R608.7(1A), (1B) or (1C), or determine the reduction factor by interpolating between 1.0 and the factor shown in this table.

TABLE R608.7(4)
REDUCTION FACTOR FOR DESIGN STRENGTH, R_3, FOR FLAT, WAFFLE- AND SCREEN-GRID WALLS[a, c]

NOMINAL THICKNESS OF WALL (inches)	VERTICAL BARS AT EACH END OF SOLID WALL SEGMENT		VERTICAL REINFORCEMENT LAYOUT DETAIL [see Figure R608.7(2)]	REDUCTION FACTOR, R_3, FOR LENGTH OF SOLID WALL			
				Horizontal and vertical shear reinforcement provided			
				No		Yes[d]	
	Number of bars	Bar size		40,000[b]	60,000[b]	40,000[b]	60,000[b]
Flat walls							
4	2	4	1	0.74	0.61	0.74	0.50
	3	4	2	0.61	0.61	0.52	0.27
	2	5	1	0.61	0.61	0.48	0.25
	3	5	2	0.61	0.61	0.26	0.18
6	2	4	3	0.70	0.48	0.70	0.48
	3	4	4	0.49	0.38	0.49	0.33
	2	5	3	0.46	0.38	0.46	0.31
	3	5	4	0.38	0.38	0.32	0.16
8	2	4	3	0.70	0.47	0.70	0.47
	3	4	5	0.47	0.32	0.47	0.32
	2	5	3	0.45	0.31	0.45	0.31
	4	4	6	0.36	0.28	0.36	0.25
	3	5	5	0.31	0.28	0.31	0.16
	4	5	6	0.28	0.28	0.24	0.12
10	2	4	3	0.70	0.47	0.70	0.47
	2	5	3	0.45	0.30	0.45	0.30
	4	4	7	0.36	0.25	0.36	0.25
	6	4	8	0.25	0.22	0.25	0.13
	4	5	7	0.24	0.22	0.24	0.12
	6	5	8	0.22	0.22	0.12	0.08
Waffle-grid walls[e]							
6	2	4	3	0.78	0.78	0.70	0.48
	3	4	4	0.78	0.78	0.49	0.25
	2	5	3	0.78	0.78	0.46	0.23
	3	5	4	0.78	0.78	0.24	0.16
8	2	4	3	0.78	0.78	0.70	0.47
	3	4	5	0.78	0.78	0.47	0.24
	2	5	3	0.78	0.78	0.45	0.23
	4	4	6	0.78	0.78	0.36	0.18
	3	5	5	0.78	0.78	0.23	0.16
	4	5	6	0.78	0.78	0.18	0.13
Screen-grid walls[e]							
6	2	4	3	0.93	0.93	0.70	0.48
	3	4	4	0.93	0.93	0.49	0.25
	2	5	3	0.93	0.93	0.46	0.23
	3	5	4	0.93	0.93	0.24	0.16

For SI: 1 inch = 25.4 mm, 1,000 pounds per square inch = 6.895 MPa.

a. See Note e to Table R608.7(1A) for application of adjustment factors in this table.

b. Yield strength in pounds per square inch of vertical wall reinforcement at ends of solid wall segments.

c. Values are based on concrete with a specified compressive strength, f'_c, of 2,500 psi. Where concrete with f'_c of not less than 3,000 psi is used, values in shaded cells are permitted to be decreased by multiplying by 0.91.

d. Horizontal and vertical shear reinforcement shall be provided in accordance with Section R608.7.2.2.

e. Each end of each solid wall segment shall have rectangular flanges. In the through-the-wall dimension, the flange shall be not less than $5^1/_2$ inches for 6-inch-nominal waffle- and screen-grid walls, and not less than $7^1/_2$ inches for 8-inch-nominal waffle-grid walls. In the in-plane dimension, flanges shall be long enough to accommodate the vertical reinforcement required by the layout detail selected from Figure R608.7(2) and provide the cover required by Section R608.5.4.1. If necessary to achieve the required dimensions, form material shall be removed or use of flat wall forms is permitted.

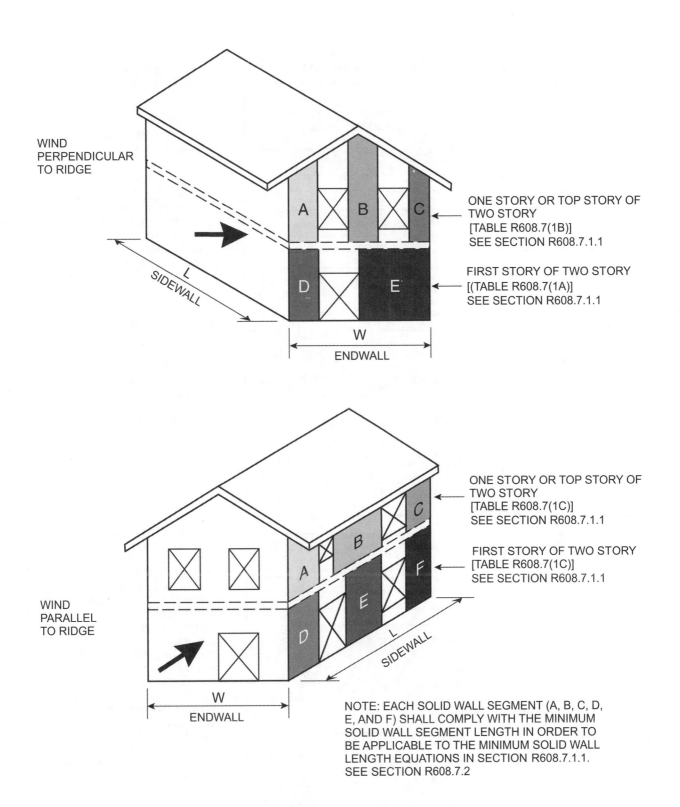

WIND
PERPENDICULAR
TO RIDGE

ONE STORY OR TOP STORY OF
TWO STORY
[TABLE R608.7(1B)]
SEE SECTION R608.7.1.1

FIRST STORY OF TWO STORY
[(TABLE R608.7(1A)]
SEE SECTION R608.7.1.1

L
SIDEWALL

W
ENDWALL

WIND
PARALLEL
TO RIDGE

ONE STORY OR TOP STORY OF
TWO STORY
[TABLE R608.7(1C)]
SEE SECTION R608.7.1.1

FIRST STORY OF TWO STORY
[TABLE R608.7(1C)]
SEE SECTION R608.7.1.1

L
SIDEWALL

W
ENDWALL

NOTE: EACH SOLID WALL SEGMENT (A, B, C, D,
E, AND F) SHALL COMPLY WITH THE MINIMUM
SOLID WALL SEGMENT LENGTH IN ORDER TO
BE APPLICABLE TO THE MINIMUM SOLID WALL
LENGTH EQUATIONS IN SECTION R608.7.1.1.
SEE SECTION R608.7.2

FIGURE R608.7(1)
MINIMUM SOLID WALL LENGTH

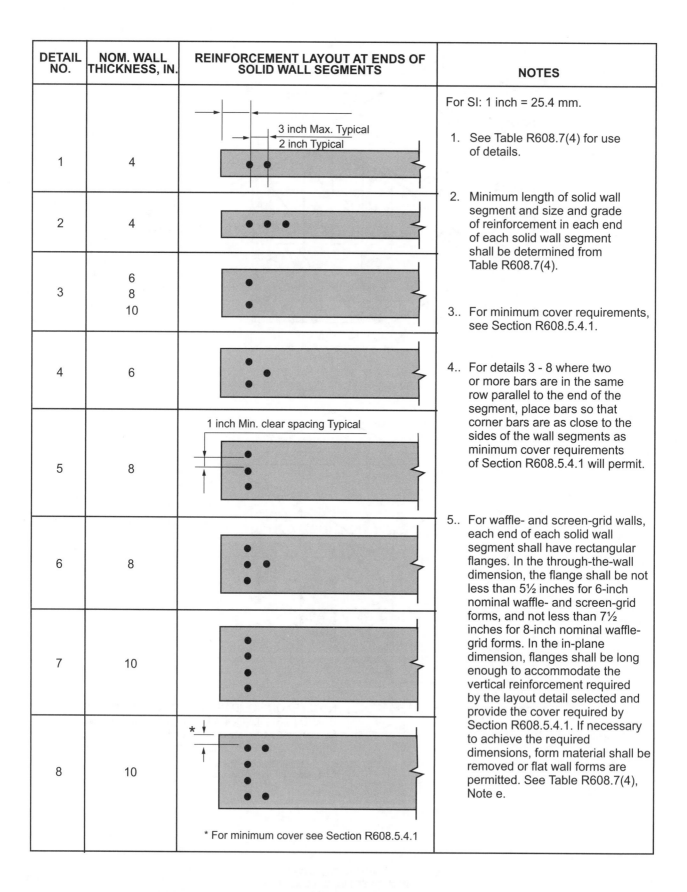

FIGURE R608.7(2)
VERTICAL REINFORCEMENT LAYOUT DETAIL

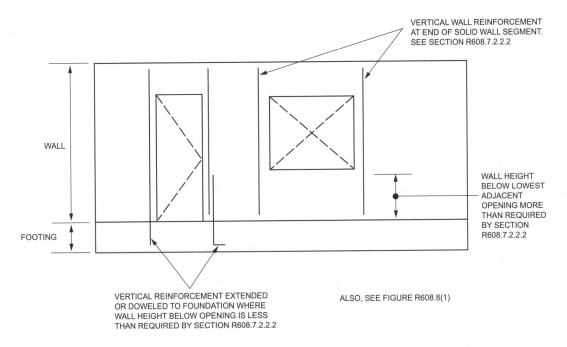

VERTICAL WALL REINFORCEMENT
AT END OF SOLID WALL SEGMENT.
SEE SECTION R608.7.2.2.2

WALL

FOOTING

WALL HEIGHT
BELOW LOWEST
ADJACENT
OPENING MORE
THAN REQUIRED
BY SECTION
R608.7.2.2.2

VERTICAL REINFORCEMENT EXTENDED
OR DOWELED TO FOUNDATION WHERE
WALL HEIGHT BELOW OPENING IS LESS
THAN REQUIRED BY SECTION R608.7.2.2.2

ALSO, SEE FIGURE R608.8(1)

FIGURE R608.7(3)
VERTICAL WALL REINFORCEMENT ADJACENT TO WALL OPENINGS

enough to develop the bar in tension in accordance with Section R608.5.4.4 and Figure R608.5.4(2), or shall be lap-spliced with a dowel that is embedded in the footing far enough to develop the dowel-bar in tension.

R608.7.2.2.3 Vertical shear reinforcement. Where reduction factors for design strength, R_3, from Table R608.7(4) based on horizontal and vertical shear reinforcement being provided are used, solid wall segments shall have vertical reinforcement consisting of minimum No. 4 bars. Vertical shear reinforcement shall be the same grade of steel required by Section R608.7.2.2.2 for the vertical reinforcement at the ends of solid wall segments. The spacing of vertical reinforcement throughout the length of the segment shall not exceed the smaller of one third the length of the segment, and 18 inches (457 mm). Vertical shear reinforcement shall be continuous between stories in accordance with Section R608.6.3, and shall terminate in accordance with Section R608.6.4. Vertical shear reinforcement required by this section is permitted to be used for vertical reinforcement required by Table R608.6(1), R608.6(2), R608.6(3) or R608.6(4), whichever is applicable.

R608.7.2.3 Solid wall segments at corners. At all interior and exterior corners of exterior walls, a solid wall segment shall extend the full height of each wall *story*. The segment shall have the length required to develop the horizontal reinforcement above and below the adjacent opening in tension in accordance with Section R608.5.4.4. For an exterior corner, the limiting dimension is measured on the outside of the wall, and for an interior corner the limiting dimension is measured on the

inside of the wall. See Section R608.8.1. The length of a segment contributing to the required length of solid wall shall comply with Section R608.7.2.1.

The end of a solid wall segment complying with the minimum length requirements of Section R608.7.2.1 shall be located not more than 6 feet (1829 mm) from each corner.

R608.8 Requirements for lintels and reinforcement around openings.

R608.8.1 Reinforcement around openings. Reinforcement shall be provided around openings in walls equal to or greater than 2 feet (610 mm) in width in accordance with this section and Figure R608.8(1), in addition to the minimum wall reinforcement required by Sections R404.1.3, R608.6 and R608.7. Vertical wall reinforcement required by this section is permitted to be used as reinforcement at the ends of solid wall segments required by Section R608.7.2.2.2 provided it is located in accordance with Section R608.8.1.2. Wall openings shall have a minimum depth of concrete over the width of the opening of 8 inches (203 mm) in flat walls and waffle-grid walls, and 12 inches (305 mm) in screen-grid walls. Wall openings in waffle-grid and screen-grid walls shall be located such that not less than one-half of a vertical core occurs along each side of the opening.

R608.8.1.1 Horizontal reinforcement. Lintels complying with Section R608.8.2 shall be provided above wall openings equal to or greater than 2 feet (610 mm) in width.

Openings equal to or greater than 2 feet (610 mm) in width shall have not less than one No. 4 bar placed within 12 inches (305 mm) of the bottom of the opening. See Figure R608.8(1).

Horizontal reinforcement placed above and below an opening shall extend beyond the edges of the opening the dimension required to develop the bar in tension in accordance with Section R608.5.4.4.

Exception: Continuous horizontal wall reinforcement placed within 12 inches (305 mm) of the top of the wall *story* as required in Sections R404.1.3.2 and R608.6.2 is permitted in lieu of top or bottom lintel reinforcement required by Section R608.8.2 provided that the continuous horizontal wall reinforcement meets the location requirements specified in Figures R608.8(2), R608.8(3), and R608.8(4) and the size requirements specified in Tables R608.8(2) through R608.8(10).

R608.8.1.2 Vertical reinforcement. Not less than one No. 4 bar [Grade 40 (280 MPa)] shall be provided on each side of openings equal to or greater than 2 feet (610 mm) in width. The vertical reinforcement required by this section shall extend the full height of the wall story and shall be located within 12 inches (305 mm) of each side of the opening. The vertical reinforcement required on each side of an opening by this section is permitted to serve as reinforcement at the ends of solid wall segments in accordance with Section R608.7.2.2.2, provided it is

located as required by the applicable detail in Figure R608.7(2). Where the vertical reinforcement required by this section is used to satisfy the requirements of Section R608.7.2.2.2 in waffle- and screen-grid walls, a concrete flange shall be created at the ends of the solid wall segments in accordance with Table R608.7(4), Note e. In the top-most story, the reinforcement shall terminate in accordance with Section R608.6.4.

R608.8.2 Lintels. Lintels shall be provided over all openings equal to or greater than 2 feet (610 mm) in width. Lintels with uniform loading shall conform to Sections R608.8.2.1 and R608.8.2.2, or Section R608.8.2.3. Lintels supporting concentrated loads, such as from roof or floor beams or girders, shall be designed in accordance with ACI 318.

R608.8.2.1 Lintels designed for gravity load-bearing conditions. Where a lintel will be subjected to gravity load conditions 1 through 5 of Table R608.8(1), the clear span of the lintel shall not exceed that permitted by Tables R608.8(2) through R608.8(8). The maximum clear span of lintels with and without stirrups in flat walls shall be determined in accordance with Tables R608.8(2) through R608.8(5), and constructed in accor-

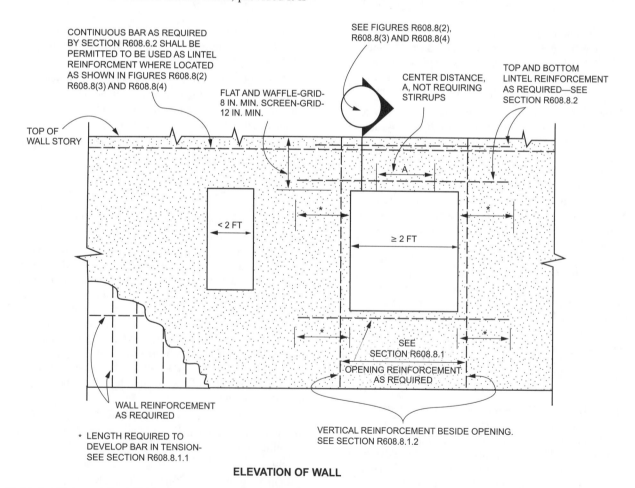

ELEVATION OF WALL

For SI: 1 inch = 25.4 mm, 1 foot = 304.8 mm.

FIGURE R608.8(1)
REINFORCEMENT OF OPENINGS

dance with Figure R608.8(2). The maximum clear span of lintels with and without stirrups in waffle-grid walls shall be determined in accordance with Tables R608.8(6) and R608.8(7), and constructed in accordance with Figure R608.8(3). The maximum clear span of lintels with and without stirrups in screen-grid walls shall be determined in accordance with Table R608.8(8), and constructed in accordance with Figure R608.8(4).

Where required by the applicable table, No. 3 stirrups shall be installed in lintels at a maximum spacing of $d/2$ where d equals the depth of the lintel, D, less the cover of the concrete as shown in Figures R608.8(2) through R608.8(4). The smaller value of d computed for the top and bottom bar shall be used to determine the maximum stirrup spacing. Where stirrups are required in a lintel with a single bar or two bundled bars in the top and bottom, they shall be fabricated like the letter "c" or "s" with 135-degree (2.36 rad) standard hooks at each end that comply with Section R608.5.4.5 and Figure R608.5.4(3) and installed as shown in Figures R608.8(2) through R608.8(4). Where two bars are required in the top and bottom of the lintel and the bars are not bundled, the bars shall be separated by not less than 1 inch (25 mm). The free end of the stirrups shall be fabricated with 90- or 135-degree (1.57 or 2.36 rad) standard hooks that comply with Section R608.5.4.5 and Figure R608.5.4(3) and installed as shown in Figures R608.8(2) and R608.8(3). For flat, waffle-grid and screen-grid lintels, stirrups are not required in the center distance, A, portion of spans in accordance with Figure R608.8(1) and Tables R608.8(2) through R608.8(8). See Section R608.8.2.2, Item 5, for requirement for stirrups through out lintels with bundled bars.

R608.8.2.2 Bundled bars in lintels. It is permitted to bundle two bars in contact with each other in lintels if all of the following are observed:

1. Bars equal to or less than No. 6 are bundled.

2. Where the wall thickness is not sufficient to provide not less than 3 inches (76 mm) of clear space beside bars (total on both sides) oriented horizontally in a bundle, the bundled bars shall be oriented in a vertical plane.

3. Where vertically oriented bundled bars terminate with standard hooks to develop the bars in tension beyond the support (see Section R608.5.4.4), the hook extensions shall be staggered to provide not less than 1 inch (25 mm) clear spacing between the extensions.

4. Bundled bars shall not be lap spliced within the lintel span and the length on each end of the lintel that is required to develop the bars in tension.

5. Bundled bars shall be enclosed within stirrups throughout the length of the lintel. Stirrups and the installation thereof shall comply with Section R608.8.2.1.

R608.8.2.3 Lintels without stirrups designed for nonload-bearing conditions. The maximum clear span of lintels without stirrups designed for nonload-bearing conditions of Table R608.8(1).1 shall be determined in accordance with this section. The maximum clear span of lintels without stirrups in flat walls shall be determined in accordance with Table R608.8(9), and the maximum clear span of lintels without stirrups in walls of waffle-grid or screen-grid construction shall be determined in accordance with Table R608.8(10).

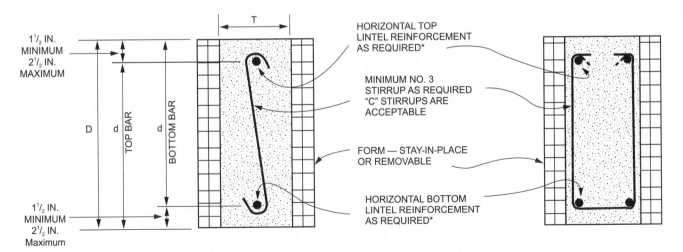

* FOR BUNDLED BARS, SEE SECTION R608.8.2.2.
SECTION CUT THROUGH FLAT WALL LINTEL

For SI: 1 inch = 25.4 mm.

FIGURE R608.8(2)
LINTEL FOR FLAT WALLS

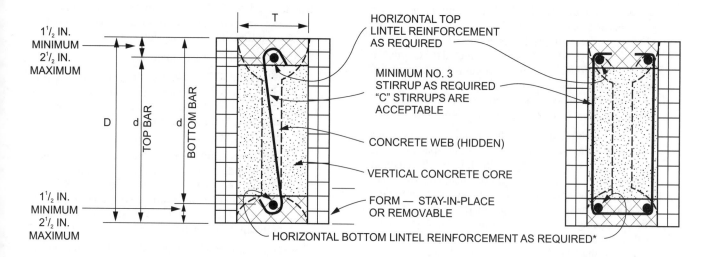

(a) SINGLE FORM HEIGHT SECTION CUT THROUGH VERTICAL CORE OF A WAFFLE-GRID LINTEL

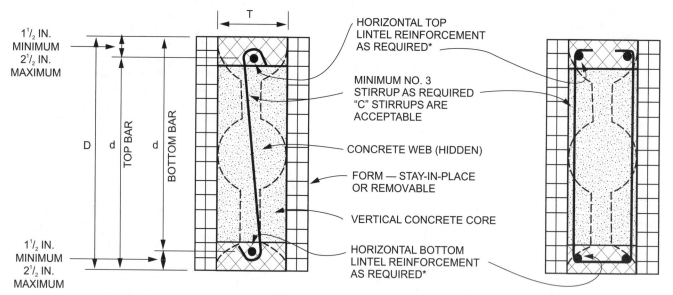

(b) DOUBLE FORM HEIGHT SECTION CUT THROUGH VERTICAL CORE OF A WAFFLE-GRID LINTEL

*FOR BUNDLED BARS, SEE SECTION R608.8.2.2.

NOTE: CROSS HATCHING REPRESENTS THE AREA IN WHICH FORM MATERIAL SHALL BE REMOVED, IF NECESSARY, TO CREATE FLANGES CONTINUOUS THE LENGTH OF THE LINTEL. FLANGES SHALL HAVE A MINIMUM THICKNESS OF 3 IN., AND A MINIMUM WIDTH OF 5 IN. AND 7 IN. IN 6 IN. NOMINAL AND 8 IN. NOMINAL WAFFLE-GRID WALLS, RESPECTIVELY. SEE NOTE a TO TABLES R608.8(6) AND R608.8(10).

For SI: 1 inch = 25.4 mm.

FIGURE R608.8(3)
LINTELS FOR WAFFLE-GRID WALLS

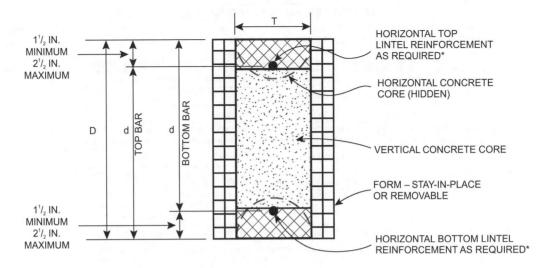

(a) SINGLE FORM HEIGHT SECTION CUT THROUGH
VERTICAL CORE OF A SCREEN-GRID LINTEL

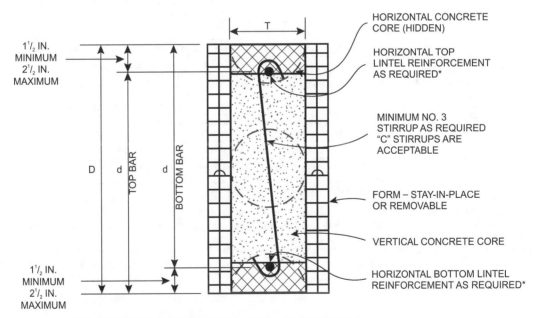

(b) DOUBLE FORM HEIGHT SECTION CUT THROUGH VERTICAL
CORE OF A SCREEN-GRID LINTEL

*FOR BUNDLED BARS, SEE SECTION R608.8.2.2

NOTE: CROSS HATCHING REPRESENTS THE AREA IN WHICH FORM MATERIAL SHALL BE REMOVED,
IF NECESSARY, TO CREATE FLANGES CONTINUOUS THE LENGTH OF THE LINTEL. FLANGES
SHALL HAVE A MINIMUM THICKNESS OF 2.5 IN. AND A MINIMUM WIDTH OF 5 IN. SEE NOTE a
TO TABLES R608.8(8) AND R608.8(10).

For SI: 1 inch = 25.4 mm.

FIGURE R608.8(4)
LINTELS FOR SCREEN-GRID WALLS

TABLE R608.8(1)
LINTEL DESIGN LOADING CONDITIONS[a, b, d]

DESCRIPTION OF LOADS AND OPENINGS ABOVE INFLUENCING DESIGN OF LINTEL			DESIGN LOAD CONDITION[c]
Opening in wall of top story of two-story building, or first story of one-story building			
Wall supporting loads from roof, including attic floor, if applicable, and	Top of lintel equal to or less than W/2 below top of wall		2
	Top of lintel greater than W/2 below top of wall		NLB
Wall not supporting loads from roof or attic floor			NLB
Opening in wall of first story of two-story building where wall immediately above is of concrete construction, or opening in basement wall of one-story building where wall immediately above is of concrete construction			
LB ledger board mounted to side of wall with bottom of ledger less than or equal to W/2 above top of lintel, and	Top of lintel greater than W/2 below bottom of opening in story above		1
	Top of lintel less than or equal to W/2 below bottom of opening in story above, and	Opening is entirely within the footprint of the opening in the story above	1
		Opening is partially within the footprint of the opening in the story above	4
LB ledger board mounted to side of wall with bottom of ledger more than W/2 above top of lintel			NLB
NLB ledger board mounted to side of wall with bottom of ledger less than or equal to W/2 above top of lintel, or no ledger board, and	Top of lintel greater than W/2 below bottom of opening in story above		NLB
	Top of lintel less than or equal to W/2 below bottom of opening in story above, and	Opening is entirely within the footprint of the opening in the story above	NLB
		Opening is partially within the footprint of the opening in the story above	1
Opening in basement wall of two-story building where walls of two stories above are of concrete construction			
LB ledger board mounted to side of wall with bottom of ledger less than or equal to W/2 above top of lintel, and	Top of lintel greater than W/2 below bottom of opening in story above		1
	Top of lintel less than or equal to W/2 below bottom of opening in story above, and	Opening is entirely within the footprint of the opening in the story above	1
		Opening is partially within the footprint of the opening in the story above	5
LB ledger board mounted to side of wall with bottom of ledger more than W/2 above top of lintel			NLB
NLB ledger board mounted to side of wall with bottom of ledger less than or equal to W/2 above top of lintel, or no ledger board, and	Top of lintel greater than W/2 below bottom of opening in story above		NLB
	Top of lintel less than or equal to W/2 below bottom of opening in story above, and	Opening is entirely within the footprint of the opening in the story above	NLB
		Opening is partially within the footprint of the opening in the story above	1
Opening in wall of first story of two-story building where wall immediately above is of light-framed construction, or opening in basement wall of one-story building where wall immediately above is of light-framed construction			
Wall supporting loads from roof, second floor and top-story wall of light-framed construction, and	Top of lintel equal to or less than W/2 below top of wall		3
	Top of lintel greater than W/2 below top of wall		NLB
Wall not supporting loads from roof or second floor			NLB

a. LB means load bearing, NLB means nonload bearing, and W means width of opening.

b. Footprint is the area of the wall below an opening in the story above, bounded by the bottom of the opening and vertical lines extending downward from the edges of the opening.

c. For design loading condition "NLB" see Tables R608.8(9) and R608.8(10). For all other design loading conditions, see Tables R608.8(2) through R608.8(8).

d. An NLB ledger board is a ledger attached to a wall that is parallel to the span of the floor, roof or ceiling framing that supports the edge of the floor, ceiling or roof.

TABLE R608.8(2)
MAXIMUM ALLOWABLE CLEAR SPANS FOR 4-INCH-NOMINAL THICK FLAT LINTELS IN LOAD-BEARING WALLS[a, b, c, d, e, f, m]
ROOF CLEAR SPAN 40 FEET AND FLOOR CLEAR SPAN 32 FEET

LINTEL DEPTH, D[g] (inches)	NUMBER OF BARS AND BAR SIZE IN TOP AND BOTTOM OF LINTEL	STEEL YIELD STRENGTH[h], f_y (psi)	DESIGN LOADING CONDITION DETERMINED FROM TABLE R608.8(1)								
			1	2		3		4		5	
			Maximum ground snow load (psf)								
			—	30	70	30	70	30	70	30	70
			Maximum clear span of lintel (feet - inches)								
8	Span without stirrups[i, j]		3-2	3-4	2-4	2-6	2-2	2-1	2-0	2-0	2-0
	1-#4	40,000	5-2	5-5	4-1	4-3	3-10	3-7	3-4	2-9	2-9
		60,000	6-2	6-5	4-11	5-1	4-6	4-2	3-8	2-11	2-10
	1-#5	40,000	6-3	6-7	5-0	5-2	4-6	4-2	3-8	2-11	2-10
		60,000	DR	DR	DR	DR	DR	DR	DR	DR	DR
	Center distance A[k, l]		1-1	1-2	0-8	0-9	0-7	0-6	0-5	0-4	0-4
12	Span without stirrups[i, j]		3-4	3-7	2-9	2-11	2-8	2-6	2-5	2-2	2-2
	1-#4	40,000	6-7	7-0	5-4	5-7	5-0	4-9	4-4	3-8	3-7
		60,000	7-11	8-6	6-6	6-9	6-0	5-9	5-3	4-5	4-4
	1-#5	40,000	8-1	8-8	6-7	6-10	6-2	5-10	5-4	4-6	4-5
		60,000	9-8	10-4	7-11	8-2	7-4	6-11	6-2	4-10	4-8
	2-#4 1-#6	40,000	9-1	9-8	7-4	7-8	6-10	6-6	6-0	4-10	4-8
		60,000	DR	DR	DR	DR	DR	DR	DR	DR	DR
	Center distance A[k, l]		1-8	1-11	1-1	1-3	1-0	0-11	0-9	0-6	0-6
16	Span without stirrups[i, j]		4-7	5-0	3-11	4-0	3-8	3-7	3-4	3-1	3-0
	1-#4	40,000	6-8	7-3	5-6	5-9	5-2	4-11	4-6	3-10	3-8
		60,000	9-3	10-1	7-9	8-0	7-2	6-10	6-3	5-4	5-2
	1-#4	40,000	9-6	10-4	7-10	8-2	7-4	6-11	6-5	5-5	5-3
		60,000	11-5	12-5	9-6	9-10	8-10	8-4	7-9	6-6	6-4
	2-#4 1-#6	40,000	10-7	11-7	8-10	9-2	8-3	7-9	7-2	6-1	5-11
		60,000	12-9	13-10	10-7	11-0	9-10	9-4	8-7	6-9	6-6
	2-#5	40,000	13-0	14-1	10-9	11-2	9-11	9-2	8-2	6-6	6-3
		60,000	DR	DR	DR	DR	DR	DR	DR	DR	DR
	Center distance A[k, l]		2-3	2-8	1-7	1-8	1-4	1-3	1-0	0-9	0-8
20	Span without stirrups A[i, j]		5-9	6-5	5-0	5-2	4-9	4-7	4-4	3-11	3-11
	1-#4	40,000	7-5	8-2	6-3	6-6	5-10	5-7	5-1	4-4	4-2
		60,000	9-0	10-0	7-8	7-11	7-1	6-9	6-3	5-3	5-1
	1-#5	40,000	9-2	10-2	7-9	8-1	7-3	6-11	6-4	5-4	5-2
		60,000	12-9	14-2	10-10	11-3	10-1	9-7	8-10	7-5	7-3
	2-#4 1-#6	40,000	11-10	13-2	10-1	10-5	9-4	8-11	8-2	6-11	6-9
		60,000	14-4	15-10	12-1	12-7	11-3	10-9	9-11	8-4	8-1
	2-#5	40,000	14-7	16-2	12-4	12-9	11-4	10-6	9-5	7-7	7-3
		60,000	17-5	19-2	14-9	15-3	13-5	12-4	11-0	8-8	8-4
	2-#6	40,000	16-4	18-11	12-7	13-3	11-4	10-6	9-5	7-7	7-3
		60,000	DR	DR	DR	DR	DR	DR	DR	DR	DR
	Center distance A[k, l]		2-9	3-5	2-0	2-2	1-9	1-7	1-4	0-11	0-11

(continued)

TABLE R608.8(2)—continued
MAXIMUM ALLOWABLE CLEAR SPANS FOR 4-INCH-NOMINAL THICK FLAT LINTELS IN LOAD-BEARING WALLS[a, b, c, d, e, f, m]
ROOF CLEAR SPAN 40 FEET AND FLOOR CLEAR SPAN 32 FEET

LINTEL DEPTH, D[g] (inches)	NUMBER OF BARS AND BAR SIZE IN TOP AND BOTTOM OF LINTEL	STEEL YIELD STRENGTH[h], f_y (psi)	DESIGN LOADING CONDITION DETERMINED FROM TABLE R608.8(1)								
			1	2		3		4		5	
			Maximum ground snow load (psf)								
			—	30	70	30	70	30	70	30	70
			Maximum clear span of lintel (feet - inches)								
24	Span without stirrups[i, j]		6-11	7-9	6-1	6-3	5-9	5-7	5-3	4-9	4-8
	1-#4	40,000	8-0	9-0	6-11	7-2	6-5	6-2	5-8	4-9	4-8
		60,000	9-9	11-0	8-5	8-9	7-10	7-6	6-11	5-10	5-8
	1-#5	40,000	10-0	11-3	8-7	8-11	8-0	7-7	7-0	5-11	5-9
		60,000	13-11	15-8	12-0	12-5	11-2	10-7	9-10	8-3	8-0
	2-#4 1-#6	40,000	12-11	14-6	11-2	11-6	10-5	9-10	9-1	7-8	7-5
		60,000	15-7	17-7	13-6	13-11	12-7	11-11	11-0	9-3	9-0
	2-#5	40,000	15-11	17-11	13-7	14-3	12-8	11-9	10-8	8-7	8-4
		60,000	19-1	21-6	16-5	17-1	15-1	14-0	12-6	9-11	9-7
	2-#6	40,000	17-7	21-1	14-1	14-10	12-8	11-9	10-8	8-7	8-4
		60,000	DR	DR	DR	DR	DR	DR	DR	DR	DR
	Center distance A[k, l]		3-3	4-1	2-5	2-7	2-1	1-11	1-7	1-2	1-1

For SI: 1 inch = 25.4 mm, 1 foot = 304.8 mm, 1 pound per square inch = 6.895 kPa, 1 pound per square foot = 0.0479 kPa, Grade 40 = 280 MPa, Grade 60 = 420 MPa.

a. See Table R608.3 for tolerances permitted from nominal thickness.

b. Table values are based on concrete with a minimum specified compressive strength of 2,500 psi. See Note j.

c. Table values are based on uniform loading. See Section R608.8.2 for lintels supporting concentrated loads.

d. Deflection criterion is $L/240$, where L is the clear span of the lintel in inches, or $^1/_2$-inch, whichever is less.

e. Linear interpolation is permitted between ground snow loads and between lintel depths.

f. DR indicates design required.

g. Lintel depth, D, is permitted to include the available height of wall located directly above the lintel, provided that the increased lintel depth spans the entire length of the lintel.

h. Stirrups shall be fabricated from reinforcing bars with the same yield strength as that used for the main longitudinal reinforcement.

i. Allowable clear span without stirrups applicable to all lintels of the same depth, D. Top and bottom reinforcement for lintels without stirrups shall be not less than the least amount of reinforcement required for a lintel of the same depth and loading condition with stirrups. All other spans require stirrups spaced at not more than $d/2$.

j. Where concrete with a minimum specified compressive strength of 3,000 psi is used, clear spans for lintels without stirrups shall be permitted to be multiplied by 1.05. If the increased span exceeds the allowable clear span for a lintel of the same depth and loading condition with stirrups, the top and bottom reinforcement shall be equal to or greater than that required for a lintel of the same depth and loading condition that has an allowable clear span that is equal to or greater than that of the lintel without stirrups that has been increased.

k. Center distance, A, is the center portion of the clear span where stirrups are not required. This is applicable to all longitudinal bar sizes and steel yield strengths.

l. Where concrete with a minimum specified compressive strength of 3,000 psi is used, center distance, A, shall be permitted to be multiplied by 1.10.

m. The maximum clear opening width between two solid wall segments shall be 18 feet. See Section R608.7.2.1. Lintel clear spans in the table greater than 18 feet are shown for interpolation and information only.

TABLE R608.8(3)
MAXIMUM ALLOWABLE CLEAR SPANS FOR 6-INCH-NOMINAL THICK FLAT LINTELS IN LOAD-BEARING WALLS[a, b, c, d, e, f, m]
ROOF CLEAR SPAN 40 FEET AND FLOOR CLEAR SPAN 32 FEET

LINTEL DEPTH, D [g] (inches)	NUMBER OF BARS AND BAR SIZE IN TOP AND BOTTOM OF LINTEL	STEEL YIELD STRENGTH[h], f_y (psi)	DESIGN LOADING CONDITION DETERMINED FROM TABLE R608.8(1)								
			1	2		3		4		5	
			Maximum ground snow load (psf)								
			—	30	70	30	70	30	70	30	70
			Maximum clear span of lintel (feet - inches)								
8	Span without stirrups[i, j]		4-2	4-8	3-1	3-3	2-10	2-6	2-3	2-0	2-0
	1-#4	40,000	5-1	5-5	4-2	4-3	3-10	3-6	3-3	2-8	2-7
		60,000	6-2	6-7	5-0	5-2	4-8	4-2	3-11	3-3	3-2
	1-#5	40,000	6-3	6-8	5-1	5-3	4-9	4-3	4-0	3-3	3-2
		60,000	7-6	8-0	6-1	6-4	5-8	5-1	4-9	3-8	3-6
	2-#4 1-#6	40,000	7-0	7-6	5-8	5-11	5-3	4-9	4-5	3-8	3-6
		60,000	DR	DR	DR	DR	DR	DR	DR	DR	DR
	Center distance A[k, l]		1-7	1-10	1-1	1-2	0-11	0-9	0-8	0-5	0-5
12	Span without stirrups[i, j]		4-2	4-8	3-5	3-6	3-2	2-11	2-9	2-5	2-4
	1-#4	40,000	5-7	6-1	4-8	4-10	4-4	3-11	3-8	3-0	2-11
		60,000	7-9	8-6	6-6	6-9	6-1	5-6	5-1	4-3	4-1
	1-#5	40,000	7-11	8-8	6-8	6-11	6-2	5-7	5-2	4-4	4-2
		60,000	9-7	10-6	8-0	8-4	7-6	6-9	6-3	5-2	5-1
	2-#4 1-#6	40,000	8-11	9-9	7-6	7-9	6-11	6-3	5-10	4-10	4-8
		60,000	10-8	11-9	8-12	9-4	8-4	7-6	7-0	5-10	5-8
	2-#5	40,000	10-11	12-0	9-2	9-6	8-6	7-8	7-2	5-6	5-3
		60,000	12-11	14-3	10-10	11-3	10-1	9-0	8-1	6-1	5-10
	2-#6	40,000	12-9	14-0	10-8	11-1	9-7	8-1	7-3	5-6	5-3
		60,000	DR	DR	DR	DR	DR	DR	DR	DR	DR
	Center distance A[k, l]		2-6	3-0	1-9	1-10	1-6	1-3	1-1	0-9	0-8
16	Span without stirrups[i, j]		5-7	6-5	4-9	4-11	4-5	4-0	3-10	3-4	3-4
	1-#4	40,000	6-5	7-2	5-6	5-9	5-2	4-8	4-4	3-7	3-6
		60,000	7-10	8-9	6-9	7-0	6-3	5-8	5-3	4-4	4-3
	1-#5	40,000	7-11	8-11	6-10	7-1	6-5	5-9	5-4	4-5	4-4
		60,000	11-1	12-6	9-7	9-11	8-11	8-0	7-6	6-2	6-0
	2-#4 1-#6	40,000	10-3	11-7	8-10	9-2	8-3	7-6	6-11	5-9	5-7
		60,000	12-5	14-0	10-9	11-1	10-0	9-0	8-5	7-0	6-9
	2-#5	40,000	12-8	14-3	10-11	11-4	10-2	9-2	8-7	6-9	6-6
		60,000	15-2	17-1	13-1	13-7	12-3	11-0	10-3	7-11	7-7
	2-#6	40,000	14-11	16-9	12-8	13-4	11-4	9-8	8-8	6-9	6-6
		60,000	DR	DR	DR	DR	DR	DR	DR	DR	DR
	Center distance A[k, l]		3-3	4-1	2-5	2-7	2-1	1-9	1-6	1-0	1-0

(continued)

TABLE R608.8(3)—continued
MAXIMUM ALLOWABLE CLEAR SPANS FOR 6-INCH-NOMINAL THICK FLAT LINTELS IN LOAD-BEARING WALLS[a, b, c, d, e, f, m]
ROOF CLEAR SPAN 40 FEET AND FLOOR CLEAR SPAN 32 FEET

LINTEL DEPTH, D[g] (inches)	NUMBER OF BARS AND BAR SIZE IN TOP AND BOTTOM OF LINTEL	STEEL YIELD STRENGTH[h], f_y (psi)	DESIGN LOADING CONDITION DETERMINED FROM TABLE R608.8(1)								
			1	2		3		4		5	
			Maximum ground snow load (psf)								
			—	30	70	30	70	30	70	30	70
			Maximum clear span of lintel (feet - inches)								
20	Span without stirrups[i, j]		6-11	8-2	6-1	6-3	5-8	5-2	4-11	4-4	4-3
	1-#5	40,000	8-9	10-1	7-9	8-0	7-3	6-6	6-1	5-1	4-11
		60,000	10-8	12-3	9-5	9-9	8-10	8-0	7-5	6-2	6-0
	2-#4 1-#6	40,000	9-11	11-4	8-9	9-1	8-2	7-4	6-10	5-8	5-7
		60,000	13-9	15-10	12-2	12-8	11-5	10-3	9-7	7-11	7-9
	2-#5	40,000	14-0	16-2	12-5	12-11	11-7	10-6	9-9	7-11	7-8
		60,000	16-11	19-6	15-0	15-6	14-0	12-7	11-9	9-1	8-9
	2-#6	40,000	16-7	19-1	14-7	15-3	13-1	11-3	10-2	7-11	7-8
		60,000	19-11	22-10	17-4	18-3	15-6	13-2	11-10	9-1	8-9
	Center distance A[k, l]		3-11	5-2	3-1	3-3	2-8	2-2	1-11	1-4	1-3
24	Span without stirrups[i, j]		8-2	9-10	7-4	7-8	6-11	6-4	5-11	5-3	5-2
	1-#5	40,000	9-5	11-1	8-7	8-10	8-0	7-3	6-9	5-7	5-5
		60,000	11-6	13-6	10-5	10-9	9-9	8-9	8-2	6-10	6-8
	2-#4 1-#6	40,000	10-8	12-6	9-8	10-0	9-0	8-2	7-7	6-4	6-2
		60,000	12-11	15-2	11-9	12-2	11-0	9-11	9-3	7-8	7-6
	2-#5	40,000	15-2	17-9	13-9	14-3	12-10	11-7	10-10	9-0	8-9
		60,000	18-4	21-6	16-7	17-3	15-6	14-0	13-1	10-4	10-0
	2-#6	40,000	18-0	21-1	16-4	16-11	14-10	12-9	11-8	9-2	8-11
		60,000	21-7	25-4	19-2	20-4	17-2	14-9	13-4	10-4	10-0
	Center distance A[k, l]		4-6	6-2	3-8	4-0	3-3	2-8	2-3	1-7	1-6

For SI: 1 inch = 25.4 mm, 1 foot = 304.8 mm, 1 pound per square inch = 6.895 kPa, 1 pound per square foot = 0.0479 kPa, Grade 40 = 280 MPa, Grade 60 = 420 MPa.

a. See Table R608.3 for tolerances permitted from nominal thickness.

b. Table values are based on concrete with a minimum specified compressive strength of 2,500 psi. See Note j.

c. Table values are based on uniform loading. See Section R608.8.2 for lintels supporting concentrated loads.

d. Deflection criterion is L/240, where L is the clear span of the lintel in inches, or $^1/_2$ inch, whichever is less.

e. Linear interpolation is permitted between ground snow loads and between lintel depths.

f. DR indicates design required.

g. Lintel depth, D, is permitted to include the available height of wall located directly above the lintel, provided that the increased lintel depth spans the entire length of the lintel.

h. Stirrups shall be fabricated from reinforcing bars with the same yield strength as that used for the main longitudinal reinforcement.

i. Allowable clear span without stirrups applicable to all lintels of the same depth, D. Top and bottom reinforcement for lintels without stirrups shall be not less than the least amount of reinforcement required for a lintel of the same depth and loading condition with stirrups. All other spans require stirrups spaced at not more than d/2.

j. Where concrete with a minimum specified compressive strength of 3,000 psi is used, clear spans for lintels without stirrups shall be permitted to be multiplied by 1.05. If the increased span exceeds the allowable clear span for a lintel of the same depth and loading condition with stirrups, the top and bottom reinforcement shall be equal to or greater than that required for a lintel of the same depth and loading condition that has an allowable clear span that is equal to or greater than that of the lintel without stirrups that has been increased.

k. Center distance, A, is the center portion of the clear span where stirrups are not required. This is applicable to all longitudinal bar sizes and steel yield strengths.

l. Where concrete with a minimum specified compressive strength of 3,000 psi is used, center distance, A, shall be permitted to be multiplied by 1.10.

m. The maximum clear opening width between two solid wall segments shall be 18 feet. See Section R608.7.2.1. Lintel clear spans in the table greater than 18 feet are shown for interpolation and information only.

TABLE R608.8(4)
MAXIMUM ALLOWABLE CLEAR SPANS FOR 8-INCH-NOMINAL THICK FLAT LINTELS IN LOAD-BEARING WALLS[a, b, c, d, e, f, m]
ROOF CLEAR SPAN 40 FEET AND FLOOR CLEAR SPAN 32 FEET

LINTEL DEPTH, D [g] (inches)	NUMBER OF BARS AND BAR SIZE IN TOP AND BOTTOM OF LINTEL	STEEL YIELD STRENGTH[h], f_y (psi)	DESIGN LOADING CONDITION DETERMINED FROM TABLE R608.8(1)								
			1	2		3		4		5	
			Maximum ground snow load (psf)								
			—	30	70	30	70	30	70	30	70
			Maximum clear span of lintel (feet - inches)								
8	Span without stirrups[i, j]		4-4	4-9	3-7	3-9	3-4	2-10	2-7	2-1	2-0
	1-#4	40,000	4-4	4-9	3-7	3-9	3-4	2-11	2-9	2-3	2-2
		60,000	6-1	6-7	5-0	5-3	4-8	4-0	3-9	3-1	3-0
	1-#5	40,000	6-2	6-9	5-2	5-4	4-9	4-1	3-10	3-2	3-1
		60,000	7-5	8-1	6-2	6-5	5-9	4-11	4-7	3-9	3-8
	2-#4 1-#6	40,000	6-11	7-6	5-9	6-0	5-4	4-7	4-4	3-6	3-5
		60,000	8-3	9-0	6-11	7-2	6-5	5-6	5-2	4-2	4-1
	2-#5	40,000	8-5	9-2	7-0	7-3	6-6	5-7	5-3	4-2	4-0
		60,000	DR	DR	DR	DR	DR	DR	DR	DR	DR
	Center distance A [k, l]		2-1	2-6	1-5	1-6	1-3	0-11	0-10	0-6	0-6
12	Span without stirrups[i, j]		4-10	5-8	4-0	4-2	3-9	3-2	3-0	2-7	2-6
	1-#4	40,000	5-5	6-1	4-8	4-10	4-4	3-9	3-6	2-10	2-10
		60,000	6-7	7-5	5-8	5-11	5-4	4-7	4-3	3-6	3-5
	1-#5	40,000	6-9	7-7	5-9	6-0	5-5	4-8	4-4	3-7	3-6
		60,000	9-4	10-6	8-1	8-4	7-6	6-6	6-1	5-0	4-10
	2-#4 1-#6	40,000	8-8	9-9	7-6	7-9	7-0	6-0	5-8	4-7	4-6
		60,000	10-6	11-9	9-1	9-5	8-5	7-3	6-10	5-7	5-5
	2-#5	40,000	10-8	12-0	9-3	9-7	8-7	7-5	6-11	5-6	5-4
		60,000	12-10	14-5	11-1	11-6	10-4	8-11	8-4	6-7	6-4
	2-#6	40,000	12-7	14-2	10-10	11-3	10-2	8-3	7-6	5-6	5-4
		60,000	DR	DR	DR	DR	DR	DR	DR	DR	DR
	Center distance A [k, l]		3-2	4-0	2-4	2-6	2-0	1-6	1-4	0-11	0-10
16	Span without stirrups[i, j]		6-5	7-9	5-7	5-10	5-2	4-5	4-2	3-7	3-6
	1-#4	40,000	6-2	7-1	5-6	5-8	5-1	4-5	4-2	3-5	3-4
		60,000	7-6	8-8	6-8	6-11	6-3	5-5	5-1	4-2	4-0
	1-#5	40,000	7-8	8-10	6-10	7-1	6-4	5-6	5-2	4-3	4-1
		60,000	9-4	10-9	8-4	8-7	7-9	6-8	6-3	5-2	5-0
	2-#4 1-#6	40,000	8-8	10-0	7-8	8-0	7-2	6-2	5-10	4-9	4-8
		60,000	12-0	13-11	10-9	11-2	10-0	8-8	8-1	6-8	6-6
	2-#5	40,000	12-3	14-2	11-0	11-4	10-3	8-10	8-3	6-9	6-7
		60,000	14-10	17-2	13-3	13-8	12-4	10-8	10-0	7-11	7-8
	2-#6	40,000	14-6	16-10	13-0	13-5	12-1	10-1	9-2	6-11	6-8
		60,000	17-5	20-2	15-7	16-1	14-6	11-10	10-8	7-11	7-8
	Center distance A [k, l]		4-1	5-5	3-3	3-6	2-10	2-1	1-10	1-3	1-2

(continued)

TABLE R608.8(4)—continued
MAXIMUM ALLOWABLE CLEAR SPANS FOR 8-INCH-NOMINAL THICK FLAT LINTELS IN LOAD-BEARING WALLS[a, b, c, d, e, f, m]
ROOF CLEAR SPAN 40 FEET AND FLOOR CLEAR SPAN 32 FEET

LINTEL DEPTH, D [g] (inches)	NUMBER OF BARS AND BAR SIZE IN TOP AND BOTTOM OF LINTEL	STEEL YIELD STRENGTH[h], f_y (psi)	DESIGN LOADING CONDITION DETERMINED FROM TABLE R608.8(1)								
			1	2		3		4		5	
			Maximum ground snow load (psf)								
			—	30	70	30	70	30	70	30	70
			Maximum clear span of lintel (feet - inches)								
20	Span without stirrups[i, j]		7-10	9-10	7-1	7-5	6-7	5-8	5-4	4-7	4-6
	1-#5	40,000	8-4	9-11	7-8	8-0	7-2	6-3	5-10	4-9	4-8
		60,000	10-2	12-1	9-5	9-9	8-9	7-7	7-1	5-10	5-8
	2-#4 1-#6	40,000	9-5	11-3	8-8	9-0	8-1	7-0	6-7	5-5	5-3
		60,000	11-6	13-8	10-7	11-0	9-11	8-7	8-0	6-7	6-5
	2-#5	40,000	11-9	13-11	10-10	11-2	10-1	8-9	8-2	6-8	6-7
		60,000	16-4	19-5	15-0	15-7	14-0	12-2	11-4	9-3	9-0
	2-#6	40,000	16-0	19-0	14-9	15-3	13-9	11-10	10-10	8-3	8-0
		60,000	19-3	22-11	17-9	18-5	16-7	13-7	12-4	9-3	9-0
	Center distance A[k, l]		4-10	6-10	4-1	4-5	3-7	2-8	2-4	1-7	1-6
24	Span without stirrups[i, j]		9-2	11-9	8-7	8-11	8-0	6-11	6-6	5-7	5-6
	1-#5	40,000	8-11	10-10	8-6	8-9	7-11	6-10	6-5	5-3	5-2
		60,000	10-11	13-3	10-4	10-8	9-8	8-4	7-10	6-5	6-3
	2-#4 1-#6	40,000	10-1	12-3	9-7	9-11	8-11	7-9	7-3	6-0	5-10
		60,000	12-3	15-0	11-8	12-1	10-11	9-5	8-10	7-3	7-1
	2-#5	40,000	12-6	15-3	11-11	12-4	11-1	9-7	9-0	7-5	7-3
		60,000	17-6	21-3	16-7	17-2	15-6	13-5	12-7	10-4	10-1
	2-#6	40,000	17-2	20-11	16-3	16-10	15-3	13-2	12-4	9-7	9-4
		60,000	20-9	25-3	19-8	20-4	18-5	15-4	14-0	10-7	10-3
	Center distance A[k, l]		5-6	8-1	4-11	5-3	4-4	3-3	2-10	1-11	1-10

For SI: 1 inch = 25.4 mm, 1 foot = 304.8 mm, 1 pound per square inch = 6.895 kPa, 1 pound per square foot = 0.0479 kPa, Grade 40 = 280 MPa; Grade 60 = 420 MPa.

Note: Top and bottom reinforcement for lintels without stirrups, as shown in shaded cells, shall be equal to or greater than that required for lintel of the same depth and loading condition that has an allowable clear span that is equal to or greater than that of the lintel without stirrups.

a. See Table R608.3 for tolerances permitted from nominal thickness.

b. Table values are based on concrete with a minimum specified compressive strength of 2,500 psi. See Note j.

c. Table values are based on uniform loading. See Section R608.8.2 for lintels supporting concentrated loads.

d. Deflection criterion is $L/240$, where L is the clear span of the lintel in inches, or $^{1}/_{2}$ inch, whichever is less.

e. Linear interpolation is permitted between ground snow loads and between lintel depths.

f. DR indicates design required.

g. Lintel depth, D, is permitted to include the available height of wall located directly above the lintel, provided that the increased lintel depth spans the entire length of the lintel.

h. Stirrups shall be fabricated from reinforcing bars with the same yield strength as that used for the main longitudinal reinforcement.

i. Allowable clear span without stirrups applicable to all lintels of the same depth, D. Top and bottom reinforcement for lintels without stirrups shall be not less than the least amount of reinforcement required for a lintel of the same depth and loading condition with stirrups. All other spans require stirrups spaced at not more than $d/2$.

j. Where concrete with a minimum specified compressive strength of 3,000 psi is used, clear spans for lintels without stirrups shall be permitted to be multiplied by 1.05. If the increased span exceeds the allowable clear span for a lintel of the same depth and loading condition with stirrups, the top and bottom reinforcement shall be equal to or greater than that required for a lintel of the same depth and loading condition that has an allowable clear span that is equal to or greater than that of the lintel without stirrups that has been increased.

k. Center distance, A, is the center portion of the clear span where stirrups are not required. This is applicable to all longitudinal bar sizes and steel yield strengths.

l. Where concrete with a minimum specified compressive strength of 3,000 psi is used, center distance, A, shall be permitted to be multiplied by 1.10.

m. The maximum clear opening width between two solid wall segments shall be 18 feet. See Section R608.7.2.1. Lintel clear spans in the table greater than 18 feet are shown for interpolation and information only.

TABLE R608.8(5)
MAXIMUM ALLOWABLE CLEAR SPANS FOR 10-INCH-NOMINAL THICK FLAT LINTELS IN LOAD-BEARING WALLS[a, b, c, d, e, f, m]
ROOF CLEAR SPAN 40 FEET AND FLOOR CLEAR SPAN 32 FEET

LINTEL DEPTH, D^g (inches)	NUMBER OF BARS AND BAR SIZE IN TOP AND BOTTOM OF LINTEL	STEEL YIELD STRENGTH[h], f_y (psi)	DESIGN LOADING CONDITION DETERMINED FROM TABLE R608.8(1)								
			1	2		3		4		5	
			Maximum ground snow load (psf)								
			—	30	70	30	70	30	70	30	70
			Maximum clear span of lintel (feet - inches)								
8	Span without stirrups[i, j]		6-0	7-2	4-7	4-10	4-1	3-1	2-11	2-3	2-2
	1-#4	40,000	4-3	4-9	3-7	3-9	3-4	2-9	2-7	2-1	2-1
		60,000	5-11	6-7	5-0	5-3	4-8	3-10	3-8	2-11	2-11
	1-#5	40,000	6-1	6-9	5-2	5-4	4-9	3-11	3-9	3-0	2-11
		60,000	7-4	8-1	6-3	6-5	5-9	4-9	4-6	3-7	3-7
	2-#4 1-#6	40,000	6-10	7-6	5-9	6-0	5-5	4-5	4-2	3-4	3-4
		60,000	8-2	9-1	6-11	7-2	6-6	5-4	5-0	4-1	4-0
	2-#5	40,000	8-4	9-3	7-1	7-4	6-7	5-5	5-1	4-1	4-0
		60,000	9-11	11-0	8-5	8-9	7-10	6-6	6-1	4-8	4-6
	2-#6	40,000	9-9	10-10	8-3	8-7	7-9	6-4	5-10	4-1	4-0
		60,000	DR	DR	DR	DR	DR	DR	DR	DR	DR
	Center distance $A^{k, 1}$		2-6	3-1	1-10	1-11	1-7	1-1	0-11	0-7	0-7
12	Span without stirrups[i, j]		5-5	6-7	4-7	4-10	4-3	3-5	3-3	2-8	2-8
	1-#4	40,000	5-3	6-0	4-8	4-10	4-4	3-7	3-4	2-9	2-8
		60,000	6-5	7-4	5-8	5-10	5-3	4-4	4-1	3-4	3-3
	1-#5	40,000	6-6	7-6	5-9	6-0	5-5	4-5	4-2	3-5	3-4
		60,000	7-11	9-1	7-0	7-3	6-7	5-5	5-1	4-2	4-0
	2-#4 1-#6	40,000	7-4	8-5	6-6	6-9	6-1	5-0	4-9	3-10	3-9
		60,000	10-3	11-9	9-1	9-5	8-6	7-0	6-7	5-4	5-3
	2-#5	40,000	10-5	12-0	9-3	9-7	8-8	7-2	6-9	5-5	5-4
		60,000	12-7	14-5	11-2	11-6	10-5	8-7	8-1	6-6	6-4
	2-#6	40,000	12-4	14-2	10-11	11-4	10-2	8-5	7-8	5-7	5-5
		60,000	14-9	17-0	13-1	13-6	12-2	10-0	9-1	6-6	6-4
	Center distance $A^{k, 1}$		3-9	4-11	2-11	3-2	2-7	1-9	1-7	1-0	1-0
16	Span without stirrups[i, j]		7-1	9-0	6-4	6-8	5-10	4-9	4-6	3-9	3-8
	1-#4	40,000	5-11	7-0	5-5	5-8	5-1	4-3	4-0	3-3	3-2
		60,000	7-3	8-7	6-8	6-11	6-3	5-2	4-10	3-11	3-10
	1-#5	40,000	7-4	8-9	6-9	7-0	6-4	5-3	4-11	4-0	3-11
		60,000	9-0	10-8	8-3	8-7	7-9	6-5	6-0	4-11	4-9
	2-#4 1-#6	40,000	8-4	9-11	7-8	7-11	7-2	5-11	5-7	4-6	4-5
		60,000	10-2	12-0	9-4	9-8	8-9	7-3	6-10	5-6	5-5
	2-#5	40,000	10-4	12-3	9-6	9-10	8-11	7-4	6-11	5-8	5-6
		60,000	14-4	17-1	13-3	13-8	12-4	10-3	9-8	7-10	7-8
	2-#6	40,000	14-1	16-9	13-0	13-5	12-2	10-1	9-6	7-0	6-10
		60,000	17-0	20-2	15-8	16-2	14-7	12-0	10-11	8-0	7-9
	Center distance $A^{k, 1}$		4-9	6-8	4-0	4-4	3-6	2-5	2-2	1-5	1-4

(continued)

TABLE R608.8(5)—continued
MAXIMUM ALLOWABLE CLEAR SPANS FOR 10-INCH-NOMINAL THICK FLAT LINTELS IN LOAD-BEARING WALLS[a, b, c, d, e, f, m]
ROOF CLEAR SPAN 40 FEET AND FLOOR CLEAR SPAN 32 FEET

LINTEL DEPTH, D^g (inches)	NUMBER OF BARS AND BAR SIZE IN TOP AND BOTTOM OF LINTEL	STEEL YIELD STRENGTH[h], f_y (psi)	DESIGN LOADING CONDITION DETERMINED FROM TABLE R608.8(1)								
			1	2		3		4		5	
			Maximum ground snow load (psf)								
			—	30	70	30	70	30	70	30	70
			Maximum clear span of lintel (feet - inches)								
20	Span without stirrups[i, j]		8-7	11-4	8-1	8-5	7-5	6-1	5-9	4-10	4-9
	1-#4	40,000	6-5	7-10	6-2	6-4	5-9	4-9	4-6	3-8	3-7
		60,000	7-10	9-7	7-6	7-9	7-0	5-10	5-6	4-5	4-4
	1-#5	40,000	8-0	9-9	7-8	7-11	7-2	5-11	5-7	4-6	4-5
		60,000	9-9	11-11	9-4	9-8	8-9	7-3	6-10	5-6	5-5
	2-#4 1-#6	40,000	9-0	11-1	8-8	8-11	8-1	6-9	6-4	5-2	5-0
		60,000	11-0	13-6	10-6	10-11	9-10	8-2	7-9	6-3	6-2
	2-#5	40,000	11-3	13-9	10-9	11-1	10-0	8-4	7-10	6-5	6-3
		60,000	15-8	19-2	15-0	15-6	14-0	11-8	11-0	8-11	8-9
	2-#6	40,000	15-5	18-10	14-8	15-2	13-9	11-5	10-9	8-6	8-3
		60,000	18-7	22-9	17-9	18-5	16-7	13-10	12-9	9-5	9-2
	Center distance $A^{k, l}$		5-7	8-4	5-1	5-5	4-5	3-1	2-9	1-10	1-9
24	Span without stirrups[i, j]		9-11	13-7	9-9	10-2	9-0	7-5	7-0	5-10	5-9
	1-#5	40,000	8-6	10-8	8-5	8-8	7-10	6-6	6-2	5-0	4-11
		60,000	10-5	13-0	10-3	10-7	9-7	8-0	7-6	6-1	6-0
	2-#4 1-#6	40,000	9-7	12-1	9-6	9-9	8-10	7-5	7-0	5-8	5-6
		60,000	11-9	14-9	11-7	11-11	10-10	9-0	8-6	6-11	6-9
	2-#5	40,000	12-0	15-0	11-9	12-2	11-0	9-2	8-8	7-1	6-11
		60,000	14-7	18-3	14-4	14-10	13-5	11-2	10-7	8-7	8-5
	2-#6	40,000	14-3	17-11	14-1	14-7	13-2	11-0	10-4	8-5	8-3
		60,000	19-11	25-0	19-7	20-3	18-4	15-3	14-5	10-10	10-7
	Center distance $A^{k, l}$		6-3	9-11	6-1	6-6	5-4	3-9	3-4	2-2	2-1

For SI: 1 inch = 25.4 mm, 1 foot = 304.8 mm, 1 pound per square inch = 6.895 kPa, 1 pound per square foot = 0.0479 kPa, Grade 40 = 280 MPa, Grade 60 = 420 MPa.

Note: Top and bottom reinforcement for lintels without stirrups, as shown in shaded cells, shall be equal to or greater than that required for lintel of the same depth and loading condition that has an allowable clear span that is equal to or greater than that of the lintel without stirrups.

a. See Table R608.3 for tolerances permitted from nominal thickness.

b. Table values are based on concrete with a minimum specified compressive strength of 2,500 psi. See Note j.

c. Table values are based on uniform loading. See Section R608.8.2 for lintels supporting concentrated loads.

d. Deflection criterion is $L/240$, where L is the clear span of the lintel in inches, or $^1/_2$ inch, whichever is less.

e. Linear interpolation is permitted between ground snow loads and between lintel depths.

f. DR indicates design required.

g. Lintel depth, D, is permitted to include the available height of wall located directly above the lintel, provided that the increased lintel depth spans the entire length of the lintel.

h. Stirrups shall be fabricated from reinforcing bars with the same yield strength as that used for the main longitudinal reinforcement.

i. Allowable clear span without stirrups applicable to all lintels of the same depth, D. Top and bottom reinforcement for lintels without stirrups shall be not less than the least amount of reinforcement required for a lintel of the same depth and loading condition with stirrups. All other spans require stirrups spaced at not more than $d/2$.

j. Where concrete with a minimum specified compressive strength of 3,000 psi is used, clear spans for lintels without stirrups shall be permitted to be multiplied by 1.05. If the increased span exceeds the allowable clear span for a lintel of the same depth and loading condition with stirrups, the top and bottom reinforcement shall be equal to or greater than that required for a lintel of the same depth and loading condition that has an allowable clear span that is equal to or greater than that of the lintel without stirrups that has been increased.

k. Center distance, A, is the center portion of the clear span where stirrups are not required. This is applicable to all longitudinal bar sizes and steel yield strengths.

l. Where concrete with a minimum specified compressive strength of 3,000 psi is used, center distance, A, shall be permitted to be multiplied by 1.10.

m. The maximum clear opening width between two solid wall segments shall be 18 feet. See Section R608.7.2.1. Lintel clear spans in the table greater than 18 feet are shown for interpolation and information only.

TABLE R608.8(6)
MAXIMUM ALLOWABLE CLEAR SPANS FOR 6-INCH-THICK WAFFLE-GRID LINTELS IN LOAD-BEARING WALLS[a, b, c, d, e, f, o]
MAXIMUM ROOF CLEAR SPAN 40 FEET AND MAXIMUM FLOOR SPAN 32 FEET

LINTEL DEPTH, D^g (inches)	NUMBER OF BARS AND BAR SIZE IN TOP AND BOTTOM OF LINTEL	STEEL YIELD STRENGTH[h], f_y (psi)	DESIGN LOADING CONDITION DETERMINED FROM TABLE R608.8(1)								
			1	2		3		4		5	
			Maximum ground snow load (psf)								
			—	30	70	30	70	30	70	30	70
			Maximum clear span of lintel (feet - inches)								
8[i]	Span without stirrups[k, l]		2-7	2-9	2-0	2-1	2-0	2-0	2-0	2-0	2-0
	1-#4	40,000	5-2	5-5	4-0	4-3	3-7	3-3	2-11	2-4	2-3
		60,000	5-9	6-3	4-0	4-3	3-7	3-3	2-11	2-4	2-3
	1-#5	40,000	5-9	6-3	4-0	4-3	3-7	3-3	2-11	2-4	2-3
		60,000	5-9	6-3	4-0	4-3	3-7	3-3	2-11	2-4	2-3
	2-#4 1-#6	40,000	5-9	6-3	4-0	4-3	3-7	3-3	2-11	2-4	2-3
		60,000	DR	DR	DR	DR	DR	DR	DR	DR	DR
	Center distance $A^{m, n}$		0-9	0-10	0-6	0-6	0-5	0-5	0-4	STL	STL
12[i]	Span without stirrups[k, l]		2-11	3-1	2-6	2-7	2-5	2-4	2-3	2-1	2-0
	1-#4	40,000	5-9	6-2	4-8	4-10	4-4	4-1	3-9	3-2	3-1
		60,000	8-0	8-7	6-6	6-9	6-0	5-5	4-11	3-11	3-10
	1-#5	40,000	8-1	8-9	6-8	6-11	6-0	5-5	4-11	3-11	3-10
		60,000	9-1	10-3	6-8	7-0	6-0	5-5	4-11	3-11	3-10
	2-#4 1-#6	40,000	9-1	9-9	6-8	7-0	6-0	5-5	4-11	3-11	3-10
	Center distance $A^{m, n}$		1-3	1-5	0-10	0-11	0-9	0-8	0-6	STL	STL
16[i]	Span without stirrups[k, l]		4-0	4-4	3-6	3-7	3-4	3-3	3-1	2-10	2-10
	1-#4	40,000	6-7	7-3	5-6	5-9	5-2	4-10	4-6	3-9	3-8
		60,000	8-0	8-10	6-9	7-0	6-3	5-11	5-5	4-7	4-5
	1-#5	40,000	8-2	9-0	6-11	7-2	6-5	6-0	5-7	4-8	4-6
		60,000	11-5	12-6	9-3	9-9	8-4	7-7	6-10	5-6	5-4
	2-#4 1-#6	40,000	10-7	11-7	8-11	9-3	8-3	7-7	6-10	5-6	5-4
		60,000	12-2	14-0	9-3	9-9	8-4	7-7	6-10	5-6	5-4
	2-#5	40,000	12-2	14-2	9-3	9-9	8-4	7-7	6-10	5-6	5-4
		60,000	DR	DR	DR	DR	DR	DR	DR	DR	DR
	Center distance $A^{m, n}$		1-8	2-0	1-2	1-3	1-0	0-11	0-9	STL	STL
20[i]	Span without stirrups[k, l]		5-0	5-6	4-6	4-7	4-3	4-1	4-0	3-8	3-8
	1-#4	40,000	7-2	8-2	6-3	6-6	5-10	5-6	5-1	4-3	4-2
		60,000	8-11	9-11	7-8	7-11	7-1	6-8	6-2	5-2	5-0
	1-#5	40,000	9-1	10-2	7-9	8-1	7-3	6-10	6-4	5-4	5-2
		60,000	12-8	14-2	10-11	11-3	10-2	9-6	8-9	7-1	6-10
	2-#4 1-#6	40,000	10-3	11-5	8-9	9-1	8-2	7-8	7-1	6-0	5-10
		60,000	14-3	15-11	11-9	12-5	10-8	9-9	8-9	7-1	6-10
	2-#5	40,000	14-6	16-3	11-6	12-1	10-4	9-6	8-6	6-11	6-8
		60,000	DR	DR	DR	DR	DR	DR	DR	DR	DR
	Center distance $A^{m, n}$		2-0	2-6	1-6	1-7	1-3	1-1	1-0	STL	STL

(continued)

TABLE R608.8(6)—continued
MAXIMUM ALLOWABLE CLEAR SPANS FOR 6-INCH-THICK WAFFLE-GRID LINTELS IN LOAD-BEARING WALLS[a, b, c, d, e, f, o]
MAXIMUM ROOF CLEAR SPAN 40 FEET AND MAXIMUM FLOOR SPAN 32 FEET

LINTEL DEPTH, D[g] (inches)	NUMBER OF BARS AND BAR SIZE IN TOP AND BOTTOM OF LINTEL	STEEL YIELD STRENGTH[h], f_y (psi)	DESIGN LOADING CONDITION DETERMINED FROM TABLE R608.8(1)								
			1	2		3		4		5	
			Maximum ground snow load (psf)								
			—	30	70	30	70	30	70	30	70
			Maximum clear span of lintel (feet - inches)								
24w[j]	Span without stirrups[k, l]		6-0	6-8	5-5	5-7	5-3	5-0	4-10	4-6	4-5
	1-#4	40,000	7-11	9-0	6-11	7-2	6-5	6-0	5-7	4-8	4-7
		60,000	9-8	10-11	8-5	8-9	7-10	7-4	6-10	5-9	5-7
	1-#5	40,000	9-10	11-2	8-7	8-11	8-0	7-6	7-0	5-10	5-8
		60,000	12-0	13-7	10-6	10-10	9-9	9-2	8-6	7-2	6-11
	2-#4 1-#6	40,000	11-1	12-7	9-8	10-1	9-1	8-6	7-10	6-7	6-5
		60,000	15-6	17-7	13-6	14-0	12-8	11-10	10-8	8-7	8-4
	2-#5	40,000	15-6	17-11	12-8	13-4	11-6	10-7	9-7	7-10	7-7
		60,000	DR	DR	DR	DR	DR	DR	DR	DR	DR
	Center distance A[m, n]		2-4	3-0	1-9	1-11	1-6	1-4	1-2	STL	STL

For SI: 1 inch = 25.4 mm, 1 foot = 304.8 mm, 1 pound per square inch = 6.895 kPa, 1 pound per square foot = 0.0479 kPa, Grade 40 = 280 MPa, Grade 60 = 420 MPa.

a. Where lintels are formed with waffle-grid forms, form material shall be removed, if necessary, to create top and bottom flanges of the lintel that are not less than 3 inches in depth (in the vertical direction), are not less than 5 inches in width for 6-inch-nominal waffle-grid forms and not less than 7 inches in width for 8-inch-nominal waffle-grid forms. See Figure R608.8(3). Flat form lintels shall be permitted in place of waffle-grid lintels. See Tables R608.8(2) through R608.8(5).

b. See Table R608.3 for tolerances permitted from nominal thicknesses and minimum dimensions and spacing of cores.

c. Table values are based on concrete with a minimum specified compressive strength of 2,500 psi. See Notes l and n. Table values are based on uniform loading. See Section R608.8.2 for lintels supporting concentrated loads.

d. Deflection criterion is $L/240$, where L is the clear span of the lintel in inches, or $^1/_2$ inch, whichever is less.

e. Linear interpolation is permitted between ground snow loads.

f. DR indicates design required. STL indicates stirrups required throughout lintel.

g. Lintel depth, D, is permitted to include the available height of wall located directly above the lintel, provided that the increased lintel depth spans the entire length of the lintel.

h. Stirrups shall be fabricated from reinforcing bars with the same yield strength as that used for the main longitudinal reinforcement.

i. Lintels less than 24 inches in depth with stirrups shall be formed from flat-wall forms [see Tables R608.8(2) through R608.8(5)], or, if necessary, form material shall be removed from waffle-grid forms so as to provide the required cover for stirrups. Allowable spans for lintels formed with flat-wall forms shall be determined from Tables R608.8(2) through R608.8(5).

j. Where stirrups are required for 24-inch-deep lintels, the spacing shall not exceed 12 inches on center.

k. Allowable clear span without stirrups applicable to all lintels of the same depth, D. Top and bottom reinforcement for lintels without stirrups shall be not less than the least amount of reinforcement required for a lintel of the same depth and loading condition with stirrups. All other spans require stirrups spaced at not more than $d/2$.

l. Where concrete with a minimum specified compressive strength of 3,000 psi is used, clear spans for lintels without stirrups shall be permitted to be multiplied by 1.05. If the increased span exceeds the allowable clear span for a lintel of the same depth and loading condition with stirrups, the top and bottom reinforcement shall be equal to or greater than that required for a lintel of the same depth and loading condition that has an allowable clear span that is equal to or greater than that of the lintel without stirrups that has been increased.

m. Center distance, A, is the center portion of the span where stirrups are not required. This is applicable to all longitudinal bar sizes and steel yield strengths.

n. Where concrete with a minimum specified compressive strength of 3,000 psi is used, center distance, A, shall be permitted to be multiplied by 1.10.

o. The maximum clear opening width between two solid wall segments shall be 18 feet. See Section R608.7.2.1. Lintel spans in the table greater than 18 feet are shown for interpolation and information only.

TABLE R608.8(7)
MAXIMUM ALLOWABLE CLEAR SPANS FOR 8-INCH-THICK WAFFLE-GRID LINTELS IN LOAD-BEARING WALLS[a, b, c, d, e, f, o]
MAXIMUM ROOF CLEAR SPAN 40 FEET AND MAXIMUM FLOOR CLEAR SPAN 32 FEET

LINTEL DEPTH, D [g] (inches)	NUMBER OF BARS AND BAR SIZE IN TOP AND BOTTOM OF LINTEL	STEEL YIELD STRENGTH[h], f_y (psi)	DESIGN LOADING CONDITION DETERMINED FROM TABLE R608.8(1)								
			1	2		3		4		5	
			Maximum ground snow load (psf)								
			—	30	70	30	70	30	70	30	70
			Maximum clear span of lintel (feet - inches)								
8[i]	Span without stirrups[k, l]		2-6	2-9	2-0	2-1	2-0	2-0	2-0	2-0	2-0
	1-#4	40,000	4-5	4-9	3-7	3-9	3-4	3-0	2-10	2-3	2-2
		60,000	5-6	6-2	4-0	4-3	3-7	3-1	2-10	2-3	2-2
	1-#5	40,000	5-6	6-2	4-0	4-3	3-7	3-1	2-10	2-3	2-2
	Center distance A[m, n]		0-9	0-10	0-6	0-6	0-5	0-4	0-4	STL	STL
12[i]	Span without stirrups[k, l]		2-10	3-1	2-6	2-7	2-5	2-3	2-2	2-0	2-0
	1-#4	40,000	5-7	6-1	4-8	4-10	4-4	3-11	3-8	3-0	2-11
		60,000	6-9	7-5	5-8	5-11	5-4	4-9	4-5	3-8	3-7
	1-#5	40,000	6-11	7-7	5-10	6-0	5-5	4-10	4-6	3-9	3-7
		60,000	8-8	10-1	6-7	7-0	5-11	5-2	4-8	3-9	3-7
	2-#4 1-#6	40,000	8-8	9-10	6-7	7-0	5-11	5-2	4-8	3-9	3-7
		60,000	8-8	10-1	6-7	7-0	5-11	5-2	4-8	3-9	3-7
	Center distance A[m, n]		1-2	1-5	0-10	0-11	0-9	0-7	0-6	STL	STL
16[i]	Span without stirrups[k, l]		3-10	4-3	3-6	3-7	3-4	3-2	3-0	2-10	2-9
	1-#4	40,000	6-5	7-2	5-6	5-9	5-2	4-8	4-4	3-7	3-6
		60,000	7-9	8-9	6-9	7-0	6-3	5-8	5-3	4-4	4-3
	1-#5	40,000	7-11	8-11	6-10	7-1	6-5	5-9	5-4	4-5	4-4
		60,000	9-8	10-11	8-4	8-8	7-10	7-0	6-6	5-2	5-1
	2-#4 1-#6	40,000	9-0	10-1	7-9	8-0	7-3	6-6	6-1	5-0	4-11
		60,000	11-5	13-10	9-2	9-8	8-3	7-2	6-6	5-2	5-1
	Center distance A[m, n]		1-6	1-11	1-2	1-3	1-0	0-10	0-8	STL	STL
20[i]	Span without stirrups[k, l]		4-10	5-5	4-5	4-7	4-3	4-0	3-11	3-7	3-7
	1-#4	40,000	7-0	8-1	6-3	6-5	5-10	5-3	4-11	4-1	3-11
		60,000	8-7	9-10	7-7	7-10	7-1	6-5	6-0	4-11	4-10
	1-#5	40,000	8-9	10-1	7-9	8-0	7-3	6-6	6-1	5-1	4-11
		60,000	10-8	12-3	9-6	9-10	8-10	8-0	7-5	6-2	6-0
	2-#4 1-#6	40,000	9-10	11-4	8-9	9-1	8-2	7-4	6-10	5-8	5-7
		60,000	12-0	13-10	10-8	11-0	9-11	9-0	8-4	6-8	6-6
	2-#5	40,000	12-3	14-1	10-10	11-3	10-2	8-11	8-1	6-6	6-4
		60,000	14-0	17-6	11-8	12-3	10-6	9-1	8-4	6-8	6-6
	Center distance A[m, n]		1-10	2-5	1-5	1-7	1-3	1-0	0-11	STL	STL

(continued)

TABLE R608.8(7)—continued
MAXIMUM ALLOWABLE CLEAR SPANS FOR 8-INCH-THICK WAFFLE-GRID LINTELS IN LOAD-BEARING WALLS[a, b, c, d, e, f, o]
MAXIMUM ROOF CLEAR SPAN 40 FEET AND MAXIMUM FLOOR CLEAR SPAN 32 FEET

LINTEL DEPTH, D [g] (inches)	NUMBER OF BARS AND BAR SIZE IN TOP AND BOTTOM OF LINTEL	STEEL YIELD STRENGTH[h], f_y (psi)	DESIGN LOADING CONDITION DETERMINED FROM TABLE R608.8(1)								
			1	2		3		4		5	
			Maximum ground snow load (psf)								
			—	30	70	30	70	30	70	30	70
			Maximum clear span of lintel (feet - inches)								
24[j]	Span without stirrups[k, l]		5-9	6-7	5-5	5-6	5-2	4-11	4-9	4-5	4-4
	1-#4	40,000	7-6	8-10	6-10	7-1	6-5	5-9	5-5	4-6	4-4
		60,000	9-2	10-9	8-4	8-8	7-10	7-1	6-7	5-6	5-4
	1-#5	40,000	9-5	11-0	8-6	8-10	8-0	7-2	6-8	5-7	5-5
		60,000	11-5	13-5	10-5	10-9	9-9	8-9	8-2	6-10	6-8
	2-#4 1-#6	40,000	10-7	12-5	9-8	10-0	9-0	8-1	7-7	6-3	6-2
		60,000	12-11	15-2	11-9	12-2	11-0	9-11	9-3	7-8	7-6
	2-#5	40,000	13-2	15-6	12-0	12-5	11-2	9-11	9-2	7-5	7-3
		60,000	16-3	21-0	14-1	14-10	12-9	11-1	10-1	8-1	7-11
	2-#6	40,000	14-4	18-5	12-6	13-2	11-5	9-11	9-2	7-5	7-3
	Center distance A [m, n]		2-1	2-11	1-9	1-10	1-6	1-3	1-1	STL	STL

For SI: 1 inch = 25.4 mm, 1 foot = 304.8 mm, 1 pound per square inch = 6.895 kPa, 1 pound per square foot = 0.0479 kPa, Grade 40 = 280 MPa, Grade 60 = 420 MPa.

a. Where lintels are formed with waffle-grid forms, form material shall be removed, if necessary, to create top and bottom flanges of the lintel that are not less than 3 inches in depth (in the vertical direction), are not less than 5 inches in width for 6-inch-nominal waffle-grid forms and not less than 7 inches in width for 8-inch-nominal waffle-grid forms. See Figure R608.8(3). Flat-form lintels shall be permitted in lieu of waffle-grid lintels. See Tables R608.8(2) through R608.8(5).

b. See Table R608.3 for tolerances permitted from nominal thicknesses and minimum dimensions and spacing of cores.

c. Table values are based on concrete with a minimum specified compressive strength of 2,500 psi. See Notes l and n. Table values are based on uniform loading. See Section R608.8.2 for lintels supporting concentrated loads.

d. Deflection criterion is $L/240$, where L is the clear span of the lintel in inches, or $^1/_2$ inch, whichever is less.

e. Linear interpolation is permitted between ground snow loads.

f. STL indicates stirrups required throughout lintel.

g. Lintel depth, D, is permitted to include the available height of wall located directly above the lintel, provided that the increased lintel depth spans the entire length of the lintel.

h. Stirrups shall be fabricated from reinforcing bars with the same yield strength as that used for the main longitudinal reinforcement.

i. Lintels less than 24 inches in depth with stirrups shall be formed from flat-wall forms [see Tables R608.8(2) through R608.8(5)], or, if necessary, form material shall be removed from waffle-grid forms so as to provide the required cover for stirrups. Allowable spans for lintels formed with flat-wall forms shall be determined from Tables R608.8(2) through R608.8(5).

j. Where stirrups are required for 24-inch-deep lintels, the spacing shall not exceed 12 inches on center.

k. Allowable clear span without stirrups applicable to all lintels of the same depth, D. Top and bottom reinforcement for lintels without stirrups shall be not less than the least amount of reinforcement required for a lintel of the same depth and loading condition with stirrups. All other spans require stirrups spaced at not more than $d/2$.

l. Where concrete with a minimum specified compressive strength of 3,000 psi is used, clear spans for lintels without stirrups shall be permitted to be multiplied by 1.05. If the increased span exceeds the allowable clear span for a lintel of the same depth and loading condition with stirrups, the top and bottom reinforcement shall be equal to or greater than that required for a lintel of the same depth and loading condition that has an allowable clear span that is equal to or greater than that of the lintel without stirrups that has been increased.

m. Center distance, A, is the center portion of the span where stirrups are not required. This is applicable to all longitudinal bar sizes and steel yield strengths.

n. Where concrete with a minimum specified compressive strength of 3,000 psi is used, center distance, A, shall be permitted to be multiplied by 1.10.

o. The maximum clear opening width between two solid wall segments shall be 18 feet. See Section R608.7.2.1. Lintel spans in the table greater than 18 feet are shown for interpolation and information only.

TABLE R608.8(8)
MAXIMUM ALLOWABLE CLEAR SPANS FOR 6-INCH-THICK SCREEN-GRID LINTELS IN LOAD-BEARING WALLS[a, b, c, d, e, f, p]
ROOF CLEAR SPAN 40 FEET AND FLOOR CLEAR SPAN 32 FEET

LINTEL DEPTH, D[g] (inches)	NUMBER OF BARS AND BAR SIZE IN TOP AND BOTTOM OF LINTEL	STEEL YIELD STRENGTH[h], f_y (psi)	DESIGN LOADING CONDITION DETERMINED FROM TABLE R608.8(1)								
			1	2		3		4		5	
			Maximum ground snow load (psf)								
			—	30	70	30	70	30	70	30	70
			Maximum clear span of lintel (feet - inches)								
12[i, j]	Span without stirrups		2-9	2-11	2-4	2-5	2-3	2-3	2-2	2-0	2-0
16[i, j]	Span without stirrups		3-9	4-0	3-4	3-5	3-2	3-1	3-0	2-9	2-9
20[i, j]	Span without stirrups		4-9	5-1	4-3	4-4	4-1	4-0	3-10	3-7	3-7
24[k]	Span without stirrups[l, m]		5-8	6-3	5-2	5-3	5-0	4-10	4-8	4-4	4-4
	1-#4	40,000	7-11	9-0	6-11	7-2	6-5	6-1	5-8	4-9	4-7
		60,000	9-9	11-0	8-5	8-9	7-10	7-5	6-10	5-9	5-7
	1-#5	40,000	9-11	11-2	8-7	8-11	8-0	7-7	7-0	5-11	5-9
		60,000	12-1	13-8	10-6	10-10	9-9	9-3	8-6	7-2	7-0
	2-#4 1-#6	40,000	11-2	12-8	9-9	10-1	9-1	8-7	7-11	6-8	6-6
		60,000	15-7	17-7	12-8	13-4	11-6	10-8	9-8	7-11	7-8
	2-#5	40,000	14-11	18-0	12-2	12-10	11-1	10-3	9-4	7-8	7-5
		60,000	DR	DR	DR	DR	DR	DR	DR	DR	DR
	Center distance A[n, o]		2-0	2-6	1-6	1-7	1-4	1-2	1-0	STL	STL

For SI: 1 inch = 25.4 mm, 1 foot = 304.8 mm, 1 pound per square inch = 6.895 kPa, 1 pound per square foot = 0.0479 kPa, Grade 40 = 280 MPa, Grade 60 = 420 MPa.

a. Where lintels are formed with screen-grid forms, form material shall be removed if necessary to create top and bottom flanges of the lintel that are not less than 5 inches in width and not less than 2.5 inches in depth (in the vertical direction). See Figure R608.8(4). Flat-form lintels shall be permitted in lieu of screen-grid lintels. See Tables R608.8(2) through R608.8(5).

b. See Table R608.3 for tolerances permitted from nominal thickness and minimum dimensions and spacings of cores.

c. Table values are based on concrete with a minimum specified compressive strength of 2,500 psi. See Notes m and o. Table values are based on uniform loading. See Section R608.7.2.1 for lintels supporting concentrated loads.

d. Deflection criterion is $L/240$, where L is the clear span of the lintel in inches, or $1/2$ inch, whichever is less.

e. Linear interpolation is permitted between ground snow loads.

f. DR indicates design required. STL indicates stirrups required throughout lintel.

g. Lintel depth, D, is permitted to include the available height of wall located directly above the lintel, provided that the increased lintel depth spans the entire length of the lintel.

h. Stirrups shall be fabricated from reinforcing bars with the same yield strength as that used for the main longitudinal reinforcement.

i. Stirrups are not required for lintels less than 24 inches in depth fabricated from screen-grid forms. Top and bottom reinforcement shall consist of a No. 4 bar having a yield strength of 40,000 psi or 60,000 psi.

j. Lintels between 12 and 24 inches in depth with stirrups shall be formed from flat-wall forms [see Tables R608.8(2) through R608.8(5)], or form material shall be removed from screen-grid forms to provide a concrete section comparable to that required for a flat wall. Allowable spans for flat lintels with stirrups shall be determined from Tables R608.8(2) through R608.8(5).

k. Where stirrups are required for 24-inch-deep lintels, the spacing shall not exceed 12 inches on center.

l. Allowable clear span without stirrups applicable to all lintels of the same depth, D. Top and bottom reinforcement for lintels without stirrups shall be not less than the least amount of reinforcement required for a lintel of the same depth and loading condition with stirrups. All other spans require stirrups spaced at not more than 12 inches.

m. Where concrete with a minimum specified compressive strength of 3,000 psi is used, clear spans for lintels without stirrups shall be permitted to be multiplied by 1.05. If the increased span exceeds the allowable clear span for a lintel of the same depth and loading condition with stirrups, the top and bottom reinforcement shall be equal to or greater than that required for a lintel of the same depth and loading condition that has an allowable clear span that is equal to or greater than that of the lintel without stirrups that has been increased.

n. Center distance, A, is the center portion of the span where stirrups are not required. This is applicable to all longitudinal bar sizes and steel yield strengths.

o. Where concrete with a minimum specified compressive strength of 3,000 psi is used, center distance, A, shall be permitted to be multiplied by 1.10.

p. The maximum clear opening width between two solid wall segments shall be 18 feet. See Section R608.7.2.1. Lintel spans in the table greater than 18 feet are shown for interpolation and information only.

TABLE R608.8(9)
MAXIMUM ALLOWABLE CLEAR SPANS FOR FLAT LINTELS WITHOUT STIRRUPS IN NONLOAD-BEARING WALLS[a, b, c, d, e, g]

LINTEL DEPTH, D^1 (inches)	NUMBER OF BARS AND BAR SIZE	STEEL YIELD STRENGTH, f_y (psi)	NOMINAL WALL THICKNESS (inches)							
			4		6		8		10	
			Lintel Supporting							
			Concrete Wall	Light-framed Gable	Concrete Wall	Light-framed Gable	Concrete Wall	Light-framed Gable	Concrete Wall	Light-framed Gable
			Maximum Clear Span of Lintel (feet - inches)							
8	1-#4	40,000	10-11	11-5	9-7	11-2	7-10	9-5	7-3	9-2
		60,000	12-5	11-7	10-11	13-5	9-11	13-2	9-3	12-10
	1-#5	40,000	12-7	11-7	11-1	13-8	10-1	13-5	9-4	13-1
		60,000	DR	DR	12-7	16-4	11-6	14-7	10-9	14-6
	2-#4 1-#6	40,000	DR	DR	12-0	15-3	10-11	15-0	10-2	14-8
		60,000	DR	DR	DR	DR	12-2	15-3	11-7	15-3
	2-#5	40,000	DR	DR	DR	DR	12-7	16-7	11-9	16-7
		60,000	DR	DR	DR	DR	DR	DR	13-3	16-7
	2-#6	40,000	DR	DR	DR	DR	DR	DR	13-2	17-8
		60,000	DR	DR	DR	DR	DR	DR	DR	DR
12	1-#4	40,000	11-5	9-10	10-6	12-0	9-6	11-6	8-9	11-1
		60,000	11-5	9-10	11-8	13-3	10-11	14-0	10-1	13-6
	1-#5	40,000	11-5	9-10	11-8	13-3	11-1	14-4	10-3	13-9
		60,000	11-5	9-10	11-8	13-3	11-10	16-0	11-9	16-9
	2-#4 1-#6	40,000	DR	DR	11-8	13-3	11-10	16-0	11-2	15-6
		60,000	DR	DR	11-8	13-3	11-10	16-0	11-11	18-4
	2-#5	40,000	DR	DR	11-8	13-3	11-10	16-0	11-11	18-4
		60,000	DR	DR	11-8	13-3	11-10	16-0	11-11	18-4
16	1-#4	40,000	13-6	13-0	11-10	13-8	10-7	12-11	9-11	12-4
		60,000	13-6	13-0	13-8	16-7	12-4	15-9	11-5	15-0
	1-#5	40,000	13-6	13-0	13-10	17-0	12-6	16-1	11-7	15-4
		60,000	13-6	13-0	13-10	17-1	14-0	19-7	13-4	18-8
	2-#4 1-#6	40,000	13-6	13-0	13-10	17-1	13-8	18-2	12-8	17-4
		60,000	13-6	13-0	13-10	17-1	14-0	20-3	14-1	—
	2-#5	40,000	13-6	13-0	13-10	17-1	14-0	20-3	14-1	—
		60,000	DR	DR	13-10	17-1	14-0	20-3	14-1	—
20	1-#4	40,000	14-11	15-10	13-0	14-10	11-9	13-11	10-10	13-2
		60,000	15-3	15-10	14-11	18-1	13-6	17-0	12-6	16-2
	1-#5	40,000	15-3	15-10	15-2	18-6	13-9	17-5	12-8	16-6
		60,000	15-3	15-10	15-8	20-5	15-9	—	14-7	20-1
	2-#4 1-#6	40,000	15-3	15-10	15-8	20-5	14-11	—	13-10	—
		60,000	15-3	15-10	15-8	20-5	15-10	—	15-11	—
	2-#5	40,000	15-3	15-10	15-8	20-5	15-10	—	15-11	—
		60,000	15-3	15-10	15-8	20-5	15-10	—	15-11	—

(continued)

TABLE R608.8(9)—continued
TABLE R608.8(9)—continued
MAXIMUM ALLOWABLE CLEAR SPANS FOR FLAT LINTELS WITHOUT STIRRUPS IN NONLOAD-BEARING WALLS[a, b, c, d, e, g]

LINTEL DEPTH, D^f (inches)	NUMBER OF BARS AND BAR SIZE	STEEL YIELD STRENGTH, f_y (psi)	NOMINAL WALL THICKNESS (inches)							
			4		6		8		10	
			Lintel Supporting							
			Concrete Wall	Light-framed Gable	Concrete Wall	Light-framed Gable	Concrete Wall	Light-framed Gable	Concrete Wall	Light-framed Gable
			Maximum Clear Span of Lintel (feet - inches)							
24	1-#4	40,000	16-1	17-1	13-11	15-10	12-7	14-9	11-8	13-10
		60,000	16-11	18-5	16-1	19-3	14-6	18-0	13-5	17-0
	1-#5	40,000	16-11	18-5	16-3	19-8	14-9	18-5	13-8	17-4
		60,000	16-11	18-5	17-4	—	17-0	—	15-8	—
	2-#4 1-#6	40,000	16-11	18-5	17-4	—	16-1	—	14-10	—
		60,000	16-11	18-5	17-4	—	17-6	—	17-1	—
	2-#5	40,000	16-11	18-5	17-4	—	17-6	—	17-4	—
		60,000	16-11	18-5	17-4	—	17-6	—	17-8	—

For SI: 1 inch = 25.4 mm, 1 foot = 304.8 mm, 1 pound per square inch = 6.895 kPa, Grade 40 = 280 MPa, Grade 60 = 420 MPa.

DR = Design Required.

a. See Table R608.3 for tolerances permitted from nominal thickness.

b. Table values are based on concrete with a minimum specified compressive strength of 2,500 psi. See Note e.

c. Deflection criterion is $L/240$, where L is the clear span of the lintel in inches, or $^1/_2$ inch, whichever is less.

d. Linear interpolation between lintels depths, D, is permitted provided the two cells being used to interpolate are shaded.

e. Where concrete with a minimum specified compressive strength of 3,000 psi is used, spans in cells that are shaded shall be permitted to be multiplied by 1.05.

f. Lintel depth, D, is permitted to include the available height of wall located directly above the lintel, provided that the increased lintel depth spans the entire length of the lintel.

g. The maximum clear opening width between two solid wall segments shall be 18 feet. See Section R608.7.2.1. Lintel spans in the table greater than 18 feet are shown for interpolation and information purposes only.

TABLE R608.8(10)
MAXIMUM ALLOWABLE CLEAR SPANS FOR WAFFLE-GRID AND SCREEN-GRID LINTELS WITHOUT STIRRUPS IN NONLOAD-BEARING WALLS[c, d, e, f, g]

LINTEL DEPTH[h], D (inches)	FORM TYPE AND NOMINAL WALL THICKNESS (inches)					
	6-inch Waffle-grid[a]		8-inch Waffle-grid[a]		6-inch Screen-grid[b]	
	Lintel supporting					
	Concrete Wall	Light-framed Gable	Concrete Wall	Light-framed Gable	Concrete Wall	Light-framed Gable
	Maximum Clear Span of Lintel (feet - inches)					
8	10-3	8-8	8-8	8-3	—	—
12	9-2	7-6	7-10	7-1	8-8	6-9
16	10-11	10-0	9-4	9-3	—	—
20	12-5	12-2	10-7	11-2	—	—
24	13-9	14-2	11-10	12-11	13-0	12-9

For SI: 1 inch = 25.4 mm, 1 foot = 304.8 mm, Grade 40 = 280 MPa, Grade 60 = 420 MPa.

a. Where lintels are formed with waffle-grid forms, form material shall be removed, if necessary, to create top and bottom flanges of the lintel that are not less than 3 inches in depth (in the vertical direction), are not less than 5 inches in width for 6-inch waffle-grid forms and not less than 7 inches in width for 8-inch waffle-grid forms. See Figure R608.8(3). Flat-form lintels shall be permitted in lieu of waffle-grid lintels. See Tables R608.8(2) through R608.8(5).

b. Where lintels are formed with screen-grid forms, form material shall be removed if necessary to create top and bottom flanges of the lintel that are not less than 5 inches in width and not less than 2.5 inches in depth (in the vertical direction). See Figure R608.8(4). Flat-form lintels shall be permitted in lieu of screen-grid lintels. See Tables R608.8(2) through R608.8(5).

c. See Table R608.3 for tolerances permitted from nominal thickness and minimum dimensions and spacing of cores.

d. Table values are based on concrete with a minimum specified compressive strength of 2,500 psi. See Note g.

e. Deflection criterion is $L/240$, where L is the clear span of the lintel in inches, or $^1/_2$ inch, whichever is less.

f. Top and bottom reinforcement shall consist of a No. 4 bar having a minimum yield strength of 40,000 psi.

g. Where concrete with a minimum specified compressive strength of 3,000 psi is used, spans in shaded cells shall be permitted to be multiplied by 1.05.

h. Lintel depth, D, is permitted to include the available height of wall located directly above the lintel, provided that the increased lintel depth spans the entire length of the lintel.

R608.9 Requirements for connections–general. Concrete walls shall be connected to footings, floors, ceilings and roofs in accordance with this section.

R608.9.1 Connections between concrete walls and light-framed floor, ceiling and roof systems. Connections between concrete walls and light-framed floor, ceiling and roof systems using the prescriptive details of Figures R608.9(1) through R608.9(12) shall comply with this section and Sections R608.9.2 and R608.9.3.

R608.9.1.1 Anchor bolts. Anchor bolts used to connect light-framed floor, ceiling and roof systems to concrete walls in accordance with Figures R608.9(1) through R608.9(12) shall have heads, or shall be rods with threads on both ends with a hex or square nut on the end embedded in the concrete. Bolts and threaded rods shall comply with Section R608.5.2.2. Anchor bolts with J- or L-hooks shall not be used where the connection details in these figures are used.

R608.9.1.2 Removal of stay-in-place form material at bolts. Holes in stay-in-place forms for installing bolts for attaching face-mounted wood ledger boards to the wall shall be not less than 4 inches (102 mm) in diameter for forms not greater than $1^1/_2$ inches (38 mm) in thickness, and increased 1 inch (25 mm) in diameter for each $^1/_2$-inch (12.7 mm) increase in form thickness. Holes in stay-in-place forms for installing bolts for attaching face-mounted cold-formed steel tracks to the wall shall be not less than 4 inches (102 mm) square. The wood ledger board or steel track shall be in direct contact with the concrete at each bolt location.

> **Exception:** A vapor retarder or other material less than or equal to $^1/_{16}$ inch (1.6 mm) in thickness is permitted to be installed between the wood ledger or cold-formed track and the concrete.

R608.9.2 Connections between concrete walls and light-framed floor systems. Connections between concrete walls and light-framed floor systems shall be in accordance with one of the following:

1. For floor systems of wood-framed construction, the provisions of Section R608.9.1 and the prescriptive details of Figures R608.9(1) through R608.9(4), where permitted by the tables accompanying those figures. Portions of connections of wood-framed floor systems not noted in the figures shall be in accordance with Section R502, or AWC WFCM, if applicable. Wood framing members shall be of a species having a specific gravity equal to or greater than 0.42.

2. For floor systems of cold-formed steel construction, the provisions of Section R608.9.1 and the prescriptive details of Figures R608.9(5) through R608.9(8), where permitted by the tables accompanying those figures. Portions of connections of cold-formed steel-framed floor systems not noted in the figures shall be in accordance with Section R505, or AISI S230, if applicable.

3. Proprietary connectors selected to resist loads and load combinations in accordance with Appendix A (ASD) or Appendix B (LRFD) of PCA 100.

4. An engineered design using loads and load combinations in accordance with Appendix A (ASD) or Appendix B (LRFD) of PCA 100.

5. An engineered design using loads and material design provisions in accordance with this code, or in accordance with ASCE 7, ACI 318, and AWC NDS for wood-framed construction or AISI S100 for cold-formed steel frame construction.

R608.9.3 Connections between concrete walls and light-framed ceiling and roof systems. Connections between concrete walls and light-framed ceiling and roof systems shall be in accordance with one of the following:

1. For ceiling and roof systems of wood-framed construction, the provisions of Section R608.9.1 and the prescriptive details of Figures R608.9(9) and R608.9(10), where permitted by the tables accompanying those figures. Portions of connections of wood-framed ceiling and roof systems not noted in the figures shall be in accordance with Section R802, or AWC WFCM, if applicable. Wood framing members shall be of a species having a specific gravity equal to or greater than 0.42.

2. For ceiling and roof systems of cold-formed steel construction, the provisions of Section R608.9.1 and the prescriptive details of Figures R608.9(11) and R608.9(12), where permitted by the tables accompanying those figures. Portions of connections of cold-formed-steel framed ceiling and roof systems not noted in the figures shall be in accordance with Section R804, or AISI S230, if applicable.

3. Proprietary connectors selected to resist loads and load combinations in accordance with Appendix A (ASD) or Appendix B (LRFD) of PCA 100.

4. An engineered design using loads and load combinations in accordance with Appendix A (ASD) or Appendix B (LRFD) of PCA 100.

5. An engineered design using loads and material design provisions in accordance with this code, or in accordance with ASCE 7, ACI 318, and AWC NDS for wood-framed construction or AISI S100 for cold-formed steel-framed construction.

R608.10 Floor, roof and ceiling diaphragms. Floors and roofs in buildings with exterior walls of concrete shall be designed and constructed as diaphragms. Where gable-end walls occur, ceilings shall be designed and constructed as diaphragms. The design and construction of floors, roofs and ceilings of wood framing or cold-formed-steel framing serving as diaphragms shall comply with the applicable requirements of this code, or AWC WFCM or AISI S230, if applicable. Wood framing members shall be of a species having a specific gravity equal to or greater than 0.42.

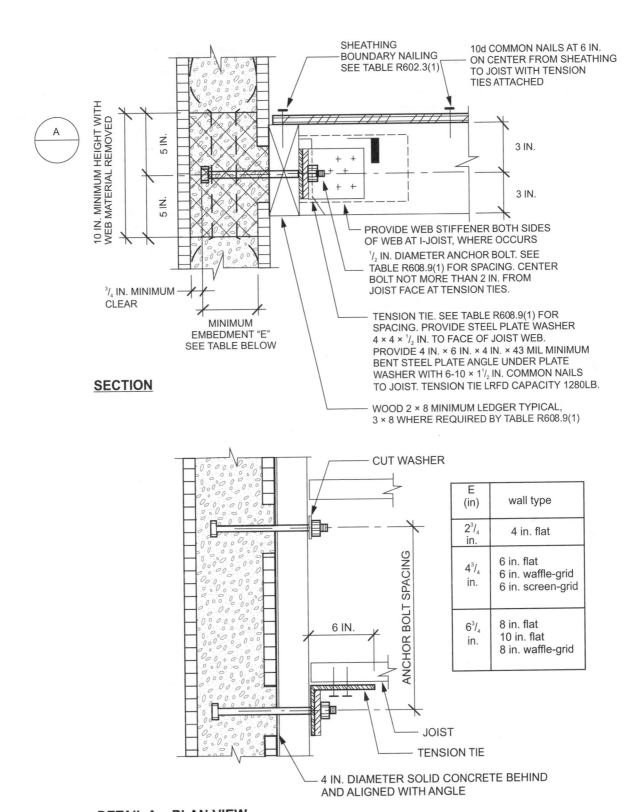

SHEATHING
BOUNDARY NAILING
SEE TABLE R602.3(1)

10d COMMON NAILS AT 6 IN.
ON CENTER FROM SHEATHING
TO JOIST WITH TENSION
TIES ATTACHED

10 IN. MINIMUM HEIGHT WITH
WEB MATERIAL REMOVED

5 IN.

5 IN.

3 IN.

3 IN.

³/₄ IN. MINIMUM
CLEAR

MINIMUM
EMBEDMENT "E"
SEE TABLE BELOW

SECTION

PROVIDE WEB STIFFENER BOTH SIDES
OF WEB AT I-JOIST, WHERE OCCURS

¹/₂ IN. DIAMETER ANCHOR BOLT. SEE
TABLE R608.9(1) FOR SPACING. CENTER
BOLT NOT MORE THAN 2 IN. FROM
JOIST FACE AT TENSION TIES.

TENSION TIE. SEE TABLE R608.9(1) FOR
SPACING. PROVIDE STEEL PLATE WASHER
4 × 4 × ¹/₂ IN. TO FACE OF JOIST WEB.
PROVIDE 4 IN. × 6 IN. × 4 IN. × 43 MIL MINIMUM
BENT STEEL PLATE ANGLE UNDER PLATE
WASHER WITH 6-10 × 1¹/₂ IN. COMMON NAILS
TO JOIST. TENSION TIE LRFD CAPACITY 1280LB.

WOOD 2 × 8 MINIMUM LEDGER TYPICAL,
3 × 8 WHERE REQUIRED BY TABLE R608.9(1)

CUT WASHER

ANCHOR BOLT SPACING

6 IN.

JOIST

TENSION TIE

4 IN. DIAMETER SOLID CONCRETE BEHIND
AND ALIGNED WITH ANGLE

DETAIL A – PLAN VIEW

E (in)	wall type
2³/₄ in.	4 in. flat
4³/₄ in.	6 in. flat 6 in. waffle-grid 6 in. screen-grid
6³/₄ in.	8 in. flat 10 in. flat 8 in. waffle-grid

For SI: 1 mil = 0.0254 mm, 1 inch = 25.4 mm, 1 pound-force = 4.448 N.

FIGURE R608.9(1)
WOOD-FRAMED FLOOR TO SIDE OF CONCRETE WALL, FRAMING PERPENDICULAR

TABLE R608.9(1)
WOOD-FRAMED FLOOR TO SIDE OF CONCRETE WALL, FRAMING PERPENDICULAR[a, b]

ANCHOR BOLT SPACING (inches)	TENSION TIE SPACING (inches)	BASIC WIND SPEED (mph)					
		115B	120B	130B	140B	150B	160B
		—	—	110C	119C	127C	136C
		—	—	—	110D	117D	125D
12	12						
12	24						
12	36						
12	48						
16	16						
16	32						
16	48						
19.2	19.2						
19.2	38.4						

For SI: 1 inch = 25.4 mm, 1 mile per hour = 0.447 m/s.

a. This table is for use with the detail in Figure R608.9(1). Use of this detail is permitted where a cell is not shaded and prohibited where shaded.

b. Wall design per other provisions of Section R608 is required.

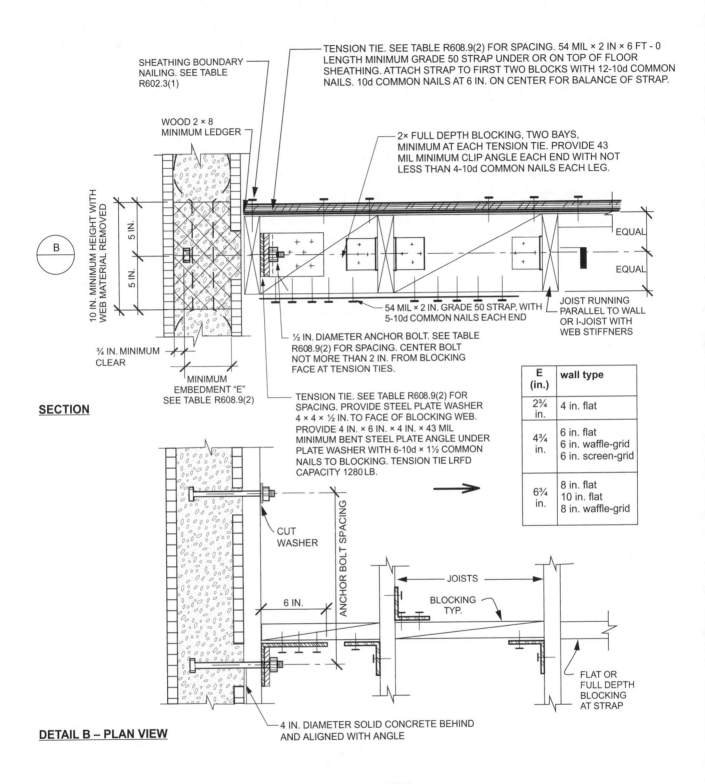

SHEATHING BOUNDARY NAILING. SEE TABLE R602.3(1)

WOOD 2 × 8 MINIMUM LEDGER

TENSION TIE. SEE TABLE R608.9(2) FOR SPACING. 54 MIL × 2 IN × 6 FT - 0 LENGTH MINIMUM GRADE 50 STRAP UNDER OR ON TOP OF FLOOR SHEATHING. ATTACH STRAP TO FIRST TWO BLOCKS WITH 12-10d COMMON NAILS. 10d COMMON NAILS AT 6 IN. ON CENTER FOR BALANCE OF STRAP.

2× FULL DEPTH BLOCKING, TWO BAYS, MINIMUM AT EACH TENSION TIE. PROVIDE 43 MIL MINIMUM CLIP ANGLE EACH END WITH NOT LESS THAN 4-10d COMMON NAILS EACH LEG.

10 IN. MINIMUM HEIGHT WITH WEB MATERIAL REMOVED

5 IN.

5 IN.

5 IN.

EQUAL

EQUAL

JOIST RUNNING PARALLEL TO WALL OR I-JOIST WITH WEB STIFFNERS

54 MIL × 2 IN. GRADE 50 STRAP, WITH 5-10d COMMON NAILS EACH END

¾ IN. MINIMUM CLEAR

MINIMUM EMBEDMENT "E" SEE TABLE R608.9(2)

½ IN. DIAMETER ANCHOR BOLT. SEE TABLE R608.9(2) FOR SPACING. CENTER BOLT NOT MORE THAN 2 IN. FROM BLOCKING FACE AT TENSION TIES.

SECTION

TENSION TIE. SEE TABLE R608.9(2) FOR SPACING. PROVIDE STEEL PLATE WASHER 4 × 4 × ½ IN. TO FACE OF BLOCKING WEB. PROVIDE 4 IN. × 6 IN. × 4 IN. × 43 MIL MINIMUM BENT STEEL PLATE ANGLE UNDER PLATE WASHER WITH 6-10d × 1½ COMMON NAILS TO BLOCKING. TENSION TIE LRFD CAPACITY 1280 LB.

E (in.)	wall type
2¾ in.	4 in. flat
4¾ in.	6 in. flat 6 in. waffle-grid 6 in. screen-grid
6¾ in.	8 in. flat 10 in. flat 8 in. waffle-grid

CUT WASHER

ANCHOR BOLT SPACING

6 IN.

JOISTS

BLOCKING TYP.

FLAT OR FULL DEPTH BLOCKING AT STRAP

DETAIL B – PLAN VIEW

4 IN. DIAMETER SOLID CONCRETE BEHIND AND ALIGNED WITH ANGLE

For SI: 1 mil = 0.0254 mm, 1 inch = 25.4 mm, 1 foot = 304.8 mm, 1 pound-force = 4.448 N.

FIGURE R608.9(2)
WOOD-FRAMED FLOOR TO SIDE OF CONCRETE WALL, FRAMING PARALLEL

TABLE R608.9(2)
WOOD-FRAMED FLOOR TO SIDE OF CONCRETE WALL, FRAMING PARALLEL[a, b]

ANCHOR BOLT SPACING (inches)	TENSION TIE SPACING (inches)	BASIC WIND SPEED (mph) AND WIND EXPOSURE CATEGORY					
		115B	120B	130B	140B	150B	160B
		—	—	110C	119C	127C	136C
		—	—	—	110D	117D	125D
12	12						
12	24						
12	36						
12	48						
16	16						
16	32						
16	48						
19.2	19.2						
19.2	38.4						
24	24						
24	48						

For SI: 1 inch = 25.4 mm, 1 mile per hour = 0.447 m/s.

a. This table is for use with the detail in Figure R608.9(2). Use of this detail is permitted where a cell is not shaded and prohibited where shaded.

b. Wall design per other provisions of Section R608 is required.

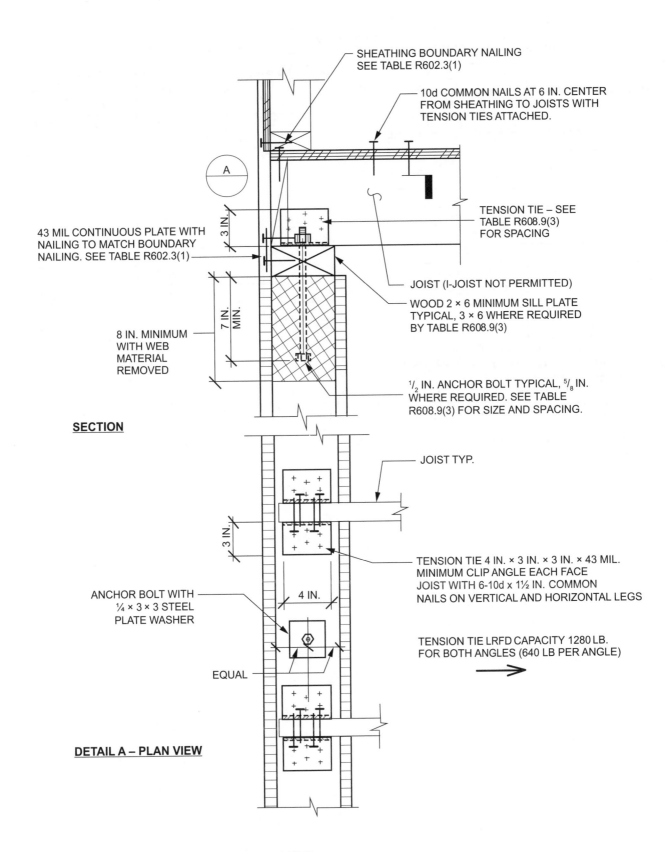

SHEATHING BOUNDARY NAILING
SEE TABLE R602.3(1)

10d COMMON NAILS AT 6 IN. CENTER
FROM SHEATHING TO JOISTS WITH
TENSION TIES ATTACHED.

TENSION TIE – SEE
TABLE R608.9(3)
FOR SPACING

43 MIL CONTINUOUS PLATE WITH
NAILING TO MATCH BOUNDARY
NAILING. SEE TABLE R602.3(1)

3 IN.

JOIST (I-JOIST NOT PERMITTED)

WOOD 2 × 6 MINIMUM SILL PLATE
TYPICAL, 3 × 6 WHERE REQUIRED
BY TABLE R608.9(3)

7 IN. MIN.

8 IN. MINIMUM
WITH WEB
MATERIAL
REMOVED

$^1/_2$ IN. ANCHOR BOLT TYPICAL, $^5/_8$ IN.
WHERE REQUIRED. SEE TABLE
R608.9(3) FOR SIZE AND SPACING.

SECTION

JOIST TYP.

3 IN.

ANCHOR BOLT WITH
$^1/_4$ × 3 × 3 STEEL
PLATE WASHER

4 IN.

TENSION TIE 4 IN. × 3 IN. × 3 IN. × 43 MIL.
MINIMUM CLIP ANGLE EACH FACE
JOIST WITH 6-10d x 1½ IN. COMMON
NAILS ON VERTICAL AND HORIZONTAL LEGS

TENSION TIE LRFD CAPACITY 1280 LB.
FOR BOTH ANGLES (640 LB PER ANGLE)

EQUAL

DETAIL A – PLAN VIEW

For SI: 1 mil = 0.0254 mm, 1 inch = 25.4 mm, 1 pound-force = 4.448 N.

FIGURE R608.9(3)
WOOD-FRAMED FLOOR TO TOP OF CONCRETE WALL FRAMING, PERPENDICULAR

TABLE R608.9(3)
WOOD-FRAMED FLOOR TO TOP OF CONCRETE WALL, FRAMING PERPENDICULAR[a, b, c, d, e]

ANCHOR BOLT SPACING (inches)	TENSION TIE SPACING (inches)	BASIC WIND SPEED (mph) AND WIND EXPOSURE CATEGORY					
		115B	120B	130B	140B	150B	160B
		—	—	110C	119C	127C	136C
		—	—	—	110D	117D	125D
12	12						6
12	24					6	6
12	36					6	6
12	48				6	6	6
16	16					6	6A
16	32				6	6	6A
16	48			6	6	6	6A
19.2	19.2				6A	6A	6B
19.2	38.4			6	6A	6A	6B
24	24			6A	6B	6B	6B
24	48		6	6A	6B	6B	8B

For SI: 1 inch = 25.4 mm, 1 mile per hour = 0.447 m/s.

a. This table is for use with the detail in Figure R608.9(3). Use of this detail is permitted where cell is not shaded.

b. Wall design per other provisions in Section R608 is required.

c. For wind design, minimum 4-inch-nominal wall is permitted in unshaded cells that do not contain a number.

d. Numbers 6 and 8 indicate minimum permitted nominal wall thickness in inches necessary to develop required strength (capacity) of connection. As a minimum, this nominal thickness shall occur in the portion of the wall indicated by the cross hatching in Figure R608.9(3). For the remainder of the wall, see Note b.

e. Letter "A" indicates that a minimum nominal 3 × 6 sill plate is required. Letter "B" indicates that a $^5/_8$-inch-diameter anchor bolt and a minimum nominal 3 × 6 sill plate are required.

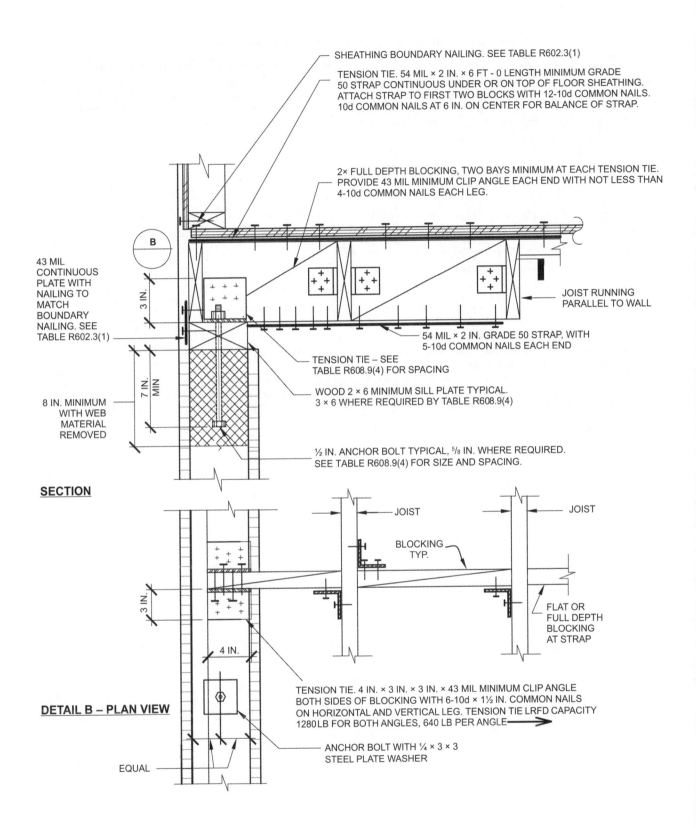

SHEATHING BOUNDARY NAILING. SEE TABLE R602.3(1)

TENSION TIE. 54 MIL × 2 IN. × 6 FT - 0 LENGTH MINIMUM GRADE 50 STRAP CONTINUOUS UNDER OR ON TOP OF FLOOR SHEATHING. ATTACH STRAP TO FIRST TWO BLOCKS WITH 12-10d COMMON NAILS. 10d COMMON NAILS AT 6 IN. ON CENTER FOR BALANCE OF STRAP.

2× FULL DEPTH BLOCKING, TWO BAYS MINIMUM AT EACH TENSION TIE. PROVIDE 43 MIL MINIMUM CLIP ANGLE EACH END WITH NOT LESS THAN 4-10d COMMON NAILS EACH LEG.

43 MIL CONTINUOUS PLATE WITH NAILING TO MATCH BOUNDARY NAILING. SEE TABLE R602.3(1)

B

3 IN.

JOIST RUNNING PARALLEL TO WALL

54 MIL × 2 IN. GRADE 50 STRAP, WITH 5-10d COMMON NAILS EACH END

TENSION TIE – SEE TABLE R608.9(4) FOR SPACING

7 IN. MIN

8 IN. MINIMUM WITH WEB MATERIAL REMOVED

WOOD 2 × 6 MINIMUM SILL PLATE TYPICAL. 3 × 6 WHERE REQUIRED BY TABLE R608.9(4)

½ IN. ANCHOR BOLT TYPICAL, ⅝ IN. WHERE REQUIRED. SEE TABLE R608.9(4) FOR SIZE AND SPACING.

SECTION

JOIST

JOIST

BLOCKING TYP.

3 IN.

FLAT OR FULL DEPTH BLOCKING AT STRAP

4 IN.

DETAIL B – PLAN VIEW

TENSION TIE. 4 IN. × 3 IN. × 3 IN. × 43 MIL MINIMUM CLIP ANGLE BOTH SIDES OF BLOCKING WITH 6-10d × 1½ IN. COMMON NAILS ON HORIZONTAL AND VERTICAL LEG. TENSION TIE LRFD CAPACITY 1280LB FOR BOTH ANGLES, 640 LB PER ANGLE

ANCHOR BOLT WITH ¼ × 3 × 3 STEEL PLATE WASHER

EQUAL

For SI: 1 mil = 0.0254 mm, 1 inch = 25.4 mm, 1 foot = 304.8 mm, 1 pound-force = 4.448 N.

FIGURE R608.9(4)
WOOD-FRAMED FLOOR TO TOP OF CONCRETE WALL, FRAMING PARALLEL

TABLE R608.9(4)
WOOD-FRAMED FLOOR TO TOP OF CONCRETE WALL, FRAMING PARALLEL[a, b, c, d, e]

ANCHOR BOLT SPACING (inches)	TENSION TIE SPACING (inches)	BASIC WIND SPEED (mph) AND WIND EXPOSURE CATEGORY					
		115B	120B	130B	140B	150B	160B
		—	—	110C	119C	127C	136C
		—	—	—	110D	117D	125D
12	12						6
12	24					6	6
12	36					6	6
12	48				6	6	6
16	16					6	6A
16	32				6	6	6A
16	48			6	6	6	6A
19.2	19.2				6A	6A	6B
19.2	38.4			6	6A	6A	6B
24	24			6A	6B	6B	6B
24	48		6	6A	6B	6B	8B

For SI: 1 inch = 25.4 mm, 1 mile per hour = 0.447 m/s.

a. This table is for use with the detail in Figure R608.9(4). Use of this detail is permitted where a cell is not shaded.

b. Wall design per other provisions of Section R608 is required.

c. For wind design, minimum 4-inch-nominal wall is permitted in unshaded cells that do not contain a number.

d. Numbers 6 and 8 indicate minimum permitted nominal wall thickness in inches necessary to develop required strength (capacity) of connection. As a minimum, this nominal thickness shall occur in the portion of the wall indicated by the cross hatching in Figure R608.9(4). For the remainder of the wall, see Note b.

e. Letter "A" indicates that a minimum nominal 3 × 6 sill plate is required. Letter "B" indicates that a $^5/_8$-inch-diameter anchor bolt and a minimum nominal 3 × 6 sill plate are required.

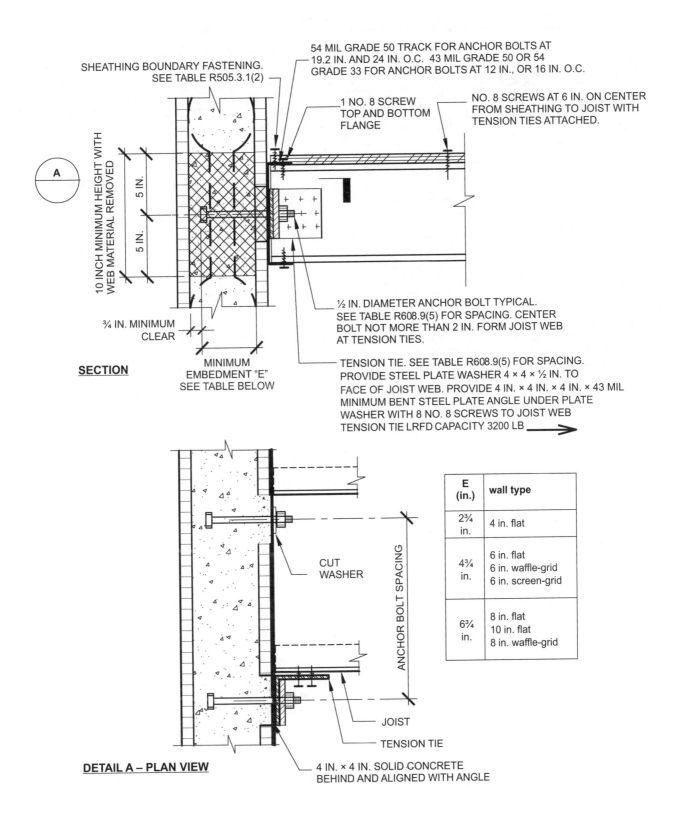

SHEATHING BOUNDARY FASTENING.
SEE TABLE R505.3.1(2)

54 MIL GRADE 50 TRACK FOR ANCHOR BOLTS AT
19.2 IN. AND 24 IN. O.C. 43 MIL GRADE 50 OR 54
GRADE 33 FOR ANCHOR BOLTS AT 12 IN., OR 16 IN. O.C.

1 NO. 8 SCREW
TOP AND BOTTOM
FLANGE

NO. 8 SCREWS AT 6 IN. ON CENTER
FROM SHEATHING TO JOIST WITH
TENSION TIES ATTACHED.

10 INCH MINIMUM HEIGHT WITH
WEB MATERIAL REMOVED

5 IN.

5 IN.

¾ IN. MINIMUM
CLEAR

SECTION

MINIMUM
EMBEDMENT "E"
SEE TABLE BELOW

½ IN. DIAMETER ANCHOR BOLT TYPICAL.
SEE TABLE R608.9(5) FOR SPACING. CENTER
BOLT NOT MORE THAN 2 IN. FORM JOIST WEB
AT TENSION TIES.

TENSION TIE. SEE TABLE R608.9(5) FOR SPACING.
PROVIDE STEEL PLATE WASHER 4 × 4 × ½ IN. TO
FACE OF JOIST WEB. PROVIDE 4 IN. × 4 IN. × 4 IN. × 43 MIL
MINIMUM BENT STEEL PLATE ANGLE UNDER PLATE
WASHER WITH 8 NO. 8 SCREWS TO JOIST WEB
TENSION TIE LRFD CAPACITY 3200 LB

CUT
WASHER

ANCHOR BOLT SPACING

E (in.)	wall type
2¾ in.	4 in. flat
4¾ in.	6 in. flat 6 in. waffle-grid 6 in. screen-grid
6¾ in.	8 in. flat 10 in. flat 8 in. waffle-grid

DETAIL A – PLAN VIEW

JOIST

TENSION TIE

4 IN. × 4 IN. SOLID CONCRETE
BEHIND AND ALIGNED WITH ANGLE

For SI: 1 mil = 0.0254 mm, 1 inch = 25.4 mm, 1 pound-force = 4.448 N.

FIGURE R608.9(5)
COLD-FORMED STEEL FLOOR TO SIDE OF CONCRETE WALL, FRAMING PERPENDICULAR

COLD-FORMED STEEL-FRAMED FLOOR TO SIDE OF CONCRETE WALL, FRAMING PERPENDICULAR[a, b, c]

ANCHOR BOLT SPACING (inches)	TENSION TIE SPACING (inches)	BASIC WIND SPEED (mph) AND WIND EXPOSURE CATEGORY					
		115B	120B	130B	140B	150B	160B
		—	—	110C	119C	127C	136C
		—	—	—	110D	117D	125D
12	12						
12	24						
12	36						
12	48						
16	16						
16	32						
16	48						
19.2	19.2						
19.2	38.4						
24	24						
24	48						

For SI: 1 inch = 25.4 mm, 1 mile per hour = 0.4470 m/s.

a. This table is for use with the detail in Figure R608.9(5). Use of this detail is permitted where a cell is not shaded.

b. Wall design per other provisions of Section R608 is required.

c. For wind design, minimum 4-inch-nominal wall is permitted in unshaded cells that do not contain a number.

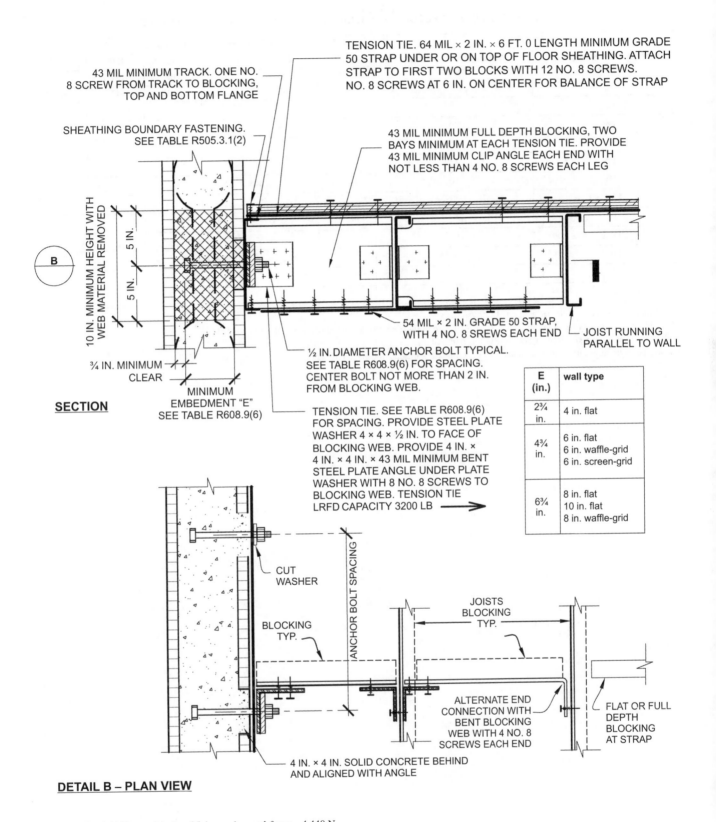

SECTION

DETAIL B – PLAN VIEW

43 MIL MINIMUM TRACK. ONE NO. 8 SCREW FROM TRACK TO BLOCKING, TOP AND BOTTOM FLANGE

SHEATHING BOUNDARY FASTENING. SEE TABLE R505.3.1(2)

10 IN. MINIMUM HEIGHT WITH WEB MATERIAL REMOVED

5 IN.

5 IN.

5 IN.

¾ IN. MINIMUM CLEAR

MINIMUM EMBEDMENT "E" SEE TABLE R608.9(6)

B

TENSION TIE. 64 MIL × 2 IN. × 6 FT. 0 LENGTH MINIMUM GRADE 50 STRAP UNDER OR ON TOP OF FLOOR SHEATHING. ATTACH STRAP TO FIRST TWO BLOCKS WITH 12 NO. 8 SCREWS. NO. 8 SCREWS AT 6 IN. ON CENTER FOR BALANCE OF STRAP

43 MIL MINIMUM FULL DEPTH BLOCKING, TWO BAYS MINIMUM AT EACH TENSION TIE. PROVIDE 43 MIL MINIMUM CLIP ANGLE EACH END WITH NOT LESS THAN 4 NO. 8 SCREWS EACH LEG

54 MIL × 2 IN. GRADE 50 STRAP, WITH 4 NO. 8 SREWS EACH END

JOIST RUNNING PARALLEL TO WALL

½ IN. DIAMETER ANCHOR BOLT TYPICAL. SEE TABLE R608.9(6) FOR SPACING. CENTER BOLT NOT MORE THAN 2 IN. FROM BLOCKING WEB.

TENSION TIE. SEE TABLE R608.9(6) FOR SPACING. PROVIDE STEEL PLATE WASHER 4 × 4 × ½ IN. TO FACE OF BLOCKING WEB. PROVIDE 4 IN. × 4 IN. × 4 IN. × 43 MIL MINIMUM BENT STEEL PLATE ANGLE UNDER PLATE WASHER WITH 8 NO. 8 SCREWS TO BLOCKING WEB. TENSION TIE LRFD CAPACITY 3200 LB

E (in.)	wall type
2¾ in.	4 in. flat
4¾ in.	6 in. flat 6 in. waffle-grid 6 in. screen-grid
6¾ in.	8 in. flat 10 in. flat 8 in. waffle-grid

CUT WASHER

BLOCKING TYP.

ANCHOR BOLT SPACING

JOISTS BLOCKING TYP.

ALTERNATE END CONNECTION WITH BENT BLOCKING WEB WITH 4 NO. 8 SCREWS EACH END

FLAT OR FULL DEPTH BLOCKING AT STRAP

4 IN. × 4 IN. SOLID CONCRETE BEHIND AND ALIGNED WITH ANGLE

For SI: 1 mil = 0.0254 mm, 1 inch = 25.4 mm, 1 pound-force = 4.448 N.

FIGURE R608.9(6)
COLD-FORMED STEEL FLOOR TO SIDE OF CONCRETE WALL, FRAMING PARALLEL

TABLE R608.9(6)
COLD-FORMED STEEL-FRAMED FLOOR TO SIDE OF CONCRETE WALL, FRAMING PARALLEL[a, b, c]

ANCHOR BOLT SPACING (inches)	TENSION TIE SPACING (inches)	BASIC WIND SPEED (mph) AND WIND EXPOSURE CATEGORY					
		115B	120B	130B	140B	150B	160B
		—	—	110C	119C	127C	136C
		—	—	—	110D	117D	125D
12	12						
12	24						
12	36						
12	48						
16	16						
16	32						
16	48						
19.2	19.2						
19.2	38.4						
24	24						
24	48						

For SI: 1 inch = 25.4 mm, 1 mile per hour = 0.447 m/s.

a. This table is for use with the detail in Figure R608.9(6). Use of this detail is permitted where a cell is not shaded.

b. Wall design per other provisions of Section R608 is required.

c. For wind design, minimum 4-inch-nominal wall is permitted in unshaded cells that do not contain a number.

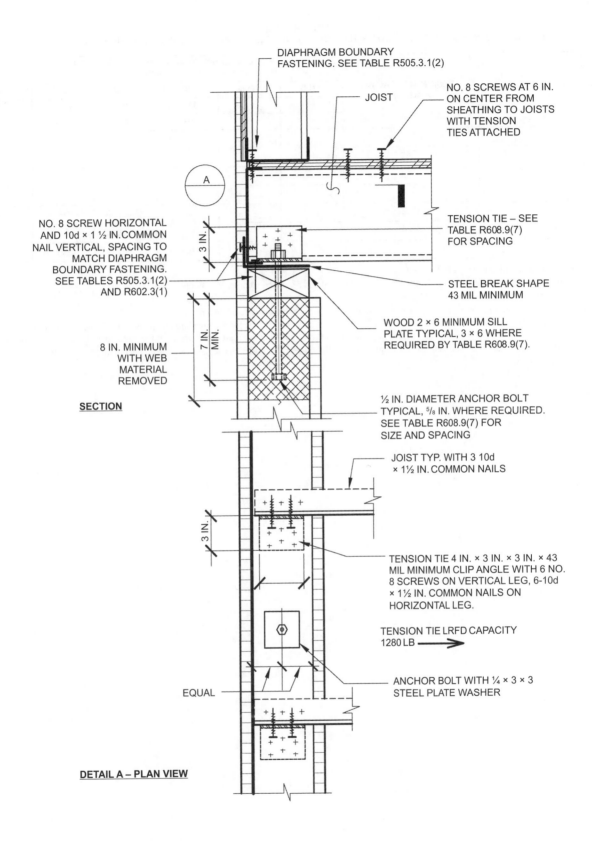

DIAPHRAGM BOUNDARY
FASTENING. SEE TABLE R505.3.1(2)

JOIST

NO. 8 SCREWS AT 6 IN.
ON CENTER FROM
SHEATHING TO JOISTS
WITH TENSION
TIES ATTACHED

A

NO. 8 SCREW HORIZONTAL
AND 10d × 1 ½ IN. COMMON
NAIL VERTICAL, SPACING TO
MATCH DIAPHRAGM
BOUNDARY FASTENING.
SEE TABLES R505.3.1(2)
AND R602.3(1)

3 IN.

TENSION TIE – SEE
TABLE R608.9(7)
FOR SPACING

STEEL BREAK SHAPE
43 MIL MINIMUM

7 IN.
MIN.

WOOD 2 × 6 MINIMUM SILL
PLATE TYPICAL, 3 × 6 WHERE
REQUIRED BY TABLE R608.9(7).

8 IN. MINIMUM
WITH WEB
MATERIAL
REMOVED

SECTION

½ IN. DIAMETER ANCHOR BOLT
TYPICAL, ⅝ IN. WHERE REQUIRED.
SEE TABLE R608.9(7) FOR
SIZE AND SPACING

JOIST TYP. WITH 3 10d
× 1½ IN. COMMON NAILS

3 IN.

TENSION TIE 4 IN. × 3 IN. × 3 IN. × 43
MIL MINIMUM CLIP ANGLE WITH 6 NO.
8 SCREWS ON VERTICAL LEG, 6-10d
× 1½ IN. COMMON NAILS ON
HORIZONTAL LEG.

TENSION TIE LRFD CAPACITY
1280 LB

ANCHOR BOLT WITH ¼ × 3 × 3
STEEL PLATE WASHER

EQUAL

DETAIL A – PLAN VIEW

For SI: 1 mil = 0.0254 mm, 1 inch = 25.4 mm, 1 pound-force = 4.448 N.

**FIGURE R608.9(7)
COLD-FORMED STEEL FLOOR TO TOP OF CONCRETE WALL, FRAMING PERPENDICULAR**

TABLE R608.9(7)
COLD-FORMED STEEL-FRAMED FLOOR TO TOP OF CONCRETE WALL, FRAMING PERPENDICULAR[a, b, c, d, e]

ANCHOR BOLT SPACING (inches)	TENSION TIE SPACING (inches)	BASIC WIND SPEED AND WIND EXPOSURE CATEGORY (mph)					
		115B	120B	130B	140B	150B	160B
		—	—	110C	119C	127C	136C
		—	—	—	110D	117D	125D
12	12						6
12	24					6	6
16	16					6	6A
16	32				6	6	6A
19.2	19.2				6A	6A	6B
19.2	38.4			6	6A	6A	6B
24	24			6A	6B	6B	6B

For SI: 1 inch = 25.4 mm, 1 mile per hour = 0.447 m/s.

a. This table is for use with the detail in Figure R608.9(7). Use of this detail is permitted where a cell is not shaded.

b. Wall design per other provisions of Section R608 is required.

c. For wind design, minimum 4-inch-nominal wall is permitted in unshaded cells that do not contain a number.

d. Number 6 indicates minimum permitted nominal wall thickness in inches necessary to develop required strength (capacity) of connection. As a minimum, this nominal thickness shall occur in the portion of the wall indicated by the cross hatching in Figure R608.9(7). For the remainder of the wall, see Note b.

e. Letter "A" indicates that a minimum nominal 3 × 6 sill plate is required. Letter "B" indicates that a $^5/_8$-inch-diameter anchor bolt and a minimum nominal 3 × 6 sill plate are required.

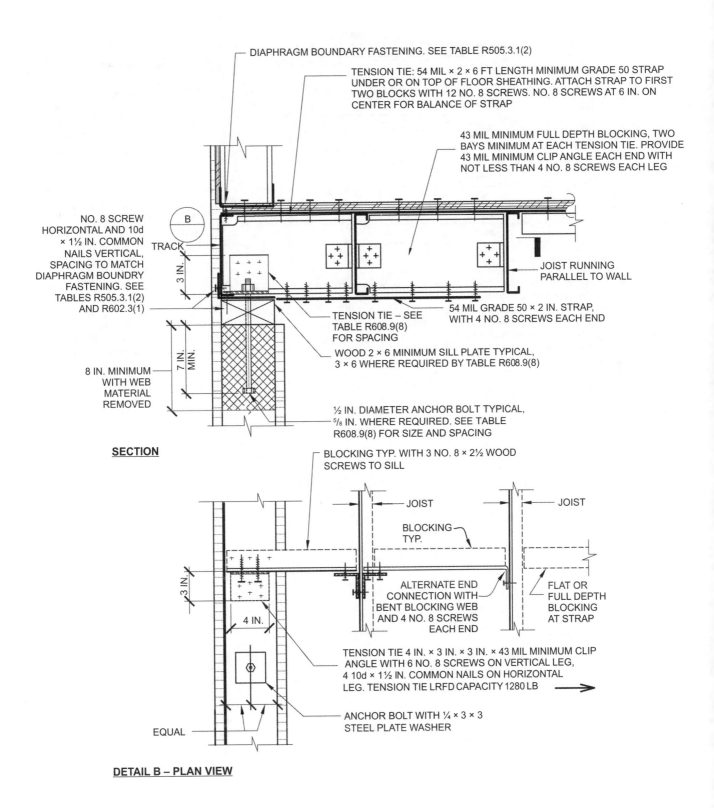

SECTION

DETAIL B – PLAN VIEW

For SI: 1 mil = 0.0254 mm, 1 inch = 25.4 mm, 1 pound-force = 4.448 N.

FIGURE R608.9(8)
COLD-FORMED STEEL FLOOR TO TOP OF CONCRETE WALL, FRAMING PARALLEL

TABLE R608.9(8)
COLD-FORMED STEEL-FRAMED FLOOR TO TOP OF CONCRETE WALL, FRAMING PARALLEL[a, b, c, d, e]

ANCHOR BOLT SPACING (inches)	TENSION TIE SPACING (inches)	BASIC WIND SPEED AND WIND EXPOSURE CATEGORY (mph)					
		115B	120B	130B	140B	150B	160B
		—	—	110C	119C	127C	136C
		—	—	—	110D	117D	125D
12	12						6
12	24					6	6
16	16					6	6A
16	32				6	6	6A
19.2	19.2				6A	6A	6B
19.2	38.4			6	6A	6A	6B
24	24			6A	6B	6B	6B

For SI: 1 inch = 25.4 mm, 1 mile per hour = 0.447 m/s.

a. This table is for use with the detail in Figure R608.9(8). Use of this detail is permitted where a cell is not shaded.

b. Wall design per other provisions of Section R608 is required.

c. For wind design, minimum 4-inch-nominal wall is permitted in unshaded cells that do not contain a number.

d. Number 6 indicates minimum permitted nominal wall thickness in inches necessary to develop required strength (capacity) of connection. As a minimum, this nominal thickness shall occur in the portion of the wall indicated by the cross hatching in Figure R608.9(8). For the remainder of the wall, see Note b.

e. Letter "A" indicates that a minimum nominal 3 × 6 sill plate is required. Letter "B" indicates that a $^5/_8$-inch-diameter anchor bolt and a minimum nominal 3 × 6 sill plate are required.

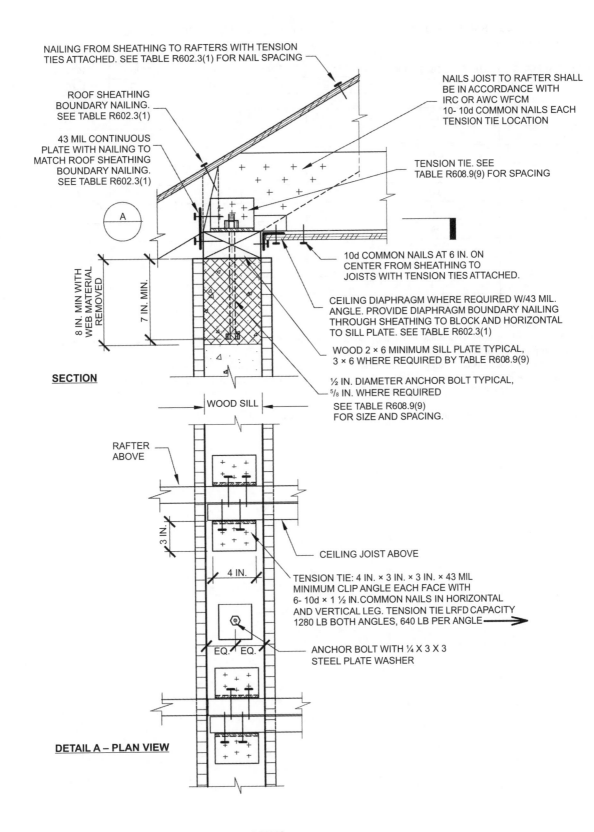

NAILING FROM SHEATHING TO RAFTERS WITH TENSION TIES ATTACHED. SEE TABLE R602.3(1) FOR NAIL SPACING

ROOF SHEATHING BOUNDARY NAILING. SEE TABLE R602.3(1)

43 MIL CONTINUOUS PLATE WITH NAILING TO MATCH ROOF SHEATHING BOUNDARY NAILING. SEE TABLE R602.3(1)

NAILS JOIST TO RAFTER SHALL BE IN ACCORDANCE WITH IRC OR AWC WFCM 10- 10d COMMON NAILS EACH TENSION TIE LOCATION

TENSION TIE. SEE TABLE R608.9(9) FOR SPACING

A

8 IN. MIN WITH WEB MATERIAL REMOVED

7 IN. MIN.

10d COMMON NAILS AT 6 IN. ON CENTER FROM SHEATHING TO JOISTS WITH TENSION TIES ATTACHED.

CEILING DIAPHRAGM WHERE REQUIRED W/43 MIL. ANGLE. PROVIDE DIAPHRAGM BOUNDARY NAILING THROUGH SHEATHING TO BLOCK AND HORIZONTAL TO SILL PLATE. SEE TABLE R602.3(1)

WOOD 2 × 6 MINIMUM SILL PLATE TYPICAL, 3 × 6 WHERE REQUIRED BY TABLE R608.9(9)

SECTION

½ IN. DIAMETER ANCHOR BOLT TYPICAL, ⅝ IN. WHERE REQUIRED SEE TABLE R608.9(9) FOR SIZE AND SPACING.

WOOD SILL

RAFTER ABOVE

3 IN.

4 IN.

CEILING JOIST ABOVE

TENSION TIE: 4 IN. × 3 IN. × 3 IN. × 43 MIL MINIMUM CLIP ANGLE EACH FACE WITH 6- 10d × 1 ½ IN.COMMON NAILS IN HORIZONTAL AND VERTICAL LEG. TENSION TIE LRFD CAPACITY 1280 LB BOTH ANGLES, 640 LB PER ANGLE ➡

EQ. EQ.

ANCHOR BOLT WITH ¼ X 3 X 3 STEEL PLATE WASHER

DETAIL A – PLAN VIEW

For SI: 1 mil = 0.0254 mm, 1 inch = 25.4 mm, 1 pound-force = 4.448 N.

FIGURE R608.9(9)
WOOD-FRAMED ROOF TO TOP OF CONCRETE WALL, FRAMING PERPENDICULAR

TABLE R608.9(9)
WOOD-FRAMED ROOF TO TOP OF CONCRETE WALL, FRAMING PERPENDICULAR[a, b, c, d, e]

ANCHOR BOLT SPACING (inches)	TENSION TIE SPACING (inches)	BASIC WIND SPEED (mph) AND WIND EXPOSURE CATEGORY					
		115B	120B	130B	140B	150B	160B
		—	—	110C	119C	127C	136C
		—	—	—	110D	117D	125D
12	12						6
12	24						6
12	36					6	6
12	48				6	6	6
16	16					6	6
16	32					6	6
16	48				6	6	6
19.2	19.2					6	6
19.2	38.4				6	6	
24	24				6		
24	48			6	8B		

For SI: 1 inch = 25.4 mm, 1 mile per hour = 0.447 m/s.

a. This table is for use with the detail in Figure R608.9(9). Use of this detail is permitted where a cell is not shaded, and prohibited where shaded.

b. Wall design per other provisions of Section R608 is required.

c. For wind design, minimum 4-inch-nominal wall is permitted in unshaded cells that do not contain a number.

d. Numbers 6 and 8 indicate minimum permitted nominal wall thickness in inches necessary to develop required strength (capacity) of connection. As a minimum, this nominal thickness shall occur in the portion of the wall indicated by the cross hatching in Figure R608.9(9). For the remainder of the wall, see Note b.

e. Letter "B" indicates that a $^5/_8$-inch-diameter anchor bolt and a minimum nominal 3 × 6 sill plate are required.

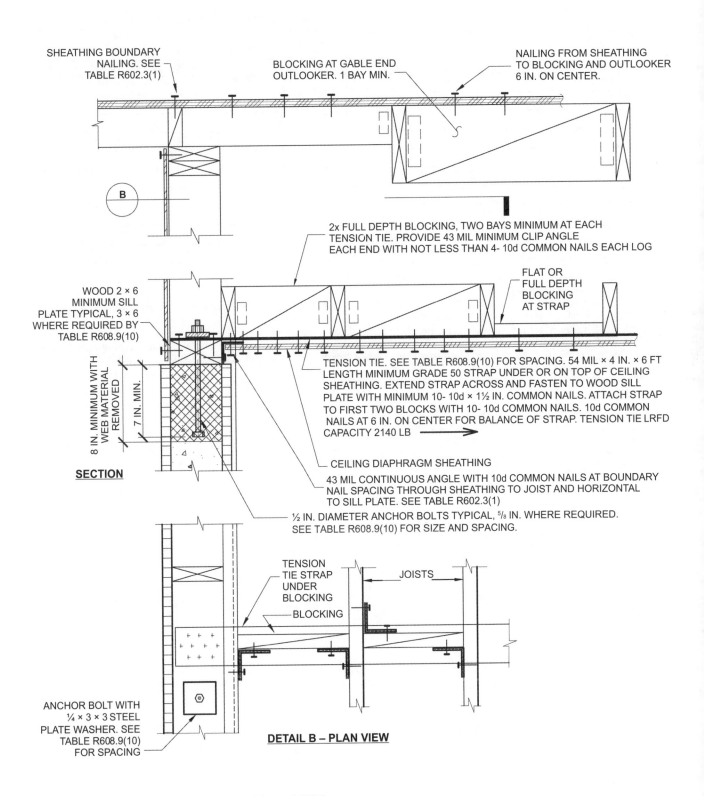

SHEATHING BOUNDARY NAILING. SEE TABLE R602.3(1)

BLOCKING AT GABLE END OUTLOOKER. 1 BAY MIN.

NAILING FROM SHEATHING TO BLOCKING AND OUTLOOKER 6 IN. ON CENTER.

B

2x FULL DEPTH BLOCKING, TWO BAYS MINIMUM AT EACH TENSION TIE. PROVIDE 43 MIL MINIMUM CLIP ANGLE EACH END WITH NOT LESS THAN 4- 10d COMMON NAILS EACH LOG

WOOD 2 × 6 MINIMUM SILL PLATE TYPICAL, 3 × 6 WHERE REQUIRED BY TABLE R608.9(10)

FLAT OR FULL DEPTH BLOCKING AT STRAP

8 IN. MINIMUM WITH WEB MATERIAL REMOVED

7 IN. MIN.

TENSION TIE. SEE TABLE R608.9(10) FOR SPACING. 54 MIL × 4 IN. × 6 FT LENGTH MINIMUM GRADE 50 STRAP UNDER OR ON TOP OF CEILING SHEATHING. EXTEND STRAP ACROSS AND FASTEN TO WOOD SILL PLATE WITH MINIMUM 10- 10d × 1½ IN. COMMON NAILS. ATTACH STRAP TO FIRST TWO BLOCKS WITH 10- 10d COMMON NAILS. 10d COMMON NAILS AT 6 IN. ON CENTER FOR BALANCE OF STRAP. TENSION TIE LRFD CAPACITY 2140 LB

SECTION

CEILING DIAPHRAGM SHEATHING

43 MIL CONTINUOUS ANGLE WITH 10d COMMON NAILS AT BOUNDARY NAIL SPACING THROUGH SHEATHING TO JOIST AND HORIZONTAL TO SILL PLATE. SEE TABLE R602.3(1)

½ IN. DIAMETER ANCHOR BOLTS TYPICAL, ⅝ IN. WHERE REQUIRED. SEE TABLE R608.9(10) FOR SIZE AND SPACING.

TENSION TIE STRAP UNDER BLOCKING

JOISTS

BLOCKING

ANCHOR BOLT WITH ¼ × 3 × 3 STEEL PLATE WASHER. SEE TABLE R608.9(10) FOR SPACING

DETAIL B – PLAN VIEW

For SI: 1 mil = 0.0254 mm, 1 inch = 25.4 mm, 1 pound-force = 4.448 N.

FIGURE R608.9(10)
WOOD-FRAMED ROOF TO TOP OF CONCRETE WALL, FRAMING PARALLEL

TABLE R608.9(10)
WOOD-FRAMED ROOF TO TOP OF CONCRETE WALL, FRAMING PARALLEL[a, b, c, d, e]

ANCHOR BOLT SPACING (inches)	TENSION TIE SPACING (inches)	BASIC WIND SPEED (mph) AND WIND EXPOSURE CATEGORY					
		115B	120B	130B	140B	150B	160B
		—	—	110C	119C	127C	136C
		—	—	—	110D	117D	125D
12	12						6
12	24						6
12	36					6	6
12	48				6	6	6
16	16					6	6
16	32					6	6
16	48				6	6	6
19.2	19.2					6	6
19.2	38.4				6	6	
24	24				6		
24	48			6	8B		

For SI: 1 inch = 25.4 mm, 1 mile per hour = 0.447 m/s.

a. This table is for use with the detail in Figure R608.9(10). Use of this detail is permitted where a cell is not shaded, and prohibited where shaded.

b. Wall design per other provisions of Section R608 is required.

c. For wind design, minimum 4-inch-nominal wall is permitted in cells that do not contain a number.

d. Numbers 6 and 8 indicate minimum permitted nominal wall thickness in inches necessary to develop required strength (capacity) of connection. As a minimum, this nominal thickness shall occur in the portion of the wall indicated by the cross hatching in Figure R608.9(10). For the remainder of the wall, see Note b.

e. Letter "B" indicates that a $^5/_8$-inch-diameter anchor bolt and a minimum nominal 3 × 6 sill plate are required.

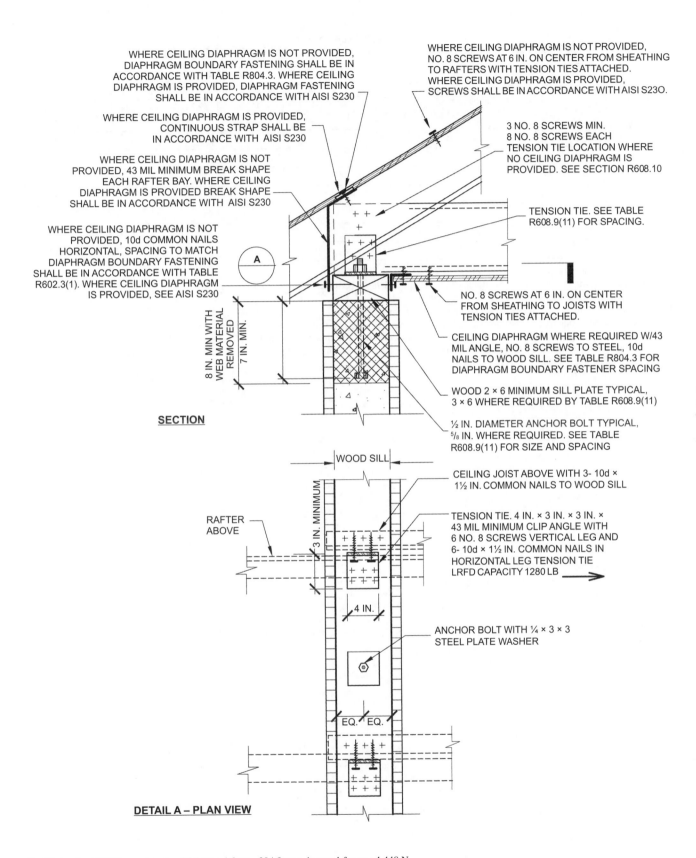

WHERE CEILING DIAPHRAGM IS NOT PROVIDED, DIAPHRAGM BOUNDARY FASTENING SHALL BE IN ACCORDANCE WITH TABLE R804.3. WHERE CEILING DIAPHRAGM IS PROVIDED, DIAPHRAGM FASTENING SHALL BE IN ACCORDANCE WITH AISI S230

WHERE CEILING DIAPHRAGM IS PROVIDED, CONTINUOUS STRAP SHALL BE IN ACCORDANCE WITH AISI S230

WHERE CEILING DIAPHRAGM IS NOT PROVIDED, 43 MIL MINIMUM BREAK SHAPE EACH RAFTER BAY. WHERE CEILING DIAPHRAGM IS PROVIDED BREAK SHAPE SHALL BE IN ACCORDANCE WITH AISI S230

WHERE CEILING DIAPHRAGM IS NOT PROVIDED, 10d COMMON NAILS HORIZONTAL, SPACING TO MATCH DIAPHRAGM BOUNDARY FASTENING SHALL BE IN ACCORDANCE WITH TABLE R602.3(1). WHERE CEILING DIAPHRAGM IS PROVIDED, SEE AISI S230

WHERE CEILING DIAPHRAGM IS NOT PROVIDED, NO. 8 SCREWS AT 6 IN. ON CENTER FROM SHEATHING TO RAFTERS WITH TENSION TIES ATTACHED. WHERE CEILING DIAPHRAGM IS PROVIDED, SCREWS SHALL BE IN ACCORDANCE WITH AISI S230.

3 NO. 8 SCREWS MIN. 8 NO. 8 SCREWS EACH TENSION TIE LOCATION WHERE NO CEILING DIAPHRAGM IS PROVIDED. SEE SECTION R608.10

TENSION TIE. SEE TABLE R608.9(11) FOR SPACING.

NO. 8 SCREWS AT 6 IN. ON CENTER FROM SHEATHING TO JOISTS WITH TENSION TIES ATTACHED.

CEILING DIAPHRAGM WHERE REQUIRED W/43 MIL ANGLE, NO. 8 SCREWS TO STEEL, 10d NAILS TO WOOD SILL. SEE TABLE R804.3 FOR DIAPHRAGM BOUNDARY FASTENER SPACING

WOOD 2 × 6 MINIMUM SILL PLATE TYPICAL, 3 × 6 WHERE REQUIRED BY TABLE R608.9(11)

½ IN. DIAMETER ANCHOR BOLT TYPICAL, ⅝ IN. WHERE REQUIRED. SEE TABLE R608.9(11) FOR SIZE AND SPACING

8 IN. MIN WITH WEB MATERIAL REMOVED

7 IN. MIN.

SECTION

WOOD SILL

3 IN. MINIMUM

RAFTER ABOVE

CEILING JOIST ABOVE WITH 3- 10d × 1½ IN. COMMON NAILS TO WOOD SILL

TENSION TIE. 4 IN. × 3 IN. × 3 IN. × 43 MIL MINIMUM CLIP ANGLE WITH 6 NO. 8 SCREWS VERTICAL LEG AND 6- 10d × 1½ IN. COMMON NAILS IN HORIZONTAL LEG TENSION TIE LRFD CAPACITY 1280 LB

4 IN.

ANCHOR BOLT WITH ¼ × 3 × 3 STEEL PLATE WASHER

EQ. EQ.

DETAIL A – PLAN VIEW

For SI: 1 mil = 0.0254 mm, 1 inch = 25.4 mm, 1 foot = 304.8 mm, 1 pound-force = 4.448 N.

FIGURE R608.9(11)
COLD-FORMED STEEL ROOF TO TOP OF CONCRETE WALL, FRAMING PERPENDICULAR

TABLE R608.9(11)
WOOD-FRAMED ROOF TO TOP OF CONCRETE WALL, FRAMING PERPENDICULAR[a, b, c, d, e]

ANCHOR BOLT SPACING (inches)	TENSION TIE SPACING (inches)	BASIC WIND SPEED (mph) AND WIND EXPOSURE CATEGORY					
		115B	120B	130B	140B	150B	160B
		—	—	110C	119C	127C	136C
		—	—	—	110D	117D	125D
12	12						6
12	24						6
16	16					6	6
16	32					6	6
19.2	19.2					6	6
19.2	38.4				6	6	6
24	24				6	6A	6B

For SI: 1 inch = 25.4 mm, 1 mile per hour = 0.447 m/s.

a. This table is for use with the detail in Figure R608.9(11). Use of this detail is permitted where a cell is not shaded.

b. Wall design per other provisions of Section R608 is required.

c. For wind design, minimum 4-inch-nominal wall is permitted in unshaded cells that do not contain a number.

d. Number 6 indicates minimum permitted nominal wall thickness in inches necessary to develop required strength (capacity) of connection. As a minimum, this nominal thickness shall occur in the portion of the wall indicated by the cross hatching in Figure R608.9(11). For the remainder of the wall, see Note b.

e. Letter "A" indicates that a minimum nominal 3 × 6 sill plate is required. Letter "B" indicates that a $5/8$-inch-diameter anchor bolt and a minimum nominal 3 × 6 sill plate are required.

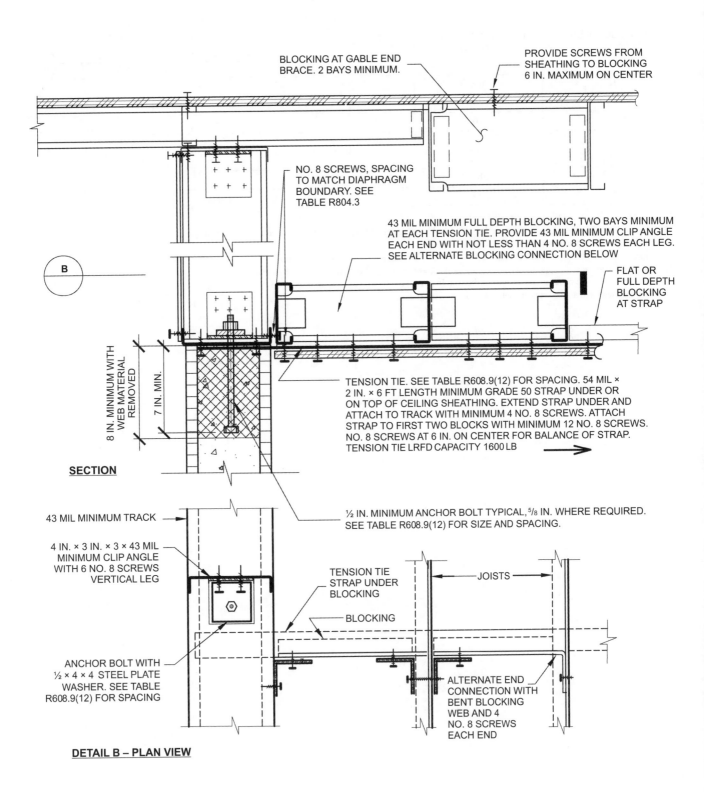

For SI: 1 mil = 0.0254 mm, 1 inch = 25.4 mm, 1 pound-force = 4.448 N.

FIGURE R608.9(12)
COLD-FORMED STEEL ROOF TO TOP OF CONCRETE WALL, FRAMING PARALLEL

TABLE R608.9(12)
COLD-FORMED STEEL ROOF TO TOP OF CONCRETE WALL, FRAMING PARALLEL[a, b, c, d, e]

ANCHOR BOLT SPACING (inches)	TENSION TIE SPACING (inches)	BASIC WIND SPEED (mph) AND WIND EXPOSURE CATEGORY					
		115B	120B	130B	140B	150B	160B
		—	—	110C	119C	127C	136C
		—	—	—	110D	117D	125D
12	12						6
12	24						6
16	16					6	6
16	32					6	6
19.2	19.2					6	6
19.2	38.4				6	6	6
24	24				6	6	6B

For SI: 1 inch = 25.4 mm, 1 mile per hour = 0.447 m/s.

a. This table is for use with the detail in Figure R608.9(12). Use of this detail is permitted where a cell is not shaded.

b. Wall design per other provisions of Section R608 is required.

c. For wind design, minimum 4-inch-nominal wall is permitted in cells that do not contain a number.

d. Number 6 indicates minimum permitted nominal wall thickness in inches necessary to develop required strength (capacity) of connection. As a minimum, this nominal thickness shall occur in the portion of the wall indicated by the cross hatching in Figure R608.9(12). For the remainder of the wall, see Note b.

e. Letter "B" indicates that a $^5/_8$-inch-diameter anchor bolt is required.

SECTION R609
EXTERIOR WINDOWS AND DOORS

R609.1 General. This section prescribes performance and construction requirements for exterior windows and doors installed in walls. Windows and doors shall be installed and flashed in accordance with the fenestration manufacturer's written instructions. Window and door openings shall be flashed in accordance with Section R703.4. Written installation instructions shall be provided by the fenestration manufacturer for each window or door.

R609.2 Performance. Exterior windows and doors shall be capable of resisting the design wind loads specified in Table R301.2(2) adjusted for height and exposure in accordance with Table R301.2(3) or determined in accordance with ASCE 7 using the allowable stress design load combinations of ASCE 7. For exterior windows and doors tested in accordance with Sections R609.3 and R609.5, required design wind pressures determined from ASCE 7 using the ultimate strength design (USD) are permitted to be multiplied by 0.6. Design wind loads for exterior glazing not part of a labeled assembly shall be permitted to be determined in accordance with Chapter 24 of the *International Building Code*. Design wind loads for exterior glazing not part of a labeled assembly shall be permitted to be determined in accordance with Chapter 24 of the *International Building Code*.

R609.3 Testing and labeling. Exterior windows and sliding doors shall be tested by an *approved* independent laboratory, and bear a *label* identifying manufacturer, performance characteristics and *approved* inspection agency to indicate compliance with AAMA/WDMA/CSA 101/I.S.2/A440. Exterior side-hinged doors shall be tested and *labeled* as conforming to AAMA/WDMA/CSA 101/I.S.2/A440 or AMD 100, or comply with Section R609.5.

Exception: Decorative glazed openings.

R609.3.1 Comparative analysis. Structural wind load design pressures for window and door units different than the size tested in accordance with Section R609.3 shall be permitted to be different than the design value of the tested unit where determined in accordance with one of the following comparative analysis methods:

1. Structural wind load design pressures for window and door units smaller than the size tested in accordance with Section R609.3 shall be permitted to be higher than the design value of the tested unit provided such higher pressures are determined by accepted engineering analysis. Components of the smaller unit shall be the same as those of the tested unit. Where such calculated design pressures are used, they shall be validated by an additional test of the window or door unit having the highest allowable design pressure.

2. In accordance with WDMA I.S.11.

R609.4 Garage doors. Garage doors shall be tested in accordance with either ASTM E330 or ANSI/DASMA 108, and shall meet the acceptance criteria of ANSI/DASMA 108.

R609.5 Other exterior window and door assemblies. Exterior windows and door assemblies not included within the scope of Section R609.3 or R609.4 shall be tested in accordance with ASTM E330. Glass in assemblies covered by this section shall comply with Section R308.5.

R609.6 Windborne debris protection. Protection of exterior windows, glass doors and doors with glass in buildings located in windborne debris regions shall be in accordance with Section R301.2.1.2.

R609.6.1 Fenestration testing and labeling. *Fenestration* shall be tested by an *approved* independent laboratory, listed by an *approved* entity, and bear a *label* identifying the manufacturer, performance characteristics and an *approved* inspection agency to indicate compliance with the requirements of the following specification(s):

1. ASTM E1886 and ASTM E1996; or

2. AAMA 506.

R609.6.2 Impact protective systems-testing and labeling. *Impact protective systems* shall be tested for impact resistance by an *approved* independent laboratory for compliance with ASTM E1886 and ASTM E1996. *Impact protective systems* shall be tested for design wind pressure by an *approved* independent laboratory for compliance with ASTM E330. Required design wind pressures shall be determined in accordance with Table R301.2(2), adjusted for height and exposure in accordance with Table R301.2(3) or determined in accordance with ASCE 7. For the purposes of this section, design wind pressures determined in accordance with ASCE 7 are permitted to be multiplied by 0.6.

Impact protective systems bear a *label* identifying the manufacturer, performance characteristics and an *approved* inspection agency. *Impact protective systems* shall have a permanent *label* providing traceability to the manufacturer, product designation and performance characteristics. The permanent *label* shall be acid etched, sand blasted, ceramic fired, laser etched, embossed or of a type that, once applied, cannot be removed without being destroyed.

R609.7 Anchorage methods. The methods cited in this section apply only to anchorage of window and glass door assemblies to the main force-resisting system.

R609.7.1 Anchoring requirements. Window and glass door assemblies shall be anchored in accordance with the published manufacturer's recommendations to achieve the design pressure specified. Substitute anchoring systems used for substrates not specified by the fenestration manufacturer shall provide equal or greater anchoring performance as demonstrated by accepted engineering practice.

R609.7.2 Anchorage details. Products shall be anchored in accordance with the minimum requirements illustrated in Figures R609.7.2(1), R609.7.2(2), R609.7.2(3), R609.7.2(4), R609.7.2(5), R609.7.2(6), R609.7.2(7) and R609.7.2(8).

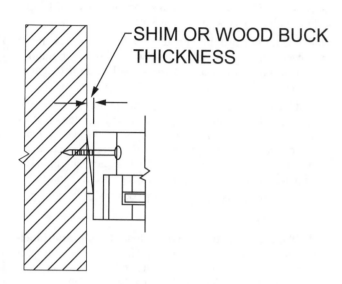

FIGURE R609.7.2(1)
THROUGH THE FRAME

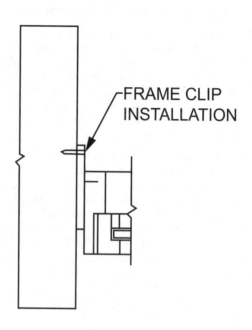

FIGURE R609.7.2(2)
FRAME CLIP

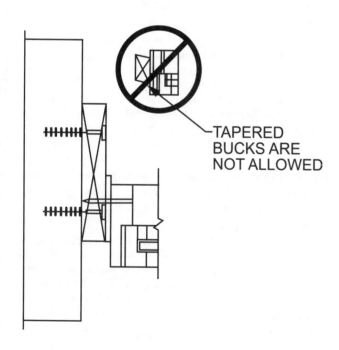

FIGURE R609.7.2(3)
THROUGH THE FRAME

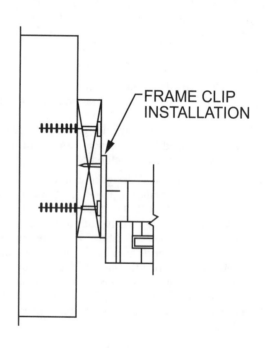

FIGURE R609.7.2(4)
FRAME CLIP

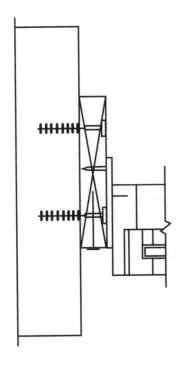

FIGURE R609.7.2(5)
THROUGH THE FLANGE

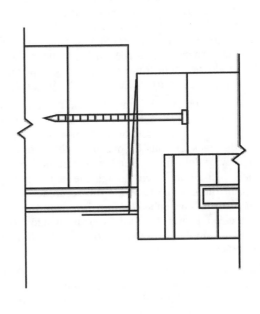

FIGURE R609.7.2(6)
THROUGH THE FLANGE

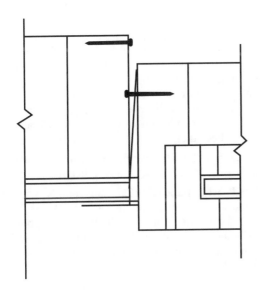

FIGURE R609.7.2(7)
FRAME CLIP

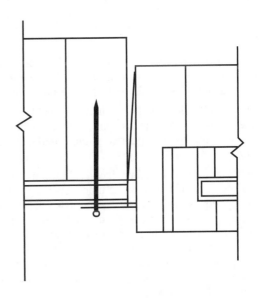

FIGURE R609.7.2(8)
THROUGH THE FLANGE

R609.7.2.1 Masonry, concrete or other structural substrate. Where the wood shim or buck thickness is less than $1^1/_2$ inches (38 mm), window and glass door assemblies shall be anchored through the jamb, or by jamb clip and anchors shall be embedded directly into the masonry, concrete or other substantial substrate material. Anchors shall adequately transfer load from the window or door frame into the rough opening substrate [see Figures R609.7.2(1) and R609.7.2(2)].

Where the wood shim or buck thickness is $1^1/_2$ inches (38 mm) or more, the buck is securely fastened to the masonry, concrete or other substantial substrate, and the buck extends beyond the interior face of the window or door frame, window and glass door assemblies shall be anchored through the jamb, or by jamb clip, or through the flange to the secured wood buck. Anchors shall be embedded into the secured wood buck to adequately transfer load from the window or door frame assembly [see Figures R609.7.2(3), R609.7.2(4) and R609.7.2(5)].

R609.7.2.2 Wood or other approved framing material. Where the framing material is wood or other *approved* framing material, window and glass door assemblies shall be anchored through the frame, or by frame clip, or through the flange. Anchors shall be embedded into the frame construction to adequately transfer load [see Figures R609.7.2(6), R609.7.2(7) and R609.7.2(8)].

R609.8 Mullions. Mullions shall be tested by an *approved* testing laboratory in accordance with AAMA 450, or be engineered in accordance with accepted engineering practice. Mullions tested as stand-alone units or qualified by engineering shall use performance criteria cited in Sections R609.8.1, R609.8.2 and R609.8.3. Mullions qualified by an actual test of an entire assembly shall comply with Sections R609.8.1 and R609.8.3.

R609.8.1 Load transfer. Mullions shall be designed to transfer the design pressure loads applied by the window and door assemblies to the rough opening substrate.

R609.8.2 Deflection. Mullions shall be capable of resisting the design pressure loads applied by the window and door assemblies to be supported without deflecting more than $L/175$, where L is the span of the mullion in inches.

R609.8.3 Structural safety factor. Mullions shall be capable of resisting a load of 1.5 times the design pressure loads applied by the window and door assemblies to be supported without exceeding the appropriate material stress levels. If tested by an *approved* laboratory, the 1.5 times the design pressure load shall be sustained for 10 seconds, and the permanent deformation shall not exceed 0.4 percent of the mullion span after the 1.5 times design pressure load is removed.

SECTION R610
STRUCTURAL INSULATED
PANEL WALL CONSTRUCTION

R610.1 General. Structural insulated panel (SIP) walls shall be designed in accordance with the provisions of this section. Where the provisions of this section are used to design structural insulated panel walls, project drawings, typical details and specifications are not required to bear the seal of the architect or engineer responsible for design, unless otherwise required by the state law of the *jurisdiction* having authority.

R610.2 Applicability limits. The provisions of this section shall control the construction of exterior structural insulated panel walls and interior load-bearing structural insulated panel walls for buildings not greater than 60 feet (18 288 mm) in length perpendicular to the joist or truss span, not greater than 40 feet (12 192 mm) in width parallel to the joist or truss span and not greater than two stories in height with each wall not greater than 10 feet (3048 mm) high. Exterior walls installed in accordance with the provisions of this section shall be considered as load-bearing walls. Structural insulated panel walls constructed in accordance with the provisions of this section shall be limited to sites where the ultimate design wind speed (V_{ult}) is not greater than 155 miles per hour (69 m/s) in Exposure B or 140 miles per hour (63 m/s) in Exposure C, the ground snow load is not greater than 70 pounds per square foot (3.35 kPa), and the seismic design category is A, B or C.

R610.3 Materials. SIPs shall comply with the requirements of ANSI/APA PRS 610.1.

R610.3.1 Lumber. The minimum lumber framing material used for SIPs prescribed in this document is NLGA graded No. 2 Spruce-pine-fir. Substitution of other wood species/grades that meet or exceed the mechanical properties and specific gravity of No. 2 Spruce-pine-fir shall be permitted.

R610.3.2 SIP screws. Screws used for the erection of SIPs as specified in Section R610.5 shall be fabricated from steel, shall be provided by the SIP manufacturer and shall be sized to penetrate the wood member to which the assembly is being attached by not less than 1 inch (25 mm). The screws shall be corrosion resistant and have a minimum shank diameter of 0.188 inch (4.7 mm) and a minimum head diameter of 0.620 inch (15.5 mm).

R610.3.3 Nails. Nails specified in Section R610 shall be common or galvanized box unless otherwise stated.

R610.4 SIP wall panels. SIPs shall comply with Figure R610.4 and shall have minimum panel thickness in accordance with Tables R610.5(1) and R610.5(2) for above-grade walls. SIPs shall be identified by grade mark or certificate of inspection issued by an *approved* agency in accordance with ANSI/APA PRS 610.1.

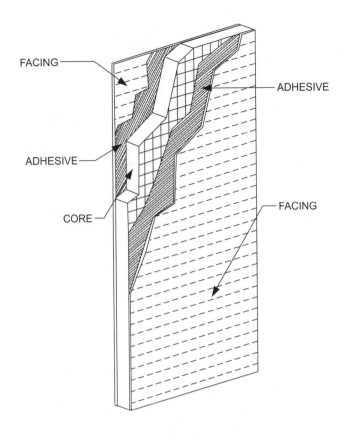

FIGURE R610.4
SIP WALL PANEL

R610.5 Wall construction. Exterior walls of SIP construction shall be designed and constructed in accordance with the provisions of this section and Tables R610.5(1) and R610.5(2) and Figures R610.5(1) through R610.5(5). SIP walls shall be fastened to other wood building components in accordance with Tables R602.3(1) through R602.3(4).

Framing shall be attached in accordance with Table R602.3(1) unless otherwise provided for in Section R610.

R610.5.1 Top plate connection. SIP walls shall be capped with a double top plate installed to provide overlapping at corner, intersections and splines in accordance with Figure R610.5.1. The double top plates shall be made up of a single 2-by (nominal 2-inch) top plate having a width equal to the width of the panel core, and shall be recessed into the SIP below. Over this top plate a cap plate shall be placed. The cap plate width shall match the SIP thickness and overlap the facers on both sides of the panel. End joints in top plates shall be offset not less than 24 inches (610 mm).

R610.5.2 Bottom (sole) plate connection. SIP walls shall have full bearing on a sole plate having a width equal to the nominal width of the foam core. Where SIP walls are supported directly on continuous foundations, the wall wood sill plate shall be anchored to the foundation in accordance with Figure R610.5.2 and Section R403.1.

R610.5.3 Panel-to-panel connection. SIPs shall be connected at vertical in-plane joints in accordance with Figure R610.8 or by other *approved* methods.

R610.5.4 Corner framing. Corner framing of SIP walls shall be constructed in accordance with Figure R610.5.4.

R610.5.5 Wall bracing. SIP walls shall be braced in accordance with Section R602.10. SIP walls shall be considered continuous wood structural panel sheathing (bracing Method CS-WSP) for purposes of computing required bracing. SIP walls shall meet the requirements of Section R602.10.4.2 except that SIP corners shall be fabricated as shown in Figure R610.8. Where SIP walls are used for wall bracing, the SIP bottom plate shall be attached to wood framing below in accordance with Table R602.3(1).

R610.5.6 Thermal barrier. SIP walls shall be separated from the interior of a building by an *approved* thermal barrier in accordance with Section R316.4.

R610.6 Interior load-bearing walls. Interior load-bearing walls shall be constructed as specified for exterior walls.

R610.7 Drilling and notching. The maximum vertical chase penetration in SIPs shall have a maximum side dimension of 2 inches (51 mm) centered in the panel. Vertical chases shall have a minimum spacing of 24 inches (610 mm) on center. Not more than two horizontal chases shall be permitted in each wall panel, one at 14 inches (360 mm) plus or minus 2 inches (51 mm) from the bottom of the panel and one at 48 inches (1220 mm) plus or minus 2 inches (51 mm) from the bottom edge of the SIP's panel. Additional penetrations are permitted where justified by analysis.

R610.8 Headers. SIP headers shall be designed and constructed in accordance with Table R610.8 and Figure R610.5.1. SIP headers shall be continuous sections without splines. Headers shall be not less than 117/8 inches (302 mm) deep. Headers longer than 4 feet (1219 mm) shall be constructed in accordance with Section R602.7. The strength axis of the factors on the header shall be oriented horizontally.

R610.8.1 Wood structural panel box headers. Wood structural panel box headers shall be allowed where SIP headers are not applicable. Wood structural panel box headers shall be constructed in accordance with Figure R602.7.3 and Table R602.7.3.

TABLE R610.5(1)
MINIMUM THICKNESS FOR SIP WALL SUPPORTING SIP OR LIGHT-FRAME ROOF ONLY (inches)[a]

ULTIMATE DESIGN WIND SPEED V_{ult} (mph)		SNOW LOAD (psf)	BUILDING WIDTH (ft)															
			24			28			32			36			40		
			Wall Height (feet)			Wall Height (feet)			Wall Height (feet)			Wall Height (feet)			Wall Height (feet)		
Exp. B	Exp. C		8	9	10	8	9	10	8	9	10	8	9	10	8	9	10
110	—	20	4.5	4.5	4.5	4.5	4.5	4.5	4.5	4.5	4.5	4.5	4.5	4.5	4.5	4.5	4.5
		30	4.5	4.5	4.5	4.5	4.5	4.5	4.5	4.5	4.5	4.5	4.5	4.5	4.5	4.5	4.5
		50	4.5	4.5	4.5	4.5	4.5	4.5	4.5	4.5	4.5	4.5	4.5	4.5	4.5	4.5	4.5
		70	4.5	4.5	4.5	4.5	4.5	4.5	4.5	4.5	4.5	4.5	4.5	6.5	4.5	4.5	6.5
115	—	20	4.5	4.5	4.5	4.5	4.5	4.5	4.5	4.5	4.5	4.5	4.5	4.5	4.5	4.5	4.5
		30	4.5	4.5	4.5	4.5	4.5	4.5	4.5	4.5	4.5	4.5	4.5	4.5	4.5	4.5	4.5
		50	4.5	4.5	4.5	4.5	4.5	4.5	4.5	4.5	4.5	4.5	4.5	4.5	4.5	4.5	6.5
		70	4.5	4.5	4.5	4.5	4.5	4.5	4.5	4.5	6.5	4.5	4.5	DR	4.5	4.5	DR
130	110	20	4.5	4.5	6.5	4.5	4.5	6.5	4.5	4.5	6.5	4.5	4.5	DR	4.5	4.5	DR
		30	4.5	4.5	6.5	4.5	4.5	6.5	4.5	4.5	DR	4.5	4.5	DR	4.5	4.5	DR
		50	4.5	4.5	DR	4.5	4.5	DR	4.5	4.5	DR	4.5	6.5	DR	4.5	DR	DR
		70	4.5	4.5	DR	4.5	DR	DR	4.5	DR	DR	4.5	DR	DR	DR	DR	DR
140	120	20	4.5	6.5	DR	4.5	6.5	DR	4.5	DR	DR	4.5	DR	DR	4.5	DR	DR
		30	4.5	6.5	DR	4.5	DR	DR	4.5	DR	DR	4.5	DR	DR	4.5	DR	DR
		50	4.5	DR	DR	4.5	DR	DR	DR	DR	DR	DR	DR	DR	DR	DR	DR
		70	4.5	DR	DR	DR	DR	DR	DR	DR	DR	DR	DR	DR	DR	DR	DR

For SI: 1 inch = 25.4 mm, 1 foot = 304.8 mm, 1 pound per square foot = 0.0479 kPa, 1 mile per hour = 0.447 m/s.

DR = Design Required.

a. Design assumptions:

Maximum deflection criteria: $L/240$.

Maximum roof dead load: 10 psf.

Maximum roof live load: 70 psf.

Maximum ceiling dead load: 5 psf.

Maximum ceiling live load: 20 psf.

Wind loads based on Table R301.2 (2).

Strength axis of facing material applied vertically.

TABLE R610.5(2)
MINIMUM THICKNESS FOR SIP WALL SUPPORTING SIP OR LIGHT-FRAME ONE STORY AND ROOF ONLY (inches)[a]

ULTIMATE DESIGN WIND SPEED V_{ult} (mph)		SNOW LOAD (psf)	BUILDING WIDTH (ft)															
			24			28			32			36			40			
Exp. B	Exp. C		Wall Height (feet)			Wall Height (feet)			Wall Height (feet)			Wall Height (feet)			Wall Height (feet)			
			8	9	10	8	9	10	8	9	10	8	9	10	8	9	10
110	—	20	4.5	4.5	4.5	4.5	4.5	4.5	4.5	4.5	6.5	4.5	4.5	DR	4.5	4.5	DR
		30	4.5	4.5	4.5	4.5	4.5	4.5	4.5	4.5	6.5	4.5	4.5	DR	4.5	6.5	DR
		50	4.5	4.5	4.5	4.5	4.5	6.5	4.5	4.5	DR	4.5	DR	DR	DR	DR	DR
		70	4.5	4.5	6.5	4.5	4.5	DR	4.5	DR	DR	DR	DR	DR	DR	DR	DR
115	—	20	4.5	4.5	4.5	4.5	4.5	6.5	4.5	4.5	DR	4.5	4.5	DR	4.5	DR	DR
		30	4.5	4.5	4.5	4.5	4.5	6.5	4.5	4.5	DR	4.5	6.5	DR	4.5	DR	DR
		50	4.5	4.5	6.5	4.5	4.5	DR	4.5	DR	DR	4.5	DR	DR	DR	DR	DR
		70	4.5	4.5	DR	4.5	DR	DR	DR	DR	DR	DR	DR	DR	DR	DR	DR
120	—	20	4.5	4.5	6.5	4.5	4.5	DR	4.5	4.5	DR	4.5	DR	DR	4.5	DR	DR
		30	4.5	4.5	DR	4.5	4.5	DR	4.5	6.5	DR	4.5	DR	DR	DR	DR	DR
		50	4.5	4.5	DR	4.5	DR	DR	4.5	DR	DR	DR	DR	DR	DR	DR	DR
		70	4.5	DR	DR	4.5	DR	DR	DR	DR	DR	DR	DR	DR	DR	DR	DR
130	110	20	4.5	6.5	DR	4.5	DR	DR	4.5	DR	DR	DR	DR	DR	DR	DR	DR
		30	4.5	DR	DR	4.5	DR	DR	DR	DR	DR	DR	DR	DR	DR	DR	DR
		50	4.5	DR	DR	DR	DR	DR	DR	DR	DR	DR	DR	DR	DR	DR	DR
		70	DR	DR	DR	DR	DR	DR	DR	DR	DR	DR	DR	DR	DR	DR	DR

For SI: 1 Inch = 25.4 mm, 1 foot = 304.8 mm, 1 pound per square foot = 0.0479 kPa, 1 mile per hour = 0.447 m/s.

DR = Design Required.

a. Design assumptions:

    Maximum deflection criteria: $L/240$.

    Maximum roof dead load: 10 psf.

    Maximum roof live load: 70 psf.

    Maximum ceiling dead load: 5 psf.

    Maximum ceiling live load: 20 psf.

    Maximum second-floor dead load: 10 psf.

    Maximum second-floor live load: 30 psf.

    Maximum second-floor dead load from walls: 10 psf.

    Maximum first-floor dead load: 10 psf.

    Maximum first-floor live load: 40 psf.

    Wind loads based on Table R301.2 (2).

    Strength axis of facing material applied vertically.

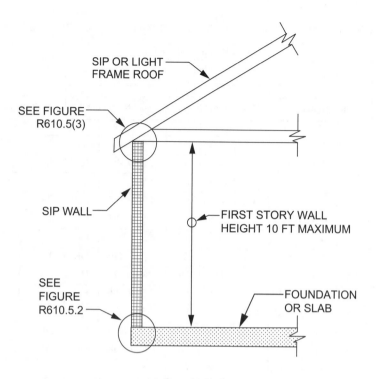

For SI: 1 foot = 304.8 mm.
Note: Figure illustrates SIP-specific attachment requirements. Other connections shall be made in accordance with Tables R602.3(1) and (2), as appropriate.

FIGURE R610.5(1)
MAXIMUM ALLOWABLE HEIGHT OF SIP WALLS

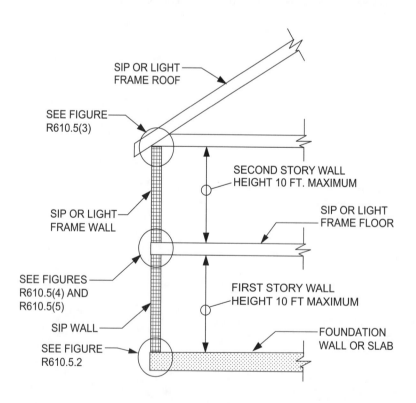

For SI: 1 foot = 304.8 mm.
Note: Figure illustrates SIP-specific attachment requirements. Other connections shall be made in accordance with Tables R602.3(1) and (2), as appropriate.

FIGURE R610.5(2)
MAXIMUM ALLOWABLE HEIGHT OF SIP WALLS

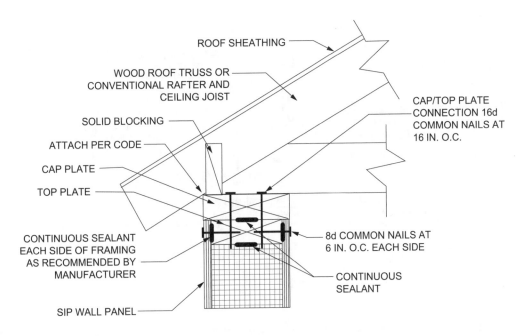

For SI: 1 inch = 25.4 mm.
Note: Figure illustrates SIP-specific attachment requirements. Other connections shall be made in accordance with Tables R602.3(1) and (2), as appropriate.

FIGURE R610.5(3)
TRUSSED ROOF TO TOP PLATE CONNECTION

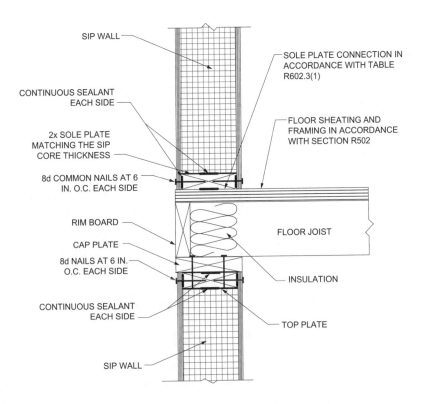

For SI: 1 inch = 25.4 mm.
Note: Figure illustrates SIP-specific attachment requirements. Other connections shall be made in accordance with Tables R602.3(1) and (2), as appropriate.

FIGURE R610.5(4)
SIP WALL-TO-WALL PLATFORM FRAME CONNECTION

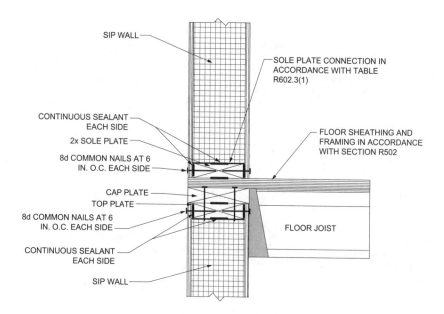

For SI: 1 inch = 25.4 mm.
Note: Figure illustrates SIP-specific attachment requirements. Other connections shall be made in accordance with Tables R602.3(1) and (2), as appropriate.

FIGURE R610.5(5)
SIP WALL-TO-WALL HANGING FLOOR FRAME CONNECTION
(I-Joist floor shown for Illustration only)

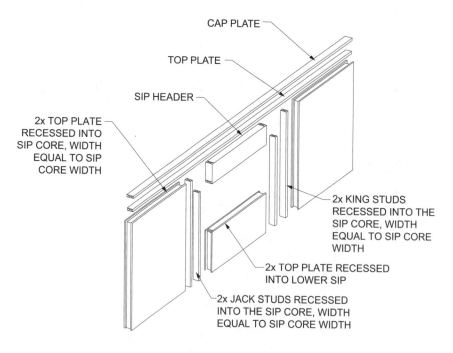

For SI: 1 inch = 25.4 mm.
Notes:
1. Top plates shall be continuous over header.
2. Lower 2x top plate shall have a width equal to the SIP core width and shall be recessed into the top edge of the panel. Cap plate shall be placed over the recessed top plate and shall have a width equal to the SIPs width.
3. SIP facing surfaces shall be nailed to framing and cripples with 8d common or galvanized box nails spaced 6 inches on center.

FIGURE R610.5.1
SIP WALL FRAMING CONFIGURATION

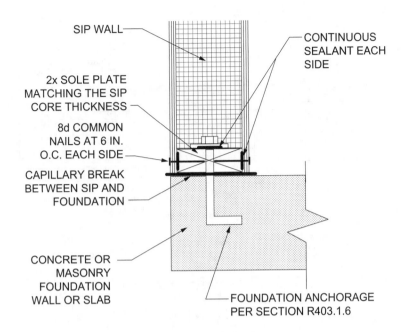

SIP WALL

CONTINUOUS SEALANT EACH SIDE

2x SOLE PLATE MATCHING THE SIP CORE THICKNESS

8d COMMON NAILS AT 6 IN. O.C. EACH SIDE

CAPILLARY BREAK BETWEEN SIP AND FOUNDATION

CONCRETE OR MASONRY FOUNDATION WALL OR SLAB

FOUNDATION ANCHORAGE PER SECTION R403.1.6

For SI: 1 inch = 25.4 mm, 1 foot = 304.8 mm.

FIGURE R610.5.2
SIP WALL TO CONCRETE SLAB FOR FOUNDATION WALL ATTACHMENT

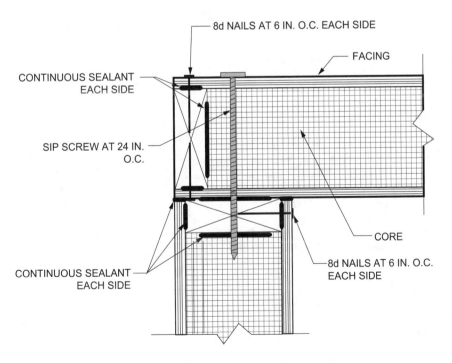

8d NAILS AT 6 IN. O.C. EACH SIDE

FACING

CONTINUOUS SEALANT EACH SIDE

SIP SCREW AT 24 IN. O.C.

CORE

CONTINUOUS SEALANT EACH SIDE

8d NAILS AT 6 IN. O.C. EACH SIDE

For SI: 1 inch = 25.4 mm.

FIGURE R610.5.4
SIP CORNER FRAMING DETAIL

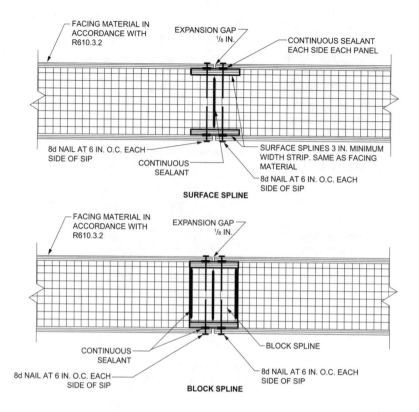

For SI: 1 inch = 25.4 mm.

FIGURE R610.8
TYPICAL SIP WALL PANEL-TO-PANEL CONNECTION DETAILS

TABLE R610.8
MAXIMUM SPANS FOR 11⁷⁄₈-INCH OR DEEPER SIP HEADERS (feet)[a, c, d]

LOAD CONDITION	SNOW LOAD (psf)	BUILDING[b] width (feet)				
		24	28	32	36	40
Supporting roof only	20	4	4	4	4	2
	30	4	4	4	2	2
	50	2	2	2	2	2
	70	2	2	2	DR	DR
Supporting roof and one-story	20	2	2	DR	DR	DR
	30	2	2	DR	DR	DR
	50	2	DR	DR	DR	DR
	70	DR	DR	DR	DR	DR

For SI: 1 inch = 25.4 mm, 1 foot = 304.8 mm, 1 pound per square foot = 0.0479 kPa.

DR = Design Required.

a. Design assumptions:
    Maximum deflection criterion: $L/240$.
    Maximum roof dead load: 10 psf.
    Maximum ceiling load: 5 psf.
    Maximum ceiling live load: 20 psf
    Maximum second-floor live load: 30 psf.
    Maximum second-floor dead load: 10 psf.
    Maximum second-floor dead load from walls: 10 psf.
    Maximum first floor dead load: 10 psf.
    Wind loads based on Table R301.2(2).
    Strength axis of facing material applied horizontally.

b. Building width is in the direction of horizontal framing members supported by the header.

c. The table provides for roof slopes between 3:12 and 12:12.

d. The maximum roof overhang is 24 inches (610 mm).

CHAPTER 7

WALL COVERING

SECTION R701
GENERAL

R701.1 Application. The provisions of this chapter shall control the design and construction of the interior and exterior wall covering for buildings.

R701.2 Installation. Products sensitive to adverse weather shall not be installed until adequate weather protection for the installation is provided. Exterior sheathing shall be dry before applying exterior cover.

SECTION R702
INTERIOR COVERING

R702.1 General. Interior coverings or wall finishes shall be installed in accordance with this chapter and Table R702.1(1), Table R702.1(2), Table R702.1(3) and Table R702.3.5. Interior masonry veneer shall comply with the requirements of

Section R703.7.1 for support and Section R703.7.4 for anchorage, except an airspace is not required. Interior finishes and materials shall conform to the flame spread and smoke-development requirements of Section R302.9.

R702.2 Interior plaster.

R702.2.1 Gypsum plaster. Gypsum plaster materials shall conform to ASTM C5, C22, C28, C35, C59, C61, C587, C631, C847, C933, C1032 and C1047, and shall be installed or applied in compliance with ASTM C841, C842 and C843. Gypsum lath or gypsum base for veneer plaster shall conform to ASTM C1396 and shall be installed in compliance with ASTM C844. Plaster shall be not less than three coats where applied over metal lath and not less than two coats where applied over other bases permitted by this section, except that veneer plaster shall be applied in one coat not to exceed $^3/_{16}$ inch (4.76 mm) thickness, provided the total thickness is in accordance with Table R702.1(1).

TABLE R702.1(1)
THICKNESS OF PLASTER

PLASTER BASE	FINISHED THICKNESS OF PLASTER FROM FACE OF LATH, MASONRY, CONCRETE (inches)	
	Gypsum Plaster	Cement Plaster
Expanded metal lath	$^5/_8$, minimum[a]	$^5/_8$, minimum[a]
Wire lath	$^5/_8$, minimum[a]	$^3/_4$, minimum (interior)[b] $^7/_8$, minimum (exterior)[b]
Gypsum lath[g]	$^1/_2$, minimum	$^3/_4$, minimum (interior)[b]
Masonry walls[c]	$^1/_2$, minimum	$^1/_2$, minimum
Monolithic concrete walls[c, d]	$^5/_8$, maximum	$^7/_8$, maximum
Monolithic concrete ceilings[c, d]	$^3/_8$, maximum[e]	$^1/_2$, maximum
Gypsum veneer base[f, g]	$^1/_{16}$, minimum	$^3/_4$, minimum (interior)[b]
Gypsum sheathing[g]	—	$^3/_4$, minimum (interior)[b] $^7/_8$, minimum (exterior)[b]

For SI: 1 inch = 25.4 mm.

a. Where measured from back plane of expanded metal lath, exclusive of ribs, or self-furring lath, plaster thickness shall be $^3/_4$ inch minimum.

b. Where measured from face of support or backing.

c. Because masonry and concrete surfaces vary in plane, thickness of plaster need not be uniform.

d. Where applied over a liquid bonding agent, finish coat shall be permitted to be applied directly to concrete surface.

e. Approved acoustical plaster shall be permitted to be applied directly to concrete or over base coat plaster, beyond the maximum plaster thickness shown.

f. Attachment shall be in accordance with Table R702.3.5.

g. Where gypsum board is used as a base for cement plaster, a water-resistive barrier complying with Section R703.2 shall be provided.

NUMBER	COAT	PLASTER BASE OR LATH	MAXIMUM VOLUME AGGREGATE PER 100 POUNDS NEAT PLASTER[b] (cubic feet)	
			Damp Loose Sand[a]	Perlite or Vermiculite[c]
Two-coat work	Base coat	Gypsum lath	2.5	2
	Base coat	Masonry	3	3
Three-coat work	First coat	Lath	2[d]	2
	Second coat	Lath	3[d]	2[e]
	First and second coats	Masonry	3	3

For SI: 1 inch = 25.4 mm, 1 cubic foot = 0.0283 m^3, 1 pound = 0.454 kg.

a. Wood-fibered gypsum plaster shall be mixed in the proportions of 100 pounds of gypsum to not more than 1 cubic foot of sand where applied on masonry or concrete.

b. Where determining the amount of aggregate in set plaster, a tolerance of 10 percent shall be allowed.

c. Combinations of sand and lightweight aggregate shall be permitted to be used, provided the volume and weight relationship of the combined aggregate to gypsum plaster is maintained.

d. If used for both first and second coats, the volume of aggregate shall be permitted to be 2.5 cubic feet.

e. Where plaster is 1 inch or more in total thickness, the proportions for the second coat may be increased to 3 cubic feet.

COAT	CEMENT PLASTER TYPE	CEMENTITIOUS MATERIALS				VOLUME OF AGGREGATE PER SUM OF SEPARATE VOLUMES OF CEMENTITIOUS MATERIALS[b]
		Portland Cement Type I, II or III; Blended Hydraulic Cement Type IP, I (S < 70), IL, or IT (S < 70); or Hydraulic Cement Type GU, HE, MS, HS or MH	Plastic Cement	Masonry Cement Type M, S or N	Lime	
First	Portland or blended	1	—	—	$^3/_4$ - $1^1/_2$[a]	$2^1/_2$ - 4
	Masonry	—	—	1	—	$2^1/_2$ - 4
	Plastic	—	1	—	—	$2^1/_2$ - 4
Second	Portland or blended	1	—	—	$^3/_4$ - $1^1/_2$	3 - 5
	Masonry	—	—	1	—	3 - 5
	Plastic	—	1	—	—	3 - 5
Finish	Portland or blended	1	—	—	$1^1/_2$ - 2	$1^1/_2$ - 3
	Masonry	—	—	1	—	$1^1/_2$ - 3
	Plastic	—	1	—	—	$1^1/_2$ - 3

For SI: 1 inch = 25.4 mm, 1 pound = 0.454 kg.

a. Lime by volume of 0 to $^3/_4$ shall be used where the plaster will be placed over low-absorption surfaces such as dense clay tile or brick.

b. The same or greater sand proportion shall be used in the second coat than used in the first coat.

R702.2.2 Cement plaster. Cement plaster materials shall conform to ASTM C91 (Type M, S or N), C150 (Types I, II and III), C595 [Types IP, I (PM), IS and I (SM), C847, C897, C933, C1032, C1047 and C1328, and shall be installed or applied in compliance with ASTM C926 and C1063. Gypsum lath shall conform to ASTM C1396. Plaster shall be not less than three coats where applied over metal lath and not less than two coats where applied over other bases permitted by this section.

R702.2.2.1 Application. Each coat shall be kept in a moist condition for not less than 24 hours prior to application of the next coat.

Exception: Applications installed in accordance with ASTM C926.

R702.2.2.2 Curing. The finish coat for two-coat cement plaster shall not be applied sooner than 48 hours after application of the first coat. For three-coat cement plaster, the second coat shall not be applied sooner than 24 hours after application of the first coat. The finish coat for three-coat cement plaster shall not be applied sooner than 48 hours after application of the second coat.

R702.2.3 Support. Support spacing for gypsum or metal lath on walls or ceilings shall not exceed 16 inches (406 mm) for $^3/_8$-inch-thick (9.5 mm) or 24 inches (610 mm) for $^1/_2$-inch-thick (12.7 mm) plain gypsum lath. Gypsum lath shall be installed at right angles to support framing with end joints in adjacent courses staggered by not less than one framing space.

R702.3 Gypsum board and gypsum panel products.

R702.3.1 Materials. Gypsum board and gypsum panel product materials and accessories shall conform to ASTM C22, C475, C514, C1002, C1047, C1177, C1178, C1278, C1396, C1658 or C1766 and shall be installed in accordance with the provisions of this section. Adhesives for the installation of gypsum board and gypsum panel products shall conform to ASTM C557.

R702.3.1.1 Adhesives. Expandable foam adhesives for the installation of gypsum board and gypsum panel products shall conform to ASTM C6464. Other adhesives for the installation of gypsum board and gypsum panel products shall conform to ASTM C557. Supports and fasteners used to attach gypsum board and gypsum panel products shall comply with Table R702.3.5 or other approved method.

R702.3.2 Wood framing. Wood framing supporting gypsum board and gypsum panel products shall be not less than 2 inches (51 mm) nominal thickness in the least dimension except that wood furring strips not less than 1-inch by 2-inch (25 mm by 51 mm) nominal dimension shall be permitted to be used over solid backing or framing spaced not more than 24 inches (610 mm) on center.

R702.3.3 Cold-formed steel framing. Cold-formed steel framing supporting gypsum board and gypsum panel products shall be not less than $1^1/_4$ inches (32 mm) wide in the least dimension. Nonload-bearing cold-formed steel framing shall comply with AISI S220. Load-bearing cold-formed steel framing shall comply with AISI S240.

R702.3.4 Insulating concrete form walls. Foam plastics for insulating concrete form walls constructed in accordance with Sections R404.1.2 and R608 on the interior of *habitable spaces* shall be protected in accordance with Section R316.4. Use of adhesives in conjunction with mechanical fasteners is permitted. Adhesives used for interior and exterior finishes shall be compatible with the insulating form materials.

R702.3.5 Application. Supports and fasteners used to attach gypsum board and gypsum panel products shall comply with Table R702.3.5. Gypsum sheathing shall be attached to exterior walls in accordance with Table R602.3(1). Gypsum board and gypsum panel products shall be applied at right angles or parallel to framing members. All edges and ends of gypsum board and gypsum panel products shall occur on the framing members, except those edges and ends that are perpendicular to the framing members. Interior gypsum board shall not be installed where it is directly exposed to the weather or to water.

R702.3.5.1 Screw fastening. Screws for attaching gypsum board and gypsum panel products to wood framing shall be Type W or Type S in accordance with ASTM C1002 and shall penetrate the wood not less than $5/_8$ inch (15.9 mm). Gypsum board and gypsum panel products shall be attached to cold-formed steel framing with mini-mum No. 6 screws. Screws for attaching gypsum board and gypsum panel products to cold-formed steel framing less than 0.033 inch (1 mm) thick shall be Type S in accordance with ASTM C1002 or bugle head style in accordance with ASTM C1513 and shall penetrate the steel not less than $3/_8$ inch (9.5 mm). Screws for attaching gypsum board and gypsum panel products to cold-formed steel framing 0.033 inch to 0.112 inch (1 mm to 3 mm) thick shall be in accordance with ASTM C954 or bugle head style in accordance with ASTM C1513. Screws for attaching gypsum board and gypsum panel products to structural insulated panels shall penetrate the wood structural panel facing not less than $7/_{16}$ inch (11.1 mm).

R702.3.6 Horizontal gypsum board diaphragm ceilings. Gypsum board and gypsum panel products shall be permitted on wood joists to create a horizontal *diaphragm* in accordance with Table R702.3.6. Gypsum board and gypsum panel products shall be installed perpendicular to ceiling framing members. End joints of adjacent courses of board and panels shall not occur on the same joist. The maximum allowable *diaphragm* proportions shall be $1^1/_2$:1 between shear resisting elements. Rotation or cantilever conditions shall not be permitted. Gypsum board or gypsum panel products shall not be used in *diaphragm* ceilings to resist lateral forces imposed by masonry or concrete construction. Perimeter edges shall be blocked using wood members not less than 2-inch by 6-inch (51 mm by 152 mm) nominal dimension. Blocking material shall be installed flat over the top plate of the wall to provide a nailing surface not less than 2 inches (51 mm) in width for the attachment of the gypsum board or gypsum panel product.

R702.3.7 Water-resistant gypsum backing board. Gypsum board used as the base or backer for adhesive application of ceramic tile or other required nonabsorbent finish material shall conform to ASTM C1178, C1278 or C1396. Use of water-resistant gypsum backing board shall be permitted on ceilings. Water-resistant gypsum board shall not be installed over a Class I or II vapor retarder in a shower or tub compartment. Cut or exposed edges, including those at wall intersections, shall be sealed as recommended by the manufacturer.

R702.3.7.1 Limitations. Water-resistant gypsum backing board shall not be used where there will be direct exposure to water, or in areas subject to continuous high humidity.

R702.4 Ceramic tile.

R702.4.1 General. Ceramic tile surfaces shall be installed in accordance with ANSI A108.1, A108.4, A108.5, A108.6, A108.11, A118.1, A118.3, A136.1 and A137.1.

R702.4.2 Backer boards. Materials used as backers for wall tile in tub and shower areas and wall panels in shower areas shall be of materials listed in Table R702.4.2, and installed in accordance with the manufacturer's recommendations.

TABLE R702.3.5
MINIMUM THICKNESS AND APPLICATION OF GYPSUM BOARD AND GYPSUM PANEL PRODUCTS

THICKNESS OF GYPSUM BOARD OR GYPSUM PANEL PRODUCTS (inches)	APPLICATION	ORIENTATION OF GYPSUM BOARD OR GYPSUM PANEL PRODUCTS TO FRAMING	MAXIMUM SPACING OF FRAMING MEMBERS (inches o.c.)	MAXIMUM SPACING OF FASTENERS (inches)		SIZE OF NAILS FOR APPLICATION TO WOOD FRAMING[c]
				Nails[a]	Screws[b]	
Application without adhesive						
$^3/_8$	Ceiling[d]	Perpendicular	16	7	12	13 gage, $1^1/_4$″ long, $^{19}/_{64}$″ head; 0.098″ diameter, $1^1/_4$″ long, annular-ringed; or 4d cooler nail, 0.080″ diameter, $1^3/_8$″ long, $^7/_{32}$″ head.
	Wall	Either direction	16	8	16	
$^1/_2$	Ceiling	Either direction	16	7	12	13 gage, $1^3/_8$″ long, $^{19}/_{64}$″ head; 0.098″ diameter, $1^1/_4$″ long, annular-ringed; 5d cooler nail, 0.086″ diameter, $1^5/_8$″ long, $^{15}/_{64}$″ head; or gypsum board nail, 0.086″ diameter, $1^5/_8$″ long, $^9/_{32}$″ head.
	Ceiling[d]	Perpendicular	24	7	12	
	Wall	Either direction	24	8	12	
	Wall	Either direction	16	8	16	
$^5/_8$	Ceiling	Either direction	16	7	12	13 gage, $1^5/_8$″ long, $^{19}/_{64}$″ head; 0.098″ diameter, $1^3/_8$″ long, annular-ringed; 6d cooler nail, 0.092″ diameter, $1^7/_8$″ long, $^1/_4$″ head; or gypsum board nail, 0.0915″ diameter, $1^7/_8$″ long, $^{19}/_{64}$″ head.
	Ceiling	Perpendicular	24	7	12	
	Type X at garage ceiling beneath habitable rooms	Perpendicular	24	6	6	$1^7/_8$″ long 6d coated nails or equivalent drywall screws. Screws shall comply with Section R702.3.5.1
	Wall	Either direction	24	8	12	13 gage, $1^5/_8$″ long, $^{19}/_{64}$″ head; 0.098″ diameter, $1^3/_8$″ long, annular-ringed; 6d cooler nail, 0.092″ diameter, $1^7/_8$″ long, $^1/_4$″ head; or gypsum board nail, 0.0915″ diameter, $1^7/_8$″ long, $^{19}/_{64}$″ head.
	Wall	Either direction	16	8	16	
Application with adhesive						
$^3/_8$	Ceiling[d]	Perpendicular	16	16	16	Same as above for $^3/_8$″ gypsum board and gypsum panel products.
	Wall	Either direction	16	16	24	
$^1/_2$ or $^5/_8$	Ceiling	Either direction	16	16	16	Same as above for $^1/_2$″ and $^5/_8$″ gypsum board and gypsum panel products, respectively.
	Ceiling[d]	Perpendicular	24	12	16	
	Wall	Either direction	24	16	24	
Two $^3/_8$ layers	Ceiling	Perpendicular	16	16	16	Base ply nailed as above for $^1/_2$″ gypsum board and gypsum panel products; face ply installed with adhesive.
	Wall	Either direction	24	24	24	

For SI: 1 inch = 25.4 mm.

a. For application without adhesive, a pair of nails spaced not less than 2 inches apart or more than $2^1/_2$ inches apart shall be permitted to be used with the pair of nails spaced 12 inches on center.

b. Screws shall be in accordance with Section R702.3.5.1. Screws for attaching gypsum board or gypsum panel products to structural insulated panels shall penetrate the wood structural panel facing not less than $^7/_{16}$ inch.

c. Where cold-formed steel framing is used with a clinching design to receive nails by two edges of metal, the nails shall be not less than $^5/_8$ inch longer than the gypsum board or gypsum panel product thickness and shall have ringed shanks. Where the cold-formed steel framing has a nailing groove formed to receive the nails, the nails shall have barbed shanks or be 5d, $13^1/_2$ gage, $1^5/_8$ inches long, $^{15}/_{64}$-inch head for $^1/_2$-inch gypsum board or gypsum panel product; and 6d, 13 gage, $1^7/_8$ inches long, $^{15}/_{64}$-inch head for $^5/_8$-inch gypsum board or gypsum panel product.

d. Three-eighths-inch-thick single-ply gypsum board or gypsum panel product shall not be used on a ceiling where a water-based textured finish is to be applied, or where it will be required to support insulation above a ceiling. On ceiling applications to receive a water-based texture material, either hand or spray applied, the gypsum board or gypsum panel product shall be applied perpendicular to framing. Where applying a water-based texture material, the minimum gypsum board thickness shall be increased from $^3/_8$ inch to $^1/_2$ inch for 16-inch on center framing, and from $^1/_2$ inch to $^5/_8$ inch for 24-inch on center framing or $^1/_2$-inch sag-resistant gypsum ceiling board shall be used.

TABLE R702.3.6
SHEAR CAPACITY FOR HORIZONTAL WOOD-FRAMED GYPSUM BOARD DIAPHRAGM CEILING ASSEMBLIES

MATERIAL	THICKNESS OF MATERIAL (min.) (inch)	SPACING OF FRAMING MEMBERS (max.) (inch)	SHEAR VALUE[a, b] (plf of ceiling)	MINIMUM FASTENER SIZE[c, d]
Gypsum board or gypsum panel product	$^1/_2$	16 o.c.	90	5d cooler or wallboard nail; $1^5/_8$-inch long; 0.086-inch shank; $^{15}/_{64}$-inch head
Gypsum board or gypsum panel product	$^1/_2$	24 o.c.	70	5d cooler or wallboard nail; $1^5/_8$-inch long; 0.086-inch shank; $^{15}/_{64}$-inch head

For SI: 1 inch = 25.4 mm, 1 pound per linear foot = 1.488 kg/m.

a. Values are not cumulative with other horizontal diaphragm values and are for short-term loading caused by wind or seismic loading. Values shall be reduced 25 percent for normal loading.

b. Values shall be reduced 50 percent in Seismic Design Categories D_0, D_1, D_2 and E.

c. $1^1/_4$-inch, No. 6 Type S or W screws shall be permitted to be substituted for the listed nails.

d. Fasteners shall be spaced not more than 7 inches on center at all supports, including perimeter blocking, and not less than $^3/_8$ inch from the edges and ends of the gypsum board.

TABLE R702.4.2
BACKER BOARD MATERIALS

MATERIAL	STANDARD
Glass mat gypsum backing panel	ASTM C1178
Fiber-reinforced gypsum panels	ASTM C1278
Nonasbestos fiber-cement backer board	ASTM C1288 or ISO 8336, Category C
Nonasbestos fiber mat-reinforced cementitious backer units	ASTM C1325

R702.5 Other finishes. Wood veneer paneling and hardboard paneling shall be placed on wood or cold-formed steel framing spaced not more than 16 inches (406 mm) on center. Wood veneer and hard board paneling less than $^1/_4$-inch (6 mm) nominal thickness shall not have less than a $^3/_8$-inch (10 mm) gypsum board or gypsum panel product backer. Wood veneer paneling not less than $^1/_4$-inch (6 mm) nominal thickness shall conform to ANSI/HPVA HP-1. Hardboard paneling shall conform to CPA/ANSI A135.5.

R702.6 Wood shakes and shingles. Wood shakes and shingles shall conform to CSSB *Grading Rules for Wood Shakes and Shingles* and shall be permitted to be installed directly to the studs with maximum 24 inches (610 mm) on-center spacing.

R702.6.1 Attachment. Nails, staples or glue are permitted for attaching shakes or shingles to the wall, and attachment of the shakes or shingles directly to the surface shall be permitted provided the fasteners are appropriate for the type of wall surface material. Where nails or staples are used, two fasteners shall be provided and shall be placed so that they are covered by the course above.

R702.6.2 Furring strips. Where furring strips are used, they shall be 1 inch by 2 inches or 1 inch by 3 inches (25 mm by 51 mm or 25 mm by 76 mm), spaced a distance on center equal to the desired exposure, and shall be attached to the wall by nailing through other wall material into the studs.

R702.7 Vapor retarders. A class I or II vapor retarder is required on the interior side of frame walls in Climate Zones 6 and 7. Class II vapor retarders are permitted only when specified on the construction documents.

R702.7.1 Class III vapor retarders. Class III vapor retarders shall be permitted where any one of the conditions in Table R702.7.1 is met.

TABLE R702.7.1
CLASS III VAPOR RETARDERS

CLIMATE ZONE	CLASS III VAPOR RETARDERS PERMITTED FOR:[a]
Marine 4	Vented cladding over wood structural panels.
	Vented cladding over fiberboard.
	Vented cladding over gypsum.
	Continuous insulation with R-value $\geq$ 2.5 over 2 × 4 wall.
	Continuous insulation with R-value $\geq$ 3.75 over 2 × 6 wall.
5	Vented cladding over wood structural panels.
	Vented cladding over fiberboard.
	Vented cladding over gypsum.
	Continuous insulation with R-value $\geq$ 5 over 2 × 4 wall.
	Continuous insulation with R-value $\geq$ 7.5 over 2 × 6 wall.
6	Vented cladding over fiberboard.
	Vented cladding over gypsum.
	Continuous insulation with R-value $\geq$ 7.5 over 2 × 4 wall.
	Continuous insulation with R-value $\geq$ 11.25 over 2 × 6 wall.
7 and 8	Continuous insulation with R-value $\geq$ 10 over 2 × 4 wall.
	Continuous insulation with R-value $\geq$ 15 over 2 × 6 wall.

For SI: 1 pound per cubic foot = 16 kg/m³.

a. Spray foam with a maximum permeance of 1.5 perms at the installed thickness, applied to the interior cavity side of wood structural panels, fiberboard, insulating sheathing or gypsum is deemed to meet the continuous insulation requirement where the spray foam R-value meets or exceeds the specified continuous insulation R-value.

R702.7.2 Material vapor retarder class. The *vapor retarder class* shall be based on the manufacturer's certified testing or a tested assembly.

The following shall be deemed to meet the class specified:

1. Class I: Sheet polyethylene, on perforated aluminum foil.

2. Class II: Kraft-faced fiberglass batts.

3. Class III: Latex or enamel paint.

R702.7.3 Minimum clear airspaces and vented openings for vented cladding. For the purposes of this section, vented cladding shall include the following minimum clear airspaces. Other openings with the equivalent vent area shall be permitted.

1. Vinyl polypropylene or horizontal aluminum siding applied over a weather-resistive barrier as specified in Table R703.3(1).

2. Brick veneer with a clear airspace as specified in Table R703.8.4.

3. Other approved vented claddings.

SECTION R703
EXTERIOR COVERING

R703.1 General. Exterior walls shall provide the building with a weather-resistant exterior wall envelope. The exterior wall envelope shall include flashing as described in Section R703.4.

Exception: Log walls designed and constructed in accordance with the provisions of ICC 400.

R703.1.1 Water resistance. The exterior wall envelope shall be designed and constructed in a manner that prevents the accumulation of water within the wall assembly by providing a water-resistant barrier behind the exterior cladding as required by Section R703.2 and a means of draining to the exterior water that penetrates the exterior cladding.

Exceptions:

1. A weather-resistant exterior wall envelope shall not be required over concrete or masonry walls designed in accordance with Chapter 6 and flashed in accordance with Section R703.4 or R703.8.

2. Compliance with the requirements for a means of drainage, and the requirements of Sections R703.2 and R703.4, shall not be required for an exterior wall envelope that has been demonstrated to resist wind-driven rain through testing of the exterior wall envelope, including joints, penetrations and intersections with dissimilar materials, in accordance with ASTM E331 under the following conditions:

   2.1. Exterior wall envelope test assemblies shall include at least one opening, one control joint, one wall/eave interface and one wall sill. All tested openings and penetrations shall be representative of the intended end-use configuration.

   2.2. Exterior wall envelope test assemblies shall be at least 4 feet by 8 feet (1219 mm by 2438 mm) in size.

   2.3. Exterior wall assemblies shall be tested at a minimum differential pressure of 6.24 pounds per square foot (299 Pa).

   2.4. Exterior wall envelope assemblies shall be subjected to the minimum test exposure for a minimum of 2 hours.

   The exterior wall envelope design shall be considered to resist wind-driven rain where the results of testing indicate that water did not penetrate control joints in the exterior wall envelope, joints at the perimeter of openings penetration or intersections of terminations with dissimilar materials.

R703.1.2 Wind resistance. Wall coverings, backing materials and their attachments shall be capable of resisting wind loads in accordance with Tables R301.2(2) and R301.2(3). Wind-pressure resistance of the siding, soffit and backing materials shall be determined by ASTM E330 or other applicable standard test methods. Where wind-pressure resistance is determined by design analysis, data from approved design standards and analysis conforming to generally accepted engineering practice shall be used to evaluate the siding, soffit and backing material and its fastening. All applicable failure modes including bending rupture of siding, fastener withdrawal and fastener head pull-through shall be considered in the testing or design analysis. Where the wall covering, soffit and backing material resist wind load as an assembly, use of the design capacity of the assembly shall be permitted.

R703.2 Water-resistive barrier. One layer of No. 15 asphalt felt, free from holes and breaks, complying with ASTM D226 for Type 1 felt or other approved water-resistive barrier shall be applied over studs or sheathing of all exterior walls. No.15 asphalt felt shall be applied horizontally, with the upper layer lapped over the lower layer not less than 2 inches (51 mm). Where joints occur, felt shall be lapped not less than 6 inches (152 mm). Other *approved* materials shall be installed in accordance with the *water-resistive barrier* manufacturer's installation instructions. The No. 15 asphalt felt or other approved water-resistive barrier material shall overlap the flashings required in Section R703.4 not less than 2 inches (51 mm). The No. 15 asphalt felt or other approved *water-resistive barrier* material shall be continuous up to the underside of the rafter or truss top chord and terminated at penetrations and building appendages in a manner to meet the requirements of the exterior wall envelope as described in Section R703.1.

R703.3 Wall covering nominal thickness and attachments. The nominal thickness and attachment of exterior wall coverings shall be in accordance with Table R703.3(1), the wall covering material requirements of this section, and the wall covering manufacturer's installation instructions. Cladding attachment over foam sheathing shall comply with the additional requirements and limitations of Sections R703.15 through R703.17. Nominal material thicknesses in Table R703.3(1) are based on a maximum stud spacing of 16 inches (406 mm) on center. Where specified by the siding manufacturer's instructions and supported by a test report or other documentation, attachment to studs with greater spacing is permitted. Fasteners for exterior wall coverings attached to wood framing shall be in accordance with Section R703.3.3 and Table R703.3(1). Exterior wall coverings shall be attached to cold-formed steel light frame construction in accordance with the cladding manufacturer's installation instructions, the requirements of Table R703.3(1) using screw fasteners substituted for the nails specified in accordance with Table R703.3(2), or an approved design.

TABLE R703.3(1)
SIDING MINIMUM ATTACHMENT AND MINIMUM THICKNESS

SIDING MATERIAL		NOMINAL THICKNESS (inches)	JOINT TREATMENT	TYPE OF SUPPORTS FOR THE SIDING MATERIAL AND FASTENERS					Number or spacing of fasteners
				Wood or wood structural panel sheathing into stud	Fiberboard sheathing into stud	Gypsum sheathing into stud	Foam plastic sheathing into stud[i]	Direct to studs	
Anchored veneer: brick, concrete, masonry or stone (see Section R703.8)		2	Section R703.8	Section R703.8					
Adhered veneer: concrete, stone or masonry (see Section R703.12)		—	Section R703.12	Section R703.12					
Fiber cement siding	Panel siding (see Section R703.10.1)	5/16	Section R703.10.1	6d common (2″ × 0.113″)	6d common (2″ × 0.113″)	6d common (2″ × 0.113″)	6d common (2″ × 0.113″)	4d common (1 1/2″ × 0.099″)	6″ panel edges 12″ inter. sup.
	Lap siding (see Section R703.10.2)	5/16	Section R703.10.2	6d common (2″ × 0.113″)	6d common (2″ × 0.113″)	6d common (2″ × 0.113″)	6d common (2″ × 0.113″)	6d common (2″ × 0.113″) or 11 gage roofing nail	Note f
Hardboard panel siding (see Section R703.5)		7/16	—	0.120″ nail (shank) with 0.225″ head	0.120″ nail (shank) with 0.225″ head	0.120″ nail (shank) with 0.225″ head	0.120″ nail (shank) with 0.225″ head	0.120″ nail (shank) with 0.225″ head	6″ panel edges 12″ inter. sup.[d]
Hardboard lap siding (see Section R703.5)		7/16	Note e	0.099″ nail (shank) with 0.240″ head	0.099″ nail (shank) with 0.240″ head	0.099″ nail (shank) with 0.240″ head	0.099″ nail (shank) with 0.240″ head	0.099″ nail (shank) with 0.240″ head	Same as stud spacing 2 per bearing
Horizontal aluminum[a]	Without insulation	0.019[b]	Lap	Siding nail 1 1/2″ × 0.120″	Siding nail 2″ × 0.120″	Siding nail 2″ × 0.120″	Siding nail[h] 1 1/2″ × 0.120″	Not allowed	Same as stud spacing
		0.024	Lap	Siding nail 1 1/2″ × 0.120″	Siding nail 2″ × 0.120″	Siding nail 2″ × 0.120″	Siding nail[h] 1 1/2″ × 0.120″	Not allowed	
	With insulation	0.019	Lap	Siding nail 1 1/2″ × 0.120″	Siding nail 2 1/2″ × 0.120″	Siding nail 2 1/2″ × 0.120″	Siding nail[h] 1 1/2″ × 0.120″	Siding nail 1 1/2″ × 0.120″	
Insulated vinyl siding[j]		0.035 (vinyl siding layer only)	Lap	0.120 nail (shank) with a 0.313 head or 16-gage crown[h, i]	0.120 nail (shank) with a 0.313 head or 16-gage crown[h]	0.120 nail (shank) with a 0.313 head or 16-gage crown[h]	0.120 nail (shank) with a 0.313 head Section R703.11.2	Not allowed	16 inches on center or specified by manufacturer instructions, test report or other sections of this code
Particleboard panels		3/8	—	6d box nail (2″ × 0.099″)	6d box nail (2″ × 0.099″)	6d box nail (2″ × 0.099″)	6d box nail (2″ × 0.099″)	Not allowed	6″ panel edges 12″ inter. sup.
		1/2	—	6d box nail (2″ × 0.099″)	6d box nail (2″ × 0.099″)	6d box nail (2″ × 0.099″)	6d box nail (2″ × 0.099″)	6d box nail (2″ × 0.099″)	
		5/8	—	6d box nail (2″ × 0.099″)	8d box nail (2 1/2″ × 0.113″)	8d box nail (2 1/2″ × 0.113″)	6d box nail (2″ × 0.099″)	6d box nail (2″ × 0.099″)	
Polypropylene siding[k]		Not applicable	Lap	Section 703.14.1	Section 703.14.1	Section 703.14.1	Section 703.14.1	Not allowed	As specified by the manufacturer instructions, test report or other sections of this code

(continued)

TABLE R703.3(1)—continued
SIDING MINIMUM ATTACHMENT AND MINIMUM THICKNESS

SIDING MATERIAL		NOMINAL THICKNESS (inches)	JOINT TREATMENT	TYPE OF SUPPORTS FOR THE SIDING MATERIAL AND FASTENERS					
				Wood or wood structural panel sheathing into stud	Fiberboard sheathing into stud	Gypsum sheathing into stud	Foam plastic sheathing into stud[l]	Direct to studs	Number or spacing of fasteners
Steel[c]		29 ga.	Lap	Siding nail ($1^3/_4''$ × 0.113") Staple–$1^3/_4''$	Siding nail ($2^3/_4''$ × 0.113") Staple–$2^1/_2''$	Siding nail ($2^1/_2''$ × 0.113") Staple–$2^1/_4''$	Siding nail ($1^3/_4''$ x 0.113") Staple–$1^3/_4''$	Not allowed	Same as stud spacing
Vinyl siding (see Section R703.11)		0.035	Lap	0.120" nail (shank) with a 0.313" head or 16-gage staple with $^3/_8$- to $^1/_2$-inch crown[h, i]	0.120" nail (shank) with a 0.313" head or 16-gage staple with $^3/_8$- to $^1/_2$-inch crown[h]	0.120" nail (shank) with a 0.313" head or 16- gage staple with $^3/_8$- to $^1/_2$-inch crown[h]	0.120" nail (shank) with a 0.313 head Section R703.11.2	Not allowed	16 inches on center or as specified by the manufacturer instructions or test report
Wood siding (see Section R703.5)	Wood rustic, drop	$^3/_8$ min.	Lap	6d box or siding nail (2" × 0.099")	6d box or siding nail (2" × 0.099")	6d box or siding nail (2" × 0.099")	6d box or siding nail (2" × 0.099")	8d box or siding nail ($2^1/_2''$ × 0.113") Staple–2"	Face nailing up to 6" widths, 1 nail per bearing; 8" widths and over, 2 nails per bearing
	Shiplap	$^{19}/_{32}$ average	Lap						
	Bevel	$^7/_{16}$							
	Butt tip	$^3/_{16}$	Lap						
Wood structural panel ANSI/APA PRP-210 siding (exterior grade) (see Section R703.5)		$^3/_8 – ^1/_2$	Note e	2" × 0.099" siding nail	$2^1/_2''$ × 0.113" siding nail	$2^1/_2''$ × 0.113" siding nail	$2^1/_2''$ × 0.113" siding nail	2" × 0.099" siding nail	6" panel edges 12" inter. sup.
Wood structural panel lap siding (see Section R703.5)		$^3/_8 – ^1/_2$	Note e Note g	2" × 0.099" siding nail	$2^1/_2''$ × 0.113" siding nail	$2^1/_2''$ × 0.113" siding nail	$2^1/_2''$ × 0.113" siding nail	2" × 0.099" siding nail	8" along bottom edge

For SI: 1 inch = 25.4 mm.

a. Aluminum nails shall be used to attach aluminum siding.

b. Aluminum (0.019 inch) shall be unbacked only where the maximum panel width is 10 inches and the maximum flat area is 8 inches. The tolerance for aluminum siding shall be +0.002 inch of the nominal dimension.

c. Shall be of approved type.

d. Where used to resist shear forces, the spacing must be 4 inches at panel edges and 8 inches on interior supports.

e. Vertical end joints shall occur at studs and shall be covered with a joint cover or shall be caulked.

f. Face nailing: one 6d common nail through the overlapping planks at each stud. Concealed nailing: one 11-gage $1^1/_2$-inch-long galv. roofing nail through the top edge of each plank at each stud in accordance with the manufacturer's installation instructions.

g. Vertical joints, if staggered, shall be permitted to be away from studs if applied over wood structural panel sheathing.

h. Minimum fastener length must be sufficient to penetrate sheathing other nailable substrate and framing a total of a minimum of $1^1/_4$ inches or in accordance with the manufacturer's installation instructions.

i. Where specified by the manufacturer's instructions and supported by a test report, fasteners are permitted to penetrate into or fully through nailable sheathing or other nailable substrate of minimum thickness specified by the instructions or test report, without penetrating into framing.

j. Insulated vinyl siding shall comply with ASTM D7793.

k. Polypropylene siding shall comply with ASTM D7254.

l. Cladding attachment over foam sheathing shall comply with the additional requirements and limitations of Sections R703.15, R703.16 and R703.17.

TABLE R703.3(2)
SCREW FASTENER SUBSTITUTION FOR SIDING ATTACHMENT TO COLD-FORMED STEEL LIGHT FRAME CONSTRUCTION[a, b, c, d, e]

NAIL DIAMETER PER TABLE R703.3(1)	MINIMUM SCREW FASTENER SIZE
0.099″	No. 6
0.113″	No. 7
0.120″	No. 8

For SI: 1 inch = 25.4 mm

a. Screws shall comply with ASTM C1513 and shall penetrate a minimum of three threads through minimum 33 mil (20 gage) cold-formed steel frame construction.

b. Screw head diameter shall be not less than the nail head diameter required by Table R703.3(1).

c. Number and spacing of screw fasteners shall comply with Table R703.3(1).

d. Pan head, hex washer head, modified truss head or other screw head types with a flat attachment surface under the head shall be used for vinyl siding attachment.

e. Aluminum siding shall not be fastened directly to cold-formed steel light frame construction.

R703.3.1 Soffit installation. Soffits shall comply with Section R703.3.1.1, Section R703.3.1.2 or the manufacturer's installation instructions.

R703.3.1.1 Wood structural panel soffit. The minimum nominal thickness for wood structural panel soffits shall be $^3/_8$ inch (9.5 mm) and shall be fastened to framing or nailing strips with 2-inch by 0.099-inch (51 mm × 2.5 mm) nails. Fasteners shall be in spaced not less than 6 inches (152 mm) on center at panel edges and 12 inches (305 mm) on center at intermediate supports.

R703.3.1.2 Vinyl soffit panels. Soffit panels shall be fastened at fascia and wall ends and to intermediate nailing strips as necessary to ensure that there is no unsupported span greater than 16 inches (406 mm), or as specified by the manufacturer's instructions.

R703.3.2 Wind limitations. Where the design wind pressure exceeds 30 psf or where the limits of Table R703.3.2 are exceeded, the attachment of wall coverings and soffits shall be designed to resist the component and cladding loads specified in Table R301.2(2) for walls, adjusted for height and exposure in accordance with Table R301.2(3). For the determination of wall covering and soffit attachment, component and cladding loads shall be determined using an effective wind area of 10 square feet (0.93 m²).

TABLE R703.3.2
LIMITS FOR ATTACHMENT PER TABLE R703.3(1)

Ultimate Wind Speed (mph 3-second gust)	MAXIMUM MEAN ROOF HEIGHT		
	Exposure		
	B	C	D
115	NL	50′	20′
120	NL	30′	DR
130	60′	15′	DR
140	35′	DR	DR

For SI: 1 foot = 304.8 mm, 1 mile per hour = 0.447 m/s.
NL = Not Limited by Table R703.3.2, DR = Design Required.

R703.3.3 Fasteners. Exterior wall coverings and roof overhang soffits shall be securely fastened with aluminum, galvanized, stainless steel or rust-preventative coated nails or staples in accordance with Table R703.3(1) or with other approved corrosion-resistant fasteners in accordance with the wall covering manufacturer's installation instructions. Nails and staples shall comply with ASTM F1667. Nails shall be T-head, modified round head, or round head with smooth or deformed shanks. Staples shall have a minimum crown width of $^7/_{16}$ inch (11.1 mm) outside diameter and be manufactured of minimum 16-gage wire. Where fiberboard, gypsum, or foam plastic sheathing backing is used, nails or staples shall be driven into the studs. Where wood or wood structural panel sheathing is used, fasteners shall be driven into studs unless otherwise permitted to be driven into sheathing in accordance with either the siding manufacturer's installation instructions or Table R703.3.3.

R703.3.4 Minimum fastener length and penetration. Fasteners shall have the greater of the minimum length specified in Table R703.3(1) or as required to provide a minimum penetration into framing as follows:

1. Fasteners for horizontal aluminum siding, steel siding, particleboard panel siding, wood structural panel siding in accordance with ANSI/APA-PRP 210, fiber-cement panel siding and fiber-cement lap siding installed over foam plastic sheathing shall penetrate not less than $1^1/_2$ inches (38 mm) into framing or shall be in accordance with the manufacturer's installation instructions.

2. Fasteners for hardboard panel and lap siding shall penetrate not less than $1^1/_2$ inches (38 mm) into framing.

3. Fasteners for vinyl siding and insulated vinyl siding installed over wood or wood structural panel sheathing shall penetrate not less than $1^1/_4$ inches (32 mm)

TABLE R703.3.3
OPTIONAL SIDING ATTACHMENT SCHEDULE FOR FASTENERS WHERE NO STUD PENETRATION NECESSARY

APPLICATION	NUMBER AND TYPE OF FASTENER	SPACING OF FASTENERS[b]
Exterior wall covering (weighing 3 psf or less) attachment to wood structural panel sheathing, either direct or over foam sheathing a maximum of 2 inches thick.[a] Note: Does not apply to vertical siding.	Ring shank roofing nail (0.120″ min. dia.)	12″ o.c.
	Ring shank nail (0.148″ min. dia.)	15″ o.c.
	No. 6 screw (0.138″ min. dia.)	12″ o.c.
	No. 8 screw (0.164″ min. dia.)	16″ o.c.

For SI: 1 inch = 25.4 mm, 1 pound per square foot = 0.479 kPa.

a. Fastener length shall be sufficient to penetrate the back side of the wood structural panel sheathing by at least $^1/_4$ inch. The wood structural panel sheathing shall be not less than $^7/_{16}$ inch in thickness.

b. Spacing of fasteners is per 12 inches of siding width. For other siding widths, multiply "Spacing of Fasteners" above by a factor of 12/s, where "s" is the siding width in inches. Fastener spacing shall never be greater than the manufacturer's minimum recommendations.

into sheathing and framing combined. Vinyl siding and insulated vinyl siding shall be permitted to be installed with fasteners penetrating into or through wood or wood structural sheathing of minimum thickness as specified by the manufacturer's instructions or test report, with or without penetration into the framing. Where the fastener penetrates fully through the sheathing, the end of the fastener shall extend not less than $^1/_4$ inch (6.4 mm) beyond the opposite face of the sheathing. Fasteners for vinyl siding and insulated vinyl siding installed over foam plastic sheathing shall be in accordance with Section R703.11.2. Fasteners for vinyl siding and insulated vinyl siding installed over fiberboard or gypsum sheathing shall penetrate not less than $1^1/_4$ inches (32 mm) into framing.

4. Fasteners for vertical or horizontal wood siding shall penetrate not less than $1^1/_2$ inches (38 mm) into studs, studs and wood sheathing combined, or blocking.

5. Fasteners for siding material installed over foam plastic sheathing shall have sufficient length to accommodate foam plastic sheathing thickness and to penetrate framing or sheathing and framing combined, as specified in Items 1 through 4.

R703.4 Flashing. Approved corrosion-resistant flashing shall be applied shingle-fashion in such a manner as to prevent entry of water into the wall cavity or penetration of water to the building structural framing components. Self-adhered membranes used as flashing shall comply with AAMA 711. Fluid-applied membranes used as flashing in exterior walls shall comply with AAMA 714. The flashing shall extend to the surface of the exterior wall finish. Approved corrosion-resistant flashings shall be installed at the following locations:

1. Exterior window and door openings. Flashing shall be installed at the head and sides of exterior window and door openings and shall extend to the surface of the exterior wall finish or to the water-resistive barrier for subsequent drainage. Flashing at exterior window and door openings shall be installed in accordance with at least one of the following:

    1.1. The fenestration manufacturer's installation and flashing instructions. When flashing is not addressed in the fenestration manufacturer's instructions, it shall be installed in accordance with the flashing manufacturer's instructions.

    1.2. In accordance with the flashing design or method of a registered design professional.

    1.3. In accordance with other approved methods.

2. At the intersection of chimneys or other masonry construction with frame or stucco walls, with projecting lips on both sides under stucco copings.

3. Under and at the ends of masonry, wood, or metal copings and sills.

4. Continuously above all projecting wood trim.

5. Where exterior porches, decks, or stairs attach to a wall or floor assembly of wood-frame construction.

6. At wall and roof intersections.

7. At built-in gutters.

8. Where exterior material meets in other than a vertical line.

9. Where the lower portion of a sloped roof stops within the plane of an intersecting wall cladding in such a manner as to divert water away from the assembly in compliance with Section R903.2.1.

10. At the intersection of the foundation and rim joist framing when the exterior wall covering does not lap the foundation insulation.

R703.4.1 Pan flashing of windows and doors. Pan flashing shall be installed in accordance with the fenestration manufacturer's installation and flashing instructions. Where flashing instructions or details are not provided, pan flashing shall be installed at the sill of exterior window and door openings. Pan flashing shall be sealed or sloped in such a manner as to direct water to the surface of the exterior wall finish or to the water-resistive barrier for subsequent drainage.

Exceptions:

1. Windows or doors installed in accordance with the manufacturer's installation instructions which include an alternate flashing method.

2. Windows or doors in detached accessory structures.

3. Skylights, bow or bay windows.

4. Doors required to meet accessibility requirements that would prevent the installation of pan flashing.

5. Repairs or replacement of existing windows and doors.

6. When a method is provided by a registered design professional.

R703.5 Wood, hardboard and wood structural panel siding. Wood, hardboard, and wood structural panel siding shall be installed in accordance with this section and Table R703.3(1). Hardboard siding shall comply with CPA/ANSI A135.6. Hardboard siding used as architectural trim shall comply with CPA/ANSI A 135.7.

R703.5.1 Vertical wood siding. Wood siding applied vertically shall be nailed to horizontal nailing strips or blocking set not more than 24 inches (610 mm) on center.

R703.5.2 Panel siding. Three-eighths-inch (9.5 mm) wood structural panel siding shall not be applied directly to studs spaced more than 16 inches (406 mm) on center where long dimension is parallel to studs. Wood structural panel siding $^7/_{16}$ inch (11.1 mm) or thinner shall not be applied directly to studs spaced more than 24 inches (610 mm) on center. The stud spacing shall not exceed the panel span rating provided by the manufacturer unless the panels are installed with the face grain perpendicular to the studs or over sheathing approved for that stud spacing.

Joints in wood, hardboard or wood structural panel siding shall be made as follows unless otherwise approved. Vertical joints in panel siding shall occur over framing members, unless wood or wood structural panel sheathing is used, and shall be shiplapped or covered with a batten. Horizontal joints in panel siding shall be lapped not less than 1 inch (25 mm) or shall be shiplapped or flashed with Z-flashing and occur over solid blocking, wood or wood structural panel sheathing.

R703.5.3 Horizontal wood siding. Horizontal lap siding shall be installed in accordance with the manufacturer's recommendations. Where there are no recommendations the siding shall be lapped not less than 1 inch (25 mm), or $^{1}/_{2}$ inch (12.7 mm) if rabbeted, and shall have the ends caulked, covered with a batten or sealed and installed over a strip of flashing.

R703.6 Wood shakes and shingles. Wood shakes and shingles shall conform to CSSB.

R703.6.1 Application. Wood shakes or shingles shall be applied either single course or double course over nominal $^{1}/_{2}$-inch (12.7 mm) wood-based sheathing or to furring strips over $^{1}/_{2}$-inch (12.7 mm) nominal nonwood sheathing. A water-resistive barrier shall be provided over all sheathing, with horizontal overlaps in the membrane of not less than 2 inches (51 mm) and vertical overlaps of not less than 6 inches (152 mm). Where horizontal furring strips are used, they shall be 1 inch by 3 inches or 1 inch by 4 inches (25 mm by 76 mm or 25 mm by 102 mm) and shall be fastened to the studs with minimum 7d or 8d box nails and shall be spaced a distance on center equal to the actual weather exposure of the shakes or shingles, not to exceed the maximum exposure specified in Table R703.6.1. When installing shakes or shingles over a nonpermeable water-resistive barrier, furring strips shall be placed first vertically over the barrier and in addition, horizontal furring strips shall be fastened to the vertical furring strips prior to attaching the shakes or shingles to the horizontal furring strips. The spacing between adjacent shingles to allow for expansion shall be $^{1}/_{8}$ inch (3.2 mm) to $^{1}/_{4}$ inch (6.4 mm) apart, and between adjacent shakes shall be $^{3}/_{8}$ inch (9.5 mm) to $^{1}/_{2}$ inch (12.7 mm) apart. The offset spacing between joints in adjacent courses shall be not less than $1^{1}/_{2}$ inches (38 mm).

TABLE R703.6.1
MAXIMUM WEATHER EXPOSURE FOR WOOD SHAKES AND SHINGLES ON EXTERIOR WALLS[a, b, c]
(Dimensions are in inches)

LENGTH	EXPOSURE FOR SINGLE COURSE	EXPOSURE FOR DOUBLE COURSE
Shingles[a]		
16	7	12[b]
18	8	14[c]
24	$10^{1}/_{2}$	16[d]
Shakes[a]		
18	8	14
24	$10^{1}/_{2}$	18

For SI: 1 inch = 25.4 mm.

a. Dimensions given are for No. 1 grade.

b. A maximum 9-inch exposure is permitted for No. 2 grade.

c. A maximum 10-inch exposure is permitted for No. 2 grade.

d. A maximum 14-inch exposure is permitted for No. 2 grade.

R703.6.2 Weather exposure. The maximum weather exposure for shakes and shingles shall not exceed that specified in Table 703.6.1.

R703.6.3 Attachment. Wood shakes or shingles shall be installed according to this chapter and the manufacturer's instructions. Each shake or shingle shall be held in place by two stainless steel Type 304, Type 316 or hot-dipped zinc-coated galvanized corrosion-resistant box nails in accordance with Table R703.6.3(1) or R703.6.3(2). The hot-dipped zinc-coated galvanizing shall be in compliance with ASTM A153, 1.0 ounce per square foot. Alternatively, 16-gage stainless steel Type 304 or Type 316 staples with crown widths $^{7}/_{16}$ inch (11 mm) minimum, $^{3}/_{4}$ inch (19 mm) maximum, shall be used and the crown of the staple shall be placed parallel with the butt of the shake or the shingle. In single-course application, the fasteners shall be concealed by the course above and shall be driven approximately 1 inch (25 mm) above the butt line of the succeeding course and $^{3}/_{4}$ inch (19 mm) from the edge. In double-course applications, the exposed shake or shingle shall be face-nailed with two fasteners, driven approximately 2 inches (51 mm) above the butt line and $^{3}/_{4}$ inch (19 mm) from each edge. Fasteners installed within 15 miles (24 km) of salt water coastal areas shall be stainless steel Type 316. Fasteners for fire-retardant-treated shakes or shingles in accordance with Section R902 or pressure-impregnated-preservative-treated shakes or shingles in accordance with AWPA U1 shall be stainless steel Type 316. The fasteners shall penetrate the sheathing or furring strips by not less than $^{1}/_{2}$ inch (13 mm) and shall not be overdriven. Fasteners for untreated (natural) and treated products shall comply with ASTM F1667.

R703.6.4 Bottom courses. The bottom courses shall be doubled.

R703.7 Exterior plaster. Installation of these materials shall be in compliance with ASTM C926 and ASTM C1063 and provisions of this code.

R703.7.1 Lath. All lath and lath attachments shall be of corrosion-resistant materials. Expanded metal or woven wire lath shall be attached with 11-gage nails having a $^{7}/_{16}$-inch (11.1 mm) head or 16-gage staples, spaced at no more than 6 inches (152 mm) or as otherwise approved. Nails or staples shall penetrate wood framing support members not less than $^{3}/_{4}$ inch (19 mm).

R703.7.1.1 Control joints and expansion joints. Provisions for the control of expansion shall be determined by the exterior plaster application designer. ASTM C1063 Sections 7.11.4 through 7.11.4.4 do not apply.

R703.7.2 Plaster. Plastering with portland cement plaster shall be in accordance with ASTM C926. Cement materials shall be in accordance with one of the following:

1. Masonry cement conforming to ASTM C91 Type M, S, or N.

2. Portland cement conforming to ASTM C150 Type I, II, or III.

3. Blended hydraulic cement conforming to ASTM C595 Type IP, IS (< 70), IL, or IT (S < 70).

4. Hydraulic cement conforming to ASTM C1157 Type GU, HE, MS, HS, or MH.

5. Plastic (stucco) cement conforming to ASTM C1328.

Plastering with portland cement plaster shall be not less than three coats when applied over metal lath or wire lath and shall be not less than two coats when applied over masonry, concrete, pressure-preservative-treated wood, or decay-resistant wood as specified in Section R317.1 or gypsum backing. If the plaster surface is completely covered by veneer or other facing material or is completely concealed, plaster application need be only two coats, provided the total thickness is as set forth in Table R702.1(1).

On wood-frame construction with an on-grade floor slab system, exterior plaster shall be applied to cover, but not extend below, lath, paper, and screed.

R703.7.2.1 Weep screeds. A minimum 0.019-inch (0.5 mm) (No. 26 galvanized sheet gage), corrosion-resistant weep screed or plastic weep screed, with a minimum vertical attachment flange of $3^{1}/_{2}$ inches (89 mm) shall be provided at or below the foundation plate line on exterior stud walls in accordance with ASTM C1063. The weep screed shall be placed a minimum of 4 inches (102 mm) above the earth or 2 inches (51 mm) above paved areas and shall be of a type that will allow trapped water to drain to the exterior of the building. The weather-resistant barrier shall lap the attachment flange. The exterior lath shall cover and terminate on the attachment flange of the weep screed.

R703.7.3 Water-resistive barriers. Water-resistive barriers shall be installed as required in Section R703.2 and, where applied over wood-based sheathing, shall include two layers of a water-resistive vapor-permeable barrier. Each layer shall meet both of the following requirements:

1. A water resistance of not less than that of 60-minute Grade D paper; or a minimum hydrostatic head of $23^{31}/_{32}$ inches (60.9 cm) when tested in accordance with hydrostatic pressure test method AATCC 127-2008; or a minimum water transudation time of 60 minutes when tested in accordance with ASTM D779.

TABLE R703.6.3(1)
SINGLE-COURSE SIDEWALL FASTENERS

SINGLE-COURSE SIDEWALL FASTENERS			
Product type	Nail type and minimum length (inches)	Minimum head diameter (inches)	Minimum shank thickness (inches)
R & R and sanded shingles			
16″ and 18″ shingles	3d box $1^{1}/_{4}$	0.19	0.08
24″ shingles	4d box $1^{1}/_{2}$	0.19	0.08
Grooved shingles			
16″ and 18″ shingles	3d box $1^{1}/_{4}$	0.19	0.08
24″ shingles	4d box $1^{1}/_{2}$	0.19	0.08
Split and sawn shakes			
18″ straight-split shakes	5d box $1^{3}/_{4}$	0.19	0.08
18″ and 24″ handsplit shakes	6d box 2	0.19	0.0915
24″ tapersplit shakes	5d box $1^{3}/_{4}$	0.19	0.08
18″ and 24″ tapersawn shakes	6d box 2	0.19	0.0915

For SI: 1 inch = 25.4 mm.

TABLE R703.6.3(2)
DOUBLE-COURSE SIDEWALL FASTENERS

DOUBLE-COURSE SIDEWALL FASTENERS			
Product type	Nail type and minimum length (inches)	Minimum head diameter (inches)	Minimum shank thickness (inches)
R & R and sanded shingles			
16,″ 8″ and 24″ shingles	5d box $1^{3}/_{4}$ or same size casing nails	0.19	0.08
Grooved shingles			
16,″ 18″ and 24″shingles	5d box $1^{3}/_{4}$	0.19	0.08
Split and sawn shakes			
18″ straight-split shakes	7d box $2^{1}/_{4}$ or 8d $2^{1}/_{2}$	0.19	0.099
18″ and 24″ handsplit shakes	7d box $2^{1}/_{4}$ or 8d $2^{1}/_{2}$	0.19	0.099
24″ tapersplit shakes	7d box $2^{1}/_{4}$ or 8d $2^{1}/_{2}$	0.19	0.099
18″ and 24″ tapersawn shakes	7d box $2^{1}/_{4}$ or 8d $2^{1}/_{2}$	0.19	0.099

For SI: 1 inch = 25.4 mm.

2. A water vapor permeance of not less than that of No. 15 felt; or a minimum permeance rating of 8.5 gr/h.ft.^{2} in Hg (US perm) (4.9×10^{10}kg/Pa.s.m^2) when tested in accordance with Procedure B of ASTM E96.

Exception: One layer *water-resistive barrier* complying with R703.2 is permitted when a drainage space that allows bulk water to flow freely behind the cladding is provided.

R703.7.4 Application. Each coat shall be kept in a moist condition for at least 48 hours prior to application of the next coat.

Exception: Applications installed in accordance with ASTM C926. The second coat is permitted to be applied as soon as the first coat has attained sufficient rigidity to receive the second coat.

R703.7.5 Curing. The finish coat for two-coat cement plaster shall not be applied sooner than seven days after application of the first coat. For three-coat cement plaster, the second coat shall not be applied sooner than 48 hours after application of the first coat, except as required in Section R703.7.4. The finish coat for three-coat cement plaster shall not be applied sooner than seven days after application of the second coat.

R703.8 Anchored stone and masonry veneer, general. Anchored stone and masonry veneer shall be installed in accordance with this chapter, Table R703.3(1) and Figure R703.8. These veneers installed over a backing of wood or cold-formed steel shall be limited to the first story above grade plane and shall not exceed 5 inches (127 mm) in thickness. See Section R602.10 for wall bracing requirements for masonry veneer for wood-framed construction and Section R603.9.5 for wall bracing requirements for masonry veneer for cold-formed steel construction.

Exceptions:

1. For buildings in Seismic Design Categories A, B and C, exterior stone or masonry veneer, as specified in Table R703.8(1), with a backing of wood or steel framing shall be permitted to the height specified in Table R703.8(1) above a noncombustible foundation.

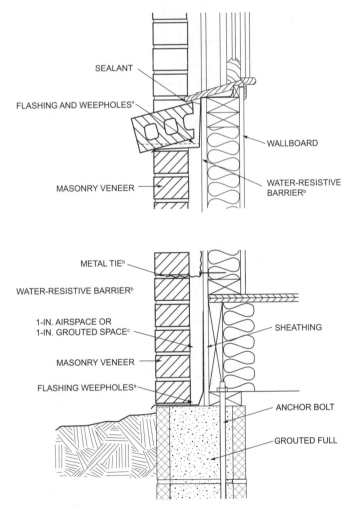

For SI: 1 inch = 24.5 mm.

FIGURE R703.8
TYPICAL MASONRY VENEER WALL DETAILS^e

(continued)

2. For detached one- or two-family dwellings in Seismic Design Categories D_0, D_1 and D_2, exterior stone or masonry veneer, as specified in Table R703.8(2), with a backing of wood framing shall be permitted to the height specified in Table R703.8(2) above a noncombustible foundation.

R703.8.1 Interior veneer support. Veneers used as interior wall finishes shall be permitted to be supported on wood or cold-formed steel floors that are designed to support the loads imposed.

R703.8.2 Exterior veneer support. Except in Seismic Design Categories D_0, D_1 and D_2, exterior masonry veneers having an installed weight of 40 pounds per square foot (195 kg/m^2) or less shall be permitted to be supported on wood or cold-formed steel construction. Where masonry veneer supported by wood or cold-formed steel construction adjoins masonry veneer supported by the foundation, there shall be a movement joint between the veneer supported by the wood or cold-formed steel construction and the veneer supported by the foundation.

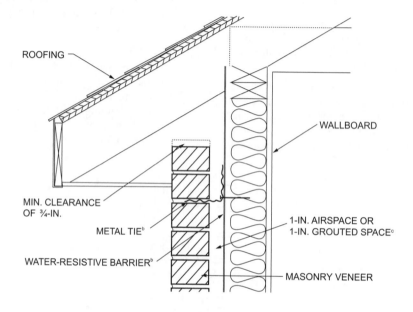

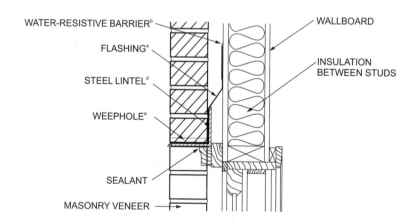

For SI: 1 inch = 25.4 mm.

a. See Sections R703.4, R703.8.5 and R703.8.6.
b. See Sections R703.2 and R703.8.4.
c. See Table R703.8.4 and Section R703.8.4.2.
d. See Section R703.8.3.
e. Figure R703.8 illustrates typical construction details for a masonry veneer wall. For the actual mandatory requirements of this code, see the indicated sections of text. Other details of masonry veneer wall construction shall be permitted provided the requirements of the indicated sections of text are met.

FIGURE R703.8—continued
TYPICAL MASONRY VENEER WALL DETAILS[e]

The wood or cold-formed steel construction supporting the masonry veneer shall be designed to limit the deflection to $^1/_{600}$ of the span for the supporting members. The design of the wood or cold-formed steel construction shall consider the weight of the veneer and any other loads.

R703.8.2.1 Support by steel angle. A minimum 6-inch by 4-inch by $^5/_{16}$-inch (152 mm by 102 mm by 8 mm) steel angle, with the long leg placed vertically, shall be anchored to double 2-inch by 4-inch (51 mm by 102 mm) wood studs or double 350S162 cold-formed steel studs at a maximum on-center spacing of 16 inches (406 mm). Anchorage of the steel angle at every double stud spacing shall be not less than two $^7/_{16}$-inch-diameter (11 mm) by 4-inch (102 mm) lag screws for wood construction or two $^7/_{16}$-inch (11.1 mm) bolts with washers for

cold-formed steel construction. The steel angle shall have a minimum clearance to underlying construction of $^1/_{16}$ inch (1.6 mm). Not less than two-thirds the width of the masonry veneer thickness shall bear on the steel angle. Flashing and weep holes shall be located in the masonry veneer in accordance with Figure R703.8.2.1. The maximum height of masonry veneer above the steel angle support shall be 12 feet 8 inches (3861 mm). The airspace separating the masonry veneer from the wood backing shall be in accordance with Sections R703.8.4 and R703.8.4.2. The method of support for the masonry veneer on wood construction shall be constructed in accordance with Figure R703.8.2.1.

The maximum slope of the roof construction without stops shall be 7:12. Roof construction with slopes

TABLE R703.8(1)
STONE OR MASONRY VENEER LIMITATIONS AND REQUIREMENTS,
WOOD OR STEEL FRAMING, SEISMIC DESIGN CATEGORIES A, B AND C

SEISMIC DESIGN CATEGORY	NUMBER OF WOOD- OR STEEL- FRAMED STORIES	MAXIMUM HEIGHT OF VENEER ABOVE NONCOMBUSTIBLE FOUNDATION[a] (feet)	MAXIMUM NOMINAL THICKNESS OF VENEER (inches)	MAXIMUM WEIGHT OF VENEER (psf)[b]	WOOD- OR STEEL- FRAMED STORY
A or B	Steel: 1 or 2 Wood: 1, 2 or 3	30	5	50	all
C	1	30	5	50	1 only
	2	30	5	50	top
					bottom
	Wood only: 3	30	5	50	top
					middle
					bottom

For SI: 1 inch = 25.4 mm, 1 foot = 304.8 mm, 1 pound per square foot = 0.479 kPa.

a. An additional 8 feet is permitted for gable end walls. See also story height limitations of Section R301.3.

b. Maximum weight is installed weight and includes weight of mortar, grout, lath and other materials used for installation. Where veneer is placed on both faces of a wall, the combined weight shall not exceed that specified in this table.

TABLE R703.8(2)
STONE OR MASONRY VENEER LIMITATIONS AND REQUIREMENTS,
ONE- AND TWO-FAMILY DETACHED DWELLINGS, SEISMIC DESIGN CATEGORIES D$_0$, D$_1$ AND D$_2$

SEISMIC DESIGN CATEGORY	NUMBER OF WOOD- FRAMED STORIES[a]	MAXIMUM HEIGHT OF VENEER ABOVE NONCOMBUSTIBLE FOUNDATION OR FOUNDATION WALL (feet)	MAXIMUM NOMINAL THICKNESS OF VENEER (inches)	MAXIMUM WEIGHT OF VENEER (psf)[b]
D$_0$	1	20[c]	4	40
	2	20[c]	4	40
	3	30[d]	4	40
D$_1$	1	20[c]	4	40
	2	20[c]	4	40
	3	20[c]	4	40
D$_2$	1	20[c]	3	30
	2	20[c]	3	30

For SI: 1 inch = 25.4 mm, 1 foot = 304.8 mm, 1 pound per square foot = 0.479 kPa, 1 pound-force = 4.448 N.

a. Cripple walls are not permitted in Seismic Design Categories D$_0$, D$_1$ and D$_2$.

b. Maximum weight is installed weight and includes weight of mortar, grout and lath, and other materials used for installation.

c. The veneer shall not exceed 20 feet in height above a noncombustible foundation, with an additional 8 feet permitted for gable end walls, or 30 feet in height with an additional 8 feet for gable end walls where the lower 10 feet have a backing of concrete or masonry wall. See story height limitations of Section R301.3.

d. The veneer shall not exceed 30 feet in height above a noncombustible foundation, with an additional 8 feet permitted for gable end walls. See story height limitations of Section R301.3.

greater than 7:12 but not more than 12:12 shall have stops of a minimum 3-inch by 3-inch by $^1/_4$-inch (76 mm by 76 mm by 6.4 mm) steel plate welded to the angle at 24 inches (610 mm) on center along the angle or as *approved* by the *building official*.

R703.8.2.2 Support by roof construction. A steel angle shall be placed directly on top of the roof construction. The roof supporting construction for the steel angle shall consist of not fewer than three 2-inch by 6-inch (51 mm by 152 mm) wood members for wood construction or three 550S162 cold-formed steel members for cold-formed steel light frame construction. A wood member abutting the vertical wall stud construction shall be anchored with not fewer than three $^5/_8$-inch (15.9 mm) diameter by 5-inch (127 mm) lag screws to every wood stud spacing. Each additional wood roof member shall be anchored by the use of two 10d nails at every wood stud spacing. A cold-formed steel member abutting the vertical wall stud shall be anchored with not fewer than nine No. 8 screws to every cold-formed steel stud. Each additional cold-formed steel roof member shall be anchored to the adjoining roof member using two No. 8 screws at every stud spacing. Not less than two-thirds the width of the masonry veneer thickness shall bear on the steel angle. Flashing and weep holes shall be located in the masonry veneer wythe in accordance with Figure R703.8.2.2. The maximum height of the masonry veneer above the steel angle support shall be 12 feet 8 inches (3861 mm). The airspace separating the masonry veneer from the wood backing shall be in accordance with Sec-

tions R703.8.4 and R703.8.4.2. The support for the masonry veneer shall be constructed in accordance with Figure R703.8.2.2.

The maximum slope of the roof construction without stops shall be 7:12. Roof construction with slopes greater than 7:12 but not more than 12:12 shall have stops of a minimum 3-inch by 3-inch by $^1/_4$-inch (76 mm by 76 mm by 6.4 mm) steel plate welded to the angle at 24 inches (610 mm) on center along the angle or as *approved* by the *building official*.

R703.8.3 Lintels. Masonry veneer shall not support any vertical load other than the dead load of the veneer above. Veneer above openings shall be supported on lintels of noncombustible materials. The lintels shall have a length of bearing not less than 4 inches (102 mm). Steel lintels shall be shop coated with a rust-inhibitive paint, except for lintels made of corrosion-resistant steel or steel treated with coatings to provide corrosion resistance. Construction of openings shall comply with either Section R703.8.3.1 or 703.8.3.2.

R703.8.3.1 Allowable span. The allowable span shall not exceed the values set forth in Table R703.8.3.1.

R703.8.3.2 Maximum span. The allowable span shall not exceed 18 feet 3 inches (5562 mm) and shall be constructed to comply with Figure R703.8.3.2 and the following:

1. Provide a minimum length of 18 inches (457 mm) of masonry veneer on each side of opening as shown in Figure R703.8.3.2.

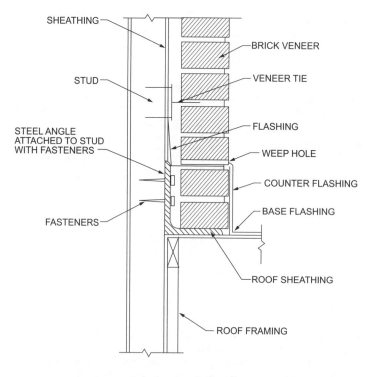

SUPPORT BY STEEL ANGLE

FIGURE R703.8.2.1
EXTERIOR MASONRY VENEER SUPPORT BY STEEL ANGLES

2. Provide a minimum 5-inch by $3^1/_2$-inch by $^5/_{16}$-inch (127 mm by 89 mm by 7.9 mm) steel angle above the opening and shore for a minimum of 7 days after installation.

3. Provide double-wire joint reinforcement extending 12 inches (305 mm) beyond each side of the opening. Lap splices of joint reinforcement not less than 12 inches (305 mm). Comply with one of the following:

   3.1. Double-wire joint reinforcement shall be $^3/_{16}$-inch (4.8 mm) diameter and shall be placed in the first two bed joints above the opening.

   3.2. Double-wire joint reinforcement shall be 9 gauge (0.144 inch or 3.66 mm diameter) and shall be placed in the first three bed joints above the opening.

4. Provide the height of masonry veneer above opening, in accordance with Table R703.8.3.2.

TABLE R703.8.3.2
HEIGHT OF MASONRY VENEER ABOVE OPENING

MINIMUM HEIGHT OF MASONRY VENEER ABOVE OPENING (INCH)	MAXIMUM HEIGHT OF MASONRY VENEER ABOVE OPENING (FEET)
13	< 5
24	5 to < 12
60	12 to height above support allowed by Section R703.8

For SI: 1 inch = 25.4 mm, 1 foot = 304.8 mm.

R703.8.4 Anchorage. Masonry veneer shall be anchored to the supporting wall studs with corrosion-resistant metal ties embedded in mortar or grout and extending into the veneer a minimum of $1^1/_2$ inches (38 mm), with not less than $^5/_8$-inch (15.9 mm) mortar or grout cover to outside face. Masonry veneer shall conform to Table R703.8.4(1). For masonry veneer tie attachment through insulating sheathing not greater than 2 inches (51 mm) in thickness to not less than 7/16 performance category wood structural panel, see Table R703.8.4(2).

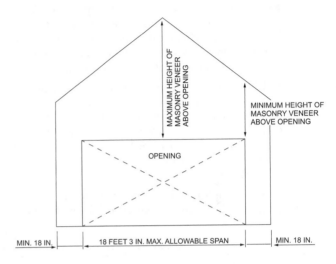

For SI: 1 inch = 25.4 mm, 1 foot = 304.8 mm.

FIGURE R703.8.3.2
MASONRY VENEER OPENING

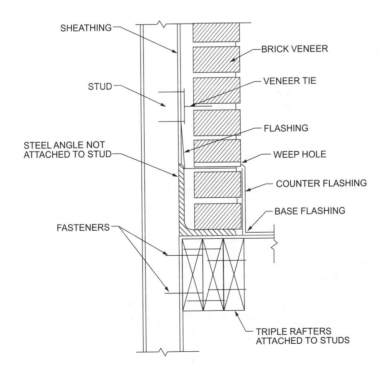

SUPPORT BY ROOF MEMBERS

FIGURE R703.8.2.2
EXTERIOR MASONRY VENEER SUPPORT BY ROOF MEMBERS

R703.8.4.1 Size and spacing. Veneer ties, if strand wire, shall be not less in thickness than No. 9 U.S. gage [(0.148 inch) (4 mm)] wire and shall have a hook embedded in the mortar joint, or if sheet metal, shall be not less than No. 22 U.S. gage by [(0.0299 inch) (0.76 mm)] $^7/_8$ inch (22 mm) corrugated. Each tie shall support not more than 2.67 square feet (0.25 m^2) of wall area and shall be spaced not more than 32 inches (813 mm) on center horizontally and 24 inches (635 mm) on center vertically.

Exception: In Seismic Design Category D$_0$, D$_1$ or D$_2$ or townhouses in Seismic Design Category C or in wind areas of more than 30 pounds per square foot pressure (1.44 kPa), each tie shall support not more than 2 square feet (0.2 m^2) of wall area.

R703.8.4.1.1 Veneer ties around wall openings. Additional metal ties shall be provided around wall openings greater than 16 inches (406 mm) in either dimension. Metal ties around the perimeter of openings shall be spaced not more than 3 feet (9144 mm) on center and placed within 12 inches (305 mm) of the wall opening.

R703.8.4.2 Grout fill. As an alternative to the airspace required by Table R703.8.4, grout shall be permitted to fill the airspace. Where the airspace is filled with grout, a water-resistive barrier is required over studs or sheathing. Where the airspace is filled, replacing the sheathing and water-resistive barrier with a wire mesh and *approved* water-resistive barrier or an *approved* water-resistive barrier-backed reinforcement attached directly to the studs is permitted.

R703.8.5 Flashing. Flashing shall be located beneath the first course of masonry above finished ground level above the foundation wall or slab and at other points of support, including structural floors, shelf angles and lintels where masonry veneers are designed in accordance with Section R703.8. See Section R703.4 for additional requirements.

R703.8.6 Weepholes. Weepholes shall be provided in the outside wythe of masonry walls at a maximum spacing of 33 inches (838 mm) on center. Weepholes shall be not less than $^3/_{16}$ inch (5 mm) in diameter. Weepholes shall be located immediately above the flashing.

R703.9 Exterior insulation and finish system (EIFS)/EIFS with drainage. Exterior insulation and finish systems (EIFS) shall comply with this chapter and Section R703.9.1. EIFS with drainage shall comply with this chapter and Section R703.9.2.

TABLE R703.8.3.1
ALLOWABLE SPANS FOR LINTELS SUPPORTING MASONRY VENEER[a, b, c, d]

SIZE OF STEEL ANGLE[a, c, d] (inches)	NO STORY ABOVE	ONE STORY ABOVE	TWO STORIES ABOVE	NO. OF $^1/_2$-INCH OR EQUIVALENT REINFORCING BARS IN REINFORCED LINTEL[b, d]
$3 \times 3 \times ^1/_4$	6'-0"	4'-6"	3'-0"	1
$4 \times 3 \times ^1/_4$	8'-0"	6'-0"	4'-6"	1
$5 \times 3^1/_2 \times ^5/_{16}$	10'-0"	8'-0"	6'-0"	2
$6 \times 3^1/_2 \times ^5/_{16}$	14'-0"	9'-6"	7'-0"	2
$2\text{-}6 \times 3^1/_2 \times ^5/_{16}$	20'-0"	12'-0"	9'-6"	4

For SI: 1 inch = 25.4 mm, 1 foot = 304.8 mm.

a. Long leg of the angle shall be placed in a vertical position.

b. Depth of reinforced lintels shall be not less than 8 inches and all cells of hollow masonry lintels shall be grouted solid. Reinforcing bars shall extend not less than 8 inches into the support.

c. Steel members indicated are adequate typical examples; other steel members meeting structural design requirements shall be permitted to be used.

d. Either steel angle or reinforced lintel shall span opening.

TABLE R703.8.4(1)
TIE ATTACHMENT AND AIRSPACE REQUIREMENTS

BACKING AND TIE	MINIMUM TIE	MINIMUM TIE FASTENER[a]	AIRSPACE[c]	
Wood stud backing with corrugated sheet metal	22 U.S. gage (0.0299 in.) × $^7/_8$ in. wide	8d common nail[b] (2$^1/_2$ in. × 0.131 in.)	Nominal 1 in. between sheathing and veneer	
Wood stud backing with metal strand wire	W1.7 (No. 9 U.S. gage; 0.148 in.) with hook embedded in mortar joint	8d common nail[b] (2$^1/_2$ in. × 0.131 in.)	Minimum nominal 1 in. between sheathing and veneer	Maximum 4$^1/_2$ in. between backing and veneer
Cold-formed steel stud backing with adjustable metal strand wire	W1.7 (No. 9 U.S. gage; 0.148 in.) with hook embedded in mortar joint	No. 10 screw extending through the steel framing a minimum of three exposed threads	Minimum nominal 1 in. between sheathing and veneer	Maximum 4$^1/_2$ in. between backing and veneer

For SI: 1 inch = 25.4 mm.

a. In Seismic Design Category D$_0$, D$_1$ or D$_2$, the minimum tie fastener shall be an 8d ring-shank nail (2$^1/_2$ in. × 0.131 in.) or a No. 10 screw extending through the steel framing a minimum of three exposed threads.

b. All fasteners shall have rust-inhibitive coating suitable for the installation in which they are being used, or be manufactured from material not susceptible to corrosion.

c. An airspace that provides drainage shall be permitted to contain mortar from construction.

TABLE R703.8.4(2)
REQUIRED BRICK TIE SPACING FOR DIRECT APPLICATION TO WOOD STRUCTURAL PANEL SHEATHING[a, b, c]

REQUIRED BRICK-TIE SPACING (VERTICAL-TIE SPACING/HORIZONTAL-TIE SPACING) (inches/inches)

FASTENER TYPE[d]	SIZE (DIA. OR SCREW #)	110 mph V Ultimate			115 mph V Ultimate			130 mph V Ultimate			140 mph V Ultimate		
		Zone 5, Exposure B	Zone 5, Exposure C	Zone 5, Exposure D	Zone 5, Exposure B	Zone 5, Exposure C	Zone 5, Exposure D	Zone 5, Exposure B	Zone 5, Exposure C	Zone 5, Exposure D	Zone 5, Exposure B	Zone 5, Exposure C	Zone 5, Exposure D
Ring Shank Nails	0.091	16/16, 16/12, 12/16, 12/12	16/12, 12/16, 12/12	12/12	16/16, 16/12, 12/16, 12/12	16/12, 12/16, 12/12	12/12	16/12, 12/16, 12/12	12/12	—	12/12	—	—
	0.148	24/16, 16/24, 16/16, 16/12, 12/16, 12/12	16/16, 16/12, 12/16, 12/12	16/16, 16/12, 12/16, 12/12	24/16, 16/24, 16/16, 16/12, 12/16, 12/12	16/16, 16/12, 12/16, 12/12	16/16, 16/12, 12/16, 12/12	16/16, 16/12, 12/16, 12/12	16/12, 12/16, 12/12	16/12, 12/16, 12/12	16/16, 16/12, 12/16, 12/12	16/12, 12/16, 12/12	12/12
Screws	#6	24/16, 16/24, 16/16, 16/12, 12/16, 12/12	16/16, 16/12, 12/16, 12/12	16/16, 16/12, 12/16, 12/12	24/16, 16/24, 16/16, 16/12, 12/16, 12/12	16/16, 16/12, 12/16, 12/12	16/16, 16/12, 12/16, 12/12	16/16, 16/12, 12/16, 12/12	16/12, 12/16, 12/12	16/12, 12/16, 12/12	16/16, 16/12, 12/16, 12/12	16/12, 12/16, 12/12	12/12
	#8	24/16, 16/24, 16/16, 16/12, 12/16, 12/12	24/16, 16/24, 16/16, 16/12, 12/16, 12/12	16/16, 16/12, 12/16, 12/12	24/16, 16/24, 16/16, 16/12, 12/16, 12/12	16/16, 16/12, 12/16, 12/12	16/16, 16/12, 12/16, 12/12	24/16, 16/24, 16/16, 16/12, 12/16, 12/12	16/16, 16/12, 12/16, 12/12	16/12, 12/16, 12/12	16/16, 16/12, 12/16, 12/12	16/12, 12/16, 12/12	16/12, 12/16, 12/12
	#10	24/16, 16/24, 16/16, 16/12, 12/16, 12/12	24/16, 16/24, 16/16, 16/12, 12/16, 12/12	24/16, 16/24, 16/16, 16/12, 12/16, 12/12	24/16, 16/24, 16/16, 16/12, 12/16, 12/12	24/16, 16/24, 16/16, 16/12, 12/16, 12/12	24/16, 16/24, 16/16, 16/12, 12/16, 12/12	24/16, 16/24, 16/16, 16/12, 12/16, 12/12	24/16, 16/24, 16/16, 16/12, 12/16, 12/12	16/16, 16/12, 12/16, 12/12	24/16, 16/24, 16/16, 16/12, 12/16, 12/12	16/16, 16/12, 12/16, 12/12	16/16, 16/12, 12/16, 12/12
	#14	24/16, 16/24, 16/16, 16/12, 12/16, 12/12	24/16, 16/24, 16/16, 16/12, 12/16, 12/12	24/16, 16/24, 16/16, 16/12, 12/16, 12/12	24/16, 16/24, 16/16, 16/12, 12/16, 12/12	24/16, 16/24, 16/16, 16/12, 12/16, 12/12	24/16, 16/24, 16/16, 16/12, 12/16, 12/12	24/16, 16/24, 16/16, 16/12, 12/16, 12/12	24/16, 16/24, 16/16, 16/12, 12/16, 12/12	16/16, 16/12, 12/16, 12/12	24/16, 16/24, 16/16, 16/12, 12/16, 12/12	16/16, 16/12, 12/16, 12/12	16/16, 16/12, 12/16, 12/12

For SI: 1 inch = 25.4 mm, 1 mph = 0.447 m/s.

a. This table is based on attachment of brick ties directly to wood structural panel sheathing only. Additional attachment of the brick tie to lumber framing is not required. The brick ties shall be permitted to be placed over any insulating sheathing, not to exceed 2 inches in thickness. Wood structural panel sheathing shall be a minimum 7/16 performance category. The table is based on a building height of 30 feet or less.

b. Wood structural panels shall have a specific gravity of 0.42 or greater in accordance with NDS.

c. Foam sheathing shall have a minimum compressive strength of 15 psi in accordance with ASTM C578 or ASTM C1289.

d. Fasteners shall be sized such that the tip of the fastener passes completely through the wood structural panel sheathing by not less than 1/4 inch.

R703.9.1 Exterior insulation and finish systems (EIFS). EIFS shall comply with the following:

1. ASTM E2568.

2. EIFS shall be limited to applications over substrates of concrete or masonry wall assemblies.

3. Flashing of EIFS shall be provided in accordance with the requirements of Section R703.4.

4. EIFS shall be installed in accordance with the manufacturer's instructions.

5. EIFS shall terminate not less than 6 inches (152 mm) above the finished ground level.

6. Decorative trim shall not be face-nailed through the EIFS.

R703.9.2 Exterior insulation and finish system (EIFS) with drainage. EIFS with drainage shall comply with the following:

1. ASTM E2568.

2. EIFS with drainage shall be required over all wall assemblies with the exception of substrates of concrete or masonry wall assemblies.

3. EIFS with drainage shall have an average minimum drainage efficiency of 90 percent when tested in accordance with ASTM E2273.

4. The water-resistive barrier shall comply with Section R703.2 or ASTM E2570.

5. The water-resistive barrier shall be applied between the EIFS and the wall sheathing.

6. Flashing of EIFS with drainage shall be provided in accordance with the requirements of Section R703.4.

7. EIFS with drainage shall be installed in accordance with the manufacturer's instructions.

8. EIFS with drainage shall terminate not less than 6 inches (152 mm) above the finished ground level.

9. Decorative trim shall not be face-nailed through the EIFS with drainage.

R703.10 Fiber cement siding.

R703.10.1 Panel siding. Fiber-cement panels shall comply with the requirements of ASTM C1186, Type A, minimum Grade II or ISO 8336, Category A, minimum Class 2. Panels shall be installed with the long dimension either parallel or perpendicular to framing. Vertical and horizontal joints shall occur over framing members and shall be protected with caulking, or with battens or flashing, or be vertical or horizontal shiplap, or otherwise designed to comply with Section R703.1. Panel siding shall be installed with fasteners in accordance with Table R703.3(1) or the approved manufacturer's instructions.

R703.10.2 Lap siding. Fiber-cement lap siding having a maximum width of 12 inches (305 mm) shall comply with the requirements of ASTM C1186, Type A, minimum Grade II or ISO 8336, Category A, minimum Class 2. Lap siding shall be lapped a minimum of $1^1/_4$ inches (32 mm) and lap siding not having tongue-and-groove end joints shall have the ends protected with caulking, covered with an H-section joint cover, located over a strip of flashing, or shall be designed to comply with Section R703.1. Lap siding courses shall be installed with the fastener heads exposed or concealed, in accordance with Table R703.3(1) or approved manufacturer's instructions.

R703.11 Vinyl siding. Vinyl siding shall be certified and *labeled* as conforming to the requirements of ASTM D3679 by an *approved* quality control agency.

R703.11.1 Installation. Vinyl siding, soffit and accessories shall be installed in accordance with the manufacturer's instructions.

R703.11.1.1 Fasteners. Unless specified otherwise by the manufacturer's instructions, fasteners for vinyl siding shall be 0.120-inch (3 mm) shank diameter nail with a 0.313-inch (8 mm) head or 16-gage staple with a $^3/_8$-inch (9.5 mm) to $^1/_2$-inch (12.7 mm) crown.

R703.11.1.2 Penetration depth. Unless specified otherwise by the manufacturer's instructions, fasteners shall penetrate into building framing. The total penetration into sheathing, furring framing or other nailable substrate shall be a minimum $1^1/_4$ inches (32 mm). Where specified by the manufacturer's instructions and supported by a test report, fasteners are permitted to penetrate into or fully through nailable sheathing or other nailable substrate of minimum thickness specified by the instructions or test report without penetrating into framing. Where the fastener penetrates fully through the sheathing, the end of the fastener shall extend a minimum of $^1/_4$ inch (6.4 mm) beyond the opposite face of the sheathing or nailable substrate.

R703.11.1.3 Spacing. Unless specified otherwise by the manufacturer's instructions, the maximum spacing between fasteners for horizontal siding shall be 16 inches (406 mm), and for vertical siding 12 inches (305 mm) both horizontally and vertically. Where specified by the manufacturer's instructions and supported by a test report, greater fastener spacing is permitted.

R703.11.2 Installation over foam plastic sheathing. Where vinyl siding or insulated vinyl siding is installed over foam plastic sheathing, the vinyl siding shall comply with Section R703.11 and shall have a design wind pressure resistance in accordance with Table R703.11.2.

Exceptions:

1. Where the foam plastic sheathing is applied directly over wood structural panels, fiberboard, gypsum sheathing or other *approved* backing capable of independently resisting the design wind pressure, the vinyl siding shall be installed in accordance with Sections R703.3.3 and R703.11.1.

2. Where the vinyl siding manufacturer's product specifications provide an approved design wind pressure rating for installation over foam plastic sheathing, use of this design wind pressure rating shall be permitted and the siding shall be installed in accordance with the *manufacturer's installation instructions.*

3. Where the foam plastic sheathing and its attachment have a design wind pressure resistance complying with Sections R316.8 and R301.2.1, the vinyl siding shall be installed in accordance with Sections R703.3.3 and R703.11.1.

R703.12 Adhered masonry veneer installation. Adhered masonry veneer shall comply with the requirements of Section R703.7.3 and the requirements in Sections 12.1 and 12.3 of TMS 402. Adhered masonry veneer shall be installed in accordance with Section R703.7.1, Article 3.3C of TMS 602 or the manufacturer's instructions.

R703.12.1 Clearances. On exterior stud walls, adhered masonry veneer shall be installed:

1. Minimum of 4 inches (102 mm) above the earth;

2. Minimum of 2 inches (51 mm) above paved areas; or

3. Minimum of $^1/_2$ inch (12.7 mm) above exterior walking surfaces that are supported by the same foundation that supports the exterior wall.

R703.12.2 Flashing at foundation. A corrosion-resistant screed or flashing of a minimum 0.019-inch (0.48 mm) or 26-gage galvanized or plastic with a minimum vertical attachment flange of $3^1/_2$ inches (89 mm) shall be installed to extend a minimum of 1 inch (25 mm) below the foundation plate line on exterior stud walls in accordance with Section R703.4.

R703.12.3 Water-resistive barrier. A water-resistive barrier shall be installed as required by Section R703.2 and shall comply with the requirements of Section R703.7.3. The water-resistive barrier shall lap over the exterior of the attachment flange of the screed or flashing provided in accordance with Section R703.12.2.

R703.13 Insulated vinyl siding. Insulated vinyl siding shall be certified and labeled as conforming to the requirements of ASTM D7793 by an approved quality control agency.

R703.13.1 Insulated vinyl siding and accessories. Insulated vinyl siding and accessories shall be installed in accordance with the manufacturer's installation instructions.

R703.14 Polypropylene siding. Polypropylene siding shall be certified and labeled as conforming to the requirements of ASTM D7254, and those of Section R703.14.2 or Section R703.14.3, by an approved quality control agency.

R703.14.1 Polypropylene siding and accessories. Polypropylene siding and accessories shall be installed in accordance with manufacturer's installation instructions.

R703.14.1.1 Installation. Polypropylene siding shall be installed over and attached to wood structural panel sheathing with minimum thickness of $^7/_{16}$ inch (11.1 mm), or other substrate, composed of wood or wood-based material and fasteners having equivalent withdrawal resistance.

R703.14.1.2 Fastener requirements. Unless otherwise specified in the approved manufacturer's instructions, nails shall be corrosion resistant, with a minimum 0.120-inch (3 mm) shank and minimum 0.313-inch (8 mm) head diameter. Nails shall be a minimum of $1^1/_4$ inches (32 mm) long or as necessary to penetrate sheathing or substrate not less than $^3/_4$ inch (19.1 mm). Where the nail fully penetrates the sheathing or nailable substrate, the end of the fastener shall extend not less than $^1/_4$ inch (6.4 mm) beyond the opposite face of the sheathing or substrate. Staples are not permitted.

R703.14.2 Fire separation. Polypropylene siding shall not be installed on walls with a fire separation distance of less than 5 feet (1524 mm) and walls closer than 10 feet (3048 mm) to a building on another lot.

Exception: Walls perpendicular to the line used to determine the fire separation distance.

R703.14.3 Flame spread index. The certification of the *flame spread index* shall be accompanied by a test report stating that all portions of the test specimen ahead of the flame front remained in position during the test in accordance with ASTM E84 or UL 723.

R703.15 Cladding attachment over foam sheathing to wood framing. Cladding shall be specified and installed in accordance with Section R703, the cladding manufacturer's

TABLE R703.11.2
ADJUSTED MINIMUM DESIGN WIND PRESSURE REQUIREMENT FOR VINYL SIDING

ULTIMATE DESIGN WIND SPEED (MPH)	ADJUSTED MINIMUM DESIGN WIND PRESSURE (ASD) (PSF)[a, b]					
	Case 1: With interior gypsum wallboard[c]			Case 2: Without interior gypsum wallboard[c]		
	Exposure			Exposure		
	B	C	D	B	C	D
110	-44.0	-61.6	-73.1	-62.9	-88.1	-104.4
115	-49.2	-68.9	-81.7	-70.3	-98.4	-116.7
120	-51.8	-72.5	-86.0	-74.0	-103.6	-122.8
130	-62.2	-87.0	-103.2	-88.8	-124.3	-147.4
> 130	Not Allowed[d]					

For SI: 1 inch = 25.4 mm, 1 foot = 304.8 mm, 1 square foot = 0.0929 m², 1 mile per hour = 0.447 m/s, 1 pound per square foot = 0.0479 kPa.

a. Linear interpolation is permitted.

b. The table values are based on a maximum 30-foot mean roof height, and effective wind area of 10 square feet Wall Zone 5 (corner), and the ASD design wind pressure from Table R301.2(2) multiplied by the following adjustment factors: 2.6 (Case 1) and 3.7 (Case 2) for wind speeds less than 130 mph and 3.7 (Case 2) for wind speeds greater than 130 mph.

c. Gypsum wallboard, gypsum panel product or equivalent.

d. For the indicated wind speed condition, foam sheathing only on the exterior of frame walls with vinyl siding is not allowed unless the vinyl siding complies with an adjusted minimum design wind pressure requirement as determined in accordance with Note b and the wall assembly is capable of resisting an impact without puncture at least equivalent to that of a wood frame wall with minimum $^7/_{16}$-inch OSB sheathing as tested in accordance with ASTM E1886.

approved instructions, including any limitations for use over foam plastic sheathing, or an approved design. In addition, the cladding or furring attachments through foam sheathing to framing shall meet or exceed the minimum fastening requirements of Section R703.15.1, Section R703.15.2, or an approved design for support of cladding weight.

Exceptions:

1. Where the cladding manufacturer has provided approved installation instructions for application over foam sheathing, those requirements shall apply.

2. For exterior insulation and finish systems, refer to Section R703.9.

3. For anchored masonry or stone veneer installed over foam sheathing, refer to Section R703.8.

R703.15.1 Direct attachment. Where cladding is installed directly over foam sheathing without the use of furring, cladding minimum fastening requirements to support the cladding weight shall be as specified in Table R703.15.1.

R703.15.2 Furred cladding attachment. Where wood furring is used to attach cladding over foam sheathing, furring minimum fastening requirements to support the cladding weight shall be as specified in Table R703.15.2. Where placed horizontally, wood furring shall be preservative-treated wood in accordance with Section R317.1 or naturally durable wood and fasteners shall be corrosion resistant in accordance Section R317.3.

R703.16 Cladding attachment over foam sheathing to cold-formed steel framing. Cladding shall be specified and installed in accordance with Section R703, the cladding manufacturer's approved instructions, including any limitations for use over foam plastic sheathing, or an approved design. In addition, the cladding or furring attachments through foam sheathing to framing shall meet or exceed the minimum fastening requirements of Section R703.16.1, Section R703.16.2 or an approved design for support of cladding weight.

Exceptions:

1. Where the cladding manufacturer has provided approved installation instructions for application over foam sheathing, those requirements shall apply.

2. For exterior insulation and finish systems, refer to Section R703.9.

3. For anchored masonry or stone veneer installed over foam sheathing, refer to Section R703.8.

R703.16.1 Direct attachment. Where cladding is installed directly over foam sheathing without the use of furring, cladding minimum fastening requirements to support the cladding weight shall be as specified in Table R703.16.1.

R703.16.2 Furred cladding attachment. Where steel or wood furring is used to attach cladding over foam sheathing, furring minimum fastening requirements to support the cladding weight shall be as specified in Table R703.16.2. Where placed horizontally, wood furring shall be preservative-treated wood in accordance with Section R317.1 or naturally durable wood and fasteners shall be corrosion

resistant in accordance with Section R317.3. Steel furring shall have a minimum G60 galvanized coating.

R703.17 Cladding attachment over foam sheathing to masonry or concrete wall construction. Cladding shall be specified and installed in accordance with Section 703.3 and the cladding manufacturer's instructions or an approved design. Foam sheathing shall be attached to masonry or concrete construction in accordance with the insulation manufacturer's installation instructions or an approved design. Furring and furring attachments through foam sheathing into concrete or masonry substrate shall be designed to resist design loads determined in accordance with Section R301, including support of cladding weight as applicable. Fasteners used to attach cladding or furring through foam sheathing to masonry or concrete substrates shall be approved for application into masonry or concrete material and shall be installed in accordance with the fastener manufacturer's instructions.

Exceptions:

1. Where the cladding manufacturer has provided approved installation instructions for application over foam sheathing and connection to a masonry or concrete substrate, those requirements shall apply.

2. For exterior insulation and finish systems, refer to Section R703.9.

3. For anchored masonry or stone veneer installed over foam sheathing, refer to Section R703.8.

TABLE R703.15.1
CLADDING MINIMUM FASTENING REQUIREMENTS FOR DIRECT ATTACHMENT
OVER FOAM PLASTIC SHEATHING TO SUPPORT CLADDING WEIGHT[a]

CLADDING FASTENER THROUGH FOAM SHEATHING	CLADDING FASTENER TYPE AND MINIMUM SIZE[b]	CLADDING FASTENER VERTICAL SPACING (inches)	MAXIMUM THICKNESS OF FOAM SHEATHING[c] (inches)							
			16″ o.c. Fastener Horizontal Spacing				24″ o.c. Fastener Horizontal Spacing			
			Cladding Weight:				Cladding Weight:			
			3 psf	11 psf	18 psf	25 psf	3 psf	11 psf	18 psf	25 psf
Wood framing (minimum 1 1/4-inch penetration)	0.113″ diameter nail	6	2.00	1.45	0.75	DR	2.00	0.85	DR	DR
		8	2.00	1.00	DR	DR	2.00	0.55	DR	DR
		12	2.00	0.55	DR	DR	1.85	DR	DR	DR
	0.120″ diameter nail	6	3.00	1.70	0.90	0.55	3.00	1.05	0.50	DR
		8	3.00	1.20	0.60	DR	3.00	0.70	DR	DR
		12	3.00	0.70	DR	DR	2.15	DR	DR	DR
	0.131″ diameter nail	6	4.00	2.15	1.20	0.75	4.00	1.35	0.70	DR
		8	4.00	1.55	0.80	DR	4.00	0.90	DR	DR
		12	4.00	0.90	DR	DR	2.70	0.50	DR	DR
	0.162″ diameter nail	6	4.00	3.55	2.05	1.40	4.00	2.25	1.25	0.80
		8	4.00	2.55	1.45	0.95	4.00	1.60	0.85	0.50
		12	4.00	1.60	0.85	0.50	4.00	0.95	DR	DR

For SI: 1 inch = 25.4 mm, 1 pound per square foot = 0.0479 kPa, 1 pound per square inch = 6.895 kPa.

DR = Design Required.

o.c. = On Center.

a. Wood framing shall be Spruce-pine-fir or any wood species with a specific gravity of 0.42 or greater in accordance with AWC NDS.

b. Nail fasteners shall comply with ASTM F1667, except nail length shall be permitted to exceed ASTM F1667 standard lengths.

c. Foam sheathing shall have a minimum compressive strength of 15 psi in accordance with ASTM C578 or ASTM C1289.

TABLE R703.15.2
FURRING MINIMUM FASTENING REQUIREMENTS FOR APPLICATION
OVER FOAM PLASTIC SHEATHING TO SUPPORT CLADDING WEIGHT[a, b]

FURRING MATERIAL	FRAMING MEMBER	FASTENER TYPE AND MINIMUM SIZE	MINIMUM PENETRATION INTO WALL FRAMING (inches)	FASTENER SPACING IN FURRING (inches)	MAXIMUM THICKNESS OF FOAM SHEATHING[d] (inches)							
					16″ o.c. Furring[e]				24″ o.c. Furring[e]			
					Siding Weight:				Siding Weight:			
					3 psf	11 psf	18 psf	25 psf	3 psf	11 psf	18 psf	25 psf
Minimum 1× wood furring[c]	Minimum 2× wood stud	0.131″ diameter nail	1 1/4	8	4.00	2.45	1.45	0.95	4.00	1.60	0.85	DR
				12	4.00	1.60	0.85	DR	4.00	0.95	DR	DR
				16	4.00	1.10	DR	DR	3.05	0.60	DR	DR
		0.162″ diameter nail	1 1/4	8	4.00	4.00	2.45	1.60	4.00	2.75	1.45	0.85
				12	4.00	2.75	1.45	0.85	4.00	1.65	0.75	DR
				16	4.00	1.90	0.95	DR	4.00	1.05	DR	DR
		No.10 wood screw	1	12	4.00	2.30	1.20	0.70	4.00	1.40	0.60	DR
				16	4.00	1.65	0.75	DR	4.00	0.90	DR	DR
				24	4.00	0.90	DR	DR	2.85	DR	DR	DR
		1/4″ lag screw	1 1/2	12	4.00	2.65	1.50	0.90	4.00	1.65	0.80	DR
				16	4.00	1.95	0.95	0.50	4.00	1.10	DR	DR
				24	4.00	1.10	DR	DR	3.25	0.50	DR	DR

For SI: 1 inch = 25.4 mm, 1 pound per square foot = 0.0479 kPa, 1 pound per square inch = 6.895 kPa.

DR = Design Required.

o.c. = On Center.

a. Wood framing and furring shall be Spruce-pine-fir or any wood species with a specific gravity of 0.42 or greater in accordance with AWC NDS.

b. Nail fasteners shall comply with ASTM F1667, except nail length shall be permitted to exceed ASTM F1667 standard lengths.

c. Where the required cladding fastener penetration into wood material exceeds 3/4 inch and is not more than 1 1/2 inches, a minimum 2× wood furring or an approved design shall be used.

d. Foam sheathing shall have a minimum compressive strength of 15 psi in accordance with ASTM C578 or ASTM C1289.

e. Furring shall be spaced not more than 24 inches on center, in a vertical or horizontal orientation. In a vertical orientation, furring shall be located over wall studs and attached with the required fastener spacing. In a horizontal orientation, the indicated 8-inch and 12-inch fastener spacing in furring shall be achieved by use of two fasteners into studs at 16 inches and 24 inches on center, respectively.

TABLE R703.16.1
CLADDING MINIMUM FASTENING REQUIREMENTS FOR DIRECT ATTACHMENT OVER FOAM PLASTIC SHEATHING TO SUPPORT CLADDING WEIGHT[a]

CLADDING FASTENER THROUGH FOAM SHEATHING INTO:	CLADDING FASTENER TYPE AND MINIMUM SIZE[b]	CLADDING FASTENER VERTICAL SPACING (inches)	MAXIMUM THICKNESS OF FOAM SHEATHING[c] (inches)							
			16" o.c. Fastener Horizontal Spacing				24" o.c. Fastener Horizontal Spacing			
			Cladding Weight:				Cladding Weight:			
			3 psf	11 psf	18 psf	25 psf	3 psf	11 psf	18 psf	25 psf
Steel framing (minimum penetration of steel thickness + 3 threads)	No. 8 screw into 33-mil steel or thicker	6	3.00	2.95	2.20	1.45	3.00	2.35	1.25	DR
		8	3.00	2.55	1.60	0.60	3.00	1.80	DR	DR
		12	3.00	1.80	DR	DR	3.00	0.65	DR	DR
	No. 10 screw into 33-mil steel	6	4.00	3.50	2.70	1.95	4.00	2.90	1.70	0.55
		8	4.00	3.10	2.05	1.00	4.00	2.25	0.70	DR
		12	4.00	2.25	0.70	DR	3.70	1.05	DR	DR
	No. 10 screw into 43-mil steel or thicker	6	4.00	4.00	4.00	3.60	4.00	4.00	3.45	2.70
		8	4.00	4.00	3.70	3.00	4.00	3.85	2.80	1.80
		12	4.00	3.85	2.80	1.80	4.00	3.05	1.50	DR

For SI: 1 inch = 25.4 mm, 1 mil = 0.0254 mm, 1 pound per square foot = 0.0479 kPa, 1 pound per square inch = 6.895 kPa.

DR = Design Required.

o.c. = On Center.

a. Steel framing shall be minimum 33 ksi steel for 33 mil and 43 mil steel, and 50 ksi steel for 54 mil steel or thicker.

b. Screws shall comply with the requirements of ASTM C1513.

c. Foam sheathing shall have a minimum compressive strength of 15 psi in accordance with ASTM C578 or ASTM C1289.

TABLE R703.16.2
FURRING MINIMUM FASTENING REQUIREMENTS FOR APPLICATION OVER FOAM PLASTIC SHEATHING TO SUPPORT CLADDING WEIGHT[a]

FURRING MATERIAL	FRAMING MEMBER	FASTENER TYPE AND MINIMUM SIZE[b]	MINIMUM PENETRATION INTO WALL FRAMING (inches)	FASTENER SPACING IN FURRING (inches)	MAXIMUM THICKNESS OF FOAM SHEATHING[d] (inches)							
					16" o.c. Furring[e]				24" o.c. Furring[e]			
					Cladding Weight:				Cladding Weight:			
					3 psf	11 psf	18 psf	25 psf	3 psf	11 psf	18 psf	25 psf
Minimum 33-mil steel furring or minimum 1× wood furring[c]	33-mil steel stud	No. 8 screw	Steel thickness + 3 threads	12	3.00	1.80	DR	DR	3.00	0.65	DR	DR
				16	3.00	1.00	DR	DR	2.85	DR	DR	DR
				24	2.85	DR	DR	DR	2.20	DR	DR	DR
		No. 10 screw	Steel thickness + 3 threads	12	4.00	2.25	0.70	DR	3.70	1.05	DR	DR
				16	3.85	1.45	DR	DR	3.40	DR	DR	DR
				24	3.40	DR	DR	DR	2.70	DR	DR	DR
	43-mil or thicker steel stud	No. 8 Screw	Steel thickness + 3 threads	12	3.00	1.80	DR	DR	3.00	0.65	DR	DR
				16	3.00	1.00	DR	DR	2.85	DR	DR	DR
				24	2.85	DR	DR	DR	2.20	DR	DR	DR
		No. 10 screw	Steel thickness + 3 threads	12	4.00	3.85	2.80	1.80	4.00	3.05	1.50	DR
				16	4.00	3.30	1.95	0.60	4.00	2.25	DR	DR
				24	4.00	2.25	DR	DR	4.00	0.65	DR	DR

For SI: 1 inch = 25.4 mm, 1 mil = 0.0254 mm, 1 pound per square foot = 0.0479 kPa, 1 pound per square inch = 6.895 kPa.

DR = Design Required.

o.c. = On Center.

a. Wood furring shall be Spruce-pine-fir or any softwood species with a specific gravity of 0.42 or greater. Steel furring shall be minimum 33-ksi steel. Steel studs shall be minimum 33-ksi steel for 33-mil and 43-mil thickness, and 50-ksi steel for 54-mil steel or thicker.

b. Screws shall comply with the requirements of ASTM C1513.

c. Where the required cladding fastener penetration into wood material exceeds $^3/_4$ inch and is not more than $1^1/_2$ inches, a minimum 2-inch nominal wood furring or an approved design shall be used.

d. Foam sheathing shall have a minimum compressive strength of 15 psi in accordance with ASTM C578 or ASTM C1289.

e. Furring shall be spaced not more than 24 inches (610 mm) on center, in a vertical or horizontal orientation. In a vertical orientation, furring shall be located over wall studs and attached with the required fastener spacing. In a horizontal orientation, the indicated 8-inch and 12-inch fastener spacing in furring shall be achieved by use of two fasteners into studs at 16 inches and 24 inches on center, respectively.

CHAPTER 8

ROOF-CEILING CONSTRUCTION

User note:

About this chapter: Chapter 8 addresses the design and construction of roof-ceiling systems. This chapter contains two roof-ceiling framing systems: wood framing and cold-formed steel framing. Allowable span tables are provided to simplify the selection of rafter and ceiling joist size for wood roof framing and cold-formed steel framing. Chapter 8 also provides requirements for the application of ceiling finishes, the proper ventilation of concealed spaces in roofs (for example, enclosed attics and rafter spaces), unvented attic assemblies and attic access.

SECTION R801
GENERAL

R801.1 Application. The provisions of this chapter shall control the design and construction of the roof-ceiling system for buildings.

R801.2 Requirements. Roof and ceiling construction shall be capable of accommodating all loads imposed in accordance with Section R301 and of transmitting the resulting loads to the supporting structural elements.

R801.3 Roof drainage. In areas where *expansive soils* or *collapsible soils* are known to exist, all *dwellings* shall have a controlled method of water disposal from roofs that will collect and discharge roof drainage to the ground surface not less than 5 feet (1524 mm) from foundation walls or to an *approved* drainage system.

SECTION R802
WOOD ROOF FRAMING

R802.1 General. Wood and wood-based products used for load-supporting purposes shall conform to the applicable provisions of this section.

R802.1.1 Sawn lumber. Sawn lumber shall be identified by a grade mark of an accredited lumber grading or inspection agency and have design values certified by an accreditation body that complies with DOC PS 20. In lieu of a grade mark, a certificate of inspection issued by a lumber grading or inspection agency meeting the requirements of this section shall be accepted.

R802.1.1.1 End-jointed lumber. *Approved* end-jointed lumber identified by a grade mark conforming to Section R802.1.1 shall be permitted to be used interchangeably with solid-sawn members of the same species and grade. End-jointed lumber used in an assembly required elsewhere in this code to have a fire-resistance rating shall have the designation "Heat-Resistant Adhesive" or "HRA" included in its grade mark.

R802.1.2 Structural glued-laminated timbers. Glued-laminated timbers shall be manufactured and identified as required in ANSI A190.1, ANSI 117 and ASTM D3737.

R802.1.3 Structural log members. Structural log members shall comply with the provisions of ICC 400.

R802.1.4 Structural composite lumber. Structural capacities for structural composite lumber shall be established and monitored in accordance with ASTM D5456.

R802.1.5 Fire-retardant-treated wood. Fire-retardant-treated wood (FRTW) is any wood product that, when impregnated with chemicals by a pressure process or other means during manufacture, shall have, when tested in accordance with ASTM E84 or UL 723, a listed flame spread index of 25 or less and does not show evidence of significant progressive combustion where the test is continued for an additional 20-minute period. In addition, the flame front shall not progress more than 10.5 feet (3200 mm) beyond the center line of the burners at any time during the test.

R802.1.5.1 Pressure process. For wood products impregnated with chemicals by a pressure process, the process shall be performed in closed vessels under pressures not less than 50 pounds per square inch gauge (psig) (344.7 kPa).

R802.1.5.2 Other means during manufacture. For wood products produced by other means during manufacture the treatment shall be an integral part of the manufacturing process of the wood product. The treatment shall provide permanent protection to all surfaces of the wood product.

R802.1.5.3 Testing. For wood products produced by other means during manufacture, other than a pressure process, all sides of the wood product shall be tested in accordance with and produce the results required in Section R802.1.5. Testing of only the front and back faces of wood structural panels shall be permitted.

R802.1.5.4 Labeling. In addition to the labels required by Section 802.1.1 for sawn lumber and Section 803.2.1 for wood structural panels, each piece of *fire-retardant-treated* lumber and wood structural panel shall be labeled. The label shall contain:

1. The identification *mark* of an *approved agency* in accordance with Section 1703.5 of the *International Building Code.*

2. Identification of the treating manufacturer.

3. The name of the fire-retardant treatment.

4. The species of wood treated.

5. Flame spread index and smoke-developed index.

6. Method of drying after treatment.

7. Conformance to applicable standards in accordance with Sections R802.1.5.5 through R802.1.5.10.

8. For FRTW exposed to weather, or a damp or wet location, the words "No increase in the listed classification when subjected to the Standard Rain Test" (ASTM D2898).

R802.1.5.5 Strength adjustments. Design values for untreated lumber and wood structural panels as specified in Section R802.1 shall be adjusted for fire-retardant-treated wood. Adjustments to design values shall be based on an *approved* method of investigation that takes into consideration the effects of the anticipated temperature and humidity to which the fire-retardant-treated wood will be subjected, the type of treatment and redrying procedures.

R802.1.5.6 Wood structural panels. The effect of treatment and the method of redrying after treatment, and exposure to high temperatures and high humidities on the flexure properties of fire-retardant-treated softwood plywood shall be determined in accordance with ASTM D5516. The test data developed by ASTM D5516 shall be used to develop adjustment factors, maximum loads and spans, or both for untreated plywood design values in accordance with ASTM D6305. Each manufacturer shall publish the allowable maximum loads and spans for service as floor and roof sheathing for their treatment.

R802.1.5.7 Lumber. For each species of wood treated, the effect of the treatment and the method of redrying after treatment and exposure to high temperatures and high humidities on the allowable design properties of fire-retardant-treated lumber shall be determined in accordance with ASTM D5664. The test data developed by ASTM D5664 shall be used to develop modification factors for use at or near room temperature and at elevated temperatures and humidity in accordance with ASTM D6841. Each manufacturer shall publish the modification factors for service at temperatures of not less than 80°F (27°C) and for roof framing. The roof framing modification factors shall take into consideration the climatological location.

R802.1.5.8 Exposure to weather. Where fire-retardant-treated wood is exposed to weather or damp or wet locations, it shall be identified as "Exterior" to indicate there is not an increase in the listed flame spread index as defined in Section R802.1.5 when subjected to ASTM D2898.

R802.1.5.9 Interior applications. Interior fire-retardant-treated wood shall have a moisture content of not over 28 percent when tested in accordance with ASTM D3201 procedures at 92-percent relative humidity. Interior fire-retardant-treated wood shall be tested in accordance with Section R802.1.5.6 or R802.1.5.7. Interior fire-retardant-treated wood designated as Type A shall be tested in accordance with the provisions of this section.

R802.1.5.10 Moisture content. Fire-retardant-treated wood shall be dried to a moisture content of 19 percent or less for lumber and 15 percent or less for wood structural panels before use. For wood kiln dried after treatment (KDAT) the kiln temperatures shall not exceed those used in kiln drying the lumber and plywood submitted for the tests described in Section R802.1.5.6 for plywood and R802.1.5.7 for lumber.

R802.1.6 Cross-laminated timber. Cross-laminated timber shall be manufactured and identified as required by ANSI/APA PRG 320.

R802.1.7 Engineered wood rim board. Engineered wood rim boards shall conform to ANSI/APA PRR 410 or shall be evaluated in accordance with ASTM D7672. Structural capacities shall be in accordance with ANSI/APA PRR 410 or established in accordance with ASTM D7672. Rim boards conforming to ANSI/APA PRR 410 shall be marked in accordance with that standard.

R802.1.8 Prefabricated wood I-joists. Structural capacities and design provisions for prefabricated wood I-joists shall be established and monitored in accordance with ASTM D5055.

R802.2 Design and construction. The roof and ceiling assembly shall provide continuous ties across the structure to prevent roof thrust from being applied to the supporting walls. The assembly shall be designed and constructed in accordance with the provisions of this chapter and Figures R606.11(1), R606.11(2) and R606.11(3) or in accordance with AWC NDS.

R802.3 Ridge. A ridge board used to connect opposing rafters shall be not less than 1 inch (25 mm) nominal thickness and not less in depth than the cut end of the rafter. Where ceiling joist or rafter ties do not provide continuous ties across the structure, a ridge beam shall be provided and supported on each end by a wall or girder.

R802.4 Rafters. Rafters shall be in accordance with this section.

R802.4.1 Rafter size. Rafters shall be sized based on the rafter spans in Tables R802.4.1(1) through R802.4.1(8). Rafter spans shall be measured along the horizontal projection of the rafter. For other grades and species and for other loading conditions, refer to the AWC STJR.

R802.4.2 Framing details. Rafters shall be framed not more than $1^{1}/_{2}$ inches (38 mm) offset from each other to a ridge board or directly opposite from each other with a collar tie, gusset plate or ridge strap in accordance with Table R602.3(1). Rafters shall be nailed to the top wall plates in accordance with Table R602.3(1) unless the roof assembly is required to comply with the uplift requirements of Section R802.11.

TABLE R802.4.1(1)
RAFTER SPANS FOR COMMON LUMBER SPECIES
(Roof live load = 20 psf, ceiling not attached to rafters, L/Δ = 180)

RAFTER SPACING (inches)	SPECIES AND GRADE		DEAD LOAD = 10 psf					DEAD LOAD = 20 psf				
			2 × 4	2 × 6	2 × 8	2 × 10	2 × 12	2 × 4	2 × 6	2 × 8	2 × 10	2 × 12
			Maximum rafter spans[a]									
			(feet - inches)	(feet - inches)	(feet - inches)	(feet - inches)	(feet - inches)	(feet - inches)	(feet - inches)	(feet - inches)	(feet - inches)	(feet - inches)
12	Douglas fir-larch	SS	11-6	18-0	23-9	Note b	Note b	11-6	18-0	23-9	Note b	Note b
	Douglas fir-larch	#1	11-1	17-4	22-5	Note b	Note b	10-6	15-4	19-5	23-9	Note b
	Douglas fir-larch	#2	10-10	16-10	21-4	26-0	Note b	10-0	14-7	18-5	22-6	26-0
	Douglas fir-larch	#3	8-9	12-10	16-3	19-10	23-0	7-7	11-1	14-1	17-2	19-11
	Hem-fir	SS	10-10	17-0	22-5	Note b	Note b	10-10	17-0	22-5	Note b	Note b
	Hem-fir	#1	10 -7	16-8	22-0	Note b	Note b	10-4	15-2	19-2	23-5	Note b
	Hem-fir	#2	10-1	15-11	20-8	25-3	Note b	9-8	14-2	17-11	21-11	25-5
	Hem-fir	#3	8-7	12-6	15-10	19-5	22-6	7-5	10-10	13-9	16-9	19-6
	Southern pine	SS	11-3	17-8	23-4	Note b	Note b	11-3	17-8	23-4	Note b	Note b
	Southern pine	#1	10-10	17-0	22-5	Note b	Note b	10-6	15-8	19-10	23-2	Note b
	Southern pine	#2	10-4	15-7	19-8	23-5	Note b	9-0	13-6	17-1	20-3	23-10
	Southern pine	#3	8-0	11-9	14-10	18-0	21-4	6-11	10-2	12-10	15-7	18-6
	Spruce-pine-fir	SS	10-7	16-8	21-11	Note b	Note b	10-7	16-8	21-9	Note b	Note b
	Spruce-pine-fir	#1	10-4	16-3	21-0	25-8	Note b	9-10	14-4	18-2	22-3	25-9
	Spruce-pine-fir	#2	10-4	16-3	21-0	25-8	Note b	9-10	14-4	18-2	22-3	25-9
	Spruce-pine-fir	#3	8-7	12-6	15-10	19-5	22-6	7-5	10-10	13-9	16-9	19-6
16	Douglas fir-larch	SS	10-5	16-4	21-7	Note b	Note b	10-5	16-3	20-7	25-2	Note b
	Douglas fir-larch	#1	10-0	15-4	19-5	23-9	Note b	9-1	13-3	16-10	20-7	23-10
	Douglas fir-larch	#2	9-10	14-7	18-5	22-6	26-0	8-7	12-7	16-0	19-6	22-7
	Douglas fir-larch	#3	7-7	11-1	14-1	17-2	19-11	6-7	9-8	12-12	14-11	17-3
	Hem-fir	SS	9-10	15-6	20-5	Note b	Note b	9-10	15-6	19-11	24-4	Note b
	Hem-fir	#1	9-8	15-2	19-2	23-5	Note b	9-0	13-1	16-7	20-4	23-7
	Hem-fir	#2	9-2	14-2	17-11	21-11	25-5	8-5	12-3	15-6	18-11	22-0
	Hem-fir	#3	7-5	10-10	13-9	16-9	19-6	6-5	9-5	11-11	14-6	16-10
	Southern pine	SS	10-3	16-1	21-2	Note b	Note b	10-3	16-1	21-2	25-7	Note b
	Southern pine	#1	9-10	15-6	19-10	23-2	Note b	9-1	13-7	17-2	20-1	23-10
	Southern pine	#2	9-0	13-6	17-1	20-3	23-10	7-9	11-8	14-9	17-6	20-8
	Southern pine	#3	6-11	10-2	12-10	15-7	18-6	6-0	8-10	11-2	13-6	16-0
	Spruce-pine-fir	SS	9-8	15-2	19-11	25-5	Note b	9-8	14-10	18-10	23-0	Note b
	Spruce-pine-fir	#1	9-5	14-4	18-2	22-3	25-9	8-6	12-5	15-9	19-3	22-4
	Spruce-pine-fir	#2	9-5	14-4	18-2	22-3	25-9	8-6	12-5	15-9	19-3	22-4
	Spruce-pine-fir	#3	7-5	10-10	13-9	16-9	19-6	6-5	9-5	11-11	14-6	16-10
19.2	Douglas fir-larch	SS	9-10	15-5	20-4	25-11	Note b	9-10	14-10	18-10	23-0	Note b
	Douglas fir-larch	#1	9-5	14-0	17-9	21-8	25-2	8-4	12-2	15-4	18-9	21-9
	Douglas fir-larch	#2	9-1	13-3	16-10	20-7	23-10	7-10	11-6	14-7	17-10	20-8
	Douglas fir-larch	#3	6-11	10-2	12-10	15-8	18-3	6-0	8-9	11-2	12-7	15-9
	Hem-fir	SS	9-3	14-7	19-2	24-6	Note b	9-3	14-4	18-2	22-3	25-9
	Hem-fir	#1	9-1	13-10	17-6	21-5	24-10	8-2	12-0	15-2	18-6	21-6
	Hem-fir	#2	8-8	12-11	16-4	20-0	23-2	7-8	11-2	14-2	17-4	20-1
	Hem-fir	#3	6-9	9-11	12-7	15-4	17-9	5-10	8-7	10-10	13-3	15-5
	Southern pine	SS	9-8	15-2	19-11	25-5	Note b	9-8	15-2	19-7	23-4	Note b
	Southern pine	#1	9-3	14-3	18-1	21-2	25-2	8-4	12-4	15-8	18-4	21-9
	Southern pine	#2	8-2	12-3	15-7	18-6	21-9	7-1	10-8	13-6	16-0	18-10
	Southern pine	#3	6-4	9-4	11-9	14-3	16-10	5-6	8-1	10-2	12-4	14-7
	Spruce-pine-fir	SS	9-1	14-3	18-9	23-11	Note b	9-1	13-7	17-2	21-0	24-4
	Spruce-pine-fir	#1	8-10	13-1	16-7	20-3	23-6	7-9	11-4	14-4	17-7	20-4
	Spruce-pine-fir	#2	8-10	13-1	16-7	20-3	23-6	7-9	11-4	14-4	17-7	20-4
	Spruce-pine-fir	#3	6-9	9-11	12-7	15-4	17-9	5-10	8-7	10-10	13-3	15-5

(continued)

TABLE R802.4.1(1)—continued
RAFTER SPANS FOR COMMON LUMBER SPECIES
(Roof live load = 20 psf, ceiling not attached to rafters, L/Δ = 180)

RAFTER SPACING (inches)	SPECIES AND GRADE		DEAD LOAD = 10 psf					DEAD LOAD = 20 psf				
			2 × 4	2 × 6	2 × 8	2 × 10	2 × 12	2 × 4	2 × 6	2 × 8	2 × 10	2 × 12
			Maximum rafter spans[a]									
			(feet - inches)	(feet - inches)	(feet - inches)	(feet - inches)	(feet - inches)	(feet - inches)	(feet - inches)	(feet - inches)	(feet - inches)	(feet - inches)
24	Douglas fir-larch	SS	9-1	14-4	18-10	23-9	Note b	9-1	13-3	16-10	20-7	23-10
	Douglas fir-larch	#1	8-7	12-6	15-10	19-5	22-6	7-5	10-10	13-9	16-9	19-6
	Douglas fir-larch	#2	8-2	11-11	15-1	18-5	21-4	7-0	10-4	13-0	15-11	18-6
	Douglas fir-larch	#3	6-2	9-1	11-6	14-1	16-3	5-4	7-10	10-0	12-2	14-1
	Hem-fir	SS	8-7	13-6	17-10	22-9	Note b	8-7	12-10	16-3	19-10	23-0
	Hem-fir	#1	8-5	12-4	15-8	19-2	22-2	7-4	10-9	13-7	16-7	19-3
	Hem-fir	#2	7-11	11-7	14-8	17-10	20-9	6-10	10-0	12-8	15-6	17-11
	Hem-fir	#3	6-1	8-10	11-3	13-8	15-11	5-3	7-8	9-9	11-10	13-9
	Southern pine	SS	8-11	14-1	18-6	23-8	Note b	8-11	13-10	17-6	20-10	24-8
	Southern pine	#1	8-7	12-9	16-2	18-11	22-6	7-5	11-1	14-0	16-5	19-6
	Southern pine	#2	7-4	11-0	13-11	16-6	19-6	6-4	9-6	12-1	14-4	16-10
	Southern pine	#3	5-8	8-4	10-6	12-9	15-1	4-11	7-3	9-1	11-0	13-1
	Spruce-pine-fir	SS	8-5	13-3	17-5	21-8	25-2	8-4	12-2	15-4	18-9	21-9
	Spruce-pine-fir	#1	8-0	11-9	14-10	18-2	21-0	6-11	10-2	12-10	15-8	18-3
	Spruce-pine-fir	#2	8-0	11-9	14-10	18-2	21-0	6-11	10-2	12-10	15-8	18-3
	Spruce-pine-fir	#3	6-1	8-10	11-3	13-8	15-11	5-3	7-8	9-9	11-10	13-9

Check sources for availability of lumber in lengths greater than 20 feet.

For SI: 1 inch = 25.4 mm, 1 foot = 304.8 mm, 1 pound per square foot = 0.0479 kPa.

a. The tabulated rafter spans assume that ceiling joists are located at the bottom of the attic space or that some other method of resisting the outward push of the rafters on the bearing walls, such as rafter ties, is provided at that location. Where ceiling joists or rafter ties are located higher in the attic space, the rafter spans shall be multiplied by the following factors:

H_C/H_R	Rafter Span Adjustment Factor
1/3	0.67
1/4	0.76
1/5	0.83
1/6	0.90
1/7.5 or less	1.00

where:

H_C = Height of ceiling joists or rafter ties measured vertically above the top of the rafter support walls.

H_R = Height of roof ridge measured vertically above the top of the rafter support walls.

b. Span exceeds 26 feet in length.

TABLE R802.4.1(2)
RAFTER SPANS FOR COMMON LUMBER SPECIES
(Roof live load = 20 psf, ceiling attached to rafters, L/Δ = 240)

RAFTER SPACING (inches)	SPECIES AND GRADE		DEAD LOAD = 10 psf					DEAD LOAD = 20 psf				
			2 × 4	2 × 6	2 × 8	2 × 10	2 × 12	2 × 4	2 × 6	2 × 8	2 × 10	2 × 12
			Maximum rafter spans[a]									
			(feet - inches)	(feet - inches)	(feet - inches)	(feet - inches)	(feet - inches)	(feet - inches)	(feet - inches)	(feet - inches)	(feet - inches)	(feet - inches)
12	Douglas fir-larch	SS	10-5	16-4	21-7	Note b	Note b	10-5	16-4	21-7	Note b	Note b
	Douglas fir-larch	#1	10-0	15-9	20-10	Note b	Note b	10-0	15-4	19-5	23-9	Note b
	Douglas fir-larch	#2	9-10	15-6	20-5	26-0	Note b	9-10	14-7	18-5	22-6	26-0
	Douglas fir-larch	#3	8-9	12-10	16-3	19-10	23-0	7-7	11-1	14-1	17-2	19-11
	Hem-fir	SS	9-10	15-6	20-5	Note b	Note b	9-10	15-6	20-5	Note b	Note b
	Hem-fir	#1	9-8	15-2	19-11	25-5	Note b	9-8	15-2	19-2	23-5	Note b
	Hem-fir	#2	9-2	14-5	19-0	24-3	Note b	9-2	14-2	17-11	21-11	25-5
	Hem-fir	#3	8-7	12-6	15-10	19-5	22-6	7-5	10-10	13-9	16-9	19-6
	Southern pine	SS	10-3	16-1	21-2	Note b	Note b	10-3	16-1	21-2	Note b	Note b
	Southern pine	#1	9-10	15-6	20-5	Note b	Note b	9-10	15-6	19-10	23-2	Note b
	Southern pine	#2	9-5	14-9	19-6	23-5	Note b	9-0	13-6	17-1	20-3	23-10
	Southern pine	#3	8-0	11-9	14-10	18-0	21-4	6-11	10-2	12-10	15-7	18-6
	Spruce-pine-fir	SS	9-8	15-2	19-11	25-5	Note b	9-8	15-2	19-11	25-5	Note b
	Spruce-pine-fir	#1	9-5	14-9	19-6	24-10	Note b	9-5	14-4	18-2	22-3	25-9
	Spruce-pine-fir	#2	9-5	14-9	19-6	24-10	Note b	9-5	14-4	18-2	22-3	25-9
	Spruce-pine-fir	#3	8-7	12-6	15-10	19-5	22-6	7-5	10-10	13-9	16-9	19-6
16	Douglas fir-larch	SS	9-6	14-11	19-7	25-0	Note b	9-6	14-11	19-7	25-0	Note b
	Douglas fir-larch	#1	9-1	14-4	18-11	23-9	Note b	9-1	13-3	16-10	20-7	23-10
	Douglas fir-larch	#2	8-11	14-1	18-5	22-6	26-0	8-7	12-7	16-0	19-6	22-7
	Douglas fir-larch	#3	7-7	11-1	14-1	17-2	19-11	6-7	9-8	12-2	14-11	17-3
	Hem-fir	SS	8-11	14-1	18-6	23-8	Note b	8-11	14-1	18-6	23-8	Note b
	Hem-fir	#1	8-9	13-9	18-1	23-1	Note b	8-9	13-1	16-7	20-4	23-7
	Hem-fir	#2	8-4	13-1	17-3	21-11	25-5	8-4	12-3	15-6	18-11	22-0
	Hem-fir	#3	7-5	10-10	13-9	16-9	19-6	6-5	9-5	11-11	14-6	16-10
	Southern pine	SS	9-4	14-7	19-3	24-7	Note b	9-4	14-7	19-3	24-7	Note b
	Southern pine	#1	8-11	14-1	18-6	23-2	Note b	8-11	13-7	17-2	20-1	23-10
	Southern pine	#2	8-7	13-5	17-1	20-3	23-10	7-9	11-8	14-9	17-6	20-8
	Southern pine	#3	6-11	10-2	12-10	15-7	18-6	6-0	8-10	11-2	13-6	16-0
	Spruce-pine-fir	SS	8-9	13-9	18-1	23-1	Note b	8-9	13-9	18-1	23-0	Note b
	Spruce-pine-fir	#1	8-7	13-5	17-9	22-3	25-9	8-6	12-5	15-9	19-3	22-4
	Spruce-pine-fir	#2	8-7	13-5	17-9	22-3	25-9	8-6	12-5	15-9	19-3	22-4
	Spruce-pine-fir	#3	7-5	10-10	13-9	16-9	19-6	6-5	9-5	11-11	14-6	16-10
19.2	Douglas fir-larch	SS	8-11	14-0	18-5	23-7	Note b	8-11	14-0	18-5	23-0	Note b
	Douglas fir-larch	#1	8-7	13-6	17-9	21-8	25-2	8-4	12-2	15-4	18-9	21-9
	Douglas fir-larch	#2	8-5	13-3	16-10	20-7	23-10	7-10	11-6	14-7	17-10	20-8
	Douglas fir-larch	#3	6-11	10-2	12-10	15-8	18-3	6-0	8-9	11-2	13-7	15-9
	Hem-fir	SS	8-5	13-3	17-5	22-3	Note b	8-5	13-3	17-5	22-3	25-9
	Hem-fir	#1	8-3	12-11	17-1	21-5	24-10	8-2	12-0	15-2	18-6	21-6
	Hem-fir	#2	7-10	12-4	16-3	20-0	23-2	7-8	11-2	14-2	17-4	20-1
	Hem-fir	#3	6-9	9-11	12-7	15-4	17-9	5-10	8-7	10-10	13-3	15-5

(continued)

TABLE R802.4.1(2)—continued
RAFTER SPANS FOR COMMON LUMBER SPECIES
(Roof live load = 20 psf, ceiling attached to rafters, L/Δ = 240)

RAFTER SPACING (inches)	SPECIES AND GRADE		DEAD LOAD = 10 psf					DEAD LOAD = 20 psf				
			2 × 4	2 × 6	2 × 8	2 × 10	2 × 12	2 × 4	2 × 6	2 × 8	2 × 10	2 × 12
			Maximum rafter spans[a]									
			(feet - inches)	(feet - inches)	(feet - inches)	(feet - inches)	(feet - inches)	(feet - inches)	(feet - inches)	(feet - inches)	(feet - inches)	(feet - inches)
19.2	Southern pine	SS	8-9	13-9	18-2	23-1	Note b	8-9	13-9	18-2	23-1	Note b
	Southern pine	#1	8-5	13-3	17-5	21-2	25-2	8-4	12-4	15-8	18-4	21-9
	Southern pine	#2	8-1	12-3	15-7	18-6	21-9	7-1	10-8	13-6	16-0	18-10
	Southern pine	#3	6-4	9-4	11-9	14-3	16-10	5-6	8-1	10-2	12-4	14-7
	Spruce-pine-fir	SS	8-3	12-11	17-1	21-9	Note b	8-3	12-11	17-1	21-0	24-4
	Spruce-pine-fir	#1	8-1	12-8	16-7	20-3	23-6	7-9	11-4	14-4	17-7	20-4
	Spruce-pine-fir	#2	8-1	12-8	16-7	20-3	23-6	7-9	11-4	14-4	17-7	20-4
	Spruce-pine-fir	#3	6-9	9-11	12-7	15-4	17-9	5-10	8-7	10-10	13-3	15-5
24	Douglas fir-larch	SS	8-3	13-0	17-2	21-10	Note b	8-3	13-0	16-10	20-7	23-10
	Douglas fir-larch	#1	8-0	12-6	15-10	19-5	22-6	7-5	10-10	13-9	16-9	19-6
	Douglas fir-larch	#2	7-10	11-11	15-1	18-5	21-4	7-0	10-4	13-0	15-11	18-6
	Douglas fir-larch	#3	6-2	9-1	11-6	14-1	16-3	5-4	7-10	10-0	12-2	14-1
	Hem-fir	SS	7-10	12-3	16-2	20-8	25-1	7-10	12-3	16-2	19-10	23-0
	Hem-fir	#1	7-8	12-0	15-8	19-2	22-2	7-4	10-9	13-7	16-7	19-3
	Hem-fir	#2	7-3	11-5	14-8	17-10	20-9	6-10	10-0	12-8	15-6	17-11
	Hem-fir	#3	6-1	8-10	11-3	13-8	15-11	5-3	7-8	9-9	11-10	13-9
	Southern pine	SS	8-1	12-9	16-10	21-6	Note b	8-1	12-9	16-10	20-10	24-8
	Southern pine	#1	7-10	12-3	16-2	18-11	22-6	7-5	11-1	14-0	16-5	19-6
	Southern pine	#2	7-4	11-0	13-11	16-6	19-6	6-4	9-6	12-1	14-4	16-10
	Southern pine	#3	5-8	8-4	10-6	12-9	15-1	4-11	7-3	9-1	11-0	13-1
	Spruce-pine-fir	SS	7-8	12-0	15-10	20-2	24-7	7-8	12-0	15-4	18-9	21-9
	Spruce-pine-fir	#1	7-6	11-9	14-10	18-2	21-0	6-11	10-2	12-10	15-8	18-3
	Spruce-pine-fir	#2	7-6	11-9	14-10	18-2	21-0	6-11	10-2	12-10	15-8	18-3
	Spruce-pine-fir	#3	6-1	8-10	11-3	13-8	15-11	5-3	7-8	9-9	11-10	13-9

Check sources for availability of lumber in lengths greater than 20 feet.

For SI: 1 inch = 25.4 mm, 1 foot = 304.8 mm, 1 pound per square foot = 0.0479 kPa.

a. The tabulated rafter spans assume that ceiling joists are located at the bottom of the attic space or that some other method of resisting the outward push of the rafters on the bearing walls, such as rafter ties, is provided at that location. Where ceiling joists or rafter ties are located higher in the attic space, the rafter spans shall be multiplied by the following factors:

H_C/H_R	Rafter Span Adjustment Factor
1/3	0.67
1/4	0.76
1/5	0.83
1/6	0.90
1/7.5 or less	1.00

where:

H_C = Height of ceiling joists or rafter ties measured vertically above the top of the rafter support walls.

H_R = Height of roof ridge measured vertically above the top of the rafter support walls.

b. Span exceeds 26 feet in length.

TABLE R802.4.1(3)
RAFTER SPANS FOR COMMON LUMBER SPECIES
(Ground snow load = 30 psf, ceiling not attached to rafters, L/Δ = 180)

RAFTER SPACING (inches)	SPECIES AND GRADE		DEAD LOAD = 10 psf					DEAD LOAD = 20 psf				
			2 × 4	2 × 6	2 × 8	2 × 10	2 × 12	2 × 4	2 × 6	2 × 8	2 × 10	2 × 12
			Maximum rafter spans[a]									
			(feet - inches)	(feet - inches)	(feet - inches)	(feet - inches)	(feet - inches)	(feet - inches)	(feet - inches)	(feet - inches)	(feet - inches)	(feet - inches)
12	Douglas fir-larch	SS	10-0	15-9	20-9	Note b	Note b	10-0	15-9	20-5	24-11	Note b
	Douglas fir-larch	#1	9-8	14-9	18-8	22-9	Note b	9-0	13-2	16-8	20-4	23-7
	Douglas fir-larch	#2	9-6	14-0	17-8	21-7	25-1	8-6	12-6	15-10	19-4	22-5
	Douglas fir-larch	#3	7-3	10-8	13-6	16-6	19-2	6-6	9-6	12-1	14-9	17-1
	Hem-fir	SS	9-6	14-10	19-7	25-0	Note b	9-6	14-10	19-7	24-1	Note b
	Hem-fir	#1	9-3	14-6	18-5	22-6	26-0	8-11	13-0	16-6	20-1	23-4
	Hem-fir	#2	8-10	13-7	17-2	21-0	24-4	8-4	12-2	15-4	18-9	21-9
	Hem-fir	#3	7-1	10-5	13-2	16-1	18-8	6-4	9-4	11-9	14-5	16-8
	Southern pine	SS	9-10	15-6	20-5	Note b	Note b	9-10	15-6	20-5	25-4	Note b
	Southern pine	#1	9-6	14-10	19-0	22-3	Note b	9-0	13-5	17-0	19-11	23-7
	Southern pine	#2	8-7	12-11	16-4	19-5	22-10	7-8	11-7	14-8	17-4	20-5
	Southern pine	#3	6-7	9-9	12-4	15-0	17-9	5-11	8-9	11-0	13-5	15-10
	Spruce-pine-fir	SS	9-3	14-7	19-2	24-6	Note b	9-3	14-7	18-8	22-9	Note b
	Spruce-pine-fir	#1	9-1	13-9	17-5	21-4	24-8	8-5	12-4	15-7	19-1	22-1
	Spruce-pine-fir	#2	9-1	13-9	17-5	21-4	24-8	8-5	12-4	15-7	19-1	22-1
	Spruce-pine-fir	#3	7-1	10-5	13-2	16-1	18-8	6-4	9-4	11-9	14-5	16-8
16	Douglas fir-larch	SS	9-1	14-4	18-10	24-1	Note b	9-1	14-0	17-8	21-7	25-1
	Douglas fir-larch	#1	8-9	12-9	16-2	19-9	22-10	7-10	11-5	14-5	17-8	20-5
	Douglas fir-larch	#2	8-3	12-1	15-4	18-9	21-8	7-5	10-10	13-8	16-9	19-5
	Douglas fir-larch	#3	6-4	9-3	11-8	14-3	16-7	5-8	8-3	10-6	12-9	14-10
	Hem-fir	SS	8-7	13-6	17-10	22-9	Note b	8-7	13-6	17-1	20-10	24-2
	Hem-fir	#1	8-5	12-7	15-11	19-6	22-7	7-8	11-3	14-3	17-5	20-2
	Hem-fir	#2	8-0	11-9	14-11	18-2	21-1	7-2	10-6	13-4	16-3	18-10
	Hem-fir	#3	6-2	9-0	11-5	13-11	16-2	5-6	8-1	10-3	12-6	14-6
	Southern pine	SS	8-11	14-1	18-6	23-8	Note b	8-11	14-1	18-5	1-11	25-11
	Southern pine	#1	8-7	13-0	16-6	19-3	22-10	7-10	11-7	14-9	17-3	20-5
	Southern pine	#2	7-6	11-2	14-2	16-10	19-10	6-8	10-0	12-8	15-1	17-9
	Southern pine	#3	5-9	8-6	10-8	13-0	15-4	5-2	7-7	9-7	11-7	13-9
	Spruce-pine-fir	SS	8-5	13-3	17-5	22-1	25-7	8-5	12-9	16-2	19-9	22-10
	Spruce-pine-fir	#1	8-2	11-11	15-1	18-5	21-5	7-3	10-8	13-6	16-6	19-2
	Spruce-pine-fir	#2	8-2	11-11	15-1	18-5	21-5	7-3	10-8	13-6	16-6	19-2
	Spruce-pine-fir	#3	6-2	9-0	11-5	13-11	16-2	5-6	8-1	10-3	12-6	14-6
19.2	Douglas fir-larch	SS	8-7	13-6	17-9	22-1	25-7	8-7	12-9	16-2	19-9	22-10
	Douglas fir-larch	#1	7-11	11-8	14-9	18-0	20-11	7-1	10-5	13-2	16-1	18-8
	Douglas fir-larch	#2	7-7	11-0	14-0	17-1	19-10	6-9	9-10	12-6	15-3	17-9
	Douglas fir-larch	#3	5-9	8-5	10-8	13-1	15-2	5-2	7-7	9-7	11-8	13-6
	Hem-fir	SS	8-1	12-9	16-9	21-4	24-8	8-1	12-4	15-7	19-1	22-1
	Hem-fir	#1	7-10	11-6	14-7	17-9	20-7	7-0	10-3	13-0	15-11	18-5
	Hem-fir	#2	7-4	10-9	13-7	16-7	19-3	6-7	9-7	12-2	14-10	17-3
	Hem-fir	#3	5-7	8-3	10-5	12-9	14-9	5-0	7-4	9-4	11-5	13-2

(continued)

TABLE R802.4.1(3)—continued
RAFTER SPANS FOR COMMON LUMBER SPECIES
(Ground snow load = 30 psf, ceiling not attached to rafters, L/Δ = 180)

RAFTER SPACING (inches)	SPECIES AND GRADE		DEAD LOAD = 10 psf					DEAD LOAD = 20 psf				
			2 × 4	2 × 6	2 × 8	2 × 10	2 × 12	2 × 4	2 × 6	2 × 8	2 × 10	2 × 12
			Maximum rafter spans[a]									
			(feet - inches)	(feet - inches)	(feet - inches)	(feet - inches)	(feet - inches)	(feet - inches)	(feet - inches)	(feet - inches)	(feet - inches)	(feet - inches)
19.2	Southern pine	SS	8-5	13-3	17-5	22-3	Note b	8-5	13-3	16-10	20-0	23-7
	Southern pine	#1	8-0	11-10	15-1	17-7	20-11	7-1	10-7	13-5	15-9	18-8
	Southern pine	#2	6-10	10-2	12-11	15-4	18-1	6-1	9-2	11-7	13-9	16-2
	Southern pine	#3	5-3	7-9	9-9	11-10	14-0	4-8	6-11	8-9	10-7	12-6
	Spruce-pine-fir	SS	7-11	12-5	16-5	20-2	23-4	7-11	11-8	14-9	18-0	20-11
	Spruce-pine-fir	#1	7-5	10-11	13-9	16-10	19-6	6-8	9-9	12-4	15-1	17-6
	Spruce-pine-fir	#2	7-5	10-11	13-9	16-10	19-6	6-8	9-9	12-4	15-1	17-6
	Spruce-pine-fir	#3	5-7	8-3	10-5	12-9	14-9	5-0	7-4	9-4	11-5	13-2
24	Douglas fir-larch	SS	8-0	12-6	16-2	19-9	22-10	7-10	11-5	14-5	17-8	20-5
	Douglas fir-larch	#1	7-1	10-5	13-2	16-1	18-8	6-4	9-4	11-9	14-5	16-8
	Douglas fir-larch	#2	6-9	9-10	12-6	15-3	17-9	6-0	8-10	11-2	13-8	15-10
	Douglas fir-larch	#3	5-2	7-7	9-7	11-8	13-6	4-7	6-9	8-7	10-5	12-1
	Hem-fir	SS	7-6	11-10	15-7	19-1	22-1	7-6	11-0	13-11	17-0	19-9
	Hem-fir	#1	7-0	10-3	13-0	15-11	18-5	6-3	9-2	11-8	14-3	16-6
	Hem-fir	#2	6-7	9-7	12-2	14-10	17-3	5-10	8-7	10-10	13-3	15-5
	Hem-fir	#3	5-0	7-4	9-4	11-5	13-2	4-6	6-7	8-4	10-2	11-10
	Southern pine	SS	7-10	12-3	16-2	20-0	23-7	7-10	11-10	15-0	17-11	21-2
	Southern pine	#1	7-1	10-7	13-5	15-9	18-8	6-4	9-6	12-0	14-1	16-8
	Southern pine	#2	6-1	9-2	11-7	13-9	16-2	5-5	8-2	10-4	12-3	14-6
	Southern pine	#3	4-8	6-11	8-9	10-7	12-6	4-2	6-2	7-10	9-6	11-2
	Spruce-pine-fir	SS	7-4	11-7	14-9	18-0	20-11	7-1	10-5	13-2	16-1	18-8
	Spruce-pine-fir	#1	6-8	9-9	12-4	15-1	17-6	5-11	8-8	11-0	13-6	15-7
	Spruce-pine-fir	#2	6-8	9-9	12-4	15-1	17-6	5-11	8-8	11-0	13-6	15-7
	Spruce-pine-fir	#3	5-0	7-4	9-4	11-5	13-2	4-6	6-7	8-4	10-2	11-10

Check sources for availability of lumber in lengths greater than 20 feet.

For SI: 1 inch = 25.4 mm, 1 foot = 304.8 mm, 1 pound per square foot = 0.0479 kPa.

a. The tabulated rafter spans assume that ceiling joists are located at the bottom of the attic space or that some other method of resisting the outward push of the rafters on the bearing walls, such as rafter ties, is provided at that location. Where ceiling joists or rafter ties are located higher in the attic space, the rafter spans shall be multiplied by the following factors:

H_C/H_R	Rafter Span Adjustment Factor
1/3	0.67
1/4	0.76
1/5	0.83
1/6	0.90
1/7.5 or less	1.00

where:

H_C = Height of ceiling joists or rafter ties measured vertically above the top of the rafter support walls.

H_R = Height of roof ridge measured vertically above the top of the rafter support walls.

b. Span exceeds 26 feet in length.

TABLE R802.4.1(4)
RAFTER SPANS FOR COMMON LUMBER SPECIES
(Ground snow load = 30 psf, ceiling attached to rafters, L/Δ = 240)

RAFTER SPACING (inches)	SPECIES AND GRADE		DEAD LOAD = 10 psf					DEAD LOAD = 20 psf				
			2 × 4	2 × 6	2 × 8	2 × 10	2 × 12	2 × 4	2 × 6	2 × 8	2 × 10	2 × 12
			Maximum rafter spans[a]									
			(feet - inches)	(feet - inches)	(feet - inches)	(feet - inches)	(feet - inches)	(feet - inches)	(feet - inches)	(feet - inches)	(feet - inches)	(feet - inches)
12	Douglas fir-larch	SS	9-1	14-4	18-10	24-1	Note b	9-1	14-4	18-10	24-1	Note b
	Douglas fir-larch	#1	8-9	13-9	18-2	22-9	Note b	8-9	13-2	16-8	20-4	23-7
	Douglas fir-larch	#2	8-7	13-6	17-8	21-7	25-1	8-6	12-6	15-10	19-4	22-5
	Douglas fir-larch	#3	7-3	10-8	13-6	16-6	19-2	6-6	9-6	12-1	14-9	17-1
	Hem-fir	SS	8-7	13-6	17-10	22-9	Note b	8-7	13-6	17-10	22-9	Note b
	Hem-fir	#1	8-5	13-3	17-5	22-3	26-0	8-5	13-0	16-6	20-1	23-4
	Hem-fir	#2	8-0	12-7	16-7	21-0	24-4	8-0	12-2	15-4	18-9	21-9
	Hem-fir	#3	7-1	10-5	13-2	16-1	18-8	6-4	9-4	11-9	14-5	16-8
	Southern pine	SS	8-11	14-1	18-6	23-8	Note b	8-11	14-1	18-6	23-8	Note b
	Southern pine	#1	8-7	13-6	17-10	22-3	Note b	8-7	13-5	17-0	19-11	23-7
	Southern pine	#2	8-3	12-11	16-4	19-5	22-10	7-8	11-7	14-8	17-4	20-5
	Southern pine	#3	6-7	9-9	12-4	15-0	17-9	5-11	8-9	11-0	13-5	15-10
	Spruce-pine-fir	SS	8-5	13-3	17-5	22-3	Note b	8-5	13-3	17-5	22-3	Note b
	Spruce-pine-fir	#1	8-3	12-11	17-0	21-4	24-8	8-3	12-4	15-7	19-1	22-1
	Spruce-pine-fir	#2	8-3	12-11	17-0	21-4	24-8	8-3	12-4	15-7	19-1	22-1
	Spruce-pine-fir	#3	7-1	10-5	13-2	16-1	18-8	6-4	9-4	11-9	14-5	16-8
16	Douglas fir-larch	SS	8-3	13-0	17-2	21-10	Note b	8-3	13-0	17-2	21-7	25-1
	Douglas fir-larch	#1	8-0	12-6	16-2	19-9	22-10	7-10	11-5	14-5	17-8	20-5
	Douglas fir-larch	#2	7-10	12-1	15-4	18-9	21-8	7-5	10-10	13-8	16-9	19-5
	Douglas fir-larch	#3	6-4	9-3	11-8	14-3	16-7	5-8	8-3	10-6	12-9	14-10
	Hem-fir	SS	7-10	12-3	16-2	20-8	25-1	7-10	12-3	16-2	20-8	24-2
	Hem-fir	#1	7-8	12-0	15-10	19-6	22-7	7-8	11-3	14-3	17-5	20-2
	Hem-fir	#2	7-3	11-5	14-11	18-2	21-1	7-2	10-6	13-4	16-3	18-10
	Hem-fir	#3	6-2	9-0	11-5	13-11	16-2	5-6	8-1	10-3	12-6	14-6
	Southern pine	SS	8-1	12-9	16-10	21-6	Note b	8-1	12-9	16-10	21-6	25-11
	Southern pine	#1	7-10	12-3	16-2	19-3	22-10	7-10	11-7	14-9	17-3	20-5
	Southern pine	#2	7-6	11-2	14-2	16-10	19-10	6-8	10-0	12-8	15-1	17-9
	Southern pine	#3	5-9	8-6	10-8	13-0	15-4	5-2	7-7	9-7	11-7	13-9
	Spruce-pine-fir	SS	7-8	12-0	15-10	20-2	24-7	7-8	12-0	15-10	19-9	22-10
	Spruce-pine-fir	#1	7-6	11-9	15-1	18-5	21-5	7-3	10-8	13-6	16-6	19-2
	Spruce-pine-fir	#2	7-6	11-9	15-1	18-5	21-5	7-3	10-8	13-6	16-6	19-2
	Spruce-pine-fir	#3	6-2	9-0	11-5	13-11	16-2	5-6	8-1	10-3	12-6	14-6
19.2	Douglas fir-larch	SS	7-9	12-3	16-1	20-7	25-0	7-9	12-3	16-1	19-9	22-10
	Douglas fir-larch	#1	7-6	11-8	14-9	18-0	20-11	7-1	10-5	13-2	16-1	18-8
	Douglas fir-larch	#2	7-4	11-0	14-0	17-1	19-10	6-9	9-1	12-6	15-3	17-9
	Douglas fir-larch	#3	5-9	8-5	10-8	13-1	15-2	5-2	7-7	9-7	11-8	13-6
	Hem-fir	SS	7-4	11-7	15-3	19-5	23-7	7-4	11-7	15-3	19-1	22-1
	Hem-fir	#1	7-2	11-4	14-7	17-9	20-7	7-0	16-3	13-0	15-11	18-5
	Hem-fir	#2	6-10	10-9	13-7	16-7	19-3	6-7	9-7	12-2	14-10	17-3
	Hem-fir	#3	5-7	8-3	10-5	12-9	14-9	5-0	7-4	9-4	11-5	13-2

(continued)

TABLE R802.4.1(4)—continued
RAFTER SPANS FOR COMMON LUMBER SPECIES
(Ground snow load = 30 psf, ceiling attached to rafters, L/Δ = 240)

RAFTER SPACING (inches)	SPECIES AND GRADE		DEAD LOAD = 10 psf					DEAD LOAD = 20 psf				
			2 × 4	2 × 6	2 × 8	2 × 10	2 × 12	2 × 4	2 × 6	2 × 8	2 × 10	2 × 12
			Maximum rafter spans[a]									
			(feet - inches)	(feet - inches)	(feet - inches)	(feet - inches)	(feet - inches)	(feet - inches)	(feet - inches)	(feet - inches)	(feet - inches)	(feet - inches)
19.2	Southern pine	SS	7-8	12-0	15-10	20-2	24-7	7-8	12-0	15-10	20-0	23-7
	Southern pine	#1	7-4	11-7	15-1	17-7	20-11	7-1	10-7	13-5	15-9	18-8
	Southern pine	#2	6-10	10-2	12-11	15-4	18-1	6-1	9-2	11-7	13-9	16-2
	Southern pine	#3	5-3	7-9	9-9	11-10	14-0	4-8	6-11	8-9	10-7	12-6
	Spruce-pine-fir	SS	7-2	11-4	14-11	19-0	23-1	7-2	11-4	14-9	18-0	20-11
	Spruce-pine-fir	#1	7-0	10-11	13-9	16-10	19-6	6-8	9-9	12-4	15-1	17-6
	Spruce-pine-fir	#2	7-0	10-11	13-9	16-10	19-6	6-8	9-9	12-4	15-1	17-6
	Spruce-pine-fir	#3	5-7	8-3	10-5	12-9	14-9	5-0	7-4	9-4	11-5	13-2
24	Douglas fir-larch	SS	7-3	11-4	15-0	19-1	22-10	7-3	11-4	14-5	17-8	20-5
	Douglas fir-larch	#1	7-0	10-5	13-2	16-1	18-8	6-4	9-4	11-9	14-5	16-8
	Douglas fir-larch	#2	6-9	9-10	12-6	15-3	17-9	6-0	8-10	11-2	13-8	15-10
	Douglas fir-larch	#3	5-2	7-7	9-7	11-8	13-6	4-7	6-9	8-7	10-5	12-1
	Hem-fir	SS	6-10	10-9	14-2	18-0	21-11	6-10	10-9	13-11	17-0	19-9
	Hem-fir	#1	6-8	10-3	13-0	15-11	18-5	6-3	9-2	11-8	14-3	16-6
	Hem-fir	#2	6-4	9-7	12-2	14-10	17-3	5-10	8-7	10-10	13-3	15-5
	Hem-fir	#3	5-0	7-4	9-4	11-5	13-2	4-6	6-7	8-4	10-2	11-10
	Southern pine	SS	7-1	11-2	14-8	18-9	22-10	7-1	11-2	14-8	17-11	21-2
	Southern pine	#1	6-10	10-7	13-5	15-9	18-8	6-4	9-6	12-0	14-1	16-8
	Southern pine	#2	6-1	9-2	11-7	13-9	16-2	5-5	8-2	10-4	12-3	14-6
	Southern pine	#3	4-8	6-11	8-9	10-7	12-6	4-2	6-2	7-10	9-6	11-2
	Spruce-pine-fir	SS	6-8	10-6	13-10	17-8	20-11	6-8	10-5	13-2	16-1	18-8
	Spruce-pine-fir	#1	6-6	9-9	12-4	15-1	17-6	5-11	8-8	11-0	13-6	15-7
	Spruce-pine-fir	#2	6-6	9-9	12-4	15-1	17-6	5-11	8-8	11-0	13-6	15-7
	Spruce-pine-fir	#3	5-0	7-4	9-4	11-5	13-2	4-6	6-7	8-4	10-2	11-10

Check sources for availability of lumber in lengths greater than 20 feet.

For SI: 1 inch = 25.4 mm, 1 foot = 304.8 mm, 1 pound per square foot = 0.0479 kPa.

a. The tabulated rafter spans assume that ceiling joists are located at the bottom of the attic space or that some other method of resisting the outward push of the rafters on the bearing walls, such as rafter ties, is provided at that location. Where ceiling joists or rafter ties are located higher in the attic space, the rafter spans shall be multiplied by the following factors:

H_C/H_R	Rafter Span Adjustment Factor
1/3	0.67
1/4	0.76
1/5	0.83
1/6	0.90
1/7.5 or less	1.00

where:

H_C = Height of ceiling joists or rafter ties measured vertically above the top of the rafter support walls.

H_R = Height of roof ridge measured vertically above the top of the rafter support walls.

b. Span exceeds 26 feet in length.

TABLE R802.4.1(5)
RAFTER SPANS FOR COMMON LUMBER SPECIES
(Ground snow load = 50 psf, ceiling not attached to rafters, L/Δ = 180)

RAFTER SPACING (inches)	SPECIES AND GRADE		DEAD LOAD = 10 psf					DEAD LOAD = 20 psf				
			2 × 4	2 × 6	2 × 8	2 × 10	2 × 12	2 × 4	2 × 6	2 × 8	2 × 10	2 × 12
			Maximum rafter spans[a]									
			(feet - inches)	(feet - inches)	(feet - inches)	(feet - inches)	(feet - inches)	(feet - inches)	(feet - inches)	(feet - inches)	(feet - inches)	(feet - inches)
12	Douglas fir-larch	SS	8-5	13-3	17-6	22-4	26-0	8-5	13-3	17-3	21-1	24-5
	Douglas fir-larch	#1	8-2	12-0	15-3	18-7	21-7	7-7	11-2	14-1	17-3	20-0
	Douglas fir-larch	#2	7-10	11-5	14-5	17-8	20-5	7-3	10-7	13-4	16-4	18-11
	Douglas fir-larch	#3	6-0	8-9	11-0	13-6	15-7	5-6	8-1	10-3	12-6	14-6
	Hem-fir	SS	8-0	12-6	16-6	21-1	25-6	8-0	12-6	16-6	20-4	23-7
	Hem-fir	#1	7-10	11-10	15-0	18-4	21-3	7-6	11-0	13-11	17-0	19-9
	Hem-fir	#2	7-5	11-1	14-0	17-2	19-11	7-0	10-3	13-0	15-10	18-5
	Hem-fir	#3	5-10	8-6	10-9	13-2	15-3	5-5	7-10	10-0	12-2	14-1
	Southern pine	SS	8-4	13-1	17-2	21-11	Note b	8-4	13-1	17-2	21-5	25-3
	Southern pine	#1	8-0	12-3	15-6	18-2	21-7	7-7	11-4	14-5	16-10	20-0
	Southern pine	#2	7-0	10-6	13-4	15-10	18-8	6-6	9-9	12-4	14-8	17-3
	Southern pine	#3	5-5	8-0	10-1	12-3	14-6	5-0	7-5	9-4	11-4	13-5
	Spruce-pine-fir	SS	7-10	12-3	16-2	20-8	24-1	7-10	12-3	15-9	19-3	22-4
	Spruce-pine-fir	#1	7-8	11-3	14-3	17-5	20-2	7-1	10-5	13-2	16-1	18-8
	Spruce-pine-fir	#2	7-8	11-3	14-3	17-5	20-2	7-1	10-5	13-2	16-1	18-8
	Spruce-pine-fir	#3	5-10	8-6	10-9	13-2	15-3	5-5	7-10	10-0	12-2	14-1
16	Douglas fir-larch	SS	7-8	12-1	15-11	19-9	22-10	7-8	11-10	14-11	18-3	21-2
	Douglas fir-larch	#1	7-1	10-5	13-2	16-1	18-8	6-7	9-8	12-2	14-11	17-3
	Douglas fir-larch	#2	6-9	9-10	12-6	15-3	17-9	6-3	9-2	11-7	14-2	16-5
	Douglas fir-larch	#3	5-2	7-7	9-7	11-18	13-6	4-9	7-0	8-10	10-10	12-6
	Hem-fir	SS	7-3	11-5	15-0	19-1	22-1	7-3	11-5	14-5	17-8	20-5
	Hem-fir	#1	7-0	10-3	13-0	15-11	18-5	6-6	9-6	12-1	14-9	17-1
	Hem-fir	#2	6-7	9-7	12-2	14-10	17-3	6-1	8-11	11-3	13-9	15-11
	Hem-fir	#3	5-0	7-4	9-4	11-5	13-2	4-8	6-10	8-8	10-6	12-3
	Southern pine	SS	7-6	11-10	15-7	19-11	23-7	7-6	11-10	15-7	18-6	21-10
	Southern pine	#1	7-1	10-7	13-5	15-9	18-8	6-7	9-10	12-5	14-7	17-3
	Southern pine	#2	6-1	9-2	11-7	13-9	16-2	5-8	8-5	10-9	12-9	15-0
	Southern pine	#3	4-8	6-11	8-9	10-7	12-6	4-4	6-5	8-1	9-10	11-7
	Spruce-pine-fir	SS	7-1	11-2	14-8	18-0	20-11	7-1	10-9	13-8	15-11	19-4
	Spruce-pine-fir	#1	6-8	9-9	12-4	15-1	17-6	6-2	9-0	11-5	13-11	16-2
	Spruce-pine-fir	#2	6-8	9-9	12-4	15-1	17-6	6-2	9-0	11-5	13-11	16-2
	Spruce-pine-fir	#3	5-0	7-4	9-4	11-5	13-2	4-8	6-10	8-8	10-6	12-3
19.2	Douglas fir-larch	SS	7-3	11-4	14-9	18-0	20-11	7-3	10-9	13-8	16-8	19-4
	Douglas fir-larch	#1	6-6	9-6	12-0	14-8	17-1	6-0	8-10	11-2	13-7	15-9
	Douglas fir-larch	#2	6-2	9-0	11-5	13-11	16-2	5-8	8-4	10-9	12-11	15-0
	Douglas fir-larch	#3	4-8	6-11	8-9	10-8	12-4	4-4	6-4	8-1	9-10	11-5
	Hem-fir	SS	6-10	10-9	14-2	17-5	20-2	6-10	10-5	13-2	16-1	18-8
	Hem-fir	#1	6-5	9-5	11-11	14-6	16-10	8-11	8-8	11-0	13-5	15-7
	Hem-fir	#2	6-0	8-9	11-1	13-7	15-9	5-7	8-1	10-3	12-7	14-7
	Hem-fir	#3	4-7	6-9	8-6	10-5	12-1	4-3	6-3	7-11	9-7	11-2

(continued)

TABLE R802.4.1(5)—continued
RAFTER SPANS FOR COMMON LUMBER SPECIES
(Ground snow load = 50 psf, ceiling not attached to rafters, L/Δ = 180)

RAFTER SPACING (inches)	SPECIES AND GRADE		DEAD LOAD = 10 psf					DEAD LOAD = 20 psf				
			2 × 4	2 × 6	2 × 8	2 × 10	2 × 12	2 × 4	2 × 6	2 × 8	2 × 10	2 × 12
			Maximum rafter spans[a]									
			(feet - inches)	(feet - inches)	(feet - inches)	(feet - inches)	(feet - inches)	(feet - inches)	(feet - inches)	(feet - inches)	(feet - inches)	(feet - inches)
19.2	Southern pine	SS	7-1	11-2	14-8	18-3	21-7	7-1	11-2	14-2	16-11	20-0
	Southern pine	#1	6-6	9-8	12-3	14-4	17-1	6-0	9-0	11-4	13-4	15-9
	Southern pine	#2	5-7	8-4	10-7	12-6	14-9	5-2	7-9	9-9	11-7	13-8
	Southern pine	#3	4-3	6-4	8-0	9-8	11-5	4-0	5-10	7-4	8-11	10-7
	Spruce-pine-fir	SS	6-8	10-6	13-5	16-5	19-1	6-8	9-10	12-5	15-3	17-8
	Spruce-pine-fir	#1	6-1	8-11	11-3	13-9	15-11	5-7	8-3	10-5	12-9	14-9
	Spruce-pine-fir	#2	6-1	8-11	11-3	13-9	15-11	5-7	8-3	10-5	12-9	14-9
	Spruce-pine-fir	#3	4-7	6-9	8-6	10-5	12-1	4-3	6-3	7-11	9-7	11-2
24	Douglas fir-larch	SS	6-8	10-5	13-2	16-1	18-8	6-7	9-8	12-2	14-11	17-3
	Douglas fir-larch	#1	5-10	8-6	10-9	13-2	15-3	5-5	7-10	10-0	12-2	14-1
	Douglas fir-larch	#2	5-6	8-1	10-3	12-6	14-6	5-1	7-6	9-5	11-7	13-5
	Douglas fir-larch	#3	4-3	6-2	7-10	9-6	11-1	3-11	5-8	7-3	8-10	10-3
	Hem-fir	SS	6-4	9-11	12-9	15-7	18-0	6-4	9-4	11-9	14-5	16-8
	Hem-fir	#1	5-9	8-5	10-8	13-0	15-1	8-4	7-9	9-10	12-0	13-11
	Hem-fir	#2	5-4	7-10	9-11	12-1	14-1	4-11	7-3	9-2	11-3	13-0
	Hem-fir	#3	4-1	6-0	7-7	9-4	10-9	3-10	5-7	7-1	8-7	10-0
	Southern pine	SS	6-7	10-4	13-8	16-4	19-3	6-7	10-0	12-8	15-2	17-10
	Southern pine	#1	5-10	8-8	11-0	12-10	15-3	5-5	8-0	10-2	11-11	14-1
	Southern pine	#2	5-0	7-5	9-5	11-3	13-2	4-7	6-11	8-9	10-5	12-3
	Southern pine	#3	3-10	5-8	7-1	8-8	10-3	3-6	5-3	6-7	8-0	9-6
	Spruce-pine-fir	SS	6-2	9-6	12-0	14-8	17-1	6-0	8-10	11-2	13-7	15-9
	Spruce-pine-fir	#1	5-5	7-11	10-1	12-4	14-3	5-0	7-4	9-4	11-5	13-2
	Spruce-pine-fir	#2	5-5	7-11	10-1	12-4	14-3	5-0	7-4	9-4	11-5	13-2
	Spruce-pine-fir	#3	4-1	6-0	7-7	9-4	10-9	3-10	5-7	7-1	8-7	10-0

Check sources for availability of lumber in lengths greater than 20 feet.

For SI: 1 inch = 25.4 mm, 1 foot = 304.8 mm, 1 pound per square foot = 0.0479 kPa

a. The tabulated rafter spans assume that ceiling joists are located at the bottom of the attic space or that some other method of resisting the outward push of the rafters on the bearing walls, such as rafter ties, is provided at that location. Where ceiling joists or rafter ties are located higher in the attic space, the rafter spans shall be multiplied by the following factors:

H_C/H_R	Rafter Span Adjustment Factor
1/3	0.67
1/4	0.76
1/5	0.83
1/6	0.90
1/7.5 or less	1.00

where:

H_C = Height of ceiling joists or rafter ties measured vertically above the top of the rafter support walls.

H_R = Height of roof ridge measured vertically above the top of the rafter support walls.

b. Span exceeds 26 feet in length.

TABLE R802.4.1(6)
RAFTER SPANS FOR COMMON LUMBER SPECIES
(Ground snow load = 50 psf, ceiling attached to rafters, L/Δ = 240)

RAFTER SPACING (inches)	SPECIES AND GRADE		DEAD LOAD = 10 psf					DEAD LOAD = 20 psf				
			2 × 4	2 × 6	2 × 8	2 × 10	2 × 12	2 × 4	2 × 6	2 × 8	2 × 10	2 × 12
			Maximum rafter spans[a]									
			(feet-inches)	(feet-inches)	(feet-inches)	(feet-inches)	(feet-inches)	(feet-inches)	(feet-inches)	(feet-inches)	(feet-inches)	(feet-inches)
12	Douglas fir-larch	SS	7-8	12-1	15-11	20-3	24-8	7-8	12-1	15-11	20-3	24-5
	Douglas fir-larch	#1	7-5	11-7	15-3	18-7	21-7	7-5	11-2	14-1	17-3	20-0
	Douglas fir-larch	#2	7-3	11-5	14-5	17-8	20-5	7-3	10-7	13-4	16-4	18-11
	Douglas fir-larch	#3	6-0	8-9	11-0	13-6	15-7	5-6	8-1	10-3	12-6	14-6
	Hem-fir	SS	7-3	11-5	15-0	19-2	23-4	7-3	11-5	15-0	19-2	23-4
	Hem-fir	#1	7-1	11-2	14-8	18-4	21-3	7-1	11-0	13-11	17-0	19-9
	Hem-fir	#2	6-9	10-8	14-0	17-2	19-11	6-9	10-3	13-0	15-10	18-5
	Hem-fir	#3	5-10	8-6	10-9	13-2	15-3	5-5	7-10	10-0	12-2	14-1
	Southern pine	SS	7-6	11-10	15-7	19-11	24-3	7-6	11-10	15-7	19-11	24-3
	Southern pine	#1	7-3	11-5	15-0	18-2	21-7	7-3	11-4	14-5	16-10	20-0
	Southern pine	#2	6-11	10-6	13-4	15-10	18-8	6-6	9-9	12-4	14-8	17-3
	Southern pine	#3	5-5	8-0	10-1	12-3	14-6	5-0	7-5	9-4	11-4	13-5
	Spruce-pine-fir	SS	7-1	11-2	14-8	18-9	22-10	7-1	11-2	14-8	18-9	22-4
	Spruce-pine-fir	#1	6-11	10-11	14-3	17-5	20-2	6-11	10-5	13-2	16-1	18-8
	Spruce-pine-fir	#2	6-11	10-11	14-3	17-5	20-2	6-11	10-5	13-2	16-1	18-8
	Spruce-pine-fir	#3	5-10	8-6	10-9	13-2	15-3	5-5	7-10	10-0	12-2	14-1
16	Douglas fir-larch	SS	7-0	11-0	14-5	18-5	22-5	7-0	11-0	14-5	18-3	21-2
	Douglas fir-larch	#1	6-9	10-5	13-2	16-1	18-8	6-7	9-8	12-2	14-11	17-3
	Douglas fir-larch	#2	6-7	9-10	12-6	15-3	17-9	6-3	9-2	11-7	14-2	16-5
	Douglas fir-larch	#3	5-2	7-7	9-7	11-8	13-6	4-9	7-0	8-10	10-10	12-6
	Hem-fir	SS	6-7	10-4	13-8	17-5	21-2	6-7	10-4	13-8	17-5	20-5
	Hem-fir	#1	6-5	10-2	13-0	15-11	18-5	6-5	9-6	12-1	14-9	17-1
	Hem-fir	#2	6-2	9-7	12-2	14-10	17-3	6-1	8-11	11-3	13-9	15-11
	Hem-fir	#3	5-0	7-4	9-4	11-5	13-2	4-8	6-10	8-8	10-6	12-3
	Southern pine	SS	6-10	10-9	14-2	18-1	22-0	6-10	10-9	14-2	18-1	21-10
	Southern pine	#1	6-7	10-4	13-5	15-9	18-8	6-7	9-10	12-5	14-7	17-3
	Southern pine	#2	6-1	9-2	11-7	13-9	16-2	5-8	8-5	10-9	12-9	15-0
	Southern pine	#3	4-8	6-11	8-9	10-7	12-6	4-4	6-5	8-1	9-10	11-7
	Spruce-pine-fir	SS	6-5	10-2	13-4	17-0	20-9	6-5	10-2	13-4	16-8	19-4
	Spruce-pine-fir	#1	6-4	9-9	12-4	15-1	17-6	6-2	9-0	11-5	13-11	16-2
	Spruce-pine-fir	#2	6-4	9-9	12-4	15-1	17-6	6-2	9-0	11-5	13-11	16-2
	Spruce-pine-fir	#3	5-0	7-4	9-4	11-5	13-2	4-8	6-10	8-8	10-6	12-3
19.2	Douglas fir-larch	SS	6-7	10-4	13-7	17-4	20-11	6-7	10-4	13-7	16-8	19-4
	Douglas fir-larch	#1	6-4	9-6	12-0	14-8	17-1	6-0	8-10	11-2	13-7	15-9
	Douglas fir-larch	#2	6-2	9-0	11-5	13-11	16-2	5-8	8-4	10-7	12-11	15-0
	Douglas fir-larch	#3	4-8	6-11	8-9	10-8	12-4	4-4	6-4	8-1	9-10	11-5
	Hem-fir	SS	6-2	9-9	12-10	16-5	19-11	6-2	9-9	12-10	16-1	18-8
	Hem-fir	#1	6-1	9-5	11-11	14-6	16-10	5-11	8-8	11-0	13-5	15-7
	Hem-fir	#2	5-9	8-9	11-1	13-7	15-9	5-7	8-1	10-3	12-7	14-7
	Hem-fir	#3	4-7	6-9	8-6	10-5	12-1	4-3	6-3	7-11	9-7	11-2

(continued)

TABLE R802.4.1(6)—continued
RAFTER SPANS FOR COMMON LUMBER SPECIES
(Ground snow load = 50 psf, ceiling attached to rafters, L/Δ = 240)

RAFTER SPACING (inches)	SPECIES AND GRADE		DEAD LOAD = 10 psf					DEAD LOAD = 20 psf				
			2 × 4	2 × 6	2 × 8	2 × 10	2 × 12	2 × 4	2 × 6	2 × 8	2 × 10	2 × 12
			Maximum rafter spans[a]									
			(feet-inches)	(feet-inches)	(feet-inches)	(feet-inches)	(feet-inches)	(feet-inches)	(feet-inches)	(feet-inches)	(feet-inches)	(feet-inches)
19.2	Southern pine	SS	6-5	10-2	13-4	17-0	20-9	6-5	10-2	13-4	16-11	20-0
	Southern pine	#1	6-2	9-8	12-3	14-4	17-1	6-0	9-0	11-4	13-4	15-9
	Southern pine	#2	5-7	8-4	10-7	12-6	14-9	5-2	7-9	9-9	11-7	13-8
	Southern pine	#3	4-3	6-4	8-0	9-8	11-5	4-0	5-10	7-4	8-11	10-7
	Spruce-pine-fir	SS	6-1	9-6	12-7	16-0	19-1	6-1	9-6	12-5	15-3	17-8
	Spruce-pine-fir	#1	5-11	8-11	11-3	13-9	15-11	5-7	8-3	10-5	12-9	14-9
	Spruce-pine-fir	#2	5-11	8-11	11-3	13-9	15-11	5-7	8-3	10-5	12-9	14-9
	Spruce-pine-fir	#3	4-7	6-9	8-6	10-5	12-1	4-3	6-3	7-11	9-7	11-2
24	Douglas fir-larch	SS	6-1	9-7	12-7	16-1	18-8	6-1	9-7	12-2	14-11	17-3
	Douglas fir-larch	#1	5-10	8-6	10-9	13-2	15-3	5-5	7-10	10-0	12-2	14-1
	Douglas fir-larch	#2	5-6	8-1	10-3	12-6	14-6	5-1	7-6	9-5	11-7	13-5
	Douglas fir-larch	#3	4-3	6-2	7-10	9-6	11-1	3-11	5-8	7-3	8-10	10-3
	Hem-fir	SS	5-9	9-1	11-11	15-2	18-0	5-9	9-1	11-9	14-5	15-11
	Hem-fir	#1	5-8	8-5	10-8	13-0	15-1	5-4	7-9	9-10	12-0	13-11
	Hem-fir	#2	5-4	7-10	9-11	12-1	14-1	4-11	7-3	9-2	11-3	13-0
	Hem-fir	#3	4-1	6-0	7-7	9-4	10-9	3-10	5-7	7-1	8-7	10-0
	Southern pine	SS	6-0	9-5	12-5	15-10	19-3	6-0	9-5	12-5	15-2	17-10
	Southern pine	#1	5-9	8-8	11-0	12-10	15-3	5-5	8-0	10-2	11-11	14-1
	Southern pine	#2	5-0	7-5	9-5	11-3	13-2	4-7	6-11	8-9	10-5	12-3
	Southern pine	#3	3-10	5-8	7-1	8-8	10-3	3-6	5-3	6-7	8-0	9-6
	Spruce-pine-fir	SS	5-8	8-10	11-8	14-8	17-1	5-8	8-10	11-2	13-7	15-9
	Spruce-pine-fir	#1	5-5	7-11	10-1	12-4	14-3	5-0	7-4	9-4	11-5	13-2
	Spruce-pine-fir	#2	5-5	7-11	10-1	12-4	14-3	5-0	7-4	9-4	11-5	13-2
	Spruce-pine-fir	#3	4-1	6-0	7-7	9-4	10-9	3-10	5-7	7-1	8-7	10-0

Check sources for availability of lumber in lengths greater than 20 feet.

For SI: 1 inch = 25.4 mm, 1 foot = 304.8 mm, 1 pound per square foot = 0.0479 kPa.

a. The tabulated rafter spans assume that ceiling joists are located at the bottom of the attic space or that some other method of resisting the outward push of the rafters on the bearing walls, such as rafter ties, is provided at that location. Where ceiling joists or rafter ties are located higher in the attic space, the rafter spans shall be multiplied by the following factors:

H_C/H_R	Rafter Span Adjustment Factor
1/3	0.67
1/4	0.76
1/5	0.83
1/6	0.90
1/7.5 or less	1.00

where:

H_C = Height of ceiling joists or rafter ties measured vertically above the top of the rafter support walls.

H_R = Height of roof ridge measured vertically above the top of the rafter support walls.

TABLE R802.4.1(7)
RAFTER SPANS FOR COMMON LUMBER SPECIES
(Ground snow load = 70 psf, ceiling not attached to rafters, L/Δ = 180)

RAFTER SPACING (inches)	SPECIES AND GRADE		DEAD LOAD = 10 psf					DEAD LOAD = 20 psf				
			2 × 4	2 × 6	2 × 8	2 × 10	2 × 12	2 × 4	2 × 6	2 × 8	2 × 10	2 × 12
			Maximum Rafter Spans[a]									
			(feet-inches)	(feet-inches)	(feet-inches)	(feet-inches)	(feet-inches)	(feet-inches)	(feet-inches)	(feet-inches)	(feet-inches)	(feet-inches)
12	Douglas fir-larch	SS	7-7	11-10	15-8	19-9	22-10	7-7	11-10	15-3	18-7	21-7
	Douglas fir-larch	#1	7-1	10-5	13-2	16-1	18-8	6-8	9-10	12-5	15-2	17-7
	Douglas fir-larch	#2	6-9	9-10	12-6	15-3	17-9	6-4	9-4	11-9	14-5	16-8
	Douglas fir-larch	#3	5-2	7-7	9-7	11-8	13-6	4-10	7-1	9-0	11-0	12-9
	Hem-fir	SS	7-2	11-3	14-9	18-10	22-1	7-2	11-3	14-8	18-0	20-10
	Hem-fir	#1	7-0	10-3	13-0	15-11	18-5	6-7	9-8	12-3	15-0	17-5
	Hem-fir	#2	6-7	9-7	12-2	14-10	17-3	6-2	9-1	11-5	14-0	16-3
	Hem-fir	#3	5-0	7-4	9-4	11-5	13-2	4-9	6-11	8-9	10-9	12-5
	Southern pine	SS	7-5	11-8	15-4	19-7	23-7	7-5	11-8	15-4	18-10	22-3
	Southern pine	#1	7-1	10-7	13-5	15-9	18-8	6-9	10-0	12-8	14-10	17-7
	Southern pine	#2	6-1	9-2	11-7	13-9	16-2	5-9	8-7	10-11	12-11	15-3
	Southern pine	#3	4-8	6-11	8-9	10-7	12-6	4-5	6-6	8-3	10-0	11-10
	Spruce-pine-fir	SS	7-0	11-0	14-6	18-0	20-11	7-0	11-0	13-11	17-0	19-8
	Spruce-pine-fir	#1	6-8	9-9	12-4	15-1	17-6	6-3	9-2	11-8	14-2	16-6
	Spruce-pine-fir	#2	6-8	9-9	12-4	15-1	17-6	6-3	9-2	11-8	14-2	16-6
	Spruce-pine-fir	#3	5-0	7-4	9-4	11-5	13-2	4-9	6-11	8-9	10-9	12-5
16	Douglas fir-larch	SS	6-10	10-9	14-0	17-1	19-10	6-10	10-5	13-2	16-1	18-8
	Douglas fir-larch	#1	6-2	9-0	11-5	13-11	16-2	5-10	8-6	10-9	13-2	15-3
	Douglas fir-larch	#2	5-10	8-7	10-10	13-3	15-4	5-6	8-1	10-3	12-6	14-6
	Douglas fir-larch	#3	4-6	6-6	8-3	10-1	11-9	4-3	6-2	7-10	9-6	11-1
	Hem-fir	SS	6-6	10-2	13-5	16-6	19-2	6-6	10-1	12-9	15-7	18-0
	Hem-fir	#1	6-1	8-11	11-3	13-9	16-0	5-9	8-5	10-8	13-0	15-1
	Hem-fir	#2	5-8	8-4	10-6	12-10	14-11	5-4	7-10	9-11	12-1	14-1
	Hem-fir	#3	4-4	6-4	8-1	9-10	11-5	4-1	6-0	7-7	9-4	10-9
	Southern pine	SS	6-9	10-7	14-0	17-4	20-5	6-9	10-7	13-9	16-4	19-3
	Southern pine	#1	6-2	9-2	11-8	13-8	16-2	5-10	8-8	11-0	12-10	15-3
	Southern pine	#2	5-3	7-11	10-0	11-11	14-0	5-0	7-5	9-5	11-3	13-2
	Southern pine	#3	4-1	6-0	7-7	9-2	10-10	3-10	5-8	7-1	8-8	10-3
	Spruce-pine-fir	SS	6-4	10-0	12-9	15-7	18-1	6-4	9-6	12-0	14-8	17-1
	Spruce-pine-fir	#1	5-9	8-5	10-8	13-1	15-2	5-5	7-11	10-1	12-4	14-3
	Spruce-pine-fir	#2	5-9	8-5	10-8	13-1	15-2	5-5	7-11	10-1	12-4	14-3
	Spruce-pine-fir	#3	4-4	6-4	8-1	9-10	11-5	4-1	6-0	7-7	9-4	10-9
19.2	Douglas fir-larch	SS	6-6	10-1	12-9	15-7	18-1	6-6	9-6	12-0	14-8	17-1
	Douglas fir-larch	#1	5-7	8-3	10-5	12-9	14-9	5-4	7-9	9-10	12-0	13-11
	Douglas fir-larch	#2	5-4	7-10	9-11	12-1	14-0	5-0	7-4	9-4	11-5	13-2
	Douglas fir-larch	#3	4-1	6-0	7-7	9-3	10-8	3-10	5-7	7-1	8-8	10-1
	Hem-fir	SS	6-1	9-7	12-4	15-1	17-4	6-1	9-2	11-8	14-2	15-5
	Hem-fir	#1	5-7	8-2	10-3	12-7	14-7	5-3	7-8	9-8	11-10	13-9
	Hem-fir	#2	5-2	7-7	9-7	11-9	13-7	4-11	7-2	9-1	11-1	12-10
	Hem-fir	#3	4-0	5-10	7-4	9-0	10-5	3-9	5-6	6-11	8-6	9-10

(continued)

TABLE R802.4.1(7)—continued
RAFTER SPANS FOR COMMON LUMBER SPECIES
(Ground snow load = 70 psf, ceiling not attached to rafters, L/Δ = 180)

RAFTER SPACING (inches)	SPECIES AND GRADE		DEAD LOAD = 10 psf					DEAD LOAD = 20 psf				
			2 × 4	2 × 6	2 × 8	2 × 10	2 × 12	2 × 4	2 × 6	2 × 8	2 × 10	2 × 12
			Maximum Rafter Spans[a]									
			(feet-inches)	(feet-inches)	(feet-inches)	(feet-inches)	(feet-inches)	(feet-inches)	(feet-inches)	(feet-inches)	(feet-inches)	(feet-inches)
19.2	Southern pine	SS	6-4	10-0	13-2	15-10	18-8	6-4	9-10	12-6	14-11	17-7
	Southern pine	#1	5-8	8-5	10-8	12-5	14-9	5-4	7-11	10-0	11-9	13-11
	Southern pine	#2	4-10	7-3	9-2	10-10	12-9	4-6	6-10	8-8	10-3	12-1
	Southern pine	#3	3-8	5-6	6-11	8-4	9-11	3-6	5-2	6-6	7-11	9-4
	Spruce-pine-fir	SS	6-0	9-2	11-8	14-3	16-6	5-11	8-8	11-0	13-5	15-7
	Spruce-pine-fir	#1	5-3	7-8	9-9	11-11	13-10	5-0	7-3	9-2	11-3	13-0
	Spruce-pine-fir	#2	5-3	7-8	9-9	11-11	13-10	5-0	7-3	9-2	11-3	13-0
	Spruce-pine-fir	#3	4-0	5-10	7-4	9-0	10-5	3-9	5-6	6-11	8-6	9-10
24	Douglas fir-larch	SS	6-0	9-0	11-5	13-11	16-2	5-10	8-6	10-9	13-2	15-3
	Douglas fir-larch	#1	5-0	7-4	9-4	11-5	13-2	4-9	6-11	8-9	10-9	12-5
	Douglas fir-larch	#2	4-9	7-0	8-10	10-10	12-6	4-6	6-7	8-4	10-2	11-10
	Douglas fir-larch	#3	3-8	5-4	6-9	8-3	9-7	3-5	5-0	6-4	7-9	9-10
	Hem-fir	SS	5-8	8-8	11-0	13-6	13-11	5-7	8-3	10-5	12-4	12-4
	Hem-fir	#1	5-0	7-3	9-2	11-3	13-0	4-8	6-10	8-8	10-7	12-4
	Hem-fir	#2	4-8	6-9	8-7	10-6	12-2	4-4	6-5	8-1	9-11	11-6
	Hem-fir	#3	3-7	5-2	6-7	8-1	9-4	3-4	4-11	6-3	7-7	8-10
	Southern pine	SS	5-11	9-3	11-11	14-2	16-8	5-11	8-10	11-2	13-4	15-9
	Southern pine	#1	5-0	7-6	9-6	11-1	13-2	4-9	7-1	9-0	10-6	12-5
	Southern pine	#2	4-4	6-5	8-2	9-9	11-5	4-1	6-1	7-9	9-2	10-9
	Southern pine	#3	3-4	4-11	6-2	7-6	8-10	3-1	4-7	5-10	7-1	8-4
	Spruce-pine-fir	SS	5-6	8-3	10-5	12-9	14-9	5-4	7-9	9-10	12-0	12-11
	Spruce-pine-fir	#1	4-8	6-11	8-9	10-8	12-4	4-5	6-6	8-3	10-0	11-8
	Spruce-pine-fir	#2	4-8	6-11	8-9	10-8	12-4	4-5	6-6	8-3	10-0	11-8
	Spruce-pine-fir	#3	3-7	5-2	6-7	8-1	9-4	3-4	4-11	6-3	7-7	8-10

Check sources for availability of lumber in lengths greater than 20 feet.

For SI: 1 inch = 25.4 mm, 1 foot = 304.8 mm, 1 pound per square foot = 0.0479 kPa.

a. The tabulated rafter spans assume that ceiling joists are located at the bottom of the attic space or that some other method of resisting the outward push of the rafters on the bearing walls, such as rafter ties, is provided at that location. Where ceiling joists or rafter ties are located higher in the attic space, the rafter spans shall be multiplied by the following factors:

H_C/H_R	Rafter Span Adjustment Factor
1/3	0.67
1/4	0.76
1/5	0.83
1/6	0.90
1/7.5 or less	1.00

where:

H_C = Height of ceiling joists or rafter ties measured vertically above the top of the rafter support walls.

H_R = Height of roof ridge measured vertically above the top of the rafter support walls.

TABLE R802.4.1(8)
RAFTER SPANS FOR COMMON LUMBER SPECIES
(Ground snow load = 70 psf, ceiling attached to rafters, L/Δ = 240)

RAFTER SPACING (inches)	SPECIES AND GRADE		DEAD LOAD = 10 psf					DEAD LOAD = 20 psf				
			2 × 4	2 × 6	2 × 8	2 × 10	2 × 12	2 × 4	2 × 6	2 × 8	2 × 10	2 × 12
			Maximum rafter spans[a]									
			(feet - inches)	(feet - inches)	(feet - inches)	(feet - inches)	(feet - inches)	(feet - inches)	(feet - inches)	(feet - inches)	(feet - inches)	(feet - inches)
12	Douglas fir-larch	SS	6-10	10-9	14-3	18-2	22-1	6-10	10-9	14-3	18-2	21-7
	Douglas fir-larch	#1	6-7	10-5	13-2	16-1	18-8	6-7	9-10	12-5	15-2	17-7
	Douglas fir-larch	#2	6-6	9-10	12-6	15-3	17-9	6-4	9-4	11-9	14-5	16-8
	Douglas fir-larch	#3	5-2	7-7	9-7	11-8	13-6	4-10	7-1	9-0	11-0	12-9
	Hem-fir	SS	6-6	10-2	13-5	17-2	20-10	6-6	10-2	13-5	17-2	20-10
	Hem-fir	#1	6-4	10-0	13-0	15-11	18-5	6-4	9-8	12-3	15-0	17-5
	Hem-fir	#2	6-1	9-6	12-2	14-10	17-3	6-1	9-1	11-5	14-0	16-3
	Hem-fir	#3	5-0	7-4	9-4	11-5	13-2	4-9	6-11	8-9	10-9	12-5
	Southern pine	SS	6-9	10-7	14-0	17-10	21-8	6-9	10-7	14-0	17-10	21-8
	Southern pine	#1	6-6	10-2	13-5	15-9	18-8	6-6	10-0	12-8	14-10	17-7
	Southern pine	#2	6-1	9-2	11-7	13-9	16-2	5-9	8-7	10-11	12-11	15-3
	Southern pine	#3	4-8	6-11	8-9	10-7	12-6	4-5	6-6	8-3	10-0	11-10
	Spruce-pine-fir	SS	6-4	10-0	13-2	16-9	20-5	6-4	10-0	13-2	16-9	19-8
	Spruce-pine-fir	#1	6-2	9-9	12-4	15-1	17-6	6-2	9-2	11-8	14-2	16-6
	Spruce-pine-fir	#2	6-2	9-9	12-4	15-1	17-6	6-2	9-2	11-8	14-2	16-6
	Spruce-pine-fir	#3	5-0	7-4	9-4	11-5	13-2	4-9	6-11	8-9	10-9	12-5
16	Douglas fir-larch	SS	6-3	9-10	12-11	16-6	19-10	6-3	9-10	12-11	16-1	18-8
	Douglas fir-larch	#1	6-0	9-0	11-5	13-11	16-2	5-10	8-6	10-9	13-2	15-3
	Douglas fir-larch	#2	5-10	8-7	10-10	13-3	15-4	5-6	8-1	10-3	12-6	14-6
	Douglas fir-larch	#3	4-6	6-6	8-3	10-1	11-9	4-3	6-2	7-10	9-6	11-1
	Hem-fir	SS	5-11	9-3	12-2	15-7	18-11	5-11	9-3	12-2	15-7	18-0
	Hem-fir	#1	5-9	8-11	11-3	13-9	16-0	5-9	8-5	10-8	13-0	15-1
	Hem-fir	#2	5-6	8-4	10-6	12-10	14-11	5-4	7-10	9-11	12-1	14-1
	Hem-fir	#3	4-4	6-4	8-1	9-10	11-5	4-1	6-0	7-7	9-4	10-9
	Southern pine	SS	6-1	9-7	12-8	16-2	19-8	6-1	9-7	12-8	16-2	19-3
	Southern pine	#1	5-11	9-2	11-8	13-8	16-2	5-10	8-8	11-0	12-10	15-3
	Southern pine	#2	5-3	7-11	10-0	11-11	14-0	5-0	7-5	9-5	11-3	13-2
	Southern pine	#3	4-1	6-0	7-7	9-2	10-10	3-10	5-8	7-1	8-8	10-3
	Spruce-pine-fir	SS	5-9	9-1	11-11	15-3	18-1	5-9	9-1	11-11	14-8	17-1
	Spruce-pine-fir	#1	5-8	8-5	10-8	13-1	15-2	5-5	7-11	10-1	12-4	14-3
	Spruce-pine-fir	#2	5-8	8-5	10-8	13-1	15-2	5-5	7-11	10-1	12-4	14-3
	Spruce-pine-fir	#3	4-4	6-4	8-1	9-10	11-5	4-1	6-0	7-7	9-4	10-9
19.2	Douglas fir-larch	SS	5-10	9-3	12-2	15-6	18-1	5-10	9-3	12-0	14-8	17-1
	Douglas fir-larch	#1	5-7	8-3	10-5	12-9	14-9	5-4	7-9	9-10	12-0	13-11
	Douglas fir-larch	#2	5-4	7-10	9-11	12-1	14-0	5-0	7-4	9-4	11-5	13-2
	Douglas fir-larch	#3	4-1	6-0	7-7	9-3	10-8	3-10	5-7	7-1	8-8	10-1
	Hem-fir	SS	5-6	8-8	11-6	14-8	17-4	5-6	8-8	11-6	14-2	15-5
	Hem-fir	#1	5-5	8-2	10-3	12-7	14-7	5-3	7-8	9-8	11-10	13-9
	Hem-fir	#2	5-2	7-7	9-7	11-9	13-7	4-11	7-2	9-1	11-1	12-10
	Hem-fir	#3	4-0	5-10	7-4	9-0	10-5	3-9	5-6	6-11	8-6	9-10

(continued)

TABLE R802.4.1(8)—continued
RAFTER SPANS FOR COMMON LUMBER SPECIES
(Ground snow load = 70 psf, ceiling attached to rafters, L/Δ = 240)

RAFTER SPACING (inches)	SPECIES AND GRADE		DEAD LOAD = 10 psf					DEAD LOAD = 20 psf				
			2 × 4	2 × 6	2 × 8	2 × 10	2 × 12	2 × 4	2 × 6	2 × 8	2 × 10	2 × 12
			Maximum rafter spans[a]									
			(feet - inches)	(feet - inches)	(feet - inches)	(feet - inches)	(feet - inches)	(feet - inches)	(feet - inches)	(feet - inches)	(feet - inches)	(feet - inches)
19.2	Southern pine	SS	5-9	9-1	11-11	15-3	18-6	5-9	9-1	11-11	14-11	17-7
	Southern pine	#1	5-6	8-5	10-8	12-5	14-9	5-4	7-11	10-0	11-9	13-11
	Southern pine	#2	4-10	7-3	9-2	10-10	12-9	4-6	6-10	8-8	10-3	12-1
	Southern pine	#3	3-8	5-6	6-11	8-4	9-11	3-6	5-2	6-6	7-11	9-4
	Spruce-pine-fir	SS	5-5	8-6	11-3	14-3	16-6	5-5	8-6	11-0	13-5	15-7
	Spruce-pine-fir	#1	5-3	7-8	9-9	11-11	13-10	5-0	7-3	9-2	11-3	13-0
	Spruce-pine-fir	#2	5-3	7-8	9-9	11-11	13-10	5-0	7-3	9-2	11-3	13-0
	Spruce-pine-fir	#3	4-0	5-10	7-4	9-0	10-5	3-9	5-6	6-11	8-6	9-10
24	Douglas fir-larch	SS	5-5	8-7	11-3	13-11	16-2	5-5	8-6	10-9	13-2	15-3
	Douglas fir-larch	#1	5-0	7-4	9-4	11-5	13-2	4-9	6-11	8-9	10-9	12-5
	Douglas fir-larch	#2	4-9	7-0	8-10	10-10	12-6	4-6	6-7	8-4	10-2	11-10
	Douglas fir-larch	#3	3-8	5-4	6-9	8-3	9-7	3-5	5-0	6-4	7-9	9-0
	Hem-fir	SS	5-2	8-1	10-8	13-6	13-11	5-2	8-1	10-5	12-4	12-4
	Hem-fir	#1	5-0	7-3	9-2	11-3	13-0	4-8	6-10	8-8	10-7	12-4
	Hem-fir	#2	4-8	6-9	8-7	10-6	12-2	4-4	6-5	8-1	9-11	11-6
	Hem-fir	#3	3-7	5-2	6-7	8-1	9-4	3-4	4-11	6-3	7-7	8-10
	Southern pine	SS	5-4	8-5	11-1	14-2	16-8	5-4	8-5	11-1	13-4	15-9
	Southern pine	#1	5-0	7-6	9-6	11-1	13-2	4-9	7-1	9-0	10-6	12-5
	Southern pine	#2	4-4	6-5	8-2	9-9	11-5	4-1	6-1	7-9	9-2	10-9
	Southern pine	#3	3-4	4-11	6-2	7-6	8-10	3-1	4-7	5-10	7-1	8-4
	Spruce-pine-fir	SS	5-0	7-11	10-5	12-9	14-9	5-0	7-9	9-10	12-0	12-11
	Spruce-pine-fir	#1	4-8	6-11	8-9	10-8	12-4	4-5	6-6	8-3	10-0	11-8
	Spruce-pine-fir	#2	4-8	6-11	8-9	10-8	12-4	4-5	6-6	8-3	10-0	11-8
	Spruce-pine-fir	#3	3-7	5-2	6-7	8-1	9-4	3-4	4-11	6-3	7-7	8-10

Check sources for availability of lumber in lengths greater than 20 feet.

For SI: 1 inch = 25.4 mm, 1 foot = 304.8 mm, 1 pound per square foot = 0.0479 kPa.

a. The tabulated rafter spans assume that ceiling joists are located at the bottom of the attic space or that some other method of resisting the outward push of the rafters on the bearing walls, such as rafter ties, is provided at that location. Where ceiling joists or rafter ties are located higher in the attic space, the rafter spans shall be multiplied by the following factors:

H_C/H_R	Rafter Span Adjustment Factor
1/3	0.67
1/4	0.76
1/5	0.83
1/6	0.90
1/7.5 or less	1.00

where:

H_C = Height of ceiling joists or rafter ties measured vertically above the top of the rafter support walls.

H_R = Height of roof ridge measured vertically above the top of the rafter support walls.

R802.4.3 Hips and valleys. Hip and valley rafters shall be not less than 2 inches (51 mm) nominal in thickness and not less in depth than the cut end of the rafter. Hip and valley rafters shall be supported at the ridge by a brace to a bearing partition or be designed to carry and distribute the specific load at that point.

R802.4.4 Rafter supports. Where the roof pitch is less than 3:12 (25-percent slope), structural members that support rafters, such as ridges, hips and valleys, shall be designed as beams, and bearing shall be provided for rafters in accordance with Section R802.6.

R802.4.5 Purlins. Installation of purlins to reduce the span of rafters is permitted as shown in Figure R802.4.5. Purlins shall be sized not less than the required size of the rafters that they support. Purlins shall be continuous and shall be supported by 2-inch by 4-inch (51 mm by 102 mm) braces installed to bearing walls at a slope not less than 45 degrees (0.79 rad) from the horizontal. The braces shall be spaced not more than 4 feet (1219 mm) on center and the unbraced length of braces shall not exceed 8 feet (2438 mm).

R802.4.6 Collar ties. Where collar ties are used to connect opposing rafters, they shall be located in the upper third of the *attic* space and fastened in accordance with Table R602.3(1). Collar ties shall be not less than 1 inch by 4 inches (25 mm × 102 mm) nominal, spaced not more than 4 feet (1220 mm) on center. Ridge straps in accordance with Table R602.3(1) shall be permitted to replace collar ties.

R802.5 Ceiling joists. Ceiling joists shall be continuous across the structure or securely joined where they meet over interior partitions in accordance with Table R802.5.2.

R802.5.1 Ceiling joist size. Ceiling joists shall be sized based on the joist spans in Tables R802.5.1(1) and R802.5.1(2). For other grades and species and for other loading conditions, refer to the AWC STJR.

R802.5.2 Ceiling joist and rafter connections. Where ceiling joists run parallel to rafters, they shall be connected to rafters at the top wall plate in accordance with Table R802.5.2. Where ceiling joists are not connected to the rafters at the top wall plate, they shall be installed in the bottom third of the rafter height in accordance with Figure R802.4.5 and Table R802.5.2. Where the ceiling joists are installed above the bottom third of the rafter height, the ridge shall be designed as a beam. Where ceiling joists do not run parallel to rafters, the ceiling joists shall be connected to top plates in accordance with Table R602.3(1). Each rafter shall be tied across the structure with a rafter tie or a 2-inch by 4-inch (51 mm × 102 mm) kicker connected to the ceiling diaphragm with nails equivalent in capacity to Table R802.5.2.

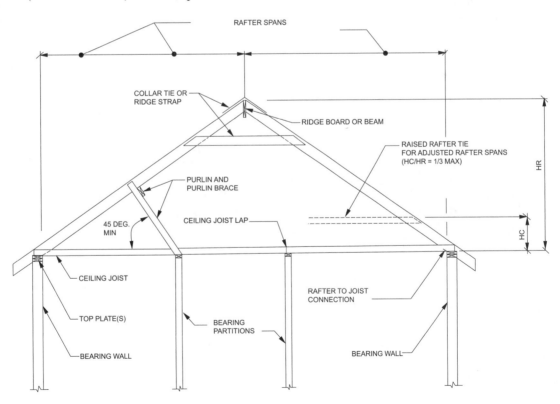

For SI: 1 inch = 25.4 mm, 1 foot = 305 mm, 1 degree = 0.018 rad.

H_C = Height of ceiling joists or rafter ties measured vertically above the top of rafter support walls.

H_R = Height of roof ridge measured vertically above the top of the rafter support walls.

**FIGURE R802.4.5
BRACED RAFTER CONSTRUCTION**

TABLE R802.5.1(1)
CEILING JOIST SPANS FOR COMMON LUMBER SPECIES
(Uninhabitable attics without storage, live load = 10 psf, L/Δ = 240)

CEILING JOIST SPACING (inches)	SPECIES AND GRADE		DEAD LOAD = 5 psf			
			2 × 4	2 × 6	2 × 8	2 × 10
			Maximum ceiling joist spans			
			(feet - inches)	(feet - inches)	(feet - inches)	(feet - inches)
12	Douglas fir-larch	SS	13-2	20-8	Note a	Note a
	Douglas fir-larch	#1	12-8	19-11	Note a	Note a
	Douglas fir-larch	#2	12-5	19-6	25-8	Note a
	Douglas fir-larch	#3	11-1	16-3	20-7	25-2
	Hem-fir	SS	12-5	19-6	25-8	Note a
	Hem-fir	#1	12-2	19-1	25-2	Note a
	Hem-fir	#2	11-7	18-2	24-0	Note a
	Hem-fir	#3	10-10	15-10	20-1	24-6
	Southern pine	SS	12-11	20-3	Note a	Note a
	Southern pine	#1	12-5	19-6	25-8	Note a
	Southern pine	#2	11-10	18-8	24-7	Note a
	Southern pine	#3	10-1	14-11	18-9	22-9
	Spruce-pine-fir	SS	12-2	19-1	25-2	Note a
	Spruce-pine-fir	#1	11-10	18-8	24-7	Note a
	Spruce-pine-fir	#2	11-10	18-8	24-7	Note a
	Spruce-pine-fir	#3	10-10	15-10	20-1	24-6
16	Douglas fir-larch	SS	11-11	18-9	24-8	Note a
	Douglas fir-larch	#1	11-6	18-1	23-10	Note a
	Douglas fir-larch	#2	11-3	17-8	23-4	Note a
	Douglas fir-larch	#3	9-7	14-1	17-10	21-9
	Hem-fir	SS	11-3	17-8	23-4	Note a
	Hem-fir	#1	11-0	17-4	22-10	Note a
	Hem-fir	#2	10-6	16-6	21-9	Note a
	Hem-fir	#3	9-5	13-9	17-5	21-3
	Southern pine	SS	11-9	18-5	24-3	Note a
	Southern pine	#1	11-3	17-8	23-10	Note a
	Southern pine	#2	10-9	16-11	21-7	25-7
	Southern pine	#3	8-9	12-11	16-3	19-9
	Spruce-pine-fir	SS	11-0	17-4	22-10	Note a
	Spruce-pine-fir	#1	10-9	16-11	22-4	Note a
	Spruce-pine-fir	#2	10-9	16-11	22-4	Note a
	Spruce-pine-fir	#3	9-5	13-9	17-5	21-3

(continued)

TABLE R802.5.1(1)—continued
CEILING JOIST SPANS FOR COMMON LUMBER SPECIES
(Uninhabitable attics without storage, live load = 10 psf, L/Δ = 240)

CEILING JOIST SPACING (inches)	SPECIES AND GRADE		DEAD LOAD = 5 psf			
			2 × 4	2 × 6	2 × 8	2 × 10
			Maximum ceiling joist spans			
			(feet - inches)	(feet - inches)	(feet - inches)	(feet - inches)
19.2	Douglas fir-larch	SS	11-3	17-8	23-3	Note a
	Douglas fir-larch	#1	10-10	17-0	22-5	Note a
	Douglas fir-larch	#2	10-7	16-8	21-4	26-0
	Douglas fir-larch	#3	8-9	12-10	16-3	19-10
	Hem-fir	SS	10-7	16-8	21-11	Note a
	Hem-fir	#1	10-4	16-4	21-6	Note a
	Hem-fir	#2	9-11	15-7	20-6	25-3
	Hem-fir	#3	8-7	12-6	15-10	19-5
	Southern -pine	SS	11-0	17-4	22-10	Note a
	Southern pine	#1	10-7	16-8	22-0	Note a
	Southern pine	#2	10-2	15-7	19-8	23-5
	Southern pine	#3	8-0	11-9	14-10	18-0
	Spruce-pine-fir	SS	10-4	16-4	21-6	Note a
	Spruce-pine-fir	#1	10-2	15-11	21-0	25-8
	Spruce-pine-fir	#2	10-2	15-11	21-0	25-8
	Spruce-pine-fir	#3	8-7	12-6	15-10	19-5
24	Douglas fir-larch	SS	10-5	16-4	21-7	Note a
	Douglas fir-larch	#1	10-0	15-9	20-1	24-6
	Douglas fir-larch	#2	9-10	15-0	19-1	23-3
	Douglas fir-larch	#3	7-10	11-6	14-7	17-9
	Hem-fir	SS	9-10	15-6	20-5	Note a
	Hem-fir	#1	9-8	15-2	19-10	24-3
	Hem-fir	#2	9-2	14-5	18-6	22-7
	Hem-fir	#3	7-8	11-2	14-2	17-4
	Southern pine	SS	10-3	16-1	21-2	Note a
	Southern pine	#1	9-10	15-6	20-5	24-0
	Southern pine	#2	9-3	13-11	17-7	20-11
	Southern pine	#3	7-2	10-6	13-3	16-1
	Spruce-pine-fir	SS	9-8	15-2	19-11	25-5
	Spruce-pine-fir	#1	9-5	14-9	18-9	22-11
	Spruce-pine-fir	#2	9-5	14-9	18-9	22-11
	Spruce-pine-fir	#3	7-8	11-2	14-2	17-4

Check sources for availability of lumber in lengths greater than 20 feet.

For SI: 1 inch = 25.4 mm, 1 foot = 304.8 mm, 1 pound per square foot = 0.0479 kPa.

a. Span exceeds 26 feet in length.

TABLE R802.5.1(2)
CEILING JOIST SPANS FOR COMMON LUMBER SPECIES
(Uninhabitable attics with limited storage, live load = 20 psf, L/Δ = 240)

CEILING JOIST SPACING (inches)	SPECIES AND GRADE		DEAD LOAD = 10 psf			
			2 × 4	2 × 6	2 × 8	2 × 10
			Maximum ceiling joist spans			
			(feet - inches)	(feet - inches)	(feet - inches)	(feet - inches)
12	Douglas fir-larch	SS	10-5	16-4	21-7	Note a
	Douglas fir-larch	#1	10-0	15-9	20-1	24-6
	Douglas fir-larch	#2	9-10	15-0	19-1	23-3
	Douglas fir-larch	#3	7-10	11-6	14-7	17-9
	Hem-fir	SS	9-10	15-6	20-5	Note a
	Hem-fir	#1	9-8	15-2	19-10	24-3
	Hem-fir	#2	9-2	14-5	18-6	22-7
	Hem-fir	#3	7-8	11-2	14-2	17-4
	Southern pine	SS	10-3	16-1	21-2	Note a
	Southern pine	#1	9-10	15-6	20-5	24-0
	Southern pine	#2	9-3	13-11	17-7	20-11
	Southern pine	#3	7-2	10-6	13-3	16-1
	Spruce-pine-fir	SS	9-8	15-2	19-11	25-5
	Spruce-pine-fir	#1	9-5	14-9	18-9	22-11
	Spruce-pine-fir	#2	9-5	14-9	18-9	22-11
	Spruce-pine-fir	#3	7-8	11-2	14-2	17-4
16	Douglas fir-larch	SS	9-6	14-11	19-7	25-0
	Douglas fir-larch	#1	9-1	13-9	17-5	21-3
	Douglas fir-larch	#2	8-11	13-0	16-6	20-2
	Douglas fir-larch	#3	6-10	9-11	12-7	15-5
	Hem-fir	SS	8-11	14-1	18-6	23-8
	Hem-fir	#1	8-9	13-7	17-2	21-0
	Hem-fir	#2	8-4	12-8	16-0	19-7
	Hem-fir	#3	6-8	9-8	12-4	15-0
	Southern pine	SS	9-4	14-7	19-3	24-7
	Southern pine	#1	8-11	14-0	17-9	20-9
	Southern pine	#2	8-0	12-0	15-3	18-1
	Southern pine	#3	6-2	9-2	11-6	14-0
	Spruce-pine-fir	SS	8-9	13-9	18-1	23-1
	Spruce-pine-fir	#1	8-7	12-10	16-3	19-10
	Spruce-pine-fir	#2	8-7	12-10	16-3	19-10
	Spruce-pine-fir	#3	6-8	9-8	12-4	15-0

(continued)

TABLE R802.5.1(2)—continued
CEILING JOIST SPANS FOR COMMON LUMBER SPECIES
(Uninhabitable attics with limited storage, live load = 20 psf, L/Δ = 240)

CEILING JOIST SPACING (inches)	SPECIES AND GRADE		DEAD LOAD = 10 psf			
			2 × 4	2 × 6	2 × 8	2 × 10
			Maximum ceiling joist spans			
			(feet - inches)	(feet - inches)	(feet - inches)	(feet - inches)
19.2	Douglas fir-larch	SS	8-11	14-0	18-5	23-7
	Douglas fir-larch	#1	8-7	12-6	15-10	19-5
	Douglas fir-larch	#2	8-2	11-11	15-1	18-5
	Douglas fir-larch	#3	6-2	9-1	11-6	14-1
	Hem-fir	SS	8-5	13-3	17-5	22-3
	Hem-fir	#1	8-3	12-4	15-8	19-2
	Hem-fir	#2	7-10	11-7	14-8	17-10
	Hem-fir	#3	6-1	8-10	11-3	13-8
	Southern pine	SS	8-9	13-9	18-2	23-1
	Southern pine	#1	8-5	12-9	16-2	18-11
	Southern pine	#2	7-4	11-0	13-11	16-6
	Southern pine	#3	5-8	8-4	10-6	12-9
	Spruce-pine-fir	SS	8-3	12-11	17-1	21-8
	Spruce-pine-fir	#1	8-0	11-9	14-10	18-2
	Spruce-pine-fir	#2	8-0	11-9	14-10	18-2
	Spruce-pine-fir	#3	6-1	8-10	11-3	13-8
24	Douglas fir-larch	SS	8-3	13-0	17-2	21-3
	Douglas fir-larch	#1	7-8	11-2	14-2	17-4
	Douglas fir-larch	#2	7-3	10-8	13-6	16-5
	Douglas fir-larch	#3	5-7	8-1	10-3	12-7
	Hem-fir	SS	7-10	12-3	16-2	20-6
	Hem-fir	#1	7-7	11-1	14-0	17-1
	Hem-fir	#2	7-1	10-4	13-1	16-0
	Hem-fir	#3	5-5	7-11	10-0	12-3
	Southern pine	SS	8-1	12-9	16-10	21-6
	Southern pine	#1	7-8	11-5	14-6	16-11
	Southern pine	#2	6-7	9-10	12-6	14-9
	Southern pine	#3	5-1	7-5	9-5	11-5
	Spruce-pine-fir	SS	7-8	12-0	15-10	19-5
	Spruce-pine-fir	#1	7-2	10-6	13-3	16-3
	Spruce-pine-fir	#2	7-2	10-6	13-3	16-3
	Spruce-pine-fir	#3	5-5	7-11	10-0	12-3

Check sources for availability of lumber in lengths greater than 20 feet.

For SI: 1 inch = 25.4 mm, 1 foot = 304.8 mm, 1 pound per square foot = 0.0479 kPa.

a. Span exceeds 26 feet in length.

TABLE R802.5.2
RAFTER/CEILING JOIST HEEL JOINT CONNECTIONS[a, b, c, d, e, g]

RAFTER SLOPE	RAFTER SPACING (inches)	GROUND SNOW LOAD (psf)															
		20[f]				30				50				70			
		Roof span (feet)															
		12	20	28	36	12	20	28	36	12	20	28	36	12	20	28	36
		Required number of 16d common nails[a, b] per heel joint splices[c, d, e]															
3:12	12	4	6	8	10	4	6	8	11	5	8	12	15	6	11	15	20
	16	5	8	10	13	5	8	11	14	6	11	15	20	8	14	20	26
	24	7	11	15	19	7	11	16	21	9	16	23	30	12	21	30	39
4:12	12	3	5	6	8	3	5	6	8	4	6	9	11	5	8	12	15
	16	4	6	8	10	4	6	8	11	5	8	12	15	6	11	15	20
	24	5	8	12	15	5	9	12	16	7	12	17	22	9	16	23	29
5:12	12	3	4	5	6	3	4	5	7	3	5	7	9	4	7	9	12
	16	3	5	6	8	3	5	7	9	4	7	9	12	5	9	12	16
	24	4	7	9	12	4	7	10	13	6	10	14	18	7	13	18	23
7:12	12	3	4	4	5	3	3	4	5	3	4	5	7	3	5	7	9
	16	3	4	5	6	3	4	5	6	3	5	7	9	4	6	9	11
	24	3	5	7	9	3	5	7	9	4	7	10	13	5	9	13	17
9:12	12	3	3	4	4	3	3	3	4	3	3	4	5	3	4	5	7
	16	3	4	4	5	3	3	4	5	3	4	5	7	3	5	7	9
	24	3	4	6	7	3	4	6	7	3	6	8	10	4	7	10	13
12:12	12	3	3	3	3	3	3	3	3	3	3	3	4	3	3	4	5
	16	3	3	4	4	3	3	3	4	3	3	4	5	3	4	5	7
	24	3	4	4	5	3	3	4	6	3	4	6	8	3	6	8	10

For SI: 1 inch = 25.4 mm, 1 foot = 304.8 mm, 1 pound per square foot = 0.0479 kPa.

a. 40d box nails shall be permitted to be substituted for 16d common nails.

b. Nailing requirements shall be permitted to be reduced 25 percent if nails are clinched.

c. Heel joint connections are not required where the ridge is supported by a load-bearing wall, header or ridge beam.

d. Where intermediate support of the rafter is provided by vertical struts or purlins to a load-bearing wall, the tabulated heel joint connection requirements shall be permitted to be reduced proportionally to the reduction in span.

e. Equivalent nailing patterns are required for ceiling joist to ceiling joist lap splices.

f. Applies to roof live load of 20 psf or less.

g. Tabulated heel joint connection requirements assume that ceiling joists or rafter ties are located at the bottom of the attic space. Where ceiling joists or rafter ties are located higher in the attic, heel joint connection requirements shall be increased by the following factors:

H_C/H_R	Heel Joint Connection Adjustment Factor
1/3	1.5
1/4	1.33
1/5	1.25
1/6	1.2
1/10 or less	1.11

where:

H_C = Height of ceiling joists or rafter ties measured vertically above the top of the rafter support walls.

H_R = Height of roof ridge measured vertically above the top of the rafter support walls.

R802.5.2.1 Ceiling joists lapped. Ends of ceiling joists shall be lapped not less than 3 inches (76 mm) or butted over bearing partitions or beams and toenailed to the bearing member. Where ceiling joists are used to provide resistance to rafter thrust, lapped joists shall be nailed together in accordance with Table R802.5.2 and butted joists shall be tied together in a manner to resist such thrust. Joists that do not resist thrust shall be permitted to be nailed in accordance with Table R602.3(1). Wood structural panel roof sheathing, in accordance with Table R503.2.1.1(1), shall not cantilever more than 9 inches (229 mm) beyond the gable endwall unless supported by gable overhang framing.

R802.5.2.2 Rafter ties. Wood rafter ties shall be not less than 2 inches by 4 inches (51 mm × 102 mm) installed in accordance with Table R802.5.2 at each rafter. Other approved rafter tie methods shall be permitted.

R802.5.2.3 Blocking. Blocking shall be not less than utility grade lumber.

R802.6 Bearing. The ends of each rafter or ceiling joist shall have not less than $1^1/_2$ inches (38 mm) of bearing on wood or metal and not less than 3 inches (76 mm) on masonry or concrete. The bearing on masonry or concrete shall be direct, or a sill plate of 2-inch (51 mm) minimum nominal thickness shall be provided under the rafter or ceiling joist. The sill plate shall provide a minimum nominal bearing area of 48 square inches (30 865 mm²).

R802.6.1 Finished ceiling material. If the finished ceiling material is installed on the ceiling prior to the attachment of the ceiling to the walls, such as in construction at a factory, a compression strip of the same thickness as the finished ceiling material shall be installed directly above the top plate of bearing walls if the compressive strength of the fin-ished ceiling material is less than the loads it will be required to withstand. The compression strip shall cover the entire length of such top plate and shall be not less than one-half the width of the top plate. It shall be of material capable of transmitting the loads transferred through it.

R802.7 Cutting, drilling and notching. Structural roof members shall not be cut, bored or notched in excess of the limitations specified in this section.

R802.7.1 Sawn lumber. Cuts, notches and holes in solid lumber joists, rafters, blocking and beams shall comply with the provisions of Section R502.8.1 except that cantilevered portions of rafters shall be permitted in accordance with Section R802.7.1.1.

R802.7.1.1 Cantilevered portions of rafters. Notches on cantilevered portions of rafters are permitted provided the dimension of the remaining portion of the rafter is not less than $3^1/_2$ inches (89 mm) and the length of the cantilever does not exceed 24 inches (610 mm) in accordance with Figure R802.7.1.1.

R802.7.1.2 Ceiling joist taper cut. Taper cuts at the ends of the ceiling joist shall not exceed one-fourth the depth of the member in accordance with Figure R802.7.1.2.

R802.7.2 Engineered wood products. Cuts, notches and holes bored in trusses, structural composite lumber, structural glue-laminated members, cross-laminated timber members or I-joists are prohibited except where permitted by the manufacturer's recommendations or where the effects of such alterations are specifically considered in the design of the member by a registered design professional.

R802.8 Lateral support. Roof framing members and ceiling joists having a depth-to-thickness ratio exceeding 5 to 1 based on nominal dimensions shall be provided with lateral support at points of bearing to prevent rotation. For roof raf-

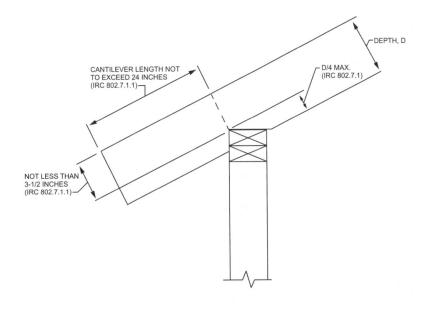

For SI: 1 inch = 25.4 mm.

FIGURE R802.7.1.1
RAFTER NOTCH

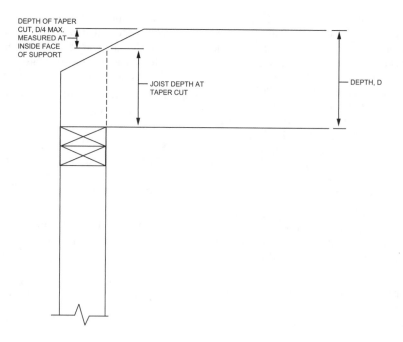

**FIGURE R802.7.1.2
CEILING JOIST TAPER CUT**

ters with ceiling joists attached in accordance with Table R602.3(1), the depth-to-thickness ratio for the total assembly shall be determined using the combined thickness of the rafter plus the attached ceiling joist.

Exception: Roof trusses shall be braced in accordance with Section R802.10.3.

R802.8.1 Bridging. Rafters and ceiling joists having a depth-to-thickness ratio exceeding 6 to 1 based on nominal dimensions shall be supported laterally by solid blocking, diagonal bridging (wood or metal) or a continuous 1-inch by 3-inch (25 mm by 76 mm) wood strip nailed across the rafters or ceiling joists at intervals not exceeding 8 feet (2438 mm).

R802.9 Framing of openings. Openings in roof and ceiling framing shall be framed with header and trimmer joists. Where the header joist span does not exceed 4 feet (1219 mm), the header joist shall be permitted to be a single member the same size as the ceiling joist or rafter. Single trimmer joists shall be permitted to be used to carry a single header joist that is located within 3 feet (914 mm) of the trimmer joist bearing. Where the header joist span exceeds 4 feet (1219 mm), the trimmer joists and the header joist shall be doubled and of sufficient cross section to support the ceiling joists or rafter framing into the header. *Approved* hangers shall be used for the header joist to trimmer joist connections where the header joist span exceeds 6 feet (1829 mm). Tail joists over 12 feet (3658 mm) long shall be supported at the header by framing anchors or on ledger strips not less than 2 inches by 2 inches (51 mm by 51 mm).

R802.10 Wood trusses.

R802.10.1 Truss design drawings. Truss design drawings, prepared in conformance to Section R802.10.1, shall be provided to the *building official* and *approved* prior to

installation. Truss design drawings shall be provided with the shipment of trusses delivered to the job site. Truss design drawings shall include, at a minimum, the following information:

1. Slope or depth, span and spacing.

2. Location of all joints.

3. Required bearing widths.

4. Design loads as applicable.

    4.1. Top chord live load (as determined from Section R301.6).

    4.2. Top chord dead load.

    4.3. Bottom chord live load.

    4.4. Bottom chord dead load.

    4.5. Concentrated loads and their points of application.

    4.6. Controlling wind and earthquake loads.

5. Adjustments to lumber and joint connector design values for conditions of use.

6. Each reaction force and direction.

7. Joint connector type and description such as size, thickness or gage and the dimensioned location of each joint connector except where symmetrically located relative to the joint interface.

8. Lumber size, species and *grade for each member*.

9. Connection requirements for:

    9.1. Truss to girder-truss.

    9.2. Truss ply to ply.

    9.3. Field splices.

10. Calculated deflection ratio or maximum description for live and total load.

11. Maximum axial compression forces in the truss members to enable the building designer to design the size, connections and anchorage of the permanent continuous lateral bracing. Forces shall be shown on the truss design drawing or on supplemental documents.

12. Required permanent truss member bracing location.

R802.10.2 Design. Wood trusses shall be designed in accordance with accepted engineering practice. The design and manufacture of metal-plate-connected wood trusses shall comply with ANSI/TPI 1. The truss design drawings shall be prepared by a registered professional where required by the statutes of the *jurisdiction* in which the project is to be constructed in accordance with Section R106.1.

R802.10.2.1 Applicability limits. The provisions of this section shall control the design of truss roof framing where snow controls for buildings that are not greater than 60 feet (18 288 mm) in length perpendicular to the joist, rafter or truss span, not greater than 36 feet (10 973 mm) in width parallel to the joist, rafter or truss span, not more than three stories above grade plane in height, and have roof slopes not smaller than 3:12 (25-percent slope) or greater than 12:12 (100-percent slope). Truss roof framing constructed in accordance with the provisions of this section shall be limited to sites subjected to a maximum design wind speed of 140 miles per hour (63 m/s), Exposure B or C, and a maximum ground snow load of 70 psf (3352 Pa). For consistent loading of all truss types, roof snow load is to be computed as: $0.7\, p_g$.

R802.10.3 Bracing. Trusses shall be braced to prevent rotation and provide lateral stability in accordance with the requirements specified in the *construction documents* for the building and on the individual truss design drawings. In the absence of specific bracing requirements, trusses shall be braced in accordance with accepted industry practice such as the SBCA *Building Component Safety Information (BCSI) Guide to Good Practice for Handling, Installing & Bracing of Metal Plate Connected Wood Trusses.*

R802.10.4 Alterations to trusses. Truss members shall not be cut, notched, drilled, spliced or otherwise altered in any way without the approval of a registered *design professional.* Alterations resulting in the addition of load such as HVAC equipment water heater that exceeds the design load for the truss shall not be permitted without verification that the truss is capable of supporting such additional loading.

R802.11 Roof tie-down.

R802.11.1 Uplift resistance. Roof assemblies shall have uplift resistance in accordance with Sections R802.11.1.1 and R802.11.1.2.

Where the uplift force does not exceed 200 pounds (90.8 kg), rafters and trusses spaced not more than 24 inches (610 mm) on center shall be permitted to be attached to their supporting wall assemblies in accordance with Table R602.3(1).

Where the basic wind speed does not exceed 115 mph, the wind exposure category is B, the roof pitch is 5:12 (42-percent slope) or greater, and the roof span is 32 feet (9754 mm) or less, rafters and trusses spaced not more than 24 inches (610 mm) on center shall be permitted to be attached to their supporting wall assemblies in accordance with Table R602.3(1).

R802.11.1.1 Truss uplift resistance. Trusses shall be attached to supporting wall assemblies by connections capable of resisting uplift forces as specified on the truss design drawings for the ultimate design wind speed as determined by Figure R301.2(5)A and listed in Table R301.2(1) or as shown on the construction documents. Uplift forces shall be permitted to be determined as specified by Table R802.11, if applicable, or as determined by accepted engineering practice.

R802.11.1.2 Rafter uplift resistance. Individual rafters shall be attached to supporting wall assemblies by connections capable of resisting uplift forces as determined by Table R802.11 or as determined by accepted engineering practice. Connections for beams used in a roof system shall be designed in accordance with accepted engineering practice.

SECTION R803
ROOF SHEATHING

R803.1 Lumber sheathing. Allowable spans for lumber used as roof sheathing shall conform to Table R803.1. Spaced lumber sheathing for wood shingle and shake roofing shall conform to the requirements of Sections R905.7 and R905.8. Spaced lumber sheathing is not allowed in Seismic Design Category D_2.

TABLE R803.1
MINIMUM THICKNESS OF LUMBER ROOF SHEATHING

RAFTER OR BEAM SPACING (inches)	MINIMUM NET THICKNESS (inches)
24	$^5/_8$
48[a]	
60[b]	$1^1/_2$ T & G
72[c]	

For SI: 1 inch = 25.4 mm.

a. Minimum 270 F_b, 340,000 E.
b. Minimum 420 F_b, 660,000 E.
c. Minimum 600F_b, 1,150,000 E.

R803.2 Wood structural panel sheathing.

R803.2.1 Identification and grade. Wood structural panels shall conform to DOC PS 1, DOC PS 2, CSA O437 or CSA O325, and shall be identified for grade, bond classification and performance category by a grade mark or certificate of inspection issued by an *approved* agency. Wood structural panels shall comply with the grades specified in Table R503.2.1.1(1).

R803.2.1.1 Exposure durability. Wood structural panels, when designed to be permanently exposed in outdoor applications, shall be of an exterior exposure durability. Wood structural panel roof sheathing exposed to the underside shall be permitted to be of interior type bonded with exterior glue, identified as Exposure 1.

TABLE R802.11
RAFTER OR TRUSS UPLIFT CONNECTION FORCES FROM WIND (ASD) (POUNDS PER CONNECTION)[a, b, c, d, e, f, g, h]

RAFTER OR TRUSS SPACING	ROOF SPAN (feet)	EXPOSURE B									
		Ultimate Design Wind Speed V_{ULT} (mph)									
		110		115		120		130		140	
		Roof Pitch		Roof Pitch		Roof Pitch		Roof Pitch		Roof Pitch	
		< 5:12	≥ 5:12	< 5:12	≥ 5:12	< 5:12	≥ 5:12	< 5:12	≥ 5:12	< 5:12	≥ 5:12
12" o.c.	12	48	43	59	53	70	64	95	88	122	113
	18	59	52	74	66	89	81	122	112	157	146
	24	71	62	89	79	108	98	149	137	192	178
	28	79	69	99	88	121	109	167	153	216	200
	32	86	75	109	97	134	120	185	170	240	222
	36	94	82	120	106	146	132	203	186	264	244
	42	106	92	135	120	166	149	230	211	300	278
	48	118	102	151	134	185	166	258	236	336	311
16" o.c.	12	64	57	78	70	93	85	126	117	162	150
	18	78	69	98	88	118	108	162	149	209	194
	24	94	82	118	105	144	130	198	182	255	237
	28	105	92	132	117	161	145	222	203	287	266
	32	114	100	145	129	178	160	246	226	319	295
	36	125	109	160	141	194	176	270	247	351	325
	42	141	122	180	160	221	198	306	281	399	370
	48	157	136	201	178	246	221	343	314	447	414
24" o.c.	12	96	86	118	106	140	128	190	176	244	226
	18	118	104	148	132	178	162	244	224	314	292
	24	142	124	178	158	216	196	298	274	384	356
	28	158	138	198	176	242	218	334	306	432	400
	32	172	150	218	194	268	240	370	340	480	444
	36	188	164	240	212	292	264	406	372	528	488
	42	212	184	270	240	332	298	460	422	600	556
	48	236	204	302	268	370	332	516	472	672	622

(continued)

TABLE R802.11—continued
RAFTER OR TRUSS UPLIFT CONNECTION FORCES FROM WIND (ASD) (POUNDS PER CONNECTION)[a, b, c, d, e, f, g, h]

RAFTER OR TRUSS SPACING	ROOF SPAN (feet)	EXPOSURE C									
		Ultimate Design Wind Speed V_{ULT} (mph)									
		110		115		120		130		140	
		Roof Pitch		Roof Pitch		Roof Pitch		Roof Pitch		Roof Pitch	
		< 5:12	≥ 5:12	< 5:12	≥ 5:12	< 5:12	≥ 5:12	< 5:12	≥ 5:12	< 5:12	≥ 5:12
12" o.c.	12	95	88	110	102	126	118	161	151	198	186
	18	121	111	141	131	163	151	208	195	257	242
	24	148	136	173	160	200	185	256	239	317	298
	28	166	152	195	179	225	208	289	269	358	335
	32	184	168	216	199	249	231	321	299	398	373
	36	202	185	237	219	274	254	353	329	438	411
	42	229	210	269	248	312	289	402	375	499	468
	48	256	234	302	278	349	323	450	420	560	524
16" o.c.	12	126	117	146	136	168	157	214	201	263	247
	18	161	148	188	174	217	201	277	259	342	322
	24	197	181	230	213	266	246	340	318	422	396
	28	221	202	259	238	299	277	384	358	476	446
	32	245	223	287	265	331	307	427	398	529	496
	36	269	246	315	291	364	338	469	438	583	547
	42	305	279	358	330	415	384	535	499	664	622
	48	340	311	402	370	464	430	599	559	745	697
24" o.c.	12	190	176	220	204	252	236	322	302	396	372
	18	242	222	282	262	326	302	416	390	514	484
	24	296	272	346	320	400	370	512	478	634	596
	28	332	304	390	358	450	416	578	538	716	670
	32	368	336	432	398	498	462	642	598	796	746
	36	404	370	474	438	548	508	706	658	876	822
	42	458	420	538	496	624	578	804	750	998	936
	48	512	468	604	556	698	646	900	840	1120	1048

For SI: 1 inch = 25.4 mm, 1 foot = 304.8 mm, 1 mile per hour = 0.447 m/s, 1 pound = 0.454 kg, 1 pound per square foot = 47.9 N/m², 1 pound per linear foot = 14.6 N/m.

a. The uplift connection forces are based on a maximum 33-foot mean roof height and Wind Exposure Category B or C. For Exposure D, the uplift connection force shall be selected from the Exposure C portion of the table using the next highest tabulated ultimate design wind speed. The adjustment coefficients in Table R301.2(3) shall not be used to multiply the tabulated forces for Exposures C and D or for other mean roof heights.

b. The uplift connection forces include an allowance for roof and ceiling assembly dead load of 15 psf.

c. The tabulated uplift connection forces are limited to a maximum roof overhang of 24 inches.

d. The tabulated uplift connection forces shall be permitted to be multiplied by 0.75 for connections not located within 8 feet of building corners.

e. For buildings with hip roofs with 5:12 and greater pitch, the tabulated uplift connection forces shall be permitted to be multiplied by 0.70. This reduction shall not be combined with any other reduction in tabulated forces.

f. For wall-to-wall and wall-to-foundation connections, the uplift connection force shall be permitted to be reduced by 60 plf for each full wall above.

g. Linear interpolation between tabulated roof spans and wind speeds shall be permitted.

h. The tabulated forces for a 12-inch on-center spacing shall be permitted to be used to determine the uplift load in pounds per linear foot.

R803.2.1.2 Fire-retardant-treated plywood. The allowable unit stresses for fire-retardant-treated plywood, including fastener values, shall be developed from an *approved* method of investigation that considers the effects of anticipated temperature and humidity to which the fire-retardant-treated plywood will be subjected, the type of treatment and redrying process. The fire-retardant-treated plywood shall be graded by an *approved agency.*

R803.2.2 Allowable spans. The maximum allowable spans for wood structural panel roof sheathing shall not exceed the values set forth in Table R503.2.1.1(1), or APA E30.

R803.2.3 Installation. Wood structural panel used as roof sheathing shall be installed with joints staggered or not staggered in accordance with Table R602.3(1), APA E30 for wood roof framing or with Table R804.3 for cold-formed steel roof framing. Wood structural panel roof sheathing in accordance with Table R503.2.1.1(1) shall not cantilever more than 9 inches (229 mm) beyond the gable endwall unless supported by gable overhang framing.

SECTION R804
COLD-FORMED STEEL ROOF FRAMING

R804.1 General. Elements shall be straight and free of any defects that would significantly affect their structural performance. Cold-formed steel roof framing members shall be in accordance with the requirements of this section.

R804.1.1 Applicability limits. The provisions of this section shall control the construction of cold-formed steel roof framing for buildings not greater than 60 feet (18 288 mm) perpendicular to the joist, rafter or truss span, not greater than 40 feet (12 192 mm) in width parallel to the joist span or truss, less than or equal to three stories above *grade* plane and with roof slopes not less than 3:12 (25-percent slope) or greater than 12:12 (100-percent slope). Cold-formed steel roof framing constructed in accordance with the provisions of this section shall be limited to sites where the ultimate design wind speed is less than 140 miles per hour (63 m/s), Exposure Category B or C, and the ground snow load is less than or equal to 70 pounds per square foot (3350 Pa).

R804.1.2 In-line framing. Cold-formed steel roof framing constructed in accordance with Section R804 shall be located in line with load-bearing studs in accordance with Figure R804.1.2 and the tolerances specified as follows:

1. The maximum tolerance shall be $^3/_4$ inch (19.1 mm) between the centerline of the horizontal framing member and the centerline of the vertical framing member.

2. Where the centerline of the horizontal framing member and bearing stiffener are located to one side of the centerline of the vertical framing member, the maximum tolerance shall be $^1/_8$ inch (3.2 mm) between the web of the horizontal framing member and the edge of the vertical framing member.

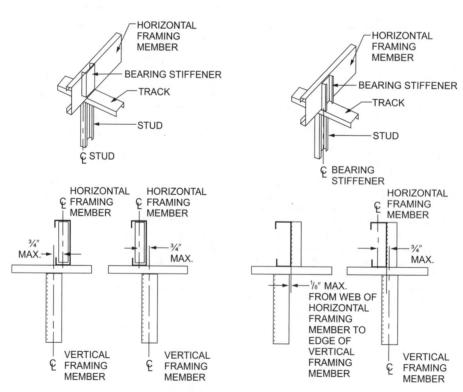

For SI: 1 inch = 25.4 mm.

FIGURE R804.1.2
IN-LINE FRAMING

R804.2 Structural framing. Load-bearing, cold-formed steel roof framing members shall be in accordance with this section.

R804.2.1 Material. Load-bearing, cold-formed steel framing members shall be cold formed to shape from structural quality sheet steel complying with the requirements of ASTM A1003, Structural Grades 33 Type H and 50 Type H.

R804.2.2 Corrosion protection. Load-bearing, cold-formed steel framing shall have a metallic coating complying with ASTM A1003 and one of the following:

1. Not less than G 60 in accordance with ASTM A653.

2. Not less than AZ 50 in accordance with ASTM A792.

R804.2.3 Dimension, thickness and material grade. Load-bearing, cold-formed steel roof framing members shall comply with Figure R804.2.3(1) and with the dimensional and thickness requirements specified in Table R804.2.3. Additionally, C-shaped sections shall have a minimum flange width of 1.625 inches (41 mm) and a maximum flange width of 2 inches (51 mm). The minimum lip size for C-shaped sections shall be $^1/_2$ inch (12.7 mm). Tracks shall comply with Figure R804.2.3(2) and shall have a minimum flange width of $1^1/_4$ inches (32 mm). Minimum Grade 33 ksi steel shall be used wherever 33 mil and 43 mil thicknesses are specified. Minimum Grade 50 ksi steel shall be used wherever 54 and 68 mil thicknesses are specified.

R804.2.4 Identification. Load-bearing, cold-formed steel framing members shall have a legible *label,* stencil, stamp or embossment with the following information as a minimum:

1. Manufacturer's identification.

2. Minimum base steel thickness in inches (mm).

3. Minimum coating designation.

4. Minimum yield strength, in kips per square inch (ksi) (MPa).

TABLE R804.2.3
LOAD-BEARING COLD-FORMED STEEL ROOF FRAMING MEMBER SIZES AND THICKNESSES

MEMBER DESIGNATION[a]	WEB DEPTH (inches)	MINIMUM BASE STEEL THICKNESS mil (inches)
350S162-t	3.5	33 (0.0329), 43 (0.0428), 54 (0.0538)
550S162-t	5.5	33 (0.0329), 43 (0.0428), 54 (0.0538), 68 (0.0677)
800S162-t	8	33 (0.0329), 43 (0.0428), 54 (0.0538), 68 (0.0677)
1000S162-t	10	43 (0.0428), 54 (0.0538), 68 (0.0677)
1200S162-t	12	43 (0.0428), 54 (0.0538), 68 (0.0677)

For SI: 1 inch = 25.4 mm

a. The member designation is defined by the first number representing the member depth in hundredths of an inch, the letter "s" representing a stud or joist member, the second number representing the flange width in hundredths of an inch and the letter "t" shall be a number representing the minimum base metal thickness in mils.

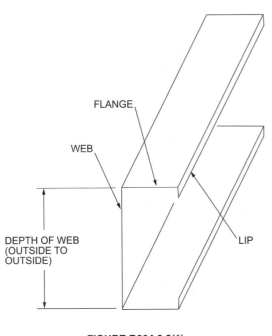

FIGURE R804.2.3(1)
C-SHAPED SECTION

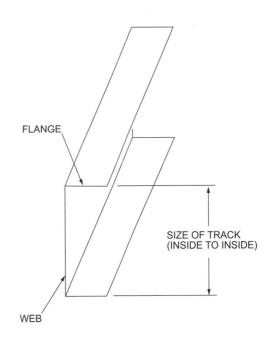

FIGURE R804.2.3(2)
TRACK SECTION

R804.2.5 Fastening requirements. Screws for steel-to-steel connections shall be installed with a minimum edge distance and center-to-center spacing of $^1/_2$ inch (12.7 mm), shall be self-drilling tapping and shall conform to ASTM C1513. Structural sheathing shall be attached to cold-formed steel roof rafters with minimum No. 8 self-drilling tapping screws that conform to ASTM C1513. Screws for attaching structural sheathing to cold-formed steel roof framing shall have a minimum head diameter of 0.292 inch (7.4 mm) with countersunk heads and shall be installed with a minimum edge distance of $^3/_8$ inch (9.5 mm). Gypsum board ceilings shall be attached to cold-formed steel joists with minimum No. 6 screws conforming to ASTM C954 or ASTM C1513 with a bugle-head style and shall be installed in accordance with Section R805. For all connections, screws shall extend through the steel not fewer than three exposed threads. Fasteners shall have rust-inhibitive coating suitable for the installation in which they are being used, or be manufactured from material not susceptible to corrosion.

R804.2.6 Web holes, web hole reinforcing and web hole patching. Web holes, web hole reinforcing and web hole patching shall be in accordance with this section.

R804.2.6.1 Web holes. Web holes in roof framing members shall comply with all of the following conditions:

1. Holes shall conform to Figure R804.2.6.1.

2. Holes shall be permitted only along the centerline of the web of the framing member.

3. Center-to-center spacing of holes shall be not less than 24 inches (610 mm).

4. The web hole width shall be not greater than one-half the member depth, or $2^1/_2$ inches (64 mm).

5. Holes shall have a web hole length not exceeding $4^1/_2$ inches (114 mm).

6. The minimum distance between the edge of the bearing surface and the edge of the web hole shall be not less than 10 inches (254 mm).

Framing members with web holes not conforming to Items 1 though 6 shall be reinforced in accordance with Section R804.2.6.2, patched in accordance with Section R804.2.6.3 or designed in accordance with accepted engineering practices.

R804.2.6.2 Web hole reinforcing. Reinforcement of web holes in ceiling joists not conforming to the requirements of Section R804.2.6.1 shall be permitted if the hole is located fully within the center 40 percent of the span and the depth and length of the hole do not exceed 65 percent of the flat width of the web. The reinforcing shall be a steel plate or C-shaped section with a hole that does not exceed the web hole size limitations of Section R804.2.6.1 for the member being reinforced. The steel reinforcing shall be the same thickness as the receiving member and shall extend not less than 1 inch (25 mm) beyond all edges of the hole. The steel reinforcing shall be fastened to the web of the receiving member with No. 8 screws spaced not greater than 1 inch (25 mm) center to center along the edges of the patch with minimum edge distance of $^1/_2$ inch (12.7 mm).

R804.2.6.3 Hole patching. Patching of web holes in roof framing members not conforming to the requirements in Section R804.2.6.1 shall be permitted in accordance with either of the following methods:

1. Framing members shall be replaced or designed in accordance with accepted engineering practices where web holes exceed either of the following size limits:

    1.1. The depth of the hole, measured across the web, exceeds 70 percent of the flat width of the web.

    1.2. The length of the hole measured along the web, exceeds 10 inches (254 mm) or the depth of the web, whichever is greater.

2. Web holes not exceeding the dimensional requirements in Section R804.2.6.3, Item 1, shall be patched with a solid steel plate, stud section or track section in accordance with Figure R804.2.6.3. The steel patch shall, as a minimum, be the same thickness as the receiving member and shall extend not

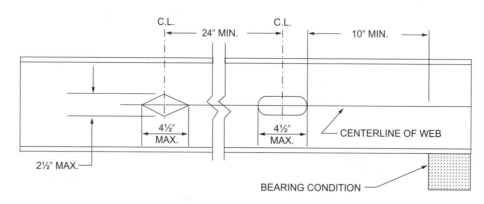

For SI: 1 inch = 25.4 mm.

FIGURE R804.2.6.1
ROOF FRAMING MEMBER WEB HOLES

less than 1 inch (25 mm) beyond all edges of the hole. The steel patch shall be fastened to the web of the receiving member with No. 8 screws spaced not greater than 1 inch (25 mm) center-to-center along the edges of the patch with minimum edge distance of $^1/_2$ inch (12.7 mm).

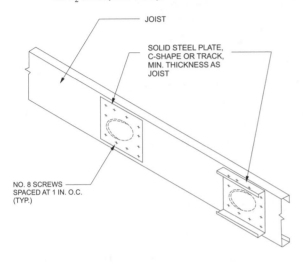

For SI: 1 inch = 25.4 mm.

FIGURE R804.2.6.3
ROOF FRAMING MEMBER WEB HOLE PATCH

R804.3 Roof construction. Cold-formed steel roof systems constructed in accordance with the provisions of this section shall consist of both ceiling joists and rafters in accordance with Figure R804.3 and fastened in accordance with Table R804.3.

R804.3.1 Ceiling joists. Cold-formed steel ceiling joists shall be in accordance with this section.

R804.3.1.1 Minimum ceiling joist size. Ceiling joist size and thickness shall be determined in accordance with the limits set forth in Tables R804.3.1.1(1) and R804.3.1.1(2). When determining the size of ceiling joists, the lateral support of the top flange shall be classified as unbraced, braced at midspan or braced at third points in accordance with Section R804.3.1.3. Where sheathing material is attached to the top flange of ceiling joists or where the bracing is spaced closer than at third points of the joists, the "third point" values from Tables R804.3.1.1(1) and R804.3.1.1(2) shall be used.

Ceiling joists shall have a bearing support length of not less than $1^1/_2$ inches (38 mm) and shall be connected to roof rafters (heel joint) with No. 10 screws in accordance with Figure R804.3.1.1 and Table R804.3.1.1(3).

Where continuous joists are framed across interior bearing supports, the interior bearing supports shall be located within 24 inches (610 mm) of midspan of the ceiling joist, and the individual spans shall not exceed the applicable spans in Tables R804.3.1.1(1) and R804.3.1.1(2).

Where the *attic* is to be used as an occupied space, the ceiling joists shall be designed in accordance with Section R505.

R804.3.1.2 Ceiling joist bottom flange bracing. The bottom flanges of ceiling joists shall be laterally braced by the application of gypsum board or continuous steel straps installed perpendicular to the joist run in accordance with one of the following:

1. Gypsum board shall be fastened with No. 6 screws in accordance with Section R702.

2. Steel straps with a minimum size of $1^1/_2$ inches by 33 mils (38 mm by 0.84 mm) shall be installed at a maximum spacing of 4 feet (1219 mm). Straps shall be fastened to the bottom flange at each joist with one No. 8 screw and shall be fastened to blocking with two No. 8 screws. Blocking shall be installed between joists at a maximum spacing of 12 feet (3658 mm) measured along a line of continuous strapping (perpendicular to the joist run), and at the termination of all straps.

R804.3.1.3 Ceiling joist top flange bracing. The top flanges of ceiling joists shall be laterally braced as required by Tables R804.3.1.1(1) and R804.3.1.1(2), in accordance with one of the following:

1. Minimum 33-mil (0.84 mm) C-shaped member in accordance with Figure R804.3.1.3(1).

2. Minimum 33-mil (0.84 mm) track section in accordance with Figure R804.3.1.3(1).

3. Minimum 33-mil (0.84 mm) hat section in accordance with Figure R804.3.1.3(1).

4. Minimum 54-mil (1.37 mm) $1^1/_2$-inch (38 mm) cold-rolled channel section in accordance with Figure R804.3.1.3(1).

5. Minimum $1^1/_2$-inch by 33-mil (38 mm by 0.84 mm) continuous steel strap in accordance with Figure R804.3.1.3(2).

Lateral bracing shall be installed perpendicular to the ceiling joists and shall be fastened to the top flange of each joist with one No. 8 screw. Blocking shall be installed between joists in line with bracing at a maximum spacing of 12 feet (3658 mm) measured perpendicular to the joists. Ends of lateral bracing shall be attached to blocking or anchored to a stable building component with two No. 8 screws.

R804.3.1.4 Ceiling joist splicing. Splices in ceiling joists shall be permitted, if ceiling joist splices are supported at interior bearing points and are constructed in accordance with Figure R804.3.1.4. The number of screws on each side of the splice shall be the same as required for the heel joint connection in Table R804.3.1.1(3).

R804.3.2 Roof rafters. Cold-formed steel roof rafters shall be in accordance with this section.

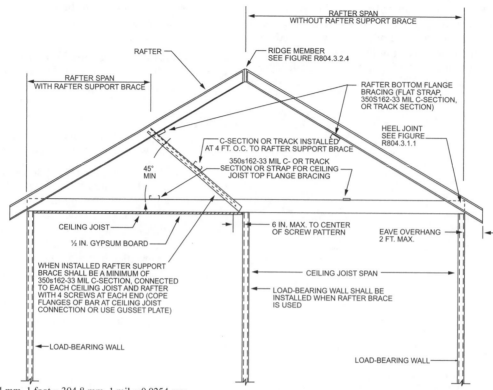

For SI: 1 inch = 25.4 mm, 1 foot = 304.8 mm, 1 mil = 0.0254 mm.

FIGURE R804.3
COLD-FORMED STEEL ROOF CONSTRUCTION

TABLE R804.3
ROOF FRAMING FASTENING SCHEDULE[a, b]

DESCRIPTION OF BUILDING ELEMENTS			NUMBER AND SIZE OF FASTENERS[a]				SPACING OF FASTENERS
Roof sheathing (oriented strand board or plywood) to rafter			No. 8 screws				6″ o.c. on edges and 12″ o.c. at interior supports. 6″ o.c. at gable end truss
Gable end truss to endwall top track			No. 10 screws				12″ o.c.
Rafter to ceiling joist			Minimum No. 10 screws, in accordance with Table R804.3.1.1(3)				Evenly spaced, not less than $^1/_2$″ from all edges.
Ceiling joist or roof truss to top track of bearing wall[b]	Ceiling Joist Spacing (in.)	Roof Span (ft)	Ultimate Design Wind Speed (mph) and Exposure Category				Each ceiling joist or roof truss
			126 B 110 C	<139 B 115 C	126 C	<139 C	
	16	24	2	2	2	3	
		28	2	2	3	3	
		32	2	2	3	4	
		36	2	2	3	4	
		40	2	2	3	4	
	24	24	2	2	3	4	
		28	2	2	4	5	
		32	2	3	4	5	
		36	2	3	4	6	
		40	2	3	5	6	

For SI: 1 inch = 25.4 mm, 1 foot = 304.8 mm, 1 pound per square foot = 0.0479 kPa, 1 mil = 0.0254 mm.

a. Screws are a minimum No. 10 unless noted otherwise.

b. Indicated number of screws shall be applied through the flanges of the truss or ceiling joist or through each leg of a 54 mil clip angle. See Section R804.3.8 for additional requirements to resist uplift forces.

TABLE R804.3.1.1(1)
CEILING JOIST SPANS
10 PSF LIVE LOAD (NO ATTIC STORAGE)[a, b, c, d]

MEMBER DESIGNATION	ALLOWABLE SPAN (feet - inches)					
	Lateral Support of Top (Compression) Flange					
	Unbraced		Midspan Bracing		Third-point Bracing	
	Ceiling Joist Spacing (inches)					
	16	24	16	24	16	24
350S162-33	9'-6"	8'-6"	11'-10"	9'-10"	11'-10"	10'-4"
350S162-43	10'-4"	9'-3"	12'-10"	11'-3"	12'-10"	11'-3"
350S162-54	11'-1"	9'-11"	13'-9"	12'-0"	13'-9"	12'-0"
350S162-68	12'-2"	10'-10"	14'-9"	12'-10"	14'-9"	12'-10"
550S162-33	10'-11"	9'-10"	15'-7"	12'-0"	16'-10"	12'-0"
550S162-43	11'-8"	10'-6"	16'-10"	14'-10"	18'-4"	16'-0"
550S162-54	12'-7"	11'-3"	18'-0"	16'-2"	19'-4"	17'-2"
550S162-68	13'-7"	12'-1"	19'-3"	17'-3"	20'-6"	18'-5"
800S162-33	—	—	—	—	—	—
800S162-43	13'-1"	11'-9"	18'-9"	16'-9"	21'-2"	18'-7"
800S162-54	13'-11"	12'-6"	20'-1"	18'-1"	21'-5"	20'-5"
800S162-68	14'-11"	13'-4"	21'-4"	19'-2"	22'-9"	21'-9"
1000S162-43	—	—	—	—	—	—
1000S162-54	14'-10"	13'-4"	21'-4"	19'-2"	22'-8"	21'-8"
1000S162-68	15'-10"	14'-3"	22'-9"	20'-5"	24'-3"	23'-3"
1200S162-43	—	—	—	—	—	—
1200S162-54	—	—	—	—	—	—
1200S162-68	16'-8"	14'-11"	23'-11"	21'-7"	25'-5"	24'-5"

For SI: 1 inch = 25.4 mm, 1 foot = 304.8 mm, 1 mil = 0.0254 mm, 1 pound per square foot = 0.0479 kPa.

a. Deflection criterion: $L/240$ for total loads.

b. Ceiling dead load = 5 psf.

c. Minimum Grade 33 ksi steel shall be used for 33 mil and 43 mil thicknesses. Minimum Grade 50 ksi steel shall be used for 54 and 68 mil thicknesses.

d. Listed allowable spans are not applicable for 350S162-33, 550S162-33, 550S162-43 and 800S162-43 continuous joist members.

TABLE R804.3.1.1(2)
CEILING JOIST SPANS
20 PSF LIVE LOAD (LIMITED ATTIC STORAGE)[a, b, c, d]

MEMBER DESIGNATION	ALLOWABLE SPAN (feet - inches)					
	Lateral Support of Top (Compression) Flange					
	Unbraced		Midspan Bracing		Third-point Bracing	
	Ceiling Joist Spacing (inches)					
	16	24	16	24	16	24
350S162-33	8'-0"	6'-5"	9'-2"	7'-5"	9'-11"	7'-5"
350S162-43	8'-11"	7'-8"	10'-9"	8'-9"	10'-0"	9'-6"
350S162-54	9'-7"	8'-7"	11'-7"	10'-2"	11'-7"	10'-2"
350S162-68	10'-4"	9'-3"	12'-5"	10'-10"	12'-5"	10'-10"
550S162-33	9'-5"	6'-11"	10'-5"	6'-11"	10'-5"	6'-11"
550S162-43	10'-2"	9'-2"	14'-2"	11'-8"	15'-2"	11'-8"
550S162-54	10'-10"	9'-9"	15'-7"	14'-0"	16'-7"	14'-5"
550S162-68	11'-8"	10'-5"	16'-7"	14'-10"	17'-9"	15'-6"
800S162-33	—	—	—	—	—	—
800S162-43	11'-4"	10'-2"	16'-1"	11'-0"	16'-6"	11'-0"
800S162-54	12'-0"	10'-10"	17'-4"	15'-7"	18'-7"	17'-7"
800S162-68	12'-10"	11'-6"	18'-6"	16'-7"	19'-11"	18'-11"
1000S162-43	—	—	—	—	—	—
1000S162-54	12'-10"	11'-7"	18'-5"	16'-6"	19'-8"	18'-8"
1000S162-68	13'-8"	12'-3"	19'-8"	17'-9"	21'-1"	20'-1"
1200S162-43	—	—	—	—	—	—
1200S162-54	—	—	—	—	—	—
1200S162-68	14'-5"	12'-11"	20'-9"	18'-7"	22'-0"	21'-0"

For SI: 1 inch = 25.4 mm, 1 foot = 304.8 mm, 1 mil = 0.0254 mm, 1 pound per square foot = 0.0479 kPa.

a. Deflection criterion: L/240 for total loads.

b. Ceiling deal load = 5 psf.

c. Minimum Grade 33 ksi steel shall be used for 33 mil and 43 mil thicknesses. Minimum Grade 50 ksi steel shall be used for 54 and 68 mil thicknesses.

d. Listed allowable spans are not applicable for 350S162-33, 350S162-43, 550S162-33, 550S162-43 and 800S162-43 continuous joist members.

TABLE R804.3.1.1(3)
NUMBER OF SCREWS REQUIRED FOR CEILING JOIST TO ROOF RAFTER CONNECTION[a]

ROOF SLOPE	NUMBER OF SCREWS																			
	Building width (feet)																			
	24				28				32				36				40			
	Ground snow load (psf)																			
	20	30	50	70	20	30	50	70	20	30	50	70	20	30	50	70	20	30	50	70
3/12	5	6	9	11	5	7	10	13	6	8	11	15	7	8	13	17	8	9	14	19
4/12	4	5	7	9	4	5	8	10	5	6	9	12	5	7	10	13	6	7	11	14
5/12	3	4	6	7	4	4	6	8	4	5	7	10	5	5	8	11	5	6	9	12
6/12	3	3	5	6	3	4	6	7	4	4	6	8	4	5	7	9	4	5	8	10
7/12	3	3	4	6	3	3	5	7	3	4	6	7	4	4	6	8	4	5	7	9
8/12	2	3	4	5	3	3	5	6	3	4	5	7	3	4	6	8	4	4	6	8
9/12	2	3	4	5	3	3	4	6	3	3	5	6	3	4	5	7	3	4	6	8
10/12	2	2	4	5	2	3	4	5	3	3	5	6	3	3	5	7	3	4	6	7
11/12	2	2	3	4	2	3	4	5	3	3	4	6	3	3	5	6	3	4	5	7
12/12	2	2	3	4	2	3	4	5	2	3	4	5	3	3	5	6	3	4	5	7

For SI: 1 inch = 25.4 mm, 1 foot = 304.8 mm, 1 pound per square foot = 0.0479kPa.

a. Screws shall be No. 10.

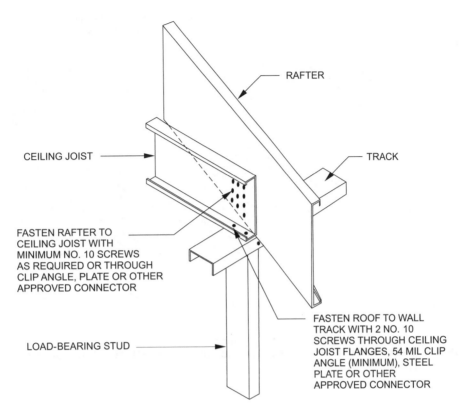

RAFTER

CEILING JOIST

TRACK

FASTEN RAFTER TO
CEILING JOIST WITH
MINIMUM NO. 10 SCREWS
AS REQUIRED OR THROUGH
CLIP ANGLE, PLATE OR OTHER
APPROVED CONNECTOR

LOAD-BEARING STUD

FASTEN ROOF TO WALL
TRACK WITH 2 NO. 10
SCREWS THROUGH CEILING
JOIST FLANGES, 54 MIL CLIP
ANGLE (MINIMUM), STEEL
PLATE OR OTHER
APPROVED CONNECTOR

For SI: 1 mil = 0.0254 mm.

**FIGURE R804.3.1.1
JOIST TO RAFTER CONNECTION**

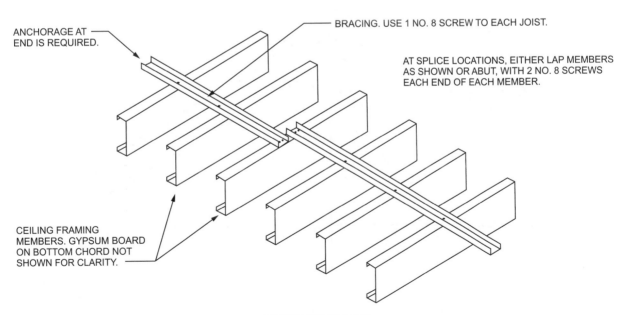

ANCHORAGE AT
END IS REQUIRED.

BRACING. USE 1 NO. 8 SCREW TO EACH JOIST.

AT SPLICE LOCATIONS, EITHER LAP MEMBERS
AS SHOWN OR ABUT, WITH 2 NO. 8 SCREWS
EACH END OF EACH MEMBER.

CEILING FRAMING
MEMBERS. GYPSUM BOARD
ON BOTTOM CHORD NOT
SHOWN FOR CLARITY.

**FIGURE R804.3.1.3(1)
CEILING JOIST TOP FLANGE BRACING WITH C-SHAPED, TRACK OR COLD-ROLLED CHANNEL**

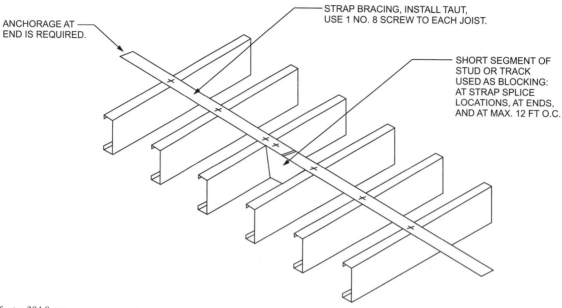

For SI: 1 foot = 304.8 mm.

FIGURE R804.3.1.3(2)
CEILING JOIST TOP FLANGE BRACING WITH CONTINUOUS STEEL STRAP AND BLOCKING

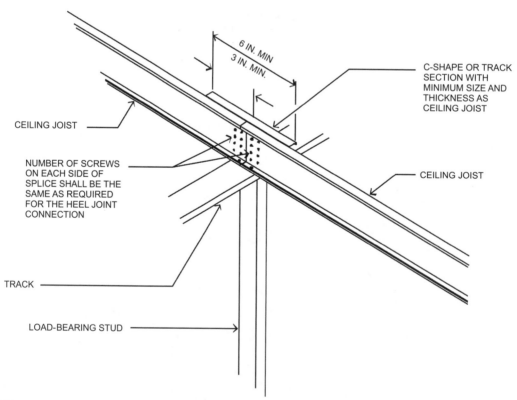

For SI: 1 inch = 25.4 mm.

FIGURE R804.3.1.4
SPLICED CEILING JOISTS

R804.3.2.1 Minimum roof rafter sizes. Roof rafter size and thickness shall be determined in accordance with the limits set forth in Table R804.3.2.1(1) based on the horizontal projection of the roof rafter span. For determination of roof rafter sizes, reduction of roof spans shall be permitted where a roof rafter support brace is installed in accordance with Section R804.3.2.2. The reduced roof rafter span shall be taken as the larger of the distances from the roof rafter support brace to the ridge or to the heel measured horizontally.

For the purpose of determining roof rafter sizes in Table R804.3.2.1(1), ultimate design wind speeds shall be converted to equivalent ground snow loads in accordance with Table R804.3.2.1(2). Roof rafter sizes shall be based on the higher of the ground snow load or the equivalent snow load converted from the ultimate design wind speed.

R804.3.2.1.1 Eave overhang. Eave overhangs shall not exceed 24 inches (610 mm) measured horizontally.

R804.3.2.1.2 Rake overhangs. Rake overhangs shall not exceed 12 inches (305 mm) measured hori-zontally. Outlookers at gable endwalls shall be installed in accordance with Figure R804.3.2.1.2.

R804.3.2.2 Roof rafter support brace. Where used to reduce roof rafter spans in determining roof rafter sizes, a roof rafter support brace shall meet all of the following conditions:

1. Minimum 350S162-33 C-shaped brace member with maximum length of 8 feet (2438 mm).

2. Minimum brace member slope of 45 degrees (0.785 rad) to the horizontal.

3. Minimum connection of brace to a roof rafter and ceiling joist with four No.10 screws at each end.

4. Maximum 6 inches (152 mm) between brace/ceiling joist connection and load-bearing wall below.

5. Each roof rafter support brace greater than 4 feet (1219 mm) in length, shall be braced with a supplemental brace having a minimum size of 350S162-33 or 350T162-33 such that the maximum unsupported length of the roof rafter support brace is 4 feet (1219 mm). The supplemental brace shall be continuous and shall be connected to each roof rafter support brace using two No. 8 screws.

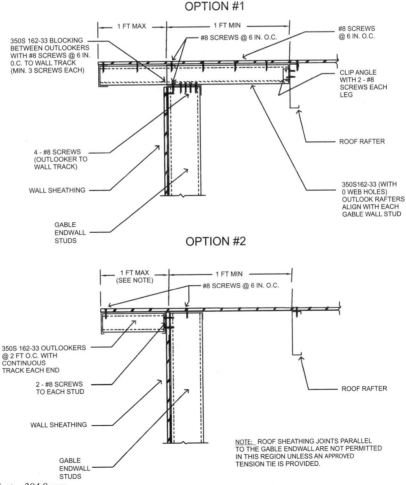

For SI: 1 inch = 25.4 mm, 1 foot = 304.8 mm.

FIGURE R804.3.2.1.2
GABLE ENDWALL OVERHANG DETAILS

TABLE R804.3.2.1(1)
ROOF RAFTER SPANS[a, b, c, d]

MEMBER DESIGNATION	ALLOWABLE SPAN MEASURED HORIZONTALLY (feet - inches)							
	Ground snow load (psf)							
	20		30		50		70	
	Rafter spacing (inches)							
	16	24	16	24	16	24	16	24
550S162-33	13'-11"	11'-4"	11'-9"	9'-7"	9'-5"	7'-8"	8'-1"	6'-7"
550S162-43	15'-9"	13'-8"	14'-3"	11'-8"	11'-4"	9'-3"	9'-9"	7'-11"
550S162-54	16'-11"	14'-10"	15'-3"	13'-4"	13'-3"	11'-7"	12'-0"	10'-6"
550S162-68	18'-2"	15'-10"	16'-5"	14'-4"	14'-3"	12'-5"	12'-11"	11'-3"
800S162-33	16'-4"	13'-4"	13'-11"	11'-4"	11'-1"	9'-0"	9'-6"	6'-7"
800S162-43	19'-7"	16'-0"	16'-8"	13'-7"	13'-4"	10'-10"	11'-5"	9'-4"
800S162-54	22'-9"	19'-11"	20'-7"	17'-11"	17'-10"	4'-9"	15'-6"	12'-7"
800S162-68	24'-7"	21'-6"	22'-2"	19'-5"	19'-3"	16'-10"	17'-5"	14'-8"
1000S162-43	22'-2"	18'-1"	18'-10"	15'-4"	15'-1"	12'-4"	12'-11"	10'-7"
1000S162-54	27'-1"	23'-8"	24'-6"	20'-9"	20'-5"	16'-8"	17'-6"	14'-3"
1000S162-68	29'-5"	25'-8"	26'-6"	23'-2"	23'-0"	19'-6"	20'-6"	16'-9"
1200S162-54	31'-3"	27'-0"	28'-1"	22'-11"	22'-6"	18'-4"	19'-4"	15'-9"
1200S162-68	34'-0"	29'-8"	30'-8"	26'-9"	26'-6"	21'-7"	22'-8"	18'-6"

For SI: 1 inch = 25.4 mm, 1 foot = 304.8 mm, 1 pound per square foot = 0.0479 kPa.

a. Table provides maximum horizontal rafter spans in feet and inches for slopes between 3:12 and 12:12.

b. Deflection criteria: L/240 for live loads and L/180 for total loads.

c. Roof dead load = 12 psf.

d. Grade 33 ksi steel is permitted to be used for 33 mil and 43 mil thicknesses. Grade 50 ksi steel shall be used for 54 and 68 mil thicknesses.

TABLE R804.3.2.1(2)
ULTIMATE DESIGN WIND SPEED TO EQUIVALENT SNOW LOAD CONVERSION

ULTIMATE WIND SPEED AND EXPOSURE		EQUIVALENT GROUND SNOW LOAD (psf)									
		Roof slope									
Exposure	Wind speed (mph)	3:12	4:12	5:12	6:12	7:12	8:12	9:12	10:12	11:12	12:12
B	115	20	20	20	20	30	20	30	30	30	50
	120	20	20	20	20	30	30	30	30	30	50
	130	20	20	20	20	30	30	30	50	50	50
	<140	20	20	20	20	30	50	50	50	50	50
C	115	20	20	20	20	30	30	30	50	50	50
	120	20	20	20	20	30	30	50	50	50	50
	130	20	20	20	30	30	50	50	50	50	70
	<140	30	30	30	50	50	50	70	70	70	—

For SI: 1 mile per hour = 0.447 m/s, 1 pound per square foot = 0.0479 kPa.

R804.3.2.3 Roof rafter splice. Roof rafters shall not be spliced.

R804.3.2.4 Roof rafter to ceiling joist and ridge member connection. Roof rafters shall be connected to a parallel ceiling joist to form a continuous tie between exterior walls in accordance with Figure R804.3.1.1 and Table R804.3.1.1(3). Ceiling joists shall be connected to the top track of the load-bearing wall in accordance with Table R804.3, either with the required number of No. 10 screws applied through the flange of the ceiling joist or by using a 54-mil (1.37 mm) clip angle with the required number of No.10 screws in each leg. Roof rafters shall be connected to a ridge member with a minimum 2-inch by 2-inch (51 mm by 51 mm) clip angle fastened with No. 10 screws to the ridge member in accordance with Figure R804.3.2.4 and Table R804.3.2.4. The clip angle shall have a steel thickness equivalent to or greater than the roof rafter thickness and shall extend the depth of the roof rafter member to the extent possible. The ridge member shall be fabricated from a C-shaped member and a track section that shall have a minimum size and steel thickness equivalent to or greater than that of adjacent roof rafters and shall be installed in accordance with Figure R804.3.2.4. The ridge member shall extend the full depth of the sloped roof rafter cut.

R804.3.2.5 Roof rafter bottom flange bracing. The bottom flanges of roof rafters shall be continuously braced, at a maximum spacing of 8 feet (2440 mm) as measured parallel to the roof rafters, with one of the following members:

1. Minimum 33-mil (0.84 mm) C-shaped member.

2. Minimum 33-mil (0.84 mm) track section.

3. Minimum $1^1/_2$-inch by 33-mil (38 mm by 0.84 mm) steel strap.

The bracing element shall be fastened to the bottom flange of each roof rafter with one No. 8 screw and shall be fastened to blocking with two No. 8 screws. Blocking shall be installed between roof rafters in-line with the continuous bracing at a maximum spacing of 12 feet (3658 mm) measured perpendicular to the roof rafters. The ends of continuous bracing shall be fastened to blocking or anchored to a stable building component with two No. 8 screws.

R804.3.3 Cutting and notching. Flanges and lips of load-bearing, cold-formed steel roof framing members shall not be cut or notched.

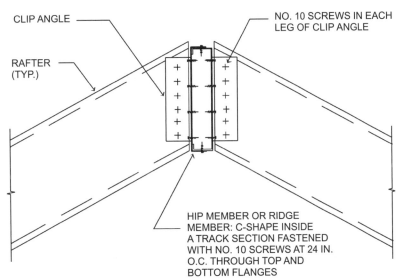

For SI: 1 inch = 25.4 mm.

FIGURE R804.3.2.4
RIDGE MEMBER CONNECTION

TABLE R804.3.2.4
SCREWS REQUIRED AT EACH LEG OF CLIP ANGLE FOR ROOF RAFTER TO RIDGE MEMBER CONNECTION[a]

BUILDING WIDTH (feet)	NUMBER OF SCREWS			
	Ground snow load (psf)			
	0 to 20	21 to 30	31 to 50	51 to 70
24	2	2	3	4
28	2	3	4	5
32	2	3	4	5
36	3	3	5	6
40	3	4	5	7

For SI: 1 inch = 25.4 mm, 1 foot = 304.8 mm, 1 pound per square foot = 0.0479 kPa.

a. Screws shall be No. 10 minimum.

R804.3.4 Headers. Roof-ceiling framing above wall openings shall be supported on headers. The allowable spans for headers in load-bearing walls shall not exceed the values set forth in Section R603.6 and Tables R603.6(1) through R603.6(6).

R804.3.5 Framing of openings in roofs and ceilings. Openings in roofs and ceilings shall be framed with header and trimmer joists. Header joist spans shall not exceed 4 feet (1219 mm) in length. Header and trimmer joists shall be fabricated from joist and track members having a minimum size and thickness equivalent to the adjacent ceiling joists or roof rafters and shall be installed in accordance with Figures R804.3.5(1) and R804.3.5(2). Each header joist shall be connected to trimmer joists with not less than four 2-inch by 2-inch (51 by 51 mm) clip angles. Each clip angle shall be fastened to both the header and trimmer joists with four No. 8 screws, evenly spaced, through each leg of the clip angle. The steel thickness of the clip angles shall be not less than that of the ceiling joist or roof rafter. Each track section for a built-up header or trimmer joist shall extend the full length of the joist (continuous).

R804.3.6 Roof trusses. Cold-formed steel trusses shall be designed and installed in accordance with AISI S240. In the absence of specific bracing requirements, trusses shall be braced in accordance with accepted industry practices, such as the SBCA *Cold-Formed Steel Building Component Safety Information (CFSBCSI) Guide to Good Practice for Handling, Installing & Bracing of Cold-Formed Steel Trusses.* Trusses shall be connected to the top track of the load-bearing wall in accordance with Table R804.3, either with two No. 10 screws applied through the flange of the truss or by using a 54-mil (1.37 mm) clip angle with two No. 10 screws in each leg.

R804.3.7 Ceiling and roof diaphragms. Ceiling and roof diaphragms shall be in accordance with this section.

R804.3.7.1 Ceiling diaphragms. At gable endwalls a ceiling *diaphragm* shall be provided by attaching a minimum $^1/_2$-inch (12.7 mm) gypsum board or a minimum $^3/_8$-inch (9.5 mm) wood structural panel sheathing, that complies with Section R803, to the bottom of ceiling joists or roof trusses and connected to wall framing in accordance with Figures R804.3.7.1(1) and R804.3.7.1(2), unless studs are designed as full height without bracing at the ceiling. Flat blocking shall consist of C-shaped or track section with a minimum thickness of 33 mils (0.84 mm). For a gypsum board sheathed ceiling, the diaphragm length shall be in accordance with Table R804.3.7.1. For a wood structural panel sheathed ceiling, the diaphragm length shall be not less than 12 feet (3658 mm) for building widths less than 36 feet (10 973 mm), or not less than 14 feet (4267 mm) for building widths greater than or equal to 36 feet (10 973 mm).

The ceiling diaphragm shall be secured with screws spaced at a maximum 6 inches (152 mm) o.c. at panel edges and a maximum 12 inches (305 mm) o.c. in the field. The required lengths in Table R804.3.7.1 for gypsum board sheathed ceiling diaphragms shall be permitted to be multiplied by 0.35 if all panel edges are blocked. Multiplying the required lengths in Table R804.3.7.1 for gypsum board sheathed ceiling diaphragms by 0.9 shall be permitted if all panel edges are secured with screws spaced at 4 inches (102 mm) o.c.

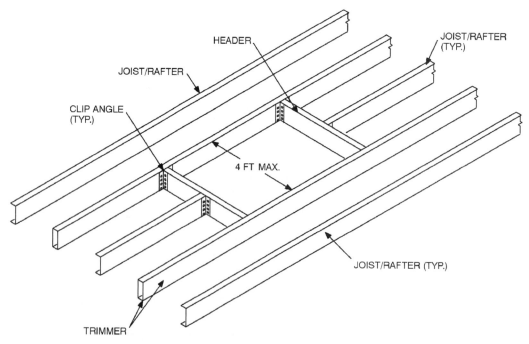

For SI: 1 foot = 304.8 mm.

FIGURE R804.3.5(1)
ROOF OR CEILING OPENING

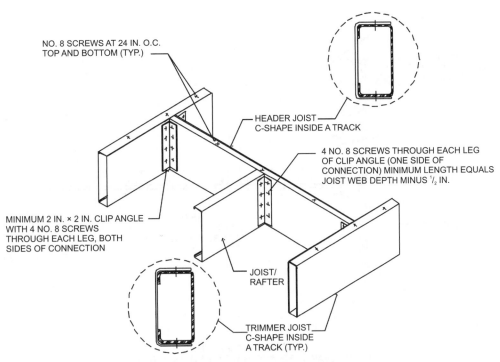

For SI: 1 inch = 25.4 mm.

FIGURE R804.3.5(2)
HEADER TO TRIMMER CONNECTION

TABLE R804.3.7.1
REQUIRED LENGTHS FOR CEILING DIAPHRAGMS AT GABLE ENDWALLS
GYPSUM BOARD SHEATHED, CEILING HEIGHT = 8 FEET[a, b, c, d, e, f, g]

EXPOSURE CATEGORY		ULTIMATE DESIGN WIND SPEED (mph)					
B		115	120	130	< 140	—	—
C		—	—	115	120	130	< 140
Roof pitch	Building endwall width (feet)	Minimum diaphragm length (feet)					
3:12 to 6:12	24 - 28	16	18	24	26	30	34
	> 28 - 32	20	20	26	32	34	40
	> 32 - 36	24	26	30	36	42	46
	> 36 - 40	26	28	36	40	48	52
6:12 to 9:12	> 24 - 28	20	20	26	30	34	38
	> 28 - 32	24	26	30	36	42	46
	> 32 - 36	26	30	38	42	48	54
	> 36 - 40	30	34	40	50	56	62
9:12 to 12:12	> 24 - 28	22	24	30	34	38	44
	> 28 - 32	26	28	36	40	46	52
	> 32 - 36	30	32	40	48	54	62
	> 36 - 40	36	38	48	56	64	72

For SI: 1 inch = 25.4 mm, 1 pound per square foot = 0.0479 kPa, 1 mile per hour = 0.447 m/s, 1 foot = 304.8 mm, 1 mil = 0.0254 mm.

a. Ceiling diaphragm is composed of $1/2$-inch gypsum board (min. thickness) secured with screws spaced at 6 inches o.c. at panel edges and 12 inches o.c. infield. Use No. 8 screws (min.) where framing members have a designation thickness of 54 mils or less and No. 10 screws (min.) where framing members have a designation thickness greater than 54 mils.

b. Maximum aspect ratio (length/width) of diaphragms is 2:1.

c. Building width is in the direction of horizontal framing members supported by the wall studs.

d. Required diaphragm lengths are to be provided at each end of the structure.

e. Multiplying required diaphragm lengths by 0.35 is permitted if all panel edges are blocked.

f. Multiplying required diaphragm lengths by 0.9 is permitted if all panel edges are secured with screws spaced at 4 inches o.c.

g. To determine the minimum diaphragm length for buildings with ceiling heights of 9 feet or 10 feet values in this table shall be multiplied by 1.15.

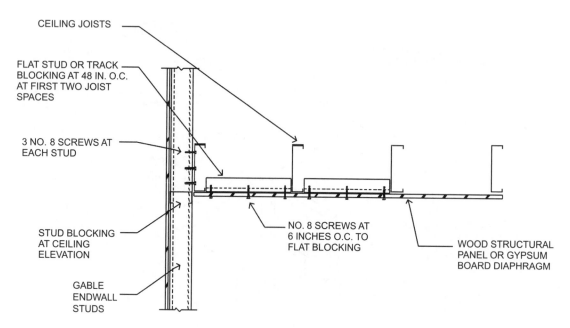

For SI: 1 inch = 25.4 mm.

FIGURE R804.3.7.1(1)
CEILING DIAPHRAGM TO GABLE ENDWALL DETAIL

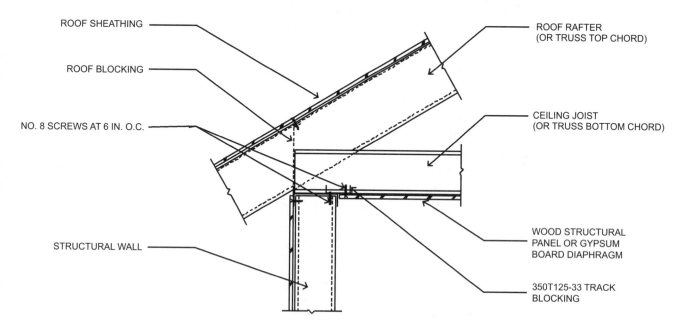

For SI: 1 inch = 25.4 mm.

FIGURE R804.3.7.1(2)
CEILING DIAPHRAGM TO SIDEWALL DETAIL

R804.3.7.2 Roof diaphragm. A roof *diaphragm* shall be provided by attaching not less than $^3/_8$-inch (9.5 mm) wood structural panel that complies with Section R803 to roof rafters or truss top chords in accordance with Table R804.3. Buildings with 3:1 or larger plan *aspect ratio* and with roof rafter slope (pitch) of 9:12 or larger shall have the roof rafters and ceiling joists blocked in accordance with Figure R804.3.7.2.

R804.3.8 Roof tie-down. Roof assemblies shall be connected to walls below in accordance with Table R804.3. A continuous load path shall be provided to transfer uplift loads to the foundation.

SECTION R805
CEILING FINISHES

R805.1 Ceiling installation. Ceilings shall be installed in accordance with the requirements for interior wall finishes as provided in Section R702.

SECTION R806
ROOF VENTILATION

R806.1 Ventilation required. Enclosed attics and enclosed rafter spaces formed where ceilings are applied directly to the underside of roof rafters shall have cross ventilation for each separate space by ventilating openings protected against the entrance of rain or snow. Ventilation openings shall have a least dimension of $^1/_{16}$ inch (1.6 mm) minimum and $^1/_4$ inch (6.4 mm) maximum. Ventilation openings having a least dimension larger than $^1/_4$ inch (6.4 mm) shall be provided with corrosion-resistant wire cloth screening, hardware cloth, perforated vinyl or similar material with openings having a least dimension of $^1/_{16}$ inch (1.6 mm) minimum and $^1/_4$ inch (6.4 mm) maximum. Openings in roof framing members shall conform to the requirements of Section R802.7. Required ventilation openings shall open directly to the outside air and shall be protected to prevent the entry of birds, rodents, snakes and other similar creatures.

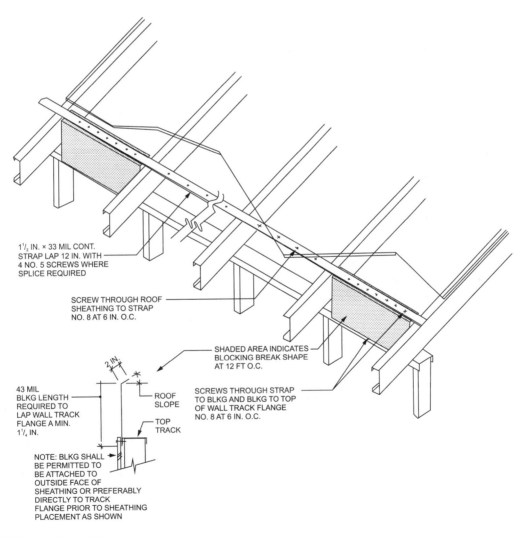

1¹/₂ IN. × 33 MIL CONT. STRAP LAP 12 IN. WITH 4 NO. 5 SCREWS WHERE SPLICE REQUIRED

SCREW THROUGH ROOF SHEATHING TO STRAP NO. 8 AT 6 IN. O.C.

43 MIL BLKG LENGTH REQUIRED TO LAP WALL TRACK FLANGE A MIN. 1¹/₄ IN.

2 IN.

ROOF SLOPE

TOP TRACK

NOTE: BLKG SHALL BE PERMITTED TO BE ATTACHED TO OUTSIDE FACE OF SHEATHING OR PREFERABLY DIRECTLY TO TRACK FLANGE PRIOR TO SHEATHING PLACEMENT AS SHOWN

SHADED AREA INDICATES BLOCKING BREAK SHAPE AT 12 FT O.C.

SCREWS THROUGH STRAP TO BLKG AND BLKG TO TOP OF WALL TRACK FLANGE NO. 8 AT 6 IN. O.C.

For SI: 1 mil = 0.0254 mm, 1 inch = 25.4 mm.

FIGURE R804.3.7.2
ROOF BLOCKING DETAIL

R806.2 Minimum vent area. The minimum net free ventilating area shall be $^1/_{150}$ of the area of the vented space.

> **Exception:** The minimum net free ventilation area shall be $^1/_{300}$ of the vented space provided both of the following conditions are met:
>
> 1. In Climate Zones 6, 7 and 8, a Class I or II vapor retarder is installed on the warm-in-winter side of the ceiling.
>
> 2. Not less than 40 percent and not more than 50 percent of the required ventilating area is provided by ventilators located in the upper portion of the attic or rafter space. Upper ventilators shall be located not more than 3 feet (914 mm) below the ridge or highest point of the space, measured vertically. The balance of the required ventilation provided shall be located in the bottom one-third of the *attic* space. Where the location of wall or roof framing members conflicts with the installation of upper ventilators, installation more than 3 feet (914 mm) below the ridge or highest point of the space shall be permitted.

R806.3 Vent and insulation clearance. Where eave or cornice vents are installed, blocking, bridging and insulation shall not block the free flow of air. Not less than a 1-inch (25 mm) space shall be provided between the insulation and the roof sheathing and at the location of the vent.

R806.4 Installation and weather protection. Ventilators shall be installed in accordance with manufacturer's instructions. Installation of ventilators in roof systems shall be in accordance with the requirements of Section R903. Installation of ventilators in wall systems shall be in accordance with the requirements of Section R703.1.

R806.5 Unvented attic and unvented enclosed rafter assemblies. Unvented *attics* and unvented enclosed roof framing assemblies created by ceilings that are applied directly to the underside of the roof framing members and structural roof sheathing applied directly to the top of the roof framing members/rafters, shall be permitted where all the following conditions are met:

1. The unvented *attic* space is completely within the *building thermal envelope*.

2. Interior Class I vapor retarders are not installed on the ceiling side (*attic* floor) of the unvented *attic* assembly or on the ceiling side of the unvented enclosed roof framing assembly.

3. Where wood shingles or shakes are used, a minimum $^1/_4$-inch (6.4 mm) vented airspace separates the shingles or shakes and the roofing underlayment above the structural sheathing.

4. In Climate Zones 5, 6, 7 and 8, any *air-impermeable insulation* shall be a Class II vapor retarder, or shall have a Class II vapor retarder coating or covering in direct contact with the underside of the insulation.

5. Insulation shall comply with Item 5.3 and either Item 5.1 or 5.2:

> 5.1. Item 5.1.1, 5.1.2, 5.1.3 or 5.1.4 shall be met, depending on the air permeability of the insulation directly under the structural roof sheathing.
>
>> 5.1.1. Where only *air-impermeable insulation* is provided, it shall be applied in direct contact with the underside of the structural roof sheathing.
>>
>> 5.1.2. Where *air-permeable insulation* is installed directly below the structural sheathing, rigid board or sheet insulation shall be installed directly above the structural roof sheathing in accordance with the *R*-values in Table R806.5 for condensation control.
>>
>> 5.1.3. Where both *air-impermeable* and *air-permeable insulation* are provided, the *air-impermeable insulation* shall be applied in direct contact with the underside of the structural roof sheathing in accordance with Item 5.1.1 and shall be in accordance with the *R*-values in Table R806.5 for condensation control. The *air-permeable insulation* shall be installed directly under the *air-impermeable insulation*.
>>
>> 5.1.4. Alternatively, sufficient rigid board or sheet insulation shall be installed directly above the structural roof sheathing to maintain the monthly average temperature of the underside of the structural roof sheathing above 45°F (7°C). For calculation purposes, an interior air temperature of 68°F (20°C) is assumed and the exterior air temperature is assumed to be the monthly average outside air temperature of the three coldest months.
>
> 5.2. In Climate Zones 1, 2 and 3, air-permeable insulation installed in unvented *attics* shall meet the following requirements:
>
>> 5.2.1. An approved *vapor diffusion port* shall be installed not more than 12 inches (305 mm) from the highest point of the roof, measured vertically from the highest point of the roof to the lower edge of the port.
>>
>> 5.2.2. The port area shall be greater than or equal to 1:600 of the ceiling area. Where there are multiple ports in the attic, the sum of the port areas shall be greater than or equal to the area requirement.
>>
>> 5.2.3. The vapor-permeable membrane in the *vapor diffusion port* shall have a vapor permeance rating of greater than or equal to 20 perms when tested in

accordance with Procedure A of ASTM E96.

5.2.4. The *vapor diffusion port* shall serve as an air barrier between the *attic* and the exterior of the building.

5.2.5. The *vapor diffusion port* shall protect the *attic* against the entrance of rain and snow.

5.2.6. Framing members and blocking shall not block the free flow of water vapor to the port. Not less than a 2-inch (51 mm) space shall be provided between any blocking and the roof sheathing. Air-permeable insulation shall be permitted within that space.

5.2.7. The roof slope shall be greater than or equal to 3:12 (vertical/horizontal).

5.2.8. Where only air-permeable insulation is used, it shall be installed directly below the structural roof sheathing.

5.2.9. *Air-impermeable insulation*, if any, shall be directly above or below the structural roof sheathing and is not required to meet the *R*-value in Table 806.5. Where directly below the structural roof sheathing, there shall be no space between the *air-impermeable insulation* and air-permeable insulation.

5.2.10. The air shall be supplied at a flow rate greater than or equal to 50 CFM (23.6 L/s) per 1,000 square feet (93 m^2) of ceiling. The air shall be supplied from ductwork providing supply air to the occupiable space when the conditioning system is operating. Alternatively, the air shall be supplied by a supply fan when the conditioning system is operating.

5.3. Where preformed insulation board is used as the air-impermeable insulation layer, it shall be sealed at the perimeter of each individual sheet interior surface to form a continuous layer.

TABLE R806.5
INSULATION FOR CONDENSATION CONTROL

CLIMATE ZONE	MINIMUM RIGID BOARD ON AIR-IMPERMEABLE INSULATION *R*-VALUE[a, b]
2B and 3B tile roof only	0 (none required)
1, 2A, 2B, 3A, 3B, 3C	R-5
4C	R-10
4A, 4B	R-15
5	R-20
6	R-25
7	R-30
8	R-35

a. Contributes to but does not supersede the requirements in Section N1102.
b. Alternatively, sufficient continuous insulation shall be installed directly above the structural roof sheathing to maintain the monthly average temperature of the underside of the structural roof sheathing above 45°F (7°C). For calculation purposes, an interior air temperature of 68°F (20°C) is assumed and the exterior air temperature is assumed to be the monthly average outside air temperature of the three coldest months.

SECTION R807
ATTIC ACCESS

R807.1 Attic access. Buildings with combustible ceiling or roof construction shall have an *attic* access opening to *attic* areas that exceed 30 square feet (2.8 m^2) and have a vertical height of 30 inches (762 mm) or greater. The vertical height shall be measured from the top of the ceiling framing members to the underside of the roof framing members.

The rough-framed opening shall be not less than 22 inches by 30 inches (559 mm by 762 mm) and shall be located in a hallway or other readily accessible location. Where located in a wall, the opening shall be not less than 22 inches wide by 30 inches high (559 mm wide by 762 mm high). Where the access is located in a ceiling, minimum unobstructed headroom in the *attic* space shall be 30 inches (762 mm) at some point above the access measured vertically from the bottom of ceiling framing members. See Minnesota Rules, Chapter 1346, the *Minnesota Mechanical Code*, for access requirements where mechanical *equipment* is located in *attics*.

ROOF ASSEMBLIES

User note:

About this chapter: Chapter 9 addresses the design and construction of roof assemblies. A roof assembly includes the roof deck, substrate or thermal barrier, insulation, vapor retarder and roof covering. This chapter provides the requirement for wind resistance of roof coverings. The types of roof covering materials and installation addressed by Chapter 9 are: asphalt shingles, clay and concrete tile, metal roof shingles, mineral-surfaced roll roofing, slate and slate-type shingles, wood shakes and shingles, built-up roofs, metal roof panels, modified bitumen roofing, thermoset and thermoplastic single-ply roofing, sprayed polyurethane foam roofing, liquid applied coatings and photovoltaic shingles. Chapter 9 also provides requirements for roof drainage, flashing, above-deck thermal insulation, rooftop-mounted photovoltaic systems and recovering or replacing an existing roof covering.

SECTION R901
GENERAL

R901.1 Scope. The provisions of this chapter shall govern the design, materials, construction and quality of roof assemblies.

SECTION R902
FIRE CLASSIFICATION

R902.1 Roofing covering materials. Roofs shall be covered with materials as set forth in Sections R904 and R905. Class A, B or C roofing shall be installed in jurisdictions designated by law as requiring their use or where the edge of the roof is less than 3 feet (914 mm) from a lot line. Class A, B and C roofing required by this section to be listed shall be tested in accordance with UL 790 or ASTM E108.

Exceptions:

1. Class A roof assemblies include those with coverings of brick, masonry and exposed concrete roof deck.

2. Class A roof assemblies include ferrous or copper shingles or sheets, metal sheets and shingles, clay or concrete roof tile, or slate installed on noncombustible decks.

3. Class A roof assemblies include minimum 16 ounces per square foot copper sheets installed over combustible decks.

4. Class A roof assemblies include slate installed over *underlayment* over combustible decks.

R902.2 Fire-retardant-treated shingles and shakes. Fire-retardant-treated wood shakes and shingles shall be treated by impregnation with chemicals by the full-cell vacuum-pressure process, in accordance with AWPA C1. Each bundle shall be marked to identify the manufactured unit and the manufacturer, and shall be *labeled* to identify the classification of the material in accordance with the testing required in Section R902.1, the treating company and the quality control agency.

R902.3 Building-integrated photovoltaic product. Building-integrated photovoltaic products installed as the roof covering shall be tested, listed and labeled for fire classification in accordance with Section R902.1.

R902.4 Rooftop-mounted photovoltaic panel systems. Rooftop-mounted *photovoltaic panel systems* installed on or above the roof covering shall be tested, listed and identified with a fire classification in accordance with UL 1703 and UL 2703. Class A, B or C *photovoltaic panel systems* and modules shall be installed in jurisdictions designated by law as requiring their use or where the edge of the roof is less than 3 feet (914 mm) from a lot line.

SECTION R903
WEATHER PROTECTION

R903.1 General. Roof decks shall be covered with *approved* roof coverings secured to the building or structure in accordance with the provisions of this chapter. Roof assemblies shall be designed and installed in accordance with this code and the *approved* manufacturer's instructions such that the *roof assembly* shall serve to protect the building or structure.

R903.2 Flashing. Flashings shall be installed in a manner that prevents moisture from entering the wall and roof through joints in copings, through moisture permeable materials and at intersections with parapet walls and other penetrations through the roof plane.

R903.2.1 Locations. Flashings shall be installed at wall and roof intersections, wherever there is a change in roof slope or direction and around roof openings. A kick-out flashing shall be installed to divert the water away from where the eave of a sloped roof intersects a vertical sidewall. The kick-out flashing on the roof shall be a minimum of $2^{1}/_{2}$ inches (63.5 mm) long. Where flashing is of metal, the metal shall be corrosion-resistant with a thickness of not less than 0.019 inch (0.5 mm) (No. 26 galvanized sheet).

R903.2.1.1 Existing buildings and structures. Kick-out flashings shall be required in accordance with Section R903.2.1 when re-siding or simultaneously re-siding and re-roofing existing buildings and structures.

Exception: Kick-out flashings are not required when only re-roofing existing buildings and structures.

R903.2.2 Crickets and saddles. A cricket or saddle shall be installed on the ridge side of any chimney or penetration more than 30 inches (762 mm) wide as measured perpendicular to the slope. Cricket or saddle coverings shall be sheet metal or of the same material as the roof covering.

Exception: Unit skylights installed in accordance with Section R308.6 and flashed in accordance with the manufacturer's instructions shall be permitted to be installed without a cricket or saddle.

R903.3 Coping. Parapet walls shall be properly coped with noncombustible, weatherproof materials of a width not less than the thickness of the parapet wall.

R903.4 Roof drainage. Unless roofs are sloped to drain over roof edges, roof drains shall be installed at each low point of the roof.

R903.4.1 Secondary (emergency overflow) drains or scuppers. Where roof drains are required, secondary emergency overflow roof drains or scuppers shall be provided where the roof perimeter construction extends above the roof in such a manner that water will be entrapped if the primary drains allow buildup for any reason. Overflow drains having the same size as the roof drains shall be installed with the inlet flow line located 2 inches (51 mm) above the low point of the roof, or overflow scuppers having three times the size of the roof drains and having a minimum opening height of 4 inches (102 mm) shall be installed in the adjacent parapet walls with the inlet flow located 2 inches (51 mm) above the low point of the roof served. The installation and sizing of overflow drains, leaders and conductors shall comply with Sections 1106 and 1108 of the *International Plumbing Code,* as applicable.

Overflow drains shall discharge to an *approved* location and shall not be connected to roof drain lines.

SECTION R904
MATERIALS

R904.1 Scope. The requirements set forth in this section shall apply to the application of roof covering materials specified herein. Roof assemblies shall be applied in accordance with this chapter and the manufacturer's installation instructions. Installation of roof assemblies shall comply with the applicable provisions of Section R905.

R904.2 Compatibility of materials. Roof assemblies shall be of materials that are compatible with each other and with the building or structure to which the materials are applied.

R904.3 Material specifications and physical characteristics. Roof covering materials shall conform to the applicable standards listed in this chapter.

R904.4 Product identification. Roof covering materials shall be delivered in packages bearing the manufacturer's identifying marks and *approved* testing agency *labels* required. Bulk shipments of materials shall be accompanied by the same information issued in the form of a certificate or on a bill of lading by the manufacturer.

SECTION R905
REQUIREMENTS FOR ROOF COVERINGS

R905.1 Roof covering application. Roof coverings shall be applied in accordance with the applicable provisions of this section and the manufacturer's installation instructions. Unless otherwise specified in this section, roof coverings shall be installed to resist the component and cladding loads specified in Table R301.2(2), adjusted for height and exposure in accordance with Table R301.2(3).

R905.1.1 Underlayment. *Underlayment* for asphalt shingles, clay and concrete tile, metal roof shingles, mineral-surfaced roll roofing, slate and slate-type shingles, wood shingles, wood shakes, metal roof panels and *photovoltaic shingles* shall conform to the applicable standards listed in this chapter. *Underlayment* materials required to comply with ASTM D226, D1970, D4869 and D6757 shall bear a label indicating compliance to the standard designation and, if applicable, type classification indicated in Table R905.1.1(1). *Underlayment* shall be applied in accordance with Table R905.1.1(2). *Underlayment* shall be attached in accordance with Table R905.1.1(3).

Exceptions:

1. As an alternative, self-adhering polymer-modified bitumen *underlayment* complying with ASTM D1970 installed in accordance with both the *underlayment* manufacturer's and roof covering manufacturer's instructions for the deck material, roof ventilation configuration and climate exposure for the roof covering to be installed, shall be permitted.

2. As an alternative, a minimum 4-inch-wide (102 mm) strip of self-adhering polymer-modified bitumen membrane complying with ASTM D1970, installed in accordance with the *manufacturer's installation instructions* for the deck material, shall be applied over all joints in the roof decking. An *approved underlayment* for the applicable roof covering for maximum ultimate design wind speeds, V_{ult}, less than 140 miles per hour shall be applied over the entire roof over the 4-inch-wide (102 mm) membrane strips.

3. As an alternative, two layers of *underlayment* complying with ASTM D226 Type II or ASTM D4869 Type III or Type IV shall be permitted to be installed as follows in 3.1–3.4:

   3.1. Apply a 19-inch-wide (483 mm) strip of *underlayment* parallel with the eave. Starting at the eave, apply 36-inch-wide (914 mm) strips of *underlayment* felt, overlapping successive sheets 19 inches (483 mm). End laps shall be 4 inches (102 mm) and shall be offset by 6 feet (1829 mm).

TABLE R905.1.1(1)
UNDERLAYMENT TYPES

ROOF COVERING	SECTION	MAXIMUM ULTIMATE DESIGN WIND SPEED, V_{ult} < 140 MPH	MAXIMUM ULTIMATE DESIGN WIND SPEED, V_{ult} ≥ 140 MPH
Asphalt shingles	R905.2	ASTM D226 Type I ASTM D4869 Type I, II, III or IV ASTM D6757	ASTM D226 Type II ASTM D4869 Type III or Type IV ASTM D6757
Clay and concrete tile	R905.3	ASTM D226 Type II ASTM D2626 Type I ASTM D6380 Class M mineral-surfaced roll roofing	ASTM D226 Type II ASTM D2626 Type I ASTM D6380 Class M mineral-surfaced roll roofing
Metal roof shingles	R905.4	ASTM D226 Type I or II ASTM D4869 Type I, II, III or IV	ASTM D226 Type II ASTM D4869 Type III or Type IV
Mineral-surfaced roll roofing	R905.5	ASTM D226 Type I or II ASTM D4869 Type I, II, III or IV	ASTM D226 Type II ASTM D4869 Type III or Type IV
Slate and slate-type shingles	R905.6	ASTM D226 Type I ASTM D4869 Type I, II, III or IV	ASTM D226 Type II ASTM D4869 Type III or Type IV
Wood shingles	R905.7	ASTM D226 Type I or II ASTM D4869 Type I, II, III or IV	ASTM D226 Type II ASTM D4869 Type III or Type IV
Wood shakes	R905.8	ASTM D226 Type I or II ASTM D4869 Type I, II, III or IV	ASTM D226 Type II ASTM D4869 Type III or Type IV
Metal panels	R905.10	Manufacturer's instructions	ASTM D226 Type II ASTM D4869 Type III or Type IV
Photovoltaic shingles	R905.16	ASTM D4869 Type I, II, III or IV ASTM D6757	ASTM D4869 Type III or Type IV ASTM D6757

For SI: 1 mile per hour = 0.447 m/s.

TABLE R905.1.1(2)
UNDERLAYMENT APPLICATION

ROOF COVERING	SECTION	MAXIMUM ULTIMATE DESIGN WIND SPEED, V_{ult} < 140 MPH	MAXIMUM ULTIMATE DESIGN WIND SPEED, V_{ult} ≥ 140 MPH
Asphalt shingles	R905.2	For roof slopes from two units vertical in 12 units horizontal (2:12), up to four units vertical in 12 units horizontal (4:12), underlayment shall be two layers applied in the following manner: apply a 19-inch strip of underlayment felt parallel to and starting at the eaves. Starting at the eave, apply 36-inch-wide sheets of underlayment, overlapping successive sheets 19 inches. Distortions in the underlayment shall not interfere with the ability of the shingles to seal. End laps shall be 4 inches and shall be offset by 6 feet. For roof slopes of four units vertical in 12 units horizontal (4:12) or greater, underlayment shall be one layer applied in the following manner: underlayment shall be applied shingle fashion, parallel to and starting from the eave and lapped 2 inches, Distortions in the underlayment shall not interfere with the ability of the shingles to seal. End laps shall be 4 inches and shall be offset by 6 feet.	Same as Maximum Ultimate Design Wind Speed, V_{ult} < 140 mph except all laps shall be not less than 4 inches.

(continued)

TABLE R905.1.1(2)—continued
UNDERLAYMENT APPLICATION

ROOF COVERING	SECTION	MAXIMUM ULTIMATE DESIGN WIND SPEED, $V_{ult} < 140$ MPH	MAXIMUM ULTIMATE DESIGN WIND SPEED, $V_{ult} \geq 140$ MPH
Clay and concrete tile	R905.3	For roof slopes from two and one-half units vertical in 12 units horizontal ($2^1/_2$:12), up to four units vertical in 12 units horizontal (4:12), underlayment shall be not fewer than two layers applied as follows: starting at the eave, apply a 19-inch strip of underlayment parallel with the eave. Starting at the eave, apply 36-inch-wide strips of underlayment felt, overlapping successive sheets 19 inches. End laps shall be 4 inches and shall be offset by 6 feet. For roof slopes of four units vertical in 12 units horizontal (4:12) or greater, underlayment shall be not fewer than one layer of underlayment felt applied shingle fashion, parallel to and starting from the eaves and lapped 2 inches. End laps shall be 4 inches and shall be offset by 6 feet.	Same as Maximum Ultimate Design Wind Speed, $V_{ult} < 140$ mph, except all laps shall be not less than 4 inches.
Metal roof shingles	R905.4	Apply in accordance with the manufacturer's installation instructions.	For roof slopes from two units vertical in 12 units horizontal (2:12), up to four units vertical in 12 units horizontal (4:12), underlayment shall be two layers applied in the following manner: apply a 19-inch strip of underlayment felt parallel to and starting at the eaves. Starting at the eave, apply 36-inch-wide sheets of underlayment, overlapping successive sheets 19 inches. End laps shall be 4 inches and shall be offset by 6 feet. For roof slopes of four units vertical in 12 units horizontal (4:12) or greater, underlayment shall be one layer applied in the following manner: underlayment shall be applied shingle fashion, parallel to and starting from the eave and lapped 4 inches. End laps shall be 4 inches and shall be offset by 6 feet.
Mineral-surfaced roll roofing	R905.5		
Slate and slate-type shingles	R905.6		
Wood shingles	R905.7		
Wood shakes	R905.8		
Metal panels	R905.10		
Photovoltaic shingles	R905.16	For roof slopes from two units vertical in 12 units horizontal (2:12), up to four units vertical in 12 units horizontal (4:12), underlayment shall be two layers applied in the following manner: apply a 19-inch strip of underlayment felt parallel to and starting at the eaves. Starting at the eave, apply 36-inch-wide sheets of underlayment, overlapping successive sheets 19 inches. Distortions in the underlayment shall not interfere with the ability of the shingles to seal. End laps shall be 4 inches and shall be offset by 6 feet. For roof slopes of four units vertical in 12 units horizontal (4:12) or greater, underlayment shall be one layer applied in the following manner: underlayment shall be applied shingle fashion, parallel to and starting from the eave and lapped 2 inches. Distortions in the underlayment shall not interfere with the ability of the shingles to seal. End laps shall be 4 inches and shall be offset by 6 feet.	Same as Maximum Ultimate Design Wind Speed, $V_{ult} < 140$ mph, except all laps shall be not less than 4 inches.

For SI: 1 inch = 25.4 mm, 1 foot = 304.8 mm, 1 mile per hour = 0.447 m/s.

TABLE R905.1.1(3)
UNDERLAYMENT ATTACHMENT

ROOF COVERING	SECTION	MAXIMUM ULTIMATE DESIGN WIND SPEED, V_{ult} < 140 MPH	MAXIMUM ULTIMATE DESIGN WIND SPEED, V_{ult} ≥ 140 MPH
Asphalt shingles	R905.2	Fastened sufficiently to hold in place	The underlayment shall be attached with corrosion-resistant fasteners in a grid pattern of 12 inches between side laps with a 6-inch spacing at side and end laps. Underlayment shall be attached using metal or plastic cap nails or cap staples with a nominal cap diameter of not less than 1 inch. Metal caps shall have a thickness of not less than 32-gage sheet metal. Power-driven metal caps shall have a minimum thickness of 0.010 inch. Minimum thickness of the outside edge of plastic caps shall be 0.035 inch. The cap nail shank shall be not less than 0.083 inch for ring shank cap nails and 0.091 inch for smooth shank cap nails. Staples shall be not less than 21 gage. Cap nail shank and cap staple legs shall have a length sufficient to penetrate through the roof sheathing or not less than $^3/_4$ inch into the roof sheathing.
Clay and concrete tile	R905.3		
Photovoltaic	R905.16		
Metal roof shingles	R905.4	Manufacturer's installation instructions.	The underlayment shall be attached with corrosion-resistant fasteners in a grid pattern of 12 inches between side laps with a 6-inch spacing at side and end laps. Underlayment shall be attached using metal or plastic cap nails or cap staples with a nominal cap diameter of not less than 1 inch. Metal caps shall have a thickness of not less than 32-gage sheet metal. Power-driven metal caps shall have a minimum thickness of 0.010 inch. Minimum thickness of the outside edge of plastic caps shall be 0.035 inch. The cap nail shank shall be not less than 0.083 inch for ring shank cap nails and 0.091 inch for smooth shank cap nails. Staples shall be not less than 21 gage. Cap nail shank and cap staple legs shall have a length sufficient to penetrate through the roof sheathing or not less than $^3/_4$ inch into the roof sheathing.
Mineral-surfaced roll roofing	R905.5		
Slate and slate-type shingles	R905.6		
Wood shingles	R905.7		
Wood shakes	R905.8		
Metal panels	R905.10		

For SI: 1 inch = 25.4 mm, 1 mile per hour = 0.447 m/s.

3.2. The *underlayment* shall be attached with corrosion-resistant fasteners in a grid pattern of 12 inches (305 mm) between side laps with a 6-inch (152 mm) spacing at side and end laps.

3.3. *Underlayment* shall be attached using metal or plastic cap nails with a nominal cap diameter of not less than 1 inch (25 mm). Metal caps shall have a thickness of not less than 32-gage sheet metal. Power-driven metal caps shall have a thickness of not less than 0.010 inch (0.25 mm). Minimum thickness of the outside edge of plastic caps shall be 0.035 inch (0.89 mm).

3.4. The cap nail shank shall be not less than 0.083 inch (2.11 mm) for ring shank cap nails and 0.091 inch (2.31 mm) for smooth shank cap nails. Cap nail shank shall have a length sufficient to penetrate through the roof sheathing or not less than $^3/_4$ inch (19 mm) into the roof sheathing.

R905.1.2 Ice barriers. In areas where there has been a history of ice forming along the eaves causing a backup of water as designated in Table R301.2(1), an ice barrier shall be installed for asphalt shingles, metal roof shingles, mineral-surfaced roll roofing, slate and slate-type shingles, wood shingles and wood shakes. The ice barrier shall consist of not fewer than two layers of *underlayment* cemented together, or a self-adhering polymer-modified bitumen sheet shall be used in place of normal *underlayment* and extend from the lowest edges of all roof surfaces to a point not less than 24 inches (610 mm) inside the exterior wall line of the building. On roofs with slope equal to or greater than eight units vertical in 12 units horizontal (67-percent slope), the ice barrier shall also be applied not less than 36 inches (914 mm) measured along the roof slope from the eave edge of the building.

Exception: Detached accessory structures not containing conditioned floor area.

R905.2 Asphalt shingles. The installation of asphalt shingles shall comply with the provisions of this section.

R905.2.1 Sheathing requirements. Asphalt shingles shall be fastened to solidly sheathed decks or 1-inch thick nominal wood boards.

R905.2.2 Slope. Asphalt shingles shall be used only on roof slopes of two units vertical in 12 units horizontal (17-percent slope) or greater. For roof slopes from two units vertical in 12 units horizontal (17-percent slope) up to four units vertical in 12 units horizontal (33-percent slope), double *underlayment* application is required in accordance with Section R905.1.1.

R905.2.3 Underlayment. *Underlayment* shall comply with Section R905.1.1.

R905.2.4 Asphalt shingles. Asphalt shingles shall comply with ASTM D3462.

R905.2.4.1 Wind resistance of asphalt shingles. Asphalt shingles shall be tested in accordance with ASTM D7158. Asphalt shingles shall meet the classification requirements of Table R905.2.4.1 for the appropriate ultimate design wind speed. Asphalt shingle packaging shall bear a label to indicate compliance with ASTM D7158 and the required classification in Table R905.2.4.1.

Exception: Asphalt shingles not included in the scope of ASTM D7158 shall be tested and labeled in accordance with ASTM D3161. Asphalt shingle packaging shall bear a label to indicate compliance with ASTM D3161 and the required classification in Table R905.2.4.1.

R905.2.5 Fasteners. Fasteners for asphalt shingles shall be galvanized steel, stainless steel, aluminum or copper roofing nails, minimum 12-gage [0.105 inch (3 mm)] shank with a minimum $^3/_8$-inch-diameter (9.5 mm) head, complying with ASTM F1667, of a length to penetrate through the roofing materials and not less than $^3/_4$ inch (19.1 mm) into the roof sheathing. Where the roof sheathing is less than $^3/_4$ inch (19.1 mm) thick, the fasteners shall penetrate through the sheathing.

TABLE R905.2.4.1
CLASSIFICATION OF ASPHALT ROOF SHINGLES

MAXIMUM ULTIMATE DESIGN WIND SPEED, V_{ult} FROM FIGURE R301.2(5)A (mph)	MAXIMUM BASIC WIND SPEED, V_{ASD} FROM TABLE R301.2.1.3 (mph)	ASTM D7158[a] SHINGLE CLASSIFICATION	ASTM D3161 SHINGLE CLASSIFICATION
110	85	D, G or H	A, D or F
116	90	D, G or H	A, D or F
129	100	G or H	A, D or F
142	110	G or H	F
155	120	G or H	F
168	130	H	F
181	140	H	F
194	150	H	F

For SI: 1 foot = 304.8 mm; 1 mile per hour = 0.447 m/s.

a. The standard calculations contained in ASTM D7158 assume Exposure Category B or C and a building height of 60 feet or less. Additional calculations are required for conditions outside of these assumptions.

R905.2.6 Attachment. Asphalt shingles shall have the minimum number of fasteners required by the manufacturer's *approved* installation instructions, but not less than four fasteners per strip shingle or two fasteners per individual shingle. Where the roof slope exceeds 21 units vertical in 12 units horizontal (21:12, 175-percent slope), shingles shall be installed in accordance with the manufacturer's *approved* installation instructions.

R905.2.7 Ice barrier. Where required, ice barriers shall comply with Section R905.1.2.

R905.2.8 Flashing. Flashing for asphalt shingles shall comply with this section and the asphalt shingle manufacturer's *approved* installation instructions.

R905.2.8.1 Base and cap flashing. Base and cap flashing shall be installed in accordance with manufacturer's instructions. Base flashing shall be of either corrosion-resistant metal of minimum nominal 0.019-inch (0.5 mm) thickness or mineral-surfaced roll roofing weighing not less than 77 pounds per 100 square feet (4 kg/m²). Cap flashing shall be corrosion-resistant metal of minimum nominal 0.019-inch (0.5 mm) thickness.

R905.2.8.2 Valleys. Valley linings shall be installed in accordance with the manufacturer's instructions before applying shingles. Valley linings of the following types shall be permitted:

1. For open valleys (valley lining exposed) lined with metal, the valley lining shall be not less than 24 inches (610 mm) wide and of any of the corrosion-resistant metals in Table R905.2.8.2.

2. For open valleys, valley lining of two plies of mineral-surfaced roll roofing, complying with ASTM D3909 or ASTM D6380 Class M, shall be permitted. The bottom layer shall be 18 inches (457 mm) and the top layer not less than 36 inches (914 mm) wide.

3. For closed valleys (valley covered with shingles), valley lining of one ply of smooth roll roofing complying with ASTM D6380 and not less than 36 inches wide (914 mm) or valley lining as described in Item 1 or 2 shall be permitted. Self-adhering polymer-modified bitumen *underlayment* complying with ASTM D1970 shall be permitted in lieu of the lining material.

R905.2.8.3 Sidewall flashing. Base flashing against a vertical sidewall shall be continuous or step flashing and shall be not less than 4 inches (102 mm) in height and 4 inches (102 mm) in width and shall direct water away from the vertical sidewall onto the roof or into the gutter. Where siding is provided on the vertical sidewall, the vertical leg of the flashing shall be continuous under the siding. Where anchored masonry veneer is provided on the vertical sidewall, the base flashing shall be provided in accordance with this section and counterflashing shall be provided in accordance with Section R703.8.2.2. Where exterior plaster or adhered masonry veneer is provided on the vertical sidewall, the base flashing shall be provided in accordance with this section and Section R703.6.3.

R905.2.8.4 Other flashing. Flashing against a vertical front wall, as well as soil stack, vent pipe and chimney flashing, shall be applied in accordance with the asphalt shingle manufacturer's printed instructions.

R905.2.8.5 Drip edge. Deleted.

R905.3 Clay and concrete tile. The installation of clay and concrete tile shall comply with the provisions of this section.

R905.3.1 Deck requirements. Concrete and clay tile shall be installed only over solid sheathing or spaced structural sheathing boards.

R905.3.2 Deck slope. Clay and concrete roof tile shall be installed on roof slopes of two and one-half units vertical in 12 units horizontal (25-percent slope) or greater. For roof slopes from two and one-half units vertical in 12 units horizontal (25-percent slope) to four units vertical in 12 units horizontal (33-percent slope), double *underlayment* application is required in accordance with Section R905.3.3.

R905.3.3 Underlayment. *Underlayment* shall comply with Section R905.1.1.

TABLE R905.2.8.2
VALLEY LINING MATERIAL

MATERIAL	MINIMUM THICKNESS (inches)	GAGE	WEIGHT (pounds)
Cold-rolled copper	0.0216 nominal	—	ASTM B370, 16 oz. per square foot
Lead-coated copper	0.0216 nominal	—	ASTM B101, 16 oz. per square foot
High-yield copper	0.0162 nominal	—	ASTM B370, 12 oz. per square foot
Lead-coated high-yield copper	0.0162 nominal	—	ASTM B101, 12 oz. per square foot
Aluminum	0.024	—	—
Stainless steel	—	28	—
Galvanized steel	0.0179	26 (zinc coated G90)	—
Zinc alloy	0.027	—	—
Lead	—	—	2¹/₂
Painted terne	—	—	20

For SI: 1 inch = 25.4 mm, 1 pound = 0.454 kg.

R905.3.4 Clay tile. Clay roof tile shall comply with ASTM C1167.

R905.3.5 Concrete tile. Concrete roof tile shall comply with ASTM C1492.

R905.3.6 Fasteners. Nails shall be corrosion resistant and not less than 11-gage, $^5/_{16}$-inch (11 mm) head, and of sufficient length to penetrate the deck not less than $^3/_4$ inch (19 mm) or through the thickness of the deck, whichever is less. Attaching wire for clay or concrete tile shall not be smaller than 0.083 inch (2 mm). Perimeter fastening areas include three tile courses but not less than 36 inches (914 mm) from either side of hips or ridges and edges of eaves and gable rakes.

R905.3.7 Application. Tile shall be applied in accordance with this chapter and the manufacturer's installation instructions, based on the following:

1. Climatic conditions.

2. Roof slope.

3. *Underlayment* system.

4. Type of tile being installed.

Clay and concrete roof tiles shall be fastened in accordance with this section and the manufacturer's installation instructions. Perimeter tiles shall be fastened with not less than one fastener per tile. Tiles with installed weight less than 9 pounds per square foot (0.4 kg/m^2) require not less than one fastener per tile regardless of roof slope. Clay and concrete roof tile attachment shall be in accordance with the manufacturer's installation instructions where applied in areas where the ultimate design wind speed exceeds 130 miles per hour (58 m/s) and on buildings where the roof is located more than 40 feet (12 192 mm) above grade. In areas subject to snow, not less than two fasteners per tile are required. In other areas, clay and concrete roof tiles shall be attached in accordance with Table R905.3.7.

TABLE R905.3.7
CLAY AND CONCRETE TILE ATTACHMENT

SHEATHING	ROOF SLOPE	NUMBER OF FASTENERS
Solid without battens	All	One per tile
Spaced or solid with battens and slope < 5:12	Fasteners not required	—
Spaced sheathing without battens	5:12 ≤ slope < 12:12	One per tile/every other row
	12:12 ≤ slope < 24:12	One per tile

R905.3.8 Flashing. At the juncture of roof vertical surfaces, flashing and counterflashing shall be provided in accordance with this chapter and the manufacturer's installation instructions and, where of metal, shall be not less than 0.019 inch (0.5 mm) (No. 26 galvanized sheet gage) corrosion-resistant metal. The valley flashing shall extend not less than 11 inches (279 mm) from the centerline each way and have a splash diverter rib not less than 1 inch (25 mm) in height at the flow line formed as part of the flashing. Sections of flashing shall have an end lap of not less than 4 inches (102 mm). For roof slopes of three units vertical in 12 units horizontal (25-percent slope) and greater, valley flashing shall have a 36-inch-wide (914 mm) *underlayment* of one layer of Type I *underlayment* running the full length of the valley, in addition to other required *underlayment*. In areas where the average daily temperature in January is 25°F (-4°C) or less, metal valley flashing *underlayment* shall be solid-cemented to the roofing *underlayment* for slopes less than seven units vertical in 12 units horizontal (58-percent slope) or be of self-adhering polymer-modified bitumen sheet.

R905.4 Metal roof shingles. The installation of metal roof shingles shall comply with the provisions of this section.

R905.4.1 Deck requirements. Metal roof shingles shall be applied to a solid or closely fitted deck, except where the roof covering is specifically designed to be applied to spaced sheathing.

R905.4.2 Deck slope. Metal roof shingles shall not be installed on roof slopes below three units vertical in 12 units horizontal (25-percent slope).

R905.4.3 Underlayment. *Underlayment* shall comply with Section R905.1.1.

R905.4.3.1 Ice barrier. Where required, ice barriers shall comply with Section R905.1.2.

R905.4.4 Material standards. Metal roof shingle roof coverings shall comply with Table R905.10.3(1). The materials used for metal roof shingle roof coverings shall be naturally corrosion resistant or be made corrosion resistant in accordance with the standards and minimum thicknesses listed in Table R905.10.3(2).

R905.4.5 Application. Metal roof shingles shall be secured to the roof in accordance with this chapter and the *approved* manufacturer's installation instructions.

R905.4.6 Flashing. Roof valley flashing shall be of corrosion-resistant metal of the same material as the roof covering or shall comply with the standards in Table R905.10.3(1). The valley flashing shall extend not less than 8 inches (203 mm) from the centerline each way and shall have a splash diverter rib not less than $^3/_4$ inch (19 mm) in height at the flow line formed as part of the flashing. Sections of flashing shall have an end lap of not less than 4 inches (102 mm). The metal valley flashing shall have a 36-inch-wide (914 mm) *underlayment* directly under it consisting of one layer of *underlayment* running the full length of the valley, in addition to *underlayment* required for metal roof shingles. In areas where the average daily temperature in January is 25°F (-4°C) or less, the metal valley flashing *underlayment* shall be solid-cemented to the roofing *underlayment* for roof slopes under seven units vertical in 12 units horizontal (58-percent slope) or self-adhering polymer-modified bitumen sheet.

R905.5 Mineral-surfaced roll roofing. The installation of mineral-surfaced roll roofing shall comply with this section.

R905.5.1 Deck requirements. Mineral-surfaced roll roofing shall be fastened to solidly sheathed roofs.

R905.5.2 Deck slope. Mineral-surfaced roll roofing shall not be applied on roof slopes below one unit vertical in 12 units horizontal (8-percent slope).

R905.5.3 Underlayment. *Underlayment* shall comply with Section R905.1.1.

R905.5.3.1 Ice barrier. Where required, ice barriers shall comply with Section R905.1.2.

R905.5.4 Material standards. Mineral-surfaced roll roofing shall conform to ASTM D3909 or ASTM D6380, Class M.

R905.5.5 Application. Mineral-surfaced roll roofing shall be installed in accordance with this chapter and the manufacturer's instructions.

R905.6 Slate shingles. The installation of slate shingles shall comply with the provisions of this section.

R905.6.1 Deck requirements. Slate shingles shall be fastened to solidly sheathed roofs.

R905.6.2 Deck slope. Slate shingles shall be used only on slopes of four units vertical in 12 units horizontal (33-percent slope) or greater.

R905.6.3 Underlayment. *Underlayment* shall comply with Section R905.1.1.

R905.6.3.1 Ice barrier. Where required, ice barriers shall comply with Section R905.1.2.

R905.6.4 Material standards. Slate shingles shall comply with ASTM C406.

R905.6.5 Application. Minimum headlap for slate shingles shall be in accordance with Table R905.6.5. Slate shingles shall be secured to the roof with two fasteners per slate. Slate shingles shall be installed in accordance with this chapter and the manufacturer's instructions.

TABLE R905.6.5
SLATE SHINGLE HEADLAP

SLOPE	HEADLAP (inches)
4:12 ≤ slope < 8:12	4
8:12 ≤ slope < 20:12	3
Slope ≥ 20:12	2

For SI: 1 inch = 25.4 mm.

R905.6.6 Flashing. Flashing and counterflashing shall be made with sheet metal. Valley flashing shall be not less than 15 inches (381 mm) wide. Valley and flashing metal shall be a minimum uncoated thickness of 0.0179-inch (0.5 mm) zinc coated G90. Chimneys, stucco or brick walls shall have not less than two plies of felt for a cap flashing consisting of a 4-inch-wide (102 mm) strip of felt set in plastic cement and extending 1 inch (25 mm) above the first felt and a top coating of plastic cement. The felt shall extend 2 inches (51 mm) over the base flashing.

R905.7 Wood shingles. The installation of wood shingles shall comply with the provisions of this section.

R905.7.1 Deck requirements. Wood shingles shall be installed on solid or spaced sheathing. Where spaced sheathing is used, sheathing boards shall be not less than 1-inch by 4-inch (25 mm by 102 mm) nominal dimensions and shall be spaced on centers equal to the weather exposure to coincide with the placement of fasteners.

R905.7.1.1 Solid sheathing required. In areas where the average daily temperature in January is 25°F (-4°C) or less, solid sheathing is required on that portion of the roof requiring the application of an ice barrier.

R905.7.2 Deck slope. Wood shingles shall be installed on slopes of three units vertical in 12 units horizontal (25-percent slope) or greater.

R905.7.3 Underlayment. *Underlayment* shall comply with Section R905.1.1.

R905.7.3.1 Ice barrier. Where required, ice barriers shall comply with Section R905.1.2.

R905.7.4 Material standards. Wood shingles shall be of naturally durable wood and comply with the requirements of Table R905.7.4.

TABLE R905.7.4
WOOD SHINGLE MATERIAL REQUIREMENTS

MATERIAL	MINIMUM GRADES	APPLICABLE GRADING RULES
Wood shingles of naturally durable wood	1, 2 or 3	CSSB

R905.7.5 Application. Wood shingles shall be installed in accordance with this chapter and the manufacturer's instructions. Wood shingles shall be laid with a side lap not less than $1^1/_2$ inches (38 mm) between joints in courses, and two joints shall not be in direct alignment in any three adjacent courses. Spacing between shingles shall be not less than $^1/_4$ inch to $^3/_8$ inch (6.4 mm to 9.5 mm). Weather exposure for wood shingles shall not exceed those set in Table R905.7.5(1). Fasteners for untreated (naturally durable) wood shingles shall be box nails in accordance with Table R905.7.5(2). Nails shall be stainless steel Type 304 or 316 or hot-dipped galvanized with a coating weight of ASTM A153 Class D (1.0 oz/ft²). Alternatively, two 16-gage stainless steel Type 304 or 316 staples with crown widths $^7/_{16}$ inch (11.1 mm) minimum, $^3/_4$ inch (19.1 mm) maximum, shall be used. Fasteners installed within 15 miles (24 km) of saltwater coastal areas shall be stainless steel Type 316. Fasteners for fire-retardant-treated shingles in accordance with Section R902 or pressure-impregnated-preservative-treated shingles of naturally durable wood in accordance with AWPA U1 shall be stainless steel Type 316. Fasteners shall have a minimum penetration into the sheathing of $^3/_4$ inch (19.1 mm). For sheathing less than $^3/_4$ inch in (19.1 mm) thickness, each fastener shall penetrate through the sheathing. Wood shingles shall be attached to the roof with two fasteners per shingle, positioned in accordance with the manufacturer's installation instructions. Fastener packaging shall bear a label indicating the appropriate grade material or coating weight.

TABLE R905.7.5(1)
WOOD SHINGLE WEATHER EXPOSURE AND ROOF SLOPE

ROOFING MATERIAL	LENGTH (inches)	GRADE	EXPOSURE (inches)	
			3:12 pitch to < 4:12	4:12 pitch or steeper
Shingles of naturally durable wood	16	No. 1	$3^3/_4$	5
		No. 2	$3^1/_2$	4
		No. 3	3	$3^1/_2$
	18	No. 1	$4^1/_4$	$5^1/_2$
		No. 2	4	$4^1/_2$
		No. 3	$3^1/_2$	4
	24	No. 1	$5^3/_4$	$7^1/_2$
		No. 2	$5^1/_2$	$6^1/_2$
		No. 3	5	$5^1/_2$

For SI: 1 inch = 25.4 mm.

TABLE R905.7.5(2)
NAIL REQUIREMENTS FOR WOOD SHAKES AND WOOD SHINGLES

SHAKES	NAIL TYPE AND MINIMUM LENGTH	MINIMUM HEAD SIZE	MINIMUM SHANK DIAMETER
18″ straight-split	5d box $1^3/_4$″	0.19″	.080″
18″ and 24″ handsplit and resawn	6d box 2″	0.19″	.0915″
24″ taper-split	5d box $1^3/_4$″	0.19″	.080″
18″ and 24″ tapersawn	6d box 2″	0.19″	.0915″
Shingles	**Nail Type and Minimum Length**	**Minimum Head Size**	**Minimum Shank Diameter**
16″ and 18″	3d box $1^1/_4$″	0.19″	.080″
24″	4d box $1^1/_2$″	0.19″	.080″

For SI: 1 inch = 25.4 mm.

R905.7.6 Valley flashing. Roof flashing shall be not less than No. 26 gage [0.019 inches (0.5 mm)] corrosion-resistant sheet metal and shall extend 10 inches (254 mm) from the centerline each way for roofs having slopes less than 12 units vertical in 12 units horizontal (100-percent slope), and 7 inches (178 mm) from the centerline each way for slopes of 12 units vertical in 12 units horizontal (100-percent slope) and greater. Sections of flashing shall have an end lap of not less than 4 inches (102 mm).

R905.7.7 Label required. Each bundle of shingles shall be identified by a *label* of an *approved* grading or inspection bureau or agency.

R905.8 Wood shakes. The installation of wood shakes shall comply with the provisions of this section.

R905.8.1 Deck requirements. Wood shakes shall be used only on solid or spaced sheathing. Where spaced sheathing is used, sheathing boards shall be not less than 1-inch by 4-inch (25 mm by 102 mm) nominal dimensions and shall be spaced on centers equal to the weather exposure to coincide with the placement of fasteners. Where 1-inch by 4-inch (25 mm by 102 mm) spaced sheathing is installed at 10 inches (254 mm) on center, additional 1-inch by 4-inch (25 mm by 102 mm) boards shall be installed between the sheathing boards.

R905.8.1.1 Solid sheathing required. In areas where the average daily temperature in January is 25°F (-4°C) or less, solid sheathing is required on that portion of the roof requiring an ice barrier.

R905.8.2 Deck slope. Wood shakes shall only be used on slopes of three units vertical in 12 units horizontal (25-percent slope) or greater.

R905.8.3 Underlayment. *Underlayment* shall comply with Section R905.1.1.

R905.8.3.1 Ice barrier. Where required, ice barriers shall comply with Section R905.1.2.

R905.8.4 Interlayment. Interlayment shall comply with ASTM D226, Type I.

R905.8.5 Material standards. Wood shakes shall comply with the requirements of Table R905.8.5.

TABLE R905.8.5
WOOD SHAKE MATERIAL REQUIREMENTS

MATERIAL	MINIMUM GRADES	APPLICABLE GRADING RULES
Wood shakes of naturally durable wood	1	Cedar Shake and Shingle Bureau
Tapersawn shakes of naturally durable wood	1 or 2	Cedar Shake and Shingle Bureau
Preservative-treated shakes and shingles of naturally durable wood	1	Cedar Shake and Shingle Bureau
Fire-retardant-treated shakes and shingles of naturally durable wood	1	Cedar Shake and Shingle Bureau
Preservative-treated tapersawn shakes of Southern pine treated in accordance with AWPA Standard U1 (Commodity Specification A, Special Requirement 4.6)	1 or 2	Forest Products Laboratory of the Texas Forest Services

R905.8.6 Application. Wood shakes shall be installed in accordance with this chapter and the manufacturer's installation instructions. Wood shakes shall be laid with a side lap not less than $1^1/_2$ inches (38 mm) between joints in adjacent courses. Spacing between shakes in the same course shall be $3/_8$ inch to $5/_8$ inch (9.5 mm to 15.9 mm) including tapersawn shakes. Weather exposures for wood shakes shall not exceed those set in Table R905.8.6. Fasteners for untreated (naturally durable) wood shakes shall be box nails in accordance with Table R905.7.5(2). Nails shall be stainless steel Type 304, or Type 316 or hot-dipped with a coating weight of ASTM A153 Class D (1.0 oz/ft²). Alternatively, two 16-gage Type 304 or Type 316 stainless steel staples, with crown widths $7/_{16}$ inch (11.1 mm) minimum, $3/_4$ inch (19.1 mm) maximum, shall be used. Fasteners installed within 15 miles (24 km) of salt-water coastal areas shall be stainless steel Type 316. Wood shakes shall be attached to the roof with two fasteners per shake positioned in accordance with the manufacturer's installation instructions Fasteners for fire-retardant-treated (as defined in Section R902) shakes or pressure-impregnated-preservative-treated shakes of naturally durable wood in accordance with AWPA U1 shall be stainless steel Type 316. Fasteners shall have a minimum penetra-

TABLE R905.8.6
WOOD SHAKE WEATHER EXPOSURE AND ROOF SLOPE

ROOFING MATERIAL	LENGTH (inches)	GRADE	EXPOSURE (inches) 4:12 pitch or steeper
Shakes of naturally durable wood	18	No. 1	$7^1/_2$
	24	No. 1	10^a
Preservative-treated tapersawn shakes of Southern Yellow Pine	18	No. 1	$7^1/_2$
	24	No. 1	10
	18	No. 2	$5^1/_2$
	24	No. 2	$7^1/_2$
Taper-sawn shakes of naturally durable wood	18	No. 1	$7^1/_2$
	24	No. 1	10
	18	No. 2	$5^1/_2$
	24	No. 2	$7^1/_2$

For SI: 1 inch = 25.4 mm.

a. For 24-inch by $^3/_8$-inch handsplit shakes, the maximum exposure is $7^1/_2$ inches.

tion into the sheathing of $^3/_4$ inch (19.1 mm). Where the sheathing is less than $^3/_4$ inch (19.1 mm) thick, each fastener shall penetrate through the sheathing. Fastener packaging shall bear a label indicating the appropriate grade material or coating weight.

R905.8.7 Shake placement. The starter course at the eaves shall be doubled and the bottom layer shall be either 15-inch (381 mm), 18-inch (457 mm) or 24-inch (610 mm) wood shakes or wood shingles. Fifteen-inch (381 mm) or 18-inch (457 mm) wood shakes shall be permitted to be used for the final course at the ridge. Shakes shall be interlaid with 18-inch-wide (457 mm) strips of not less than No. 30 felt shingled between each course in such a manner that felt is not exposed to the weather by positioning the lower edge of each felt strip above the butt end of the shake it covers a distance equal to twice the weather exposure.

R905.8.8 Valley flashing. Roof valley flashing shall be not less than No. 26 gage [0.019 inch (0.5 mm)] corrosion-resistant sheet metal and shall extend not less than 11 inches (279 mm) from the centerline each way. Sections of flashing shall have an end lap of not less than 4 inches (102 mm).

R905.8.9 Label required. Each bundle of shakes shall be identified by a *label* of an *approved* grading or inspection bureau or agency.

R905.9 Built-up roofs. The installation of built-up roofs shall comply with the provisions of this section and the manufacturer's *approved* installation instructions.

R905.9.1 Slope. Built-up roofs shall have a design slope of not less than one-fourth unit vertical in 12 units horizontal (2-percent slope) for drainage, except for coal-tar built-up roofs, which shall have a design slope of a minimum one-eighth unit vertical in 12 units horizontal (1-percent slope).

R905.9.2 Material standards. Built-up roof covering materials shall comply with the standards in Table R905.9.2 or UL 55A.

R905.9.3 Application. Built-up roofs shall be installed in accordance with this chapter and the manufacturer's instructions.

R905.10 Metal roof panels. The installation of metal roof panels shall comply with the provisions of this section.

R905.10.1 Deck requirements. Metal roof panel roof coverings shall be applied to solid or spaced sheathing, except where the roof covering is specifically designed to be applied to spaced supports.

R905.10.2 Slope. Minimum slopes for metal roof panels shall comply with the following:

1. The minimum slope for lapped, nonsoldered-seam metal roofs without applied lap sealant shall be three units vertical in 12 units horizontal (25-percent slope).

2. The minimum slope for lapped, nonsoldered-seam metal roofs with applied lap sealant shall be one-half unit vertical in 12 units horizontal (4-percent slope). Lap sealants shall be applied in accordance with the *approved* manufacturer's installation instructions.

3. The minimum slope for standing-seam roof systems shall be one-quarter unit vertical in 12 units horizontal (2-percent slope).

R905.10.3 Material standards. Metal-sheet roof covering systems that incorporate supporting structural members shall be designed in accordance with the *International Building Code.* Metal-sheet roof coverings installed over structural decking shall comply with Table R905.10.3(1). The materials used for metal-sheet roof coverings shall be naturally corrosion resistant or provided with corrosion resistance in accordance with the standards and minimum thicknesses shown in Table R905.10.3(2).

TABLE R905.9.2
BUILT-UP ROOFING MATERIAL STANDARDS

MATERIAL STANDARD	STANDARD
Acrylic coatings used in roofing	ASTM D6083
Aggregate surfacing	ASTM D1863
Asphalt adhesive used in roofing	ASTM D3747
Asphalt cements used in roofing	ASTM D2822; D3019; D4586
Asphalt-coated glass fiber base sheet	ASTM D4601
Asphalt coatings used in roofing	ASTM D1227; D2823; D2824; D4479
Asphalt glass felt	ASTM D2178
Asphalt primer used in roofing	ASTM D41
Asphalt-saturated and asphalt-coated organic felt base sheet	ASTM D2626
Asphalt-saturated organic felt (perforated)	ASTM D226
Asphalt used in roofing	ASTM D312
Coal-tar cements used in roofing	ASTM D4022; D5643
Coal-tar primer used in roofing, dampproofing and waterproofing	ASTM D43
Coal-tar saturated organic felt	ASTM D227
Coal-tar used in roofing	ASTM D450, Type I or II
Glass mat, coal tar	ASTM D4990
Glass mat, venting type	ASTM D4897
Mineral-surfaced inorganic cap sheet	ASTM D3909
Thermoplastic fabrics used in roofing	ASTM D5665; D5726

TABLE R905.10.3(1)
METAL ROOF COVERING STANDARDS

ROOF COVERING TYPE	STANDARD APPLICATION RATE/THICKNESS
Galvanized steel	ASTM A653 G90 Zinc coated
Stainless steel	ASTM A240, 300 Series alloys
Steel	ASTM A924
Lead-coated copper	ASTM B101
Cold-rolled copper	ASTM B370 minimum 16 oz/sq ft and 12 oz/sq ft high-yield copper for metal-sheet roof-covering systems; 12 oz/sq ft for preformed metal shingle systems.
Hard lead	2 lb/sq ft
Soft lead	3 lb/sq ft
Aluminum	ASTM B209, 0.024 minimum thickness for roll-formed panels and 0.019-inch minimum thickness for press-formed shingles.
Terne (tin) and terne-coated stainless	Terne coating of 40 lb per double base box, field painted where applicable in accordance with manufacturer's installation instructions.
Zinc	0.027 inch minimum thickness: 99.995% electrolytic high-grade zinc with alloy additives of copper (0.08 - 0.20%), titanium (0.07% - 0.12%) and aluminum (0.015%).

For SI: 1 ounce per square foot = 0.305 kg/m^2, 1 pound per square foot = 4.214 kg/m^2, 1 inch = 25.4 mm, 1 pound = 0.454 kg.

TABLE R905.10.3(2)
MINIMUM CORROSION RESISTANCE

55% aluminum-zinc-alloy-coated steel	ASTM A792 AZ 50
5% aluminum alloy-coated steel	ASTM A875 GF60
Aluminum-coated steel	ASTM A463 T2 65
Galvanized steel	ASTM A653 G-90
Prepainted steel	ASTM A755[a]

a. Paint systems in accordance with ASTM A755 shall be applied over steel products with corrosion-resistant coatings complying with ASTM A792, ASTM A875, ASTM A463, or ASTM A653.

R905.10.4 Attachment. Metal roof panels shall be secured to the supports in accordance with this chapter and the manufacturer's installation instructions. In the absence of manufacturer's installation instructions, the following fasteners shall be used:

1. Galvanized fasteners shall be used for steel roofs.

2. Copper, brass, bronze, copper alloy and 300-series stainless steel fasteners shall be used for copper roofs.

3. Stainless steel fasteners are acceptable for metal roofs.

R905.10.5 Underlayment. *Underlayment* shall comply with Section R905.1.1.

R905.11 Modified bitumen roofing. The installation of modified bitumen roofing shall comply with the provisions of this section and the manufacturer's *approved* installation instructions.

R905.11.1 Slope. Modified bitumen roofing shall have a design slope of not less than one-fourth unit vertical in 12 units horizontal (2-percent slope) for drainage.

R905.11.2 Material standards. Modified bitumen roofing shall comply with the standards in Table R905.11.2.

TABLE R905.11.2
MODIFIED BITUMEN ROOFING MATERIAL STANDARDS

MATERIAL	STANDARD
Acrylic coating	ASTM D6083
Asphalt adhesive	ASTM D3747
Asphalt cement	ASTM D3019
Asphalt coating	ASTM D1227; D2824
Asphalt primer	ASTM D41
Modified bitumen roof membrane	ASTM D6162; D6163; D6164; D6222; D6223; D6298

R905.11.2.1 Base sheet. A base sheet that complies with the requirements of Section 1507.11.2 of the *International Building Code*, ASTM D1970, or ASTM D4601 shall be permitted to be used with a modified bitumen cap sheet.

R905.11.3 Application. Modified bitumen roofs shall be installed in accordance with this chapter and the manufacturer's instructions.

R905.12 Thermoset single-ply roofing. The installation of thermoset single-ply roofing shall comply with the provisions of this section.

R905.12.1 Slope. Thermoset single-ply membrane roofs shall have a design slope of not less than one-fourth unit vertical in 12 units horizontal (2-percent slope) for drainage.

R905.12.2 Material standards. Thermoset single-ply roof coverings shall comply with ASTM D4637 or ASTM D5019.

R905.12.3 Application. Thermoset single-ply roofs shall be installed in accordance with this chapter and the manufacturer's instructions.

R905.13 Thermoplastic single-ply roofing. The installation of thermoplastic single-ply roofing shall comply with the provisions of this section.

R905.13.1 Slope. Thermoplastic single-ply membrane roofs shall have a design slope of not less than one-fourth unit vertical in 12 units horizontal (2-percent slope).

R905.13.2 Material standards. Thermoplastic single-ply roof coverings shall comply with ASTM D4434, ASTM D6754 or ASTM D6878.

R905.13.3 Application. Thermoplastic single-ply roofs shall be installed in accordance with this chapter and the manufacturer's instructions.

R905.14 Sprayed polyurethane foam roofing. The installation of sprayed polyurethane foam roofing shall comply with the provisions of this section.

R905.14.1 Slope. Sprayed polyurethane foam roofs shall have a design slope of not less than one-fourth unit vertical in 12 units horizontal (2-percent slope) for drainage.

R905.14.2 Material standards. Spray-applied polyurethane foam insulation shall comply with ASTM C1029, Type III or IV or ASTM D7425.

R905.14.3 Application. Foamed-in-place roof insulation shall be installed in accordance with this chapter and the manufacturer's instructions. A liquid-applied protective coating that complies with Table R905.14.3 shall be applied not less than 2 hours nor more than 72 hours following the application of the foam.

TABLE R905.14.3
PROTECTIVE COATING MATERIAL STANDARDS

MATERIAL	STANDARD
Acrylic coating	ASTM D6083
Silicone coating	ASTM D6694
Moisture-cured polyurethane coating	ASTM D6947

R905.14.4 Foam plastics. Foam plastic materials and installation shall comply with Section R316.

R905.15 Liquid-applied roofing. The installation of liquid-applied roofing shall comply with the provisions of this section.

R905.15.1 Slope. Liquid-applied roofing shall have a design slope of not less than one-fourth unit vertical in 12 units horizontal (2-percent slope).

R905.15.2 Material standards. Liquid-applied roofing shall comply with ASTM C836, C957, D1227, D3468, D6083, D6694 or D6947.

R905.15.3 Application. Liquid-applied roofing shall be installed in accordance with this chapter and the manufacturer's installation instructions.

R905.16 Photovoltaic shingles. The installation of *photovoltaic shingles* shall comply with the provisions of this section, Section R324 and NFPA 70.

R905.16.1 Deck requirements. *Photovoltaic shingles* shall be applied to a solid or closely-fitted deck, except where the roof covering is specifically designed to be applied over spaced sheathing.

R905.16.2 Deck slope. *Photovoltaic shingles* shall be used only on roof slopes of two units vertical in 12 units horizontal (2:12) or greater.

R905.16.3 Underlayment. *Underlayment* shall comply with Section R905.1.1.

R905.16.3.1 Ice barrier. Where required, ice barriers shall comply with Section R905.1.2.

R905.16.4 Material standards. *Photovoltaic shingles* shall be listed and labeled in accordance with UL 1703.

R905.16.5 Attachment. *Photovoltaic shingles* shall be attached in accordance with the manufacturer's installation instructions.

R905.16.6 Wind resistance. *Photovoltaic shingles* shall be tested in accordance with procedures and acceptance criteria in ASTM D3161. *Photovoltaic shingles* shall comply with the classification requirements of Table R905.2.4.1 for the appropriate maximum basic wind speed. *Photovoltaic shingle* packaging shall bear a label to indicate compliance with the procedures in ASTM D3161 and the required classification from Table R905.2.4.1.

R905.17 Building-integrated Photovoltaic (BIPV) roof panels applied directly to the roof deck. The installation of *BIPV roof panels* shall comply with the provisions of this section, Section R324 and NFPA 70.

R905.17.1 Deck requirements. *BIPV roof panels* shall be applied to a solid or closely-fitted deck, except where the roof covering is specifically designed to be applied over spaced sheathing.

R905.17.2 Deck slope. *BIPV roof panels* shall be used only on roof slopes of two units vertical in 12 units horizontal (17-percent slope) or greater.

R905.17.3 Underlayment. *Underlayment* shall comply with Section 905.1.1.

R905.17.3.1 Ice barrier. Where required, an ice barrier shall comply with Section R905.1.2.

R905.17.4 Ice barrier. In areas where there has been a history of ice forming along the eaves causing a backup of water, as designated in Table R301.2(1), an ice barrier that consists of not less than two layers of *underlayment* cemented together or of a self-adhering polymer-modified bitumen sheet shall be used in lieu of normal *underlayment* and extend from the lowest edges of all roof surfaces to a point not less than 24 inches (610 mm) inside the exterior wall line of the building.

Exception: Detached accessory structures that do not contain conditioned floor area.

R905.17.5 Material standards. *BIPV roof panels* shall be *listed* and *labeled* in accordance with UL 1703.

R905.17.6 Attachment. *BIPV roof panels* shall be attached in accordance with the manufacturer's installation instructions.

R905.17.7 Wind resistance. *BIPV roof panels* shall be tested in accordance with UL 1897. *BIPV roof panel* packaging shall bear a *label* to indicate compliance with UL 1897.

SECTION R906
ROOF INSULATION

R906.1 General. The use of above-deck thermal insulation shall be permitted provided that such insulation is covered with an *approved* roof covering and complies with FM 4450 or UL 1256.

R906.2 Material standards. Above-deck thermal insulation board shall comply with the standards in Table R906.2.

TABLE R906.2
MATERIAL STANDARDS FOR ROOF INSULATION

Cellular glass board	ASTM C552
Composite boards	ASTM C1289, Type III, IV, V or VI
Expanded polystyrene	ASTM C578
Extruded polystyrene board	ASTM C578
Fiber-reinforced gypsum board	ASTM C1278
Glass-faced gypsum board	ASTM C1177
Mineral wool board	ASTM C726
Perlite board	ASTM C728
Polyisocyanurate board	ASTM C1289, Type I or II
Wood fiberboard	ASTM C208

SECTION R907
ROOFTOP-MOUNTED
PHOTOVOLTAIC PANEL SYSTEMS

R907.1 Rooftop-mounted photovoltaic panel systems. Rooftop-mounted *photovoltaic panel systems* shall be designed and installed in accordance with Section R324 and NFPA 70.

SECTION R908
REROOFING

R908.1 General. Materials and methods of application used for re-covering or replacing an existing roof covering shall comply with the requirements of Chapter 9.

Exceptions:

1. Reroofing shall not be required to meet the minimum design slope requirement of one-quarter unit vertical in 12 units horizontal (2-percent slope) in Section R905 for roofs that provide positive roof drainage.

2. For roofs that provide positive drainage, re-covering or replacing an existing roof covering shall not require the secondary (emergency overflow) drains or scuppers of Section R903.4.1 to be added to an existing roof.

R908.2 Structural and construction loads. The structural roof components shall be capable of supporting the roof covering system and the material and equipment loads that will be encountered during installation of the roof covering system.

R908.3 Roof replacement. Roof replacement shall include the removal of existing layers of roof coverings down to the roof deck.

Exception: Where the existing *roof assembly* includes an ice barrier membrane that is adhered to the roof deck, the existing ice barrier membrane shall be permitted to remain in place and covered with an additional layer of ice barrier membrane in accordance with Section R905.

R908.3.1 Roof recover. The installation of a new roof covering over an existing roof covering shall be permitted where any of the following conditions occur:

1. Where the new roof covering is installed in accordance with the roof covering manufacturer's approved instructions

2. Complete and separate roofing systems, such as standing-seam metal roof systems, that are designed to transmit the roof loads directly to the building's structural system and do not rely on existing roofs and roof coverings for support, shall not require the removal of existing roof coverings.

3. Metal panel, metal shingle and concrete and clay tile roof coverings shall be permitted to be installed over existing wood shake roofs where applied in accordance with Section R908.4.

4. The application of a new protective *roof coating* over an existing protective *roof coating*, metal roof panel, metal roof shingle, mineral surfaced roll roofing, built-up roof, modified bitumen roofing, thermoset and thermoplastic single-ply roofing and spray polyurethane foam roofing system shall be permitted without tear-off of existing roof coverings.

R908.3.1.1 Roof recover not allowed. A *roof recover* shall not be permitted where any of the following conditions occur:

1. Where the existing roof or roof covering is water soaked or has deteriorated to the point that the existing roof or roof covering is not adequate as a base for additional roofing.

2. Where the existing roof covering is slate, clay, cement or asbestos-cement tile.

3. Where the existing roof has two or more applications of any type of roof covering.

R908.4 Roof recovering. Where the application of a new roof covering over wood shingle or shake roofs creates a combustible concealed space, the entire existing surface shall be covered with gypsum board, mineral fiber, glass fiber or other *approved* materials securely fastened in place.

R908.5 Reinstallation of materials. Existing slate, clay or cement tile shall be permitted for reinstallation, except that damaged, cracked or broken slate or tile shall not be reinstalled. Any existing flashings, edgings, outlets, vents or similar devices that are a part of the assembly shall be replaced where rusted, damaged or deteriorated. Aggregate surfacing materials shall not be reinstalled.

R908.6 Flashings. Flashings shall be reconstructed in accordance with *approved* manufacturer's installation instructions. Metal flashing to which bituminous materials are to be adhered shall be primed prior to installation.

CHAPTER 10

CHIMNEYS AND FIREPLACES

User note:

About this chapter: Chapter 10 contains requirements for the construction, seismic reinforcing and anchorage of masonry chimneys and fireplaces; and establishes standards for the use and installation of factory-built chimneys, fireplaces and masonry heaters. Chimneys and fireplaces constructed of masonry rely on prescriptive requirements for the details of their construction; factory-built versions rely on the listing and labeling method of approval.

SECTION R1001
MASONRY FIREPLACES

R1001.1 General. Masonry fireplaces shall be constructed in accordance with this section and the applicable provisions of Chapters 3 and 4.

R1001.2 Footings and foundations. Footings for masonry fireplaces and their chimneys shall be constructed of concrete or *solid masonry* not less than 12 inches (305 mm) thick and shall extend not less than 6 inches (152 mm) beyond the face of the fireplace or foundation wall on all sides. Footings shall be founded on natural, undisturbed earth or engineered fill below frost depth. In areas not subjected to freezing, footings shall be not less than 12 inches (305 mm) below finished *grade*.

R1001.2.1 Ash dump cleanout. Cleanout openings located within foundation walls below fireboxes, where provided, shall be equipped with ferrous metal or masonry doors and frames constructed to remain tightly closed except when in use. Cleanouts shall be located to allow *access* so that ash removal will not create a hazard to combustible materials.

R1001.3 Seismic reinforcing. Masonry or concrete chimneys in Seismic Design Category D_0, D_1 or D_2 shall be reinforced. Reinforcing shall conform to the requirements set forth in Table R1001.1 and Section R606.

R1001.3.1 Vertical reinforcing. For chimneys up to 40 inches (1016 mm) wide, four No. 4 continuous vertical bars shall be placed between wythes of *solid masonry* or within the cells of hollow unit masonry and grouted in accordance with Section R606. Grout shall be prevented from bonding with the flue liner so that the flue liner is free to move with thermal expansion. For chimneys more than 40 inches (1016 mm) wide, two additional No. 4 vertical bars shall be provided for each additional flue incorporated into the chimney or for each additional 40 inches (1016 mm) in width or fraction thereof.

R1001.3.2 Horizontal reinforcing. Vertical reinforcement shall be placed within $^1/_4$-inch (6.4 mm) ties, or other reinforcing of equivalent net cross-sectional area, placed in the bed joints in accordance with Section R606 at not less than every 18 inches (457 mm) of vertical height. Two such ties shall be installed at each bend in the vertical bars.

R1001.4 Seismic anchorage. Masonry or concrete chimneys in Seismic Design Category D_0, D_1 or D_2 shall be anchored at each floor, ceiling or roof line more than 6 feet (1829 mm) above *grade*, except where constructed completely within the exterior walls. Anchorage shall conform to the requirements of Section R1001.4.1.

R1001.4.1 Anchorage. Two $^3/_{16}$-inch by 1-inch (5 mm by 25 mm) straps shall be embedded not less than 12 inches (305 mm) into the chimney. Straps shall be hooked around the outer bars and extend 6 inches (152 mm) beyond the bend. Each strap shall be fastened to not less than four floor ceiling or floor joists or rafters with two $^1/_2$-inch (12.7 mm) bolts.

R1001.4.1.1 Cold-formed steel framing. Where cold-formed steel framing is used, the location where the $^1/_2$-inch (12.7 mm) bolts are used to attach the straps to the framing shall be reinforced with not less than a 3-inch × 3-inch × 0.229-inch (76 mm × 76 mm × 5.8 mm) steel plate on top of the strap that is screwed to the framing with not fewer than seven No. 6 screws for each bolt.

R1001.5 Firebox walls. Masonry fireboxes shall be constructed of *solid masonry* units, hollow masonry units grouted solid, stone or concrete. Where a lining of firebrick not less than 2 inches (51 mm) thick or other *approved* lining is provided, the minimum thickness of back and sidewalls shall each be 8 inches (203 mm) of *solid masonry*, including the lining. The width of joints between firebricks shall not be greater than $^1/_4$ inch (6.4 mm). Where a lining is not provided, the total minimum thickness of back and side walls shall be 10 inches (254 mm) of *solid masonry*. Firebrick shall conform to ASTM C27 or C1261 and shall be laid with medium-duty refractory mortar conforming to ASTM C199.

R1001.5.1 Steel fireplace units. Installation of steel fireplace units with *solid masonry* to form a masonry fireplace is permitted where installed either in accordance with the requirements of their listing or the requirements of this section. Steel fireplace units incorporating a steel firebox lining shall be constructed with steel not less than $^1/_4$ inch (6.4 mm) thick, and an air-circulating chamber that is ducted to the interior of the building. The firebox lining shall be encased with *solid masonry* to provide a total thickness at the back and sides of not less than 8 inches (203 mm), of which not less than 4 inches (102 mm) shall be of *solid masonry* or concrete. Circulating air ducts used with steel fireplace units shall be constructed of metal or masonry.

TABLE R1001.1
SUMMARY OF REQUIREMENTS FOR MASONRY FIREPLACES AND CHIMNEYS

ITEM	LETTER[a]	REQUIREMENTS
Hearth slab thickness	A	4″
Hearth extension (each side of opening)	B	8″ fireplace opening < 6 square feet. 12″ fireplace opening ≥ 6 square feet.
Hearth extension (front of opening)	C	16″ fireplace opening < 6 square feet. 20″ fireplace opening ≥ 6 square feet.
Hearth slab reinforcing	D	Reinforced to carry its own weight and all imposed loads.
Thickness of wall of firebox	E	10″ solid brick or 8″ where a firebrick lining is used. Joints in firebrick $\frac{1}{4}$″ maximum.
Distance from top of opening to throat	F	8″
Smoke chamber wall thickness Unlined walls	G	6″ 8″
Chimney Vertical reinforcing[b]	H	Four No. 4 full-length bars for chimney up to 40″ wide. Add two No. 4 bars for each additional 40″ or fraction of width or each additional flue.
Horizontal reinforcing	J	$\frac{1}{4}$″ ties at 18″ and two ties at each bend in vertical steel.
Bond beams	K	No specified requirements.
Fireplace lintel	L	Noncombustible material.
Chimney walls with flue lining	M	Solid masonry units or hollow masonry units grouted solid with not less than 4-inch nominal thickness.
Distances between adjacent flues	—	See Section R1003.13.
Effective flue area (based on area of fireplace opening)	P	See Section R1003.15.
Clearances Combustible material Mantel and trim Above roof	R	See Sections R1001.11 and R1003.18. See Section R1001.11, Exception 4. 3′ at roofline and 2′ at 10′.
Anchorage[b] Strap Number Embedment into chimney Fasten to Bolts	S	$\frac{3}{16}$″ × 1″ Two 12″ hooked around outer bar with 6″ extension. 4 joists Two $\frac{1}{2}$″ diameter.
Footing Thickness Width	T	12″ min. 6″ each side of fireplace wall.

For SI: 1 inch = 25.4 mm, 1 foot = 304.8 mm, 1 square foot = 0.0929 m².

Note: This table provides a summary of major requirements for the construction of masonry chimneys and fireplaces. Letter references are to Figure R1001.1, which shows examples of typical construction. This table does not cover all requirements, nor does it cover all aspects of the indicated requirements. For the actual mandatory requirements of the code, see the indicated section of text.

a. The letters refer to Figure R1001.1.

b. Not required in Seismic Design Category A, B or C.

R1001.6 Firebox dimensions. The firebox of a concrete or masonry fireplace shall have a depth of not less than 20 inches (508 mm). The throat shall be not less than 8 inches (203 mm) above the fireplace opening. The throat opening shall be not less than 4 inches (102 mm) deep. The cross-sectional area of the passageway above the firebox, including the throat, damper and smoke chamber, shall be not less than the cross-sectional area of the flue.

Exception: Rumford fireplaces shall be permitted provided that the depth of the fireplace is not less than 12 inches (305 mm) and not less than one-third of the width of the fireplace opening, that the throat is not less than 12 inches (305 mm) above the lintel and is not less than one-twentieth the cross-sectional area of the fireplace opening.

R1001.7 Lintel and throat. Masonry over a fireplace opening shall be supported by a lintel of noncombustible material. The minimum required bearing length on each end of the fireplace opening shall be 4 inches (102 mm). The fireplace throat or damper shall be located not less than 8 inches (203 mm) above the lintel.

R1001.7.1 Damper. Masonry fireplaces shall be equipped with a ferrous metal damper located not less than 8 inches (203 mm) above the top of the fireplace opening. Dampers shall be installed in the fireplace or the chimney venting the fireplace, and shall be operable from the room containing the fireplace.

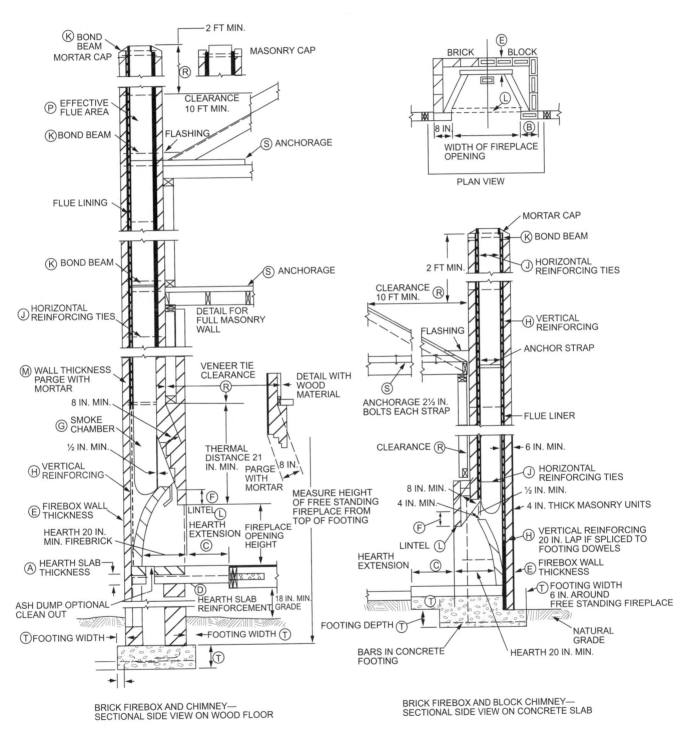

For SI: 1 inch = 25.4 mm, 1 foot = 304.8 mm.

FIGURE R1001.1
FIREPLACE AND CHIMNEY DETAILS

R1001.8 Smoke chamber. Smoke chamber walls shall be constructed of *solid masonry* units, hollow masonry units grouted solid, stone or concrete. The total minimum thickness of front, back and side walls shall be 8 inches (203 mm) of *solid masonry*. The inside surface shall be parged smooth with refractory mortar conforming to ASTM C199. Where a lining of firebrick not less than 2 inches (51 mm) thick, or a lining of vitrified clay not less than $\frac{5}{8}$ inch (16 mm) thick, is provided, the total minimum thickness of front, back and side walls shall be 6 inches (152 mm) of *solid masonry*, including the lining. Firebrick shall conform to ASTM C1261 and shall be laid with medium-duty refractory mortar conforming to ASTM C199. Vitrified clay linings shall conform to ASTM C315.

R1001.8.1 Smoke chamber dimensions. The inside height of the smoke chamber from the fireplace throat to the beginning of the flue shall not be greater than the inside width of the fireplace opening. The inside surface of the smoke chamber shall not be inclined more than 45 degrees (0.79 rad) from vertical where prefabricated smoke chamber linings are used or where the smoke chamber walls are rolled or sloped rather than corbeled. Where the inside surface of the smoke chamber is formed by corbeled masonry, the walls shall not be corbeled more than 30 degrees (0.52 rad) from vertical.

R1001.9 Hearth and hearth extension. Masonry fireplace hearths and hearth extensions shall be constructed of concrete or masonry, supported by noncombustible materials, and reinforced to carry their own weight and all imposed loads. Combustible material shall not remain against the underside of hearths and hearth extensions after construction.

R1001.9.1 Hearth thickness. The minimum thickness of fireplace hearths shall be 4 inches (102 mm).

R1001.9.2 Hearth extension thickness. The minimum thickness of hearth extensions shall be 2 inches (51 mm).

Exception: Where the bottom of the firebox opening is raised not less than 8 inches (203 mm) above the top of the hearth extension, a hearth extension of not less than $\frac{3}{8}$-inch-thick (10 mm) brick, concrete, stone, tile or other *approved* noncombustible material is permitted.

R1001.10 Hearth extension dimensions. Hearth extensions shall extend not less than 16 inches (406 mm) in front of and not less than 8 inches (203 mm) beyond each side of the fireplace opening. Where the fireplace opening is 6 square feet (0.6 m²) or larger, the hearth extension shall extend not less than 20 inches (508 mm) in front of and not less than 12 inches (305 mm) beyond each side of the fireplace opening.

R1001.11 Fireplace clearance. Wood beams, joists, studs and other combustible material shall have a clearance of not less than 2 inches (51 mm) from the front faces and sides of masonry fireplaces and not less than 4 inches (102 mm) from the back faces of masonry fireplaces. The airspace shall not be filled, except to provide fireblocking in accordance with Section R1001.12.

Exceptions:

1. Masonry fireplaces *listed* and *labeled* for use in contact with combustibles in accordance with UL 127 and installed in accordance with the manufacturer's instructions are permitted to have combustible material in contact with their exterior surfaces.

2. Where masonry fireplaces are part of masonry or concrete walls, combustible materials shall not be in contact with the masonry or concrete walls less than 12 inches (306 mm) from the inside surface of the nearest firebox lining.

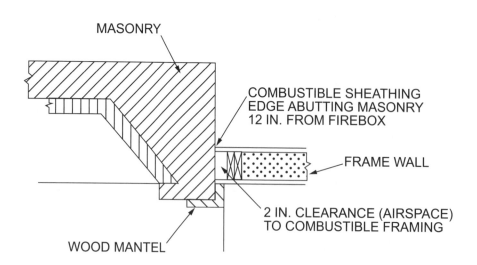

For SI: 1 inch = 25.4 mm.

FIGURE R1001.11
CLEARANCE FROM COMBUSTIBLES

3. Exposed combustible trim and the edges of sheathing materials such as wood siding, flooring and gypsum board shall be permitted to abut the masonry fireplace sidewalls and hearth extension in accordance with Figure R1001.11, provided such combustible trim or sheathing is not less than 12 inches (305 mm) from the inside surface of the nearest firebox lining.

4. Exposed combustible mantels or trim is permitted to be placed directly on the masonry fireplace front surrounding the fireplace opening providing such combustible materials are not placed within 6 inches (152 mm) of a fireplace opening. Combustible material within 12 inches (306 mm) of the fireplace opening shall not project more than $^1/_8$ inch (3 mm) for each 1-inch (25 mm) distance from such an opening.

R1001.12 Fireplace fireblocking. Fireplace fireblocking shall comply with the provisions of Section R602.8.

SECTION R1002
MASONRY HEATERS

R1002.1 Definition. A masonry heater is a heating *appliance* constructed of concrete or *solid masonry*, hereinafter referred to as masonry, that is designed to absorb and store heat from a solid-fuel fire built in the firebox by routing the exhaust gases through internal heat exchange channels in which the flow path downstream of the firebox includes flow in a horizontal or downward direction before entering the chimney and that delivers heat by radiation from the masonry surface of the heater.

R1002.2 Installation. Masonry heaters shall be installed in accordance with this section and comply with one of the following:

1. Masonry heaters shall comply with the requirements of ASTM E1602.

2. Masonry heaters shall be *listed* and *labeled* in accordance with UL 1482 or CEN 15250 and installed in accordance with the manufacturer's instructions.

R1002.3 Footings and foundation. The firebox floor of a masonry heater shall be a minimum thickness of 4 inches (102 mm) of noncombustible material and be supported on a noncombustible footing and foundation in accordance with Section R1003.2.

R1002.4 Seismic reinforcing. In Seismic Design Categories D_0, D_1 and D_2, masonry heaters shall be anchored to the masonry foundation in accordance with Section R1003.3. Seismic reinforcing shall not be required within the body of a masonry heater whose height is equal to or less than 3.5 times its body width and where the masonry chimney serving the heater is not supported by the body of the heater. Where the masonry chimney shares a common wall with the facing of the masonry heater, the chimney portion of the structure shall be reinforced in accordance with Section R1003.

R1002.5 Masonry heater clearance. Combustible materials shall not be placed within 36 inches (914 mm) of the outside surface of a masonry heater in accordance with NFPA 211 Section 8-7 (clearances for solid-fuel-burning *appliances*), and the required space between the heater and combustible material shall be fully vented to permit the free flow of air around all heater surfaces.

Exceptions:

1. Where the masonry heater wall is not less than 8 inches (203 mm) thick of *solid masonry* and the wall of the heat exchange channels is not less than 5 inches (127 mm) thick of *solid masonry*, combustible materials shall not be placed within 4 inches (102 mm) of the outside surface of a masonry heater. A clearance of not less than 8 inches (203 mm) shall be provided between the gas-tight capping slab of the heater and a combustible ceiling.

2. Masonry heaters listed and labeled in accordance with UL 1482 or CEN 15250 shall be installed in accordance with the listing specifications and the manufacturer's written instructions.

SECTION R1003
MASONRY CHIMNEYS

R1003.1 Definition. A masonry chimney is a chimney constructed of *solid masonry* units, hollow masonry units grouted solid, stone or concrete, hereinafter referred to as masonry. Masonry chimneys shall be constructed, anchored, supported and reinforced as required in this chapter.

R1003.2 Footings and foundations. Footings for masonry chimneys shall be constructed of concrete or *solid masonry* not less than 12 inches (305 mm) thick and shall extend not less than 6 inches (152 mm) beyond the face of the foundation or support wall on all sides. Footings shall be founded on natural undisturbed earth or engineered fill below frost depth. In areas not subjected to freezing, footings shall be not less than 12 inches (305 mm) below finished *grade*.

R1003.3 Seismic reinforcing. Masonry or concrete chimneys shall be constructed, anchored, supported and reinforced as required in this chapter. In Seismic Design Category D_0, D_1 or D_2 masonry and concrete chimneys shall be reinforced and anchored as detailed in Sections R1003.3.1, R1003.3.2 and R1003.4. In Seismic Design Category A, B or C, reinforcement and seismic anchorage are not required.

R1003.3.1 Vertical reinforcing. For chimneys up to 40 inches (1016 mm) wide, four No. 4 continuous vertical bars, anchored in the foundation, shall be placed in the concrete, or between wythes of *solid masonry*, or within the cells of hollow unit masonry, and grouted in accordance with Section R608.1.1. Grout shall be prevented from bonding with the flue liner so that the flue liner is free to move with thermal expansion. For chimneys more than 40 inches (1016 mm) wide, two additional No. 4 vertical bars shall be installed for each additional 40 inches (1016 mm) in width or fraction thereof.

R1003.3.2 Horizontal reinforcing. Vertical reinforcement shall be placed enclosed within $^1/_4$-inch (6.4 mm) ties, or other reinforcing of equivalent net cross-sectional area, spaced not to exceed 18 inches (457 mm) on center in concrete, or placed in the bed joints of unit masonry, at not less than every 18 inches (457 mm) of vertical height. Two such ties shall be installed at each bend in the vertical bars.

R1003.4 Seismic anchorage. Masonry and concrete chimneys and foundations in Seismic Design Category D_0, D_1 or D_2 shall be anchored at each floor, ceiling or roof line more than 6 feet (1829 mm) above *grade*, except where constructed completely within the exterior walls. Anchorage shall conform to the requirements in Section R1003.4.1.

R1003.4.1 Anchorage. Two $^3/_{16}$-inch by 1-inch (5 mm by 25 mm) straps shall be embedded not less than 12 inches (305 mm) into the chimney. Straps shall be hooked around the outer bars and extend 6 inches (152 mm) beyond the bend. Each strap shall be fastened to not less than four floor joists with two $^1/_2$-inch (12.7 mm) bolts.

R1003.4.1.1 Cold-formed steel framing. Where cold-formed steel framing is used, the location where the $^1/_2$-inch (12.7 mm) bolts are used to attach the straps to the framing shall be reinforced with not less than a 3-inch × 3-inch × 0.229-inch (76 mm × 76 mm × 5.8 mm) steel plate on top of a strap that is screwed to the framing with not fewer than seven No. 6 screws for each bolt.

R1003.5 Corbeling. Masonry chimneys shall not be corbeled more than one-half of the chimney's wall thickness from a wall or foundation, nor shall a chimney be corbeled from a wall or foundation that is less than 12 inches (305 mm) thick unless it projects equally on each side of the wall, except that on the second *story* of a two-story *dwelling*, corbeling of chimneys on the exterior of the enclosing walls shall be permitted to be equal to the wall thickness. The projection of a single course shall not exceed one-half the unit height or one-third of the unit bed depth, whichever is less.

R1003.6 Changes in dimension. The chimney wall or chimney flue lining shall not change in size or shape within 6 inches (152 mm) above or below where the chimney passes through floor components, ceiling components or roof components.

R1003.7 Offsets. Where a masonry chimney is constructed with a fireclay flue liner surrounded by one wythe of masonry, the maximum offset shall be such that the centerline of the flue above the offset does not extend beyond the center of the chimney wall below the offset. Where the chimney offset is supported by masonry below the offset in an *approved* manner, the maximum offset limitations shall not apply. Each individual corbeled masonry course of the offset shall not exceed the projection limitations specified in Section R1003.5.

R1003.8 Additional load. Chimneys shall not support loads other than their own weight unless they are designed and constructed to support the additional load. Construction of masonry chimneys as part of the masonry walls or reinforced concrete walls of the building shall be permitted.

R1003.9 Termination. Chimneys shall extend not less than 2 feet (610 mm) higher than any portion of a building within 10 feet (3048 mm), but shall be not less than 3 feet (914 mm) above the highest point where the chimney passes through the roof.

R1003.9.1 Chimney caps. Masonry chimneys shall have a concrete, metal or stone cap, a drip edge and a caulked bond break around any flue liners in accordance with ASTM C1283. The concrete, metal or stone cap shall be sloped to shed water.

R1003.9.2 Spark arrestors. Where a spark arrestor is installed on a masonry chimney, the spark arrestor shall meet all of the following requirements:

1. The net free area of the arrestor shall be not less than four times the net free area of the outlet of the chimney flue it serves.

2. The arrestor screen shall have heat and corrosion resistance equivalent to 19-gage galvanized steel or 24-gage stainless steel.

3. Openings shall not permit the passage of spheres having a diameter greater than $^1/_2$ inch (12.7 mm) nor block the passage of spheres having a diameter less than $^3/_8$ inch (9.5 mm).

4. The spark arrestor shall be located with *access* for cleaning and the screen or chimney cap shall be removable to allow for cleaning of the chimney flue.

R1003.9.3 Rain caps. Where a masonry or metal rain cap is installed on a masonry chimney, the net free area under the cap shall be not less than four times the net free area of the outlet of the chimney flue it serves.

R1003.10 Wall thickness. Masonry chimney walls shall be constructed of *solid masonry* units or hollow masonry units grouted solid with not less than a 4-inch (102 mm) nominal thickness.

R1003.10.1 Masonry veneer chimneys. Where masonry is used to veneer a frame chimney, through-flashing and weep holes shall be installed as required by Section R703.

R1003.11 Flue lining (material). Masonry chimneys shall be lined. The lining material shall be appropriate for the type of *appliance* connected, in accordance with the terms of the *appliance* listing and manufacturer's instructions.

R1003.11.1 Residential-type appliances (general). Flue lining systems shall comply with one of the following:

1. Clay flue lining complying with the requirements of ASTM C315.

2. Listed and labeled chimney lining systems complying with UL 1777.

3. Factory-built chimneys or chimney units listed for installation within masonry chimneys.

4. Other *approved* materials that will resist corrosion, erosion, softening or cracking from flue gases and condensate at temperatures up to 1,800°F (982°C).

R1003.11.2 Flue linings for specific appliances. Flue linings other than these covered in Section R1003.11.1, intended for use with specific types of *appliances*, shall comply with Sections R1003.11.3 through R1003.11.6.

R1003.11.3 Gas appliances. Flue lining systems for gas *appliances* shall be in accordance with Chapter 24.

R1003.11.4 Pellet fuel-burning appliances. Flue lining and vent systems for use in masonry chimneys with pellet fuel-burning *appliances* shall be limited to the following:

1. Flue lining systems complying with Section R1003.11.1.

2. Pellet vents listed for installation within masonry chimneys (see Section R1003.11.6 for marking).

R1003.11.5 Oil-fired appliances approved for use with Type L vent. Flue lining and vent systems for use in masonry chimneys with oil-fired *appliances approved* for use with Type L vent shall be limited to the following:

1. Flue lining systems complying with Section R1003.11.1.

2. Listed chimney liners complying with UL 641 (see Section R1003.11.6 for marking).

R1003.11.6 Notice of usage. Where a flue is relined with a material not complying with Section R1003.11.1, the chimney shall be plainly and permanently identified by a *label* attached to a wall, ceiling or other conspicuous location adjacent to where the connector enters the chimney. The *label* shall include the following message or equivalent language:

THIS CHIMNEY FLUE IS FOR USE ONLY WITH [TYPE OR CATEGORY OF APPLIANCE] APPLIANCES THAT BURN [TYPE OF FUEL]. DO NOT CONNECT OTHER TYPES OF APPLIANCES.

R1003.12 Clay flue lining (installation). Clay flue liners shall be installed in accordance with ASTM C1283 and extend from a point not less than 8 inches (203 mm) below the lowest inlet or, in the case of fireplaces, from the top of the smoke chamber to a point above the enclosing walls. The lining shall be carried up vertically, with a slope not greater than 30 degrees (0.52 rad) from the vertical.

Clay flue liners shall be laid in medium-duty water insoluble refractory mortar conforming to ASTM C199 with tight mortar joints left smooth on the inside and installed to maintain an airspace or insulation not to exceed the thickness of the flue liner separating the flue liners from the interior face of the chimney masonry walls. Flue liners shall be supported on all sides. Only enough mortar shall be placed to make the joint and hold the liners in position.

R1003.12.1 Listed materials. *Listed* materials used as flue linings shall be installed in accordance with the terms of their listings and manufacturer's instructions.

R1003.12.2 Space around lining. The space surrounding a chimney lining system or vent installed within a masonry chimney shall not be used to vent any other *appliance*.

> **Exception:** This shall not prevent the installation of a separate flue lining in accordance with the manufacturer's instructions.

R1003.13 Multiple flues. Where two or more flues are located in the same chimney, masonry wythes shall be built between adjacent flue linings. The masonry wythes shall be not less than 4 inches (102 mm) thick and bonded into the walls of the chimney.

> **Exception:** Where venting only one *appliance*, two flues shall be permitted to adjoin each other in the same chimney with only the flue lining separation between them. The joints of the adjacent flue linings shall be staggered not less than 4 inches (102 mm).

R1003.14 Flue area (appliance). Chimney flues shall not be smaller in area than that of the area of the connector from the *appliance* [see Tables R1003.14(1) and R1003.14(2)]. The sizing of a chimney flue to which multiple *appliance* venting systems are connected shall be in accordance with Section M1805.3.

TABLE R1003.14(1)
NET CROSS-SECTIONAL AREA OF ROUND FLUE SIZES[a]

FLUE SIZE, INSIDE DIAMETER (inches)	CROSS-SECTIONAL AREA (square inches)
6	28
7	38
8	50
10	78
$10^3/_4$	90
12	113
15	176
18	254

For SI: 1 inch = 25.4 mm, 1 square inch = 645.16 mm².

a. Flue sizes are based on ASTM C315.

TABLE R1003.14(2)
NET CROSS-SECTIONAL AREA OF SQUARE AND RECTANGULAR FLUE SIZES

FLUE SIZE, OUTSIDE NOMINAL DIMENSIONS (inches)	CROSS-SECTIONAL AREA (square inches)
4.5 × 8.5	23
4.5 × 13	34
8 × 8	42
8.5 × 8.5	49
8 × 12	67
8.5 × 13	76
12 × 12	102
8.5 × 18	101
13 × 13	127
12 × 16	131
13 × 18	173
16 × 16	181
16 × 20	222
18 × 18	233
20 × 20	298
20 × 24	335
24 × 24	431

For SI: 1 inch = 25.4 mm, 1 square inch = 645.16 mm².

R1003.15 Flue area (masonry fireplace). Flue sizing for chimneys serving fireplaces shall be in accordance with Section R1003.15.1 or R1003.15.2.

R1003.15.1 Option 1. Round chimney flues shall have a minimum net cross-sectional area of not less than one-twelfth of the fireplace opening. Square chimney flues shall have a minimum net cross-sectional area of one-tenth of the fireplace opening. Rectangular chimney flues with an *aspect ratio* less than 2 to 1 shall have a minimum net cross-sectional area of one-tenth of the fireplace opening. Rectangular chimney flues with an *aspect ratio* of 2 to 1 or more shall have a minimum net cross-sectional area of one-eighth of the fireplace opening. Cross-sectional areas of clay flue linings are shown in Tables R1003.14(1) and R1003.14(2) or as provided by the manufacturer or as measured in the field.

R1003.15.2 Option 2. The minimum net cross-sectional area of the chimney flue shall be determined in accordance with Figure R1003.15.2. A flue size providing not less than the equivalent net cross-sectional area shall be used. Cross-sectional areas of clay flue linings are shown in Tables R1003.14(1) and R1003.14(2) or as provided by the manufacturer or as measured in the field. The height of the chimney shall be measured from the firebox floor to the top of the chimney flue.

R1003.16 Inlet. Inlets to masonry chimneys shall enter from the side. Inlets shall have a thimble of fireclay, rigid refractory material or metal that will prevent the connector from pulling out of the inlet or from extending beyond the wall of the liner.

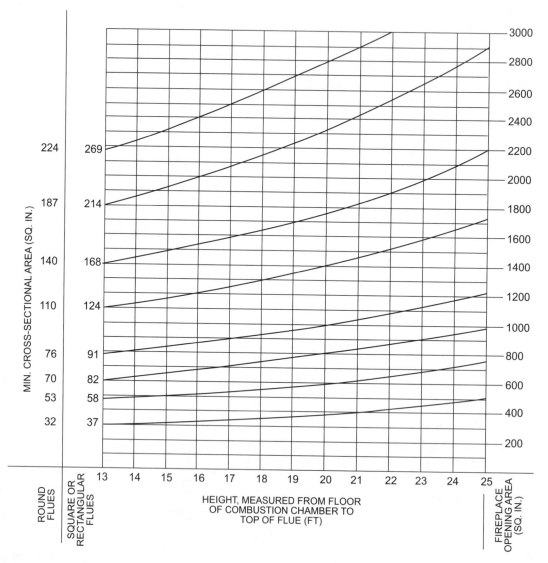

For SI: 1 foot = 304.8 mm, 1 square inch = 645.16 mm².

FIGURE R1003.15.2
FLUE SIZES FOR MASONRY CHIMNEYS

R1003.17 Masonry chimney cleanout openings. Cleanout openings shall be provided within 6 inches (152 mm) of the base of each flue within every masonry chimney. The upper edge of the cleanout shall be located not less than 6 inches (152 mm) below the lowest chimney inlet opening. The height of the opening shall be not less than 6 inches (152 mm). The cleanout shall be provided with a noncombustible cover.

Exception: Chimney flues serving masonry fireplaces where cleaning is possible through the fireplace opening.

R1003.18 Chimney clearances. Any portion of a masonry chimney located in the interior of the building or within the exterior wall of the building shall have a minimum airspace clearance to combustibles of 2 inches (51 mm). Chimneys located entirely outside the exterior walls of the building, including chimneys that pass through the soffit or cornice, shall have a minimum airspace clearance of 1 inch (25 mm). The airspace shall not be filled, except to provide fire blocking in accordance with Section R1003.19.

Exceptions:

1. Masonry chimneys equipped with a chimney lining system listed and *labeled* for use in chimneys in contact with combustibles in accordance with UL 1777 and installed in accordance with the manufacturer's instructions are permitted to have combustible material in contact with their exterior surfaces.

2. Where masonry chimneys are constructed as part of masonry or concrete walls, combustible materials shall not be in contact with the masonry or concrete wall less than 12 inches (305 mm) from the inside surface of the nearest flue lining.

3. Exposed combustible trim and the edges of sheathing materials, such as wood siding and flooring, shall be permitted to abut the masonry chimney side walls, in accordance with Figure R1003.18, provided such combustible trim or sheathing is not less than 8 inches (203 mm) from the inside surface of the nearest flue lining.

R1003.19 Chimney fireblocking. Spaces between chimneys and floors and ceilings through which chimneys pass shall be fireblocked with noncombustible material securely fastened in place. The fireblocking of spaces between chimneys and wood joists, beams or headers shall be self-supporting or be placed on strips of metal or metal lath laid across the spaces between combustible material and the chimney.

R1003.20 Chimney crickets. Chimneys shall be provided with crickets where the dimension parallel to the ridgeline is greater than 30 inches (762 mm) and does not intersect the ridgeline. The intersection of the cricket and the chimney shall be flashed and counterflashed in the same manner as normal roof-chimney intersections. Crickets shall be constructed in compliance with Figure R1003.20 and Table R1003.20.

TABLE R1003.20
CRICKET DIMENSIONS

ROOF SLOPE	H
12:12	$^1/_2$ of W
8:12	$^1/_3$ of W
6:12	$^1/_4$ of W
4:12	$^1/_6$ of W
3:12	$^1/_8$ of W

SECTION R1004
FACTORY-BUILT FIREPLACES

R1004.1 General. Factory-built fireplaces shall be *listed* and *labeled* and shall be installed in accordance with the conditions of the *listing*. Factory-built fireplaces shall be tested in accordance with UL 127.

R1004.2 Hearth extensions. Hearth extensions of *approved* factory-built fireplaces shall be installed in accordance with the *listing* of the fireplace. The hearth extension shall be readily distinguishable from the surrounding floor area. Listed and labeled hearth extensions shall comply with UL 1618.

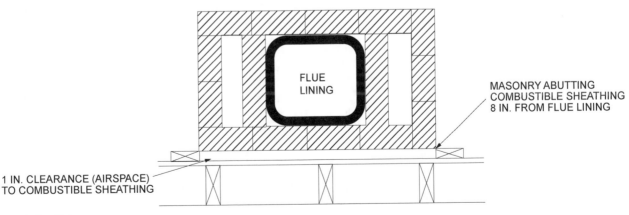

For SI: 1 inch = 25.4 mm.

FIGURE R1003.18
CLEARANCE FROM COMBUSTIBLES

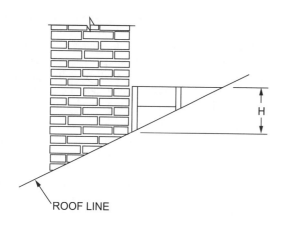

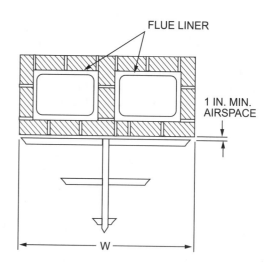

FLUE LINER

1 IN. MIN. AIRSPACE

W

ROOF LINE

H

For SI: 1 inch = 25.4 mm.

FIGURE R1003.20
CHIMNEY CRICKET

R1004.3 Decorative shrouds. Decorative shrouds shall not be installed at the termination of chimneys for factory-built fireplaces except where the shrouds are listed and *labeled* for use with the specific factory-built fireplace system and installed in accordance with the manufacturer's instructions.

R1004.4 Unvented gas log heaters. An unvented gas log heater shall not be installed in a factory-built fireplace unless the fireplace system has been specifically tested, *listed* and *labeled* for such use in accordance with UL 127.

R1004.5 Gasketed fireplace doors. A gasketed fireplace door shall not be installed on a factory-built fireplace except where the fireplace system has been specifically tested, *listed* and *labeled* for such use in accordance with UL 127.

SECTION R1005
FACTORY-BUILT CHIMNEYS

R1005.1 Listing. *Factory-built chimneys* shall be *listed* and *labeled* and shall be installed and terminated in accordance with the *manufacturer's installation instructions*.

R1005.2 Decorative shrouds. Decorative shrouds shall not be installed at the termination of *factory-built chimneys* except where the shrouds are *listed* and *labeled* for use with the specific *factory-built chimney* system and installed in accordance with the *manufacturer's installation instructions*.

R1005.3 Solid-fuel appliances. *Factory-built chimneys* installed in *dwelling units* with solid-fuel-burning *appliances* shall comply with the Type HT requirements of UL 103 and shall be marked "Type HT and "Residential Type and Building Heating Appliance Chimney."

> **Exception:** *Chimneys* for use with open combustion chamber fireplaces shall comply with the requirements of UL 103 and shall be marked "Residential Type and Building Heating Appliance Chimney."

Chimneys for use with open combustion chamber *appliances* installed in buildings other than *dwelling units* shall comply with the requirements of UL 103 and shall be marked "Building Heating Appliance Chimney" or "Residential Type and Building Heating Appliance Chimney."

R1005.4 Factory-built fireplaces. *Chimneys* for use with factory-built fireplaces shall comply with the requirements of UL 127.

R1005.5 Support. Where *factory-built chimneys* are supported by structural members, such as joists and rafters, those members shall be designed to support the additional load.

R1005.6 Medium-heat appliances. *Factory-built chimneys* for medium-heat *appliances* producing flue gases having a temperature above 1,000°F (538°C), measured at the entrance to the *chimney*, shall comply with UL 959.

R1005.7 Factory-built chimney offsets. Where a *factory-built chimney* assembly incorporates offsets, no part of the *chimney* shall be at an angle of more than 30 degrees (0.52 rad) from vertical at any point in the assembly and the chimney assembly shall not include more than four elbows.

R1005.8 Insulation shield. Where *factory-built chimneys* pass through insulated assemblies, an insulation shield constructed of steel having a thickness of not less than 0.0187 inch (0.4712 mm) (No. 26 gage) shall be installed to provide clearance between the *chimney* and the insulation material. The clearance shall be not less than the clearance to combustibles specified by the chimney *manufacturer's installation instructions*. Where *chimneys* pass through attic space, the shield shall terminate not less than 2 inches (51 mm) above the insulation materials and shall be secured in place to prevent displacement. Insulation shields provided as part of a *listed* chimney system shall be installed in accordance with the manufacturer's installation instructions.

SECTION R1006
EXTERIOR AIR SUPPLY

R1006.1 Exterior air. Factory-built or masonry fireplaces covered in this chapter shall be equipped with an exterior air supply to ensure proper fuel combustion unless the room is mechanically ventilated and controlled so that the indoor pressure is neutral or positive.

R1006.1.1 Factory-built fireplaces. Exterior *combustion air* ducts for factory-built fireplaces shall be a *listed* component of the fireplace and shall be installed in accordance with the fireplace manufacturer's instructions.

R1006.1.2 Masonry fireplaces. *Listed combustion air* ducts for masonry fireplaces shall be installed in accordance with the terms of their *listing* and the manufacturer's instructions.

R1006.2 Exterior air intake. The exterior air intake shall be capable of supplying all *combustion air* from the exterior of the *dwelling* or from spaces within the *dwelling* ventilated with outdoor air such as nonmechanically ventilated crawl or *attic* spaces. The exterior air intake shall not be located within the garage or basement of the dwelling. The exterior air intake, for other than listed factory-built fireplaces, shall not be located at an elevation higher than the firebox. The exterior air intake shall be covered with a corrosion-resistant screen of $^1/_4$-inch (6.4 mm) mesh.

R1006.3 Clearance. Unlisted *combustion air* ducts shall be installed with a minimum 1-inch (25 mm) clearance to combustibles for all parts of the duct within 5 feet (1524 mm) of the duct outlet.

R1006.4 Passageway. The *combustion air* passageway shall be not less than 6 square inches (3870 mm^2) and not more than 55 square inches (0.035 m^2), except that *combustion air* systems for listed fireplaces shall be constructed in accordance with the fireplace manufacturer's instructions.

R1006.5 Outlet. The exterior air outlet shall be located in the back or side of the firebox chamber or shall be located outside of the firebox, at the level of the hearth and not greater than 24 inches (610 mm) from the firebox opening. The outlet shall be closable and designed to prevent burning material from dropping into concealed combustible spaces.

CHAPTER 11 [RE]

ENERGY EFFICIENCY

Provisions for energy, energy conservation, or references to the International Energy Conservation Code are deleted and replaced with Minnesota Rules, Chapters 1322 and 1323, Minnesota Energy Code.

CHAPTER 12

MECHANICAL ADMINISTRATION

Provisions for mechanical or references to the International Mechanical Code, which include Chapters 12 through 24 of the IRC, are deleted and replaced with Minnesota Rules, Chapter 1346, Minnesota Mechanical Code.

CHAPTER 25

PLUMBING ADMINISTRATION

Provisions for plumbing or references to the International Plumbing Code, which include Chapters 25 through 33 of the IRC, are deleted and replaced with Minnesota Rules, Chapter 4714, Minnesota Plumbing Code. Except for Section P2904, which is kept.

SECTION 2904

DWELLING UNIT FIRE SPRINKLER SYSTEMS

P2904.1 General. The design and installation of residential fire sprinkler systems shall be in accordance with NFPA 13D or Section P2904, which shall be considered to be equivalent to NFPA 13D. Partial residential sprinkler systems shall be permitted to be installed only in buildings not required to be equipped with a residential sprinkler system. Section P2904 shall apply to stand-alone and multipurpose wet-pipe sprinkler systems that do not include the use of antifreeze. A multipurpose fire sprinkler system shall provide domestic water to both fire sprinklers and plumbing fixtures. A stand-alone sprinkler system shall be separate and independent from the water distribution system. A backflow preventer shall not be required to separate a sprinkler system from the water distribution system, provided that the sprinkler system complies with all of the following:

1. The system complies with NFPA 13D or Section P2904.

2. The piping material complies with Section P2906.

3. The system does not contain antifreeze.

4. The system does not have a fire department connection.

P2904.1.1 Required sprinkler locations. Sprinklers shall be installed to protect all areas of a *dwelling unit*.

Exceptions:

1. Attics, crawl spaces and normally unoccupied concealed spaces that do not contain fuel-fired appliances do not require sprinklers. In *attics*, crawl spaces and normally unoccupied concealed spaces that contain fuel-fired equipment, a sprinkler shall be installed above the equipment; however, sprinklers shall not be required in the remainder of the space.

2. Clothes closets, linen closets and pantries not exceeding 24 square feet (2.2 m²) in area, with the smallest dimension not greater than 3 feet (915 mm) and having wall and ceiling surfaces of gypsum board.

3. Bathrooms not more than 55 square feet (5.1 m²) in area.

4. Garages; carports; exterior porches; unheated entry areas, such as mud rooms, that are adjacent to an exterior door; and similar areas.

P2904.2 Sprinklers. Sprinklers shall be new listed residential sprinklers and shall be installed in accordance with the sprinkler manufacturer's instructions.

P2904.2.1 Temperature rating and separation from heat sources. Except as provided for in Section P2904.2.2, sprinklers shall have a temperature rating of not less than 135°F (57°C) and not more than 170°F (77°C). Sprinklers shall be separated from heat sources as required by the sprinkler manufacturer's installation instructions.

P2904.2.2 Intermediate temperature sprinklers. Sprinklers shall have an intermediate temperature rating not less than 175°F (79°C) and not more than 225°F (107°C) where installed in the following locations:

1. Directly under skylights, where the sprinkler is exposed to direct sunlight.

TABLE P2904.2.2
LOCATIONS WHERE INTERMEDIATE TEMPERATURE SPRINKLERS ARE REQUIRED

HEAT SOURCE	RANGE OF DISTANCE FROM HEAT SOURCE WITHIN WHICH INTERMEDIATE TEMPERATURE SPRINKLERS ARE REQUIRED[a, b] (inches)
Fireplace, side of open or recessed fireplace	12 to 36
Fireplace, front of recessed fireplace	36 to 60
Coal and wood burning stove	12 to 42
Kitchen range top	9 to 18
Oven	9 to 18
Vent connector or chimney connector	9 to 18
Heating duct, not insulated	9 to 18
Hot water pipe, not insulated	6 to 12
Side of ceiling or wall warm air register	12 to 24
Front of wall mounted warm air register	18 to 36
Water heater, furnace or boiler	3 to 6
Luminaire up to 250 watts	3 to 6
Luminaire 250 watts up to 499 watts	6 to 12

For SI: 1 inch = 25.4 mm.

a. Sprinklers shall not be located at distances less than the minimum table distance unless the sprinkler listing allows a lesser distance.

b. Distances shall be measured in a straight line from the nearest edge of the heat source to the nearest edge of the sprinkler.

2. In *attics*.

3. In concealed spaces located directly beneath a roof.

4. Within the distance to a heat source as specified in Table P2904.2.2.

P2904.2.3 Freezing areas. Piping shall be protected from freezing as required by Section P2603.5. Where sprinklers are required in areas that are subject to freezing, dry-sidewall or dry-pendent sprinklers extending from a nonfreezing area into a freezing area shall be installed.

P2904.2.4 Sprinkler coverage. Sprinkler coverage requirements and sprinkler obstruction requirements shall be in accordance with Sections P2904.2.4.1 and P2904.2.4.2.

P2904.2.4.1 Coverage area limit. The area of coverage of a single sprinkler shall not exceed 400 square feet (37 m²) and shall be based on the sprinkler *listing* and the sprinkler manufacturer's installation instructions.

P2904.2.4.2 Obstructions to coverage. Sprinkler discharge shall not be blocked by obstructions unless additional sprinklers are installed to protect the obstructed area. Additional sprinklers shall not be required where the sprinkler separation from obstructions complies with either the minimum distance indicated in Figure P2904.2.4.2 or the minimum distances specified in the sprinkler manufacturer's instructions where the manufacturer's instructions permit a lesser distance.

P2904.2.4.2.1 Additional requirements for pendent sprinklers. Pendent sprinklers within 3 feet (915 mm) of the center of a ceiling fan, surface-mounted ceiling luminaire or similar object shall be considered to be obstructed, and additional sprinklers shall be installed.

P2904.2.4.2.2 Additional requirements for sidewall sprinklers. Sidewall sprinklers within 5 feet (1524 mm) of the center of a ceiling fan, surface-mounted ceiling luminaire or similar object shall be considered to be obstructed, and additional sprinklers shall be installed.

P2904.2.5 Sprinkler installation on systems assembled with solvent cement. The solvent cementing of threaded adapter fittings shall be completed and threaded adapters for sprinklers shall be verified as being clear of excess cement prior to the installation of sprinklers on systems assembled with solvent cement.

P2904.2.6 Sprinkler modifications prohibited. Painting, caulking or modifying of sprinklers shall be prohibited. Sprinklers that have been painted, caulked, modified or damaged shall be replaced with new sprinklers.

P2904.3 Sprinkler piping system. Sprinkler piping shall be supported in accordance with requirements for cold water distribution piping. Sprinkler piping shall comply with the requirements for cold water distribution piping. For multipurpose piping systems, the sprinkler piping shall connect to and be a part of the cold water distribution piping system.

Exception: For plastic piping, it shall be permissible to follow the manufacturer's installation instructions.

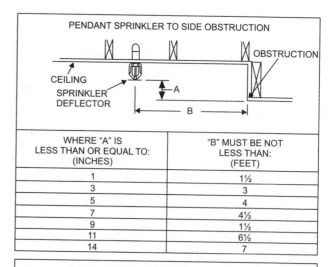

PENDANT SPRINKLER TO SIDE OBSTRUCTION

WHERE "A" IS LESS THAN OR EQUAL TO: (INCHES)	"B" MUST BE NOT LESS THAN: (FEET)
1	1½
3	3
5	4
7	4½
9	6
11	6½
14	7

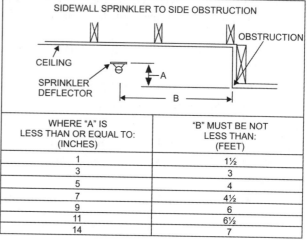

SIDEWALL SPRINKLER TO SIDE OBSTRUCTION

WHERE "A" IS LESS THAN OR EQUAL TO: (INCHES)	"B" MUST BE NOT LESS THAN: (FEET)
1	1½
3	3
5	4
7	4½
9	6
11	6½
14	7

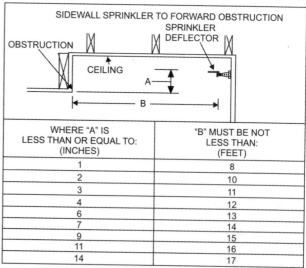

SIDEWALL SPRINKLER TO FORWARD OBSTRUCTION

WHERE "A" IS LESS THAN OR EQUAL TO: (INCHES)	"B" MUST BE NOT LESS THAN: (FEET)
1	8
2	10
3	11
4	12
6	13
7	14
9	15
11	16
14	17

For SI: 1 inch = 25.4 mm, 1 foot = 304.8 mm.

FIGURE P2904.2.4.2
MINIMUM ALLOWABLE DISTANCE BETWEEN SPRINKLER AND OBSTRUCTION

P2904.3.1 Nonmetallic pipe and tubing. Nonmetallic pipe and tubing, such as CPVC, PEX, and PE-RT shall be *listed* for use in residential fire sprinkler systems.

P2904.3.1.1 Nonmetallic pipe protection. Nonmetallic pipe and tubing systems shall be protected from exposure to the living space by a layer of not less than $^3/_8$-inch-thick (9.5 mm) gypsum wallboard, $^1/_2$-inch-thick (13 mm) plywood, or other material having a 15-minute fire rating.

Exceptions:

1. Pipe protection shall not be required in areas that do not require protection with sprinklers as specified in Section P2904.1.1.

2. Pipe protection shall not be required where exposed piping is permitted by the pipe *listing*.

P2904.3.2 Shutoff valves prohibited. With the exception of shutoff valves for the entire water distribution system, valves shall not be installed in any location where the valve would isolate piping serving one or more sprinklers.

P2904.3.3 Single dwelling limit. Piping beyond the service valve located at the beginning of the water distribution system shall not serve more than one *dwelling*.

P2904.3.4 Drain. A means to drain the sprinkler system shall be provided on the system side of the water distribution shutoff valve.

P2904.4 Determining system design flow. The flow for sizing the sprinkler piping system shall be based on the flow rating of each sprinkler in accordance with Section P2904.4.1 and the calculation in accordance with Section P2904.4.2.

P2904.4.1 Determining required flow rate for each sprinkler. The minimum required flow for each sprinkler shall be determined using the sprinkler manufacturer's published data for the specific sprinkler model based on all of the following:

1. The area of coverage.

2. The ceiling configuration.

3. The temperature rating.

4. Any additional conditions specified by the sprinkler manufacturer.

P2904.4.2 System design flow rate. The design flow rate for the system shall be based on the following:

1. The design flow rate for a room having only one sprinkler shall be the flow rate required for that sprinkler, as determined by Section P2904.4.1.

2. The design flow rate for a room having two or more sprinklers a shall be determined by identifying the sprinkler in that room with the highest required flow rate, based on Section P2904.4.1, and multiplying that flow rate by 2.

3. Where the sprinkler manufacturer specifies different criteria for ceiling configurations that are not

smooth, flat and horizontal, the required flow rate for that room shall comply with the sprinkler manufacturer's instructions.

4. The design flow rate for the sprinkler system shall be the flow required by the room with the largest flow rate, based on Items 1, 2 and 3.

5. For the purpose of this section, it shall be permissible to reduce the design flow rate for a room by subdividing the space into two or more rooms, where each room is evaluated separately with respect to the required design flow rate. Each room shall be bounded by walls and a ceiling. Openings in walls shall have a lintel not less than 8 inches (203 mm) in depth and each lintel shall form a solid barrier between the ceiling and the top of the opening.

P2904.5 Water supply. The water supply shall provide not less than the required design flow rate for sprinklers in accordance with Section P2904.4.2 at a pressure not less than that used to comply with Section P2904.6.

P2904.5.1 Water supply from individual sources. Where a *dwelling unit* water supply is from a tank system, a private well system or a combination of these, the available water supply shall be based on the minimum pressure control setting for the pump.

P2904.5.2 Required capacity. The water supply shall have the capacity to provide the required design flow rate for sprinklers for a period of time as follows:

1. Seven minutes for *dwelling units* one *story* in height and less than 2,000 square feet (186 m²) in area.

2. Ten minutes for *dwelling units* two or more stories in height or equal to or greater than 2,000 square feet (186 m²) in area.

Where a well system, a water supply tank system or a combination thereof is used, any combination of well capacity and tank storage shall be permitted to meet the capacity requirement.

P2904.6 Pipe sizing. The piping to sprinklers shall be sized for the flow required by Section P2904.4.2. The flow required to supply the plumbing fixtures shall not be required to be added to the sprinkler design flow.

P2904.6.1 Method of sizing pipe. Piping supplying sprinklers shall be sized using the prescriptive method in Section P2904.6.2 or by hydraulic calculation in accordance with NFPA 13D. The minimum pipe size from the water supply source to any sprinkler shall be $^3/_4$ inch (19 mm) nominal. Threaded adapter fittings at the point where sprinklers are attached to the piping shall be not less than $^1/_2$ inch (13 mm) nominal.

P2904.6.2 Prescriptive pipe sizing method. Pipe shall be sized by determining the available pressure to offset friction loss in piping and identifying a piping material, diameter and length using the equation in Section P2904.6.2.1 and the procedure in Section P2904.6.2.2.

P2904.6.2.1 Available pressure equation. The pressure available to offset friction loss in the interior piping system (P_t) shall be determined in accordance with the Equation 29-1.

$$P_t = P_{sup} - PL_{svc} - PL_m - PL_d - PL_e - P_{sp} \quad \textbf{(Equation 29-1)}$$

where:

P_t = Pressure used in applying Tables P2904.6.2(4) through P2904.6.2(9).

P_{sup} = Pressure available from the water supply source.

PL_{svc} = Pressure loss in the water service pipe. (Table P2904.6.2(1))

PL_m = Pressure loss in the water meter. (Table P2904.6.2(2))

PL_d = Pressure loss from devices other than the water meter.

PL_e = Pressure loss associated with changes in elevation. (Table P2904.6.2(3))

P_{sp} = Maximum pressure required by a sprinkler.

P2904.6.2.2 Calculation procedure. Determination of the required size for water distribution piping shall be in accordance with the following procedure:

Step 1—Determine P_{sup}

Obtain the static supply pressure that will be available from the water main from the water purveyor, or for an individual source, the available supply pressure shall be in accordance with Section P2904.5.1.

Step 2—Determine PL_{svc}

Use Table P2904.6.2(1) to determine the pressure loss in the water service pipe based on the selected size of the water service.

Step 3—Determine PL_m

Use Table P2904.6.2(2) to determine the pressure loss from the water meter, based on the selected water meter size.

Step 4—Determine PL_d

Determine the pressure loss from devices other than the water meter installed in the piping system supplying sprinklers, such as pressure-reducing valves, backflow preventers, water softeners or water filters. Device pressure losses shall be based on the device manufacturer's specifications. The flow rate used to determine pressure loss shall be the rate from Section P2904.4.2, except that 5 gpm (0.3 L/s) shall be added where the device is installed in a water service pipe that supplies more than one *dwelling*. As an alternative to deducting pressure loss for a device, an automatic bypass valve shall be installed to divert flow around the device when a sprinkler activates.

Step 5—Determine PL_e

Use Table P2904.6.2(3) to determine the pressure loss associated with changes in elevation. The elevation used in applying the table shall be the difference between the elevation where the water source pressure was measured and the elevation of the highest sprinkler.

Step 6—Determine P_{sp}

Determine the maximum pressure required by any individual sprinkler based on the flow rate from Section P2904.4.1. The required pressure is provided in the sprinkler manufacturer's published data for the specific sprinkler model based on the selected flow rate.

Step 7—Calculate P_t

Using Equation 29-1, calculate the pressure available to offset friction loss in water-distribution piping between the service valve and the sprinklers.

Step 8—Determine the maximum allowable pipe length

Use Tables P2904.6.2(4) through P2904.6.2(9) to select a material and size for water distribution piping. The piping material and size shall be acceptable if the *developed length* of pipe between the service valve and the most remote sprinkler does not exceed the maximum allowable length specified by the applicable table. Interpolation of P_t between the tabular values shall be permitted.

The maximum allowable length of piping in Tables P2904.6.2(4) through P2904.6.2(9) incorporates an adjustment for pipe fittings. Additional consideration of friction losses associated with pipe fittings shall not be required.

P2904.7 Instructions and signs. An owner's manual for the fire sprinkler system shall be provided to the owner. A sign or valve tag shall be installed at the main shutoff valve to the water distribution system stating the following: "Warning, the water system for this home supplies fire sprinklers that require certain flows and pressures to fight a fire. Devices that restrict the flow or decrease the pressure or automatically shut off the water to the fire sprinkler system, such as water softeners, filtration systems and automatic shutoff valves, shall not be added to this system without a review of the fire sprinkler system by a fire protection specialist. Do not remove this sign."

P2904.8 Inspections. The water distribution system shall be inspected in accordance with Sections P2904.8.1 and P2904.8.2.

P2904.8.1 Preconcealment inspection. The following items shall be verified prior to the concealment of any sprinkler system piping:

1. Sprinklers are installed in all areas as required by Section P2904.1.1.

2. Where sprinkler water spray patterns are obstructed by construction features, luminaires or ceiling fans, additional sprinklers are installed as required by Section P2904.2.4.2.

3. Sprinklers are the correct temperature rating and are installed at or beyond the required separation distances from heat sources as required by Sections P2904.2.1 and P2904.2.2.

4. The pipe size equals or exceeds the size used in applying Tables P2904.6.2(4) through P2904.6.2(9) or, if the piping system was hydraulically calculated in accordance with Section P2904.6.1, the size used in the hydraulic calculation.

5. The pipe length does not exceed the length permitted by Tables P2904.6.2(4) through P2904.6.2(9) or, if the piping system was hydraulically calculated in accordance with Section P2904.6.1, pipe lengths and fittings do not exceed those used in the hydraulic calculation.

6. Nonmetallic piping that conveys water to sprinklers is *listed* for use with fire sprinklers.

7. Piping is supported in accordance with the pipe manufacturer's and sprinkler manufacturer's installation instructions.

8. The piping system is tested in accordance with Section P2503.7.

P2904.8.2 Final inspection. The following items shall be verified upon completion of the system:

1. Sprinkler are not painted, damaged or otherwise hindered from operation.

2. Where a pump is required to provide water to the system, the pump starts automatically upon system water demand.

3. Pressure-reducing valves, water softeners, water filters or other impairments to water flow that were not part of the original design have not been installed.

4. The sign or valve tag required by Section P2904.7 is installed and the owner's manual for the system is present.

TABLE P2904.6.2(1)
WATER SERVICE PRESSURE LOSS (PL_{svc})[a, b]

FLOW RATE[c] (gpm)	3/4-INCH WATER SERVICE PRESSURE LOSS (psi)				1-INCH WATER SERVICE PRESSURE LOSS (psi)				1 1/4-INCH WATER SERVICE PRESSURE LOSS (psi)			
	Length of water service pipe (feet)				Length of water service pipe (feet)				Length of water service pipe (feet)			
	40 or less	41 to 75	76 to 100	101 to 150	40 or less	41 to 75	76 to 100	101 to 150	40 or less	41 to 75	76 to 100	101 to 150
8	5.1	8.7	11.8	17.4	1.5	2.5	3.4	5.1	0.6	1.0	1.3	1.9
10	7.7	13.1	17.8	26.3	2.3	3.8	5.2	7.7	0.8	1.4	2.0	2.9
12	10.8	18.4	24.9	NP	3.2	5.4	7.3	10.7	1.2	2.0	2.7	4.0
14	14.4	24.5	NP	NP	4.2	7.1	9.6	14.3	1.6	2.7	3.6	5.4
16	18.4	NP	NP	NP	5.4	9.1	12.4	18.3	2.0	3.4	4.7	6.9
18	22.9	NP	NP	NP	6.7	11.4	15.4	22.7	2.5	4.3	5.8	8.6
20	27.8	NP	NP	NP	8.1	13.8	18.7	27.6	3.1	5.2	7.0	10.4
22	NP	NP	NP	NP	9.7	16.5	22.3	NP	3.7	6.2	8.4	12.4
24	NP	NP	NP	NP	11.4	19.3	26.2	NP	4.3	7.3	9.9	14.6
26	NP	NP	NP	NP	13.2	22.4	NP	NP	5.0	8.5	11.4	16.9
28	NP	NP	NP	NP	15.1	25.7	NP	NP	5.7	9.7	13.1	19.4
30	NP	NP	NP	NP	17.2	NP	NP	NP	6.5	11.0	14.9	22.0
32	NP	NP	NP	NP	19.4	NP	NP	NP	7.3	12.4	16.8	24.8
34	NP	NP	NP	NP	21.7	NP	NP	NP	8.2	13.9	18.8	NP
36	NP	NP	NP	NP	24.1	NP	NP	NP	9.1	15.4	20.9	NP

For SI: 1 inch = 25.4 mm, 1 foot = 304.8 mm, 1 gallon per minute = 0.063 L/s, 1 pound per square inch = 6.895 kPa.

NP = Not Permitted. Pressure loss exceeds reasonable limits.

a. Values are applicable for underground piping materials listed in Table P2905.4 and are based on an SDR of 11 and a Hazen Williams C Factor of 150.

b. Values include the following length allowances for fittings: 25% length increase for actual lengths up to 100 feet and 15% length increase for actual lengths over 100 feet.

c. Flow rate from Section P2904.4.2. Add 5 gpm to the flow rate required by Section P2904.4.2 where the water service pipe supplies more than one dwelling.

TABLE P2904.6.2(2)
MINIMUM WATER METER PRESSURE LOSS (PL_m)[a]

FLOW RATE (gallons per minute, gpm)[b]	⁵/₈-INCH METER PRESSURE LOSS (pounds per square inch, psi)	³/₄-INCH METER PRESSURE LESS (pounds per square inch, psi)	1-INCH METER PRESSURE LOSS (pounds per square inch, psi)
8	2	1	1
10	3	1	1
12	4	1	1
14	5	2	1
16	7	3	1
18	9	4	1
20	11	4	2
22	NP	5	2
24	NP	5	2
26	NP	6	2
28	NP	6	2
30	NP	7	2
32	NP	7	3
34	NP	8	3
36	NP	8	3

For SI: 1 inch = 25.4 mm, 1 pound per square inch = 6.895 kPa, 1 gallon per minute = 0.063 L/s.

NP = Not permitted unless the actual water meter pressure loss is known.

a. Table P2904.6.2(2) establishes conservative values for water meter pressure loss or installations where the water meter loss is unknown. Where the actual water meter pressure loss is known, P_m shall be the actual loss.

b. Flow rate from Section P2904.4.2. Add 5 gpm to the flow rate required by Section P2904.4.2 where the water service pipe supplies more than one dwelling.

TABLE P2904.6.2(3)
ELEVATION LOSS (PL_e)

ELEVATION (feet)	PRESSURE LOSS (psi)
5	2.2
10	4.4
15	6.5
20	8.7
25	10.9
30	13
35	15.2
40	17.4

For SI: 1 foot = 304.8 mm, 1 pound per square inch = 6.895 kPa.

TABLE P2904.6.2(4)
ALLOWABLE PIPE LENGTH FOR $^3/_4$-INCH TYPE M COPPER WATER TUBING

SPRINKLER FLOW RATE[a] (gpm)	WATER DISTRIBUTION SIZE (inch)	AVAILABLE PRESSURE—P_t (psi)									
		15	20	25	30	35	40	45	50	55	60
		Allowable length of pipe from service valve to farthest sprinkler (feet)									
8	$^3/_4$	217	289	361	434	506	578	650	723	795	867
9	$^3/_4$	174	232	291	349	407	465	523	581	639	697
10	$^3/_4$	143	191	239	287	335	383	430	478	526	574
11	$^3/_4$	120	160	200	241	281	321	361	401	441	481
12	$^3/_4$	102	137	171	205	239	273	307	341	375	410
13	$^3/_4$	88	118	147	177	206	235	265	294	324	353
14	$^3/_4$	77	103	128	154	180	205	231	257	282	308
15	$^3/_4$	68	90	113	136	158	181	203	226	248	271
16	$^3/_4$	60	80	100	120	140	160	180	200	220	241
17	$^3/_4$	54	72	90	108	125	143	161	179	197	215
18	$^3/_4$	48	64	81	97	113	129	145	161	177	193
19	$^3/_4$	44	58	73	88	102	117	131	146	160	175
20	$^3/_4$	40	53	66	80	93	106	119	133	146	159
21	$^3/_4$	36	48	61	73	85	97	109	121	133	145
22	$^3/_4$	33	44	56	67	78	89	100	111	122	133
23	$^3/_4$	31	41	51	61	72	82	92	102	113	123
24	$^3/_4$	28	38	47	57	66	76	85	95	104	114
25	$^3/_4$	26	35	44	53	61	70	79	88	97	105
26	$^3/_4$	24	33	41	49	57	65	73	82	90	98
27	$^3/_4$	23	30	38	46	53	61	69	76	84	91
28	$^3/_4$	21	28	36	43	50	57	64	71	78	85
29	$^3/_4$	20	27	33	40	47	53	60	67	73	80
30	$^3/_4$	19	25	31	38	44	50	56	63	69	75
31	$^3/_4$	18	24	29	35	41	47	53	59	65	71
32	$^3/_4$	17	22	28	33	39	44	50	56	61	67
33	$^3/_4$	16	21	26	32	37	42	47	53	58	63
34	$^3/_4$	NP	20	25	30	35	40	45	50	55	60
35	$^3/_4$	NP	19	24	28	33	38	42	47	52	57
36	$^3/_4$	NP	18	22	27	31	36	40	45	49	54
37	$^3/_4$	NP	17	21	26	30	34	38	43	47	51
38	$^3/_4$	NP	16	20	24	28	32	36	40	45	49
39	$^3/_4$	NP	15	19	23	27	31	35	39	42	46
40	$^3/_4$	NP	NP	18	22	26	29	33	37	40	44

For SI: 1 inch = 25.4 mm, 1 foot = 304.8 mm, 1 pound per square inch = 6.895 kPa, 1 gallon per minute = 0.963 L/s.

NP = Not Permitted.

a. Flow rate from Section P2904.4.2.

TABLE P2904.6.2(5)
TABLE P2904.6.2(5)
ALLOWABLE PIPE LENGTH FOR 1-INCH TYPE M COPPER WATER TUBING

SPRINKLER FLOW RATE[a] (gpm)	WATER DISTRIBUTION SIZE (inch)	AVAILABLE PRESSURE—P_t (psi)									
		15	20	25	30	35	40	45	50	55	60
		Allowable length of pipe from service valve to farthest sprinkler (feet)									
8	1	806	1075	1343	1612	1881	2149	2418	2687	2955	3224
9	1	648	864	1080	1296	1512	1728	1945	2161	2377	2593
10	1	533	711	889	1067	1245	1422	1600	1778	1956	2134
11	1	447	586	745	894	1043	1192	1341	1491	1640	1789
12	1	381	508	634	761	888	1015	1142	1269	1396	1523
13	1	328	438	547	657	766	875	985	1094	1204	1313
14	1	286	382	477	572	668	763	859	954	1049	1145
15	1	252	336	420	504	588	672	756	840	924	1008
16	1	224	298	373	447	522	596	671	745	820	894
17	1	200	266	333	400	466	533	600	666	733	799
18	1	180	240	300	360	420	479	539	599	659	719
19	1	163	217	271	325	380	434	488	542	597	651
20	1	148	197	247	296	345	395	444	493	543	592
21	1	135	180	225	270	315	360	406	451	496	541
22	1	124	165	207	248	289	331	372	413	455	496
23	1	114	152	190	228	267	305	343	381	419	457
24	1	106	141	176	211	246	282	317	352	387	422
25	1	98	131	163	196	228	261	294	326	359	392
26	1	91	121	152	182	212	243	273	304	334	364
27	1	85	113	142	170	198	226	255	283	311	340
28	1	79	106	132	159	185	212	238	265	291	318
29	1	74	99	124	149	174	198	223	248	273	298
30	1	70	93	116	140	163	186	210	233	256	280
31	1	66	88	110	132	153	175	197	219	241	263
32	1	62	83	103	124	145	165	186	207	227	248
33	1	59	78	98	117	137	156	176	195	215	234
34	1	55	74	92	111	129	148	166	185	203	222
35	1	53	70	88	105	123	140	158	175	193	210
36	1	50	66	83	100	116	133	150	166	183	199
37	1	47	63	79	95	111	126	142	158	174	190
38	1	45	60	75	90	105	120	135	150	165	181
39	1	43	57	72	86	100	115	129	143	158	172
40	1	41	55	68	82	96	109	123	137	150	164

For SI: 1 inch = 25.4 mm, 1 foot = 304.8 mm, 1 pound per square inch = 6.895 kPa, 1 gallon per minute = 0.963 L/s.

a. Flow rate from Section P2904.4.2.

TABLE P2904.6.2(6)
ALLOWABLE PIPE LENGTH FOR ³/₄-INCH CPVC PIPE

SPRINKLER FLOW RATE[a] (gpm)	WATER DISTRIBUTION SIZE (inch)	AVAILABLE PRESSURE—P_t (psi)									
		15	20	25	30	35	40	45	50	55	60
		Allowable length of pipe from service valve to farthest sprinkler (feet)									
8	³/₄	348	465	581	697	813	929	1045	1161	1278	1394
9	³/₄	280	374	467	560	654	747	841	934	1027	1121
10	³/₄	231	307	384	461	538	615	692	769	845	922
11	³/₄	193	258	322	387	451	515	580	644	709	773
12	³/₄	165	219	274	329	384	439	494	549	603	658
13	³/₄	142	189	237	284	331	378	426	473	520	568
14	³/₄	124	165	206	247	289	330	371	412	454	495
15	³/₄	109	145	182	218	254	290	327	363	399	436
16	³/₄	97	129	161	193	226	258	290	322	354	387
17	³/₄	86	115	144	173	202	230	259	288	317	346
18	³/₄	78	104	130	155	181	207	233	259	285	311
19	³/₄	70	94	117	141	164	188	211	234	258	281
20	³/₄	64	85	107	128	149	171	192	213	235	256
21	³/₄	58	78	97	117	136	156	175	195	214	234
22	³/₄	54	71	89	107	125	143	161	179	197	214
23	³/₄	49	66	82	99	115	132	148	165	181	198
24	³/₄	46	61	76	91	107	122	137	152	167	183
25	³/₄	42	56	71	85	99	113	127	141	155	169
26	³/₄	39	52	66	79	92	105	118	131	144	157
27	³/₄	37	49	61	73	86	98	110	122	135	147
28	³/₄	34	46	57	69	80	92	103	114	126	137
29	³/₄	32	43	54	64	75	86	96	107	118	129
30	³/₄	30	40	50	60	70	81	91	101	111	121
31	³/₄	28	38	47	57	66	76	85	95	104	114
32	³/₄	27	36	45	54	63	71	80	89	98	107
33	³/₄	25	34	42	51	59	68	76	84	93	101
34	³/₄	24	32	40	48	56	64	72	80	88	96
35	³/₄	23	30	38	45	53	61	68	76	83	91
36	³/₄	22	29	36	43	50	57	65	72	79	86
37	³/₄	20	27	34	41	48	55	61	68	75	82
38	³/₄	20	26	33	39	46	52	59	65	72	78
39	³/₄	19	25	31	37	43	50	56	62	68	74
40	³/₄	18	24	30	35	41	47	53	59	65	71

For SI: 1 inch = 25.4 mm, 1 foot = 304.8 mm, 1 pound per square inch = 6.895 kPa, 1 gallon per minute = 0.963 L/s.

a. Flow rate from Section P2904.4.2.

TABLE P2904.6.2(7)
ALLOWABLE PIPE LENGTH FOR 1-INCH CPVC PIPE

SPRINKLER FLOW RATE[a] (gpm)	WATER DISTRIBUTION SIZE (inch)	AVAILABLE PRESSURE—P_t (psi)									
		15	20	25	30	35	40	45	50	55	60
		Allowable length of pipe from service valve to farthest sprinkler (feet)									
8	1	1049	1398	1748	2098	2447	2797	3146	3496	3845	4195
9	1	843	1125	1406	1687	1968	2249	2530	2811	3093	3374
10	1	694	925	1157	1388	1619	1851	2082	2314	2545	2776
11	1	582	776	970	1164	1358	1552	1746	1940	2133	2327
12	1	495	660	826	991	1156	1321	1486	1651	1816	1981
13	1	427	570	712	854	997	1139	1281	1424	1566	1709
14	1	372	497	621	745	869	993	1117	1241	1366	1490
15	1	328	437	546	656	765	874	983	1093	1202	1311
16	1	291	388	485	582	679	776	873	970	1067	1164
17	1	260	347	433	520	607	693	780	867	954	1040
18	1	234	312	390	468	546	624	702	780	858	936
19	1	212	282	353	423	494	565	635	706	776	847
20	1	193	257	321	385	449	513	578	642	706	770
21	1	176	235	293	352	410	469	528	586	645	704
22	1	161	215	269	323	377	430	484	538	592	646
23	1	149	198	248	297	347	396	446	496	545	595
24	1	137	183	229	275	321	366	412	458	504	550
25	1	127	170	212	255	297	340	382	425	467	510
26	1	118	158	197	237	276	316	355	395	434	474
27	1	111	147	184	221	258	295	332	368	405	442
28	1	103	138	172	207	241	275	310	344	379	413
29	1	97	129	161	194	226	258	290	323	355	387
30	1	91	121	152	182	212	242	273	303	333	364
31	1	86	114	143	171	200	228	257	285	314	342
32	1	81	108	134	161	188	215	242	269	296	323
33	1	76	102	127	152	178	203	229	254	280	305
34	1	72	96	120	144	168	192	216	240	265	289
35	1	68	91	114	137	160	182	205	228	251	273
36	1	65	87	108	130	151	173	195	216	238	260
37	1	62	82	103	123	144	165	185	206	226	247
38	1	59	78	98	117	137	157	176	196	215	235
39	1	56	75	93	112	131	149	168	187	205	224
40	1	53	71	89	107	125	142	160	178	196	214

For SI: 1 inch = 25.4 mm, 1 foot = 304.8 mm, 1 pound per square inch = 6.895 kPa, 1 gallon per minute = 0.963 L/s.

a. Flow rate from Section P2904.4.2.

TABLE P2904.6.2(8)
ALLOWABLE PIPE LENGTH FOR 3/4-INCH PEX AND PE-RT TUBING

SPRINKLER FLOW RATE[a] (gpm)	WATER DISTRIBUTION SIZE (inch)	AVAILABLE PRESSURE—P_t (psi)									
		15	20	25	30	35	40	45	50	55	60
		Allowable length of pipe from service valve to farthest sprinkler (feet)									
8	3/4	93	123	154	185	216	247	278	309	339	370
9	3/4	74	99	124	149	174	199	223	248	273	298
10	3/4	61	82	102	123	143	163	184	204	225	245
11	3/4	51	68	86	103	120	137	154	171	188	205
12	3/4	44	58	73	87	102	117	131	146	160	175
13	3/4	38	50	63	75	88	101	113	126	138	151
14	3/4	33	44	55	66	77	88	99	110	121	132
15	3/4	29	39	48	58	68	77	87	96	106	116
16	3/4	26	34	43	51	60	68	77	86	94	103
17	3/4	23	31	38	46	54	61	69	77	84	92
18	3/4	21	28	34	41	48	55	62	69	76	83
19	3/4	19	25	31	37	44	50	56	62	69	75
20	3/4	17	23	28	34	40	45	51	57	62	68
21	3/4	16	21	26	31	36	41	47	52	57	62
22	3/4	NP	19	24	28	33	38	43	47	52	57
23	3/4	NP	17	22	26	31	35	39	44	48	52
24	3/4	NP	16	20	24	28	32	36	40	44	49
25	3/4	NP	NP	19	22	26	30	34	37	41	45
26	3/4	NP	NP	17	21	24	28	31	35	38	42
27	3/4	NP	NP	16	20	23	26	29	33	36	39
28	3/4	NP	NP	15	18	21	24	27	30	33	36
29	3/4	NP	NP	NP	17	20	23	26	28	31	34
30	3/4	NP	NP	NP	16	19	21	24	27	29	32
31	3/4	NP	NP	NP	15	18	20	23	25	28	30
32	3/4	NP	NP	NP	NP	17	19	21	24	26	28
33	3/4	NP	NP	NP	NP	16	18	20	22	25	27
34	3/4	NP	NP	NP	NP	NP	17	19	21	23	25
35	3/4	NP	NP	NP	NP	NP	16	18	20	22	24
36	3/4	NP	NP	NP	NP	NP	15	17	19	21	23
37	3/4	NP	NP	NP	NP	NP	NP	16	18	20	22
38	3/4	NP	NP	NP	NP	NP	NP	16	17	19	21
39	3/4	NP	NP	NP	NP	NP	NP	NP	16	18	20
40	3/4	NP	NP	NP	NP	NP	NP	NP	16	17	19

For SI: 1 inch = 25.4 mm, 1 foot = 304.8 mm, 1 pound per square inch = 6.895 kPa, 1 gallon per minute = 0.963 L/s.

NP = Not Permitted.

a. Flow rate from Section P2904.4.2.

TABLE P2904.6.2(9)
ALLOWABLE PIPE LENGTH FOR 1-INCH PEX AND PE-RT TUBING

SPRINKLER FLOW RATE[a] (gpm)	WATER DISTRIBUTION SIZE (inch)	AVAILABLE PRESSURE—P_t (psi)									
		15	20	25	30	35	40	45	50	55	60
		Allowable length of pipe from service valve to farthest sprinkler (feet)									
8	1	314	418	523	628	732	837	941	1046	1151	1255
9	1	252	336	421	505	589	673	757	841	925	1009
10	1	208	277	346	415	485	554	623	692	761	831
11	1	174	232	290	348	406	464	522	580	638	696
12	1	148	198	247	296	346	395	445	494	543	593
13	1	128	170	213	256	298	341	383	426	469	511
14	1	111	149	186	223	260	297	334	371	409	446
15	1	98	131	163	196	229	262	294	327	360	392
16	1	87	116	145	174	203	232	261	290	319	348
17	1	78	104	130	156	182	208	233	259	285	311
18	1	70	93	117	140	163	187	210	233	257	280
19	1	63	84	106	127	148	169	190	211	232	253
20	1	58	77	96	115	134	154	173	192	211	230
21	1	53	70	88	105	123	140	158	175	193	211
22	1	48	64	80	97	113	129	145	161	177	193
23	1	44	59	74	89	104	119	133	148	163	178
24	1	41	55	69	82	96	110	123	137	151	164
25	1	38	51	64	76	89	102	114	127	140	152
26	1	35	47	59	71	83	95	106	118	130	142
27	1	33	44	55	66	77	88	99	110	121	132
28	1	31	41	52	62	72	82	93	103	113	124
29	1	29	39	48	58	68	77	87	97	106	116
30	1	27	36	45	54	63	73	82	91	100	109
31	1	26	34	43	51	60	68	77	85	94	102
32	1	24	32	40	48	56	64	72	80	89	97
33	1	23	30	38	46	53	61	68	76	84	91
34	1	22	29	36	43	50	58	65	72	79	86
35	1	20	27	34	41	48	55	61	68	75	82
36	1	19	26	32	39	45	52	58	65	71	78
37	1	18	25	31	37	43	49	55	62	68	74
38	1	18	23	29	35	41	47	53	59	64	70
39	1	17	22	28	33	39	45	50	56	61	67
40	1	16	21	27	32	37	43	48	53	59	64

For SI: 1 inch = 25.4 mm, 1 foot = 304.8 mm, 1 pound per square inch = 6.895 kPa, 1 gallon per minute = 0.963 L/s.

a. Flow rate from Section P2904.4.2.

CHAPTER 34

GENERAL REQUIREMENTS

Provisions for electrical or references to the National Electrical Code, which includes Chapters 34 through 43 of the IRC, are deleted and replaced with Minnesota Rules, Chapter 1315, Minnesota Electrical Code.

CHAPTER 44

REFERENCED STANDARDS

User note:

About this chapter: The one- and two-family dwelling code contains numerous references to standards promulgated by other organizations that are used to provide requirements for materials, products and methods of construction. Chapter 44 contains a comprehensive list of all standards that are referenced in this code. These standards, in essence, are part of this code to the extent of the reference to the standard.

This chapter lists the standards that are referenced in various sections of this document. The standards are listed herein by the promulgating agency of the standard, the standard identification, the effective date and title, and the section or sections of this document that reference the standard. The application of the referenced standards shall be as specified in Section R102.4.

AAMA

American Architectural Manufacturers Association
1827 Walden Office Square, Suite 550
Schaumburg, IL 60173

AAMA/WDMA/CSA 101/I.S.2/A440—17: North American Fenestration Standards/Specifications for Windows, Doors and Skylights
R308.6.9, R609.3, N1102.4.3

450—10: Voluntary Performance Rating Method for Mulled Fenestration Assemblies
R609.8

506—16: Voluntary Specifications for Hurricane Impact and Cycle Testing of Fenestration Products
R609.6.1

711—13: Voluntary Specification for Self-adhering Flashing Used for Installation of Exterior Wall Fenestration Products
R703.4

712—14: Voluntary Specification for Mechanically Attached Flexible Flashing
R703.4

714—15: Voluntary Specification for Liquid Applied Flashing Used to Create a Water-resistive Seal around Exterior Wall Openings in Buildings
R703.4

AAMA/NPEA/NSA 2100—12: Specifications for Sunrooms
R301.2.1.1.1

ACCA

Air Conditioning Contractors of America
2800 Shirlington Road, Suite 300
Arlington, VA 22206

Manual D—2016: Residential Duct Systems
Table R301.2(1), M1601.1, M1602.2

Manual J—2016: Residential Load Calculation—Eighth Edition
N1103.7, M1401.3

Manual S—2014: Residential Equipment Selection
N1103.7, M1401.3

ACI

American Concrete Institute
38800 Country Club Drive
Farmington Hills, MI 48331

318—14: Building Code Requirements for Structural Concrete
R301.2.2.2.5, R402.2, Table R404.1.2(2), Table R404.1.2(5), Table R404.1.2(6), Table R404.1.2(7), Table R404.1.2(8), R404.1.3, R404.1.3.1, R404.1.3.3, R404.1.3.4, R404.1.4.2, R404.5.1, R608.1, R608.1.1, R608.1.2, R608.2, R608.5.1, R608.6.1, R608.8.2, R608.9.2, R608.9.3

ACI—continued

332—14: Residential Code Requirements for Structural Concrete
R402.2, R403.1, R404.1.3, R404.1.3.4, R404.1.4.2, R506.1

AISI

American Iron and Steel Institute
25 Massachusetts Avenue, NW Suite 800
Washington, DC 20001

AISI S100—16: North American Specification for the Design of Cold-formed Steel Structural Members, 2016
R608.9.2, R608.9.3

AISI S220—15: North American Standard for Cold-formed Steel Framing—Nonstructural Members, 2015
R702.3.3

AISI S230—15: Standard for Cold-formed Steel Framing—Prescriptive Method for One- and Two-family Dwellings, 2015
R301.1.1, R301.2.1.1, R301.2.2.7, R301.2.2.8, R603.6, R603.9.4.1, R603.9.4.2, R608.9.2, R608.9.3, Figure 608.9(11), R608.10

AISI S240—15: North American Standard for Cold-Formed Steel Structural Framing
R505.1.3, R603.6, R702.3.3, R804.3.6

AMCA

Air Movement and Control Association International
30 West University Drive
Arlington Heights, IL 60004

ANSI/AMCA 210-ANSI/ASHRAE 51—07: Laboratory Methods of Testing Fans for Aerodynamic Performance Rating
Table M1505.3

ANCE

Association of the Electric Sector
Av. Lázaro Cardenas No. 869
Col. Nueva Industrial Vallejo
C.P. 07700 México D.F.

NMX-J-521/2-40-ANCE—2014/CAN/CSA-22.2 No. 60335-2-40—12/UL 60335-2-40: Safety of Household and Similar Electric Appliances, Part 2-40: Particular Requirements for Heat Pumps, Air-Conditioners and Dehumidifiers
M1403.1, M1412.1, M1413.1

ANSI

American National Standards Institute
25 West 43rd Street, 4th Floor
New York, NY 10036

A108.1A—16: Installation of Ceramic Tile in the Wet-set Method, with Portland Cement Mortar
R702.4.1

A108.1B—99: Installation of Ceramic Tile, Quarry Tile on a Cured Portland Cement Mortar Setting Bed with Dry-set or Latex Portland Mortar
R702.4.1

A108.4—99: Installation of Ceramic Tile with Organic Adhesives or Water-Cleanable Tile-setting Epoxy Adhesive
R702.4.1

A108.5—99: Installation of Ceramic Tile with Dry-set Portland Cement Mortar or Latex Portland Cement Mortar
R702.4.1

A108.6—99: Installation of Ceramic Tile with Chemical-resistant, Water-cleanable Tile-setting and -grouting Epoxy
R702.4.1

A108.11—99: Interior Installation of Cementitious Backer Units
R702.4.1

ANSI 117—2015: Standard Specifications for Structural Glued Laminated Timber of Softwood Species
R502.1.3, R602.1.3, R802.1.3

A118.1—16: American National Standard Specifications for Dry-set Portland Cement Mortar
R702.4.1

ANSI—continued

A118.3—13: American National Standard Specifications for Chemical-resistant, Water-cleanable Tile-setting and -grouting Epoxy, and Water-cleanable Tile-setting Epoxy Adhesive
> R702.4.1

A118.4—16: American National Standard Specifications for Modified Dry-Set Cement Mortar
> R606.2.11

A118.10—99: Specification for Load-bearing, Bonded, Waterproof Membranes for Thin-set Ceramic Tile and Dimension Stone Installation
> P2709.2, P2709.2.4

A136.1—08: American National Standard Specifications for Organic Adhesives for Installation of Ceramic Tile
> R702.4.1

A137.1—17: American National Standard Specifications for Ceramic Tile
> R702.4.1

LC1/CSA 6.26—13: Fuel Gas Piping Systems Using Corrugated Stainless Steel Tubing (CSST)
> G2414.5.4, G2411.3, G2415.5

LC4/CSA 6.32—12: Press-connect Metallic Fittings for Use in Fuel Gas Distribution Systems
> G2414.10.1, G2414.10.2, G2414.10.3, G2415.5

Z21.1—2010: Household Cooking Gas Appliances
> G2447.1, M1503.2

Z21.5.1/CSA 7.1—14: Gas Clothes Dryers—Volume I—Type I Clothes Dryers
> G2438.1

Z21.8—94 (R2002): Installation of Domestic Gas Conversion Burners
> G2443.1

Z21.10.1/CSA 4.1—12: Gas Water Heaters—Volume I—Storage Water Heaters with Input Ratings of 75,000 Btu per hour or Less
> G2448.1

Z21.10.3/CSA 4.3—11: Gas Water Heaters—Volume III—Storage Water Heaters with Input Ratings above 75,000 Btu per hour, Circulating and Instantaneous
> G2448.1

Z21.11.2—11: Gas-fired Room Heaters—Volume II—Unvented Room Heaters
> G2445.1

Z21.13/CSA 4.9—11: Gas-fired Low-pressure Steam and Hot Water Boilers
> G2452.1

Z21.15/CSA 9.1—09: Manually Operated Gas Valves for Appliances, Appliance Connector Valves and Hose End Valves
> Table G2420.1.1

Z21.22—99 (R2003): Relief Valves for Hot Water Supply Systems—with Addenda Z21.22a—2000 (R2003) and 21.22b—2001 (R2003)
> P2804.2, P2804.7

Z21.24/CSA 6.10—06: Connectors for Gas Appliances
> G2422.1, G2422.2

Z21.40.1/CSA 2.91—96 (R2011): Gas-fired, Heat-activated Air-conditioning and Heat Pump Appliances
> G2449.1

Z21.40.2/CSA 2.92—96 (R2011): Air-conditioning and Heat Pump Appliances (Thermal Combustion)
> G2449.1

Z21.42—2014: Gas-fired Illuminating Appliances
> G2450.1

Z21.47/CSA 2.3—12: Gas-fired Central Furnaces
> G2442.1

Z21.50/CSA 2.22—16: Vented Gas Fireplaces
> G2434.1

Z21.54—2009: Gas Hose Connectors for Portable Outdoor Gas-fired Appliances
> G2422.1

Z21.56/CSA 4.7—17: Gas-fired Pool Heaters
> G2441.1

ANSI—continued

Z21.58—95/CSA 1.6—13: Outdoor Cooking Gas Appliances
G2447.1

Z21.60/CSA 2.26—12: Decorative Gas Appliances for Installation in Solid Fuel-burning Fireplaces
G2432.1

Z21.69/CSA 6.16—09: Connectors for Movable Gas Appliances
G2422.1.5

Z21.75/CSA 6.27—07: Connectors for Outdoor Gas Appliances and Manufactured Homes
G2422.1

Z21.80/CSA 6.22—11: Line Pressure Regulators
G2421.1

ANSI/CSA FC 1—12: Stationary Fuel Cell Power Systems
M1903.1

Z21.84—12: Manually Listed, Natural Gas Decorative Gas Appliances for Installation in Solid Fuel-burning Fireplaces
G2432.1, G2432.2

Z21.86/CSA 2.32—08: Gas-fired Vented Space Heating Appliances
G2436.1, G2437.1, G2446.1

Z21.88/CSA 2.33—16: Vented Gas Fireplace Heaters
G2435.1

Z21.91—07: Ventless Firebox Enclosures for Gas-fired Unvented Decorative Room Heaters
G2445.7.1

Z21.93/CSA 6.30—13: Excess Flow Valves for Natural and LP Gas with Pressures up to 5 psig
G2421.4

Z21.97—12: Outdoor Decorative Appliances
G2454.1

Z83.6—90 (R1998): Gas-fired Infrared Heaters
G2451.1

Z83.8/CSA 2.6—09: Gas-fired Unit Heaters, Gas Packaged Heaters, Gas Utility Heaters and Gas-fired Duct Furnaces
G2444.1

Z83.19—01 (R2009): Gas-fuel High-intensity Infrared Heaters
G2451.1

Z83.20—08: Gas-fired Low-intensity Infared Heaters Outdoor Decorative Appliances
G2451.1

Z97.1—2014: Safety Glazing Materials Used in Buildings—Safety Performance Specifications and Methods of Test
R308.1.1, R308.3.1, Table R303.3.1(2)

APA

APA—The Engineered Wood Association
7011 South 19th
Tacoma, WA 98466

ANSI/A190.1—2017: Structural Glued-laminated Timber
R502.1.3, R602.1.3, R802.1.2

ANSI/APA PRP 210—2014: Standard for Performance-rated Engineered Wood Siding
R604.1, Table R703.3(1), R703.3.4

ANSI/APA PRG 320—2017: Standard for Performance-rated Cross Laminated Timber
R502.1.6, R602.1.6, R802.1.6

ANSI/APA PRR 410—2016: Standard for Performance-rated Engineered Wood Rim Boards
R502.1.7, R602.1.7, R802.1.7

ANSI/APA PRS 610.1—2013: Standard for Performance-Rated Structural Insulated Panels in Wall Applications
R602.1.11, R610.3, R610.4

APA E30—15: Engineered Wood Construction Guide
Table R503.2.1.1(1), R503.2.2, R803.2.2, R803.2.3

APSP

The Association of Pool & Spa Professionals
211 Eisenhower Avenue, Suite 500
Alexander, VA 22314

ANSI/APSP/ICC 14—2014: American National Standard for Portable Electric Spa Energy Efficiency
N1103.11

ANSI/APSP/ICC 15a—2011: American National Standard for Residential Swimming Pool and Spa Energy Efficiency—includes Appendix A Approved January 9, 2013
N1103.12

ASCE/SEI

American Society of Civil Engineers
Structural Engineering Institute
1801 Alexander Bell Drive
Reston, VA 20191-4400

7—16: Minimum Design Loads and Associated Criteria for Buildings and Other Structures
R301.2.1.1, R301.2.1.2, R301.2.1.2.1, R301.2.1.5, R301.2.1.5.1, Table R608.6(1), Table R608.6(2), Table R608.6(3), Table R608.6(4), Table R608.7(1A), Table R608.7(1B), Table R608.7(1C), R608.9.2, R608.9.3, R609.2, R609.6.2, AH107.4.3

24—14: Flood-resistant Design and Construction
R301.2.4, R301.2.4.1, R322.1, R322.1.1, R322.1.6, R322.1.9, R322.2.2, R322.3.3

32—01: Design and Construction of Frost-protected Shallow Foundations
R403.1.4.1

ASHRAE

ASHRE
1791 Tullie Circle NE
Atlanta, GA 30329

ASHRAE—2001: 2001 ASHRAE Handbook of Fundamentals
Table N1105.5.2(1)

ASHRAE—2017: ASHRAE Handbook of Fundamentals
N1102.1.5, P3001.2, P3101.4

ASHRAE 193—2010(RA 2014): Method of Test for Determining Air Tightness of HVAC Equipment
N1103.3.2.1

34—2016: Designation and Safety Classification of Refrigerants
M1411.1

ASME

American Society of Mechanical Engineers
Two Park Avenue
New York, NY 10016-5990

ASME A17.1—2016/CSA B44—16: Safety Code for Elevators and Escalators
R321.1

A18.1—2014: Safety Standard for Platforms and Stairway Chair Lifts
R321.2

A112.1.2—2012: Air Gaps in Plumbing Systems (For Plumbing Fixtures and Water Connected Receptors)
P2717.1, Table P2902.3, P2902.3.1

A112.1.3—2000 (Reaffirmed 2015): Air Gap Fittings for Use with Plumbing Fixtures, Appliances and Appurtenances
Table P2701.1, P2717.1, Table P2902.3, P2902.3.1

A112.3.1—2007(R2012): Stainless Steel Drainage Systems for Sanitary, DWV, Storm and Vacuum Applications Above and Below Ground
Table P3002.1(1), Table P3002.1(2), Table P3002.2, Table P3002.3, Table P3302.1

A112.3.4—2013/CSA B45.9—13: Macerating Toilet Systems and Related Components
Table P2701.1, P3007.5

ASME—continued

A112.4.1—2009: Water Heater Relief Valve Drain Tubes
    P2804.6.1

ASME A112.4.2—2015/CSA B45.16—15: Water-closet Personal Hygiene Devices
    P2722.5

A112.4.3—1999 (R2010): Plastic Fittings for Connecting Water Closets to the Sanitary Drainage System
    P3003.14

A112.4.14—2004 (R2016): Manually Operated, Quarter-turn Shutoff Valves for Use in Plumbing Systems
    Table P2903.9.4

A112.6.2—2000 (R2016): Framing-affixed Supports for Off-the-floor Water Closets with Concealed Tanks
    Table P2701.1, P2702.4

A112.6.3—2001 (R2016): Floor and Trench Drains
    Table P2701.1

A112.14.1—03(2012): Backwater Valves
    P3008.3

A112.18.1—2017/CSA B125.1—2017: Plumbing Supply Fittings
    Table P2701.1, P2708.5, P2722.1, P2722.3, P2727.2, P2902.2, Table P2903.9.4

A112.18.2—2015/CSA B125.2—2015: Plumbing Waste Fittings
    Table P2701.1, P2702.2

A112.18.3—2002(R2012): Performance Requirements for Backflow Protection Devices and Systems in Plumbing Fixture Fittings
    P2708.5, P2722.3

A112.18.6—2017/CSA B125.6—17: Flexible Water Connectors
    P2906.7

A112.19.1—2013/CSA B45.2—2013: Enameled Cast-iron and Enameled Steel Plumbing Fixtures
    Table P2701.1, P2711.1

A112.19.2—2013/CSA B45.1—2013: Ceramic Plumbing Fixtures
    Table P2701.1, P2705.1, P2711.1, P2712.1, P2712.2, P2712.9

A112.19.3—2008/CSA B45.4—08 (R2013): Stainless Steel Plumbing Fixtures
    Table P2701.1, P2705.1, P2711.1, P2712.1

A112.19.5—2017/CSA B45.15—2017: Flush Valves and Spuds for Water-closets, Urinals and Tanks
    Table P2701.1

A112.19.7—2017/CSA B45.10—2017: Hydromassage Bathtub Systems
    Table P2701.1

A112.19.12—2014: Wall-mounted and Pedestal-mounted, Adjustable, Elevating, Tilting, and Pivoting Lavatory and Sink, and Shampoo Bowl Carrier Systems and Drain Waste Systems
    Table P2701.1, P2711.4, P2714.2

A112.19.14—2013: Six-Liter Water Closets Equipped with Dual Flushing Device
    P2712.1

A112.19.15—2012: Bathtub/Whirlpool Bathtubs with Pressure-sealed Doors
    Table P2701.1, P2713.2

A112.36.2m—1991 (R2012): Cleanouts
    P3005.2.10.2

ASSE 1002—2015/ASME A112.1002—2015/CSA B125.12—15: Anti-Siphon Fill Valves
    Table P2701.1, Table P2902.3, P2902.4.1

B1.20.1—2013: Pipe Threads, General-purpose (Inch)
    G2414.9, P3003.3.3, P3003.6.4, P3003.7.1, P3003.9.3

B16.3—2016: Malleable-iron-threaded Fittings, 150 and 300
    Table P2906.6

B16.4—2016: Gray-iron-threaded Fittings
    Table P2906.6, Table P3002.3

B16.9—2012: Factory-made, Wrought-steel Buttwelding Fittings
    Table P2906.6

ASME—continued

B16.11—2016: Forged Fittings, Socket-welding and Threaded
Table P2906.6

B16.12—2009 (R2014): Cast-iron-threaded Drainage Fittings
Table P3002.3

B16.15—2013: Cast-Alloy-threaded Fittings: Classes 125 and 250
Table P2906.6, Table P3002.3

B16.18—2012: Cast-copper-alloy Solder Joint Pressure Fittings
Table P2906.6, Table P3002.3

B16.22—2013: Wrought-copper and Copper-alloy Solder Joint Pressure Fittings
Table P2906.6, Table P3002.3

B16.23—2016: Cast-copper-alloy Solder Joint Drainage Fittings (DWV)
Table P3002.3

B16.26—2016: Cast-copper-alloy Fittings for Flared Copper Tubes
Table P2906.6, Table P3002.3

B16.28—1994: Wrought-steel Buttwelding Short Radius Elbows and Returns
Table P2906.6

B16.29—2012: Wrought-copper and Wrought-copper-alloy Solder Joint Drainage Fittings (DWV)
Table P3002.3

B16.33—2012: Manually Operated Metallic Gas Valves for Use in Gas Piping Systems up to 125 psig (Sizes $^1/_2$ through 2)
Table G2420.1.1

B16.34—2015: Valves—Flanged, Threaded and Welding End
Table P2903.9.4

B16.44—2012: Manually Operated Metallic Gas Valves for Use in Above-ground Piping Systems up to 5 psi
Table G2420.1.1

B16.51—2013: Copper and Copper Alloy Press-Connect Pressure Fittings
Table M2101.1, M2103.3, Table P2906.6

B36.10M—2004(R2015): Welded and Seamless Wrought-steel Pipe
G2414.4.2

BPVC—2015: ASME Boiler and Pressure Vessel Code (Sections I, II, IV, V, VI and VIII)
M2001.1.1, G2452.1

CSD-1—2016: Controls and Safety Devices for Automatically Fired Boilers
M2001.1.1, G2452.1

ASSE 1016—2017/ASME 112.1016—2017/CSA B125.16—2017: Performance Requirements for Automatic Compensating Valves for Individual Showers and Tub/Shower Combinations
Table P2701.1, P2708.4, P2722.2

ASSE 1070—2015/ASME A112.1070—2015/CSA B125.70—15: Performance Requirements for Water-temperature-limiting Devices
P2713.3, P2721.2

ASSE

ASSE International
18927 Hickory Creek Drive, Suite 220
Mokena, IL 60448

1001—2016: Performance Requirements for Atmospheric-type Vacuum Breakers
Table P2902.3, P2902.3.2

ASSE 1002—2015/ASME A112.1002—2015/CSA B125.12—15: Anti-Siphon Fill Valves
Table P2701.1, Table P2902.3, P2902.4.1

1003—2009: Performance Requirements for Water-pressure-reducing Valves for Domestic Water Distribution Systems
P2903.3.1

1008—2006: Performance Requirements for Plumbing Aspects of Residential Food Waste Disposer Units
Table P2701.1

1010—2004: Performance Requirements for Water Hammer Arresters
P2903.5

ASSE—continued

1011—2016: Performance Requirements for Hose Connection Vacuum Breakers
Table P2902.3, P2902.3.2

1012—2009: Performance Requirements for Backflow Preventers with Intermediate Atmospheric Vent
Table P2902.3, P2902.3.3, P2902.5.1, P2902.5.5.3

1013—2017: Performance Requirements for Reduced Pressure Principle Backflow Preventers and Reduced Pressure Principle Fire Protection Backflow Preventers
Table P2902.3, P2902.3.5, P2902.5.1, P2902.5.5.3

1015—2017: Performance Requirements for Double Check Backflow Prevention Assemblies and Double Check Fire Protection Backflow Prevention Assemblies
Table P2902.3, P2902.3.6

ASSE 1016—2017/ASME 112.1016—2017/CSA B125.16—2017: Performance Requirements for Automatic Compensating Valves for Individual Showers and Tub/Shower Combinations
Table P2701.1, P2708.4, P2722.2

1017—2010: Performance Requirements for Temperature-actuated Mixing Valves for Hot Water Distribution Systems
P2724.1, P2802.1, P2803.2

1018—2017: Performance Requirements for Trap Seal Primer Valves; Potable Water Supplied
P3201.2.1, P3201.2.2

1019—2016: Performance Requirements for Freeze-resistant, Wall Hydrants, Vacuum Breaker, Draining Types
Table P2701.1, Table P2902.3, P2902.3.2

1020—2004: Performance Requirements for Pressure Vacuum Breaker Assembly
Table P2902.3, P2902.3.4

1023—2016: Performance Requirements for Hot Water Dispensers, Household-storage-type—Electrical
Table P2701.1

1024—2016: Performance Requirements for Dual Check Backflow Preventers, Anti-siphon-type, Residential Applications
Table P2902.3, P2902.3.7

1035—2008: Performance Requirements for Laboratory Faucet Backflow Preventers
Table P2902.3, P2902.3.2

ASSE 1037—2015/ASME A112.1037—2015/CSA B125.37—15: Performance Requirements for Pressurized Flushing Devices for Plumbing Fixtures
Table P2701.1

1044—2010: Performance Requirements for Trap Seal Primer Devices Drainage Types and Electronic Design Types
P3201.2.1.3

1047—2017: Performance Requirements for Reduced Pressure Detector Fire Protection Backflow Prevention Assemblies
Table P2902.3, P2902.3.5

1048—2017: Performance Requirements for Double Check Detector Fire Protection Backflow Prevention Assemblies
Table P2902.3, P2902.3.6

1050—2009: Performance Requirements for Stack Air Admittance Valves for Sanitary Drainage Systems
P3114.1

1051—2009: Performance Requirements for Individual and Branch-type Air Admittance Valves for Plumbing Drainage Systems
P3114.1

1052—2016: Performance Requirements for Hose Connection Backflow Preventers
Table P2701.1, Table P2902.3, P2902.3.2

1056—2013: Performance Requirements for Spill-resistant Vacuum Breakers
Table P2902.3, P2902.3.4

1060—2016: Performance Requirements for Outdoor Enclosures for Fluid-conveying Components
P2902.6.1

1061—2015: Performance Requirements for Push Fit Fittings
Table P2906.6, P2906.21

1062—2016: Performance Requirements for Temperature-actuated, Flow Reduction (TAFR) Valves for Individual Supply Fittings
Table P2701.1, P2724.2

ASSE—continued

1066—2016: Performance Requirements for Individual Pressure Balancing In-line Valves for Individual Fixture Fittings
P2722.4

ASSE 1070—2015/ASME A112.1070—2015/CSA B125.70—15 : Performance Requirements for Water-temperature-limiting Devices
P2713.3, P2721.2, P2724.1

1072—2007: Performance Requirements for Barrier-type Floor Drain Trap Seal Protection Devices
P3201.2.1.4

ASTM

ASTM International
100 Barr Harbor Drive, P.O. Box C700
West Conshohocken, PA 19428

A36/A36M—14: Specification for Carbon Structural Steel
R606.15, R608.5.2.2

A53/A53M—12: Specification for Pipe, Steel, Black and Hot-dipped, Zinc-coated Welded and Seamless
R407.3, Table M2101.1, G2414.4.2, Table P2906.4, Table P2906.5, Table P3002.1(1)

A74—15: Specification for Cast-iron Soil Pipe and Fittings
Table P3002.1(1), Table P3002.1(2), Table P3002.2, Table P3002.3, P3005.2.6, Table P3302.1

A106/A106M—14: Specification for Seamless Carbon Steel Pipe for High-temperature Service
Table M2101.1, G2414.4.2

A123/A123M—15: Standard Specification for Zinc (Hot-Dip Galvanized) Coatings on Iron and Steel Products
Table 507.2.3

A126—04(2014): Gray Iron Castings for Valves, Flanges and Pipe Fittings
Table P2903.9.4

A153/A153M—09: Specification for Zinc Coating (Hot Dip) on Iron and Steel Hardware
R317.3, Table 507.2.3, Table R606.3.4.1, R703.6.3, R905.7.5, R905.8.6

A167—99(2009): Specification for Stainless and Heat-resisting Chromium-nickel Steel Plate, Sheet and Strip
Table R606.3.4.1

A240/A240M—15A: Standard Specification for Chromium and Chromium-nickel Stainless Steel Plate, Sheet and Strip for Pressure Vessels and for General Applications
Table R905.10.3(1)

A254—12: Specification for Copper Brazed Steel Tubing
Table M2101.1, G2414.5.1

A268—2010: Standard Specification for Seamless and Welded Ferritic and Martensitic Stainless Steel Tubing for General Service
G2414.5.2

A269—2015: Standard Specification for Seamless and Welded Austenitic Stainless Steel Tubing for General Service
G2414.5.2

A307—14: Specification for Carbon Steel Bolts and Studs, 60,000 psi Tensile Strength
R608.5.2.2, Table R507.2.3

A312/A312M—15A: Specification for Seamless, Welded and Heavily Cold Worked Austenitic Stainless Steel Pipes
Table P2906.4, Table P2906.5, Table P2906.6, P2906.13.2

A463/A463M—15: Standard Specification for Steel Sheet, Aluminum-coated by the Hot-dip Process
Table R905.10.3(2)

A539—99: Specification for Electric-resistance-welded Coiled Steel Tubing for Gas and Fuel Oil Lines
M2202.1

A563—15: Standard Specification for Carbon and Alloy Steel Nuts
Table R507.2.3

A615/A615M—2015aE1: Specification for Deformed and Plain Carbon-steel Bars for Concrete Reinforcement
R402.3.1, R403.1.3.5.1, R404.1.3.3.7.1, R608.5.2.1

A641/A641M—09a(2014): Specification for Zinc-coated (Galvanized) Carbon Steel Wire
Table R606.3.4.1

ASTM—continued

A653/A653M—15: Specification for Steel Sheet, Zinc-coated (Galvanized) or Zinc-iron Alloy-coated (Galvannealed) by the Hot-dip Process
R317.3.1, R505.2.2, Table R507.2.3, R603.2.2, Table R606.3.4.1, R608.5.2.3, R804.2.2, R804.2.3, Table R905.10.3(1), Table R905.10.3(2), M1601.1.1

A706/A706M—15: Specification for Low-alloy Steel Deformed and Plain Bars for Concrete Reinforcement
R402.3.1, R403.1.3.5.1, R404.1.3.3.7.1, R608.5.2.1

A755/A755M—2015: Specification for Steel Sheet, Metallic Coated by the Hot-dip Process and Prepainted by the Coil-coating Process for Exterior Exposed Building Products
Table R905.10.3(2)

A778/A778M—15: Specification for Welded Unannealed Austenitic Stainless Steel Tubular Products
Table P2906.4, Table P2906.5, Table P2906.6

A792/A792M—10(2015): Specification for Steel Sheet, 55% Aluminum-zinc Alloy-coated by the Hot-dip Process
R505.2.2, R603.2.2, R608.5.2.3, R804.2.2, Table 905.10.3(2)

A875/A875M—13: Specification for Steel Sheet, Zinc-5%, Aluminum Alloy-coated by the Hot-dip Process
R608.5.2.3, Table R905.10.3(2)

A888—15: Specification for Hubless Cast Iron Soil Pipe and Fittings for Sanitary and Storm Drain, Waste and Vent Piping Application
Table P3002.1(1), Table P3002.1(2), Table P3002.2, Table P3002.3, Table P3302.1

A924/A924M—14: Standard Specification for General Requirements for Steel Sheet, Metallic-coated by the Hot-dip Process
Table R905.10.3(1)

A996/A996M—15: Specifications for Rail-steel and Axle-steel Deformed Bars for Concrete Reinforcement
R403.1.3.5.1, R403.2.1, Table R404.1.2(9), R404.1.3.3.7.1, R608.5.2.1, Table R608.5.4(2)

A1003/A1003M—15: Standard Specification for Steel Sheet, Carbon, Metallic and Nonmetallic-coated for Cold-formed Framing Members
R505.2.1, R505.2.2, R603.2.1, R603.2.2, R804.2.1, R804.2.2

B32—08(2014): Specification for Solder Metal
P3003.6.3

B42—2015A: Specification for Seamless Copper Pipe, Standard Sizes
Table M2101.1, Table P2906.4, Table P2906.5, Table P3002.1(1)

B43—15: Specification for Seamless Red Brass Pipe, Standard Sizes
Table M2101.1, Table P2906.4, Table P2906.5, Table P3002.1(1)

B75/B75M—11: Specification for Seamless Copper Tube
Table M2101.1, Table P2906.4, Table P2906.5, Table P3002.1(1), Table P3002.1(2), Table P3002.2

B88—14: Specification for Seamless Copper Water Tube
Table M2101.1, G2414.5.2, Table P2906.4, Table P2906.5, Table P3002.1(1), Table P3002.1(2), Table P3002.2

B101—12: Specification for Lead-coated Copper Sheet and Strip for Building Construction
Table R905.2.8.2, Table R905.10.3(1)

B135—10: Specification for Seamless Brass Tube
Table M2101.1

B209—14: Specification for Aluminum and Aluminum-alloy Sheet and Plate
Table 905.10.3(1)

B251—10: Specification for General Requirements for Wrought Seamless Copper and Copper-alloy Tube
Table M2101.1, Table P2906.4, Table P2906.5, Table P3002.1(1), Table P3002.1(2), Table P3002.2

B302—12: Specification for Threadless Copper Pipe, Standard Sizes
Table M2101.1, Table P2906.4, Table P2906.5, Table P3002.1(1)

B306—13: Specification for Copper Drainage Tube (DWV)
Table M2101.1, Table P3002.1(1), Table P3002.1(2)

B370—12: Specification for Copper Sheet and Strip for Building Construction
Table R905.2.8.2, Table R905.10.3(1), Table P2701.1

B447—12a: Specification for Welded Copper Tube
Table P2906.4, Table P2906.5

ASTM—continued

B695—04(2009): Standard Specification for Coatings of Zinc Mechanically Deposited on Iron and Steel
R317.3.1, R317.3.3, Table R507.2.3

B813—10: Specification for Liquid and Paste Fluxes for Soldering Applications of Copper and Copper Alloy Tube
Table M2101.1, M2103.3, P2906.15, P3003.6.3

B828—02(2010): Practice for Making Capillary Joints by Soldering of Copper and Copper Alloy Tube and Fittings
M2103.3, P2906.15, P3003.6.3

C4—04(2014): Specification for Clay Drain Tile and Perforated Clay Drain Tile
Table P3302.1

C5—10: Specification for Quicklime for Structural Purposes
R702.2.1

C14—15a: Specification for Non-reinforced Concrete Sewer, Storm Drain and Culvert Pipe
Table P3002.2

C22/C22M—2015: Specification for Gypsum
R702.2.1, R702.3.1

C27—98(2013): Specification for Standard Classification of Fireclay and High-alumina Refractory Brick
R1001.5

C28/C28M—10(2015): Specification for Gypsum Plasters
R702.2.1

C33/C33M—13: Specification for Concrete Aggregates
R403.4.1

C34—13: Specification for Structural Clay Load-bearing Wall Tile
Table R301.2(1), R606.2.2

C35/C35M—(2014): Specification for Inorganic Aggregates for Use in Gypsum Plaster
R702.2.1

C55—2014A: Specification for Concrete Building Brick
R202, Table R301.2(1), R606.2.1

C56—13: Standard Specification for Structural Clay Nonloadbearing Tile
R606.2.2

C59/C59M—00(2015): Specification for Gypsum Casting Plaster and Molding Plaster
R702.2.1

C61/C61M—00(2015): Specification for Gypsum Keene's Cement
R702.2.1

C62—13A: Standard Specification for Building Brick (Solid Masonry Units Made from Clay or Shale)
R202, Table R301.2(1), R606.2.2

C73—14: Specification for Calcium Silicate Face Brick (Sand Lime Brick)
R202, Table R301.2(1), R606.2.1

C76—15A: Specification for Reinforced Concrete Culvert, Storm Drain and Sewer Pipe
Table P3002.2

C90—14: Specification for Load-bearing Concrete Masonry Units
Table R301.2(1), 606.2.1

C91/C91M—12: Specification for Masonry Cement
R702.2.2, R703.7.2

C94/C94M—15A: Standard Specification for Ready-mixed Concrete
R404.1.3.3.2, R608.5.1.2

C126—15: Standard Specification for Ceramic Glazed Structural Clay Facing Tile, Facing Brick, and Solid Masonry Units
R606.2.2

C129—14A: Specification for Nonload-bearing Concrete Masonry Units
Table R301.2(1)

C143/C143M—15: Test Method for Slump of Hydraulic Cement Concrete
R404.1.3.3.4, R608.5.1.4

C145—85: Specification for Solid Load-bearing Concrete Masonry Units
R202, Table R301.2(1)

C150/C150M—15: Specification for Portland Cement
R608.5.1.1, R702.7.2

C199—84(2011): Test Method for Pier Test for Refractory Mortar
R1001.5, R1001.8, R1003.12

C203—05a(2012): Standard Test Methods for Breaking Load and Flexural Properties of Block-type Thermal Insulation
Table R610.3.1

C207—06(2011): Specification for Hydrated Lime for Masonry Purposes
Table R606.2.8

C208—12: Specification for Cellulosic Fiber Insulating Board
R602.1.10, Table R602.3(1), Table R906.2

C212—14: Standard Specification for Structural Clay Facing Tile
R602.2.2

C216—15: Specification for Facing Brick (Solid Masonry Units Made from Clay or Shale)
R202, Table R301.2(1), R606.2.2

C270—14A: Specification for Mortar for Unit Masonry
R606.2.8, Table R606.2.8, R606.2.11

C315—07(2011): Specification for Clay Flue Liners and Chimney Pots
R1001.8, R1003.11.1, Table R1003.14(1), G2425.12

C406/C406M—2015: Specifications for Roofing Slate
R905.6.4

C411—11: Test Method for Hot-surface Performance of High-temperature Thermal Insulation
M1601.3

C425—04(2013): Specification for Compression Joints for Vitrified Clay Pipe and Fittings
Table P3002.2, P3003.10, P3003.13

C443—12: Specification for Joints for Concrete Pipe and Manholes, Using Rubber Gaskets
P3003.5, P3003.13

C475/C475M—15: Specification for Joint Compound and Joint Tape for Finishing Gypsum Wallboard
R702.3.1

C476—10: Specification for Grout for Masonry
R606.2.12

C503/C503M—2010: Standard Specification for Marble Dimension Stone
R606.2.4

C514—04(2014): Specification for Nails for the Application of Gypsum Wallboard
R702.3.1

C552—15: Standard Specification for Cellular Glass Thermal Insulation
Table R906.2

C557—03(2009)e01: Specification for Adhesives for Fastening Gypsum Wallboard to Wood Framing
R702.3.1.1

C564—14: Specification for Rubber Gaskets for Cast Iron Soil Pipe and Fittings
P3003.4.2, P3003.4.3, P3003.13

C568/C568M—2010: Standard Specification for Limestone Dimension Stone
R606.2.4

C578—15: Specification for Rigid, Cellular Polystyrene Thermal Insulation
R316.8, R403.3, Table 703.8.4(2), Table R703.15.1, Table R703.15.2, Table R703.16.1,
Table R703.16.2, Table R906.2

C587—04(2014): Specification for Gypsum Veneer Plaster
R702.2.1

C595/C595M—14E1: Specification for Blended Hydraulic Cements
R608.5.1.1, R702.2.2, R703.7.2

C615/C615M—11: Standard Specification for Granite Dimension Stone
R606.2.4

ASTM—continued

C616/C616M—10: Standard Specification for Quartz-based Dimension Stone
R606.2.4

C629/C629M—10: Standard Specification for Slate Dimension Stone
R606.2.4

C631—09(2014): Specification for Bonding Compounds for Interior Gypsum Plastering
R702.2.1

C645—14: Specification for Nonstructural Steel Framing Members
R702.3.3

C652—15: Specification for Hollow Brick (Hollow Masonry Units Made from Clay or Shale)
R202, Table R301.2(1), R606.2.2

C685/C685M—14: Specification for Concrete Made by Volumetric Batching and Continuous Mixing
R404.1.3.3.2, R608.5.1.2

C700—13: Specification for Vitrified Clay Pipe, Extra Strength, Standard Strength and Perforated
Table P3002.2, Table P3002.3, Table P3302.1

C726—12: Standard Specification for Mineral Wool Roof Insulation Board
Table R906.2

C728—15: Standard Specification for Perlite Thermal Insulation Board
Table R906.2

C744—14: Standard Specification for Prefaced Concrete and Calcium Silicate Masonry Units
R606.2.1

C836/C836M—15: Specification for High Solids Content, Cold Liquid-applied Elastomeric Waterproofing Membrane for Use with Separate Wearing Course
R905.15.2

C841—03(2013): Standard Specification for Installation of Interior Lathing and Furring
R702.2.1

C842—05(2015): Standard Specification for Application of Interior Gypsum Plaster
R702.2.1

C843—99(2012): Specification for Application of Gypsum Veneer Plaster
R702.2.1

C844—2015: Specification for Application of Gypsum Base to Receive Gypsum Veneer Plaster
R702.2.1

C847—14A: Specification for Metal Lath
R702.2.1, R702.2.2

C887—13: Specification for Packaged, Dry, Combined Materials for Surface Bonding Mortar
R406.1, R606.2.9

C897—15: Specification for Aggregate for Job-mixed Portland Cement-based Plasters
R702.2.2

C920—14A: Standard Specification for Elastomeric Joint Sealants
R406.4.1

C926—15B: Specification for Application of Portland Cement-based Plaster
R702.2.2, R702.2.2.1, R703.7, R703.7.2, R703.7.2.1, R703.7.4

C933—14: Specification for Welded Wire Lath
R702.2.1, R702.2.2

C946—10: Standard Practice for Construction of Dry-Stacked, Surface-Bonded Walls
R606.2.9

C954—15: Specification for Steel Drill Screws for the Application of Gypsum Panel Products or Metal Plaster Bases to Steel Studs from 0.033 in (0.84 mm) or to 0.112 in. (2.84 mm) in Thickness
R505.2.5, R603.2.5, R702.3.5.1, R804.2.5

C957/C957M—15: Specification for High-solids Content, Cold Liquid-applied Elastomeric Waterproofing Membrane for Use with Integral Wearing Surface
R905.15.2

ASTM—continued

C1002—14: Specification for Steel Self-piercing Tapping Screws for the Application of Gypsum Panel Products or Metal Plaster Bases to Wood Studs or Steel Studs
R702.3.1, R702.3.5.1

C1029—15: Specification for Spray-applied Rigid Cellular Polyurethane Thermal Insulation
R905.14.2

C1032—14: Specification for Woven Wire Plaster Base
R702.2.1, R702.2.2

C1047—14a: Specification for Accessories for Gypsum Wallboard and Gypsum Veneer Base
R702.2.1, R702.2.2, R702.3.1

C1063—15A: Specification for Installation of Lathing and Furring to Receive Interior and Exterior Portland Cement-based Plaster
R702.2.2, R703.7, R703.7.1

C1088—14: Standard Specification for Thin Veneer Brick Units Made from Clay or Shale
R606.2.2

C1107/C1107M—14A: Standard Specification for Packaged Dry, Hydraulic-cement Grout (Nonshrink)
R402.3.1

C1116/C116M—10(2015): Standard Specification for Fiber-reinforced Concrete and Shotcrete
R402.3.1

C1157—11/C1157M—11: Standard Performance Specification for Hydraulic Cement
R608.5.1.1, R703.7.2

C1167—11: Specification for Clay Roof Tiles
R905.3.4

C1173—10(2014): Specification for Flexible Transition Couplings for Underground Piping Systems
P3003.3.1, P3003.5, P3003.9.1, P3003.10, P3003.12.2, P3003.13

C1177/C1177M—13: Specification for Glass Mat Gypsum Substrate for Use as Sheathing
R702.3.1, Table 906.2

C1178/C1178M—13: Specification for Glass Mat Water-resistant Gypsum Backing Panel
R702.3.1, R702.3.7, Table R702.4.2

C1186—08(2012): Specification for Flat Fiber Cement Sheets
R703.10.1, R703.10.2

C1261—13: Specification for Firebox Brick for Residential Fireplaces
R1001.5, R1001.8

C1277—15: Specification for Shielded Couplings Joining Hubless Cast Iron Soil Pipe and Fittings
P3003.4.3

C1278/C1278M—07a(2011): Specification for Fiber-reinforced Gypsum Panels
R702.3.1, R702.3.7, Table R702.4.2, Table R906.2

C1283—11: Practice for Installing Clay Flue Lining
R1003.9.1, R1003.12

C1288—14: Standard Specification for Discrete Nonasbestos Fiber-cement Interior Substrate Sheets
Table R503.2.1.1(1), Table R503.2.1.1(2), Table 602.3(2), Table R702.4.2

C1289—15: Standard Specification for Faced Rigid Cellular Polyisocyanurate Thermal Insulation Board
R316.8, Table R703.15.1, Table R703.15.2, Table R703.16.1, Table R703.16.2, R708.8.4(2), Table R906.2

C1325—14: Standard Specification for Nonasbestos Fiber-mat Reinforced Cement Interior Substrate Sheets Backer Units
Table R702.4.2

C1328/C1328M—12: Specification for Plastic (Stucco) Cement
R702.2.2, R703.7.2

C1363—11: The Standard Test Method for Thermal Performance of Building Materials and Envelope Assemblies by Means of a Hot Box Apparatus
N1101.10.4.1

C1364—10B: Standard Specification for Architectural Cast Stone
R606.2.5

C1396/C1396M—2014A: Specification for Gypsum Board
Table R602.3(1), R702.2.1, R702.2.2, R702.3.1, R702.3.7

ASTM—continued

C1405—15: Standard Specification for Glazed Brick (Single Fired, Brick Units)
R606.2.2

C1440—08(2013): Specification for Thermoplastic Elastomeric (TPE) Gasket Materials for Drain, Waste and Vent (DWV), Sewer, Sanitary and Storm Plumbing Systems
P3003.13

C1460—2012: Specification for Shielded Transition Couplings for Use with Dissimilar DWV Pipe and Fittings Above Ground
P3003.13

C1461—08(2013): Specification for Mechanical Couplings Using Thermoplastic Elastomeric (TPE) Gaskets for Joining Drain, Waste and Vent (DWV) Sewer, Sanitary and Storm Plumbing Systems for Above and Below Ground Use
P3003.13

C1492—03(2009): Specification for Concrete Roof Tile
R905.3.5

C1513—2013: Standard Specification for Steel Tapping Screws for Cold-formed Steel Framing Connections
R505.2.5, R603.2.5, R702.3.5.1, Table R703.3(2), Table R703.16.1, Table R703.16.2, R804.2.5

C1540—15: Specification for Heavy Duty Shielded Couplings Joining Hubless Cast-iron Soil Pipe and Fittings
P3003.4.3

C1634—15: Standard Specification for Concrete Facing Brick
R606.2.1

C1658/C1658M—13: Standard Specification for Glass Mat Gypsum Panels
R702.3.1

C1668—13a: Standard Specification for Externally Applied Reflective Insulation Systems on Rigid Duct in Heating, Ventilation, and Air Conditioning (HVAC) Systems
M1601.3

C1670/1670M—16: Standard Specification for Adhered Manufactured Stone Masonry Veneer Units
R606.2.6

C1691—11: Standard Specification for Unreinforced Autoclaved Aerated Concrete (AAC) Masonry Units
R606.2.3

C1693—11: Standard Specification for Autoclaved Aerated Concrete (AAC)
R606.2.3

C1766—13: Standard Specification for Factory-Laminated Gypsum Panel Products
R702.3.1

D41/D41M—2011: Specification for Asphalt Primer Used in Roofing, Dampproofing and Waterproofing
Table R905.9.2, Table R905.11.2

D43/D43M—2000(2012)E1: Specification for Coal Tar Primer Used in Roofing, Dampproofing and Waterproofing
Table R905.9.2

D226/D226M—09: Specification for Asphalt-saturated (Organic Felt) Used in Roofing and Waterproofing
R703.2, R905.1.1, Table R905.1.1(1), R905.8.4, Table R905.9.2

D227/D227M—03(2011)e1: Specification for Coal Tar Saturated (Organic Felt) Used in Roofing and Waterproofing
Table R905.9.2

D312/D321M—15: Specification for Asphalt Used in Roofing
Table R905.9.2

D422—63(2007)E2: Test Method for Particle-size Analysis of Soils
R403.1.8.1

D449/D449M—03(2014)E1: Specification for Asphalt Used in Dampproofing and Waterproofing
R406.2

D450/D450M—07(2013)E1: Specification for Coal-tar Pitch Used in Roofing, Dampproofing and Waterproofing
Table R905.9.2

D1227—13: Specification for Emulsified Asphalt Used as a Protective Coating for Roofing
Table R905.9.2, Table R905.11.2, R905.15.2

D1248—12: Specification for Polyethylene Plastics Extrusion Materials for Wire and Cable
M1601.1.2

D1527—99(2005): Specification for Acrylonitrile-butadiene-styrene (ABS) Plastic Pipe, Schedules 40 and 80
Table P2906.4

ASTM—continued

D1693—15: Test Method for Environmental Stress-cracking of Ethylene Plastics
Table M2101.1

D1784—11: Standard Specification for Rigid Poly (Vinyl Chloride) (PVC) Compounds and Chlorinated Poly (Vinyl Chloride) (CPVC) Compounds
M1601.1.2

D1785—15: Specification for Poly (Vinyl Chloride) (PVC) Plastic Pipe, Schedules 40, 80 and 120
Table P2906.4, Table AG101.1

D1863/D1863M—05(2011)e1: Specification for Mineral Aggregate Used in Built-up Roofs
Table R905.9.2

D1869—15: Specification for Rubber Rings for Fiber-Reinforced Cement Pipe
P2906.18, P3003.13

D1970/D1970M—2015A: Specification for Self-adhering Polymer Modified Bitumen Sheet Materials Used as Steep Roofing Underlayment for Ice Dam Protection
R905.1.1, R905.2.8.2, R905.11.2.1

D2104—03: Specification for Polyethylene (PE) Plastic Pipe, Schedule 40
Table P2906.4

D2178/D2178M—15: Specification for Asphalt Glass Felt Used in Roofing and Waterproofing
Table R905.9.2

D2235—04(2011): Specification for Solvent Cement for Acrylonitrile-butadiene-styrene (ABS) Plastic Pipe and Fittings
P2906.9.1.1, P3003.3.2

D2239—12A: Specification for Polyethylene (PE) Plastic Pipe (SIDR-PR) Based on Controlled Inside Diameter
Table P2906.4, Table AG101.1

D2241—15: Specification for Poly (Vinyl Chloride) (PVC) Pressure-rated Pipe (SDR-Series)
Table P2906.4, Table AG101.1

D2282—99(2005): Specification for Acrylonitrile-butadiene-styrene (ABS) Plastic Pipe (SDR-PR)
Table P2905.4

D2412—11: Test Method for Determination of External Loading Characteristics of Plastic Pipe by Parallel-plate Loading
M1601.1.2

D2447—03: Specification for Polyethylene (PE) Plastic Pipe Schedules 40 and 80, Based on Outside Diameter
Table M2101.1

D2464—15: Specification for Threaded Poly (Vinyl Chloride) (PVC) Plastic Pipe Fittings, Schedule 80
Table P2906.6

D2466—15: Specification for Poly (Vinyl Chloride) (PVC) Plastic Pipe Fittings, Schedule 40
Table P2906.6

D2467—15: Specification for Poly (Vinyl Chloride) (PVC) Plastic Pipe Fittings, Schedule 80
Table P2906.6

D2468—96a: Specification for Acrylonitrile-butadiene-styrene (ABS) Plastic Pipe Fittings, Schedule 40
Table P2906.6

D2513—2014e1: Specification for Gas Pressure Pipe, Tubing and Fittings
Table M2101.1, G2414.6, G2414.6.1, G2414.11, G2415.17.2

D2564—12: Specification for Solvent Cements for Poly (Vinyl Chloride) (PVC) Plastic Piping Systems
P2906.9.1.4, P3003.9.2

D2609—15: Specification for Plastic Insert Fittings for Polyethylene (PE) Plastic Pipe
Table P2906.6

D2626/D2626M—04 (2012)e1: Specification for Asphalt-saturated and Coated Organic Felt Base Sheet Used in Roofing
Table R905.1.1(1), Table R905.9.2

D2657—07: Standard Practice for Heat Fusion-joining of Polyolefin Pipe Fittings
M2105.11.1, P2906.3.1, P2906.20.2, P3003.12.1

D2661—14: Specification for Acrylonitrile-butadiene-styrene (ABS) Schedule 40 Plastic Drain, Waste, and Vent Pipe and Fittings
Table P3002.1(1), Table P3002.1(2), Table P3002.2, Table P3002.3, P3003.3.2

D2665—14: Specification for Poly (Vinyl Chloride) (PVC) Plastic Drain, Waste and Vent Pipe and Fittings
Table P3002.1(1), Table P3002.1(2), Table P3002.2, Table P3002.3, Table AG101.1

ASTM—continued

D2672—14: Specification for Joints for IPS PVC Pipe Using Solvent Cement
Table P2906.4

D2683—14: Specification for Socket-type Polyethylene Fittings for Outside Diameter-controlled Polyethylene Pipe and Tubing
Table M2105.5, M2105.11.1, Table P2606.6, P2906.20.2, P3002.3, P3010.5

D2729—11: Specification for Poly (Vinyl Chloride) (PVC) Sewer Pipe and Fittings
P3009.11, Table P3302.1, Table AG101.1

D2737—2012A: Specification for Polyethylene (PE) Plastic Tubing
Table P2906.4, Table AG101.1

D2751—05: Specification for Acrylonitrile-butadiene-styrene (ABS) Sewer Pipe and Fittings
Table P3002.2, Table P3002.3

D2822/D2822M—05(2011)e1: Specification for Asphalt Roof Cement, Asbestos Containing
Table R905.9.2

D2823/D2823M—05(2011)e1: Specification for Asphalt Roof Coatings, Asbestos Containing
Table R905.9.2

D2824/D2824M—2013: Specification for Aluminum-pigmented Asphalt Roof Coatings, Nonfibered, Asbestos Fibered and Fibered without Asbestos
Table R905.9.2, Table R905.11.2

D2846/D2846M—14: Specification for Chlorinated Poly (Vinyl Chloride) (CPVC) Plastic Hot- and Cold-water Distribution Systems
Table M2101.1, Table P2906.4, Table P2906.5, Table P2906.6, P2906.9.1.2, P2906.9.1.3, Table AG101.1

D2855—96(2010): Standard Practice for Making Solvent-cemented Joints with Poly (Vinyl Chloride) (PVC) Pipe and Fittings
P3003.9.2

D2898—10: Test Methods for Accelerated Weathering of Fire-retardant-treated Wood for Fire Testing
R802.1.5.4, R802.1.5.8

D2949—10: Specification for 3.25-in. Outside Diameter Poly (Vinyl Chloride) (PVC) Plastic Drain, Waste and Vent Pipe and Fittings
Table P3002.1(1), Table P3002.1(2), Table P3002.2, Table P3002.3, Table AG101.1

D3019—08: Specification for Lap Cement Used with Asphalt Roll Roofing, Nonfibered, Asbestos Fibered and Nonasbestos Fibered
Table R905.9.2, Table R905.11.2

D3034—14a: Specification for Type PSM Poly (Vinyl Chloride) (PVC) Sewer Pipe and Fittings
Table P3002.2, Table P3002.3, Table P3202.1, Table AG101.1

D3035—15: Specification for Polyethylene (PE) Plastic Pipe (DR-PR) Based On Controlled Outside Diameter
Table M2105.4, Table AG101.1

D3138—04(2011): Standard Specification for Solvent Cements for Transition Joints Between Acrylonitrile-Butadiene-Styrene (ABS) and Poly (Vinyl Chloride) (PVC) Non-Pressure Piping Components
P3003.13.4

D3161/D3161M—15: Test Method for Wind-Resistance of Steep Slope Roofing Products (Fan Induced Method)
R905.2.4.1, Table R905.2.4.1, R905.16.6

D3201/D3201M—2013: Test Method for Hygroscopic Properties of Fire-retardant Wood and Wood-base Products
R802.1.5.9

D3212—07(2013): Specification for Joints for Drain and Sewer Plastic Pipes Using Flexible Elastomeric Seals
P3003.3.1, P3003.9.1, P3003.12.2

D3261—12E1: Specification for Butt Heat Fusion Polyethylene (PE) Plastic Fittings for Polyethylene (PE) Plastic Pipe and Tubing
Table M2101.1, Table M2105.5, M2105.11.1, M2105.13.3, Table P2606.6, P2906.20.2

D3309—96a(2002): Specification for Polybutylene (PB) Plastic Hot- and Cold-water Distribution System
Table M2101.1

D3311—11: Specification for Drain, Waste and Vent (DWV) Plastic Fittings Patterns
P3002.3

D3350—14: Specification for Polyethylene Plastic Pipe and Fitting Materials
Table M2101.1

D3462/D3462M—10A: Specification for Asphalt Shingles Made From Glass Felt and Surfaced with Mineral Granules
R905.2.4

ASTM—continued

D3468/D3468M—99(2013)E1: Specification for Liquid-applied Neoprene and Chlorosulfanated Polyethylene Used in Roofing and Waterproofing
R905.15.2

D3679—13: Specification for Rigid Poly (Vinyl Chloride) (PVC) Siding
R703.11

D3737—2012: Practice for Establishing Allowable Properties for Structural Glued Laminated Timber (Glulam)
R502.1.3, R602.1.3, R802.1.2

D3747—79(2007): Specification for Emulsified Asphalt Adhesive for Adhering Roof Insulation
Table R905.9.2, Table R905.11.2

D3909/D3909M—14: Specification for Asphalt Roll Roofing (Glass Felt) Surfaced with Mineral Granules
R905.2.8.2, R905.5.4, Table R905.9.2

D4022/D4022M—2007(2012)e1: Specification for Coal Tar Roof Cement, Asbestos Containing
Table R905.9.2

D4068—15: Specification for Chlorinated Polyethylene (CPE) Sheeting for Concealed Water Containment Membrane
P2709.2, P2709.2.2

D4318—10E1: Test Methods for Liquid Limit, Plastic Limit and Plasticity Index of Soils
R403.1.8.1

D4434/D4434M—12: Specification for Poly (Vinyl Chloride) Sheet Roofing
R905.13.2

D4479/D4479M—07(2012)e1: Specification for Asphalt Roof Coatings—asbestos-free
Table R905.9.2

D4551—12: Specification for Poly (Vinyl Chloride) (PVC) Plastic Flexible Concealed Water-containment Membrane
P2709.2, P2709.2.1

D4586/D4586M—07(2012)e1: Specification for Asphalt Roof Cement—asbestos-free
Table R905.9.2

D4601/D4601M—04(2012)e1: Specification for Asphalt-coated Glass Fiber Base Sheet Used in Roofing
Table R905.9.2, R905.11.2.1

D4637/D4637M—14E1: Specification for EPDM Sheet Used in Single-ply Roof Membrane
R905.12.2

D4829—11: Test Method for Expansion Index of Soils
R403.1.8.1

D4869/D4869M—15: Specification for Asphalt-saturated (Organic Felt) Underlayment Used in Steep Slope Roofing
R905.1.1, Table R905.1.1(1)

D4897/D4897M—01(2009): Specification for Asphalt Coated Glass-fiber Venting Base Sheet Used in Roofing
Table R905.9.2

D4990—1997a(2013): Specification for Coal Tar Glass Felt Used in Roofing and Waterproofing
Table R905.9.2

D5019—07a: Specification for Reinforced Nonvulcanized Polymeric Sheet Used in Roofing Membrane
R905.12.2

D5055—13E1: Specification for Establishing and Monitoring Structural Capacities of Prefabricated Wood I-joists
R502.1.2, R802.1.8

D5456—14B: Standard Specification for Evaluation of Structural Composite Lumber Products
R502.1.5, R602.1.5, R802.1.4

D5516—09: Test Method for Evaluating the Flexural Properties of Fire-retardant-treated Softwood Plywood Exposed to the Elevated Temperatures
R802.1.5.6

D5643/D5643M—06(2012)e1: Specification for Coal Tar Roof Cement Asbestos-free
Table R905.9.2

D5664—10: Test Methods For Evaluating the Effects of Fire-retardant Treatments and Elevated Temperatures on Strength Properties of Fire-retardant-treated Lumber
R802.1.5.7

D5665/D5665M—99a(2014)E1: Specification for Thermoplastic Fabrics Used in Cold-applied Roofing and Waterproofing
Table R905.9.2

ASTM—continued

D5726—98(2013): Specification for Thermoplastic Fabrics Used in Hot-applied Roofing and Waterproofing
Table R905.9.2

D6083—05e01: Specification for Liquid-applied Acrylic Coating Used in Roofing
Table R905.9.2, Table R905.11.2, Table R905.14.3, R905.15.2

D6162/D6162M—2000a(2015)E1: Specification for Styrene Butadiene Styrene (SBS) Modified Bituminous Sheet Materials Using a Combination of Polyester and Glass Fiber Reinforcements
Table R905.11.2

D6163/D6163M—2000(2015)E1: Specification for Styrene Butadiene Styrene (SBS) Modified Bituminous Sheet Materials Using Glass Fiber Reinforcements
Table R905.11.2

D6164/D6164M—11: Specification for Styrene Butadiene Styrene (SBS) Modified Bituminous Sheet Materials Using Polyester Reinforcements
Table R905.11.2

D6222/D6222M—11: Specification for Atactic Polypropylene (APP) Modified Bituminous Sheet Materials Using Polyester Reinforcements
Table R905.11.2

D6223/D6223M—02(2009)E1: Specification for Atactic Polypropylene (APP) Modified Bituminous Sheet Materials Using a Combination of Polyester and Glass Fiber Reinforcement
Table R905.11.2

D6298—13: Specification for Fiberglass-reinforced Styrene Butadiene Styrene (SBS) Modified Bituminous Sheets with a Factory Applied Metal Surface
Table R905.11.2

D6305—08(2015)E1: Practice for Calculating Bending Strength Design Adjustment Factors for Fire-retardant-treated Plywood Roof Sheathing
R802.1.5.6

D6380/D6380—03(2013)E1: Standard Specification for Asphalt Roll Roofing (Organic Felt)
Table R905.1.1(1), R905.2.8.2, R905.5.4

D6464—03a(2009)e1: Standard Specification for Expandable Foam Adhesives for Fastening Gypsum Wallboard to Wood Framing
R702.3.1.1

D6694/D6694M—08(2013)E1: Standard Specification for Liquid-applied Silicone Coating Used in Spray Polyurethane Foam Roofing Systems
Table R905.14.3, R905.15.2

D6754/D6754M—10: Standard Specification for Ketone-ethylene-ester-based Sheet Roofing
R905.13.2

D6757—2013: Specification for Underlayment Felt Containing Inorganic Fibers Used with Steep Slope Roofing
Table R905.1.1(1), R905.1.1

D6841—08: Standard Practice for Calculating Design Value Treatment Adjustment Factors for Fire-retardant-treated Lumber
R802.1.5.7

D6878/D6878M—13: Standard Specification for Thermoplastic-polyolefin-based Sheet Roofing
R905.13.2

D6947/D6947M—07(2013)E1: Standard Specification for Liquid Applied Moisture Cured Polyurethane Coating Used in Spray Polyurethane Foam Roofing System
Table R905.14.3, R905.15.2

D7032—14: Standard Specification for Establishing Performance Ratings for Wood-plastic Composite Deck Boards and Guardrail Systems (Guards or Handrails)
R507.2.2, R507.2.2.1, 507.2.2.3, 507.2.2.4

D7158—D7158M—2016: Standard Test Method for Wind Resistance of Asphalt Shingles (Uplift Force/Uplift Resistance Method)
R905.2.4.1, Table R905.2.4.1

D7254—15: Standard Specification for Polypropylene (PP) siding
Table R703.3(1), R703.14

D7425/D7425M—13: Standard Specification for Spray Polyurethane Foam Used for Roofing Application
R905.14.2

D7672—14: Standard Specification for Evaluating Structural Capacities of Rim Board Products and Assemblies
R502.1.7, R602.1.7, R802.1.7

ASTM—continued

D7793—13: Standard Specification for Insulated Vinyl Siding
R703.13, Table R703.3(1)

E84—2016: Standard Test Method for Surface Burning Characteristics of Building Materials
R202, R302.9.3, R302.9.4, R302.10.1, R302.10.2, R316.3, R316.5.9, R316.5.11, R507.2.2.2, R703.14.3, R802.1.5, M1601.3, M1601.5.2, P2801.6

E96/E96M—2015: Test Method for Water Vapor Transmission of Materials
R202, Table R806.5, M1411.6, M1601.4.6

E108—2016: Test Methods for Fire Tests of Roof Coverings
R302.2.4, R902.1

E119—2016: Test Methods for Fire Tests of Building Construction and Materials
Table R302.1(1), Table R302.1(2), R302.2.1, R302.2.2, R302.3, R302.4.1, R302.11.1, R606.2.2

E136—2016: Test Method for Behavior of Materials in a Vertical Tube Furnace at 750°C
R202, R302.11

E283—04(2012): Test Method for Determining the Rate of Air Leakage through Exterior Windows, Curtain Walls and Doors Under Specified Pressure Differences across the Specimen
R202, N1102.4.5

E330/E330M—14: Test Method for Structural Performance of Exterior Windows, Curtain Walls and Doors by Uniform Static Air Pressure Difference
R609.4, R609.5, R609.6.2, R703.1.2

E331—00(2009): Test Method for Water Penetration of Exterior Windows, Skylights, Doors and Curtain Walls by Uniform Static Air Pressure Difference
R703.1.1

E779—10: Standard Test Method for Determining Air Leakage Rate by Fan Pressurization
N1102.4.1.2

E814—2013A: Standard Test Method for Fire Tests of Penetration Firestop Systems
R302.4.1.2

E970—14: Standard Test Method for Critical Radiant Flux of Exposed Attic Floor Insulation Using a Radiant Heat Energy Source
R302.10.5

E1509—12: Standard Specification for Room Heaters, Pellet Fuel-burning Type
M1410.1

E1602—03(2010)e1: Guide for Construction of Solid Fuel Burning Masonry Heaters
R1002.2

E1827—11: Standard Test Methods for Determining Airtightness of Building Using an Orifice Blower Door
N1102.4.1.2

E1886—13A: Test Method for Performance Impact Protective Systems Impacted by Missile(s) and Exposed to Cyclic Pressure Differentials
R301.2.1.2, R609.6.1, R609.6.2, Table R703.11.2

E1996—2014a: Standard Specification for Performance of Exterior Windows, Curtain Walls, Doors and Impact Protective Systems Impacted by Windborne Debris in Hurricanes
R301.2.1.2, R301.2.1.2.1, R609.6.1, R609.6.2

E2178—2013: Standard Test Method for Air Permeance of Building Materials
R202

E2231—15: Standard Practice for Specimen Preparation and Mounting of Pipe and Duct Insulation Materials to Assess Surface Burning Characteristics
M1601.3

E2273—03(2011): Standard Test Method for Determining the Drainage Efficiency of Exterior Insulation and Finish Systems (EIFS) Clad Wall Assemblies
R703.9.2

E2568—09e1: Standard Specification for PB Exterior Insulation and Finish Systems
R703.9.1, R703.9.2

E2570/E2570M—07(2014)E1: Standard Test Methods for Evaluating Water-resistive Barrier (WRB) Coatings Used Under Exterior Insulation and Finish Systems (EIFS) or EIFS with Drainage
R703.9.2

ASTM—continued

E2634—11(2015): Standard Specification for Flat Wall Insulating Concrete Form (ICF) Systems
R404.1.3.3.6.1, R608.4.4

F405—05: Specification for Corrugated Polyethylene (PE) Pipe and Fittings
Table P3009.11, Table P3302.1, Table AG101.1

F409—12: Specification for Thermoplastic Accessible and Replaceable Plastic Tube and Tubular Fittings
Table P2701.1, P2702.2, P2702.3

F437—15: Specification for Threaded Chlorinated Poly (Vinyl Chloride) (CPVC) Plastic Pipe Fittings, Schedule 80
Table P2906.6

F438—15: Specification for Socket-type Chlorinated Poly (Vinyl Chloride) (CPVC) Plastic Pipe Fittings, Schedule 40
Table P2906.6

F439—13: Specification for Chlorinated Poly (Vinyl Chloride) (CPVC) Plastic Pipe Fittings, Schedule 80
Table P2906.6

F441/F441M—15: Specification for Chlorinated Poly (Vinyl Chloride) (CPVC) Plastic Pipe, Schedules 40 and 80
Table P2906.4, Table P2906.5, Table AG101.1

F442/F442M—13E1: Specification for Chlorinated Poly (Vinyl Chloride) (CPVC) Plastic Pipe (SDR-PR)
Table P2906.4, Table P2906.5, Table AG101.1

F477—14: Specification for Elastomeric Seals (Gaskets) for Joining Plastic Pipe
P2906.18, P3003.13

F493—14: Specification for Solvent Cements for Chlorinated Poly (Vinyl Chloride) (CPVC) Plastic Pipe and Fittings
P2906.9.1.2, P2906.9.1.3, P2906.18.2

F628—12E1: Specification for Acrylonitrile-butadiene-styrene (ABS) Schedule 40 Plastic Drain, Waste and Vent Pipe with a Cellular Core
Table P3002.1(1), Table P3002.1(2), Table P3002.2, Table P3002.3, P3003.3.2, Table AG101.1

F656—15: Specification for Primers for Use in Solvent Cement Joints of Poly (Vinyl Chloride)(PVC) Plastic Pipe and Fittings
P2906.9.1.4, P3003.9.2

F714—13: Specification for Polyethylene (PE) Plastic Pipe (SDR-PR) Based on Outside Diameter
Table P3002.2, Table P3002.1(2), P3010.4

F844—07a(2013): Standard Specification for Washers, Steel, Plain (Flat), Unhardened for General Use
Table R507.2.3

F876—15A: Specification for Cross-linked Polyethylene (PEX) Tubing
Table M2101.1, Table P2906.4, Table P2906.5, Table AG101.1

F877—2011A: Specification for Cross-linked Polyethylene (PEX) Plastic Hot- and Cold-water Distribution Systems
Table M2101.1, Table P2906.6

F891—10: Specification for Coextruded Poly (Vinyl Chloride) (PVC) Plastic Pipe with a Cellular Core
Table P3002.1(1), Table P3002.1(2), Table P3002.2, Table P3302.1, Table AG101.1

F1055—13: Specification for Electrofusion Type Polyethylene Fittings for Outside Diameter Controlled Polyethylene and Crosslinked Polyethylene Pipe and Tubing
Table M2105.5, M2105.11.2, Table P2606.6, P2906.20.2

F1281—11: Specification for Cross-linked Polyethylene/Aluminum/Cross-linked Polyethylene (PEX-AL-PEX) Pressure Pipe
Table M2101.1, Table P2906.4, Table P2906.5, Table P2906.6, P2506.12.1, Table AG101.1

F1282—10: Specification for Polyethylene/Aluminum/Polyethylene (PE-AL-PE) Composite Pressure Pipe
Table M2101.1, Table P2906.4, Table P2906.5, Table P2906.6, P2906.12.1, Table AG101.1

F1412—09: Specification for Polyolefin Pipe and Fittings for Corrosive Waste Drainage
Table P3002.1(2), Table P3002.2, Table P3002.3, P3003.11.1

F1488—14: Specification for Coextruded Composite Pipe
Table P3002.1(1), Table P3002.1(2), Table P3002.2, Table P3009.11

F1504—2014: Standard Specification for Folded Poly (Vinyl Chloride) (PVC) for Existing Sewer and Conduit Rehabilitation
P3011.4

F1554—15: Specification for Anchor Bolts, Steel, 36, 55 and 105-ksi Yield Strength
R608.5.2.2

ASTM—continued

F1667—15: Specification for Driven Fasteners, Nails, Spikes and Staples
R317.3, Table R507.2.3, Table R602.3(1), R703.3.3, R703.6.3, Table R703.15.1, Table R703.15.2, R905.2.5

F1807—15: Specification for Metal Insert Fittings Utilizing a Copper Crimp Ring for SDR9 Cross-linked Polyethylene (PEX) Tubing and SDR9 Polyethylene of Raised Temperature (PE-RT) Tubing
Table M2101.1, Table P2906.6

F1866—13: Specification for Poly (Vinyl Chloride) (PVC) Plastic Schedule 40 Drainage and DWV Fabricated Fittings
Table P3002.3

F1871—2011: Standard Specification for Folded/Formed Poly (Vinyl Chloride) Pipe Type A for Existing Sewer and Conduit Rehabilitation
P3011.4

F1924—12: Standard Specification for Plastic Mechanical Fittings for Use on Outside Diameter Controlled Polyethylene Gas Distribution Pipe and Tubing
M2105.11.1

F1960—15: Specification for Cold Expansion Fittings with PEX Reinforcing Rings for Use with Cross-linked Polyethylene (PEX) Tubing
Table M2101.1, Table P2906.6

F1970—12E1: Standard Specification for Special Engineered Fittings, Appurtenances or Valves for Use in Poly (Vinyl Chloride) (PVC) or Chlorinated Poly (Vinyl Chloride) (CPVC) Systems
M2105.5, Table 2903.9.4

F1973—13E1: Standard Specification for Factory Assembled Anodeless Risers and Transition Fittings in Polyethylene (PE) and Polyamide 11 (PA 11) Fuel Gas Distribution Systems
G2415.15.2

F1974—09(2015): Specification for Metal Insert Fittings for Polyethylene/Aluminum/Polyethylene and Cross-linked Polyethylene/Aluminum/Cross-linked Polyethylene Composite Pressure Pipe
Table P2906.6, P2906.12.1

F1986—01(2011): Multilayer Pipe Type 2, Compression Joints for Hot and Cold Drinking Water Systems
Table P2906.4, Table P2906.5, Table P2906.6

F2080—15: Specification for Cold-expansion Fittings with Metal Compression-sleeves for Cross-linked Polyethylene (PEX) Pipe
Table P2906.6

F 2090—17: Specification for Window Fall Prevention Devices with Emergency Escape (Egress) Release Mechanisms
R310.1.1, R312.2.1, R312.2.2

F2098—08: Standard Specification for Stainless Steel Clamps for Securing SDR9 Cross-linked Polyethylene (PEX) Tubing to Metal Insert and Plastic Insert Fittings
Table M2101.1, Table P2906.6

F2159—14: Standard Specification for Plastic Insert Fittings Utilizing a Copper Crimp Ring for SDR9 Cross-linked Polyethylene (PEX) Tubing and SDR9 Polyethylene of Raised Temperature (PE-RT) Tubing
Table P2906.6

F2262—09: Standard Specification for Cross-linked Polyethylene/Aluminum/Cross-linked Polyethylene Tubing OD Controlled SDR9
Table P2906.4, Table P2906.5

F2389—15: Standard for Pressure-rated Polypropylene (PP) Piping Systems
Table M2105.12.1, Table P2906.4, Table P2906.5, Table P2906.6, P2906.11.1, Table AG101.1

F2434—14: Standard Specification for Metal Insert Fittings Utilizing a Copper Crimp Ring for Polyethylene/Aluminum/Cross-linked Polyethylene (PEX-AL-PEX) Tubing
Table P2906.6

F2623—14: Standard Specification for Polyethylene of Raised Temperature (PE-RT) SDRG Tubing
Table M2101.1, Table AG101.1

F2735—09: Standard Specification for Plastic Insert Fittings for SDR9 Cross-linked Polyethylene (PEX) and Polyethylene of Raised Temperature (PE-RT) Tubing
Table M2101.1, Table P2906.6

F2769—14: Polyethylene or Raised Temperature (PE-RT) Plastic Hot and Cold-Water Tubing and Distribution Systems
Table M2101.1, Table P2906.4, Table P2906.5, Table P2906.6, Table AG101.1

F2806—10(2015): Standard Specification for Acrylonitrile-butadiene-styrene (ABS) Plastic Pipe (Metric SDR-PR)
Table M2101.1

ASTM—continued

F2855—12: Standard Specification for Chlorinated Poly (Vinyl Chloride)/Aluminum/Chlorinated Poly (Vinyl Chloride) (CPVC AL CPVC) Composite Pressure Tubing
Table P2906.4, Table P2906.5, Table AG101.1

F2945—2015: Standard Specification for Polyamide 11 Gas Pressure Pipe, Tubing and Fittings
G2414.6

F2969—12: Standard Specification for Acrylonitrile-butadiene-styrene (ABS) IPS Dimensioned Pressure Pipe
Table M2101.1

AWC

American Wood Council
222 Catoctin Circle SE, Suite 201
Leesburg, VA 20175

AWC STJR—2015: Span Tables for Joists and Rafters
R502.3, R802.4.1, R802.5.1

ANSI/AWC WFCM—2018: Wood Frame Construction Manual for One- and Two-family Dwellings
R301.1.1, R301.2.1.1, R602.10.8.2, R608.9.2, Figure R608.9(9), R608.9.3, R608.10

ANSI/AWC NDS—2018: National Design Specification (NDS) for Wood Construction—with 2018 Supplement
R404.2.2, R502.2, Table R503.1, R507.2.1, R602.3, R608.9.2, R608.9.3, Table R703.15.1, Table R703.15.2, R802.2

ANSI/AWC PWF—2015: Permanent Wood Foundation Design Specification
R317.3.2, R401.1, R404.2.3

AWPA

American Wood Protection Association
P.O. Box 361784
Birmingham, AL 35236-1784

C1—03: All Timber Products—Preservative Treatment by Pressure Processes
R902.2

M4—16: Standard for the Care of Preservative-treated Wood Products
R317.1.1, R318.1.2

U1—16: USE CATEGORY SYSTEM: User Specification for Treated Wood Except Commodity Specification H
R317.1, R402.1.2, R504.3, R703.6.3, R905.7.5, Table R905.8.5, R905.8.6

AWS

American Welding Society
8669 NW 36 Street, #130
Miami, FL 33166

A5.8M/A5.8—2011: Specifications for Filler Metals for Brazing and Braze Welding
P3003.6.1

ANSI/AWS A5.31M/A5.31—2012: Specification for Fluxes for Brazing and Braze Welding Edition: 2nd
M2103.3, M2202.2, P2906.15

AWWA

American Water Works Association
6666 West Quincy Avenue
Denver, CO 80235

C104/A21.4—13: Cement-mortar Lining for Ductile-iron Pipe and Fittings
P2906.4

C110/A21.10—12: Ductile-iron and Gray-iron Fittings
Table P2906.6, P3002.3

C115/A21.15—11: Flanged Ductile-iron Pipe with Ductile-iron or Gray-iron Threaded Flanges
Table P2906.4

C151/A21.51—09: Ductile-iron Pipe, Centrifugally Cast, for Water
Table P2906.4

C153/A21.53—11: Ductile-iron Compact Fittings for Water Service
Table P2906.6

C500—09: Standard for Metal-seated Gate Valves for Water Supply Service
Table P2903.9.4

C504—10: Standard for Rubber-seated Butterfly Valves
Table P2903.9.4

C507—15: Standard for Ball Valves, 6 In. Through 60 In. (150 mm through 1,500 mm)
Table P2903.9.4

C510—07: Double Check Valve Backflow Prevention Assembly
Table P2902.3, P2902.3.6

C511—07: Reduced-pressure Principle Backflow Prevention Assembly
Table P2902.3, P2902.3.5, P2902.5.1

C901—16: Polyethylene (PE) Pressure Pipe and Tubing $^1/_2$ in. (13 mm) through 3 in. (76 mm) for Water Service
P2906.4, Table AG101.1

C903—16: Polyethylene-aluminum-polyethylene (PE-AL-PE) Composite Pressure Pipe, 12 mm ($^1/_2$ in.) through 50 mm (2 in.), for Water Service
Table M2101

C904—16: Cross-linked Polyethylene (PEX) Pressure Tubing, $^1/_2$ in. (13 mm) through 3 in. (76 mm) for Water Service
P2906.4, Table AG101.1

CEN

European Committee for Standardization (EN)
Central Secretariat
Rue de Stassart 36
B-10 50 Brussels

EN 15250-2007: Slow Heat Release Appliances Fired by Solid Fuel Requirements and Test Methods
R1002.2

CISPI

Cast Iron Soil Pipe Institute
2401 Fieldcrest Drive
Mundelein, IL 60060

301—12: Standard Specification for Hubless Cast Iron Soil Pipe and Fittings for Sanitary and Storm Drain, Waste and Vent Piping Applications
Table P3002.1(1), Table P3002.1(2), Table P3002.2, Table P3002.3, Table P3302.1

310—12: Standard Specification for Coupling for Use in Connection with Hubless Cast Iron Soil Pipe and Fittings for Sanitary and Storm Drain, Waste and Vent Piping Applications
P3003.4.3

CPA

Composite Panel Association
19465 Deerfield Avenue, Suite 306
Leesburg, VA 20176

ANSI A135.4—2012: Basic Hardboard
Table R602.3(2)

ANSI A135.5—2012: Prefinished Hardboard Paneling
R702.5

ANSI A135.6—2012: Engineered Wood Siding
R703.5

ANSI A135.7—2012: Engineered Wood Trim
R703.5

A208.1—2016: Particleboard
R503.3.1, R602.1.9, R605.1

CPSC

Consumer Product Safety Commission
4330 East-West Highway
Bethesda, MD 20814

16 CFR, Part 1201—(2002): Safety Standard for Architectural Glazing
R308.1.1, R308.3.1, Table R308.3.1(1)

16 CFR, Part 1209—(2002): Interim Safety Standard for Cellulose Insulation
R302.10.3

16 CFR, Part 1404—(2002): Cellulose Insulation
R302.10.3

CSA

CSA Group
8501 East Pleasant Valley Road
Cleveland, OH 44131-5516

AAMA/WDMA/CSA 101/I.S.2/A440—17: North American Fenestration Standard/Specification for Windows, Doors and Unit Skylights
R308.6.9, R609.3, N1102.4.3

ANSI/CSA FC I—2014: Fuel Cell Technologies—Part 3-100; Stationary fuel cell power systems-Safety
M1903.1

ASME A112.3.4—2013/CSA B45.9—13: Macerating Toilet Systems and Related Components
Table P2701.1, P3007.5

ASME A112.4.2—2015/CSA B45.16—15: Water-closet Personal Hygiene Device
P2722.5

ASME A112.18.1—2017/CSA B125.1—2017: Plumbing Supply Fittings
Table P2701.1, P2708.4, P2708.5, P2722.1, P2722.3, P2902.2, Table P2903.9.4

ASME A112.18.2—2015/CSA B125.2—2015: Plumbing Waste Fittings
Table P2701.1, P2702.2

A112.18.6—2017/CSA B125.6—2017: Flexible Water Connectors
P2906.7

ASME A112.19.1—2013/CSA B45.2—13: Enameled Cast-iron and Enameled Steel Plumbing Fixtures
Table P2701.1, P2711.1

ASME A112.19.2—2013/CSA B45.1—13: Ceramic Plumbing Fixtures
Table P2701.1, P2705.1, P2711.1, P2712.1, P2712.2, P2712.9

ASME A112.19.3—2008/CSA B45.4—08 (R2013): Stainless Steel Plumbing Fixtures
Table P2701.1, P2705.1, P2711.1, P2712.1

ASSE 1002—2015/ASME A112.1002—2015/CSA B125.12—15: Anti-Siphon Fill Valves
Table P2701.1, Table P2902.3, P2902.4.1

ASSE 1016—2017/ASME 112.1016—2017/CSA B125.16—2017: Performance Requirements for Automatic Compensating Valves for Individual Showers and Tub/Shower Combinations
Table P2701.1, P2708.4, P2722.2

ASSE 1070—2015/ASME A112.1070—2015/CSA B125.70—15: Performance Requirements for Water-temperature-limiting Devices
P2713.3, P2721.2, P2724.1

A112.19.5—2011/CSA B45.15—2011: Flush Valves and Spuds for Water-closets, Urinals and Tanks
Table P2701.1

A112.19.7—2017/CSA B45.10—2017: Hydromassage Bathtub Systems
Table P2701.1

ASME A17.1/CSA B44—2016: Safety Code for Elevators and Escalators
R321.1

CSA 8—93: Requirements for Gas Fired Log Lighters for Wood Burning Fireplaces
G2433.1

CSA A257.1—2014: Non-reinforced Circular Concrete Culvert, Storm Drain, Sewer Pipe and Fittings
Table P3002.2

CSA—continued

A257.2—14: Reinforced Circular Concrete Culvert, Storm Drain, Sewer Pipe and Fittings
Table P3002.2, P3003.13

A257.3—14: Joints for Circular Concrete Sewer and Culvert Pipe, Manhole Sections and Fittings Using Rubber Gaskets
P3003.5, P3003.13

B44—2013: Safety Code for Elevators and Escalators
R321.1

B55.1—2015: Test Method for Measuring Efficiency and Pressure Loss of Drain Water Heat Recovery Units
N1103.5.4

B55.2—2015: Drain Water Heat Recovery Units
N1103.5.4

B64.1.1—16: Vacuum Breakers, Atmospheric Type (AVB)
Table P2902.3, P2902.3.2

B64.1.2—16: Pressure Vacuum Breakers (PVB)
Table P2902.3, P2902.3.4

B64.1.3—16: Spill Resistant Pressure Vacuum Breakers (SRPVB)
Table P2902.3

B64.2—16: Vacuum Breakers, Hose Connection Type (HCVB)
Table P2902.3, P2902.3.2

B64.2.1—16: Hose Connection Vacuum Breakers (HCVB) with Manual Draining Feature
Table P2902.3, P2902.3.2

B64.2.1.1—16: Hose Connection Dual Check Vacuum Breakers (HCDVB)
Table P2902.3, P2902.3.2

B64.2.2—16: Vacuum Breakers, Hose Connection Type (HCVB) with Automatic Draining Feature
Table P2902.3, P2902.3.2

B64.3—16: Dual Check Backflow Preventers with Atmospheric Port (DCAP)
Table P2902.3, P2902.3.2, P2902.5.1

B64.4—16: Backflow Preventers, Reduced Pressure Principle Type (RP)
Table P2902.3, P2902.3.5, P2903.5.1

B64.4.1—16: Reduced Pressure Principle for Fire Sprinklers (RPF)
Table P2902.3, P2902.3.5

B64.5—16: Double Check Backflow Preventers (DCVA)
Table P2902.3, P2902.3.6

B64.5.1—16: Double Check Valve Backflow Preventers, Type for Fire Systems (DCVAF)
Table P2902.3, P2902.3.6

B64.6—16: Dual Check Valve Backflow Preventers (DuC)
Table P2902.3, P2902.3.7

B64.7—16: Laboratory Faucet Vacuum Breakers (LFVB)
Table P2902.3, P2902.3.2

B125.3—12: Plumbing Fittings
Table P2701.1, P2713.3, P2721.2, Table P2902.3, P2902.4.1, Table P2903.9.4

B137.1—16: Polyethylene (PE) Pipe, Tubing and Fittings for Cold Water Pressure Services
Table P2906.4, Table P2906.6

B137.2—16: Polyvinylchloride PVC Injection-moulded Gasketed Fittings for Pressure Applications
Table P2906.6

B137.3—16: Rigid Poly (Vinyl Chloride) (PVC) Pipe for Pressure Applications
Table P2906.4, Table P2906.6, P3003.9.2, Table AG101.1

B137.5—16: Cross-linked Polyethylene (PEX) Tubing Systems for Pressure Applications
Table P2906.4, Table P2906.5, Table P2906.6, Table AG101.1

B137.6—16: Chlorinated polyvinylchloride CPVC Pipe, Tubing and Fittings For Hot- and Cold-water Distribution Systems
Table P2906.4, Table P2906.5, Table 2906.6, Table AG101.1

B137.9—16: Polyethylene/Aluminum/Polyethylene (PE-AL-PE) Composite Pressure Pipe Systems
Table M2101.1, Table P2906.4, P9506.12.1

CSA—continued

B137.10—13: Cross-linked Polyethylene/Aluminum/Cross-linked Polyethylene (PE-AL-PE) Composite Pressure Pipe Systems
Table M2101.1, Table P2906.4, Table P2906.5, Table P2906.6, P2906.12.1

B137.11—16: Polypropylene (PP-R) Pipe and Fittings for Pressure Applications
Table P2906.4, Table P2906.5, Table P2906.6, Table AG101.1

B137.18—13: Polyethylene of Raised Temperature (PE-RT) Tubing Systems for Pressure Applications
Table M2101.1, Table M2105.4, Table M2105.5, Table P2906.4, Table P2906.5, Table P2906.6

B181.1—15: Acrylonitrile-butadiene-styrene (ABS) Drain, Waste and Vent Pipe and Pipe Fittings
Table P3002.1(1), Table P3002.1(2), Table P3002.3, P3003.3.2

B181.2—15: Polyvinylchloride (PVC) and chlorinated polyvinylchloride (CPVC) Drain, Waste and Vent Pipe and Pipe Fittings
Table P3002.1(1), Table P3002.1(2), P3003.9.2, P3008.3

B181.3—15: Polyolefin and polyvinylidene (PVDF) Laboratory Drainage Systems
Table P3002.1(1), Table P3002.1(2), Table P3002.2, Table P3002.3, P3003.11.1

B182.2—11: PSM Type polyvinylchloride (PVC) Sewer Pipe and Fittings
Table P3002.2, Table P3302.1

B182.4—15: Profile polyvinylchloride (PVC) Sewer Pipe & Fittings
Table P3002.2, Table P3302.1

B182.6—15: Profile Polyethylene (PE) Sewer Pipe and Fittings for leak-proof Sewer Applications
Table P3302.1

B182.8—15: Profile Polyethylene (PE) Storm Sewer and Drainage Pipe and Fittings
Table P3302.1

B356—10: Water Pressure Reducing Valves for Domestic Water Supply Systems
P2903.3.1

B483.1—07(R2012): Drinking Water Treatment Systems
P2909.1, P2909.2

B602—15: Mechanical Couplings for Drain, Waste and Vent Pipe and Sewer Pipe
P3003.3.1, P3003.4.3, P3003.5, P3003.9.1, P3003.10, P3003.12.2, P3003.13

CSA B45.5—17/IAPMO Z124—17: Plastic Plumbing Fixtures
Table P2701.1, P2711.1, P2711.2, P2712.1

C22.2 No. 218.1—M89(R2011): Spas, Hot Tubs and Associated Equipment
M2006.1

C22.2 No. 236—15: Heating and Cooling Equipment
M2006.1

CSA C448 Series—16: Design and Installation of Earth Energy Systems
Table M2105.4, Table M2105.5

CSA O325—07: Construction Sheathing
R503.2.1, R602.1.8, R604.1, R803.2.1

O437-Series—93: Standards on OSB and Waferboard (Reaffirmed 2006)
R503.2.1, R602.1.8, R604.1, R803.2.1

CAN/CSA/C22.2 No. 60335-2-40—2012: Safety of Household and Similar Electrical Appliances, Part 2-40: Particular Requirements for Electrical Heat Pumps, Air-Conditioners and Dehumidifiers
M1403.1, M1412.1, M1413.1

CSSB

Cedar Shake & Shingle Bureau
P.O. Box 1178
Sumas, WA 98295-1178

CSSB—97: Grading and Packing Rules for Western Red Cedar Shakes and Western Red Shingles of the Cedar Shake and Shingle Bureau
R702.6, R703.6

DASMA

Door & Access Systems Manufacturers Association International
1300 Sumner Avenue
Cleveland, OH 44115-2851

105—2016: Test Method for Thermal Transmittance and Air Infiltration of Garage Doors and Rolling Doors
N1101.10.3

108—2017: Standard Method for Testing Garage Doors, Rolling Doors and Flexible Doors; Determination of Structural Performance Under Uniform Static Air Pressure Difference
R609.4

115—2016: Standard Method for Testing Sectional Garage Doors, Rolling Doors and Flexible Doors: Determination of Structural Performance Under Missile Impact and Cyclic Wind Pressure
R301.2.1.2

DOC

United States Department of Commerce
1401 Constitution Avenue, NW
Washington, DC 20230

PS 1—09: Structural Plywood
R404.2.1, Table R404.2.3, R503.2.1, R602.1.8, R604.1, R803.2.1

PS 2—10: Performance Standard for Wood-based Structural-use Panels
R404.2.1, Table R404.2.3, R503.2.1, R602.1.8, R604.1, R803.2.1

PS 20—05: American Softwood Lumber Standard
R404.2.1, R502.1.1, R602.1.1, R802.1.1

DOTn

U.S. Department of Transportation
1200 New Jersey Avenue SE
East Building, 2nd floor
Washington, DC 20590

49 CFR, Parts 192.281(e) & 192.283 (b) (2009): Transportation of Natural and Other Gas by Pipeline: Minimum Federal Safety Standards
G2414.6.1

FEMA

Federal Emergency Management Agency
500 C Street SW
Washington, DC 20472

FEMA TB-2—08: Flood Damage-resistant Materials Requirements
R322.1.8

FEMA TB-11—01: Crawlspace Construction for Buildings Located in Special Flood Hazard Area
R408.7

FM

FM Approvals
Headquarters Office
1151 Boston-Providence Turnpike
P.O. Box 9102
Norwood, MA 02062

4450—(1989): Approval Standard for Class 1 Insulated Steel Deck Roofs—with Supplements through July 1992
R906.1

4880—(2015): Approval Standard for Class 1 Rating of Building Panels or Interior Finish Materials
R316.6

GA

Gypsum Association
6525 Belcrest Road, Suite 480
Hyattsville, MD 20782

GA-253—2016: Application of Gypsum Sheathing
Table R602.3(1)

HPVA

Hardwood Plywood & Veneer Association
1825 Michael Faraday Drive
Reston, Virginia 20190

ANSI/HPVA HP-1—2016: American National Standard for Hardwood and Decorative Plywood
R702.5

HVI

Home Ventilating Institute
1000 North Rand Road Suite 214
Wauconda, Il 60084

916—09 Airflow Test Procedure
Table N1103.6.1

IAPMO

IAPMO Group
4755 E. Philadelphia Street
Ontario, CA 91761-USA

CSA B45.5—17/IAPMO Z124—2017: Plastic Plumbing Fixtures
Table P2701.1, P2711.1, P2711.2, P2712.1

ICC

International Code Council, Inc.
500 New Jersey Avenue NW
6th Floor
Washington, DC 20001

ANSI/RESNET/ICC 301—2014: Standard for the Calculation and Labeling of the Energy Performance of Low-Rise Residential Buildings using the Energy Rating Index, March 7, 2014, republished 2016
N1106.3

ANSI/RESNET/ICC 380—2016: Standard for Testing Airtightness of Building Enclosures, Airtightness of Heating and Cooling Air Distribution and Airflow of Mechanical Ventilation Systems
N1102.4.1.2

IBC—18: International Building Code®
R101.2, R202, R301.1.1, R301.1.3, R301.2.1.1, R301.2.2.1.1, R301.2.2.1.2, Table R302.1(1), Table R302.1(2), R301.3, R302.2.1, R302.2.2, R302.3, R308.5, R320.1, R320.1.1, R321.3, R403.1.8, Table R602.10.3(3), Table R606.12.2.1, R609.2, R802.1.5.4, R905.10.3, G2402.3

ICC/ANSI A117.1—09: Accessible and Usable Buildings and Facilities
R321.3

ICC 400—17: Standard on the Design and Construction of Log Structures
R301.1.1, R502.1.4, R602.1.4, R703.1, R802.1.3, N1102.1, Table N1102.4.1.1

ICC 500—14: ICC/NSSA Standard on the Design and Construction of Storm Shelters
R323.1

ICC 600—14: Standard for Residential Construction in High-wind Regions
R301.2.1.1

ICC 900/SRCC 300—2015: Solar Thermal System Standard
M2301.2.2.2, M2301.2.3, M2301.2.6, M2301.2.7, M2301.2.8, M2301.2.10, M2301.4

ICC 901/SRCC 100—2015: Solar Thermal Collector Standard
M2301.3.1

IEBC—18: International Existing Building Code®
R110.2

IECC—18: International Energy Conservation Code®
N1101.1, N1101.13.1, N1103.8, Table N1105.5.2(1)

IECC—06: International Energy Conservation Code®
N1101.6

IFC—18: International Fire Code®
R102.7, R324.2, M2201.7, G2402.3, G2412.2

IFGC—18: International Fuel Gas Code®
G2401.1, G2402.3, G2423.1

IMC—18: International Mechanical Code®
G2402.3

IPC—18: International Plumbing Code®
Table R301.2(1), R903.4.1, G2402.3, P2601.1

IPMC—18: International Property Maintenance Code®
R102.7

IPSDC—18: International Private Sewage Disposal Code®
R322.1.7

IRC—15: International Residential Code®
Table N1106.4

ISPSC—18: International Swimming Pool and Spa Code®
R326.1

IEEE

Institute of Electrical and Electronic Engineers, Inc.
3 Park Avenue, 17th Floor
New York, NY 10016-5997

515.1—2012: IEEE Standard for the Testing, Design, Installation and Maintenance of Electrical Resistance Trace Heating for Commercial Applications
N1103.5.1.2

ISO

International Organization for Standardization
Chemin de Blandonnet 8
CP 401
1214 Vernier
Geneva, Switzerland

8336—2009: Fibre-cement Flat Sheets-product Specification and Test Methods
Table R503.2.1.1(1), Table R503.2.1.1(2), Table R602.3(2), Table R702.4.2, R703.10.1, R703.10.2

15874—2002: Polypropylene Plastic Piping Systems for Hot and Cold Water Installations
Table M2101.1

MSS

Manufacturers Standardization Society of the Valve and Fittings Industry
127 Park Street, NE
Vienna, VA 22180

SP-42—2013: Corrosion Resistant Gate, Globe, Angle and Check Valves with Flanged and Butt Weld Ends (Classes 150, 300 & 600)
Table P2903.9.4

SP-58—09: Pipe Hangers and Supports—Materials, Design, Manufacture, Selection, Application and Installation
G2418.2

SP-67—11: Butterfly Valves
Table P2903.9.4

MSS—continued

SP-70—2011: Gray Iron Gate Valves, Flanged and Threaded Ends
Table P2903.9.4

SP-71—2013: Gray Iron Swing Check Valves, Flanged and Threaded Ends
Table P2903.9.4

SP-72—2010a: Ball Valves with Flanged or Butt-Welding Ends for General Service
P2903.9.4

SP-78—2011: Cast Iron Plug Valves, Flanged and Threaded Ends
Table P2903.9.4

SP-80—2013: Bronze Gate, Globe, Angle and Check Valves
Table P2903.9.4

SP-110—2010a: Ball Valves, Threaded, Socket Welded, Solder Joint, Grooved and Flared Ends
Table P2903.9.4

SP-122—2012: Plastic Industrial Ball Valves
Table P2903.9.4

SP-139—2014: Copper Alloy Gate, Globe, Angle, and Check Valves for Low Pressure/ Low Temperature Plumbing Applications
Table P2903.9.4

NAIMA

North American Insulation Manufacturers Association
11 Canal Center Plaza, Suite 101
Alexandria, VA 22314

AH 116—09: Fibrous Glass Duct Construction Standards, Fifth Edition
M1601.1.1

NFPA

National Fire Protection Association
1 Batterymarch Park
Quincy, MA 02169-7471

13—16: Standard for Installation of Sprinkler Systems
R302.3

13D—16: Standard for the Installation of Sprinkler Systems in One- and Two-family Dwellings and Manufactured Homes
R313.1.1, R313.2.1, R324.6.2.1, P2904.1, P2904.6.1

13R—16: Standard for the Installation of Sprinkler Systems in Low-Rise Residential Occupancies
R325.5

31—16: Standard for the Installation of Oil-burning Equipment
M1701.1, M1801.3.1, M1805.3, M2201.2

58—17: Liquefied Petroleum Gas Code
G2412.2, G2414.6.2

70—17: National Electrical Code
R107.3, R324.3, R327.2, R327.4, E3401.1, E3401.2, E4301.1, Table E4303.2, E4304.3, E4304.4

72—16: National Fire Alarm and Signaling Code
R314.1, R314.7.1

85—15: Boiler and Combustion Systems Hazards Code
G2452.1

211—16: Standard for Chimneys, Fireplaces, Vents and Solid Fuel Burning Appliances
R1002.5, G2427.5.5.1

259—18: Standard for Test Method for Potential Heat of Building Materials
R316.5.7, R316.5.8

275—17: Standard Method of Fire Tests for the Evaluation of Thermal Barriers
R316.4

286—15: Standard Methods of Fire Tests for Evaluating Contribution of Wall and Ceiling Interior Finish to Room Fire Growth
R302.9.4, R316.6

501—17: Standard on Manufactured Housing
R202

720—15: Standard for the Installation of Carbon Monoxide (CO) Detectors and Warning Equipment
R315.7.1, R315.7.2

853—15: Standard on the Installation of Stationary Fuel Cell Power Systems
M1903.1

NFRC

National Fenestration Rating Council, Inc.
6305 Ivy Lane, Suite 140
Greenbelt, MD 20770

100—2017: Procedure for Determining Fenestration Products *U*-Factors
N1101.10.3

200—2017: Procedure for Determining Fenestration Product Solar Heat Gain Coefficients and Visible Transmittance at Normal Incidence
N1101.10.3

400—2017: Procedure for Determining Fenestration Product Air Leakage
N1102.4.3

NGWA

National Ground Water Association
601 Dempsey Road
Westerville, OH 43081

ANSI/NGWA 01—14: Water Well Construction Standard
P2602.1

NSF

NSF International
789 N. Dixboro Road
P.O. Box 130140
Ann Arbor, MI 48105

14—2015: Plastics Piping System Components and Related Materials
M1301.4, P2609.3, P2909.3

41—2011: Nonliquid Saturated Treatment Systems (Composting Toilets)
P2725.1

42—2015: Drinking Water Treatment Units—Anesthetic Effects
P2909.1, P2909.3

44—2015: Residential Cation Exchange Water Softeners
P2909.1, P2909.3

50—2015: Equipment for Swimming Pools, Hot Tubs and Other Recreational Water Facilities
P2911.8.1

53—2015: Drinking Water Treatment Units—Health Effects
P2909.1, P2909.3

58—2015: Reverse Osmosis Drinking Water Treatment Systems
P2909.2, P2909.3

61—2015: Drinking Water System Components—Health Effects
P2609.5, P2722.1, P2903.9.4, P2906.4, P2906.5, P2906.6, P2909.3

350—2014: Onsite Residential and Commercial Water Reuse Treatment Systems
P2911.6.1

358-1—2014: Polyethylene Pipe and Fittings for Water-based Ground Source "Geothermal" Heat Pump Systems
M2105.4, M2105.5, Table AG101.1

358-2—2012: Polypropylene Pipe and Fittings for Water-based Ground Source "Geothermal" Heat Pump Systems
Table M2105.4, M2105.5

359—2012: Valves for Crosslinked Polyethylene (PEX) Water Distribution Tubing Systems
Table P2903.9.4

372—2011: Drinking Water Systems Components—Lead Content
P2906.2.1

PCA

Portland Cement Association
5420 Old Orchard Road
Skokie, IL 60077

100—12: Prescriptive Design of Exterior Concrete Walls for One- and Two-family Dwellings (Pub. No. EB241)
R301.2.2.5, R301.2.2.3.4, R404.1.3, R404.1.3.2.1, R404.1.3.2.2, R404.1.3.4, R404.1.4.2, R608.1, R608.2, R608.5.1, R608.9.2, R608.9.3

SBCA

Structural Building Components Association
6300 Enterprise Lane
Madison, WI 53719

BCSI—2013 (Updated March 2015): Building Component Safety Information Guide to Good Practice for Handling, Installing, Restraining & Bracing of Metal Plate Connected Wood Trusses
R502.11.2, R802.10.3

CFS-BCSI—2008: Cold-formed Steel Building Component Safety Information (CFSBCSI) Guide to Good Practice for Handling, Installing & Bracing of Cold-formed Steel Trusses
R505.1.3, R804.3.6

FS100—12: Standard Requirements for Wind Pressure Resistance of Foam Plastic Insulating Sheathing Used in Exterior Wall Covering Assemblies
R316.8

SMACNA

Sheet Metal & Air Conditioning Contractors National Assoc. Inc.
4021 Lafayette Center Road
Chantilly, VA 22021

SMACNA—10: Fibrous Glass Duct Construction Standards (2003)
M1601.1.1, M1601.4.1

SMACNA/ANSI—2016: HVAC Duct Construction Standards—Metal and Flexible 4th Edition (ANSI) 2016
M1601.4.1

TMS

The Masonry Society
105 South Sunset Street, Suite Q
Longmont, CO 80501

402—2016: Building Code Requirements for Masonry Structures
R404.1.2, R606.1, R606.1.1, R606.12.1, R606.12.2.3.1, R606.12.3.1, R703.12

403—2017: Direct Design Handbook for Masonry Structures
R606.1, R606.1.1, R606.12.1, R606.12.3.1

404—2016: Standard for the Design of Architectural Cast Stone
R606.1

602—2016: Specification for Masonry Structures
R606.2.10, R606.2.13, R703.12

TPI

Truss Plate Institute
218 N. Lee Street, Suite 312
Alexandria, VA 22314

TPI 1—2014: National Design Standard for Metal-plate-connected Wood Truss Construction
R502.11.1, R802.10.2

UL

UL LLC
333 Pfingsten Road
Northbrook, IL 60062

17—2008: Vent or Chimney Connector Dampers for Oil-fired Appliances—with revisions through September 2013
M1802.2.2

55A—04: Materials for Built-up Roof Coverings
R905.9.2

58—96: Steel Underground Tanks for Flammable and Combustible Liquids—with Revisions through July 1998
M2201.1

80—2007: Steel Tanks for Oil-burner Fuel—with revisions through January 2014
M2201.1

103—2010: Factory-built Chimneys for Residential Type and Building Heating Appliances—with revisions through July 2012
R202, R1005.3, G2430.1

127—2011: Factory-built Fireplaces—with revisions through May 2015
R1001.11, R1004.1, R1004.4, R1004.5, R1005.4, N1102.4.2, G2445.7

174—04: Household Electric Storage Tank Water Heaters—with revisions through April 2015
M2005.1

180—2012: Liquid-level Indicating Gauges for Oil Burner Fuels and Other Combustible Liquids
M2201.5

181—05: Factory-made Air Ducts and Air Connectors—with revisions through May 2003
M1601.1.1, M1601.4.1

181A—2013: Closure Systems for Use with Rigid Air Ducts and Air Connectors—with revisions through December 1998
M1601.2, M1601.4.1

181B—2013: Closure Systems for Use with Flexible Air Ducts and Air Connectors—with revisions through August 2003
M1601.4.1

217—06: Single- and Multiple-station Smoke Alarms—with revisions through October 2015
R314.1.1, R315.1.1

263—2011: Standards for Fire Test of Building Construction and Materials—with revisions through June 2015
Table 302.1(1), Table R302.1(2), R302.2, R302.2.1, R302.2.2, R302.4.1, R302.11.1, Table R312.1(1), R606.2.2

268—2009: Smoke Detectors for Fire Alarm Systems
R314.7.1, R314.7.4, R315.7.4

325—02: Door, Drapery, Gate, Louver and Window Operations and Systems—with revisions through May 2015
R309.4

343—2008: Pumps for Oil-burning Appliances—with revisions through June 2013
M2204.1

378—06: Draft Equipment—with revisions through June 12, 2014
M1804.2.6, G2427.3.3

441—10: Gas Vents—with revisions through June 12, 2014
G2426.1, G2427.6.1

507—99: Standard for Electric Fans
M1503.2

508—99: Industrial Control Equipment—with revisions through October 2013
M1411.3.1

UL—continued

815—11: Electrical Resistance Heat Tracing for Commercial and Industrial Applications Including Revisions through July 2015
N1103.5.1.2

536—97: Flexible Metallic Hose—with revisions through December 2014
M2202.3

641—2010: Type L, Low-temperature Venting Systems—with revisions through June 2013
R202, R1003.11.5, M1804.2.4, G2426.1, G2427.6.1

651—2011: Schedule 40 and Schedule 80 Rigid PVC Conduit and Fittings—with revisions through May 2014
G2414.6.3

705—04: Standard for Power Ventilators—with revisions through December 2013
M1502.4.4

723—08: Standard for Test for Surface Burning Characteristics of Building Materials—with revisions through August 2013
R202, R302.9.3, R302.9.4, R302.10.1, R302.10.2, R316.3, R316.5.9, R316.5.11, R507.2.2.2, R703.14.3, R802.1.5, M1601.3, M1601.5.2, P2801.6

726—95: Oil-fired Boiler Assemblies—with revisions through October 2013
M2001.1.1, M2006.1

727—06: Oil-fired Central Furnaces—with revisions through October 2013
M1402.1

729—03: Oil-fired Floor Furnaces—with revisions through October 2013
M1408.1

730—03: Oil-fired Wall Furnaces—with revisions through October 2013
M1409.1

732—95: Oil-fired Storage Tank Water Heaters—with revisions through October 2013
M2005.1

737—2011: Fireplaces Stoves—with revisions through August 2015
M1414.1, M1901.2

790—04: Standard Test Methods for Fire Tests of Roof Coverings—with revisions through July 2014
R302.2.4, R902.1

795—2011: Commercial-industrial Gas Heating Equipment—with revisions through November 2013
G2442.1, G2452.1

834—04: Heating, Water Supply and Power Boilers—Electric—with revisions through December 2013
M2001.1.1

842—07: Valves for Flammable Fluids—with revisions through May 2015
M2204.2

858—05: Household Electric Ranges—with revisions through June 2015
M1901.2, M1503.2

875—09: Electric Dry-bath Heaters—with revisions through December 2013
M1902.2

896—93: Oil-burning Stoves—with revisions through November 2013
M1410.1

923—2013: Microwave Cooking Appliances—with revisions through June 2015
M1504.1, M1503.2, M1901.2

959—2010: Medium Heat Appliance Factory-built Chimneys—with revisions through June 2014
R1005.6

1026—2012: Electric Household Cooking and Food Serving Appliances—with revisions through August 2015
M1901.2

1040—96: Fire Test of Insulated Wall Construction—with revisions through October 2012
R316.6

1042—2009: Electric Baseboard Heating Equipment—with revisions through September 2014
M1405.1

1256—02: Fire Test of Roof Deck Construction—with revisions through July 2013
R906.1

UL—continued

1261—01: Electric Water Heaters for Pools and Tubs—with revisions through July 2012
M2006.1

1479—03: Fire Tests of Through-Penetration Firestops—with revisions through June 2015
R302.4.1.2

1482—2011: Solid-Fuel-type Room Heaters—with revisions through August 2015
R1002.2, R1002.5, M1410.1

1563—2009: Standard for Electric Spas, Hot Tubs and Associated Equipment—with revisions through March 2015
M2006.1

1618—09: Wall Protectors, Floor Protectors, and Hearth Extensions—with revisions through October 2015
R1004.2, M1410.2

1693—2010: Electric Radiant Heating Panels and Heating Panel Sets—with revisions through October 2011
M1406.1

1703—02: Flat-plate Photovoltaic Modules and Panels—with revisions through October 2015
R324.3.1, R902.4, R905.16.4, R907.17.5

1715—97: Fire Test of Interior Finish Material—with revisions through January 2013
R316.6

1738—2010: Venting Systems for Gas-burning Appliances, Categories II, III and IV—with revisions through November 2014
G2426.1, G2427.4.1, G2427.4.1.1, G2427.4.2

1741—2010: Inverters, Converters, Controllers and Interconnection System Equipment with Distributed Energy Resources—with revisions through January 2015
R324.3.1, R327.4

1777—07: Chimney Liners—with revisions through October 2015
R1003.11.1, R1003.18, G2425.12, G2425.15.4, M1801.3.4, G2427.5.1, G2427.5.2

1897—12: Uplift Tests for Roof Covering Systems—with revisions through September 2015
R905.17.7

1995—2011: Heating and Cooling Equipment—with revisions through July 2015
M1402.1, M1403.1, M1407.1, M1412.1, M1413.1, M2006.1

1996—2009: Electric Duct Heaters—with revisions through June 2014
M1402.1, M1407.1

2034—08: Standard for Single- and Multiple-station Carbon Monoxide Alarms—with revisions through March 2015
R314.1.1, R315.1.1

2075—2013: Standard for Gas and Vapor Detectors and Sensors
R314.7.4, R315.7.1, R315.7.4

2158A—2010: Outline of Investigation for Clothes Dryer Transition Duct
M1502.4.3, G2439.7.3

2523—09: Standard for Solid Fuel-fired Hydronic Heating Appliances, Water Heaters and Boilers—with revisions through February 2013
M2005.1, M2001.1.1

2703—14: Mounting Systems, Mounting Devices, Clamping/Retention Devices and Ground Lugs for Use with Flat-Plate Photovoltaic Modules and Panels
R902.4

9540—14: Outline of Investigation for Energy Storage Systems and Equipment
R327.2, R327.4

UL/CSA/ANCE 60335-2-40—2012: Standard for Household and Similar Electrical Appliances, Part 2: Particular Requirements for Motor-compressors
M1403.1, M1412.1, M1413.1

ULC

ULC
13775 Commerce Parkway
Richmond, BC V6V 2V4

CAN/ULC S 102.2—2010: Standard Methods for Test for Surface Burning Characteristics of Building Materials and Assemblies
R302.10.1, R302.10.2

US-FTC

United States-Federal Trade Commission
600 Pennsylvania Avenue NW
Washington, DC 20580

CFR Title 16(2015): R-value Rule
N1101.10.4

WDMA

Window and Door Manufacturers Association
2025 M Street NW, Suite 800
Washington, DC 20036-3309

AAMA/WDMA/CSA 101/I.S2/A440—17: North American Fenestration Standard/Specifications for Windows, Doors and Skylights
R308.6.9, R609.3, N1102.4.3

I.S. 11—13: Industry Standard Analytical Method for Design Pressure (DP) Ratings of Fenestration Products
R308.6.9.1, R609.3.1

WMA

World Millwork Alliance (formerly Association of Millwork Distributors Standards AMD)
10047 Robert Trent Parkway
New Port Richey, FL 34655-4649

ANSI WMA 100—2016: Standard Method of Determining Structural Performance Ratings of Side Hinged Exterior Door Systems and Procedures for Component Substitution
R609.3

APPENDICES A through J
DELETED

APPENDIX K

SOUND TRANSMISSION

The provisions contained in this appendix are not mandatory unless specifically referenced in the adopting ordinance.

User note:

About this appendix: *Sound transmission relates directly to the psychological and long-term physical well-being of building occupants. Many human activities cannot be accommodated efficiently or comfortably in various types of building spaces without proper attention to the mitigation of sound transmission from other spaces within the building, or from outside of the building. In Appendix K, attention is specifically paid to the mitigation of sound transmission between dwelling units and other dwelling units and occupancies.*

SECTION AK101
GENERAL

AK101.1 General. Wall and floor-ceiling assemblies separating *dwelling units*, including those separating adjacent *townhouse* units, shall provide airborne sound insulation for walls, and both airborne and impact sound insulation for floor-ceiling assemblies.

SECTION AK102
AIRBORNE SOUND

AK102.1 General. Airborne sound insulation for wall and floor-ceiling assemblies shall meet a sound transmission class (STC) rating of 45 when tested in accordance with ASTM E90. Penetrations or openings in construction assemblies for piping; electrical devices; recessed cabinets; bathtubs; soffits; or heating, ventilating or exhaust ducts shall be sealed, lined, insulated or otherwise treated to maintain the required ratings. *Dwelling unit* entrance doors, which share a common space, shall be tight fitting to the frame and sill.

AK102.1.1 Masonry. The sound transmission class of concrete masonry and clay masonry assemblies shall be calculated in accordance with TMS 0302 or determined through testing in accordance with ASTM E90.

SECTION AK103
STRUCTURAL-BORNE SOUND

AK103.1 General. Floor/ceiling assemblies between *dwelling units*, or between a *dwelling unit* and a public or service area within a structure, shall have an impact insulation class (IIC) rating of not less than 45 when tested in accordance with ASTM E492.

SECTION AK104
REFERENCED STANDARDS

ASTM E90—09	Test Method for Laboratory Measurement of Airborne Sound Transmission Loss of Building Partitions and Elements	AK102.1 AK102.1.1
ASTM E492—09	Specification for Laboratory Measurement of Impact Sound Transmission through Floor-ceiling Assemblies Using the Tapping Machine	AK103.1
TMS 0302—12	Standard for Determining the Sound Transmission Class Rating for Masonry Walls	AK102.1.1

APPENDICES L through P

DELETED

APPENDIX Q

TINY HOUSES

This provisions contained in this appendix are not mandatory unless specifically referenced in the adopting ordinance.

User note:

About this appendix: Appendix Q relaxes various requirements in the body of the code as they apply to houses that are 400 square feet in area or less. Attention is specifically paid to features such as compact stairs, including stair handrails and headroom, ladders, reduced ceiling heights in lofts and guard and emergency escape and rescue opening requirements at lofts.

SECTION AQ101
GENERAL

AQ101.1 Scope. This appendix shall be applicable to *tiny houses* used as single *dwelling units*. *Tiny houses* shall comply with this code except as otherwise stated in this appendix.

SECTION AQ102
DEFINITIONS

AQ102.1 General. The following words and terms shall, for the purposes of this appendix, have the meanings shown herein. Refer to Chapter 2 of this code for general definitions.

EGRESS ROOF ACCESS WINDOW. A *skylight* or roof window designed and installed to satisfy the emergency escape and rescue opening requirements of Section R310.2.

LANDING PLATFORM. A landing provided as the top step of a stairway accessing a *loft*.

LOFT. A floor level located more than 30 inches (762 mm) above the main floor, open to the main floor on one or more sides with a ceiling height of less than 6 feet 8 inches (2032 mm) and used as a living or sleeping space.

TINY HOUSE. A *dwelling* that is 400 square feet (37 m²) or less in floor area excluding *lofts*.

SECTION AQ103
CEILING HEIGHT

AQ103.1 Minimum ceiling height. *Habitable space* and hallways in *tiny houses* shall have a ceiling height of not less than 6 feet 8 inches (2032 mm). Bathrooms, toilet rooms and kitchens shall have a ceiling height of not less than 6 feet 4 inches (1930 mm). Obstructions including, but not limited to, beams, girders, ducts and lighting, shall not extend below these minimum ceiling heights.

Exception: Ceiling heights in *lofts* are permitted to be less than 6 feet 8 inches (2032 mm).

SECTION AQ104
LOFTS

AQ104.1 Minimum loft area and dimensions. *Lofts* used as a sleeping or living space shall meet the minimum area and dimension requirements of Sections AQ104.1.1 through AQ104.1.3.

AQ104.1.1 Minimum area. *Lofts* shall have a floor area of not less than 35 square feet (3.25 m²).

AQ104.1.2 Minimum dimensions. *Lofts* shall be not less than 5 feet (1524 mm) in any horizontal dimension.

AQ104.1.3 Height effect on loft area. Portions of a *loft* with a sloped ceiling measuring less than 3 feet (914 mm) from the finished floor to the finished ceiling shall not be considered as contributing to the minimum required area for the loft.

Exception: Under gable roofs with a minimum slope of 6 units vertical in 12 units horizontal (50-percent slope), portions of a *loft* with a sloped ceiling measuring less than 16 inches (406 mm) from the finished floor to the finished ceiling shall not be considered as contributing to the minimum required area for the *loft*.

AQ104.2 Loft access. The access to and primary egress from *lofts* shall be of any type described in Sections AQ104.2.1 through AQ104.2.4.

AQ104.2.1 Stairways. Stairways accessing *lofts* shall comply with this code or with Sections AQ104.2.1.1 through AQ104.2.1.5.

AQ104.2.1.1 Width. Stairways accessing a *loft* shall not be less than 17 inches (432 mm) in clear width at or above the handrail. The width below the handrail shall be not less than 20 inches (508 mm).

AQ104.2.1.2 Headroom. The headroom in stairways accessing a *loft* shall be not less than 6 feet 2 inches (1880 mm), as measured vertically, from a sloped line connecting the tread or landing platform nosings in the middle of their width.

AQ104.2.1.3 Treads and risers. Risers for stairs accessing a *loft* shall be not less than 7 inches (178 mm) and not more than 12 inches (305 mm) in height. Tread depth and riser height shall be calculated in accordance with one of the following formulas:

1. The tread depth shall be 20 inches (508 mm) minus four-thirds of the riser height.

2. The riser height shall be 15 inches (381 mm) minus three-fourths of the tread depth.

AQ104.2.1.4 Landing platforms. The top tread and riser of stairways accessing *lofts* shall be constructed as a *landing platform* where the *loft* ceiling height is less than 6 feet 2 inches (1880 mm) where the stairway meets the *loft*. The *landing platform* shall be 18 inches to 22 inches (457 to 559 mm) in depth measured from the nosing of the landing platform to the edge of the *loft*, and 16 to 18 inches (406 to 457 mm) in height measured from the *landing platform* to the *loft* floor.

AQ104.2.1.5 Handrails. Handrails shall comply with Section R311.7.8.

AQ104.2.1.6 Stairway guards. Guards at open sides of stairways shall comply with Section R312.1.

AQ104.2.2 Ladders. Ladders accessing *lofts* shall comply with Sections AQ104.2.1 and AQ104.2.2.

AQ104.2.2.1 Size and capacity. Ladders accessing *lofts* shall have a rung width of not less than 12 inches (305 mm), and 10-inch (254 mm) to 14-inch (356 mm) spacing between rungs. Ladders shall be capable of supporting a 200-pound (75 kg) load on any rung. Rung spacing shall be uniform within $^3/_8$ inch (9.5 mm).

AQ104.2.2.2 Incline. Ladders shall be installed at 70 to 80 degrees from horizontal.

AQ104.2.3 Alternating tread devices. Alternating tread devices accessing *lofts* shall comply with Sections R311.7.11.1 and R311.7.11.2. The clear width at and below the handrails shall be not less than 20 inches (508 mm).

AQ104.2.4 Ships ladders. Ships ladders accessing *lofts* shall comply with Sections R311.7.12.1 and R311.7.12.2. The clear width at and below handrails shall be not less than 20 inches (508 mm).

AQ104.2.5 Loft Guards. *Loft* guards shall be located along the open side of *lofts*. *Loft* guards shall be not less than 36 inches (914 mm) in height or one-half of the clear height to the ceiling, whichever is less.

SECTION AQ105
EMERGENCY ESCAPE AND RESCUE OPENINGS

AQ105.1 General. *Tiny houses* shall meet the requirements of Section R310 for emergency escape and rescue openings.

Exception: *Egress roof access windows* in *lofts* used as sleeping rooms shall be deemed to meet the requirements of Section R310 where installed such that the bottom of the opening is not more than 44 inches (1118 mm) above the *loft* floor, provided the egress roof access window complies with the minimum opening area requirements of Section R310.2.1.

APPENDICES R through T
DELETED

INDEX

E

F

S

Y

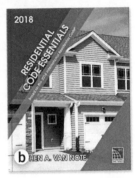

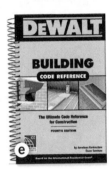

ASSESSMENT center

The ICC Assessment Center (formerly known as ICC Certification & Testing) provides nationally recognized credentials that demonstrate a confirmed commitment to protect public health, safety, and welfare. Raise the professionalism of your department and further your career by pursuing an ICC Certification.

ICC Certifications offer:

- Nationwide recognition
- Increased earning potential
- Career advancement
- Superior knowledge
- Validation of your expertise
- Personal and professional satisfaction

Exams are developed and maintained to the highest standards, which includes continuous peer review by national committees of experienced, practicing professionals. ICC is continually evolving exam offerings, testing options, and technology to ensure that all building and fire safety officials have access to the tools and resources needed to advance in today's fast-paced and rapidly-changing world.

Enhancing Exam Options

Effective July 2018, the Assessment Center enhanced and streamlined exam options and now offers only computer based testing (CBT) at a test site and PRONTO. We no longer offer paper/pencil exams.

Proctored Remote Online Testing Option (PRONTO)

Taking your next ICC certification exam is more convenient, more comfortable and more efficient than ever before with PRONTO.

PRONTO provides a convenient testing experience that is accessible 24 hours a day, 7 days a week, 365 days a year. Required hardware/ software is minimal – you will need a webcam and microphone, as well as a reasonably recent operating system.

Whether testing in your office or in the comfort of your home, your ICC exam will continue to maintain its credibility while offering more convenience, allowing you to focus on achieving your professional goals. The Assessment Center continues to add exams to the PRONTO exam catalog regularly.

18-15617

Checkout all the ICC Assessment Center has to offer at iccsafe.org/certification